**HYGRADE®**

# CATALOG & PRICE GUIDE OF
# TOPPS, BOWMAN, DONRUSS, FLEER,
# LEAF, O-PEE-CHEE, SCORE, AND UPPER DECK

# BASEBALL CARDS

## Features card values of virtually every baseball card issued by these manufacturers:

- TOPPS—years 1951 to 1992
- BOWMAN—years 1989 to 1991
- DONRUSS—years 1981 to 1992
- FLEER—years 1981 to 1992
- LEAF—years 1990 to 1991
- O-PEE-CHEE—year 1991
- SCORE—years 1988 to 1992
- UPPER DECK—years 1989 to 1992

Published annually in March—
every year since 1986.

Seventh Edition (1)

**Publisher: HYGRADE SPORTS CARD CO., 5 East 17th Street, New York, N.Y. 10003**

## General Information

Card values in this catalog represent approximate retail values as of **Feb., 1992**. Due to high demand, the values of popular cards (especially rookies cards of star players from the past few years) have been fluctuating every few weeks. Keep up-to-date on the latest market values with a monthly price guide.

Information on card values was compiled from various sources including dealer ads in card magazines, dealer catalogs, card auctions, offers at card conventions, etc. **The card values in this catalog do not represent an offer to buy or sell by the publisher. We are not responsible for typographical errors.**

## What Makes a Card Valuable?

The value of a card is determined by *supply* (how many cards are offered for sale at a certain price), and *demand* (how many cards buyers are willing and able to purchase at a certain price). When the demand is greater than the supply, the card's value *increases;* when supply exceeds demand, the card's value *decreases.* However, as with stamps and coins, the *condition* of a card also affects its value. Cards which have been preserved in *mint* condition are much more in demand by collectors, and therefore worth more than the same cards in worn condition. If the card shows *very light wear*, its value is usually about 65% to 80% of the price for the same card in mint condition. The more wear or damage the card shows, the less it is worth. So if you eventually hope to sell your collection for a profit, try to buy cards in the best possible condition.

## Rookie Cards

A *rookie* card is a player's first regular issue card from a major card set. Today the major card sets are Topps (Main Set, Traded, and Stadium Club); Bowman; Donruss (Main Set, Rookies and Studio); Fleer (Main Set, Update, Ultra, Ultra Update); Leaf; O-Pee-Chee Premier: Score (Main Set and Traded); Upper Deck (Main Set, Extended and Final).

Sometimes several players are shown on one rookie card. Occasionally a rookie card is issued one or more years after the player's actual rookie season. From 1956 to 1980 Topps was the only major card manufacturer, so each player had only one rookie card. Today there are many major card sets—so each player can have several rookie cards.

## Complete Sets

The total cost of the individual cards in a set is always much greater than the complete set price—which makes the complete set an economical purchase. This is because a complete set includes many common cards, and minor-star cards which a dealer will sell at a reduced price when sold as a group. The complete set value usually does not include any error or variety cards. Factory sealed sets generally sell for a premium over hand-collated sets.

## Double-Printed Cards

Baseball cards are not printed individually, but are printed on big sheets that have space for up to 132 cards. Once printed, these sheets are cut apart, and the cards are sorted and packaged. If the number of cards on a sheet is the same as the number of cards in a set, or divides evenly into that set number, then each of the cards on the sheet shows a different player. From 1973 to 1977, Topps issued baseball sets of 660 cards. These were printed on five sheets, each with 132 different cards. But beginning in 1978 and continuing until 1981, Topps changed the number of cards in its sets from 660 to 726, an increase of 66 cards. Rather than print a sixth sheet only half filled, Topps decided to *double-printed* (print twice the quantity) 66 cards in each set.

## Common Cards

*Common* cards are the lowest valued cards in a set. They are cards that feature ordinary players, not stars or popular personalities. There is very little demand by collectors for individual common cards. They are often sold in lots and used primarily to assemble card sets. A typical Topps card set includes about 60% *common* cards, 25% *minor star* cards and 15% *star* cards.

## High-Numbers

During the period from 1952 to 1973 Topps released their annual cards sets in series, rather than issuing the complete set at one time as they do now. Most Topps sets consisted of six or seven card series, each released a few weeks or months apart. For example, the first series of the 1970 Topps card set had 132 cards, numbers 1 to 132, the second series contained numbers 133 to 263, etc. Since sales of the cards tended to become less and less as the season progressed, Topps usually printed fewer of the later card series, which contained the high number cards. Because the high number cards are scarcer today, they are generally more valuable as a group, than the low number cards of the same set. If the last series is not scarce, compared to other series in the same set, it is not a high number series. Every Topps set issued from 1952 to 1973 has a high number series except years 1954, 1956, 1957, 1958 and 1969.

Several Topps card sets from 1952 to 1973 also have a *semi-high-number* series. This is the next to the last series of a card set in which there is also a high number series, and the semi-high number cards are scarce. Semi-high number cards as a group are generally worth less than high numbers, but more than low numbers. Beginning in 1974 and continuing until today, Topps changed their policy and distributed their card sets all at one time, thus eliminating high numbers.

# TOPPS® SPECIAL CARDS

### ALL STAR GLOSSY "INSERT" (2½" x 3½")
22 card set features the starting players, managers, and captains of the previous year's All-Star Game. One random card was inserted in rack packs.

**1984-$5, 1985-$5, 1986-$5, 1987-$4, 1988-$4, 1989-$3, 1990-$3**

### ALL STAR GLOSSY "MAIL-IN" (2½" x 3½")
From 1983 to 1985 the set consisted of 40 cards; 1986 to date—60 cards. The set was offered by Topps directly to the consumer through the mail.

**1983-$13, 1984-$14, 1985-$14, 1986-$13, 1987-$13, 1988-$13, 1989-$10, 1990-$9**

### ROOKIES GLOSSY (2½" x 3½")
22 card set features the top rookies from the previous season. One random card was inserted in supermarket jumbo rack packs.

**1987-$10, 1988-$8, 1989-$7, 1990—$8 (33 cds.)**

### WAX BOX CARDS
Printed on the bottom of wax boxes of the main card set (except 1987 printed on the side of the box). Printed in panels of four cards per box. All sets include 16 cards (2½" x 3½") except 1987 has 8 cards (2⅛" x 3"). Values are for full panels—cut cards are worth 60% less.

**1986-$10, 1987-$4, 1988-$5, 1989-$4, 1990-$4, 1991-$3**

### MINI LEAGUE LEADERS (2⅛" x 2¹⁵/₁₆")
Features the highest rated players statistically from the previous year. All sets include 77 cards except 1986 has 66 cards and 1990 has 88 cards.

**1986-$7, 1987-$6, 1988-$6, 1989-$6, 1990-$6**

### BIG BASEBALL (2⅝" x 3¾")
The design was styled after the Topps 1956 card set. Each set was distributed in wax packs and released in three different series.

**1988 (264 cards)-$30, 1989 (330 cards)-$25, 1990 (330 cards)-$20**

### SENIOR LEAGUE (2½" x 3½")
Features players from the first Senior League season. The 132 card set was packaged in its own box.

**1989/90-$7**

### CAREER BATTING LEADERS
22 card set features the major leaguers with the highest lifetime batting averages. One card was distributed in special Topps packages sold only at K Mart.

**1989-$5, 1990-$5**

### MAJOR LEAGUE DEBUT
Each card features the date of the player's first major league game.

**1990-$12**

### CHAIN STORE SETS (2½" x 3½")
Topps sold each card set exclusively to the chain stores listed below. Each set features a high gloss finish and is individually boxed. All sets include 33 cards—unless otherwise noted. Worth about $4. each.

AMES—1989 20/20 club, 1990 All Stars
BOARDWALK & BASEBALL—1987 Run Makers
CIRCLE K—1985 Home Run Kings
CUMBERLAND FARMS—1989 Superstars
HILLS—1989 Team MVP's, 1990 Hit Men
K-MART—1982 MVP (44 cards). 1987 Stars of Decade, 1988 Memorable Moments, 1989 Dream Team, 1990 Superstars, 1990 Batting Leaders
KAY BEE—1986 Young Superstars, 1987 to 1989 Superstars, 1990 Kings of Baseball
REVCO—1988 League Leaders
RITE AID—1988 Team MVP's
TOYS R US—1987 to 1990 Rookies
WOOLWORTH—1985 All-Time Record Holders (44 cards). 1986 Champion Superstars, 1987 to 1990 Baseball Highlights

### MISCELLANEOUS (1984 to 1989)
1989  United Kingdom (88 cards, size 2⅛" x 3")-$7
1989  Double Header All-Star (24 cards)-$18
1989  Heads Up (24 cards)
1988  United Kingdom (88 cards, size 2⅛" x 3")-$8
1986  Three Dimensional (30 cards, size 4½" x 6")-$10
1986  Supers (60 cards, 4⅞" x 6⅞")-$10
1985  Three Dimensional (30 cards, size 4½" x 6")-$15
1985  Supers (60 cards, size 4⅞" x 6⅞")-$15
1984  Supers (30 cards, size 4⅞" x 6⅞")-$10

### TOPPS GOLD (2½" x 3½")
Each card in the main set was issued as a gold card featuring the player and team name engraved in gold foil. One card was randomly inserted in every 36 wax packs, 18 cello packs, 12 rack packs and 6 jumbo packs. Every vending box had 5 cards and the factory set—10 cards.

**1992 (792 cards)—$450.00**

# DONRUSS® SPECIAL CARDS

## ACTION ALL STARS (3½" x 5")
Each 60 card set features an action shot of an All Star Player. The cards were sold in wax packs.

**1983-$7, 1984-$7, 1985-$7**

## ALL STARS
Issued in conjunction with Donruss Pop-Up cards. Each wax pack includes one Pop-Up and three All Star Cards.

1986 (60 cards, 3½" x 5")—$7
1987 60 cards (3½" x 5")—$7,
1988 (64 cards, 2½" x 3½")—$7
1989 (64 cards, 2½" x 3½")—$7

## POP-UPS
Issued in conjunction with Donruss All Star cards. Each wax pack includes one Pop-Up and three All Star Cards. Features the starting lineup of the previous year's All Star Game. The cards are die-cut and fold out to stand up.

1986 (18 cards, 2½" x 5")—$7
1987 (20 cards, 2½" x 5")—$7,
1988 (20 cards, 2½" x 3½")—$6,
1989 (20 cards, 2½" x 3½")—$6

## SUPER DIAMOND KINGS (4¾" x 6¾")
These are enlarged versions of the Diamond King cards of the main card set. All sets include 26 cards. Available through the mail directly from Perez Steele Galleries.

**1985-$9, 1986-$9, 1987-$9, 1988-$9, 1989-$7, 1990-$9 1991-$10**

## BONUS MVP's (2½" x 3½")
26 card set features Donruss' selection of MVP for each team. One card was inserted in wax and rack packs.

**1988-$9, 1989-$5, 1990-$4**

## GRAND SLAMMERS (2½" x 3½")
12 card set features players who hit grand slams. One random card was distributed in cello packs and the complete set was included in the factory set.

**1989-$3, 1990-$3**

## MISCELLANEOUS (1981 to 1989)
1983  Hall of Fame Heroes (44 cards, 2½" x 3½")—$4
1984  Grand Champions (60 cards, size 3½" x 5")—$6
1987  Opening Day (272 cards, size 2½" x 3½")—$20
1989  Traded (56 cards, size 2½" x 3½")—$6

## PREVIEW (2½" x 3½")
12 card set. Two cards were sent to each dealer in the Donruss network.

**1990-$250.00: 1991-$275.00**

## BASEBALLS BEST (2½" x 3½")
Cards look like the main card set except they have a different color border. The card set is packaged in a plastic gift tray.

**1988 (336 cards)—$20, 1989 (336 cards)—$20, 1990 AL (144 cards)—$9, 1990 NL (144 cards)—$9**

## HIGHLIGHTS (2½" x 3½")
56 card glossy set features highlights of the season and Player of the Month. Packaged in a printed box.

**1985-$20, 1986-$9, 1987-$7**

## WAX BOX CARDS (2½" x 3½")
Four cards were printed in panels on the bottom of wax and cello boxes of the main card set. All sets include four cards. Values are for panels—cut cards are worth 60% less.

**1985-$7, 1986-$2, 1987-$3**

## "ALL STAR" WAX BOX CARDS (2½" x 3½")
Four cards were printed in panels on the bottom of wax boxes of All Star cards. All sets include four cards. Values are for full panels—cut cards are worth 60% less.

**1986-$4, 1987-$3**

## ELITE (2½" x 3½")
Limited to 10,000 of each card. One card was randomly inserted in Donruss wax packs. The cards were numbered 1 of 10,000, etc.

**1991 (8 cards)-$1250.00, 1992 (10 cards)-**

## SIGNATURE (2½" x 3½")
Limited to 5,000 cards. One card was randomly inserted in Donruss wax. The cards were numbered 1 of 5,000, etc.

**1991 (R. Sandberg)-$250.00, 1992 (Cal Ripken)-**

## LEGENDS (2½" x 3½")
Limited to 7,500 cards. One card was randomly inserted in Donruss wax. The cards were numbered 1 of 7,500, etc.

**1991-(N. Ryan)-$325.00, 1992 (Rickey Henderson)**

## DIAMOND KINGS—GOLD FOIL (2½" x 3½")
26 card insert set (not part of the main set for the first time). 13 cards were in each of the two series numbered DK1 through DK27. The cards were coated with gold foil. One card was randomly inserted in packs.

**1992-**

Note—Values not available for 1992 cards at press time.

# FLEER® SPECIAL CARDS

**ALL STAR TEAM (2½″ x 3½″)**
12 card set features Fleer's selection of players for an All Star team. One card was inserted in wax and cello packs.

**1986-$16, 1987-$15, 1988-$13, 1989-$10, 1990-$8 1991-$15**
**(10 cards-only in cello)**

**FUTURE HALL OF FAMERS (2½″ x 3½″)**
6 card set features Fleer's selection of players who would probably enter the Hall of Fame. One random card was inserted in three-pack racks.

**1986-$8**

**HEADLINERS (2½″ x 3½″)**
6 card set features players who made news headlines the previous season. One card was inserted in rack packs.

**1987-$7, 1988-$7**

**FOR THE RECORD (2½″ x 3½″)**
6 card set features players who broke records in the previous season. One card was inserted in rack packs.

**1989-$5**

**SOARING STARS (2½″ x 3½″)**
12 card set features popular rookies. One random card was inserted in jumbo cello packs.

**1990-$5**

**WORLD SERIES (2½″ x 3½″)**
12 card set features highlights from the previous year's World Series. The complete set was packaged as a bonus with the Fleer factory sealed sets.

**1987-$4, 1988-$4, 1989-$3, 1990-$3**

**WAX BOX CARDS (2½″ x 3½″)**
Printed on the bottom of wax and cello boxes in panels of four cards per box. Values are for full panels—cut cards are worth 60% less.

**1986-(8 cards)—$3, 1987—(16 cards)—$6, 1988-(16 cards)—$5, 1989 (28 cards)—$6, 1990 (28 cards)—$5, 1991 (12 cards—$1)**

**ROOKIE SENSATIONS (2½″ x 3½″)**
20 limited edition cards. One card was randomly inserted in 42-card rack packs. Each card was UV coated and gold foil stamped.

**1992-**

**ULTRA GOLD (2½″ x 3½″)**
10 card set. One card was randomly inserted in Ultra packs.

**1991-$12**

**TEAM LEADERS (2½″ x 3½″)**
20 card set. Each card was UV coated and gold foiled. One card was randomly packaged in rack packs.

**1992-**

**LEAGUE STANDOUTS (2½″ x 3½″)**
Six card set features baseball's top players. One card was inserted in rack packs.

**1990-$5**

**CLASSIC MINI (1⅞″ x 2⅝″)**
120 card glossy coated set sold as a complete set and packaged in a printed box.

**1986-$10, 1987-$10, 1988-$9**

**CHAIN STORE SETS (2½″ x 3½″)**
Fleer sold each card set exclusively to the chain stores listed below. Each set features a high gloss finish and is individually boxed. All sets include 44 cards—worth about $4 each

BEN FRANKLIN—1987 to 1990 All Stars
CUMBERLAND FARMS—1987 to 1989 Exciting Stars
ECKERD DRUG—1987 to 1988 Record Setters
HILLS—1990 Award Winners
KAYBEE—1988 Team Leaders
McCRORY—1985 to 1989 Superstars, 1986 to 1988 Sluggers vs. Pitchers (some store display boxes feature cards printed on the bottom)
McCRORY—1985 to 1989 Superstars (from 1987 to 1989 six cards are printed on store display boxes); 1986 to 1988 Sluggers vs. Pitchers (six cards are printed on store display boxes).
PAY 'N SAVE—1987 Game Winners.
REVCO DRUG—1987 to 1988 Hottest Stars
7-ELEVEN—1987 to 1988 and 1990 Award Winners
TOYS R US—1988 to 1990 MVP's
WALGREEN—1986 to 1990 League Leaders
WOOLWORTH—1989 Heroes of Baseball

**PRO-VISIONS (2½″ x 3½″)**
12 card set features drawings by artist Terry Smith. One card was inserted in wax and rack packs.

**1991-$4**

**PRO-VISIONS (2½″ x 3½″)**
4 card set features drawings by artist Terry Smith. The four card set was inserted in the factory set.

**1991-$3**

**CAREER HIGHLIGHTS (2½″ x 3½″)**
12 card set with glossy UV coating and gold foil stamping. One card was randomly inserted in all pack types.

**1992 (Roger Clemens)—**

**AUTOGRAPHED CARDS (2½″ x 3½″)**
Personally autographed UV, glossy coated card randomly inserted in all pack types.

**1992 (Roger Clemens—over 2,000 issued)-**

**3-CARD MAIL-IN (2½″ x 3½″)**
Limited edition subset only available for a limited time by a mail offer—$1.00 with 10 Fleer wrappers. Cards are numbered 13 to 15 continuing from the 12 card inserts.

**1992 (Roger Clemens)-**

**ALL STARS—GOLD FOIL (2½″ x 3½″)**
24 limited-edition cards (12 from each league). One card was randomly inserted in wax packs. Each card was UV coated and gold foil stamped.

**1992-**

Note—Values not available for 1992 cards at press time.

# SCORE® SPECIAL CARDS

### YOUNG SUPERSTARS (2½" x 3½")
Each 40 or 42 card set features a high gloss finish and is packaged in a printed box.

**1988 Series No. 1—$8, 1988 Series No. 2—$8,
1989 Series No. 1—$7, 1989 Series No. 2—$7,
1990 Series No. 1—$6, 1990 Series No. 2—$6**

### WAX BOX BOTTOMS (2½" x 3½")
There are six panels (each with 3 players and a trivia card).

**1988—$6**

### SCOREMASTERS (2½" x 3½")
Sold as a boxed set of 42 cards.

**1989—$10**

### NAT WEST YANKEES (2½" x 3½")
33 card boxed set given away at a Yankee home game.

**1989—$12, 1990-$10**

### PEPSI RED SOX (2½" x 3½")
20 card set.

**1990-$10**

### ROOKIE DREAM TEAM
The 10 card set was included in early shipped Score factory sets.

**1990-$15**

### RISING STARS (2½" x 3½")
100 card set was sold with a 48 page book featuring information about each player.

**1989-$6, 1990-$6, 1991-$10**

### SUPER STARS (2½" x 3½")
100 card set was sold with a 48 page book featuring information about each player.

**1989-$6, 1990-$6, 1991-$10**

### 5-CARD INSERT
150,000 unsigned cards of a 5-card set were issued. One card was randomly inserted in series one packs.

**1992 (Joe DiMaggio)-**

### AUTOGRAPHED CARDS
2,495 personally autographed cards were randomly inserted in packs.

**1992 (Joe DiMaggio)-**

# UPPER DECK® SPECIAL CARDS

### AUTOGRAPHED CARDS
2,500 officially signed and personally numbered 1 of 2,500 etc. One card was randomly inserted in foil packs.

**1990 Extended foil (Reggie Jackson)-$400.00
1991 Series One Foil (Nolan Ryan)-$450.00
1991 Extended Foil (Hank Aaron)-$300.00
1992 Series One Foil (Ted Williams)-**

### BASEBALL HEROES
9 card set. One card was randomly inserted in foil packs. An unnumbered title card (not part of set) was also issued for each player.

**1990 Extended Foil (Reggie Jackson—No's 1 to 9) - $35
1991 Series One Foil (Nolan Ryan—No's 10 to 18) - $8
1991 Extended Foil (Hank Aaron—No's 19 to 27) - $6
1992 Series One Foil (Ted Williams—No's 28 to 36) -**

### SILVER SLUGGERS
18 card insert. One card was randomly inserted in packs.

**1991-$50**

# LEAF® SPECIAL CARDS

### GOLD BONUS
26 card set. One card was randomly inserted in Leaf packs.

**1991-$90**

# BOWMAN® SPECIAL CARDS

### REPRINTS
The 11 card set features reprints of Bowman cards from the 1950's. One unnumbered card was included in Bowman wax packs.

**1989-$2, 1990-$2**

Note—Values not available for 1992 cards at press time.

## LEGEND

**R**—the player's rookie card. Only rookie cards of "star" players are noted.

**RR**—the manufacturer's first card for that player, which is in the Traded Update or Rookie set.

**\***—there is a special feature of this card, which can be determined by referring to the headline for the set.

**AS**—a card featuring a player who was on the previous year's all-star team.

**DK**—abbreviation for Diamond King, which is a Donruss card with artwork by the Perez-Steele Gallery.

**Mgr.**—a card featuring the manager of a baseball team.

**MVP**—Most Valuable Player award

## 1951 Topps "Red Backs" . . . Complete Set of 52 Cards—Value $375.00 (Exc.); $700.00 (Near Mint)

This set, as well as the 1951 "Blue Backs", was Topps' first baseball card issue. The backs of the 2" x 2⅝" cards can be used to play a baseball card game. Card 36 was issued as either White Sox or Athletics. Card 52 was issued as either Hartford or Braves.

| NO. PLAYER | NR. MT. | NO. PLAYER | NR. MT. | NO. PLAYER | NR. MT. | NO. PLAYER | NR. MT. |
|---|---|---|---|---|---|---|---|
| 1 Yogi Berra | 110.00 | 14 Wayne Terwilliger | 6.00 | 27 Wally Westlake | 6.00 | 40 Mike Garcia | 8.00 |
| 2 Sid Gordon | 5.00 | 15 Ralph Kiner | 25.00 | 28 Elmer Valo | 6.00 | 41 Whitey Lockman | 6.00 |
| 3 Ferris Fain | 8.00 | 16 Preacher Roe | 10.00 | 29 Bob Kennedy | 6.00 | 42 Ray Scarborough | 6.00 |
| 4 Verne Stephens | 9.00 | 17 Dave Bell | 7.50 | 30 Warren Spahn | 40.00 | 43 Maurice McDermott | 6.00 |
| 5 Phil Rizzuto | 30.00 | 18 Gerry Coleman | 7.50 | 31 Gil Hodges | 30.00 | 44 Sid Hudson | 6.00 |
| 6 Allie Reynolds | 11.00 | 19 Dick Kokos | 6.00 | 32 Henry Thompson | 6.00 | 45 Andy Seminick | 6.00 |
| 7 Howie Pollet | 6.00 | 20 Dominick DiMaggio | 11.00 | 33 William Werle | 6.00 | 46 Billy Goodman | 6.00 |
| 8 Early Wynn | 25.00 | 21 Larry Jansen | 6.00 | 34 Grady Hatton | 6.00 | 47 Tom Glaviano | 6.00 |
| 9 Roy Sievers | 10.00 | 22 Bob Feller | 40.00 | 35 Al Rosen | 10.00 | 48 Ed Stanky | 8.00 |
| 10 Mel Parnell | 10.00 | 23 Ray Boone | 8.00 | 36 Gus Zernial* | 20.00 | 49 Al Zarilla | 6.00 |
| 11 Gene Hermanski | 6.00 | 24 Hank Bauer | 12.00 | 37 Wes Westrum | 8.00 | 50 M. Irvin | 35.00 |
| 12 Jim Hegan | 6.00 | 25 Cliffe Chambers | 6.00 | 38 Duke Snider | 70.00 | 51 Eddie Robinson | 6.00 |
| 13 Dale Mitchell | 6.00 | 26 Luke Easter | 8.00 | 39 Ted Kluszewski | 15.00 | 52 Tommy Holmes* | 22.00 |

## 1951 Topps "Blue Backs" . . . Complete Set of 52 Cards—Value $1150.00 (Exc.); $2000.00 (Near Mint)

Similar in format to the 1951 "Red Backs." The backs of the 2" x 2⅝" cards can be used to play a baseball card game.

| NO. PLAYER | NR. MT. | NO. PLAYER | NR. MT. | NO. PLAYER | NR. MT. | NO. PLAYER | NR. MT. |
|---|---|---|---|---|---|---|---|
| 1 Eddie Yost | 45.00 | 14 George Munger | 30.00 | 27 Andy Pafko | 30.00 | 40 Vic Wertz | 35.00 |
| 2 Hank Majeski | 30.00 | 15 Eddie Joost | 30.00 | 28 Harry Brecheen | 30.00 | 41 Johnny Schmitz | 30.00 |
| 3 Richie Ashburn | 150.00 | 16 Murry Dickson | 30.00 | 29 Granville Hamner | 30.00 | 42 Bruce Edwards | 30.00 |
| 4 Del Ennis | 30.00 | 17 Roy Smalley | 30.00 | 30 Enos Slaughter | 120.00 | 43 Willie Jones | 30.00 |
| 5 Johnny Pesky | 35.00 | 18 Ned Garver | 30.00 | 31 Lou Brissie | 30.00 | 44 Johnny Wyrostek | 30.00 |
| 6 Al Schoendienst | 100.00 | 19 Phil Masi | 30.00 | 32 Bob Elliott | 30.00 | 45 Bill Pierce (R) | 35.00 |
| 7 Gerald Staley | 30.00 | 20 Ralph Branca | 35.00 | 33 Don Lenhardt | 30.00 | 46 Gerry Priddy | 30.00 |
| 8 Dick Sisler | 30.00 | 21 Bill Johnson | 30.00 | 34 Earl Torgeson | 30.00 | 47 Herman Wehmeier | 30.00 |
| 9 Johnny Sain | 45.00 | 22 Bob Kuzava | 30.00 | 35 Tom Byrne (R) | 30.00 | 48 Billy Cox | 35.00 |
| 10 Joe Page | 35.00 | 23 Dizzy Trout | 30.00 | 36 Cliff Fannin | 30.00 | 49 Hank Sauer | 35.00 |
| 11 Johnny Groth | 30.00 | 24 Sherman Lollar | 30.00 | 37 Bobby Doerr | 100.00 | 50 John Mize | 125.00 |
| 12 Sam Jethroe | 30.00 | 25 Sam A. Mele | 30.00 | 38 Irv Noren | 30.00 | 51 Ed Waitkus | 30.00 |
| 13 Mickey Vernon | 30.00 | 26 Chico Carrasquel | 30.00 | 39 Ed Lopat | 40.00 | 52 Sam Chapman | 50.00 |

# 1952 Topps . . . Complete Set of 407 Cards—Value $24,000.00 (Exc.); $55,000.00 (Near Mint)

Features the rookie cards of Hoyt Wilhelm, Billy Martin and Eddie Mathews. This is Topps' first *major* baseball card set. Cards 1 to 80 were printed with *black* or *red* backs. The high number series is 311 to 407. Semi-high numbers are 251 to 310. Topps introduced a new card size—2⅝" x 3¾", used until 1956. Cards 48 and 49 exist with each other's backs transposed—worth $275.00 each.

| NO. PLAYER | NR. MT. | NO. PLAYER | NR. MT. | NO. PLAYER | NR. MT. | NO. PLAYER | NR. MT. |
|---|---|---|---|---|---|---|---|
| 1 Andy Pafko (exc. $125.00) | 1250.00 | 69 Virgil Stallcup | .50.00 | 137 Roy McMillan | .20.00 | 205 Clyde King | .20.00 |
| 2 James Runnels | 70.00 | 70 Al Zarilla | .50.00 | 138 Bill MacDonald | .20.00 | 206 Joe Ostrowski | .20.00 |
| 3 Hank Thompson | 50.00 | 71 Tom Upton | .50.00 | 139 Ken Wood | .20.00 | 207 Mickey Harris | .20.00 |
| 4 Donald Lenhardt | 50.00 | 72 Karl Olson | .50.00 | 140 John Antonelli | .20.00 | 208 Marlin Stuart | .20.00 |
| 5 Larry Jansen | 50.00 | 73 William Werle | .50.00 | 141 Clint Hartung | .20.00 | 209 Howie Fox | .20.00 |
| 6 Grady Hatton | 50.00 | 74 Andy Hansen | .50.00 | 142 Harry Perkowski | .20.00 | 210 Dick Fowler | .20.00 |
| 7 Wayne Terwilliger | 50.00 | 75 Wes Westrum | .50.00 | 143 Les Moss | .20.00 | 211 Ray Coleman | .20.00 |
| 8 Fred Marsh | 50.00 | 76 Eddie Stanky | .50.00 | 144 Edward Blake | .20.00 | 212 Ned Garver | .20.00 |
| 9 Bob Hogue | 50.00 | 77 Bob Kennedy | .50.00 | 145 Joe Haynes | .20.00 | 213 Nippy Jones | .20.00 |
| 10 Al Rosen | 80.00 | 78 Ellis Kinder | .50.00 | 146 Frank House | .20.00 | 214 Johnny Hopp | .20.00 |
| 11 Phil Rizzuto | 170.00 | 79 Gerald Staley | .50.00 | 147 Bob Young | .20.00 | 215 Hank Bauer | .45.00 |
| 12 Monty Basgall | 50.00 | 80 Herman Wehmeier | .50.00 | 148 John Klippstein | .20.00 | 216 Richie Ashburn | .90.00 |
| 13 Johnny Wyrostek | 50.00 | 81 Vernon Law | .20.00 | 149 Dick Kryhoski | .20.00 | 217 George Stirnweiss | .20.00 |
| 14 Bob Elliott | 50.00 | 82 Duane Pillette | .20.00 | 150 Ted Beard | .20.00 | 218 Clyde McCullough | .20.00 |
| 15 Johnny Pesky | 60.00 | 83 Billy Johnson | .20.00 | 151 Wally Post | .20.00 | 219 Bobby Shantz | .30.00 |
| 16 Gene Hermanski | 50.00 | 84 Vern Stephens | .20.00 | 152 Al Evans | .20.00 | 220 Joe Presko | .20.00 |
| 17 Jim Hegan | 50.00 | 85 Bob Kuzava | .20.00 | 153 Bob Rush | .20.00 | 221 Granny Hamner | .20.00 |
| 18 Merrill Combs | 50.00 | 86 Teddy Gray | .20.00 | 154 Joe Muir | .20.00 | 222 Walter Evers | .20.00 |
| 19 John Bucha | 50.00 | 87 Dale Coogan | .20.00 | 155 Frank Overmire | .20.00 | 223 Del Ennis | .20.00 |
| 20 Billy Loes | 100.00 | 88 Bob Feller | 140.00 | 156 Frank Hiller | .20.00 | 224 Bruce Edwards | .20.00 |
| 21 Ferris Fain | 50.00 | 89 Johnny Lipon | 20.00 | 157 Bob Usher | .20.00 | 225 Frank Baumholtz | .20.00 |
| 22 Dom DiMaggio | 80.00 | 90 Mickey Grasso | 20.00 | 158 Eddie Waitkus | .20.00 | 226 Dave Philley | .20.00 |
| 23 Billy Goodman | 50.00 | 91 Al Schoendienst | 70.00 | 159 Saul Rogovin | .20.00 | 227 Joe Garagiola | .125.00 |
| 24 Luke Easter | 50.00 | 92 Dale Mitchell | 20.00 | 160 Owen Friend | .20.00 | 228 Al Brazle | .20.00 |
| 25 Johnny Grothe | 50.00 | 93 Al Sima | 20.00 | 161 Bud Byerly | .20.00 | 229 Gene Bearden | .20.00 |
| 26 Monte Irvin | 100.00 | 94 Sam Mele | 20.00 | 162 Del Crandall | .20.00 | 230 Matt Batts | .20.00 |
| 27 Sam Jethroe | 50.00 | 95 Ken Holcombe | 20.00 | 163 Stan Rojek | .20.00 | 231 Sam Zoldak | .20.00 |
| 28 Jerry Priddy | 50.00 | 96 Willard Marshall | 20.00 | 164 Walt Dubiel | .20.00 | 232 Billy Cox | .20.00 |
| 29 Ted Kluszewski | 85.00 | 97 Earl Torgeson | 20.00 | 165 Ed Kazak | .20.00 | 233 Bob Friend | .20.00 |
| 30 Mel Parnell | 50.00 | 98 Bill Pierce | 30.00 | 166 Paul LaPalme | .20.00 | 234 Steve Souchock | .20.00 |
| 31 Gus Zernial | 50.00 | 99 Gene Woodling | 50.00 | 167 Bill Howerton | 20.00 | 235 Walt Dropo | .20.00 |
| 32 Eddie Robinson | 50.00 | 100 Del Rice | .20.00 | 168 Charlie Silvera | 25.00 | 236 Ed Fitzgerald | .20.00 |
| 33 Warren Spahn | 225.00 | 101 Max Lanier | .20.00 | 169 Howie Judson | .20.00 | 237 Jerry Coleman | .20.00 |
| 34 Elmer Valo | 50.00 | 102 Bill Kennedy | .20.00 | 170 Gus Bell | 20.00 | 238 Art Houtteman | .20.00 |
| 35 Hank Sauer | 50.00 | 103 Cliff Mapes | .20.00 | 171 Ed Erautt | .20.00 | 239 Rocky Bridges | .20.00 |
| 36 Gil Hodges | 150.00 | 104 Don Kolloway | .20.00 | 172 Eddie Miksis | .20.00 | 240 Jack Phillips | .20.00 |
| 37 Duke Snider | 260.00 | 105 John Pramesa | .20.00 | 173 Roy Smalley | 20.00 | 241 Tommy Byrne | .20.00 |
| 38 Wally Westlake | .50.00 | 106 Mickey Vernon | .20.00 | 174 Clarence Marshall | 20.00 | 242 Tom Poholsky | .20.00 |
| 39 Dizzy Trout | .50.00 | 107 Connie Ryan | .20.00 | 175 Billy Martin (R) | .350.00 | 243 Larry Doby | .45.00 |
| 40 Irv Noren | .50.00 | 108 Jimmy Konstanty | .20.00 | 176 Hank Edwards | .20.00 | 244 Vic Wertz | .20.00 |
| 41 Bob Wellman | .50.00 | 109 Ted Wilks | .20.00 | 177 Bill Wight | 20.00 | 245 Sherry Robertson | .20.00 |
| 42 Lou Kretlow | .50.00 | 110 Dutch Leonard | .20.00 | 178 Cass Michaels | 20.00 | 246 George Kell | .65.00 |
| 43 Ray Scarborough | .50.00 | 111 Harry Lowrey | .20.00 | 179 Frank Smith | 20.00 | 247 Randy Gumpert | .20.00 |
| 44 Con Dempsey | .50.00 | 112 Henry Majeski | .20.00 | 180 Charley Maxwell | 20.00 | 248 Frank Shea | .20.00 |
| 45 Ed Joost | .50.00 | 113 Dick Sisler | .20.00 | 181 Bob Swift | 20.00 | 249 Bobby Adams | .20.00 |
| 46 Gordon Goldsberry | .50.00 | 114 Willard Ramsdell | .20.00 | 182 Bill Hitchcock | 20.00 | 250 Carl Erskine | .60.00 |
| 47 Willie Jones | .50.00 | 115 George Munger | .20.00 | 183 Erv Dusak | 20.00 | 251 Chico Carrasquel | .35.00 |
| 48 Joe Page* | .75.00 | 116 Carl Scheib | .20.00 | 184 Bob Ramazzotti | 20.00 | 252 Vern Bickford | .35.00 |
| 49 Johnny Sain* | .90.00 | 117 Sherman Lollar | .20.00 | 185 Bill Nicholson | 20.00 | 253 Johnny Berardino | .50.00 |
| 50 Marv Rickertt | .50.00 | 118 Ken Raffensberger | .20.00 | 186 Walt Masterson | 20.00 | 254 Joe Dobson | .35.00 |
| 51 Jim Russell | .50.00 | 119 Maurice McDermott | .20.00 | 187 Bob Miller | 20.00 | 255 Clyde Vollmer | .35.00 |
| 52 Don Mueller | .50.00 | 120 Bob Chakales | .20.00 | 188 Clarence Podbielan | 20.00 | 256 Pete Suder | .35.00 |
| 53 Chris Van Cuyk | .50.00 | 121 Gus Niarhos | .20.00 | 189 Harold Reiser | 30.00 | 257 Bob Avila | .35.00 |
| 54 Leo Kiely | .50.00 | 122 Jack Jensen | .60.00 | 190 Don Johnson | 20.00 | 258 Steve Gromek | .35.00 |
| 55 Ray Boone | .50.00 | 123 Eddie Yost | .20.00 | 191 Yogi Berra | .375.00 | 259 Bob Addis | .35.00 |
| 56 Tom Glaviano | .50.00 | 124 Monte Kennedy | .20.00 | 192 Myron Ginsberg | 20.00 | 260 Pete Castiglione | .35.00 |
| 57 Eddie Lopat | 100.00 | 125 Bill Rigney | .20.00 | 193 Harry Simpson | 20.00 | 261 Willie Mays | .1500.00 |
| 58 Bob Mahoney | .50.00 | 126 Fred Hutchinson | .20.00 | 194 Joe Hatten | 20.00 | 262 Virgil Trucks | .35.00 |
| 59 Robin Roberts | .125.00 | 127 Paul Minner | .20.00 | 195 Orestes Minoso (R) | 100.00 | 263 Harry Brecheen | .35.00 |
| 60 Sid Hudson | .50.00 | 128 Don Bollweg | .20.00 | 196 Solly Hemus | 20.00 | 264 Roy Hartsfield | .35.00 |
| 61 Tookie Gilbert | .50.00 | 129 Johnny Mize | .80.00 | 197 George Strickland | 20.00 | 265 Chuck Diering | .35.00 |
| 62 Chuck Stobbs | .50.00 | 130 Sheldon Jones | .20.00 | 198 Phil Haugstad | 20.00 | 266 Murry Dickson | .35.00 |
| 63 Howie Pollett | .50.00 | 131 Morris Martin | .20.00 | 199 George Zuverink | 20.00 | 267 Sid Gordon | .35.00 |
| 64 Roy Sievers | .50.00 | 132 Clyde Klutz | .20.00 | 200 Ralph Houk (R) | 60.00 | 268 Bob Lemon | .175.00 |
| 65 Enos Slaughter | .120.00 | 133 Al Widmar | .20.00 | 201 Alex Kellner | 20.00 | 269 Willard Nixon | .35.00 |
| 66 Preacher Roe | 90.00 | 134 Joe Tipton | .20.00 | 202 Joe Collins | 25.00 | 270 Lou Brissie | .35.00 |
| 67 Allie Reynolds | 90.00 | 135 Dixie Howell | .20.00 | 203 Curt Simmons | 20.00 | 271 Jim Delsing | .35.00 |
| 68 Cliff Chambers | 50.00 | 136 Johnny Schmitz | .20.00 | 204 Ron Northey | 20.00 | 272 Mike Garcia | .35.00 |

| NO. | PLAYER | NR. MT. |
|---|---|---|
| 273 | Erv Palica | 35.00 |
| 274 | Ralph Branca | 75.00 |
| 275 | Pat Mullin | 35.00 |
| 276 | Jim Wilson | 35.00 |
| 277 | Early Wynn | 175.00 |
| 278 | Al Clark | 35.00 |
| 279 | Ed Stewart | 35.00 |
| 280 | Cloyd Boyer | 35.00 |
| 281 | Tom Brown | 45.00 |
| 282 | Birdie Tebbetts | 45.00 |
| 283 | Phil Masi | 45.00 |
| 284 | Hank Arft | 45.00 |
| 285 | Cliff Fannin | 45.00 |
| 286 | Joe DeMaestri | 45.00 |
| 287 | Steve Bilko | 45.00 |
| 288 | Chet Nichols | 45.00 |
| 289 | Tommy Holmes | 45.00 |
| 290 | Joe Astroth | 45.00 |
| 291 | Gil Coan | 45.00 |
| 292 | Floyd Baker | 45.00 |
| 293 | Sibby Sisti | 45.00 |
| 294 | Walker Cooper | 45.00 |
| 295 | Phil Cavarretta | 45.00 |
| 296 | Red Rolfe | 45.00 |
| 297 | Andy Seminick | 45.00 |
| 298 | Bob Ross | 45.00 |
| 299 | Ray Murray | 45.00 |
| 300 | Barney McCosky | 45.00 |
| 301 | Bob Porterfield | 35.00 |
| 302 | Max Surkont | 35.00 |
| 303 | Harry Dorish | 35.00 |
| 304 | Sam Dente | 35.00 |
| 305 | Paul Richards | 35.00 |
| 306 | Lou Sleater | 35.00 |
| 307 | Frank Campos | 35.00 |
| 308 | Luis Aloma | 35.00 |
| 309 | Jim Busby | 35.00 |
| 310 | George Metkovich | 35.00 |
| 311 | M. Mantle (exc. $7500.00) | 20,000.00 |
| 312 | Jackie Robinson | 1000.00 |
| 313 | Bobby Thomson | 200.00 |
| 314 | Roy Campanella | 1500.00 |
| 315 | Leo Durocher (Mgr) | 300.00 |
| 316 | Dave Williams | 150.00 |
| 317 | Connie Marrerro | 150.00 |
| 318 | Hal Gregg | 150.00 |
| 319 | Al Walker | 150.00 |
| 320 | John Rutherford | 150.00 |
| 321 | Joe Black (R) | 225.00 |
| 322 | Randy Jackson | 150.00 |
| 323 | Bubba Church | 150.00 |
| 324 | Warren Hacker | 150.00 |
| 325 | Bill Serena | 150.00 |
| 326 | George Shuba | 150.00 |
| 327 | Archie Wilson | 150.00 |
| 328 | Bob Borkowski | 150.00 |
| 329 | Ivan Delock | 150.00 |
| 330 | Turk Lown | 150.00 |
| 331 | Tom Morgan | 150.00 |
| 332 | Anthony Bartirome | 150.00 |
| 333 | Pee Wee Reese | 900.00 |
| 334 | Wilmer Mizell | 150.00 |
| 335 | Ted Lepcio | 150.00 |
| 336 | Dave Koslo | 150.00 |
| 337 | Jim Hearn | 150.00 |
| 338 | Sal Yvars | 150.00 |
| 339 | Russ Meyer | 150.00 |
| 340 | Bob Hooper | 150.00 |
| 341 | Hal Jeffcoat | 150.00 |
| 342 | Clem Labine | 150.00 |
| 343 | Dick Gernert | 150.00 |
| 344 | Ewell Blackwell | 150.00 |
| 345 | Sammy White | 150.00 |
| 346 | George Spencer | 150.00 |
| 347 | Joe Adcock | 175.00 |
| 348 | Bob Kelly | 150.00 |
| 349 | Bob Cain | 150.00 |
| 350 | Cal Abrams | 150.00 |
| 351 | Alvin Dark | 200.00 |
| 352 | Karl Drews | 150.00 |
| 353 | Robert Del Greco | 150.00 |
| 354 | Fred Hatfield | 150.00 |
| 355 | Bobby Morgan | 150.00 |
| 356 | Toby Atwell | 150.00 |
| 357 | Smokey Burgess | 200.00 |
| 358 | John Kucab | 150.00 |
| 359 | Dee Fondy | 150.00 |
| 360 | George Crowe | 150.00 |
| 361 | Bill Posedel | 150.00 |
| 362 | Kenny Heintzelman | 150.00 |
| 363 | Dick Rozek | 150.00 |
| 364 | Clyde Sukeforth | 150.00 |
| 365 | Cookie Lavagetto | 150.00 |
| 366 | Dave Madison | 150.00 |
| 367 | Bob Thorpe | 150.00 |
| 368 | Ed Wright | 150.00 |
| 369 | Dick Groat (R) | 275.00 |
| 370 | Bill Hoeft | 150.00 |
| 371 | Bob Hofman | 150.00 |
| 372 | Gil McDougald (R) | 250.00 |
| 373 | Jim Turner | 150.00 |
| 374 | Al Benton | 150.00 |
| 375 | Jack Merson | 150.00 |
| 376 | Faye Throneberry | 150.00 |
| 377 | Chuck Dressen | 175.00 |
| 378 | Les Fusselman | 150.00 |
| 379 | Joe Rossi | 150.00 |
| 380 | Clem Koshorek | 150.00 |
| 381 | Milton Stock | 150.00 |
| 382 | Samuel Jones | 150.00 |
| 383 | Del Wilber | 150.00 |
| 384 | Frank Crosetti | 250.00 |
| 385 | Herman Franks | 150.00 |
| 386 | Eddie Yuhas | 150.00 |
| 387 | Bill Meyer | 150.00 |
| 388 | Bob Chipman | 150.00 |
| 389 | Ben Wade | 150.00 |
| 390 | Glenn Nelson | 150.00 |
| 391 | Ben Chapman (photo of Sam Chapman) | 150.00 |
| 392 | Hoyt Wilhelm (R) | 550.00 |
| 393 | Ebba St. Claire | 150.00 |
| 394 | Billy Herman | 225.00 |
| 395 | Jake Pitler | 150.00 |
| 396 | Dick Williams (R) | 250.00 |
| 397 | Forrest Main | 150.00 |
| 398 | Hal Rice | 150.00 |
| 399 | Jim Fridley | 150.00 |
| 400 | Bill Dickey | 550.00 |
| 401 | Bob Schultz | 150.00 |
| 402 | Earl Harrist | 150.00 |
| 403 | Bill Miller | 150.00 |
| 404 | Dick Brodowski | 150.00 |
| 405 | Eddie Pellagrini | 150.00 |
| 406 | Joseph Nuxhall (R) | 225.00 |
| 407 | E. Mathews (R) (exc. $600.00) | 2500.00 |

## 1953 Topps . . . Complete Set of 274 Cards—Value $4500.00 (Exc.); $12,000.00 (Near Mint)

Features the rookie cards of Johnny Padres and Jim Gilliam. Although the cards are numbered up to 280, there are only 274 cards in the set. Six cards were not issued—numbers 253, 261, 267, 268, 271 and 275. The high number series is 221 to 280. Card size 2⅝" x 3¾".

MICKEY MANTLE · WILLIE MAYS · JIM GILLIAM · JOHN PODRES · MILT BOLLING

| NO. | PLAYER | NR. MT. |
|---|---|---|
| 1 | J. Robinson (Exc. $150.00) | 600.00 |
| 2 | Luke Easter | 20.00 |
| 3 | George Crowe | 20.00 |
| 4 | Benjamin Wade | 20.00 |
| 5 | Joe Dobson | 20.00 |
| 6 | Sam Jones | 20.00 |
| 7 | Bob Borkowski | 15.00 |
| 8 | Clem Koshorek | 15.00 |
| 9 | Joe Collins | 25.00 |
| 10 | Smokey Burgess | 30.00 |
| 11 | Sal Yvars | 20.00 |
| 12 | Howie Judson | 15.00 |
| 13 | Connie Marrero | 20.00 |
| 14 | Clem Labine | 15.00 |
| 15 | Bobo Newsom | 15.00 |
| 16 | Harry Lowrey | 14.00 |
| 17 | Billy Hitchcock | 18.00 |
| 18 | Ted Lepcio | 15.00 |
| 19 | Melvin Parnell | 20.00 |
| 20 | Hank Thompson | 20.00 |
| 21 | Billy Johnson | 20.00 |
| 22 | Howie Fox | 20.00 |
| 23 | Toby Atwell | 20.00 |
| 24 | Ferris Fain | 20.00 |
| 25 | R. Boone | 20.00 |
| 26 | Dale Mitchell | 20.00 |
| 27 | Roy Campanella | 175.00 |
| 28 | Eddie Pellagrini | 20.00 |
| 29 | Hal Jeffcoat | 20.00 |
| 30 | Willard Nixon | 20.00 |
| 31 | Ewell Blackwell | 30.00 |
| 32 | Clyde Vollmer | 20.00 |
| 33 | Bob Kennedy | 20.00 |
| 34 | George Shuba | 20.00 |
| 35 | Irv Noren | 20.00 |
| 36 | Johnny Groth | 20.00 |
| 37 | Ed Mathews | 100.00 |
| 38 | Jim Hearn | 20.00 |
| 39 | Eddie Miksis | 20.00 |
| 40 | Johnny Lipon | 20.00 |
| 41 | Enos Slaughter | 75.00 |
| 42 | Gus Zernial | 20.00 |
| 43 | Gil McDougald | 35.00 |
| 44 | Ellis Kinder | 20.00 |
| 45 | Grady Hatton | 20.00 |
| 46 | John Klippstein | 20.00 |
| 47 | Bubba Church | 20.00 |
| 48 | Bob Del Greco | 20.00 |
| 49 | Faye Throneberry | 20.00 |
| 50 | Chuck Dressenn | 20.00 |
| 51 | Frank Campos | 20.00 |
| 52 | Ted Gray | 20.00 |
| 53 | Sherman Lollar | 20.00 |
| 54 | Bob Feller | 90.00 |
| 55 | Maurice McDermott | 20.00 |
| 56 | Gerald Staley | 20.00 |
| 57 | Carl Scheib | 20.00 |
| 58 | George Metkovich | 20.00 |
| 59 | Karl Drews | 20.00 |
| 60 | Cloyd Boyer | 20.00 |
| 61 | Early Wynn | 75.00 |
| 62 | Monte Irvin | 35.00 |
| 63 | Gus Niarhos | 15.00 |
| 64 | David Philley | 20.00 |
| 65 | Earl Harrist | 20.00 |
| 66 | Orestes Minoso | 35.00 |
| 67 | Roy Sievers | 20.00 |
| 68 | Del Rice | 20.00 |
| 69 | Dick Brodowski | 20.00 |
| 70 | Eddie Yuhas | 20.00 |
| 71 | Tony Bartirome | 20.00 |
| 72 | Fred Hutchison | 25.00 |
| 73 | Eddie Robinson | 20.00 |
| 74 | Joe Rossi | 20.00 |
| 75 | Mike Garcia | 20.00 |
| 76 | Pee Wee Reese | 130.00 |
| 77 | John Mize | 60.00 |
| 78 | Al Schoendienst | 55.00 |
| 79 | Johnny Wyrostek | 20.00 |
| 80 | Jim Hegan | 20.00 |
| 81 | Joe Black | 50.00 |
| 82 | Mickey Mantle | 2400.00 |
| 83 | Howie Pollett | 20.00 |
| 84 | Bob Hooper | 20.00 |
| 85 | Bobby Morgan | 20.00 |
| 86 | Billy Martin | 125.00 |
| 87 | Ed Lopat | 35.00 |
| 88 | Willie Jones | 15.00 |

| NO. | PLAYER | NR. MT. |
|---|---|---|
| 89 | Chuck Stobbs | 16.00 |
| 90 | Hank Edwards | 16.00 |
| 91 | Ebba St. Claire | 16.00 |
| 92 | Paul Minner | 16.00 |
| 93 | Hal Rice | 16.00 |
| 94 | William Kennedy | 16.00 |
| 95 | Willard Marshall | 16.00 |
| 96 | Virgil Trucks | 16.00 |
| 97 | Don Kolloway | 16.00 |
| 98 | Cal Abrams | 16.00 |
| 99 | Dave Madison | 16.00 |
| 100 | Bill Miller | 16.00 |
| 101 | Ted Wilks | 16.00 |
| 102 | Connie Ryan | 16.00 |
| 103 | Joe Astroth | 16.00 |
| 104 | Yogi Berra | 200.00 |
| 105 | Joe Nuxhall | 20.00 |
| 106 | John Antonelli | 20.00 |
| 107 | Danny O'Connell | 20.00 |
| 108 | Bob Porterfield | 20.00 |
| 109 | Alvin Dark | 30.00 |
| 110 | Herman Wehmeier | 16.00 |
| 111 | Hank Sauer | 16.00 |
| 112 | Ned Garver | 16.00 |
| 113 | Jerry Priddy | 16.00 |
| 114 | Phil Rizzuto | 100.00 |
| 115 | George Spencer | 20.00 |
| 116 | Frank Smith | 20.00 |
| 117 | Sidney Gordon | 20.00 |
| 118 | Gus Bell | 20.00 |
| 119 | Johnny Sain | 40.00 |
| 120 | Davey Williams | 20.00 |
| 121 | Walt Dropo | 20.00 |
| 122 | Elmer Valo | 20.00 |
| 123 | Tommy Byrne | 20.00 |
| 124 | Sibby Sisti | 20.00 |
| 125 | Dick Williams | 18.00 |
| 126 | Billy Connelly | 16.00 |
| 127 | Clint Courtney | 16.00 |
| 128 | Wilmer Mizell | 16.00 |
| 129 | Keith Thomas | 16.00 |
| 130 | Turk Lown | 16.00 |
| 131 | Harry Byrd | 16.00 |
| 132 | Tom Morgan | 16.00 |
| 133 | Gil Coan | 16.00 |
| 134 | Rube Walker | 16.00 |
| 135 | Al Rosen | 30.00 |
| 136 | Ken Heintzelman | 20.00 |
| 137 | John Rutherford | 20.00 |
| 138 | George Kell | 50.00 |
| 139 | Sammy White | 18.00 |
| 140 | Tommy Glaviano | 18.00 |
| 141 | Allie Reynolds | 35.00 |
| 142 | Vic Wertz | 22.00 |
| 143 | Billy Pierce | 25.00 |
| 144 | Bob Schultz | 16.00 |
| 145 | Harry Dorish | 16.00 |
| 146 | Granville Hamner | 16.00 |
| 147 | Warren Spahn | 120.00 |
| 148 | Mickey Grasso | 16.00 |
| 149 | Dom DiMaggio | 30.00 |
| 150 | Harry Simpson | 16.00 |
| 151 | Hoyt Wilhelm | 60.00 |
| 152 | Bob Adams | 16.00 |
| 153 | Andy Seminick | 16.00 |
| 154 | Dick Groat | 30.00 |
| 155 | Dutch Leonard | 16.00 |
| 156 | Jim Rivera | 16.00 |
| 157 | Bob Addis | 16.00 |
| 158 | John Logan | 25.00 |
| 159 | Wayne Terwilliger | 16.00 |
| 160 | Bob Young | 16.00 |
| 161 | Vern Bickford | 16.00 |
| 162 | Ted Kluszewski | 36.00 |
| 163 | Fred Hatfield | 16.00 |
| 164 | Frank Shea | 16.00 |
| 165 | Billy Hoeft | 16.00 |
| 166 | Bill Hunter | 15.00 |
| 167 | Art Schult | 15.00 |
| 168 | Willard Schmidt | 15.00 |
| 169 | Dizzy Trout | 15.00 |
| 170 | Bill Werle | 15.00 |
| 171 | Bill Glynn | 15.00 |
| 172 | Rip Repulski | 15.00 |
| 173 | Preston Ward | 15.00 |
| 174 | Billy Loes | 15.00 |
| 175 | Ronald Kline | 15.00 |
| 176 | Don Hoak | 15.00 |
| 177 | Jim Dyck | 15.00 |
| 178 | Jim Waugh | 15.00 |
| 179 | Gene Hermanski | 15.00 |
| 180 | Virgil Stallcup | 15.00 |
| 181 | Al Zarilla | 15.00 |
| 182 | Robert Hofman | 15.00 |
| 183 | Stuart Miller | 20.00 |
| 184 | Hal Brown | 15.00 |
| 185 | Jim Pendleton | 15.00 |
| 186 | Charles Bishop | 15.00 |
| 187 | Jim Fridley | 15.00 |
| 188 | Andy Carey | 22.00 |
| 189 | Ray Jablonski | 15.00 |
| 190 | Dixie Walker | 15.00 |
| 191 | Ralph Kiner | 50.00 |
| 192 | Wally Westlake | 15.00 |
| 193 | Mike Clark | 15.00 |
| 194 | Eddie Kazak | 15.00 |
| 195 | Eddie McGhee | 15.00 |
| 196 | Bob Keegan | 15.00 |
| 197 | Del Crandall | 15.00 |
| 198 | Forrest Main | 15.00 |
| 199 | Marion Fricano | 15.00 |
| 200 | Gordon Goldsberry | 15.00 |
| 201 | Paul LaPalme | 15.00 |
| 202 | Carl Sawatski | 15.00 |
| 203 | Cliff Fannin | 15.00 |
| 204 | Dick Bokelmann | 15.00 |
| 205 | Vern Benson | 15.00 |
| 206 | Ed Bailey | 15.00 |
| 207 | Whitey Ford | 160.00 |
| 208 | Jim Wilson | 15.00 |
| 209 | Jim Greengrass | 15.00 |
| 210 | Bob Cerv | 20.00 |
| 211 | J.W. Porter | 15.00 |
| 212 | Jack Dittmer | 15.00 |
| 213 | Ray Scarborough | 15.00 |
| 214 | Bill Bruton | 20.00 |
| 215 | Gene Conley | 20.00 |
| 216 | Jim Hughes | 15.00 |
| 217 | Murray Wall | 15.00 |
| 218 | Les Fusselman | 15.00 |
| 219 | Pete Runnels | 15.00 |
| | (Photo of Don Johnson) | |
| 220 | Satchell Paige | 400.00 |
| 221 | Bob Milliken | 70.00 |
| 222 | Vic Janowicz | 50.00 |
| 223 | John O'Brien | 50.00 |
| 224 | Lou Sleater | 50.00 |
| 225 | Bobby Shantz | 80.00 |
| 226 | Edward Erautt | 70.00 |
| 227 | Morris Martin | 70.00 |
| 228 | Hal Newhouser | 100.00 |
| 229 | Rocky Krsnich | 70.00 |
| 230 | Johnny Lindell | 50.00 |
| 231 | Solly Hemus | 45.00 |
| 232 | Dick Kokos | 70.00 |
| 233 | Al Aber | 70.00 |
| 234 | Ray Murray | 50.00 |
| 235 | John Hetki | 50.00 |
| 236 | Harold Perkowski | 50.00 |
| 237 | Clarence Podbielan | 50.00 |
| 238 | Cal Hogue | 50.00 |
| 239 | Jim Delsing | 70.00 |
| 240 | Fred Marsh | 70.00 |
| 241 | Al Sima | 50.00 |
| 242 | Charlie Silvera | 75.00 |
| 243 | Carlos Bernier | 50.00 |
| 244 | Willie Mays | 1750.00 |
| 245 | Bill Norman | 45.00 |
| 246 | Roy Face (R) | 80.00 |
| 247 | Mike Sandlock | 45.00 |
| 248 | Gene Stephens | 40.00 |
| 249 | Ed O'Brien | 40.00 |
| 250 | Bob Wilson | 40.00 |
| 251 | Sid Hudson | 40.00 |
| 252 | Henry Foiles | 40.00 |
| 254 | Preacher Roe | 90.00 |
| 255 | Dixie Howell | 40.00 |
| 256 | Les Peden | 40.00 |
| 257 | Bob Boyd | 40.00 |
| 258 | Jim Gilliam (R) | 300.00 |
| 259 | Roy McMillan | 45.00 |
| 260 | Sam Calderone | 40.00 |
| 262 | Bob Oldis | 40.00 |
| 263 | John Podres (R) | 250.00 |
| 264 | Gene Woodling | 70.00 |
| 265 | Jackie Jensen | 100.00 |
| 266 | Bob Cain | 70.00 |
| 269 | Duane Pillette | 70.00 |
| 270 | Vern Stephens | 70.00 |
| 272 | Bill Antonello | 70.00 |
| 273 | Harvey Haddix (R) | 110.00 |
| 274 | John Riddle | 70.00 |
| 276 | Ken Raffensberger | 70.00 |
| 277 | Don Lund | 70.00 |
| 278 | Willie Miranda | 70.00 |
| 279 | Joe Coleman | 40.00 |
| 280 | M. Boling (R) (Exc. $45.00) | 300.00 |

## 1954 Topps . . . Complete Set of 250 Cards—Value $2750.00 (Exc.); $7000.00 (Near Mint)

Features the rookie cards of Hank Aaron, Al Kaline and Ernie Banks. Card size 2⅝" x 3¾". Topps' signed Ted Williams to a special contract for this set, and he appears on two cards.

| NO. | PLAYER | NR. MT. |
|---|---|---|
| 1 | Ted Williams (Exc. $120.00) | 550.00 |
| 2 | Gus Zernial | 10.00 |
| 3 | Monte Irvin | 30.00 |
| 4 | Hank Sauer | 12.00 |
| 5 | Ed Lopat | 20.00 |
| 6 | Pete Runnels | 12.00 |
| 7 | Ted Kluszewski | 25.00 |
| 8 | Bobby Young | 12.00 |
| 9 | Harvey Haddix | 12.00 |
| 10 | Jackie Robinson | 225.00 |
| 11 | Paul Smith | 12.00 |
| 12 | Del Crandall | 12.00 |
| 13 | Billy Martin | 75.00 |
| 14 | Preacher Roe | 18.00 |
| 15 | Al Rosen | 20.00 |
| 16 | Vic Janowicz | 12.00 |
| 17 | Phil Rizzuto | 65.00 |
| 18 | Walt Dropo | 12.00 |
| 19 | Johnny Lipon | 12.00 |
| 20 | Warren Spahn | 90.00 |

| NO. PLAYER | NR. MT. | NO. PLAYER | NR. MT. | NO. PLAYER | NR. MT. | NO. PLAYER | NR. MT. |
|---|---|---|---|---|---|---|---|
| 21 Bobby Shantz | 15.00 | 79 Andy Pafko | 12.00 | 137 Wally Moon | 20.00 | 193 Johnny Hopp | 12.00 |
| 22 Jim Greengrass | 12.00 | 80 Jackie Jensen | 20.00 | 138 Bob Borkowski | 12.00 | 194 Bill Sarni | 12.00 |
| 23 Luke Easter | 12.00 | 81 Dave Hoskins | 12.00 | 139 The O'Brien's: | 25.00 | 195 Bill Consolo | 12.00 |
| 24 Granny Hamner | 12.00 | 82 Milt Bolling | 12.00 | Johnny O'Brien, | | 196 Stan Jok | 12.00 |
| 25 Harv. Kuenn (R) | 35.00 | 83 Joe Collins | 12.00 | Eddie O'Brien | | 197 L. Rowe | 12.00 |
| 26 Ray Jablonski | 12.00 | 84 Dick Cole | 12.00 | 140 Tom Wright | 12.00 | 198 Carl Sawatski | 12.00 |
| 27 Ferris Fain | 12.00 | 85 Bob Turley (R) | 25.00 | 141 Joe Jay | 12.00 | 199 Glenn Nelson | 12.00 |
| 28 Paul Minner | 12.00 | 86 Billy Herman | 20.00 | 142 Tom Poholsky | 12.00 | 200 Larry Jansen | 12.00 |
| 29 Jim Hegan | 12.00 | 87 Roy Face | 15.00 | 143 Rollie Hemsley | 12.00 | 201 Al Kaline (R) | 650.00 |
| 30 Ed Mathews | 90.00 | 88 Matt Batts | 15.00 | 144 Bill Werle | 12.00 | 202 Bob Purkey | 12.00 |
| 31 John Klippstein | 12.00 | 89 Howie Pollet | 15.00 | 145 Elmer Valo | 12.00 | 203 Harry Brecheen | 12.00 |
| 32 Duke Snider | 125.00 | 90 Willie Mays | 400.00 | 146 Don Johnson | 12.00 | 204 Angel Scull | 12.00 |
| 33 Johnny Schmitz | 12.00 | 91 Bob Oldis | 12.00 | 147 John Riddle | 12.00 | 205 Johnny Sain | 25.00 |
| 34 Jim Rivera | 12.00 | 92 Wally Westlake | 12.00 | 148 Bob Trice | 12.00 | 206 Ray Crone | 12.00 |
| 35 Junior Gilliam | 25.00 | 93 Sid Hudson | 12.00 | 149 Jim Robertson | 12.00 | 207 Tom Oliver | 12.00 |
| 36 Hoyt Wilhelm | 40.00 | 94 Ernie Banks (R) | 650.00 | 150 Dick Kryhoski | 12.00 | 208 Grady Hatton | 12.00 |
| 37 Whitey Ford | 100.00 | 95 Hal Rice | 12.00 | 151 Alex Grammas | 12.00 | 209 Charlie Thompson | 12.00 |
| 38 Eddie Stanky | 12.00 | 96 Charlie Silvera | 12.00 | 152 Mike Blyzka | 12.00 | 210 Bob Buhl | 16.00 |
| 39 Sherm Lollar | 12.00 | 97 Jerry Lane | 12.00 | 153 Albert Walker | 12.00 | 211 Don Hoak | 12.00 |
| 40 Mel Parnell | 12.00 | 98 Joe Black | 18.00 | 154 Mike Fornieles | 12.00 | 212 Bob Micelotta | 12.00 |
| 41 Willie Jones | 12.00 | 99 Bob Hofman | 12.00 | 155 Bob Kennedy | 12.00 | 213 John Fitzpatrick | 12.00 |
| 42 Don Mueller | 12.00 | 100 Bob Keegan | 12.00 | 156 Joe Coleman | 12.00 | 214 A. Portocarrero | 12.00 |
| 43 Dick Groat | 13.00 | 101 Gene Woodling | 18.00 | 157 Don Lenhardt | 12.00 | 215 Ed McGhee | 12.00 |
| 44 Ned Garver | 12.00 | 102 Gil Hodges | 75.00 | 158 Peanuts Lowrey | 12.00 | 216 Al Sima | 12.00 |
| 45 Richie Ashburn | 35.00 | 103 Jim Lemon | 12.00 | 159 Dave Philley | 12.00 | 217 Paul Schreiber | 12.00 |
| 46 Ken Raffensberger | 12.00 | 104 Mike Sandlock | 12.00 | 160 Red Kress | 12.00 | 218 Fred Marsh | 12.00 |
| 47 Ellis Kinder | 12.00 | 105 Andy Carey | 12.00 | 161 John Hetki | 12.00 | 219 Charles Kress | 12.00 |
| 48 Bill Hunter | 12.00 | 106 Dick Kokos | 12.00 | 162 Herman Wehmeier | 12.00 | 220 Ruben Gomez | 12.00 |
| 49 Ray Murray | 12.00 | 107 Duane Pillette | 12.00 | 163 Frank House | 12.00 | 221 Dick Brodowski | 12.00 |
| 50 Y. Berra | 230.00 | 108 Thornton Kipper | 12.00 | 164 Stuart Miller | 12.00 | 222 Bill Wilson | 12.00 |
| 51 Johnny Lindell | 27.00 | 109 Bill Bruton | 12.00 | 165 Jim Pendleton | 12.00 | 223 Joe Haynes | 12.00 |
| 52 Vic Power | 27.00 | 110 Harry Dorish | 12.00 | 166 Johnny Podres | 25.00 | 224 Dick Weik | 12.00 |
| 53 Jack Dittmer | 27.00 | 111 Jim Delsing | 12.00 | 167 Don Lund | 12.00 | 225 Don Liddle | 12.00 |
| 54 Vern Stephens | 27.00 | 112 Bill Renna | 12.00 | 168 Morrie Martin | 12.00 | 226 Jehosie Heard | 12.00 |
| 55 Phil Cavarretta | 32.00 | 113 Bob Boyd | 12.00 | 169 Jim Hughes | 12.00 | 227 Buster Mills | 12.00 |
| 56 Willie Miranda | 27.00 | 114 Dean Stone | 12.00 | 170 Jim Rhodes | 12.00 | 228 Gene Hermanski | 12.00 |
| 57 Luis Aloma | 27.00 | 115 Rip Repulski | 12.00 | 171 Leo Kiely | 12.00 | 229 Bob Talbot | 12.00 |
| 58 Bob Wilson | 27.00 | 116 Steve Bilko | 12.00 | 172 Hal Brown | 12.00 | 230 Bob Kuzava | 12.00 |
| 59 Gene Conley | 27.00 | 117 Solly Hemus | 12.00 | 173 Jack Harshman | 12.00 | 231 Roy Smalley | 12.00 |
| 60 Frank Baumholtz | 27.00 | 118 Carl Scheib | 12.00 | 174 Tom Qualters | 12.00 | 232 Lou Limmer | 12.00 |
| 61 Bob Cain | 27.00 | 119 John Antonelli | 12.00 | 175 Frank Leja | 12.00 | 233 Augie Galan | 12.00 |
| 62 Eddie Robinson | 27.00 | 120 Roy McMillan | 12.00 | 176 Robert Kelley | 12.00 | 234 Jerry Lynch | 12.00 |
| 63 Johnny Pesky | 32.00 | 121 Clem Labine | 12.00 | 177 Bob Milliken | 12.00 | 235 Vernon Law | 12.00 |
| 64 Hank Thompson | 27.00 | 122 Johnny Logan | 12.00 | 178 Bill Glynn | 12.00 | 236 Paul Penson | 12.00 |
| 65 Bob Swift | 27.00 | 123 Bobby Adams | 12.00 | 179 Gair Allie | 12.00 | 237 Mike Ryba | 12.00 |
| 66 Thad Lepcio | 27.00 | 124 Marion Fricano | 12.00 | 180 Wes Westrum | 12.00 | 238 Al Aber | 12.00 |
| 67 Jim Willis | 27.00 | 125 Harry Perkowski | 12.00 | 181 Mel Roach | 12.00 | 239 Bill Skowron (R) | 80.00 |
| 68 Sammy Calderone | 27.00 | 126 Ben Wade | 12.00 | 182 Chuck Harmon | 12.00 | 240 Sam Mele | 12.00 |
| 69 Bud Podbielan | 27.00 | 127 Steve O'Neill | 12.00 | 183 Earle Combs | 25.00 | 241 Bob Miller | 12.00 |
| 70 Larry Doby | 60.00 | 128 Hank Aaron (R) | 1500.00 | 184 Ed Bailey | 12.00 | 242 Curt Roberts | 12.00 |
| 71 Frank Smith | 27.00 | 129 Forrest Jacobs | 12.00 | 185 Chuck Stobbs | 12.00 | 243 Ray Blades | 12.00 |
| 72 Preston Ward | 27.00 | 130 Hank Bauer | 30.00 | 186 Karl Olson | 12.00 | 244 Leroy Wheat | 12.00 |
| 73 Wayne Terwilliger | 27.00 | 131 Reno Bertoia | 12.00 | 187 Heinie Manush | 20.00 | 245 Roy Sievers | 15.00 |
| 74 Bill Taylor | 27.00 | 132 Tommy Lasorda (R) | 175.00 | 188 Dave Jolly | 12.00 | 246 Howie Fox | 12.00 |
| 75 Fred Haney | 27.00 | 133 Del Baker | 12.00 | 189 Bob Ross | 12.00 | 247 Ed Mayo | 12.00 |
| 76 Bob Scheffing | 12.00 | 134 Cal Hogue | 12.00 | 190 Ray Herbert | 12.00 | 248 Al Smith | 12.00 |
| 77 Ray Boone | 12.00 | 135 Joe Presko | 12.00 | 191 Dick Schofield | 12.00 | 249 Wilmer Mizell | 12.00 |
| 78 Ted Kazanski | 12.00 | 136 Connie Ryan | 12.00 | 192 Ellis Deal | 12.00 | 250 Ted Williams (Exc. $120.00) | 650.00 |

## 1955 Topps . . . Complete Set of 206 Cards—Value $2750.00 (Exc.) $7000.00 (Near Mint)

Features the rookie cards of Roberto Clemente, Sandy Koufax and Harmon Killebrew. Topps' switched to a horizontal format in 1955. Card size 2⅝" x 3¾". Four cards originally intended to be issued—175, 186, 203 and 209 were withdrawn. The high number series is 161 to 210.

| NO. PLAYER | NR. MT. |
|---|---|
| 1 Dusty Rhodes (Exc. $8.00) | 45.00 |
| 2 Ted Williams | 350.00 |
| 3 Art Fowler | 7.50 |
| 4 Al Kaline | 200.00 |
| 5 Jim Gilliam | 12.00 |
| 6 Stan Hack | 10.00 |
| 7 Jim Hegan | 7.50 |
| 8 Hal Smith | 7.50 |
| 9 Bob Miller | 7.50 |
| 10 Bob Keegan | 7.50 |
| 11 Ferris Fain | 7.50 |
| 12 Vernon Thies | 7.50 |
| 13 Fred Marsh | 7.50 |
| 14 Jim Finigan | 7.50 |
| 15 Jim Pendleton | 7.50 |
| 16 Roy Sievers | 7.50 |
| 17 Bobby Hofman | 7.50 |
| 18 Russ Kemmerer | 7.50 |
| 19 Billy Herman | 12.50 |
| 20 Andy Carey | 7.50 |
| 21 Alex Grammas | 7.50 |
| 22 Bill Skowron | 17.50 |
| 23 Jack Parks | 7.50 |
| 24 Hal Newhouser | 12.00 |
| 25 Johnnie Podres | 15.00 |
| 26 Dick Groat | 9.00 |
| 27 Billy Gardner | 7.50 |
| 28 Ernie Banks | 175.00 |
| 29 Herman Wehmeier | 7.50 |
| 30 Vic Power | 7.50 |
| 31 Warren Spahn | 75.00 |
| 32 Ed McGhee | 7.50 |
| 33 Tom Qualters | 7.50 |
| 34 Wayne Terwilliger | 7.50 |
| 35 Dave Jolly | 7.50 |
| 36 Leo Kiely | 7.50 |
| 37 Joe Cunningham | 10.00 |
| 38 Bob Turley | 12.00 |
| 39 Billy Glynn | 7.50 |
| 40 Don Hoak | 7.50 |
| 41 Chuck Stobbs | 7.50 |
| 42 John McCall | 7.50 |
| 43 Harvey Haddix | 9.00 |
| 44 Harold Valentine | 7.50 |
| 45 Hank Sauer | 7.50 |
| 46 Ted Kazanski | 7.50 |
| 47 Hank Aaron | 350.00 |
| 48 Bob Kennedy | 7.50 |
| 49 J.W. Porter | 7.50 |
| 50 Jack Robinson | 225.00 |
| 51 Jim Hughes | 7.50 |
| 52 Bill Tremel | 7.50 |

| NO. PLAYER | NR. MT. |
|---|---|
| 53 Bill Taylor | 7.50 |
| 54 Lou Limmer | 7.50 |
| 55 Eldon Repulski | 7.50 |
| 56 Ray Jablonski | 7.50 |
| 57 Bill O'Dell | 7.50 |
| 58 Manuel Rivera | 7.50 |
| 59 Gair Allie | 7.50 |
| 60 Dean Stone | 7.50 |
| 61 Forrest Jacobs | 7.50 |
| 62 Thornton Kipper | 7.50 |
| 63 Joe Collins | 8.00 |
| 64 Gus Triandos | 8.00 |
| 65 Ray Boone | 7.50 |
| 66 Ron Jackson | 7.50 |
| 67 Wally Moon | 7.50 |
| 68 Jim Davis | 7.50 |
| 69 Ed Bailey | 7.50 |
| 70 Al Rosen | 13.00 |
| 71 Ruben Gomez | 7.50 |
| 72 Karl Olson | 7.50 |
| 73 Jack Shepard | 7.50 |
| 74 Bob Borkowski | 7.50 |
| 75 Sandy Amoros (R) | 15.00 |
| 76 Howie Pollet | 7.50 |
| 77 Arnold Portocarrero | 7.50 |
| 78 Gordon Jones | 7.50 |
| 79 Clyde Schell | 7.50 |
| 80 Bob Grim (R) | 12.00 |
| 81 Gene Conley | 7.50 |
| 82 Chuck Harmon | 7.50 |
| 83 Thomas Brewer | 7.50 |
| 84 Camilo Pascual (R) | 9.00 |
| 85 Don Mossi (R) | 12.00 |
| 86 Bill Wilson | 7.50 |
| 87 Frank House | 7.50 |
| 88 Bob Skinner | 7.50 |
| 89 Joe Frazier | 7.50 |
| 90 Karl Spooner | 11.00 |
| 91 Milton Bolling | 7.50 |
| 92 Don Zimmer (R) | 35.00 |
| 93 Steve Bilko | 7.50 |
| 94 Reno Bertoia | 7.50 |
| 95 Preston Ward | 7.50 |
| 96 Charlie Bishop | 7.50 |
| 97 Carlos Paula | 7.50 |
| 98 Johnny Riddle | 7.50 |
| 99 Frank Leja | 7.50 |
| 100 Monte Irvin | 24.00 |
| 101 Johnny Gray | 7.50 |
| 102 Wally Westlake | 7.50 |
| 103 Charlie White | 7.50 |

| NO. PLAYER | NR. MT. |
|---|---|
| 104 Jack Harshman | 7.50 |
| 105 Chuck Diering | 7.50 |
| 106 Frank Sullivan | 7.50 |
| 107 Curt Roberts | 7.50 |
| 108 Rube Walker | 7.50 |
| 109 Ed Lopat | 13.00 |
| 110 Gus Zernial | 7.50 |
| 111 Bob Milliken | 7.50 |
| 112 Nelson King | 7.50 |
| 113 Harry Brecheen | 7.50 |
| 114 Louie Ortiz | 7.50 |
| 115 Ellis Kinder | 7.50 |
| 116 Tom Hurd | 7.50 |
| 117 Mel Roach | 7.50 |
| 118 Bob Purkey | 7.50 |
| 119 Bob Lennon | 7.50 |
| 120 Ted Kluszewski | 20.00 |
| 121 Bill Renna | 7.50 |
| 122 Carl Sawatski | 7.50 |
| 123 Sandy Koufax (R) | 1000.00 |
| 124 Harmon Killebrew (R) | 325.00 |
| 125 Ken Boyer (R) | 65.00 |
| 126 Dick Hall | 7.50 |
| 127 Dale Long | 7.50 |
| 128 Ted Lepcio | 7.50 |
| 129 Elvin Tappe | 7.50 |
| 130 Mayo Smith | 7.50 |
| 131 Grady Hatton | 7.50 |
| 132 Bob Trice | 7.50 |
| 133 Dave Hoskins | 7.50 |
| 134 Joe Jay | 7.50 |
| 135 Johnny O'Brien | 7.50 |
| 136 Bunky Stewart | 7.50 |
| 137 Harry Elliott | 7.50 |
| 138 Ray Herbert | 7.50 |
| 139 Steve Kraly | 7.50 |
| 140 Mel Parnell | 7.50 |
| 141 Tom Wright | 7.50 |
| 142 Jerry Lynch | 7.50 |
| 143 Dick Schofield | 7.50 |
| 144 Joe Amalfitano | 7.50 |
| 145 Elmer Valo | 7.50 |
| 146 Dick Donovan | 7.50 |
| 147 Laurin Pepper | 7.50 |
| 148 Hal Brown | 7.50 |
| 149 Ray Crone | 7.50 |
| 150 Michael Higgins | 7.50 |
| 151 Ralph Kress | 15.00 |
| 152 Harry Agganis (R) | 75.00 |
| 153 Bud Podbielan | 15.00 |
| 154 Willie Miranda | 15.00 |

| NO. PLAYER | NR. MT. |
|---|---|
| 155 Eddie Mathews | 115.00 |
| 156 Joe Black | 25.00 |
| 157 Bob Miller | 15.00 |
| 158 Tommy Carroll | 15.00 |
| 159 Johnny Schmitz | 15.00 |
| 160 Raymond Narleski | 15.00 |
| 161 Chuck Tanner (R) | 35.00 |
| 162 Joe Coleman | 25.00 |
| 163 Faye Throneberry | 25.00 |
| 164 Roberto Clemente (R) | 1200.00 |
| 165 Don Johnson | 25.00 |
| 166 Hank Bauer | 45.00 |
| 167 Tom Casagrande | 25.00 |
| 168 Duane Pillette | 25.00 |
| 169 Bob Oldis | 25.00 |
| 170 Jim Pearce | 15.00 |
| 171 Dick Brodowski | 25.00 |
| 172 Frank Baumholtz | 15.00 |
| 173 Bob Kline | 25.00 |
| 174 Rudy Minarcin | 25.00 |
| 176 Norm Zauchin | 25.00 |
| 177 Jim Robertson | 25.00 |
| 178 Bobby Adams | 25.00 |
| 179 Jim Bolger | 25.00 |
| 180 Clem Labine | 25.00 |
| 181 Roy McMillan | 25.00 |
| 182 Humberto Robinson | 25.00 |
| 183 Anthony Jacobs | 25.00 |
| 184 Harry Perkowski | 15.00 |
| 185 Don Ferrarese | 25.00 |
| 187 Gil Hodges | 135.00 |
| 188 Charlie Silvera | 15.00 |
| 189 Phil Rizzuto | 135.00 |
| 190 Gene Woodling | 25.00 |
| 191 Eddie Stanky | 25.00 |
| 192 Jim Delsing | 25.00 |
| 193 Johnny Sain | 35.00 |
| 194 Willie Mays | 425.00 |
| 195 Eddie Roebuck | 25.00 |
| 196 Gale Wade | 25.00 |
| 197 Al Smith | 25.00 |
| 198 Yogi Berra | 260.00 |
| 199 Bert Hamrick | 25.00 |
| 200 Jack Jensen | 45.00 |
| 201 Sherman Lollar | 25.00 |
| 202 Jim Owens | 25.00 |
| 204 Frank Smith | 25.00 |
| 205 Gene Freese | 25.00 |
| 206 Pete Daley | 25.00 |
| 207 Bill Consolo | 25.00 |
| 208 Ray Moore | 25.00 |
| 210 Duke Snider (exc. $100.00) | 500.00 |

## 1956 Topps . . . Complete Set of 340 Cards—Value $3000.00 (Exc.) $6750.00 (Near Mint)

In 1956 Topps bought its competitor—Bowman Card Co., including all of its player contracts. Topps card sets would now be larger and more complete. Card size 2⅝" x 3¾". Features the rookie card of Luis Aparicio. Card numbers 1 to 180 were printed with *gray* or *white* backs. The six team cards indicated by an *asterisk* were issued with three different *face* designs. The team card dated *1955* is worth about four times the value of the other team cards. The two checklists are not included in the complete set price.

| NO. PLAYER | NR. MT. |
|---|---|
| 1 W. Harridge (Exc. $10.00) (AL President) | 125.00 |
| 2 Warren Giles (NL President) | 20.00 |

| NO. PLAYER | NR. MT. |
|---|---|
| 3 Elmer Valo | 7.00 |
| 4 Carlos Paula | 7.00 |
| 5 Ted Williams | 275.00 |
| 6 Ray Boone | 7.00 |

| NO. PLAYER | NR. MT. |
|---|---|
| 7 Ron Negray | 7.00 |
| 8 Walter Alston (Mgr) | 35.00 |
| 9 Ruben Gomez | 7.00 |
| 10 Warren Spahn | 75.00 |

| NO. PLAYER | NR. MT. |
|---|---|
| 11 Chicago Cubs* | 25.00 |
| 12 Andy Carey | 7.00 |
| 13 Roy Face | 7.00 |
| 14 Ken Boyer | 15.00 |

| NO. PLAYER | NR. MT. | NO. PLAYER | NR. MT. | NO. PLAYER | NR. MT. | NO. PLAYER | NR. MT. |
|---|---|---|---|---|---|---|---|
| 15 Ernie Banks | 75.00 | 97 Jerry Lynch | 7.00 | 179 Harry Chiti | 9.00 | 261 Bobby Shantz | 12.00 |
| 16 Hector Lopez | 9.00 | 98 Camilo Pascual | 7.00 | 180 Robin Roberts | 25.00 | 262 Howie Pollett | 12.00 |
| 17 Gene Conley | 7.00 | 99 Don Zimmer | 18.00 | 181 Billy Martin | 90.00 | 263 Bob Miller | 12.00 |
| 18 Dick Donovan | 7.00 | 100 Baltimore Orioles* | 25.00 | 182 Paul Minner | 12.50 | 264 Ray Monzant | 12.00 |
| 19 Chuck Diering | 7.00 | 101 Roy Campanella | 120.00 | 183 Stan Lopata | 12.50 | 265 Sandy Consuegra | 12.00 |
| 20 Al Kaline | 100.00 | 102 Jim Davis | 9.00 | 184 Don Bessent | 12.50 | 266 Don Ferrarese | 12.00 |
| 21 Joe Collins | 8.00 | 103 Willie Miranda | 9.00 | 185 Bill Bruton | 12.50 | 267 Bob Nieman | 12.00 |
| 22 Jim Finigan | 7.00 | 104 Bob Lennon | 9.00 | 186 Ron Jackson | 12.50 | 268 Dale Mitchell | 12.00 |
| 23 Freddie Marsh | 7.00 | 105 Al Smith | 9.00 | 187 Early Wynn | 35.00 | 269 Jack Meyer | 12.00 |
| 24 Dick Groat | 10.00 | 106 Joe Astroth | 9.00 | 188 Chicago White Sox | 30.00 | 270 Billy Loes | 12.00 |
| 25 Ted Kluszeski | 20.00 | 107 Ed Mathews | 50.00 | 189 Ned Garver | 12.50 | 271 Foster Castleman | 12.00 |
| 26 Grady Hatton | 7.00 | 108 Laurin Pepper | 9.00 | 190 Carl Furillo | 20.00 | 272 Danny O'Connell | 12.00 |
| 27 Nelson Burbrink | 7.00 | 109 Enos Slaughter | 25.00 | 191 Frank Lary | 13.50 | 273 Walker Cooper | 12.00 |
| 28 Bobby Hofman | 7.00 | 110 Yogi Berra | 135.00 | 192 Smokey Burgess | 15.00 | 274 Frank Baumholtz | 12.00 |
| 29 Jack Harshman | 7.00 | 111 Boston Red Sox | 25.00 | 193 Wilmer Mizell | 12.50 | 275 Jim Greengrass | 12.00 |
| 30 Jackie Robinson | 150.00 | 112 Dee Fondy | 9.00 | 194 Monte Irvin | 30.00 | 276 George Zuverink | 12.00 |
| 31 Hank Aaron | 225.00 | 113 Phil Rizzuto | 50.00 | 195 George Kell | 30.00 | 277 Daryl Spencer | 12.00 |
| 32 Frank House | 7.00 | 114 Jim Owens | 9.00 | 196 Tom Poholsky | 12.50 | 278 Chet Nichols | 12.00 |
| 33 Roberto Clemente | 350.00 | 115 Jackie Jensen | 12.00 | 197 Granny Hamner | 12.50 | 279 Johnny Groth | 12.00 |
| 34 Tom Brewer | 7.00 | 116 Eddie O'Brien | 9.00 | 198 Ed Fitzgerald | 12.50 | 280 Jim Gilliam | 15.00 |
| 35 Al Rosen | 10.00 | 117 Virgil Trucks | 9.00 | 199 Hank Thompson | 12.50 | 281 Art Houtteman | 12.00 |
| 36 Rudy Minarcin | 7.00 | 118 Nellie Fox | 30.00 | 200 Bob Feller | 120.00 | 282 Warren Hacker | 12.00 |
| 37 Alex Grammas | 7.00 | 119 Larry Jackson | 11.00 | 201 Rip Repulski | 12.50 | 283 Hal Smith | 12.00 |
| 38 Bob Kennedy | 7.00 | 120 Richie Ashburn | 30.00 | 202 Jim Hearn | 12.50 | 284 Ike Delock | 12.00 |
| 39 Don Mossi | 7.00 | 121 Pittsburgh Pirates | 25.00 | 203 Bill Tuttle | 12.50 | 285 Eddie Miksis | 12.00 |
| 40 Bob Turley | 10.00 | 122 Willard Nixon | 9.00 | 204 Arthur Swanson | 12.50 | 286 Bill Wight | 12.00 |
| 41 Hank Sauer | 7.00 | 123 Roy McMillan | 9.00 | 205 Whitey Lockman | 12.50 | 287 Bobby Adams | 12.00 |
| 42 Sandy Amoros | 8.00 | 124 Don Kaiser | 9.00 | 206 Erv Palica | 12.50 | 288 Bob Cerv | 20.00 |
| 43 Ray Moore | 7.00 | 125 Minnie Minoso | 18.00 | 207 Jim Small | 12.50 | 289 Hal Jeffcoat | 12.00 |
| 44 Windy McCall | 7.00 | 126 Jim Brady | 9.00 | 208 Elston Howard | 45.00 | 290 Curt Simmons | 12.00 |
| 45 Gus Zernial | 7.00 | 127 Willie Jones | 9.00 | 209 Max Surkont | 12.50 | 291 Frank Kellert | 12.00 |
| 46 Gene Freese | 7.00 | 128 Eddie Yost | 9.00 | 210 Mike Garcia | 12.50 | 292 Luis Aparicio (R) | 135.00 |
| 47 Art Fowler | 7.00 | 129 Jake Martin | 9.00 | 211 Murry Dickson | 12.50 | 293 Stu Miller | 12.00 |
| 48 Jim Hegan | 7.00 | 130 Willie Mays | 275.00 | 212 Johnny Temple | 12.50 | 294 Ernie Johnson | 12.00 |
| 49 Pedro Ramos | 7.00 | 131 Bob Roselli | 9.00 | 213 Detroit Tigers | 40.00 | 295 Clem Labine | 12.00 |
| 50 Dusty Rhode | 7.00 | 132 Bobby Avila | 9.00 | 214 Bob Rush | 12.50 | 296 Andy Seminick | 12.00 |
| 51 Ernie Oravetz | 7.00 | 133 Ray Narleski | 9.00 | 215 Tommy Byrne | 12.50 | 297 Bob Skinner | 12.00 |
| 52 Bob Grim | 7.00 | 134 St. Louis Cardinals | 25.00 | 216 Jerry Schoonmaker | 12.50 | 298 Johnny Schmitz | 12.00 |
| 53 Arnold Portocarrero | 7.00 | 135 Mickey Mantle | 900.00 | 217 Billy Klaus | 12.50 | 299 Charley Neal | 20.00 |
| 54 Bob Keegan | 7.00 | 136 Johnny Logan | 9.00 | 218 Joe Nuxhall | 12.50 | 300 Vic Wertz | 12.00 |
| 55 Wally Moon | 7.00 | 137 Al Silvera | 9.00 | 219 Lew Burdette | 15.00 | 301 Marv Grissom | 12.00 |
| 56 Dale Long | 7.00 | 138 Johnny Antonelli | 9.00 | 220 Del Ennis | 12.50 | 302 Eddie Robinson | 12.00 |
| 57 Duke Maas | 7.00 | 139 Tommy Carroll | 9.00 | 221 Bob Friend | 12.50 | 303 Jim Dyck | 12.00 |
| 58 Ed Roebuck | 7.00 | 140 Herb Score (R) | 24.00 | 222 Dave Philley | 12.50 | 304 Frank Malzone | 18.00 |
| 59 Jose Santiago | 7.00 | 141 Joe Frazier | 9.00 | 223 Randy Jackson | 12.50 | 305 Brooks Lawrence | 12.00 |
| 60 Mayo Smith | 7.00 | 142 Gene Baker | 9.00 | 224 Bud Podbielan | 12.50 | 306 Curt Roberts | 12.00 |
| 61 Bill Skowron | 13.00 | 143 Jimmy Piersall | 11.00 | 225 Gil McDougald | 25.00 | 307 Hoyt Wilhelm | 30.00 |
| 62 Hal Smith | 7.00 | 144 Leroy Powell | 9.00 | 226 New York Giants | 65.00 | 308 Charles Harmon | 12.00 |
| 63 Roger Craig (R) | 25.00 | 145 Gil Hodges | 45.00 | 227 Russ Meyer | 12.50 | 309 Don Blasingame | 12.00 |
| 64 Luis Arroyo | 7.00 | 146 Washington Nat'l | 25.00 | 228 Mickey Vernon | 12.50 | 310 Steve Gromek | 12.00 |
| 65 Johnny O'Brien | 7.00 | 147 Earl Torgeson | 9.00 | 229 Harry Brecheen | 12.50 | 311 Hal Naragon | 12.00 |
| 66 Bob Speake | 7.00 | 148 Alvin Dark | 11.00 | 230 Chico Carrasquel | 12.50 | 312 Andy Pafko | 12.00 |
| 67 Vic Power | 7.00 | 149 Dixie Howell | 9.00 | 231 Bob Hale | 12.50 | 313 Gene Stephens | 12.00 |
| 68 Chuck Stobbs | 7.00 | 150 Duke Snider | 135.00 | 232 Toby Atwell | 12.50 | 314 Hobie Landrith | 12.00 |
| 69 Chuck Tanner | 9.00 | 151 Spook Jacobs | 9.00 | 233 Carl Erskine | 20.00 | 315 Milt Bolling | 12.00 |
| 70 Jim Rivera | 7.00 | 152 Billy Hoeft | 9.00 | 234 Pete Runnels | 12.50 | 316 Jerry Coleman | 12.00 |
| 71 Frank Sullivan | 7.00 | 153 Frank Thomas | 9.00 | 235 Don Newcombe | 45.00 | 317 Al Aber | 12.00 |
| 72 Philadelphia Phillies* | 25.00 | 154 David Pope | 9.00 | 236 Kansas C. Athletics | 25.00 | 318 Fred Hatfield | 12.00 |
| 73 Wayne Terwilliger | 7.00 | 155 Harvey Kuenn | 12.00 | 237 Jose Valdivielso | 12.50 | 319 Jack Crimian | 12.00 |
| 74 Jim King | 7.00 | 156 Wes Westrum | 9.00 | 238 Walt Dropo | 12.50 | 320 Joe Adcock | 12.00 |
| 75 Roy Sievers | 8.00 | 157 Dick Brodowski | 9.00 | 239 Harry Simpson | 12.50 | 321 Jim Konstanty | 12.00 |
| 76 Ray Crone | 7.00 | 158 Wally Post | 9.00 | 240 Whitey Ford | 120.00 | 322 Karl Olson | 12.00 |
| 77 Harvey Haddix | 8.00 | 159 Clint Courtney | 9.00 | 241 Don Mueller | 12.50 | 323 Willard Schmidt | 12.00 |
| 78 Herman Wehmeier | 7.00 | 160 Billy Pierce | 11.00 | 242 Hershell Freeman | 12.50 | 324 Rocky Bridges | 12.00 |
| 79 Sandy Koufax | 350.00 | 161 Joe DeMaestri | 9.00 | 243 Sherm Lollar | 12.50 | 325 Don Liddle | 12.00 |
| 80 Gus Triandos | 8.00 | 162 Gus Bell | 9.00 | 244 Bob Buhl | 12.50 | 236 Connie Johnson | 12.00 |
| 81 Wally Westlake | 7.00 | 163 Gene Woodling | 9.00 | 245 Billy Goodman | 12.50 | 327 Bob Wiesler | 12.00 |
| 82 Bill Renna | 7.00 | 164 Harmon Killebrew | 135.00 | 246 Tom Gorman | 12.50 | 328 Preston Ward | 12.00 |
| 83 Karl Spooner | 7.00 | 165 Red Schoendienst | 25.00 | 247 Bill Sarni | 12.50 | 329 Lou Berberet | 12.00 |
| 84 Babe Birrer | 7.00 | 166 Brooklyn Dodgers | 175.00 | 248 Bob Porterfield | 12.50 | 330 Jim Busby | 12.00 |
| 85 Cleveland Indians* | 25.00 | 167 Harry Dorish | 9.00 | 249 Johnny Klippstein | 12.50 | 331 Dick Hall | 12.00 |
| 86 Ray Jablonski | 7.00 | 168 Sammy White | 9.00 | 250 Larry Doby | 20.00 | 332 Don Larsen | 30.00 |
| 87 Dean Stone | 7.00 | 169 Bob Nelson | 9.00 | 251 New York Yankees | 200.00 | 333 Rube Walker | 12.00 |
| 88 Johnny Kucks | 8.00 | 170 Bill Virdon | 12.00 | 252 Vernon Law | 12.50 | 334 Bob Miller | 12.00 |
| 89 Norm Zauchin | 7.00 | 171 Jim Wilson | 9.00 | 253 Irv Noren | 15.00 | 335 Don Hoak | 12.00 |
| 90 Cincinnati Redlegs* | 25.00 | 172 Frank Torre | 9.00 | 254 George Crowe | 12.50 | 336 Ellis Kinder | 12.00 |
| 91 Gail Harris | 7.00 | 173 Johnny Podres | 15.00 | 255 Bob Lemon | 30.00 | 337 Bobby Morgan | 12.00 |
| 92 Red Wilson | 7.00 | 174 Glen Gorbous | 9.00 | 256 Tom Hurd | 12.50 | 338 Jim Delsing | 12.00 |
| 93 George Susce Jr. | 7.00 | 175 Del Crandall | 9.00 | 257 Bobby Thomson | 18.00 | 339 Rance Pless | 12.00 |
| 94 Ronald Kline | 7.00 | 176 Alex Kellner | 9.00 | 258 Art Ditmar | 12.50 | 340 M. McDermott (exc. $10.00) | 40.00 |
| 95 Milwaukee Braves* | 25.00 | 177 Hank Bauer | 20.00 | 259 Sam Jones | 12.50 | — Checklist 1/3 | 250.00 |
| 96 Bill Tremel | 7.00 | 178 Joe Black | 11.00 | 260 Pee Wee Reese | 135.00 | — Checklist 2/4 | 250.00 |

# 1957 Topps . . . Complete Set of 407 Cards—Value $2750.00 (Exc.), $7250.00 (Near Mint)

Topps' switched to a 2½" x 3½" card size. The 1957 set features the rookie cards of Don Drysdale, Frank Robinson, Tony Kubek and Brooks Robinson. The four checklists are not included in the complete set price.

| NO. PLAYER | NR. MT. | NO. PLAYER | NR. MT. | NO. PLAYER | NR. MT. | NO. PLAYER | NR. MT. |
|---|---|---|---|---|---|---|---|
| 1 Ted Williams (Exc. $75.00) | 400.00 | 65 Wally Moon | 7.50 | 130 Don Newcombe | 12.00 | 196 Larry Jackson | 5.00 |
| 2 Yogi Berra | 140.00 | 66 Brooks Lawrence | 7.50 | 131 Milt Bolling | 6.00 | 197 Hank Sauer | 5.00 |
| 3 Dale Long | 7.50 | 67 Chico Carrasquel | 7.50 | 132 Art Ditmar | 6.00 | 198 Detroit Tigers | 12.00 |
| 4 Johnny Logan | 7.50 | 68 Ray Crone | 7.50 | 133 Del Crandall | 6.00 | 199 Vernon Law | 5.00 |
| 5 Sal Maglie | 10.00 | 69 Roy McMillan | 7.50 | 134 Don Kaiser | 6.00 | 200 Gil McDougald | 11.00 |
| 6 Hector Lopez | 7.50 | 70 Richie Ashburn | 20.00 | 135 Bill Skowron | 13.00 | 201 Sandy Amoros | 5.00 |
| 7 Luis Aparicio | 30.00 | 71 Murry Dickson | 7.50 | 136 Jim Hegan | 6.00 | 202 Dick Gernert | 5.00 |
| 8 Don Mossi | 7.50 | 72 Bill Tuttle | 7.50 | 137 Bob Rush | 6.00 | 203 Hoyt Wilhelm | 18.00 |
| 9 Johnny Temple | 7.50 | 73 George Crowe | 7.50 | 138 Minnie Minoso | 12.00 | 204 Kansas C. Athletics | 11.00 |
| 10 Willie Mays | 200.00 | 74 Vito Valentinetti | 7.50 | 139 Lou Kretlow | 6.00 | 205 Charlie Maxwell | 5.00 |
| 11 George Zuverink | 7.50 | 75 Jim Piersall | 10.00 | 140 Frank Thomas | 6.00 | 206 Willard Schmidt | 5.00 |
| 12 Dick Groat | 10.00 | 76 Roberto Clemente | 200.00 | 141 Al Aber | 6.00 | 207 Bill Hunter | 5.00 |
| 13 Wally Burnette | 7.50 | 77 Paul Foytack | 7.50 | 142 Charley Thompson | 6.00 | 208 Lew Burdette | 8.00 |
| 14 Bob Nieman | 7.50 | 78 Vic Wertz | 7.50 | 143 Andy Pafko | 6.00 | 209 Bob Skinner | 5.00 |
| 15 Robin Roberts | 25.00 | 79 Lindy McDaniel | 9.00 | 144 Ray Narleski | 6.00 | 210 Roy Campanella | 100.00 |
| 16 Walt Moryn | 7.50 | 80 Gil Hodges | 40.00 | 145 Al Smith | 6.00 | 211 Camilo Pascual | 5.00 |
| 17 Billy Gardner | 7.50 | 81 Herman Wehmeier | 7.50 | 146 Don Ferrarese | 6.00 | 212 Rocco Colavito (R) | 125.00 |
| 18 Don Drysdale (R) | 225.00 | 82 Elston Howard | 16.00 | 147 Al Walker | 6.00 | 213 Les Moss | 5.00 |
| 19 Bob Wilson | 7.50 | 83 Lou Skizas | 7.50 | 148 Don Mueller | 6.00 | 214 Philadelphia Phillies | 12.00 |
| 20 Hank Aaron | 275.00 | 84 Moe Drabowsky | 7.50 | 149 Bob Kennedy | 6.00 | 215 Enos Slaughter | 25.00 |
| (negative reversed) | | 85 Larry Doby | 10.00 | 150 Bob Friend | 6.00 | 216 Marv Grissom | 5.00 |
| 21 Frank Sullivan | 7.50 | 86 Bill Sarni | 7.50 | 151 Willie Miranda | 6.00 | 217 Gene Stephens | 5.00 |
| 22 Jerry Snyder | 7.50 | 87 Tom Gorman | 7.50 | 152 Jack Harshman | 6.00 | 218 Ray Jablonski | 5.00 |
| (photo of Ed Fitzgerald) | | 88 Harvey Kuenn | 9.00 | 153 Karl Olson | 6.00 | 219 Tom Acker | 5.00 |
| 23 Sherm Lollar | 7.50 | 89 Roy Sievers | 7.00 | 154 Red Schoendienst | 20.00 | 220 Jackie Jensen | 12.00 |
| 24 Bill Mazeroski (R) | 50.00 | 90 Warren Spahn | 70.00 | 155 Jim Brosnan | 6.00 | 221 Dixie Howell | 5.00 |
| 25 W. Ford | 60.00 | 91 Mack Burk | 6.00 | 156 Gus Triandos | 6.00 | 222 Alex Grammas | 5.00 |
| 26 Bob Boyd | 7.50 | 92 Mickey Vernon | 6.00 | 157 Wally Post | 6.00 | 223 Frank House | 5.00 |
| 27 Ted Kazanski | 7.50 | 93 Hal Jeffcoat | 6.00 | 158 Curt Simmons | 6.00 | 224 Marv Blaylock | 5.00 |
| 28 Gene Conley | 7.50 | 94 Bobby Del Greco | 6.00 | 159 Solly Drake | 6.00 | 225 Harry Simpson | 5.00 |
| 29 Whitey Herzog | 25.00 | 95 Mickey Mantle | 800.00 | 160 Billy Pierce | 8.00 | 226 Preston Ward | 5.00 |
| 30 Pee Wee Reese | 60.00 | 96 Hank Aguirre | 6.00 | 161 Pittsburgh Pirates | 12.00 | 227 Jerry Staley | 5.00 |
| 31 Ron Northey | 7.50 | 97 New York Yankees | 50.00 | 162 Jack Meyer | 6.00 | 228 Smokey Burgess | 5.00 |
| 32 Hersh Freeman | 7.50 | 98 Alvin Dark | 8.00 | 163 Sammy White | 6.00 | 229 George Susce | 5.00 |
| 33 Jim Small | 7.50 | 99 Bob Keegan | 6.00 | 164 Tommy Carroll | 6.00 | 230 George Kell | 18.00 |
| 34 Tom Sturdivant | 7.50 | 100 Giles and Harridge | 10.00 | 165 Ted Kluszewski | 25.00 | 231 Solly Hemus | 5.00 |
| 35 Frank Robinson (R) | 275.00 | (League Presidents) | | 166 Roy Face | 6.00 | 232 Whitey Lockman | 5.00 |
| 36 Bob Grim | 7.50 | 101 Chuck Stobbs | 6.00 | 167 Vic Power | 6.00 | 233 Art Fowler | 5.00 |
| 37 Frank Torre | 7.50 | 102 Ray Boone | 6.00 | 168 Frank Lary | 6.00 | 234 Dick Cole | 5.00 |
| 38 Nellie Fox | 20.00 | 103 Joe Nuxhall | 6.00 | 169 Herb Plews | 6.00 | 235 Tom Poholsky | 5.00 |
| 39 Al Worthington | 7.50 | 104 Hank Foiles | 6.00 | 170 Duke Snider | 100.00 | 236 Joe Ginsberg | 5.00 |
| 40 Early Wynn | 20.00 | 105 Johnny Antonelli | 6.00 | 171 Boston Red Sox | 12.00 | 237 Foster Catleman | 5.00 |
| 41 Hal Smith | 7.50 | 106 Ray Moore | 6.00 | 172 Gene Woodling | 6.00 | 238 Eddie Robinson | 5.00 |
| 42 Dee Fondy | 7.50 | 107 Jim Rivera | 6.00 | 173 Roger Craig | 12.00 | 239 Tom Morgan | 5.00 |
| 43 Connie Johnson | 7.50 | 108 Tommy Byrne | 6.00 | 174 Willie Jones | 6.00 | 240 Hank Bauer | 12.00 |
| 44 Joe DeMaestri | 7.50 | 109 Hank Thompson | 6.00 | 175 Don Larsen | 15.00 | 241 Joe Lonnett | 5.00 |
| 45 Carl Furillo | 12.00 | 110 Bill Virdon | 8.00 | 176 Gene Baker | 6.00 | 242 Charlie Neal | 5.00 |
| 46 Bob Miller | 7.50 | 111 Hal Smith | 6.00 | 177 Eddie Yost | 5.00 | 243 St. Louis Cardinals | 5.00 |
| 47 Don Blasingame | 7.50 | 112 Tom Brewer | 6.00 | 178 Don Bessent | 5.00 | 244 Billy Loes | 5.00 |
| 48 Bill Bruton | 7.50 | 113 Wilmer Mizell | 6.00 | 179 Ernie Oravetz | 5.00 | 245 Rip Repulski | 5.00 |
| 49 Daryl Spencer | 7.50 | 114 Milwaukee Braves | 15.00 | 180 Dave Bell | 5.00 | 246 Jose Valdivielso | 5.00 |
| 50 Herb A. Score | 12.00 | 115 Jim Gilliam | 10.00 | 181 Dick Donovan | 5.00 | 247 Turk Lown | 5.00 |
| 51 Clint Courtney | 7.50 | 116 Mike Fornieles | 6.00 | 182 Hobie Landrith | 5.00 | 248 Jim Finigan | 5.00 |
| 52 Lee Walls | 7.50 | 117 Joe Adcock | 9.00 | 183 Chicago Cubs | 12.00 | 249 Dave Pope | 5.00 |
| 53 Clem Labine | 7.50 | 118 Bob Porterfield | 6.00 | 184 Tito Francona | 5.00 | 250 Ed Mathews | 35.00 |
| 54 Elmer Valo | 7.50 | 119 Stan Lopata | 6.00 | 185 Johnny Kucks | 5.00 | 251 Baltimore Orioles | 12.00 |
| 55 Ernie Banks | 100.00 | 120 Bob Lemon | 20.00 | 186 Jim King | 5.00 | 252 Carl Erskine | 10.00 |
| 56 Dave Sisler | 7.50 | 121 Cletis Boyer | 15.00 | 187 Virgil Trucks | 5.00 | 253 Gus Zernial | 5.00 |
| 57 Jim Lemon | 7.50 | 122 Ken Boyer | 12.00 | 188 Felix Mantilla | 5.00 | 254 Ron Negray | 5.00 |
| 58 Ruben Gomez | 7.50 | 123 Steve Ridzik | 6.00 | 189 Willard Nixon | 5.00 | 255 Charlie Silvera | 5.00 |
| 59 Dick Williams | 7.50 | 124 Dave Philley | 6.00 | 190 Randy Jackson | 5.00 | 256 Ronnie Kline | 5.00 |
| 60 Billy Hoeft | 7.50 | 125 Al Kaline | 75.00 | 191 Joe Margoneri | 5.00 | 257 Walt Dropo | 5.00 |
| 61 Dusty Rhodes | 7.50 | 126 Bob Wiesler | 6.00 | 192 Gerry Coleman | 5.00 | 258 Steve Gromek | 5.00 |
| 62 Billy Martin | 50.00 | 127 Bob Buhl | 6.00 | 193 Del Rice | 5.00 | 259 Eddie O'Brien | 5.00 |
| 63 Ike Delock | 7.50 | 128 Ed Bailey | 6.00 | 194 Hal Brown | 5.00 | 260 Del Ennis | 5.00 |
| 64 Pete Runnels | 7.50 | 129 Saul Rogovin | 6.00 | 195 Bobby Avila | 5.00 | 261 Bob Chakales | 5.00 |

| NO. | PLAYER | NR. MT. |
|---|---|---|
| 262 | Bobby Thomson | 15.00 |
| 263 | George Strickland | 5.00 |
| 264 | Bob Turley | 10.00 |
| 265 | Harvey Haddix | 22.00 |
| 266 | Kenny Kuhn | 20.00 |
| 267 | Danny Kravitz | 20.00 |
| 268 | Jackie Collum | 20.00 |
| 269 | Bob Cerv | 20.00 |
| 270 | Washington Senators | 40.00 |
| 271 | Danny O'Connell | 20.00 |
| 272 | Bobby Shantz | 25.00 |
| 273 | Jim Davis | 20.00 |
| 274 | Don Hoak | 20.00 |
| 275 | Cleveland Indians | 40.00 |
| 276 | Jim Pyburn | 20.00 |
| 277 | Johnny Podres | 55.00 |
| 278 | Fred Hatfield | 20.00 |
| 279 | Bob Thurman | 20.00 |
| 280 | Alex Kellner | 20.00 |
| 281 | Gail Harris | 20.00 |
| 282 | Jack Dittmer | 20.00 |
| 283 | Wes Covington | 20.00 |
| 284 | Don Zimmer | 30.00 |
| 285 | Ned Garver | 20.00 |
| 286 | Bobby Richardson (R) | 100.00 |
| 287 | Sam Jones | 20.00 |
| 288 | Ted Lepcio | 20.00 |
| 289 | Jim Bolger | 20.00 |
| 290 | Andy Carey | 20.00 |
| 291 | Windy McCall | 20.00 |
| 292 | Bill Klaus | 20.00 |
| 293 | Ted Abernathy | 20.00 |
| 294 | Rocky Bridges | 20.00 |
| 295 | Joe Collins | 20.00 |
| 296 | Johnny Klippstein | 20.00 |
| 297 | Jack Crimian | 20.00 |
| 298 | Irv Noren | 20.00 |
| 299 | Chuck Harmon | 20.00 |
| 300 | Mike Garcia | 20.00 |

| NO. | PLAYER | NR. MT. |
|---|---|---|
| 301 | Sam Esposito | 20.00 |
| 302 | Sandy Koufax | 325.00 |
| 303 | Billy Goodman | 20.00 |
| 304 | Joe Cunningham | 20.00 |
| 305 | Chico Fernandez | 20.00 |
| 306 | Darrell Johnson | 20.00 |
| 307 | Jack Phillips | 20.00 |
| 308 | Dick Hall | 20.00 |
| 309 | Jim Busby | 20.00 |
| 310 | Max Surkont | 20.00 |
| 311 | Al Pilarcik | 20.00 |
| 312 | Tony Kubek (R) | 120.00 |
| 313 | Mel Parnell | 20.00 |
| 314 | Ed Bouchee | 20.00 |
| 315 | Lou Berberet | 20.00 |
| 316 | Billy O'Dell | 20.00 |
| 317 | New York Giants | 50.00 |
| 318 | Mickey McDermott | 20.00 |
| 319 | Gino Cimoli | 20.00 |
| 320 | Neil Chrisley | 20.00 |
| 321 | Red Murff | 20.00 |
| 322 | Cincinnati Redlegs | 50.00 |
| 323 | Wes Westrum | 20.00 |
| 324 | Brooklyn Dodgers | 100.00 |
| 325 | Frank Bolling | 20.00 |
| 326 | Pedro Ramos | 20.00 |
| 327 | Jim Pendleton | 20.00 |
| 328 | Brooks Robinson (R) | 350.00 |
| 329 | Chicago White Sox | 40.00 |
| 330 | Jim Wilson | 20.00 |
| 331 | Ray Katt | 20.00 |
| 332 | Bob Bowman | 20.00 |
| 333 | Ernie Johnson | 20.00 |
| 334 | Jerry Schoonmaker | 20.00 |
| 335 | Granny Hamner | 20.00 |
| 336 | Haywood Sullivan | 20.00 |
| 337 | Rene Valdes | 20.00 |
| 338 | Jim Bunning (R) | 130.00 |

| NO. | PLAYER | NR. MT. |
|---|---|---|
| 339 | Bob Speake | 20.00 |
| 340 | Bill Wight | 20.00 |
| 341 | Don Gross | 20.00 |
| 342 | Gene Mauch | 21.00 |
| 343 | Taylor Phillips | 20.00 |
| 344 | Paul LaPalme | 20.00 |
| 345 | Paul Smith | 20.00 |
| 346 | Dick Littlefield | 20.00 |
| 347 | Hal Naragon | 20.00 |
| 348 | Jim Hearn | 20.00 |
| 349 | Nelson King | 20.00 |
| 350 | Eddie Miksis | 20.00 |
| 351 | Dave Hillman | 20.00 |
| 352 | Ellis Kinder | 20.00 |
| 353 | Cal Neeman | 5.00 |
| 354 | Rip Coleman | 5.00 |
| 355 | Frank Malzone | 5.00 |
| 356 | Faye Throneberry | 5.00 |
| 357 | Earl Torgeson | 5.00 |
| 358 | Jerry Lynch | 5.00 |
| 359 | Tom Cheney | 5.00 |
| 360 | Johnny Groth | 5.00 |
| 361 | Curt Barclay | 5.00 |
| 362 | Roman Mejias | 5.00 |
| 363 | Eddie Kasko | 5.00 |
| 364 | Cal McLish | 5.00 |
| 365 | Ossie Virgil | 5.00 |
| 366 | Ken Lehman | 5.00 |
| 367 | Ed Fitzgerald | 5.00 |
| 368 | Bob Purkey | 5.00 |
| 369 | Milt Graff | 5.00 |
| 370 | Warren Hacker | 5.00 |
| 371 | Bob Lennon | 5.00 |
| 372 | Norm Zauchin | 5.00 |
| 373 | Pete Whisenant | 5.00 |
| 374 | Don Cardwell | 5.00 |
| 375 | Jim Landis | 5.00 |
| 376 | Don Elston | 5.00 |

| NO. | PLAYER | NR. MT. |
|---|---|---|
| 377 | Andre Rodgers | 5.00 |
| 378 | Elmer Singleton | 5.00 |
| 379 | Don Lee | 5.00 |
| 380 | Walker Cooper | 5.00 |
| 381 | Dean Stone | 5.00 |
| 382 | Jim Brideweser | 5.00 |
| 383 | Juan Pizarro | 5.00 |
| 384 | Bobby Smith | 5.00 |
| 385 | Art Houtteman | 5.00 |
| 386 | Lyle Luttrell | 5.00 |
| 387 | Jack Sanford (R) | 8.00 |
| 388 | Pete Daley | 5.00 |
| 389 | Dave Jolly | 5.00 |
| 390 | Reno Bertoia | 5.00 |
| 391 | Ralph Terry (R) | 10.00 |
| 392 | Chuck Tanner | 5.00 |
| 393 | Raul Sanchez | 5.00 |
| 394 | Luis Aroyo | 5.00 |
| 395 | Bubba Phillips | 5.00 |
| 396 | Casey Wise | 5.00 |
| 397 | Roy Smalley | 5.00 |
| 398 | Al Cicotte | 5.00 |
| 399 | Billy Consolo | 5.00 |
| 400 | Dodgers' Sluggers: Carl Furillo, Gil Hodges Duke Snider, Roy Campanella | 175.00 |
| 401 | Earl Battey | 5.00 |
| 402 | Jim Pisani | 5.00 |
| 403 | Dick Hyde | 5.00 |
| 404 | Harry Anderson | 5.00 |
| 405 | Duke Maas | 5.00 |
| 406 | Bob Hale | 5.00 |
| 407 | Yanks' Power Hitters: M. Mantle, Y. Berra (exc. $75.00) | 350.00 |
| — | Checklist 1/2 | 200.00 |
| — | Checklist 2/3 | 350.00 |
| — | Checklist 3/4 | 600.00 |
| — | Checklist 4/5 | 700.00 |

## 1958 Topps . . . Complete Set of 494 Cards—Value $1900.00 (Exc.); $4750.00 (Near Mint)

Features the rookie cards of Roger Maris and Orlando Cepeda, 33 cards exist with the player's name or team in *yellow* type. These cards are worth more than the cards with *white* type. Card 145 was not issued. Prices for team checklists (377, 397, 408 and 428) are with the teams listed in alphabetical order. Team checklists with the teams in numerical order are worth about $60.00 each.

| NO. | PLAYER | NR. MT. |
|---|---|---|
| 1 | Ted Williams (exc. $55.00) | 350.00 |
| 2 | Bob Lemon | 16.00 |
| 2 | Bob Lemon (yellow type) | 32.00 |
| 3 | Alex Kellner | 6.00 |
| 4 | Hank Foiles | 6.00 |
| 5 | Willie Mays | 175.00 |
| 6 | George Zuverink | 6.00 |
| 7 | Dale Long | 7.00 |
| 8 | Eddie Kasko | 7.00 |
| 8 | Eddie Kasko (yellow type) | 22.00 |
| 9 | Hank Bauer | 10.00 |
| 10 | Lou Burdette | 8.00 |
| 11 | Jim Rivera | 6.00 |

| NO. | PLAYER | NR. MT. |
|---|---|---|
| 11 | Jim Rivera (yellow type) | 18.00 |
| 12 | George Crowe | 6.00 |
| 13 | Billy Hoeft | 6.00 |
| 13 | Billy Hoeft (yellow type) | 20.00 |
| 14 | Rip Repulski | 6.00 |
| 15 | Jim Lemon | 6.00 |
| 16 | Charley Neal | 6.00 |
| 17 | Felix Mantilla | 6.00 |
| 18 | Frank Sullivan | 6.00 |
| 19 | New York Giants | 25.00 |
| 20 | Gil McDougald | 10.00 |
| 20 | Gil McDougald (yellow type) | 25.00 |

| NO. | PLAYER | NR. MT. |
|---|---|---|
| 21 | Curt Barclay | 6.00 |
| 22 | Hal Naragon | 6.00 |
| 23 | Bill Tuttle | 6.00 |
| 23 | Bill Tuttle (yellow type) | 20.00 |
| 24 | Hobie Landrith | 6.00 |
| 24 | Hobie Landrith (yellow type) | 20.00 |
| 25 | Don Drysdal | 65.00 |
| 26 | Ron Jackson | 6.00 |
| 27 | Bud Freeman | 6.00 |
| 28 | Jim Busby | 6.00 |
| 29 | Ted Lepcio | 6.00 |
| 30 | Hank Aaron | 175.00 |
| 30 | Hank Aaron (yellow letters) | 300.00 |

| NO. | PLAYER | NR. MT. |
|---|---|---|
| 31 | Tex Clevenger | 6.00 |
| 32 | J.W. Porter | 6.00 |
| 32 | J.W. Porter (yellow letters) | 20.00 |
| 33 | Cal Neeman | 6.00 |
| 33 | Cal Neeman (yellow letters) | 20.00 |
| 34 | Bob Thurman | 6.00 |
| 35 | Don Mossi | 6.00 |
| 35 | Don Mossi (yellow letters) | 20.00 |
| 36 | Ted Kazanski | 6.00 |
| 37 | Mike McCormick (photo of Ray Monzant) | 8.00 |
| 38 | Dick Gernert | 6.00 |

| NO. PLAYER | NR. MT. | NO. PLAYER | NR. MT. | NO. PLAYER | NR. MT. | NO. PLAYER | NR. MT. |
|---|---|---|---|---|---|---|---|
| 39 Bob Martyn | 6.00 | 89 Bill Klaus | 6.00 | 160 Don Hoak | 5.00 | 241 Dick Littlefield | 4.00 |
| 40 George Kell | 13.00 | 90 Robin Roberts | 16.00 | 161 Don Larsen | 9.00 | 242 Johnny Klippstein | 4.00 |
| 41 Dave Hillman | 6.00 | 91 Chuck Tanner | 6.00 | 162 Gil Hodges | 22.00 | 243 Larry Raines | 4.00 |
| 42 John Roseboro (R) | 10.00 | 92 Clint Courtney | 6.00 | 163 Jim Wilson | 5.00 | 244 Don Demeter | 4.00 |
| 43 Sal Maglie | 9.00 | 92 Clint Courtney | 20.00 | 164 Bob Taylor | 5.00 | 245 Frank Lary | 4.00 |
| 44 Wash Senators | 15.00 | (yellow letters) | | 165 Bob Nieman | 5.00 | 246 New York Yankees | 35.00 |
| 45 Dick Groat | 9.00 | 93 Sandy Amoros | 6.00 | 166 Danny O'Connell | 5.00 | 247 Casey Wise | 4.00 |
| 46 Lou Sleater | 6.00 | 94 Bob Skinner | 6.00 | 167 Frank Baumann | 5.00 | 248 Herm Wehmeier | 4.00 |
| 46 Lou Sleater | 20.00 | 95 Frank Bolling | 6.00 | 168 Joe Cunningham | 5.00 | 249 Ray Moore | 4.00 |
| (yellow letters) | | 96 Joseph Durham | 6.00 | 169 Ralph Terry | 5.00 | 250 Roy Sievers | 4.00 |
| 47 Roger Maris (R) | 360.00 | 97 Larry Jackson | 6.00 | 170 Vic Wertz | 5.00 | 251 Warren Hacker | 4.00 |
| 48 Chuck Harmon | 6.00 | 97 Larry Jackson | 20.00 | 171 Harry Anderson | 5.00 | 252 Bob Trowbridge | 4.00 |
| 49 Smokey Burgess | 6.00 | (yellow letters) | | 172 Don Gross | 5.00 | 253 Don Mueller | 4.00 |
| 50 Billy Pierce | 6.00 | 98 Bill Hunter | 6.00 | 173 Eddie Yost | 5.00 | 254 Alex Grammas | 4.00 |
| 50 Billy Pierc | 20.00 | 98 Bill Hunter | 20.00 | 174 Kansas C. Athletics | 12.00 | 255 Bob Turley | 8.00 |
| (yellow letters) | | (yellow letters) | | 175 Marv Throneberry (R) | 10.00 | 256 Chicago White Sox | 12.00 |
| 51 Del Rice | 6.00 | 99 Bobby Adams | 6.00 | 176 Bob Buhl | 4.00 | 257 Hal Smith | 4.00 |
| 52 Bob Clemente | 150.00 | 100 Early Wynn | 17.50 | 177 Al Smith | 4.00 | 258 Carl Erskine | 7.00 |
| 52 Bob Clemente | 250.00 | 100 Early Wynn | 35.00 | 178 Ted Kluszewski | 10.00 | 259 Alan Pilarcik | 4.00 |
| 53 Morrie Martin | 6.00 | (yellow letters) | | 179 Willy Miranda | 4.00 | 260 Frank Malzone | 4.00 |
| 53 Morrie Martin | 20.00 | 101 Bob Richardson | 18.00 | 180 Lindy McDaniel | 4.00 | 261 Turk Lown | 4.00 |
| (yellow letters) | | 101 Bob Richardson | 36.00 | 181 Willie Jones | 4.00 | 262 John Groth | 4.00 |
| 54 Norm Siebern | 8.00 | (yellow letters) | | 182 Joe Caffie | 4.00 | 263 Ed Bressoud | 4.00 |
| 55 Chico Carrasquel | 6.00 | 102 George Strickland | 6.00 | 183 Dave Jolly | 4.00 | 264 Jack Sanford | 4.00 |
| 56 Bill Fischer | 6.00 | 103 Jerry Lynch | 6.00 | 184 Elvin Tappe | 4.00 | 265 Pete Runnels | 4.00 |
| 57 Tim Thompson | 6.00 | 104 Jim Pendleton | 6.00 | 185 Ray Boone | 4.00 | 266 Connie Johnson | 4.00 |
| 57 Tim Thompson | 20.00 | 105 Billy Gardner | 6.00 | 186 Jack Meyer | 4.00 | 267 Sherm Lollar | 4.00 |
| (yellow letters) | | 106 Dick Schofield | 6.00 | 187 Sandy Koufax | 175.00 | 268 Granny Hamner | 4.00 |
| 58 Art Schult | 6.00 | 107 Ossie Virgil | 6.00 | 188 Milt Bolling | 4.00 | 269 Paul Smith | 4.00 |
| 58 Art Schult | 20.00 | 108 Jim Landis | 6.00 | (photo of Lou Berberet) | | 270 Warren Spahn | 50.00 |
| (yellow letters) | | 108 Jim Landis | 20.00 | 189 George Susce | 4.00 | 271 Billy Martin | 20.00 |
| 59 Dave Sisler | 6.00 | (yellow letters) | | 190 Red Schoendienst | 15.00 | 272 Ray Crone | 4.00 |
| 60 Del Ennis | 6.00 | 109 Herb Plews | 6.00 | 191 Art Ceccarelli | 4.00 | 273 Hal Smith | 4.00 |
| 60 Del Ennis | 20.00 | 110 Johnny Logan | 6.00 | 192 Milt Graff | 4.00 | 274 Rocky Bridges | 4.00 |
| (yellow letters) | | 111 Stu Miller | 5.00 | 193 Jerry Lumpe | 4.00 | 275 Elston Howard | 10.00 |
| 61 Darrell Johnson | 6.00 | 112 Gus Zernial | 5.00 | 194 Roger Craig | 8.00 | 276 Bobby Avila | 4.00 |
| 61 Darrell Johnson | 20.00 | 113 Jerry Walker | 5.00 | 195 Whitey Lockman | 5.00 | 277 Virgil Trucks | 4.00 |
| (yellow letters) | | 114 Irv Noren | 5.00 | 196 Mike Garcia | 5.00 | 278 Mack Burk | 4.00 |
| 62 Joe DeMaestri | 6.00 | 115 Jim Bunning | 16.00 | 197 Haywood Sullivan | 5.00 | 279 Bob Boyd | 4.00 |
| 63 Joe Nuxhall | 6.00 | 116 Dave Philley | 6.00 | 198 Bill Virdon | 5.00 | 280 Jim Piersall | 6.00 |
| 64 Joe Lonnett | 6.00 | 117 Frank Torre | 6.00 | 199 Don Blasingame | 4.00 | 281 Sam Taylor | 4.00 |
| 65 Von McDaniel | 6.00 | 118 Harvey Haddix | 6.00 | 200 Bob Keegan | 4.00 | 282 Paul Foytack | 4.00 |
| 65 Von McDaniel | 20.00 | 119 Harry Chiti | 6.00 | 201 Jim Bolger | 4.00 | 283 Ray Shearer | 4.00 |
| (yellow letters) | | 120 Johnny Podres | 8.00 | 202 Woody Held | 4.00 | 284 Ray Katt | 4.00 |
| 66 Lee Walls | 6.00 | 121 Ed Miksis | 5.00 | 203 Al Walker | 4.00 | 285 Frank Robinson | 75.00 |
| 67 Joe Ginsberg | 6.00 | 122 Walter Moryn | 5.00 | 204 Leo Kiely | 4.00 | 286 Gino Cimoli | 4.00 |
| 68 Daryl Spencer | 6.00 | 123 Dick Tomanek | 5.00 | 205 Johnny Temple | 4.00 | 287 Sam Jones | 4.00 |
| 69 Wally Burnette | 6.00 | 124 Bobby Usher | 5.00 | 206 Bob Shaw | 4.00 | 288 Harmon Killebrew | 75.00 |
| 70 Al Kaline | 70.00 | 125 Al Dark | 5.00 | 207 Solly Hemus | 4.00 | 289 Hurling Rivals: | 10.00 |
| 70 Al Kaline | 120.00 | 126 Stan Palys | 5.00 | 208 Cal McLish | 4.00 | Lou Burdette, Bobby Shantz | |
| (yellow letters) | | 127 Tom Sturdivant | 5.00 | 209 Bob Anderson | 4.00 | 290 Dick Donovan | 4.00 |
| 71 Brooklyn Dodgers | 35.00 | 128 Willie Kirkland | 5.00 | 210 Wally Moon | 4.00 | 291 Don Landrum | 4.00 |
| 72 Bud Byerly | 6.00 | 129 Jim Derrington | 5.00 | 211 Pete Burnside | 4.00 | 292 Ned Garver | 4.00 |
| 73 Pete Daley | 6.00 | 130 Jackie Jensen | 10.00 | 212 Bubba Phillips | 4.00 | 293 Gene Freese | 4.00 |
| 74 Roy Face | 6.00 | 131 Bob Henrich | 5.00 | 213 Red Wilson | 4.00 | 294 Hal Jeffcoat | 4.00 |
| 75 Gus Bell | 6.00 | 132 Vernon Law | 5.00 | 214 Willard Schmidt | 4.00 | 295 Minnie Minoso | 8.00 |
| 76 Dick Farrell | 6.00 | 133 Russ Nixon | 6.00 | 215 Jim Gilliam | 7.50 | 296 Ryne Duren | 9.00 |
| 76 Dick Farrell | 20.00 | 134 Philadelphia Phillies | 12.00 | 216 St. Louis Cardinals | 12.00 | 297 Don Buddin | 4.00 |
| (yellow letters) | | 135 Mike Drabowsky | 5.00 | 217 Jack Harshman | 4.00 | 298 Jim Hearn | 4.00 |
| 77 Don Zimmer | 10.00 | 136 Jim Finigan | 5.00 | 218 Dick Rand | 4.00 | 299 Harry Simpson | 4.00 |
| 77 Don Zimmer | 20.00 | 137 Russ Kemmerer | 5.00 | 219 Camilo Pascual | 4.00 | 300 Harridge and Giles | 8.00 |
| (yellow letters) | | 138 Earl Torgeson | 5.00 | 220 Tom Brewer | 4.00 | League Presidents | |
| 78 Ernie Johnson | 6.00 | 139 George Brunet | 5.00 | 221 Jerry Kindall | 4.00 | 301 Randy Jackson | 4.00 |
| 78 Ernie Johnson | 20.00 | 140 Wes Covington | 5.00 | 222 Bud Daley | 4.00 | 302 Mike Baxes | 4.00 |
| (yellow letters) | | 141 Ken Lehman | 5.00 | 223 Andy Pafko | 4.00 | 303 Neil Chrisley | 4.00 |
| 79 Dick Williams | 6.00 | 142 Enos Slaughter | 20.00 | 224 Bob Grim | 4.00 | 304 Tigers' Big Bats: | 13.00 |
| 79 Dick Williams | 20.00 | 143 Billy Muffett | 5.00 | 225 Billy Goodman | 4.00 | Harvey Kuenn, Al Kaline | |
| (yellow letters) | | 144 Bobby Morgan | 5.00 | 226 Bob Smith | 4.00 | 305 Clem Labine | 4.00 |
| 80 Dick Drott | 6.00 | 146 Dick Gray | 5.00 | 227 Gene Stephens | 4.00 | 306 Whammy Douglas | 4.00 |
| 81 Steve Boros | 6.00 | 147 Don McMahon | 5.00 | 228 Duke Maas | 4.00 | 307 Brooks Robinson | 90.00 |
| 81 Steve Boros | 20.00 | 148 Billy Consolo | 5.00 | 229 Frank Zupo | 4.00 | 308 Paul Giel | 4.00 |
| (yellow letters) | | 149 Tom Acker | 5.00 | 230 Richie Ashburn | 15.00 | 309 Gail Harris | 4.00 |
| 82 Ronnie Kline | 6.00 | 150 Mickey Mantle | 500.00 | 231 Lloyd Merritt | 4.00 | 310 Ernie Banks | 80.00 |
| 83 Bob Hazle | 6.00 | 151 Buddy Pritchard | 5.00 | 232 Reno Bertoia | 4.00 | 311 Bob Purkey | 4.00 |
| 84 Billy O'Dell | 6.00 | 152 Johnny Antonelli | 5.00 | 233 Mickey Vernon | 4.00 | 312 Boston Red Sox | 13.00 |
| 85 Luis Aparicio | 25.00 | 153 Les Moss | 5.00 | 234 Carl Sawatski | 4.00 | 313 Bob Rush | 4.00 |
| 85 Luis Aparicio | 40.00 | 154 Harry Byrd | 5.00 | 235 Tom Gorman | 4.00 | 314 Boss and Power | 4.00 |
| (yellow letters) | | 155 Hector Lopez | 5.00 | 236 Ed Fitzgerald | 4.00 | Duke Snider, Walt Alston | |
| 86 Valmy Thomas | 6.00 | 156 Dick Hyde | 5.00 | 237 Bill Wight | 4.00 | 315 Bob Friend | 4.00 |
| 87 Johnny Kucks | 6.00 | 157 Dee Fondy | 5.00 | 238 Bill Mazeroski | 12.00 | 316 Tito Francona | 4.00 |
| 88 Duke Snider | 75.00 | 158 Cleveland Indians | 12.00 | 239 Chuck Stobbs | 4.00 | 317 Albie Pearson | 4.00 |
| | | 159 Taylor Phillips | 5.00 | 240 Moose Skowron | 10.00 | 318 Frank House | 4.00 |

| NO. | PLAYER | NR. MT. |
|---|---|---|
| 319 | Lou Skizas | 4.00 |
| 320 | Whitey Ford | 50.00 |
| 321 | Sluggers Supreme: | 36.00 |
| | Ted Kluszewski, | |
| | Ted Williams | |
| 322 | Harding Peterson | 4.00 |
| 323 | Elmer Valo | 4.00 |
| 324 | Hoyt Wilhelm | 15.00 |
| 325 | Joe Adcock | 5.00 |
| 326 | Bob Miller | 4.00 |
| 327 | Chicago Cubs | 12.00 |
| 328 | Ike Delock | 4.00 |
| 329 | Bob Cerv | 4.00 |
| 330 | Ed Bailey | 4.00 |
| 331 | Pedro Ramos | 4.00 |
| 332 | Jim King | 4.00 |
| 333 | Andy Carey | 4.00 |
| 334 | Mound Aces: | 5.00 |
| | Bob Friend, Billy Pierce | |
| 335 | Ruben Gomez | 4.00 |
| 336 | Bert Hamric | 4.00 |
| 337 | Hank Aguirre | 4.00 |
| 338 | Walter Dropo | 4.00 |
| 339 | Fred Hatfield | 4.00 |
| 340 | Don Newcombe | 8.00 |
| 341 | Pittsburgh Pirates | 12.00 |
| 342 | Jim Brosnan | 4.00 |
| 343 | Orlando Cepeda (R) | 65.00 |
| 344 | Bob Porterfield | 4.00 |
| 345 | Jim Hegan | 4.00 |
| 346 | Steve Bilko | 4.00 |
| 347 | Don Rudolph | 4.00 |
| 348 | Chico Fernandez | 4.00 |
| 349 | Murry Dickson | 4.00 |
| 350 | Ken Boyer | 10.00 |
| 351 | Braves Fence Busters: | 25.00 |
| | Del Crandall, Eddie Mathews, | |
| | Hank Aaron, Joe Adcock | |
| 352 | Herb Score | 6.00 |
| 353 | Stan Lopata | 3.50 |
| 354 | Art Ditmar | 3.50 |
| 355 | Billy Bruton | 3.50 |
| 356 | Bob Malkmus | 3.50 |
| 357 | Danny McDevitt | 3.50 |
| 358 | Gene Baker | 3.50 |
| 359 | Billy Loes | 3.50 |
| 360 | Roy McMillan | 3.50 |
| 361 | Mike Fornieles | 3.50 |

| NO. | PLAYER | NR. MT. |
|---|---|---|
| 362 | Ray Jablonski | 3.50 |
| 363 | Don Elston | 3.50 |
| 364 | Earl Battey | 3.50 |
| 365 | Tom Morgan | 3.50 |
| 366 | Gene Green | 3.50 |
| 367 | Jack Urban | 3.50 |
| 368 | Rocky Colavito | 25.00 |
| 369 | Ralph Lumenti | 3.50 |
| 370 | Yogi Berra | 85.00 |
| 371 | Marty Keough | 3.50 |
| 372 | Don Cardwell | 3.50 |
| 373 | Joe Pignatano | 3.50 |
| 374 | Brooks Lawrence | 3.50 |
| 375 | Pee Wee Reese | 50.00 |
| 376 | Charley Rabe | 3.00 |
| 377 | Milwaukee Braves* | 11.00 |
| 378 | Hank Sauer | 3.50 |
| 379 | Ray Herbert | 3.50 |
| 380 | Charley Maxwell | 3.50 |
| 381 | Hal Brown | 3.50 |
| 382 | Al Cicotte | 3.50 |
| 383 | Lou Berberet | 3.50 |
| 384 | John Goryl | 3.50 |
| 385 | Wilmer Mizell | 3.50 |
| 386 | Young Sluggers: | 9.00 |
| | Ed Bailey, Birdie Tebbetts, | |
| | Frank Robinson | |
| 387 | Wally Post | 3.50 |
| 388 | Billy Moran | 3.50 |
| 389 | Bill Taylor | 3.50 |
| 390 | Del Crandall | 3.50 |
| 391 | Dave Melton | 3.50 |
| 392 | Bennie Daniels | 3.50 |
| 393 | Tony Kubek | 15.00 |
| 394 | Jim Grant | 3.50 |
| 395 | Willard Nixon | 3.50 |
| 396 | Dutch Dotterer | 3.50 |
| 397 | Detroit Tigers* | 11.00 |
| 398 | Gene Woodling | 3.50 |
| 399 | Marv Grissom | 3.50 |
| 400 | Nellie Fox | 12.00 |
| 401 | Don Bessent | 3.50 |
| 402 | Bobby Gene Smith | 3.50 |
| 403 | Steve Korcheck | 3.50 |
| 404 | Curt Simmons | 3.50 |
| 405 | Ken Aspromonte | 3.50 |
| 406 | Vic Power | 3.50 |

| NO. | PLAYER | NR. MT. |
|---|---|---|
| 407 | Carlton Willey | 3.50 |
| 408 | Baltimore Orioles* | 11.00 |
| 409 | Frank Thomas | 3.50 |
| 410 | Murray Wall | 3.50 |
| 411 | Tony Taylor | 6.00 |
| 412 | Jerry Staley | 3.50 |
| 413 | Jim Davenport | 3.50 |
| 414 | Sammy White | 3.50 |
| 415 | Bob Bowman | 3.50 |
| 416 | Foster Castleman | 3.50 |
| 417 | Carl Furillo | 9.00 |
| 418 | W. Series Batting Foes: | 135.00 |
| | Mickey Mantle, Hank Aaron | |
| 419 | Bobby Shantz | 3.50 |
| 420 | Vada Pinson | 22.00 |
| 421 | Dixie Howell | 3.50 |
| 422 | Norm Zauchin | 3.50 |
| 423 | Phil Clark | 3.50 |
| 424 | Larry Doby | 6.00 |
| 425 | Sam Esposito | 3.50 |
| 426 | Johnny O'Brien | 3.50 |
| 427 | Al Worthington | 3.50 |
| 428 | Cincinnati Redlegs* | 12.00 |
| 429 | Gus Triandos | 3.50 |
| 430 | Bobby Thomson | 6.00 |
| 431 | Gene Conley | 3.50 |
| 432 | John Powers | 3.50 |
| 433 | Pancho Herrera | 3.50 |
| 433 | Pancho Herrer | 500.00 |
| | (name spelled wrong) | |
| 434 | Harvey Kuenn | 6.00 |
| 435 | Ed Roebuck | 6.00 |
| 436 | Rival Fence Busters: | 50.00 |
| | Willie Mays, Duke Snider | |
| 437 | Bob Speake | 3.50 |
| 438 | Whitey Herzog | 3.50 |
| 439 | Ray Narleski | 3.50 |
| 440 | Eddie Mathews | 30.00 |
| 441 | Jim Marshall | 3.50 |
| 442 | Phil Paine | 3.50 |
| 443 | Billy Harrell | 7.00 |
| 444 | Danny Kravitz | 3.50 |
| 445 | Bob Smith | 3.50 |
| 446 | Carroll Hardy | 5.00 |
| 447 | Ray Monzant | 3.50 |
| 448 | Charlie Lau | 6.00 |
| 449 | Gene Fodge | 3.50 |

| NO. | PLAYER | NR. MT. |
|---|---|---|
| 450 | Preston Ward | 7.00 |
| 451 | Joe Taylor | 3.50 |
| 452 | Roman Mejias | 3.50 |
| 453 | Tom Qualters | 3.50 |
| 454 | Harry Hanebrink | 3.50 |
| 455 | Hal Griggs | 3.50 |
| 456 | Dick Brown | 3.50 |
| 457 | Milt Pappas (R) | 6.00 |
| 458 | Julio Becquer | 3.50 |
| 459 | Ron Blackburn | 3.50 |
| 460 | Chuck Essegian | 3.50 |
| 461 | Ed Mayer | 3.50 |
| 462 | Gary Geiger | 6.00 |
| 463 | Vito Valentinetti | 3.50 |
| 464 | Curt Flood (R) | 20.00 |
| 465 | Arnie Portocarrero | 3.50 |
| 466 | Pete Whisenant | 3.50 |
| 467 | Glen Hobbie | 3.50 |
| 468 | Bob Schmidt | 3.50 |
| 469 | Don Ferrarese | 3.50 |
| 470 | R.C. Stevens | 3.50 |
| 471 | Lenny Green | 3.50 |
| 472 | Joe Jay | 3.50 |
| 473 | Bill Renna | 3.50 |
| 474 | Roman Semproch | 3.50 |
| 475 | All-Star Managers: | 15.00 |
| | Stengel, Haney | |
| 476 | Stan Musial (AS) | 35.00 |
| 477 | Bill Skowron (AS) | 5.00 |
| 478 | Johnny Temple (AS) | 4.00 |
| 479 | Nellie Fox (AS) | 7.00 |
| 480 | Eddie Mathews (AS) | 13.00 |
| 481 | Frank Malzone (AS) | 4.00 |
| 482 | Ernie Banks (AS) | 18.00 |
| 483 | Luis Aparicio (AS) | 12.00 |
| 484 | Frank Robinson (AS) | 16.00 |
| 485 | Ted Williams (AS) | 60.00 |
| 486 | Willie Mays (AS) | 40.00 |
| 487 | Mickey Mantle (AS) | 100.00 |
| 488 | Hank Aaron (AS) | 40.00 |
| 489 | Jackie Jensen (AS) | 5.00 |
| 490 | Ed Bailey (AS) | 4.00 |
| 491 | Sherm Lollar (AS) | 4.00 |
| 492 | Bob Friend (AS) | 4.00 |
| 493 | Bob Turley (AS) | 4.00 |
| 494 | Warren Spahn (AS) | 15.00 |
| 495 | H. Score (AS) (exc. $3.00) | 15.00 |

## 1959 Topps . . . Complete Set of 572 Cards—Value $2100.00 (Exc.); $5000.00 (Near Mint)

Includes Bob Gibson's rookie card. The high numbers are 507 to 572. Cards 199 to 286 were issued with *white* or *gray* backs. Cards 316, 321, 322, 336 and 362 exist without the *option* or *traded* line—worth $85.00 each.

| NO. | PLAYER | NR. MT. |
|---|---|---|
| 1 | BB Commissioner | 75.00 |
| | Ford Frick (exc. $10.00) | |
| 2 | Eddie Yost | 5.00 |
| 3 | Don McMahon | 5.00 |
| 4 | Albie Pearson | 5.00 |
| 5 | Dick Donovan | 5.00 |
| 6 | Alex Grammas | 5.00 |
| 7 | Al Pilarcik | 5.00 |
| 8 | Philadelphia Phillies | 20.00 |
| 9 | Paul Giel | 5.00 |

| NO. | PLAYER | NR. MT. |
|---|---|---|
| 10 | Mickey Mantle | 350.00 |
| 11 | Billy Hunter | 5.00 |
| 12 | Vern Law | 6.00 |
| 13 | Dick Gernert | 5.00 |
| 14 | Pete Whisenant | 5.00 |
| 15 | Dick Drott | 5.00 |
| 16 | Joe Pignatano | 5.00 |
| 17 | Danny's All-Stars: | 7.00 |
| | Frank Thomas, Danny | |
| | Murtaugh, Ted Kluszewski | |

| NO. | PLAYER | NR. MT. |
|---|---|---|
| 18 | Jack Urban | 5.00 |
| 19 | Ed Bressoud | 5.00 |
| 20 | Duke Snider | 60.00 |
| 21 | Connie Johnson | 5.00 |
| 22 | Al Smith | 5.00 |
| 23 | Murry Dickson | 5.00 |
| 24 | Red Wilson | 5.00 |
| 25 | Dan Hoak | 5.00 |
| 26 | Chuck Stobbs | 5.00 |
| 27 | Andy Pafko | 5.00 |

| NO. | PLAYER | NR. MT. |
|---|---|---|
| 28 | Red Worthington | 5.00 |
| 29 | Jim Bolger | 5.00 |
| 30 | Nellie Fox | 13.00 |
| 31 | Ken Lehman | 5.00 |
| 32 | Don Buddin | 5.00 |
| 33 | Ed Fizgerald | 5.00 |
| 34 | Pitchers Beware: | 10.00 |
| | Al Kaline, Charley Maxwell | |
| 35 | Ted Kluszewski | 9.00 |
| 36 | Hank Aguirre | 5.00 |

| NO. PLAYER | NR. MT. |
|---|---|
| 37 Gene Green | 5.00 |
| 38 Morrie Martin | 5.00 |
| 39 Ed Bouchee | 5.00 |
| 40 Warren Spahn | 50.00 |
| 41 Bob Martyn | 5.00 |
| 42 Murray Wall | 5.00 |
| 43 Steven Bilko | 5.00 |
| 44 Vito Valentinetti | 5.00 |
| 45 Andy Carey | 5.00 |
| 46 Bill Henry | 5.00 |
| 47 Jim Finigan | 5.00 |
| 48 Baltimore Orioles | 16.00 |
| 49 Bill Hall | 5.00 |
| 50 Willie May | 135.00 |
| 51 Rip Coleman | 5.00 |
| 52 Coot Veal | 5.00 |
| 53 Stan Williams | 5.00 |
| 54 Mel Roach | 5.00 |
| 55 Tom Brewer | 5.00 |
| 56 Carl Sawatski | 5.00 |
| 57 Al Cicotte | 5.00 |
| 58 Eddie Miksis | 5.00 |
| 59 Irv Noren | 5.00 |
| 60 Bob Turley | 7.00 |
| 61 Dick Brown | 5.00 |
| 62 Tony Taylor | 5.00 |
| 63 Jim Hearn | 5.00 |
| 64 Joe DeMaestri | 5.00 |
| 65 Frank Torre | 5.00 |
| 66 Joe Ginsberg | 5.00 |
| 67 Brooks Lawrence | 5.00 |
| 68 Dick Schofield | 5.00 |
| 69 San F. Giants | 12.00 |
| 70 Harvey Kuenn | 6.00 |
| 71 Don Bessent | 5.00 |
| 72 Bill Renna | 5.00 |
| 73 Ron Jackson | 5.00 |
| 74 Directing the Power: | 5.00 |
| Jim Lemon, Cookie | |
| Lavagetto, Roy Sievers | |
| 75 Sam Jones | 5.00 |
| 76 Bobby Richardson | 12.00 |
| 77 John Goryl | 5.00 |
| 78 Pedro Ramos | 5.00 |
| 79 Harry Chiti | 5.00 |
| 80 Minnie Minoso | 8.00 |
| 81 Hal Jeffcoat | 5.00 |
| 82 Bob Boyd | 5.00 |
| 83 Bob Smith | 5.00 |
| 84 Reno Bertoia | 5.00 |
| 85 Harry Anderson | 5.00 |
| 86 Bob Keegan | 5.00 |
| 87 Danny O'Connell | 5.00 |
| 88 Herb Score | 6.00 |
| 89 Billy Gardner | 5.00 |
| 90 Bill Skowron | 10.00 |
| 91 Herb Moford | 5.00 |
| 92 David Philley | 5.00 |
| 93 Julio Becquer | 5.00 |
| 94 Chicago White Sox | 15.00 |
| 95 Carl Willey | 5.00 |
| 96 Lou Berberet | 5.00 |
| 97 Jerry Lynch | 5.00 |
| 98 Arnie Portocarrero | 5.00 |
| 99 Ted Kazanski | 5.00 |
| 100 Bob Cerv | 5.00 |
| 101 Alex Kellner | 5.00 |
| 102 Felipe Alou (R) | 12.00 |
| 103 Billy Goodman | 5.00 |
| 104 Del Rice | 5.00 |
| 105 Lee Walls | 5.00 |
| 106 Hal Woodeshick | 5.00 |
| 107 Norm Larker | 5.00 |
| 108 Zack Monroe | 5.00 |
| 109 Bob Schmidt | 5.00 |
| 110 George Witt | 5.00 |
| 111 Cincinnati Redlegs | 9.00 |
| 112 Billy Consolo | 3.00 |
| 113 Taylor Phillips | 3.00 |
| 114 Earl Battey | 3.00 |
| 115 Mickey Vernon | 3.00 |

| NO. PLAYER | NR. MT. |
|---|---|
| **No. 116 to 146 Rookie Stars** | |
| 116 Bob Allison | 6.00 |
| 117 John Blanchard | 3.00 |
| 118 John Buzhardt | 3.00 |
| 119 John Callison | 6.00 |
| 120 Chuck Coles | 3.00 |
| 121 Bob Conley | 3.00 |
| 122 Bennie Daniels | 3.00 |
| 123 Donald Dillard | 3.00 |
| 124 Dan Dobbek | 3.00 |
| 125 Ron Fairly | 6.00 |
| 126 Eddie Haas | 3.00 |
| 127 Kent Hadley | 3.00 |
| 128 Bob Hartman | 3.00 |
| 129 Frank Herrera | 3.00 |
| 130 Lou Jackson | 3.00 |
| 131 Deron Johnson | 4.00 |
| 132 Don Lee | 3.00 |
| 133 Bob Lillis | 3.00 |
| 134 Jim McDaniel | 3.00 |
| 135 Gene Oliver | 3.00 |
| 136 Jim O'Toole | 3.00 |
| 137 Dick Ricketts | 3.00 |
| 138 John Romano | 3.00 |
| 139 Ed Sadowski | 3.00 |
| 140 Charlie Secrest | 3.00 |
| 141 Joe Shipley | 3.00 |
| 142 Dick Stigman | 3.00 |
| 143 Willie Tasby | 3.00 |
| 144 Jerry Walker | 3.00 |
| 145 Dom Zanni | 3.00 |
| 146 Jerry Zimmerman | 3.00 |
| 147 Cubs' Clubbers: | 10.00 |
| Dale Long, Ernie Banks, | |
| Walt Moryn | |
| 148 Mike McCormick | 3.00 |
| 149 Jim Bunning | 10.00 |
| 150 Stan Musial | 150.00 |
| 151 Bob Malkmus | 3.00 |
| 152 Johnny Klippstein | 3.00 |
| 153 Jim Marshall | 3.00 |
| 154 Ray Herbert | 3.00 |
| 155 Enos Slaughter | 15.00 |
| 156 Ace Hurlers: | 5.00 |
| Billy Pierce, Robin Roberts | |
| 157 Felix Mantilla | 3.00 |
| 158 Walt Dropo | 3.00 |
| 159 Bob Shaw | 3.00 |
| 160 Dick Groat | 6.00 |
| 161 Frank Baumann | 3.00 |
| 162 Bobby Smith | 3.00 |
| 163 Sandy Koufax | 135.00 |
| 164 Johnny Groth | 3.00 |
| 165 Bill Bruton | 3.00 |
| 166 Destruction Crew: | 6.00 |
| Minnie Minoso, Rocky | |
| Colavito, Larry Doby | |
| 167 Duke Maas | 3.00 |
| 168 Carroll Hardy | 3.00 |
| 169 Ted Abernathy | 3.00 |
| 170 Gene Woodling | 3.00 |
| 171 Willard Schmidt | 3.00 |
| 172 Kansas C. Athletics | 8.00 |
| 173 Bill Monbouquette | 3.00 |
| 174 Jim Pendleton | 3.00 |
| 175 Dick Farrell | 3.00 |
| 176 Preston Ward | 3.00 |
| 177 John Briggs | 3.00 |
| 178 Ruben Amaro | 3.00 |
| 179 Don Rudolph | 3.00 |
| 180 Yogi Berra | 75.00 |
| 181 Bob Porterfield | 3.00 |
| 182 Milt Graff | 3.00 |
| 183 Stu Miller | 3.00 |
| 184 Harvey Haddix | 4.00 |
| 185 Jim Busby | 3.00 |
| 186 Mudcat Grant | 3.00 |
| 187 Bubba Phillips | 3.00 |
| 188 Juan Pizarro | 3.00 |
| 189 Neil Chrisley | 3.00 |
| 190 Bill Virdon | 6.00 |

| NO. PLAYER | NR. MT. |
|---|---|
| 191 Russ Kemmerer | 3.00 |
| 192 Charley Beamon | 3.00 |
| 193 Sammy Taylor | 3.00 |
| 194 Jim Brosnan | 3.00 |
| 195 Rip Repulski | 3.00 |
| 196 Billy Moran | 3.00 |
| 197 Ray Semproch | 3.00 |
| 198 Jim Davenport | 3.00 |
| 199 Leo Kiely | 3.00 |
| 200 NL President: | |
| Warren Giles | 4.00 |
| 201 Tom Acker | 3.00 |
| 202 Roger Maris | 135.00 |
| 203 Ozzie Virgil | 3.00 |
| 204 Casey Wise | 3.00 |
| 205 Don Larsen | 5.00 |
| 206 Carl Furillo | 5.00 |
| 207 George Strickland | 3.00 |
| 208 Willie Jones | 3.00 |
| 209 Lenny Green | 3.00 |
| 210 Ed Bailey | 3.00 |
| 211 Bob Blaylock | 3.00 |
| 212 Fence Busters: | 35.00 |
| Hank Aaron, Eddie Mathews | |
| 213 Jim Rivera | 3.00 |
| 214 Marcelino Solis | 3.00 |
| 215 Jim Lemon | 3.00 |
| 216 Andre Rodgers | 3.00 |
| 217 Carl Erskine | 4.00 |
| 218 Roman Mejias | 3.00 |
| 219 George Zuverink | 3.00 |
| 220 Frank Malzone | 3.00 |
| 221 Bob Bowman | 3.00 |
| 222 Bobby Shantz | 3.00 |
| 223 St. Louis Cardinals | 9.00 |
| 224 Claude Osteen (R) | 4.00 |
| 225 Johnny Logan | 3.00 |
| 226 Art Ceccarelli | 3.00 |
| 227 Hal Smith | 3.00 |
| 228 Don Gross | 3.00 |
| 229 Vic Power | 3.00 |
| 230 Bill Fischer | 3.00 |
| 231 Ellis Burton | 3.00 |
| 232 Eddie Kasko | 3.00 |
| 233 Paul Foytack | 3.00 |
| 234 Chuck Tanner | 5.00 |
| 235 Valmy Thomas | 3.00 |
| 236 Ted Bowsfield | 3.00 |
| 237 Run Preventers: | 5.00 |
| Gil McDougald, Bob Turley, | |
| Bobby Richardson | |
| 238 Gene Baker | 3.00 |
| 239 Bob Trowbridge | 3.00 |
| 240 Hank Bauer | 5.00 |
| 241 Billy Muffett | 3.00 |
| 242 Ron Samford | 3.00 |
| 243 Marv Grissom | 3.00 |
| 244 Dick Gray | 3.00 |
| 245 Ned Garver | 3.00 |
| 246 J.W. Porter | 3.00 |
| 247 Don Ferrarese | 3.00 |
| 248 Boston Red Sox | 9.00 |
| 249 Bobby Adams | 3.00 |
| 250 Billy O'Dell | 3.00 |
| 251 Cletis Boyer | 5.00 |
| 252 Ray Boone | 3.00 |
| 253 Seth Morehead | 3.00 |
| 254 Zeke Bella | 3.00 |
| 255 Del Ennis | 3.00 |
| 256 Jerry Davie | 3.00 |
| 257 Leon Wagner | 3.00 |
| 258 Fred Kipp | 3.00 |
| 259 Jim Pisoni | 3.00 |
| 260 Early Wynn | 13.00 |
| 261 Gene Stephens | 3.00 |
| 262 Hitters' Foes: | 5.00 |
| Johnny Podres, Clem | |
| Labine, Don Drysdale | |
| 263 Buddy Daley | 3.00 |
| 264 Chico Carrasquel | 3.00 |
| 265 Ron Kline | 3.00 |

| NO. PLAYER | NR. MT. |
|---|---|
| 266 Woody Held | 3.00 |
| 267 John Romonosky | 3.00 |
| 268 Tito Francona | 3.00 |
| 269 Jack Mayer | 3.00 |
| 270 Gil Hodges | 16.00 |
| 271 Orlando Pena | 3.00 |
| 272 Jerry Lumpe | 3.00 |
| 273 Joey Jay | 3.00 |
| 274 Jerry Kindall | 3.00 |
| 275 Jack Sanford | 3.00 |
| 276 Pete Daley | 3.00 |
| 277 Turk Lown | 3.00 |
| 278 Chuck Essegian | 3.00 |
| 279 Ernie Johnson | 3.00 |
| 280 Frank Bolling | 3.00 |
| 281 Walt Craddock | 3.00 |
| 282 R.C. Stevens | 3.00 |
| 283 Russ Heman | 3.00 |
| 284 Steve Korcheck | 3.00 |
| 285 Joe Cunningham | 3.00 |
| 286 Dean Stone | 3.00 |
| 287 Don Zimmer | 3.00 |
| 288 Dutch Dotterer | 3.00 |
| 289 Johnny Kucks | 3.00 |
| 290 Wes Covington | 3.00 |
| 291 Pitching Partners: | 4.00 |
| Pedro Ramos, | |
| Camilo Pascual | |
| 292 Dick Williams | 3.00 |
| 293 Ray Moore | 3.00 |
| 294 Hank Foiles | 3.00 |
| 295 Billy Martin | 13.00 |
| 296 Ernie Broglio | 3.00 |
| 297 Jackie Brandt | 3.00 |
| 298 Tex Clevenger | 3.00 |
| 299 Billy Klaus | 3.00 |
| 300 Richie Ashburn | 11.00 |
| 301 Earl Averill | 3.00 |
| 302 Don Mossi | 3.00 |
| 303 Marty Keough | 3.00 |
| 304 Chicago Cubs | 9.00 |
| 305 Curt Raydon | 3.00 |
| 306 Jim Gilliam | 5.00 |
| 307 Curt Barclay | 3.00 |
| 308 Norm Siebern | 3.00 |
| 309 Sal Maglie | 4.00 |
| 310 Luis Aparicio | 15.00 |
| 311 Norm Zauchin | 3.00 |
| 312 Don Newcombe | 5.00 |
| 313 Frank House | 3.00 |
| 314 Don Cardwell | 3.00 |
| 315 Joe Adcock | 3.00 |
| 316 Ralph Lumenti* | 3.00 |
| (photo of Camilo Pascual) | |
| 317 Hitting Kings: | 18.00 |
| Willie Mays, Richie Ashburn | |
| 318 Rocky Bridges | 3.00 |
| 319 Dave Hillmann | 3.00 |
| 320 Bob Skinner | 3.00 |
| 321 Bob Giallombardo* | 3.00 |
| 322 Harry Hanebrink* | 3.00 |
| 323 Frank Sullivan | 3.00 |
| 324 Donald Demeter | 3.00 |
| 325 Ken Boyer | 6.00 |
| 326 Marv Throneberry | 4.00 |
| 327 Gary Bell | 3.00 |
| 328 Lou Skizas | 3.00 |
| 329 Detroit Tigers | 9.00 |
| 330 Gus Triandos | 3.00 |
| 331 Steve Boros | 3.00 |
| 332 Ray Monzant | 3.00 |
| 333 Harry Simpson | 3.00 |
| 334 Glen Hobbie | 3.00 |
| 335 Johnny Temple | 3.00 |
| 336 Billy Loes* | 3.00 |
| 337 George Crowe | 3.00 |
| 338 Sparky Anderson (R) | 30.00 |
| 339 Roy Face | 4.00 |
| 340 Roy Sievers | 5.00 |
| 341 Tom Qualters | 3.00 |
| 342 Ray Jablonski | 3.00 |

| NO. PLAYER | NR. MT. | NO. PLAYER | NR. MT. | NO. PLAYER | NR. MT. | NO. PLAYER | NR. MT. |
|---|---|---|---|---|---|---|---|
| 343 Billy Hoeft | 3.00 | 401 Ron Blackburn | 3.00 | 458 Gordon Jones | 3.00 | 518 Mike Cueller (R) | 20.00 |
| 344 Russ Nixon | 3.00 | 402 Hector Lopez | 3.00 | 459 Bill Tuttle | 3.00 | 519 Infield Power: | 14.00 |
| 345 Gil McDougald | 6.00 | 403 Clem Labine | 3.00 | 460 Bob Friend | 3.00 | Pete Runnels, Dick |  |
| 346 Batter Bafflers: | 3.00 | 404 Hank Sauer | 3.00 | 461 Mantle Hits 42nd HR | 40.00 | Gernert, Frank Malzone |  |
| Tom Brewer, Dave Sisler |  | 405 Roy McMillan | 3.00 | 462 Colavito's Catch | 6.00 | 520 Don Elston | 12.50 |
| 347 Bob Buhl | 3.00 | 406 Solly Drake | 3.00 | 463 Kaline Bat Champ | 12.00 | 521 Gary Geiger | 12.50 |
| 348 Ted Lepcio | 3.00 | 407 Moe Drabowsky | 3.00 | 464 Mays' Series Catch | 18.00 | 522 Gene Snyder | 12.50 |
| 349 Hoyt Wilhelm | 13.00 | 408 Keystone Combo: | 6.00 | 465 Sievers HR Mark | 4.00 | 523 Harry Bright | 12.50 |
| 350 Ernie Banks | 55.00 | Nellie Fox, Luis Aparicio |  | 466 Pierce All-Star | 4.00 | 524 Larry Osborne | 12.50 |
| 351 Earl Torgeson | 3.00 | 409 Gus Zernial | 3.00 | 467 Aaron Clubs Homer | 20.00 | 525 Jim Coates | 12.50 |
| 352 Robin Roberts | 15.00 | 410 Billy Pierce | 4.00 | 468 Snider's Play | 12.00 | 526 Bob Speake | 12.50 |
| 353 Curt Flood | 4.00 | 411 Whitey Lockman | 3.00 | 469 Banks MVP | 12.00 | 527 Solly Hemus | 12.50 |
| 354 Pete Burnside | 3.00 | 412 Stan Lopata | 3.00 | 470 Musial's 3000 Hits | 16.00 | 528 Pittsburgh Pirates | 35.00 |
| 355 Jim Piersall | 4.00 | 413 Camillo Pascual | 3.00 | 471 Tom Sturdivant | 3.00 | 529 George Bamberger (R) | 15.00 |
| 356 Bob Mabe | 3.00 | 414 Dale Long | 3.00 | 472 Gene Freese | 3.00 | 530 Wally Moon | 12.50 |
| 357 Dick Stuart (R) | 4.00 | 415 Bill Mazeroski | 6.00 | 473 Mike Fornieles | 3.00 | 531 Ray Webster | 12.50 |
| 358 Ralph Terry | 3.00 | 416 Haywood Sullivan | 3.00 | 474 Moe Thacker | 3.00 | 532 Mark Freeman | 12.50 |
| 359 Bill White (R) | 22.00 | 417 Virgil Trucks | 3.00 | 475 Jack Harshman | 3.00 | 533 Darrell Johnson | 12.50 |
| 360 Al Kaline | 55.00 | 418 Gino Cimoli | 3.00 | 476 Cleveland Indians | 8.00 | 534 Faye Throneberry | 12.50 |
| 361 Willard Nixon | 3.00 | 419 Milwuakee Braves | 7.00 | 477 Barry Latman | 3.00 | 535 Ruben Gomez | 12.50 |
| 362 Dolan Nichols* | 3.00 | 420 Rocky Colavito | 15.00 | 478 Bob Clemente | 100.00 | 536 Dan Kravitz | 12.50 |
| 363 Bobby Avila | 3.00 | 421 Herm Wehmeier | 3.00 | 479 Lindy McDaniel | 3.00 | 537 Rudolph Arias | 12.50 |
| 364 Danny McDevitt | 3.00 | 422 Hobie Landrith | 3.00 | 480 Red Schoendienst | 13.00 | 538 Chick King | 12.50 |
| 365 Gus Bell | 3.00 | 423 Bob Grim | 3.00 | 481 Charlie Maxwell | 3.00 | 539 Gary Blaylock | 12.50 |
| 366 Humberto Robinson | 3.00 | 424 Ken Aspromonte | 3.00 | 482 Russ Meyer | 3.00 | 540 Willie Miranda | 12.50 |
| 367 Cal Neeman | 3.00 | 425 Del Crandall | 3.00 | 483 Clint Courtney | 3.00 | 541 Bob Thurman | 12.50 |
| 368 Don Mueller | 3.00 | 426 Jerry Staley | 3.00 | 484 Willie Kirkland | 3.00 | 542 Jim Perry (R) | 20.00 |
| 369 Dick Tomanek | 3.00 | 427 Charlie Neal | 3.00 | 485 Ryne Duren | 3.00 | 543 Corsair Outfield Trio: | 50.00 |
| 370 Pete Runnels | 3.00 | 428 Buc Hill Aces: | 5.00 | 486 Sammy White | 3.00 | Bob Skinner, Bll Virdon, |  |
| 371 Dick Brodowski | 3.00 | Ron Kline, Bob Friend, |  | 487 Hal Brown | 3.00 | Roberto Clemente |  |
| 372 Jim Hegan | 3.00 | Vernon Law, Roy Face |  | 488 Walt Moryn | 3.00 | 544 Lee Tate | 12.50 |
| 373 Herb Plews | 3.00 | 429 Bobby Thomson | 4.00 | 489 John Powers | 3.00 | 545 Tom Morgan | 12.50 |
| 374 Art Ditmar | 3.00 | 430 Whitey Ford | 40.00 | 490 Frank Thomas | 3.00 | 546 Al Schroll | 12.50 |
| 375 Bob Nieman | 3.00 | 431 Whammy Douglas | 3.00 | 491 Don Blasingame | 3.00 | 547 Jim Baxes | 12.50 |
| 376 Hal Naragon | 3.00 | 432 Smokey Burgess | 3.00 | 492 Gene Conley | 3.00 | 548 Elmer Singleton | 12.50 |
| 377 Johnny Antonelli | 3.00 | 433 Billy Harrell | 3.00 | 493 Jim Landis | 3.00 | 549 Howie Nunn | 12.50 |
| 378 Gail Harris | 3.00 | 434 Hal Griggs | 3.00 | 494 Don Pavletich | 3.00 | 550 Symbol of Courage: | 135.00 |
| 379 Bob Miller | 3.00 | 435 Frank Robinson | 40.00 | 495 Johnny Podres | 5.00 | Roy Campanella |  |
| 380 Hank Aaron | 100.00 | 436 Granny Hamner | 3.00 | 496 Wayne Terwilliger | 3.00 | 551 F. Haney—Mgr.(AS) | 12.50 |
| 381 Mike Baxes | 3.00 | 437 Ike Delock | 3.00 | 497 Hal R. Smith | 3.00 | 552 C. Stengel—Mgr. (AS) | 30.00 |
| 382 Curt Simmons | 3.00 | 438 Sam Esposito | 3.00 | 498 Dick Hyde | 3.00 | 553 Orlando Cepeda (AS) | 20.00 |
| 383 Words of Wisdom: | 6.00 | 439 Brooks Robinson | 45.00 | 499 Johnny O'Brien | 3.00 | 554 Bll Skowron (AS) | 16.00 |
| Don Larsen, Casey Stengel |  | 440 Lou Burdette | 6.00 | 500 Vic Wertz | 3.00 | 555 Bill Mazeroski (AS) | 16.00 |
| 384 Dave Sisler | 3.00 | 441 John Roseboro | 3.00 | 501 Bobby Tiefenauer | 3.00 | 556 Nellie Fox (AS) | 20.00 |
| 385 Sherm Lollar | 3.00 | 442 Ray Narleski | 3.00 | 502 Al Dark | 3.00 | 557 Ken Boyer (AS) | 15.00 |
| 386 Jim Delsing | 3.00 | 443 Daryl Spencer | 3.00 | 503 Jim Owens | 3.00 | 558 Frank Malzone (AS) | 14.00 |
| 387 Don Drysdale | 35.00 | 444 Ronnie Hansen | 3.00 | 504 Ossie Alvarez | 3.00 | 559 Ernie Banks (AS) | 50.00 |
| 388 Bob Will | 3.00 | 445 Cal McLish | 3.00 | 505 Tony Kubek | 9.00 | 560 Luis Aparicio (AS) | 25.00 |
| 389 Joe Nuxhall | 3.00 | 446 Rocky Nelson | 3.00 | 506 Bob Purkey | 3.00 | 561 Hank Aaron (AS) | 100.00 |
| 390 Orlando Cepeda | 16.00 | 447 Bob Anderson | 3.00 | 507 Bob Hale | 12.50 | 562 Al Kaline (AS) | 45.00 |
| 391 Milt Pappas | 3.00 | 448 Vada Pinson | 5.00 | 508 Art Fowler | 12.50 | 563 Willie Mays (AS) | 105.00 |
| 392 Whitey Herzog | 5.00 | 449 Tom Gorman | 3.00 | 509 Norm Cash (R) | 50.00 | 564 Mickey Mantle (AS) | 225.00 |
| 393 Frank Lary | 3.00 | 450 Ed Mathews | 25.00 | 510 New York Yankees | 60.00 | 565 Wes Covington (AS) | 14.00 |
| 394 Randy Jackson | 3.00 | 451 Jimmy Constable | 3.00 | 511 George Susce | 12.50 | 566 Roy Sievers (AS) | 14.00 |
| 395 Elston Howard | 8.00 | 452 Chico Fernandez | 3.00 | 512 George Altman | 12.50 | 567 Del Crandall (AS) | 14.00 |
| 396 Bob Rush | 3.00 | 453 Les Moss | 3.00 | 513 Tommy Carroll | 12.50 | 568 Gus Triandos (AS) | 14.00 |
| 397 Washington Senators | 9.00 | 454 Phil Clark | 3.00 | 514 Bob Gibson (R) | 375.00 | 569 Bob Friend (AS) | 14.00 |
| 398 Wally Post | 3.00 | 455 Larry Doby | 4.00 | 515 Harmon Killebrew | 135.00 | 570 Bob Turley (AS) | 14.00 |
| 399 Larry Jackson | 3.00 | 456 Jerry Casale | 3.00 | 516 Mike Garcia | 12.50 | 571 Warren Spahn (AS) | 35.00 |
| 400 Jackie Jensen | 4.00 | 457 Los Angeles Dodgers | 15.00 | 517 Joe Koppe | 12.50 | 572 B. Pierce (AS) (exc. $7.50) | 30.00 |

## 1960 Topps . . . Complete Set of 572 Cards—Value $1600.00 (Exc.); $3750.00 (Near Mint)

This set features the rookie cards of Willie McCovey and Carl Yastrzemski. The high numbers are 507 to 572. Semi-high numbers are 441 to 506. Topps' switched to a predominantly horizontal format, and used it for the last time. Cards 375 to 440 exist with *gray* or *white* backs.

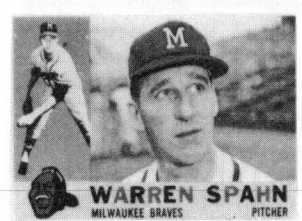

| NO. PLAYER | NR. MT. |
|---|---|
| 1 E. Wynn (exc. $8.00) | 40.00 |
| 2 Roman Mejias | 3.00 |
| 3 Joe Adcock | 4.00 |
| 4 Bob Purkey | 3.00 |
| 5 Wally Moon | 3.00 |
| 6 Lou Berberet | 3.00 |
| 7 Master & Mentor: | 15.00 |
| Willie Mays, Bill Rigney | |
| 8 Bud Daley | 3.00 |
| 9 Faye Throneberry | 3.00 |
| 10 Ernie Banks | 45.00 |
| 11 Norm Siebern | 3.00 |
| 12 Milt Pappas | 3.00 |
| 13 Wally Post | 3.00 |
| 14 Jim Grant | 3.00 |
| 15 Pete Runnels | 3.00 |
| 16 Ernie Broglio | 3.00 |
| 17 John Callison | 3.00 |
| 18 Los Angeles Dodgers | 15.00 |
| 19 Felix Mantilla | 3.00 |
| 20 Roy Face | 4.00 |
| 21 Dutch Dotterer | 3.00 |
| 22 Rocky Bridges | 3.00 |
| 23 Eddie Fisher | 3.00 |
| 24 Dick Gray | 3.00 |
| 25 Ray Sievers | 3.00 |
| 26 Wayne Terwilliger | 3.00 |
| 27 Dick Drott | 3.00 |
| 28 Brooks Robinson | 40.00 |
| 29 Clem Labine | 3.00 |
| 30 Tito Francona | 3.00 |
| 31 Sammy Esposito | 3.00 |
| 32 Sophomore Stalwarts: | 4.00 |
| Jim O'Toole, Vada Pinson | |
| 33 Tom Morgan | 3.00 |
| 34 Sparky Anderson | 7.00 |
| 35 Whitey Ford | 35.00 |
| 36 Russ Nixon | 3.00 |
| 37 Bill Bruton | 3.00 |
| 38 Jerry Casale | 3.00 |
| 39 Earl Averill | 3.00 |
| 40 Joe Cunningham | 3.00 |
| 41 Barry Latman | 3.00 |
| 42 Hobie Landrith | 3.00 |
| 43 Washington Senators | 6.00 |
| 44 Bobby Locke | 3.00 |
| 45 Roy McMillan | 3.00 |
| 46 Jack Fisher | 3.00 |
| 47 Don Zimmer | 7.00 |
| 48 Hal Smith | 3.00 |
| 49 Curt Raydon | 3.00 |
| 50 Al Kaline | 40.00 |
| 51 Jim Coates | 3.00 |
| 52 Dave Philley | 3.00 |
| 53 Jackie Brandt | 3.00 |
| 54 Mike Fornieles | 3.00 |
| 55 Bill Mazeroski | 5.00 |
| 56 Steve Korcheck | 3.00 |
| 57 Win Savers: | 4.00 |
| Turk Lown, Jerry Staley | |
| 58 Gino Cimoli | 3.00 |
| 59 Juan Pizarro | 3.00 |
| 60 Gus Triandos | 3.00 |
| 61 Eddie Kasko | 3.00 |
| 62 Roger Craig | 4.00 |
| 63 George Strickland | 3.00 |
| 64 Jack Meyer | 3.00 |
| 65 Elston Howard | 6.00 |
| 66 Bob Trowbridge | 3.00 |
| 67 Jose Pagan | 3.00 |
| 68 Dave Hillman | 3.00 |
| 69 Billy Goodman | 3.00 |
| 70 Lou Burdette | 4.00 |
| 71 Marty Keough | 3.00 |
| 72 Detroit Tigers | 6.00 |
| 73 Bob Gibson | 50.00 |
| 74 Walt Moryn | 3.00 |
| 75 Vic Power | 3.00 |
| 76 Bill Fischer | 3.00 |
| 77 Hank Foiles | 3.00 |
| 78 Bob Grim | 3.00 |
| 79 Walt Dropo | 3.00 |

| NO. PLAYER | NR. MT. |
|---|---|
| 80 Johnny Antonelli | 3.00 |
| 81 Russ Snyder | 3.00 |
| 82 Ruben Gomez | 3.00 |
| 83 Tony Kubek | 6.00 |
| 84 Hal Smith | 3.00 |
| 85 Frank Lary | 3.00 |
| 86 Dick Gernert | 3.00 |
| 87 John Romonosky | 3.00 |
| 88 John Roseboro | 3.00 |
| 89 Hal Brown | 3.00 |
| 90 Bobby Avila | 3.00 |
| 91 Bennie Daniels | 3.00 |
| 92 Whitey Herzog | 4.00 |
| 93 Art Schult | 3.00 |
| 94 Leo Kiely | 3.00 |
| 95 Frank Thomas | 3.00 |
| 96 Ralph Terry | 3.00 |
| 97 Ted Lepcio | 3.00 |
| 98 Gordon Jones | 3.00 |
| 99 Lenny Green | 3.00 |
| 100 Nellie Fox | 8.00 |
| 101 Bob Miller | 3.00 |
| 102 Kent Hadley | 3.00 |
| 103 Dick Farrell | 3.00 |
| 104 Dick Schofield | 3.00 |
| 105 Larry Sherry (R) | 4.00 |
| 106 Billy Gardner | 3.00 |
| 107 Carl Willey | 3.00 |
| 108 Pete Daley | 3.00 |
| 109 Cletis Boyer | 4.00 |
| 110 Cal McLish | 3.00 |
| 111 Vic Wertz | 2.50 |
| 112 Jack Harshman | 2.50 |
| 113 Bob Skinner | 2.50 |
| 114 Ken Apromonte | 2.50 |
| 115 Fork & Knuckler: | 5.00 |
| Roy Face, Hoyt Wilhelm | |
| 116 Jim Rivera | 2.50 |
| **No. 117 to 148—ROOKIE STARS** | |
| 117 Tom Borland | 2.50 |
| 118 Bob Bruce | 2.50 |
| 119 Chico Cardenas | 2.50 |
| 120 Duke Carmel | 2.50 |
| 121 Camilo Carreon | 2.50 |
| 122 Don Dillard | 2.50 |
| 123 Dan Dobbek | 2.50 |
| 124 Jim Donohue | 2.50 |
| 125 Dick Ellsworth | 2.50 |
| 126 Chuck Estrada (R) | 4.00 |
| 127 Ronnie Hansen | 2.50 |
| 128 Bill Harris | 2.50 |
| 129 Bob Hartman | 2.50 |
| 130 Frank Herrera | 2.50 |
| 131 Ed Hobaugh | 2.50 |
| 132 Frank Howard (R) | 15.00 |
| 133 Manuel Javier | 2.50 |
| 134 Deron Johnson | 2.50 |
| 135 Ken Johnson | 2.50 |
| 136 Jim Kaat (R) | 30.00 |
| 137 Lou Klimchock | 2.50 |
| 138 Art Mahaffey | 2.50 |
| 139 Carl Mathias | 2.50 |
| 140 Julio Navarro | 2.50 |
| 141 Jim Proctor | 2.50 |
| 142 Bill Short | 2.50 |
| 143 Al Spangler | 2.50 |
| 144 Al Stieglitz | 2.50 |
| 145 Jim Umbricht | 2.50 |
| 146 Ted Wieand | 2.50 |
| 147 Bob Will | 2.50 |
| 148 Carl Yastrzemski (R) | 300.00 |
| 149 Bob Nieman | 2.50 |
| 150 Billy Pierce | 4.00 |
| 151 San F. Giants | 8.00 |
| 152 Gail Harris | 2.50 |
| 153 Bobby Thomson | 3.00 |
| 154 Jim Davenport | 2.50 |
| 155 Charlie Neal | 2.50 |
| 156 Art Ceccarelli | 2.50 |
| 157 Rocky Nelson | 2.50 |
| 158 Wes Covington | 2.50 |

| NO. PLAYER | NR. MT. |
|---|---|
| 159 Jim Piersall | 3.00 |
| 160 Rival All-Stars: | 45.00 |
| Mickey Mantle, Ken Boyer | |
| 161 Ray Narleski | 2.50 |
| 162 Sammy Taylor | 2.50 |
| 163 Hector Lopez | 2.50 |
| 164 Cincinnati Reds | 6.00 |
| 165 Jack Sanford | 2.50 |
| 166 Chuck Essegian | 2.50 |
| 167 Valmy Thomas | 2.50 |
| 168 Alex Grammas | 2.50 |
| 169 Jake Striker | 2.50 |
| 170 Del Crandall | 2.50 |
| 171 Johnny Groth | 2.50 |
| 172 Willie Kirkland | 2.50 |
| 173 Billy Martin | 10.00 |
| 174 Cleveland Indians | 6.00 |
| 175 Pedro Ramos | 2.50 |
| 176 Vada Pinson | 5.00 |
| 177 Johnny Kucks | 2.50 |
| 178 Woody Held | 2.50 |
| 179 Rip Coleman | 2.50 |
| 180 Harry Simpson | 2.50 |
| 181 Billy Loes | 2.50 |
| 182 Glen Hobbie | 2.50 |
| 183 Eli Grba | 2.50 |
| 184 Gary Geiger | 2.50 |
| 185 Jim Owens | 2.50 |
| 186 Dave Sisler | 2.50 |
| 187 Jay Hook | 2.50 |
| 188 Dick Williams | 2.50 |
| 189 Don McMahon | 2.50 |
| 190 Gene Woodling | 2.50 |
| 191 Johnny Klippstein | 2.50 |
| 192 Danny O'Connell | 2.50 |
| 193 Dick Hyde | 2.50 |
| 194 Bobby Gene Smith | 2.50 |
| 195 Lindy McDaniel | 2.50 |
| 196 Andy Carey | 2.50 |
| 197 Ron Kline | 2.50 |
| 198 Jerry Lynch | 2.50 |
| 199 Dick Donovan | 2.50 |
| 200 Willie Mays | 110.00 |
| 201 Larry Osborne | 2.50 |
| 202 Fred Kipp | 2.50 |
| 203 Sammy White | 2.50 |
| 204 Ryne Duren | 2.50 |
| 205 Johnny Logan | 2.50 |
| 206 Claude Osteen | 2.50 |
| 207 Bob Boyd | 2.50 |
| 208 Chicago White Sox | 6.00 |
| 209 Ron Blackburn | 2.50 |
| 210 Harmon Killebrew | 27.00 |
| 211 Taylor Phillips | 2.50 |
| 212 Walt Alston (Mgr.) | 10.00 |
| 213 Chuck Dressen (Mgr.) | 3.00 |
| 214 Jim Dykes (Mgr.) | 3.00 |
| 215 Bob Elliott (Mgr.) | 3.00 |
| 216 Joe Gordon (Mgr.) | 3.00 |
| 217 Charley Grimm (Mgr.) | 3.00 |
| 218 Solly Hemus (Mgr.) | 3.00 |
| 219 Fred Hutchinson (Mgr.) | 3.00 |
| 220 Billy Jurges (Mgr.) | 3.00 |
| 221 Cookie Lavagetto (Mgr.) | 3.00 |
| 222 Al Lopez (Mgr.) | 6.00 |
| 223 Danny Murtaugh (Mgr.) | 3.00 |
| 224 Paul Richards (Mgr.) | 3.00 |
| 225 Bill Rigney (Mgr.) | 3.00 |
| 226 Eddie Sawyer (Mgr.) | 3.00 |
| 227 Casey Stengel (Mgr.) | 15.00 |
| 228 Ernie Johnson | 3.00 |
| 229 Joe Morgan | 5.00 |
| 230 Mound Magicians: | 7.00 |
| Lou Burdette, Warren Spahn, Bob Buhl | |
| 231 Hal Naragon | 2.50 |
| 232 Jim Busby | 2.50 |
| 233 Don Elston | 2.50 |
| 234 Don Demeter | 2.50 |
| 235 Gus Bell | 2.50 |
| 236 Dick Ricketts | 2.50 |
| 237 Elmer Valo | 2.50 |

| NO. PLAYER | NR. MT. |
|---|---|
| 238 Danny Kravitz | 2.50 |
| 239 Joe Shipley | 2.50 |
| 240 Luis Aparicio | 13.00 |
| 241 Albie Pearson | 2.50 |
| 242 St. Louis Cardinals | 6.00 |
| 243 Bubba Phillips | 2.50 |
| 244 Hal Griggs | 2.50 |
| 245 Eddie Yost | 2.50 |
| 246 Lee Maye | 2.50 |
| 247 Gil McDougald | 4.00 |
| 248 Del Rice | 2.50 |
| 249 Earl Wilson | 2.50 |
| 250 Stan Musial | 100.00 |
| 251 Bobby Malkmus | 2.50 |
| 252 Ray Herbert | 2.50 |
| 253 Eddie Bressoud | 2.50 |
| 254 Arnie Portocarrero | 2.50 |
| 255 Jim Gilliam | 4.00 |
| 256 Dick Brown | 2.50 |
| 257 Gordy Coleman | 2.50 |
| 258 Dick Groat | 4.00 |
| 259 George Altman | 2.50 |
| 260 Power Plus: | 4.00 |
| Rocky Colavito, Tito Francona | |
| 261 Pete Burnside | 2.50 |
| 262 Hank Bauer | 2.50 |
| 263 Darrell Johnson | 2.50 |
| 264 Robin Roberts | 12.00 |
| 265 Rip Repulski | 2.50 |
| 266 Joe Jay | 2.50 |
| 267 Jim Marshall | 2.50 |
| 268 Al Worthington | 2.50 |
| 269 Gene Green | 2.50 |
| 270 Bob Turley | 3.00 |
| 271 Julio Bequer | 2.50 |
| 272 Fred Green | 2.50 |
| 273 Neil Chrisley | 2.50 |
| 274 Tom Acker | 2.50 |
| 275 Curt Flood | 4.00 |
| 276 Ken McBride | 2.50 |
| 277 Harry Bright | 2.50 |
| 278 Stan Williams | 2.50 |
| 279 Chuck Tanner | 2.50 |
| 280 Frank Sullivan | 2.50 |
| 281 Ray Boone | 2.50 |
| 282 Joe Nuxhall | 2.50 |
| 283 John Blanchard | 2.50 |
| 284 Don Gross | 2.50 |
| 285 Harry Anderson | 2.50 |
| 286 Ray Semproch | 2.50 |
| 287 Felipe Alou | 3.50 |
| 288 Bob Mabe | 3.00 |
| 289 Willie Jones | 3.00 |
| 290 Jerry Lumpe | 3.00 |
| 291 Bob Keegan | 3.00 |
| 292 Dodger Backstops: | 4.00 |
| Joe Pignatano, John Roseboro | |
| 293 Gene Conley | 3.00 |
| 294 Tony Taylor | 3.00 |
| 295 Gil Hodges | 15.00 |
| 296 Nelson Chittum | 3.00 |
| 297 Reno Bertoia | 3.00 |
| 298 George Witt | 3.00 |
| 299 Earl Torgeson | 3.00 |
| 300 Hank Aaron | 100.00 |
| 301 Jerry Davie | 3.00 |
| 302 Philadelphia Phillies | 6.00 |
| 303 Billy O'Dell | 3.00 |
| 304 Joe Ginsberg | 3.00 |
| 305 Richie Ashburn | 9.00 |
| 306 Frank Baumann | 3.00 |
| 307 Gene Oliver | 3.00 |
| 308 Dick Hall | 3.00 |
| 309 Bob Hale | 3.00 |
| 310 Frank Malzone | 3.00 |
| 311 Raul Sanchez | 3.00 |
| 312 Charlie Lau | 3.00 |
| 313 Turk Lown | 3.00 |
| 314 Chico Fernandez | 3.00 |
| 315 Bobby Shantz | 4.00 |

| NO. | PLAYER | NR. MT. |
|---|---|---|
| 316 | Willie McCovey (R) | 225.00 |
| 317 | Pumpsie Green | 3.00 |
| 318 | Jim Baxes | 3.00 |
| 319 | Joe Koppe | 3.00 |
| 320 | Bob Allison | 3.00 |
| 321 | Ron Fairly | 3.00 |
| 322 | Willie Tasby | 3.00 |
| 323 | Johnny Romano | 3.00 |
| 324 | Jim Perry | 4.00 |
| 325 | Jim O'Toole | 3.00 |
| 326 | Bob Clemente | 100.00 |
| 327 | Ray Sadecki | 3.00 |
| 328 | Earl Battey | 3.00 |
| 329 | Zack Monroe | 3.00 |
| 330 | Harvey Kuenn | 4.00 |
| 331 | Henry Mason | 3.00 |
| 332 | New York Yankees | 20.00 |
| 333 | Danny McDevitt | 3.00 |
| 334 | Ted Abernathy | 3.00 |
| 335 | Red Schoendienst | 10.00 |
| 336 | Ike Delock | 3.00 |
| 337 | Cal Neeman | 3.00 |
| 338 | Ray Monzant | 3.00 |
| 339 | Harry Chiti | 3.00 |
| 340 | Harvey Haddix | 5.00 |
| 341 | Carroll Hardy | 3.00 |
| 342 | Casey Wise | 3.00 |
| 343 | Sandy Koufax | 115.00 |
| 344 | Clint Courtney | 3.00 |
| 345 | Don Newcombe | 4.00 |
| 346 | J.C. Martin (photo of Gary Peters | 3.00 |
| 347 | Ed Bouchee | 3.00 |
| 348 | Barry Shetrone | 3.00 |
| 349 | Moe Drabowsky | 3.00 |
| 350 | Mickey Mantle | 350.00 |
| 351 | Don Nottebart | 3.00 |
| 352 | Cincy Clouters: Gus Bell, Frank Robinson, Jerry Lync | 5.00 |
| 353 | Don Larsen | 4.00 |
| 354 | Bob Lillis | 3.00 |
| 355 | Bill White | 6.00 |
| 356 | Joe Amalfitano | 3.00 |
| 357 | Al Schroll | 3.00 |
| 358 | Joe DeMaestri | 3.00 |
| 359 | Buddy Gilbert | 3.00 |
| 360 | Herb Score | 4.00 |
| 361 | Bob Oldis | 3.00 |
| 362 | Russ Kemmerer | 3.00 |
| 363 | Gene Stephens | 3.00 |
| 364 | Paul Foytack | 3.00 |
| 365 | Minnie Minoso | 4.00 |
| 366 | Dallas Green (R) | 10.00 |
| 367 | Bill Tuttle | 3.00 |
| 368 | Daryl Spencer | 3.00 |
| 369 | Billy Hoeft | 3.00 |
| 370 | Bill Skowron | 6.00 |
| 371 | Bud Byerly | 3.00 |
| 372 | Frank House | 3.00 |
| 373 | Don Hoak | 3.00 |
| 374 | Bob Buhl | 3.00 |
| 375 | Dale Long | 3.00 |
| 376 | Johnny Briggs | 3.00 |
| 377 | Roger Maris | 120.00 |
| 378 | Stu Miller | 3.00 |
| 379 | Red Wilson | 3.00 |
| 380 | Bob Shaw | 3.00 |
| 381 | Milwaukee Braves | 6.00 |
| 382 | Ted Bowsfield | 3.00 |
| 383 | Leon Wagner | 3.00 |
| 384 | Don Cardwell | 3.00 |
| 385 | World Series Game 1 .. Neal Steals Second | 5.00 |

| NO. | PLAYER | NR. MT. |
|---|---|---|
| 386 | World Series Game 2 ... Neal Belts 2nd Homer | 6.00 |
| 387 | World Series Game 3 ... Furillo Breaks Up Game | 6.00 |
| 388 | World Series Game 4 ... Hodges' Winning Homer | 6.00 |
| 389 | World Series Game 5 ... Luis Swipes Base | 6.00 |
| 390 | World Series Game 6 ... Scrambling After Ball | 6.00 |
| 391 | World Series ......... The Champs Celebrate | 6.00 |
| 392 | Tex Clevenger | 3.00 |
| 393 | Smokey Burgess | 3.50 |
| 394 | Norm Larker | 3.00 |
| 395 | Hoyt Wilhelm | 10.00 |
| 396 | Steve Bilko | 3.00 |
| 397 | Don Blasingame | 3.00 |
| 398 | Mike Cuellar | 3.00 |
| 399 | Young Hill Stars: Milt Pappas, Jack Fisher, Jerry Walker | 3.00 |
| 400 | Rocky Colavito | 9.00 |
| 401 | Bob Duliba | 3.00 |
| 402 | Dick Stuart | 3.00 |
| 403 | Ed Sadowski | 3.00 |
| 404 | Bob Rush | 3.00 |
| 405 | Bobby Richardson | 6.00 |
| 406 | Billy Klaus | 3.00 |
| 407 | Gary Peters (photo of J.C. Martin) | 4.00 |
| 408 | Carl Furillo | 5.00 |
| 409 | Ron Samford | 3.00 |
| 410 | Sam Jones | 3.00 |
| 411 | Ed Bailey | 3.00 |
| 412 | Bob Anderson | 3.00 |
| 413 | Kansas C. Athletics | 6.00 |
| 414 | Don Williams | 3.00 |
| 415 | Bob Cerv | 3.00 |
| 416 | Humberto Robinson | 3.00 |
| 417 | Chuck Cottier (R) | 3.50 |
| 418 | Don Mossi | 3.00 |
| 419 | George Crowe | 3.00 |
| 420 | Ed Mathews | 30.00 |
| 421 | Duke Maas | 3.00 |
| 422 | Johnny Powers | 3.00 |
| 423 | Ed Fitzgerald | 3.00 |
| 424 | Pete Whisenant | 3.00 |
| 425 | Johnny Podres | 4.00 |
| 426 | Ron Jackson | 3.00 |
| 427 | Al Grunwald | 3.00 |
| 428 | Al Smith | 3.00 |
| 429 | Amer. League Kings: Nellie Fox, Harvey Kuenn | 5.00 |
| 430 | Art Ditmar | 3.00 |
| 431 | Andre Rodgers | 3.00 |
| 432 | Chuck Stobbs | 3.00 |
| 433 | Irv Noren | 3.00 |
| 434 | Brooks Lawrence | 3.00 |
| 435 | Gene Freese | 3.00 |
| 436 | Marv Throneberry | 3.50 |
| 437 | Bob Friend | 3.00 |
| 438 | Jim Coker | 3.00 |
| 439 | Tom Brewer | 3.00 |
| 440 | Jim Lemon | 3.00 |
| 441 | Gary Bell | 4.00 |
| 442 | Joe Pignatano | 4.00 |
| 443 | Charlie Maxwell | 4.00 |
| 444 | Jerry Kindall | 4.00 |
| 445 | Warren Spahn | 40.00 |
| 446 | Ellis Burton | 4.00 |
| 447 | Ray Moore | 4.00 |
| 448 | Jim Gentile | 8.00 |

| NO. | PLAYER | NR. MT. |
|---|---|---|
| 449 | Jim Brosnan | 4.00 |
| 450 | Orlando Cepeda | 12.00 |
| 451 | Curt Simmons | 5.00 |
| 452 | Ray Webster | 5.00 |
| 453 | Vern Law | 6.00 |
| 454 | Hal Woodeschick | 3.00 |
| 455 | Orioles Coaches: Robinson, Brecheen, Harris | 5.00 |
| 456 | Red Sox Coaches: York, Herman, Maglie, Baker | 6.00 |
| 457 | Cubs Coaches: Klein, Tappe, Root | 5.00 |
| 458 | White Sox Coaches: Cooney, Gutteridge, Cuccinello, Berres | 5.00 |
| 459 | Reds Coaches: Deal, Moses, Otero | 5.00 |
| 460 | Indians Coaches: White, Lemon, Harder, Kress | 5.00 |
| 461 | Tigers Coaches: Ferrick, Appling, Hitchcock | 5.00 |
| 462 | Athletics Coaches: Cooper, Fitzsimmons, Heffner | 5.00 |
| 463 | Dodgers Coaches: Bragan, Reiser, Becker, Mulleavy | 5.00 |
| 464 | Braves Coaches: Scheffing, Myatt, Wyatt, Pafko | 5.00 |
| 465 | Yankees Coaches: Dickey, Houk, Lopat, Crosetti | 12.00 |
| 466 | Phillies Coaches: Silvestri, Cohen, Carter | 5.00 |
| 467 | Pirates Coaches: Vernon, Oceak, Narron, Burwell | 5.00 |
| 468 | Cardinals Coaches: Keane, Pollet, Katt, Walker | 5.00 |
| 469 | Giants Coaches: Westrum, Parker, Posedel | 5.00 |
| 470 | Senators Coaches: Swift, Mele, Clary | 5.00 |
| 471 | Ned Garver | 4.00 |
| 472 | Al Dark | 5.00 |
| 473 | Al Cicotte | 4.00 |
| 474 | Haywood Sullivan | 4.00 |
| 475 | Don Drysdale | 40.00 |
| 476 | Lou Johnson | 4.00 |
| 477 | Don Ferrarese | 4.00 |
| 478 | Frank Torre | 4.00 |
| 479 | Georges Maranda | 4.00 |
| 480 | Yogi Berra | 70.00 |
| 481 | Wes Stock | 5.00 |
| 482 | Frank Bolling | 4.00 |
| 483 | Camilo Pascual | 4.00 |
| 484 | Pittsburgh Pirates | 15.00 |
| 485 | Ken Boyer | 7.50 |
| 486 | Bobby Del Greco | 4.00 |
| 487 | Tom Sturdivant | 4.00 |
| 488 | Norm Cash | 7.00 |
| 489 | Steve Ridzik | 4.00 |
| 490 | Frank Robinson | 50.00 |
| 491 | Mel Roach | 4.00 |
| 492 | Larry Jackson | 4.00 |
| 493 | Duke Snider | 55.00 |
| 494 | Baltimore Orioles | 10.00 |
| 495 | Sherm Lollar | 4.00 |
| 496 | Bill Virdon | 5.00 |
| 497 | John Tsitouris | 4.00 |
| 498 | Al Pilarcik | 4.00 |

| NO. | PLAYER | NR. MT. |
|---|---|---|
| 499 | Johnny James | 4.00 |
| 500 | Johnny Temple | 4.00 |
| 501 | Bob Schmidt | 4.00 |
| 502 | Jim Bunning | 10.00 |
| 503 | Don Lee | 4.00 |
| 504 | Seth Morehead | 4.00 |
| 505 | Ted Kluszewski | 8.00 |
| 506 | Lee Walls | 4.00 |
| 507 | Dick Stigman | 10.00 |
| 508 | Billy Consolo | 10.00 |
| 509 | Tommy Davis (R) | 20.00 |
| 510 | Jerry Staley | 10.00 |
| 511 | Ken Walters | 10.00 |
| 512 | Joe Gibbon | 10.00 |
| 513 | Chicago Cubs | 30.00 |
| 514 | Steve Barber | 10.00 |
| 515 | Stan Lopata | 10.00 |
| 516 | Marty Kutyna | 10.00 |
| 517 | Charley James | 10.00 |
| 518 | Tony Gonzalez | 10.00 |
| 519 | Ed Roebuck | 10.00 |
| 520 | Don Buddin | 10.00 |
| 521 | Mike Lee | 10.00 |
| 522 | Ken Hunt | 10.00 |
| 523 | Clay Dalrymple | 10.00 |
| 524 | Bill Henry | 10.00 |
| 525 | Marv Breeding | 10.00 |
| 526 | Paul Giel | 10.00 |
| 527 | Jose Valdivielso | 10.00 |
| 528 | Ben Johnson | 10.00 |
| 529 | Norm Sherry (R) | 10.00 |
| 530 | Mike McCormick | 10.00 |
| 531 | Sandy Amoros | 10.00 |
| 532 | Mike Garcia | 10.00 |
| 533 | L. Clinton | 10.00 |
| 534 | Ken Mackenzie | 10.00 |
| 535 | Whitey Lockman | 10.00 |
| 536 | Wynn Hawkins | 10.00 |
| 537 | Boston Red Sox | 35.00 |
| 538 | Frank Barnes | 10.00 |
| 539 | Gene Baker | 10.00 |
| 540 | Jerry Walker | 10.00 |
| 541 | Tony Curry | 10.00 |
| 542 | Ken Hamlin | 10.00 |
| 543 | Elio Chacon | 10.00 |
| 544 | Bill Monbouquette | 10.00 |
| 545 | Carl Sawatski | 10.00 |
| 546 | Hank Aguirre | 10.00 |
| 547 | Bob Aspromonte | 10.00 |
| 548 | Don Mincher | 10.00 |
| 549 | John Buzhardt | 10.00 |
| 550 | Jim Landis | 10.00 |
| 551 | Ed Rakow | 10.00 |
| 552 | Walt Bond | 10.00 |
| 553 | Bill Skowron (AS) | 15.00 |
| 554 | Willie McCovey (AS) | 60.00 |
| 555 | Nellie Fox (AS) | 15.00 |
| 556 | Charlie Neal (AS) | 12.00 |
| 557 | Frank Malzone (AS) | 12.00 |
| 558 | Eddie Mathews (AS) | 30.00 |
| 559 | Luis Aparicio (AS) | 20.00 |
| 560 | Ernie Banks (AS) | 40.00 |
| 561 | Al Kaline (AS) | 40.00 |
| 562 | Joe Cunningham (AS) | 12.00 |
| 563 | Mickey Mantle (AS) | 225.00 |
| 564 | Willie Mays (AS) | 100.00 |
| 565 | Roger Maris (AS) | 100.00 |
| 566 | Hank Aaron (AS) | 100.00 |
| 567 | Sherm Lollar (AS) | 12.00 |
| 568 | Del Crandall (AS) | 12.00 |
| 569 | Camilo Pascual (AS) | 12.00 |
| 570 | Don Drysdale (AS) | 25.00 |
| 571 | Billy Pierce (AS) | 12.00 |
| 572 | J.Antonelli (AS) (exc. $8.00) | 25.00 |

# 1961 Topps . . . Complete Set of 587 Cards—Value $2200.00 (Exc.); $5500.00 (Near Mint)

Juan Marichal and Billy Williams' rookie cards are in this set. The high numbers are 523 to 589. Cards 587 and 588 were not issued. Card 426 (Braves team) was mistakenly numbered 463.

| NO. | PLAYER | NR. MT. |
|---|---|---|
| 1 | Dick Groat (exc. $3.00) | 20.00 |
| 2 | Roger Maris | 150.00 |
| 3 | John Buzhardt | 2.00 |
| 4 | Lenny Green | 2.00 |
| 5 | Johnny Romano | 2.00 |
| 6 | Ed Roebuck | 2.00 |
| 7 | Chicago White Sox | 5.00 |
| 8 | Dick Williams | 2.00 |
| 9 | Bob Purkey | 2.00 |
| 10 | Brooks Robinson | 30.00 |
| 11 | Curt Simmons | 1.50 |
| 12 | Moe Thacker | 2.00 |
| 13 | Chuck Cottier | 2.00 |
| 14 | Don Mossi | 2.00 |
| 15 | Willie Kirkland | 2.00 |
| 16 | Billy Muffett | 2.00 |
| 17 | Checklist No. 1 | 8.00 |
| 18 | Jim Grant | 2.00 |
| 19 | Cletis Boyer | 4.00 |
| 20 | Robin Roberts | 11.00 |
| 21 | Zorro Versalles | 3.00 |
| 22 | Clem Labine | 2.00 |
| 23 | Don Demeter | 2.00 |
| 24 | Ken Johnson | 2.00 |
| 25 | Reds' Heavy Artillery: Vada Pinson, Gus Bell, Frank Robinson | 5.00 |
| 26 | Wes Stock | 2.00 |
| 27 | Jerry Kindall | 2.00 |
| 28 | Hector Lopez | 2.00 |
| 29 | Don Nottebart | 2.00 |
| 30 | Nellie Fox | 6.00 |
| 31 | Bob Schmidt | 2.00 |
| 32 | Ray Sadecki | 2.00 |
| 33 | Gary Geiger | 2.00 |
| 34 | Wynn Hawkins | 2.00 |
| 35 | Ron Santo (R) | 40.00 |
| 36 | Jack Kralick | 2.00 |
| 37 | Charlie Maxwell | 2.00 |
| 38 | Bob Lillis | 2.00 |
| 39 | Leo Posada | 2.00 |
| 40 | Bob Turley | 2.50 |
| 41 | NL Batting Leaders: Willie Mays, Dick Gorat, Norm Larker, Roberto Clemente | 6.00 |
| 42 | AL Batting Leaders: Pete Runnels, Minnie Minoso, Al Smith, Bill Skowron | 3.50 |
| 43 | NL Home Run Leaders: Ernie Banks, Ed Mathe Hank Aaron, Ken Boye | 7.00 |
| 44 | AL Home Run Leaders: Mickey Mantle, Roger Maris, Jim Lemon, Rocky Colavito | 25.00 |
| 45 | NL ERA Leaders: Mike McCormick, Ernie Broglio, Don Drysdale, Bob Friend, Stan Williams | 4.00 |
| 46 | AL ERA Leaders: Frank Baumann, Jim Bunning, Art Ditmar, Hal Brown | 4.00 |
| 47 | NL Pitching Leaders: E. Broglio, W. Spahn, Vern Law, Lou Burdette | 4.00 |

| NO. | PLAYER | NR. MT. |
|---|---|---|
| 48 | AL Pitching Leaders: Chuck Estrada, Jim Perry, Bud Daley, Art Ditmar, Frank Lary, Milt Pappas | 4.00 |
| 49 | NL Strikeout Leaders: Don Drysdale, Sandy Koufax, Sam Jones, Ernie Broglio | 5.00 |
| 50 | AL Strikeout Leaders: Jim Bunning, Pedro Ramos, Early Wynn, Frank Lary | 4.00 |
| 51 | Detroit Tigers | 5.00 |
| 52 | George Crowe | 2.00 |
| 53 | Russ Nixon | 2.00 |
| 54 | Earl Francis | 2.00 |
| 55 | Jim Davenport | 2.00 |
| 56 | Russ Kemmerer | 2.00 |
| 57 | Marv Throneberry | 4.00 |
| 58 | Joe Schaffernoth | 2.00 |
| 59 | Jim Woods | 2.00 |
| 60 | Woodie Held | 2.00 |
| 61 | Ron Piche | 2.00 |
| 62 | Al Pilarcik | 2.00 |
| 63 | Jim Kaat | 8.00 |
| 64 | Alex Grammas | 2.00 |
| 65 | Ted Kluszewski | 4.00 |
| 66 | Bill Henry | 2.00 |
| 67 | Ossie Virgil | 2.00 |
| 68 | Deron Johnson | 2.00 |
| 69 | Earl Wilson | 2.00 |
| 70 | Bill Virdon | 3.00 |
| 71 | Jerry Adair | 2.00 |
| 72 | Stu Miller | 2.00 |
| 73 | Al Spangler | 2.00 |
| 74 | Joe Pignatano | 2.00 |
| 75 | Lindy Shows Larry: Lindy McDaniel, Larry Jackson | 3.00 |
| 76 | Harry Anderson | 2.00 |
| 77 | Dick Stigman | 2.00 |
| 78 | Lee Walls | 2.00 |
| 79 | Joe Ginsberg | 2.00 |
| 80 | Harmon Killebrew | 20.00 |
| 81 | Tracy Stallard | 2.00 |
| 82 | Joe Christopher | 2.00 |
| 83 | Bob Bruce | 2.00 |
| 84 | Lee Maye | 2.00 |
| 85 | Jerry Walker | 2.00 |
| 86 | Los Angeles Dodgers | 5.00 |
| 87 | Joe Amalfitano | 2.00 |
| 88 | Richie Ashburn | 7.00 |
| 89 | Billy Martin | 8.00 |
| 90 | Jerry Staley | 2.00 |
| 91 | Walt Moryn | 2.00 |
| 92 | Hal Naragon | 2.00 |
| 93 | Tony Gonzalez | 2.00 |
| 94 | John Kucks | 2.00 |
| 95 | Norm Cash | 4.00 |
| 96 | Bill O'Dell | 2.00 |
| 97 | Jerry Lynch | 2.00 |
| 98 | Checklist No. 2 | 9.00 |
| 99 | Don Buddin | 2.00 |
| 100 | Harvey Haddix | 4.00 |
| 101 | Bubba Phillips | 2.00 |
| 102 | Gene Stephens | 2.00 |
| 103 | Ruben Amaro | 2.00 |
| 104 | John Blanchard | 2.00 |

| NO. | PLAYER | NR. MT. |
|---|---|---|
| 105 | Carl Willey | 2.00 |
| 106 | Whitey Herzog | 3.00 |
| 107 | Seth Morehead | 2.00 |
| 108 | Dan Dobbek | 2.00 |
| 109 | Johnny Podres | 3.00 |
| 110 | Vada Pinson | 3.50 |
| 111 | Jack Meyer | 2.50 |
| 112 | Chico Fernandez | 2.50 |
| 113 | Mike Fornieles | 2.50 |
| 114 | Hobie Landrith | 2.50 |
| 115 | Johnny Antonelli | 2.50 |
| 116 | Joe DeMaestri | 2.50 |
| 117 | Dale Long | 2.50 |
| 118 | Chris Cannizzaro | 2.50 |
| 119 | A's Big Armor: Norm Siebern, Hank Bauer, Jerry Lumpe | 3.00 |
| 120 | Ed Mathews | 22.00 |
| 121 | Eli Grba | 2.50 |
| 122 | Chicago Cubs | 5.00 |
| 123 | Billy Gardner | 2.50 |
| 124 | J.C. Martin | 2.50 |
| 125 | Steve Barber | 2.50 |
| 126 | Dick Stuart | 2.50 |
| 127 | Ron Kline | 2.50 |
| 128 | Rip Repulski | 2.50 |
| 129 | Ed Hobaugh | 2.50 |
| 130 | Norm Larker | 2.50 |
| 131 | Paul Richards (Mgr.) | 3.00 |
| 132 | Al Lopez (Mgr.) | 4.00 |
| 133 | Ralph Houk (Mgr.) | 4.00 |
| 134 | Mickey Vernon (Mgr.) | 3.00 |
| 135 | Fred Hutchinson (Mgr.) | 3.00 |
| 136 | Walt Alston (Mgr.) | 6.00 |
| 137 | Chuck Dressen (Mgr.) | 2.50 |
| 138 | Danny Murtaugh (Mgr.) | 2.50 |
| 139 | Solly Hemus (Mgr.) | 2.50 |
| 140 | Gus Triandos | 2.50 |
| 141 | Billy Williams (R) | 115.00 |
| 142 | Luis Arroyo | 2.50 |
| 143 | Russ Snyder | 2.50 |
| 144 | Jim Coker | 2.50 |
| 145 | Bob Buhl | 2.50 |
| 146 | Marty Keough | 2.50 |
| 147 | Ed Rakow | 2.50 |
| 148 | Julian Javier | 2.50 |
| 149 | Bob Oldis | 2.50 |
| 150 | Willie Mays | 100.00 |
| 151 | Jim Donohue | 2.50 |
| 152 | Earl Torgeson | 2.50 |
| 153 | Don Lee | 2.50 |
| 154 | Bobby Del Greco | 2.50 |
| 155 | Johnny Temple | 2.50 |
| 156 | Ken Hunt | 2.50 |
| 157 | Cal McLish | 2.50 |
| 158 | Pete Daley | 2.50 |
| 159 | Baltimore Orioles | 5.00 |
| 160 | Whitey Ford | 35.00 |
| 161 | Sherman Jones | 2.50 |
| 162 | Jay Hook | 2.50 |
| 163 | Ed Sadowski | 2.50 |
| 164 | Felix Mantilla | 2.50 |
| 165 | Gino Cimoli | 2.50 |
| 166 | Danny Kravitz | 2.50 |
| 167 | San F. Giants | 5.00 |
| 168 | Tommy Davis | 2.50 |
| 169 | Don Elston | 2.50 |

| NO. | PLAYER | NR. MT. |
|---|---|---|
| 170 | Al Smith | 2.50 |
| 171 | Paul Foytack | 2.50 |
| 172 | Don Dillard | 2.50 |
| 173 | Beantown Bombers: Frank Malzone, Vic Wertz, Jackie Jensen | 3.00 |
| 174 | Ray Semproch | 2.50 |
| 175 | Gene Freese | 2.50 |
| 176 | Ken Aspromonte | 2.50 |
| 177 | Don Larsen | 3.00 |
| 178 | Bob Nieman | 2.50 |
| 179 | Joe Koppe | 2.50 |
| 180 | Bobby Richardson | 6.00 |
| 181 | Fred Green | 2.50 |
| 182 | Dave Nicholson | 2.50 |
| 183 | Andre Rodgers | 2.50 |
| 184 | Steve Bilko | 2.50 |
| 185 | Herb Score | 3.00 |
| 186 | Elmer Valo | 2.50 |
| 187 | Billy Klaus | 2.50 |
| 188 | Jim Marshall | 2.50 |
| 189 | Checklist No. 3 | 8.00 |
| 190 | Stan Williams | 2.50 |
| 191 | Mike De La Hoz | 2.50 |
| 192 | Dick Brown | 2.50 |
| 193 | Gene Conley | 2.50 |
| 194 | Gordy Coleman | 2.50 |
| 195 | Jerry Casale | 2.50 |
| 196 | Ed Bouchee | 2.50 |
| 197 | Dick Hall | 2.50 |
| 198 | Carl Sawatski | 2.50 |
| 199 | Bob Boyd | 2.50 |
| 200 | Warren Spahn | 25.00 |
| 201 | Pete Whisenant | 2.50 |
| 202 | Al Neiger | 2.50 |
| 203 | Eddie Bressoud | 2.50 |
| 204 | Bob Skinner | 2.50 |
| 205 | Bill Pierce | 2.50 |
| 206 | Gene Green | 2.50 |
| 207 | Dodger Southpaws: Sandy Koufax, J. Podres | 18.00 |
| 208 | Larry Osborne | 2.50 |
| 209 | Ken McBride | 2.50 |
| 210 | Pete Runnels | 2.50 |
| 211 | Bob Gibson | 35.00 |
| 212 | Haywood Sullivan | 2.50 |
| 213 | Bill Stafford | 2.50 |
| 214 | Danny Murphy | 2.50 |
| 215 | Gus Bell | 2.50 |
| 216 | Ted Bowsfield | 2.50 |
| 217 | Mel Roach | 2.50 |
| 218 | Hal Brown | 2.50 |
| 219 | Gene Mauch (Mgr.) | 2.50 |
| 220 | Al Dark (Mgr.) | 2.50 |
| 221 | Mike Higgins (Mgr.) | 2.50 |
| 222 | Jimmie Dykes (Mgr.) | 2.50 |
| 223 | Bob Scheffing (Mgr.) | 2.50 |
| 224 | Joe Gordon (Mgr.) | 2.50 |
| 225 | Bill Rigney (Mgr.) | 2.50 |
| 226 | Harry Lavagetto (Mgr.) | 2.50 |
| 227 | Juan Pizarro | 2.50 |
| 228 | New York Yankees | 22.00 |
| 229 | Rudy Hernandez | 2.50 |
| 230 | Don Hoak | 2.50 |
| 231 | Dick Drott | 2.50 |
| 232 | Bill White | 4.00 |
| 233 | Joe Jay | 2.50 |

| NO. | PLAYER | NR. MT. |
|---|---|---|
| 234 | Ted Lepcio | 2.50 |
| 235 | Camilo Pascual | 2.50 |
| 236 | Don Gile | 2.50 |
| 237 | Billy Loes | 2.50 |
| 238 | Jim Gilliam | 3.50 |
| 239 | Dave Sisler | 2.50 |
| 240 | Ron Hansen | 2.50 |
| 241 | Al Cicotte | 2.50 |
| 242 | Hal Smith | 2.50 |
| 243 | Frank Lary | 2.50 |
| 244 | Chico Cardenas | 2.50 |
| 245 | Joe Adcock | 3.00 |
| 246 | Bob Davis | 2.50 |
| 247 | Billy Goodman | 2.50 |
| 248 | Ed Keegan | 2.50 |
| 249 | Cincinnati Reds | 5.00 |
| 250 | Buc Hill Aces: Vern Law, Roy Face | 3.00 |
| 251 | Bill Bruton | 2.50 |
| 252 | Bill Short | 2.50 |
| 253 | Sammy Taylor | 2.50 |
| 254 | Ted Sadowski | 2.50 |
| 255 | Vic Power | 2.50 |
| 256 | Billy Hoeft | 2.50 |
| 257 | Carroll Hardy | 2.50 |
| 258 | Jack Sanford | 2.50 |
| 259 | John Schaive | 2.50 |
| 260 | Don Drysdale | 25.00 |
| 261 | Charlie Lau | 2.50 |
| 262 | Tony Curry | 2.50 |
| 263 | Ken Hamlin | 2.50 |
| 264 | Glen Hobbie | 2.50 |
| 265 | Tony Kubek | 7.00 |
| 266 | Lindy McDaniel | 2.50 |
| 267 | Norm Siebern | 2.50 |
| 268 | Ike Delock | 2.50 |
| 269 | Harry Chiti | 2.50 |
| 270 | Bob Friend | 2.50 |
| 271 | Jim Landis | 2.50 |
| 272 | Tom Morgan | 2.50 |
| 273 | Checklist No. 4 | 8.00 |
| 274 | Gary Bell | 2.50 |
| 275 | Gene Woodling | 2.50 |
| 276 | Ray Rippelmeyer | 2.50 |
| 277 | Hank Foiles | 2.50 |
| 278 | Don McMahon | 2.50 |
| 279 | Jose Pagan | 2.50 |
| 280 | Frank Howard | 4.00 |
| 281 | Frank Sullivan | 2.50 |
| 282 | Faye Throneberry | 2.50 |
| 283 | Bob Anderson | 2.50 |
| 284 | Dick Gernert | 2.50 |
| 285 | Sherm Lollar | 2.50 |
| 286 | George Witt | 2.50 |
| 287 | Carl Yastrzemski | 150.00 |
| 288 | Albie Pearson | 2.50 |
| 289 | Ray Moore | 2.50 |
| 290 | Stan Musial | 90.00 |
| 291 | Tex Clevenger | 2.50 |
| 292 | Jim Baumer | 2.50 |
| 293 | Tom Sturdivant | 2.50 |
| 294 | Don Blasingame | 2.50 |
| 295 | Milt Pappas | 2.50 |
| 296 | Wes Covington | 2.50 |
| 297 | Kansas C. Athletics | 5.00 |
| 298 | Jim Golden | 2.50 |
| 299 | Clay Dalrymple | 2.50 |
| 300 | Mickey Mantle | 350.00 |
| 301 | Chet Nichols | 2.50 |
| 302 | Al Heist | 2.50 |
| 303 | Gary Peters | 2.50 |
| 304 | Rocky Nelson | 2.50 |
| 305 | Mike McCormick | 2.50 |
| 306 | World Series Game 1 .. Virdon Saves Game | 6.00 |
| 307 | World Series Game 2 .. Mantle Slams 2 Homers | 30.00 |
| 308 | World Series Game 3 .. Richardson is Hero | 6.00 |
| 309 | World Series Game 4 .. Cimoli Safe | 6.00 |

| NO. | PLAYER | NR. MT. |
|---|---|---|
| 310 | World Series Game 5 .. Face Saves the Day | 6.00 |
| 311 | World Series Game 6 .. Ford Shutout | 8.00 |
| 312 | World Series Game 7 .. Mazeroski's Homer | 8.00 |
| 313 | W.S. Celebration | 6.00 |
| 314 | Bob Miller | 2.50 |
| 315 | Earl Battey | 2.50 |
| 316 | Bobby Gene Smith | 2.50 |
| 317 | Jim Brewer | 2.50 |
| 318 | Danny O'Connell | 2.50 |
| 319 | Valmy Thomas | 2.50 |
| 320 | Lou Burdette | 4.00 |
| 321 | Marv Breeding | 2.50 |
| 322 | Bill Kunkel | 2.50 |
| 323 | Sammy Esposito | 2.50 |
| 324 | Hank Aguirre | 2.50 |
| 325 | Wally Moon | 2.50 |
| 326 | Dave Hillman | 2.50 |
| 327 | Matty Alou (R) | 5.00 |
| 328 | Jim O'Toole | 2.50 |
| 329 | Julio Becquer | 2.50 |
| 330 | Rocky Colavito | 8.00 |
| 331 | Ned Garver | 2.50 |
| 332 | Dutch Dotterer (photo of Tommy Dotterer) | 2.50 |
| 333 | Fritz Brickell | 2.50 |
| 334 | Walt Bond | 2.50 |
| 335 | Frank Bolling | 2.50 |
| 336 | Don Mincher | 2.50 |
| 337 | Al's Aces: Herb Score, Early Wynn, Al Lopez | 5.00 |
| 338 | Don Landrum | 2.50 |
| 339 | Gene Baker | 2.50 |
| 340 | Vic Wertz | 2.50 |
| 341 | Jim Owens | 2.50 |
| 342 | Clint Courtney | 2.50 |
| 343 | Earl Robinson | 2.50 |
| 344 | Sandy Koufax | 95.00 |
| 345 | Jim Piersall | 3.50 |
| 346 | Howie Nunn | 2.50 |
| 347 | St. Louis Cardinals | 5.00 |
| 348 | Steve Boros | 2.50 |
| 349 | Danny McDevitt | 2.50 |
| 350 | Ernie Banks | 35.00 |
| 351 | Jim King | 2.50 |
| 352 | Bob Shaw | 2.50 |
| 353 | Howie Bedell | 2.50 |
| 354 | Billy Harrell | 2.50 |
| 355 | Bob Allison | 2.50 |
| 356 | Ryne Duren | 2.50 |
| 357 | Daryl Spencer | 2.50 |
| 358 | Earl Averill | 2.50 |
| 359 | Dallas Green | 5.00 |
| 360 | Frank Robinson | 40.00 |
| 361 | Checklist No. 5 | 8.00 |
| 362 | Frank Funk | 2.50 |
| 363 | John Roseboro | 2.50 |
| 364 | Moe Drabowski | 2.50 |
| 365 | Jerry Lumpe | 2.50 |
| 366 | Eddie Fisher | 2.50 |
| 367 | Jim Rivera | 2.50 |
| 368 | Bennie Daniels | 2.50 |
| 369 | Dave Philley | 2.50 |
| 370 | Roy Face | 3.00 |
| 371 | Bill Skowron | 30.00 |
| 372 | Bob Hendley | 2.50 |
| 373 | Boston Red Sox | 6.00 |
| 374 | Paul Giel | 3.00 |
| 375 | Ken Boyer | 5.00 |
| 376 | Mike Roarke | 3.00 |
| 377 | Ruben Gomez | 3.00 |
| 378 | Wally Post | 3.00 |
| 379 | Bobby Shantz | 3.00 |
| 380 | Minnie Minoso | 5.00 |
| 381 | Dave Wickersham | 3.00 |
| 382 | Frank Thomas | 3.00 |
| 383 | Frisco First Liners: Mike McCormick, Jack Sanford, Billy O'Dell | 3.00 |

| NO. | PLAYER | NR. MT. |
|---|---|---|
| 384 | Chuck Essegian | 3.00 |
| 385 | Jim Perry | 3.00 |
| 386 | Joe Hicks | 3.00 |
| 387 | Duke Maas | 3.00 |
| 388 | Bob Clemente | 90.00 |
| 389 | Ralph Terry | 3.00 |
| 390 | Del Crandall | 3.00 |
| 391 | Winston Brown | 3.00 |
| 392 | Reno Bertoia | 3.00 |
| 393 | Batter Bafflers: Don Cardwell, Glen Hobbie | 3.00 |
| 394 | Ken Walters | 3.00 |
| 395 | Chuck Estrada | 3.00 |
| 396 | Bob Aspromonte | 3.00 |
| 397 | Hal Woodeschick | 3.00 |
| 398 | Hank Bauer | 3.00 |
| 399 | Cliff Cook | 3.00 |
| 400 | Vern Law | 3.00 |
| 401 | Ruth 60th Homer | 25.00 |
| 402 | Larsen—Perfect Game | 15.00 |
| 403 | 26 Inning Tie | 6.00 |
| 404 | Honsby .424 Average | 8.00 |
| 405 | Gehrig—2,130 Games | 15.00 |
| 406 | Mantle 565 Ft. HR | 40.00 |
| 407 | Chesbro Wins 41 | 6.00 |
| 408 | Mathewson 267 SO's | 7.00 |
| 409 | Johnson Shutouts | 7.00 |
| 410 | Haddix Perfect Game | 5.00 |
| 411 | Tony Taylor | 3.00 |
| 412 | Larry Sherry | 3.00 |
| 413 | Eddie Yost | 3.00 |
| 414 | Dick Donovan | 3.00 |
| 415 | Hank Aaron | 110.00 |
| 416 | Dick Howser (R) | 8.00 |
| 417 | Juan Marichal (R) | 135.00 |
| 418 | Ed Bailey | 3.00 |
| 419 | Tom Borland | 3.00 |
| 420 | Ernie Broglio | 3.00 |
| 421 | Ty Cline | 3.00 |
| 422 | Bud Daley | 3.00 |
| 423 | Charlie Neal | 3.00 |
| 424 | Turk Lown | 3.00 |
| 425 | Yogi Berra | 75.00 |
| 426 | Milwaukee Braves (error—numbered 463) | 7.00 |
| 427 | Dick Ellsworth | 3.00 |
| 428 | Ray Barker | 3.00 |
| 429 | Al Kaline | 40.00 |
| 430 | Bill Mazeroski | 30.00 |
| 431 | Chuck Stobbs | 3.00 |
| 432 | Coot Veal | 3.00 |
| 433 | Art Mahaffey | 3.00 |
| 434 | Tom Brewer | 3.00 |
| 435 | Orlando Cepeda | 9.00 |
| 436 | Jim Maloney (R) | 7.00 |
| 437 | Checklist No. 6 | 8.00 |
| 438 | Curt Flood | 4.00 |
| 439 | Phil Regan | 3.00 |
| 440 | Luis Aparicio | 13.00 |
| 441 | Dick Bertell | 3.00 |
| 442 | Gordon Jones | 3.00 |
| 443 | Duke Snider | 45.00 |
| 444 | Joe Nuxhall | 3.00 |
| 445 | Frank Malzone | 3.00 |
| 446 | Bob Taylor | 3.00 |
| 447 | Harry Bright | 4.00 |
| 448 | Del Rice | 4.00 |
| 449 | Bobby Bolin | 4.00 |
| 450 | Jim Lemon | 4.00 |
| 451 | Power for Ernie: Daryl Spencer, Bill White, Ernie Broglio | 4.00 |
| 452 | Bob Allen | 4.00 |
| 453 | Dick Schofield | 4.00 |
| 454 | Pumpsie Green | 4.00 |
| 455 | Early Wynn | 11.00 |
| 456 | Hal Bevan | 4.00 |
| 457 | Johnny James | 4.00 |
| 458 | Willie Tasby | 4.00 |
| 459 | Terry Fox | 4.00 |
| 460 | Gil Hodges | 15.00 |
| 461 | Smoky Burgess | 4.00 |

| NO. | PLAYER | NR. MT. |
|---|---|---|
| 462 | Lou Klimchock | 4.00 |
| 463 | Jack Fisher (see #426) | 4.00 |
| 464 | Leroy Thomas | 4.00 |
| 465 | Roy McMillan | 4.00 |
| 466 | Ron Moeller | 4.00 |
| 467 | Cleveland Indians | 5.00 |
| 468 | John Callison | 4.00 |
| 469 | Ralph Lumenti | 4.00 |
| 470 | Roy Sievers | 4.00 |
| 471 | Phil Rizzuto (MVP) | 15.00 |
| 472 | Yogi Berra (MVP) | 40.00 |
| 473 | Bobby Shantz (MVP) | 6.00 |
| 474 | Al Rosen (MVP) | 6.00 |
| 475 | Mickey Mantle (MVP) | 110.00 |
| 476 | Jackie Jensen (MVP) | 4.00 |
| 477 | Nellie Fox (MVP) | 4.00 |
| 478 | Roger Maris (MVP) | 40.00 |
| 479 | Jim Konstanty (MVP) | 6.00 |
| 480 | R. Campanella (MVP) | 30.00 |
| 481 | Hank Sauer (MVP) | 6.00 |
| 482 | Willie Mays (MVP) | 45.00 |
| 483 | Don Newcombe (MVP) | 6.00 |
| 484 | Hank Aaron (MVP) | 40.00 |
| 485 | Ernie Banks (MVP) | 25.00 |
| 486 | Dick Groat (MVP) | 6.00 |
| 487 | Gene Oliver | 4.00 |
| 488 | Joe McClain | 4.00 |
| 489 | Walt Dropo | 4.00 |
| 490 | Jim Bunning | 8.00 |
| 491 | Philadelphia Phillies | 5.00 |
| 492 | Ron Fairly | 4.00 |
| 493 | Don Zimmer | 5.00 |
| 494 | Tom Cheney | 4.00 |
| 495 | Elston Howard | 7.00 |
| 496 | Ken MacKenzie | 4.00 |
| 497 | Willie Jones | 4.00 |
| 498 | Ray Herbert | 4.00 |
| 499 | Chuck Schilling | 4.00 |
| 500 | Harvey Kuenn | 5.00 |
| 501 | John DeMerit | 4.00 |
| 502 | Clarence Coleman | 4.00 |
| 503 | Tito Francona | 4.00 |
| 504 | Billy Consolo | 4.00 |
| 505 | Red Schoendienst | 15.00 |
| 506 | Willie Davis (R) | 12.00 |
| 507 | Pete Burnside | 4.00 |
| 508 | Rocky Bridges | 4.00 |
| 509 | Camilo Carreon | 4.00 |
| 510 | Art Ditmar | 4.00 |
| 511 | Joe Morgan | 5.00 |
| 512 | Bob Will | 4.00 |
| 513 | Jim Brosnan | 4.00 |
| 514 | Jake Wood | 4.00 |
| 515 | Jackie Brandt | 4.00 |
| 516 | Checklist No. 7 | 8.00 |
| 517 | Willie McCovey | 60.00 |
| 518 | Andy Carey | 4.00 |
| 519 | Jim Pagliaroni | 4.00 |
| 520 | Joe Cunningham | 4.00 |
| 521 | Brother Battery: Norm Sherry, Larry Sherry | 4.00 |
| 522 | Dick Farrell | 30.00 |
| 523 | Joe Gibbon | 30.00 |
| 524 | Johnny Logan | 30.00 |
| 525 | Ron Perranoski | 30.00 |
| 526 | R.C. Stevens | 30.00 |
| 527 | Gene Leek | 30.00 |
| 528 | Pedro Ramos | 30.00 |
| 529 | Bob Roselli | 30.00 |
| 530 | Bobby Malkmus | 30.00 |
| 531 | Jim Coates | 30.00 |
| 532 | Bob Hale | 30.00 |
| 533 | Jack Curtis | 30.00 |
| 534 | Eddie Kasko | 30.00 |
| 535 | Larry Jackson | 30.00 |
| 536 | Bill Tuttle | 30.00 |
| 537 | Bobby Locke | 30.00 |
| 538 | Chuck Hiller | 30.00 |
| 539 | John Klippstein | 30.00 |
| 540 | Jackie Jensen | 30.00 |
| 541 | Roland Sheldon | 30.00 |
| 542 | Minnesota Twins | 60.00 |

| NO. PLAYER | NR. MT. | NO. PLAYER | NR. MT. | NO. PLAYER | NR. MT. | NO. PLAYER | NR. MT. |
|---|---|---|---|---|---|---|---|
| 543 Roger Craig | 35.00 | 555 Sam Jones | 30.00 | 566 P. Richards—Mgr. (AS) | 35.00 | 577 Hank Aaron (AS) | 160.00 |
| 544 George Thomas | 30.00 | 556 Ken R. Hunt | 30.00 | 567 D. Murtaugh—Mgr. (AS) | 35.00 | 578 Mickey Mantle (AS) | 400.00 |
| 545 Hoyt Wilhelm | 60.00 | 557 Jose Valdivielso | 30.00 | 568 Bill Skowron (AS) | 35.00 | 579 Willie Mays (AS) | 135.00 |
| 546 Marty Kutyna | 30.00 | 558 Don Ferrarese | 30.00 | 569 Frank Herrera (AS) | 35.00 | 580 Al Kaline (AS) | 85.00 |
| 547 Leon Wagner | 30.00 | 559 Jim Gentile | 30.00 | 570 Nellie Fox (AS) | 40.00 | 581 Frank Robinson (AS) | 90.00 |
| 548 Ted Wills | 30.00 | 560 Barry Latman | 30.00 | 571 Bill Mazeroski (AS) | 35.00 | 582 Earl Battey (AS) | 30.00 |
| 549 Hal R. Smith | 30.00 | 561 Charley James | 30.00 | 572 Brooks Robinson | 90.00 | 583 Del Crandall (AS) | 30.00 |
| 550 Frank Baumann | 30.00 | 562 Bill Monbouquette | 30.00 | 573 Ken Boyer (AS) | 35.00 | 584 Jim Perry (AS) | 30.00 |
| 551 George Altman | 30.00 | 563 Bob Cerv | 35.00 | 574 Luis Aparicio (AS) | 50.00 | 585 Bob Friend (AS) | 30.00 |
| 552 Jim Archer | 30.00 | 564 Don Cardwell | 30.00 | 575 Ernie Banks (AS) | 90.00 | 586 Whitey Ford (AS) | 85.00 |
| 553 Bill Fischer | 30.00 | 565 Felipe Alou | 30.00 | 576 Roger Maris (AS) | 125.00 | 589 W.Spahn (AS) (exc. $40.00) | 140.00 |
| 554 Pittsburgh Pirates | 50.00 | | | | | | |

## 1962 Topps . . . Complete Set of 598 Cards—Value $1600.00 (Exc.); $4800.00 (Near Mint)

The rookie cards of Lou Brock, Gaylord Perry and Bob Uecker are in this set. The high numbers are 523 to 598. Nine cards were reprinted with different photos. These are worth a premium. The value of the complete set does not include the *variety* cards.

| NO. PLAYER | NR. MT. | NO. PLAYER | NR. MT. | NO. PLAYER | NR. MT. | NO. PLAYER | NR. MT. |
|---|---|---|---|---|---|---|---|
| 1 Roger Maris (exc. $30.00) | 210.00 | 42 Jim King | 2.00 | 62 Steve Boros | 2.00 | 104 Ted Savage | 2.00 |
| 2 Jim Brosnan | 2.00 | 43 Los Angeles Dodgers | 5.00 | 63 Tony Cloninger | 2.00 | 105 Don Mossi | 2.00 |
| 3 Pete Runnels | 2.00 | 44 Don Taussig | 2.00 | 64 Russ Snyder | 2.00 | 106 Carl Sawatski | 2.00 |
| 4 John DeMerit | 2.00 | 45 Brooks Robinson | 30.00 | 65 Bobby Richardson | 5.00 | 107 Mike McCormick | 2.00 |
| 5 Sandy Koufax | 120.00 | 46 Jack Baldschun | 2.00 | 66 Cuno Barragon | 2.00 | 108 Willie Davis | 2.00 |
| 6 Marv Breeding | 2.00 | 47 Bob Will | 2.00 | 67 Harvey Haddix | 2.00 | 109 Bob Shaw | 2.00 |
| 7 Frank Thomas | 2.00 | 48 Ralph Terry | 2.00 | 68 Ken Hunt | 2.00 | 110 Bill Skowron | 4.00 |
| 8 Ray Herbert | 2.00 | 49 Hal Jones | 2.00 | 69 Phil Ortega | 2.00 | 111 Dallas Green | 3.00 |
| 9 Jim Davenport | 2.00 | 50 Stan Musal | 90.00 | 70 Harmon Killebrew | 20.00 | 112 Hank Foiles | 2.00 |
| 10 Bob Clemente | 100.00 | 51 AL Batting Leaders: | 3.00 | 71 Dick Le May | 2.00 | 113 Chicago White Sox | 5.00 |
| 11 Tom Morgan | 2.00 | Al Kaline, Norm Cash, | | 72 Bob's Pupils: | 2.00 | 114 Howie Koplitz | 2.00 |
| 12 Harry Craft (Mgr.) | 2.00 | Jim Piersall, Elston Howard | | Steve Boros, Bob | | 115 Bob Skinner | 2.00 |
| 13 Dick Howser | 2.50 | 52 NL Batting Leaders: | 5.00 | Scheffing, Jake Wood | | 116 Herb Score | 3.00 |
| 14 Bill White | 4.00 | Wally Moon, Bob Clemente, | | 73 Nellie Fox | 6.00 | 117 Gary Geiger | 2.00 |
| 15 Dick Donovan | 2.00 | Vada Pinson, Ken Boyer | | 74 Bob Lillis | 2.00 | 118 Julian Javier | 2.00 |
| 16 Darrell Johnson | 2.00 | 53 AL Home Run Leaders: | 30.00 | 75 Milt Pappas | 2.00 | 119 Danny Murphy | 2.00 |
| 17 Johnny Callison | 2.00 | Jim Gentile, Roger | | 76 Howie Bedell | 2.00 | 120 Bob Purkey | 2.00 |
| 18 Managers' Dream: | 110.00 | Maris, Mickey Mantle, | | 77 Tony Taylor | 2.00 | 121 Billy Hitchcock | 2.00 |
| Mickey Mantle, Willie Mays | | Harmon Killebrew | | 78 Gene Green | 2.00 | 122 Norm Bass | 2.00 |
| 19 Ray Washburn | 2.00 | 54 NL Home Run Leaders: | 5.00 | 79 Ed Hobaugh | 2.00 | 123 Mike De La Hoz | 2.00 |
| 20 Rocky Colavito | 7.00 | Orlando Cepeda, Willie | | 80 Vada Pinson | 3.00 | 124 Bill Pleis | 2.00 |
| 21 Jim Kaat | 5.00 | Mays, Frank Robinson | | 81 Jim Pagliaroni | 2.00 | 125 Gene Woodling | 2.00 |
| 22 Checklist No. 1 | 8.00 | 55 AL ERA Leaders: | 3.00 | 82 Deron Johnson | 2.00 | 126 Al Cicotte | 2.00 |
| 23 Norm Larker | 2.00 | Dick Donovan, Bill Stafford, | | 83 Larry Jackson | 2.00 | 127 Pride of A's: | 2.00 |
| 24 Detroit Tigers | 5.00 | Don Mossi, Milt Pappas | | 84 Lenny Green | 2.00 | Norm Siebern, Hank Bauer, |  |
| 25 Ernie Bank | 35.00 | 56 NL ERA Leaders: | 3.00 | 85 Gil Hodges | 14.00 | Jerry Lumpe |  |
| 26 Chris Cannizzaro | 2.00 | Warren Spahn, Jim | | 86 Donn Clendenon | 2.00 | 128 Art Fowler | 2.00 |
| 27 Chuck Cottier | 2.00 | O'Toole, Curt Simmons, | | 87 Mike Roarke | 2.00 | 129 Lee Walls (faces right) | 2.00 |
| 28 Minnie Minoso | 4.00 | Mike McCormick | | 88 Ralph Houk | 2.50 | 129 Lee Walls (faces left) | 18.00 |
| 29 Casey Stengel (Mgr.) | 15.00 | 57 AL Win Leaders: | 3.00 | 89 Barney Schultz | 2.00 | 130 Frank Bolling | 2.00 |
| 30 Ed Mathews | 18.00 | Frank Lary, Whitey Ford, | | 90 Jim Piersall | 2.50 | 131 Pete Richert | 2.00 |
| 31 Tom Tresh (R) | 10.00 | Steve Barber, Jim Bunning | | 91 J.C. Martin | 2.00 | 132 Los Angeles Angels* | 5.00 |
| 32 John Roseboro | 2.00 | 58 NL Win Leaders: | 3.00 | 92 Sam Jones | 2.00 | 133 Felipe Alou | 2.00 |
| 33 Don Larsen | 2.00 | Warren Spahn, Joe Jay, | | 93 John Blanchard | 2.00 | 134 Billy Hoeft (faces right) | 2.00 |
| 34 Johnny Temple | 2.00 | Jim O'Toole | | 94 Jay Hook | 2.00 | 134 Billy Hoeft (faces front) | 18.00 |
| 35 Don Schwall | 2.00 | 59 AL Strikeout Leaders: | 3.00 | 95 Don Hoak | 2.00 | 135 Babe Ruth Special: | 12.00 |
| 36 Don Leppert | 2.00 | Camilo Pascual, Whitey | | 96 Eli Grba | 2.00 | Babe as a Boy |  |
| 37 Tribe Hill Trio: | 2.00 | Ford, Jim Bunning, | | 97 Tito Francona | 2.00 | 136 Babe Ruth Special: | 12.00 |
| Barry Latman, Dick | | Juan Pizzaro | | 98 Checklist No. 2 | 7.00 | Babe Joins Yanks |  |
| Stigman, Jim Perry | | 60 NL Strikeout Leaders: | 6.00 | 99 John Powell (R) | 15.00 | 137 Babe Ruth Special: | 12.00 |
| 38 Gene Stephens | 2.00 | Sandy Koufax, Stan | | 100 Warren Spahn | 30.00 | Babe and Mgr. Huggins |  |
| 39 Joe Koppe | 2.00 | Williams, Don Drysdale, | | 101 Carroll Hardy | 2.00 | 138 Babe Ruth Special: | 12.00 |
| 40 Orlando Cepeda | 7.00 | Jim O'Toole | | 102 Al Schroll | 2.00 | Famous Slugger |  |
| 41 Cliff Cook | 2.00 | 61 St. Louis Cardinals | 5.00 | 103 Don Blasingame | 2.00 | | |

| NO. | PLAYER | NR. MT. |
|---|---|---|
| 139 | Babe Ruth Special | 15.00 |
| | Babe Hits 60 | |
| | See Card no. 159 | |
| 140 | Babe Ruth Special: | 12.00 |
| | Gehrig and Ruth | |
| 141 | Babe Ruth Special: | 12.00 |
| | Twilight Years | |
| 142 | Babe Ruth Special: | 12.00 |
| | Coaching for Dodgers | |
| 143 | Babe Ruth Special: | 12.00 |
| | Greatest Sports Hero | |
| 144 | Babe Ruth Special: | 12.00 |
| | Farewell Speech | |
| 145 | Barry Latman | 2.00 |
| 146 | Don Demeter | 2.00 |
| 147 | Bill Kunkel (head shot) | 3.00 |
| 147 | Bill Kunkel (pitching) | 18.00 |
| 148 | Wally Post | 2.00 |
| 149 | Bob Duliba | 2.00 |
| 150 | Al Kaline | 30.00 |
| 151 | Johnny Klippstein | 2.00 |
| 152 | Mickey Vernon (Mgr.) | 2.50 |
| 153 | Pumpsie Green | 2.00 |
| 154 | Lee Thomas | 2.00 |
| 155 | Stu Miller | 2.00 |
| 156 | Merritt Ranew | 2.00 |
| 157 | Wes Covington | 2.00 |
| 158 | Milwaukee Braves | 5.00 |
| 159 | Hal Reniff | 2.00 |
| 159 | Hal Reniff (head shot) | 18.00 |
| | Error—reads no. 139 | |
| 159 | Hal Reniff (pitching) | 60.00 |
| | Error—reads no. 139 | |
| 160 | Dick Stuart | 2.50 |
| 161 | Frank Baumann | 2.00 |
| 162 | Sammy Drake | 2.00 |
| 163 | Hot Corner Guardians: | 2.50 |
| | Billy Gardner, Cletis Boyer | |
| 164 | Hal Naragon | 2.00 |
| 165 | Jackie Brandt | 2.00 |
| 166 | Don Lee | 2.00 |
| 167 | Tim McCarver (R) | 25.00 |
| 168 | Leo Posada | 2.00 |
| 169 | Bob Cerv | 2.00 |
| 170 | Ron Santo | 8.00 |
| 171 | Dave Sisler | 2.00 |
| 172 | Fred Hutchinson (Mgr.) | 2.00 |
| 173 | Chico Fernandez | 2.00 |
| 174 | Carl Willey (no hat) | 2.50 |
| 174 | Carl Willey (with hat) | 18.00 |
| 175 | Frank Howard | 3.00 |
| 176 | Eddie Yost (head shot) | 2.00 |
| 176 | Eddie Yost (with bat) | 18.00 |
| 177 | Bobby Shantz | 2.50 |
| 178 | Camilo Carreon | 2.00 |
| 179 | Tom Sturdivant | 2.00 |
| 180 | Bob Allison | 2.00 |
| 181 | Paul Brown | 2.00 |
| 182 | Bob Nieman | 2.00 |
| 183 | Roger Craig | 2.50 |
| 184 | Haywood Sullivan | 2.00 |
| 185 | Roland Sheldon | 2.00 |
| 186 | Mack Jones | 2.00 |
| 187 | Gene Conley | 2.00 |
| 188 | Chuck Hiller | 2.00 |
| 189 | Dick Hall | 2.00 |
| 190 | Wally Moon (head shot) | 2.00 |
| 190 | Wally Moon (with bat) | 18.00 |
| 191 | Jim Brewer | 2.00 |
| 192 | Checklist No. 3 | 7.00 |
| 193 | Eddie Kasko | 2.00 |
| 194 | Dean Chance | 3.00 |
| 195 | Joe Cunningham | 2.00 |
| 196 | Terry Fox | 2.00 |
| 197 | Daryl Spencer | 2.50 |
| 198 | Johnny Keane (Mgr.) | 2.50 |
| 199 | Gaylord Perry (R) | 150.00 |
| 200 | Mickey Mantle | 400.00 |
| 201 | Ike Delock | 2.50 |
| 202 | Carl Warwick | 2.50 |
| 203 | Jack Fisher | 2.50 |
| 204 | Johnny Weekly | 2.50 |

| NO. | PLAYER | NR. MT. |
|---|---|---|
| 205 | Gene Freese | 2.50 |
| 206 | Washington Senators | 5.00 |
| 207 | Pete Burnside | 2.50 |
| 208 | Billy Martin | 7.00 |
| 209 | Jim Fregosi (R) | 6.00 |
| 210 | Roy Face | 3.00 |
| 211 | Midway Masters: | 3.00 |
| | Frank Bolling, Roy McMillan | |
| 212 | Jim Owens | 2.50 |
| 213 | Richie Ashburn | 8.00 |
| 214 | Dom Zanni | 1.50 |
| 215 | Woody Held | 1.50 |
| 216 | Ron Kline | 1.50 |
| 217 | Walt Alston (Mgr.) | 5.00 |
| 218 | Joe Torre (R) | 16.00 |
| 219 | Al Downing (R) | 4.00 |
| 220 | Roy Sievers | 3.00 |
| 221 | Bill Short | 2.50 |
| 222 | Jerry Zimmerman | 2.50 |
| 223 | Alex Grammas | 2.50 |
| 224 | Don Rudolph | 2.50 |
| 225 | Frank Malzone | 2.50 |
| 226 | San F. Giants | 5.00 |
| 227 | Bobby Tiefenauer | 2.50 |
| 228 | Dale Long | 2.50 |
| 229 | Jesus McFarlane | 2.50 |
| 230 | Camilo Pascual | 2.50 |
| 231 | Ernie Bowman | 2.50 |
| 232 | World Series Game 1: | 4.00 |
| | Yanks Win Opener | |
| 233 | World Series Game 2: | 4.00 |
| | Jay Ties It Up | |
| 234 | World Series Game 3: | 12.00 |
| | Maris Wins In 9th | |
| 235 | World Series Game 4: | 7.00 |
| | Ford Sets New Mark | |
| 236 | World Series Game 5: | 4.00 |
| | Yanks Crush Reds | |
| 237 | World Series | 4.00 |
| | Winners Celebrate | |
| 238 | Norm Sherry | 3.00 |
| 239 | Cecil Butler | 2.50 |
| 240 | George Altman | 2.50 |
| 241 | Johnny Kucks | 2.50 |
| 242 | Mel McGaha (Mgr.) | 2.50 |
| 243 | Robin Roberts | 11.00 |
| 244 | Don Gile | 2.50 |
| 245 | Ron Hansen | 2.50 |
| 246 | Art Ditmar | 2.50 |
| 247 | Joe Pignatano | 2.50 |
| 248 | Bob Aspromonte | 2.50 |
| 249 | Ed Keegan | 2.50 |
| 250 | Norm Cash | 4.00 |
| 251 | New York Yankees | 16.00 |
| 252 | Earl Francis | 2.50 |
| 253 | Harry Chiti | 2.50 |
| 254 | Gordon Windhorn | 2.50 |
| 255 | Joan Pizarro | 2.50 |
| 256 | Elio Chacon | 2.50 |
| 257 | Jack Spring | 2.50 |
| 258 | Marty Keough | 2.50 |
| 259 | Lou Klimchock | 2.50 |
| 260 | Bill Pierce | 3.00 |
| 261 | George Alusik | 2.50 |
| 262 | Bob Schmidt | 2.50 |
| 263 | The Right Pitch: | 2.50 |
| | Bob Purkey, Jim Turner, | |
| | Joe Jay | |
| 264 | Dick Ellsworth | 2.50 |
| 265 | Joe Adcock | 3.00 |
| 266 | John Anderson | 2.50 |
| 267 | Dan Dobbek | 2.50 |
| 268 | Ken McBride | 2.50 |
| 269 | Bob Oldis | 2.50 |
| 270 | Dick Groat | 3.00 |
| 271 | Ray Rippelmeyer | 2.50 |
| 272 | Earl Robinson | 2.50 |
| 273 | Gary Bell | 2.50 |
| 274 | Sammy Taylor | 2.50 |
| 275 | Norm Siebern | 2.50 |
| 276 | Hal Kolstad | 2.50 |
| 277 | Checklist No. 4 | 7.00 |

| NO. | PLAYER | NR. MT. |
|---|---|---|
| 278 | Ken Johnson | 2.50 |
| 279 | Hobie Landrith | 2.50 |
| 280 | Johnny Podres | 4.00 |
| 281 | Jake Gibbs | 3.00 |
| 282 | Dave Hillman | 2.50 |
| 283 | Charlie Smith | 2.50 |
| 284 | Ruben Amaro | 3.00 |
| 285 | Curt Simmons | 3.00 |
| 286 | Al Lopez (Mgr.) | 4.00 |
| 287 | George Witt | 3.00 |
| 288 | Billy Williams | 35.00 |
| 289 | Mike Krsnich | 3.00 |
| 290 | Jim Gentile | 4.00 |
| 291 | Hal Stowe | 3.00 |
| 292 | Jerry Kindall | 3.00 |
| 293 | Bob Miller | 3.00 |
| 294 | Philadelphia Phillies | 5.00 |
| 295 | Vern Law | 4.00 |
| 296 | Ken Hamlin | 3.00 |
| 297 | Ron Perranoski | 3.00 |
| 298 | Bill Tuttle | 3.00 |
| 299 | Don Wert | 3.00 |
| 300 | Willie Mays | 120.00 |
| 301 | Galen Cisco | 3.00 |
| 302 | John Edwards | 3.00 |
| 303 | Frank Torre | 3.00 |
| 304 | Dick Farrell | 3.00 |
| 305 | Jerry Lumpe | 3.00 |
| 306 | Redbird Rippers: | 3.00 |
| | Lindy McDaniel, | |
| | Larry Jackson | |
| 307 | Jim Grant | 3.00 |
| 308 | Neil Chrisley | 3.00 |
| 309 | Moe Morhardt | 3.00 |
| 310 | Whitey Ford | 35.00 |
| 311 | Kubek Double Play | 5.00 |
| 312 | Spahn No-Hit | 9.00 |
| 313 | Maris Blasts 61 HR | 15.00 |
| 314 | Colavito's Power | 5.00 |
| 315 | Ford Curveball | 8.00 |
| 316 | Killebrew's Orbit | 9.00 |
| 317 | Musial's 21st Season | 17.00 |
| 318 | Switch Hitter Mantle | 40.00 |
| 319 | McCormick in Action | 4.00 |
| 320 | Hank Aaron | 125.00 |
| 321 | Lee Stange | 3.00 |
| 322 | Al Dark (Mgr.) | 3.50 |
| 323 | Don Landrum | 3.00 |
| 324 | Joe McClain | 3.00 |
| 325 | Luis Aparicio | 12.00 |
| 326 | Tom Parsons | 3.00 |
| 327 | Ozzie Virgil | 3.00 |
| 328 | Ken Walters | 3.00 |
| 329 | Bob Bolin | 3.00 |
| 330 | Johnny Romano | 3.00 |
| 331 | Moe Drabowsky | 3.00 |
| 332 | Don Buddin | 3.00 |
| 333 | Frank Cipriani | 3.00 |
| 334 | Boston Red Sox | 5.00 |
| 335 | Bill Bruton | 3.00 |
| 336 | Bill Muffett | 3.00 |
| 337 | Jim Marshall | 3.00 |
| 338 | Billy Gardner | 3.50 |
| 339 | Jose Valdivielso | 3.00 |
| 340 | Don Drysdale | 35.00 |
| 341 | Mike Hershberger | 3.00 |
| 342 | Ed Rakow | 3.00 |
| 343 | Albie Pearson | 3.00 |
| 344 | Ed Bauta | 3.00 |
| 345 | Chuck Schilling | 3.00 |
| 346 | Jack Kralick | 3.00 |
| 347 | Chuck Hinton | 3.00 |
| 348 | Larry Burright | 3.00 |
| 349 | Paul Foytack | 3.00 |
| 350 | Frank Robinson | 40.00 |
| 351 | Braves' Backstops: | 4.00 |
| | Joe Torre, Del Crandall | |
| 352 | Frank Sullivan | 3.00 |
| 353 | Bill Mazeroski | 5.00 |
| 354 | Roman Mejias | 3.00 |
| 355 | Steve Barber | 3.00 |
| 356 | Tom Haller | 3.00 |

| NO. | PLAYER | NR. MT. |
|---|---|---|
| 357 | Jerry Walker | 3.00 |
| 358 | Tommy Davis | 5.00 |
| 359 | Bobby Locke | 3.00 |
| 360 | Yogi Berra | 60.00 |
| 361 | Bob Hendley | 3.00 |
| 362 | Ty Cline | 3.00 |
| 363 | Bob Roselli | 3.00 |
| 364 | Ken Hunt | 3.00 |
| 365 | Charley Neal | 3.00 |
| 366 | Phil Regan | 3.00 |
| 367 | Checklist No. 5 | 7.00 |
| 368 | Bob Tillman | 3.00 |
| 369 | Ted Bowsfield | 3.00 |
| 370 | Ken Boyer | 6.00 |
| 371 | Earl Battey | 4.00 |
| 372 | Jack Curtis | 4.00 |
| 373 | Al Heist | 4.00 |
| 374 | Gene Mauch (Mgr.) | 4.00 |
| 375 | Ron Fairly | 4.00 |
| 376 | Bud Daley | 4.00 |
| 377 | Johnny Orsino | 4.00 |
| 378 | Bennie Daniels | 4.00 |
| 379 | Chuck Essegian | 4.00 |
| 380 | Lou Burdette | 5.00 |
| 381 | Chico Cardenas | 4.00 |
| 382 | Dick Williams | 6.00 |
| 383 | Ray Sadecki | 4.00 |
| 384 | K.C. Athletics | 8.00 |
| 385 | Early Wynn | 15.00 |
| 386 | Don Mincher | 4.00 |
| 387 | Lou Brock (R) | 175.00 |
| 388 | Ryne Duren | 4.00 |
| 389 | Smoky Burgess | 4.00 |
| 390 | Orlando Cepeda (AS) | 6.00 |
| 391 | Bill Mazeroski (AS) | 5.00 |
| 392 | Ken Boyer (AS) | 5.00 |
| 393 | Roy McMillan (AS) | 5.00 |
| 394 | Hank Aaron (AS) | 35.00 |
| 395 | Willie Mays (AS) | 35.00 |
| 396 | Frank Robinson (AS) | 13.00 |
| 397 | John Roseboro (AS) | 5.00 |
| 398 | Don Drysdale (AS) | 10.00 |
| 399 | Warren Spahn (AS) | 10.00 |
| 400 | Elston Howard | 8.00 |
| 401 | AL & NL Homer Kings: | 30.00 |
| | Roger Maris, O. Cepeda | |
| 402 | Gino Cimoli | 4.00 |
| 403 | Chet Nichols | 4.00 |
| 404 | Tim Harkness | 4.00 |
| 405 | Jim Perry | 4.00 |
| 406 | Bob Taylor | 4.00 |
| 407 | Hank Aguirre | 4.00 |
| 408 | Gus Bell | 4.00 |
| 409 | Pittsburgh Pirates | 8.00 |
| 410 | Al Smith | 4.00 |
| 411 | Danny O'Connell | 4.00 |
| 412 | Charlie James | 4.00 |
| 413 | Matty Alou | 5.00 |
| 414 | Joe Gaines | 4.00 |
| 415 | Bill Virdon | 5.00 |
| 416 | Bob Scheffing (Mgr.) | 4.00 |
| 417 | Joe Azcue | 4.00 |
| 418 | Andy Carey | 4.00 |
| 419 | Bob Bruce | 4.00 |
| 420 | Gus Triandos | 4.00 |
| 421 | Ken MacKenzie | 4.00 |
| 422 | Steve Bilko | 4.00 |
| 423 | Rival Relief Aces: | 6.00 |
| | Roy Face, Hoyt Wilhelm | |
| 424 | Al McBean | 4.00 |
| 425 | Carl Yastrzemski | 200.00 |
| 426 | Bob Farley | 4.00 |
| 427 | Jake Wood | 4.00 |
| 428 | Joe Hicks | 4.00 |
| 429 | Billy O'Dell | 4.00 |
| 430 | Tony Kubek | 9.00 |
| 431 | Bob Rodgers | 6.00 |
| 432 | Jim Pendleton | 4.00 |
| 433 | Jim Archer | 4.00 |
| 434 | Clay Dalrymple | 4.00 |
| 435 | Larry Sherry | 4.00 |
| 436 | Felix Mantilla | 4.00 |

| NO. | PLAYER | NR. MT. |
|-----|--------|---------|
| 437 | Ray Moore | 4.00 |
| 438 | Dick Brown | 4.00 |
| 439 | Jerry Buchek | 4.00 |
| 440 | Joe Jay | 4.00 |
| 441 | Checklist No. 6 | 7.00 |
| 442 | Wes Stock | 4.00 |
| 443 | Del Crandall | 5.00 |
| 444 | Ted Wills | 4.00 |
| 445 | Vic Power | 4.00 |
| 446 | Don Elston | 4.00 |
| 447 | Willie Kirland | 5.00 |
| 448 | Joe Gibbon | 5.00 |
| 449 | Jerry Adair | 5.00 |
| 450 | Jim O'Toole | 5.00 |
| 451 | Jose Tartabull | 5.00 |
| 452 | Earl Averill | 5.00 |
| 453 | Cal McLish | 5.00 |
| 454 | Floyd Robinson | 5.00 |
| 455 | Luis Arroyo | 5.00 |
| 456 | Joe Amalfitano | 5.00 |
| 457 | Lou Clinton | 5.00 |
| 458 | Bob Buhl ("M" on hat) | 6.00 |
| 458 | Bob Buhl (without "M" on hat) | 50.00 |
| 459 | Ed Bailey | 5.00 |
| 460 | Jim Bunning | 9.00 |
| 461 | Ken Hubbs (R) | 15.00 |
| 462 | Willie Tasby ("W" on hat) | 5.00 |
| 462 | Willie Tasby (without "W" on hat) | 50.00 |
| 463 | Hank Bauer (Mgr.) | 6.00 |
| 464 | Al Jackson | 6.00 |
| 465 | Cincinnati Reds | 8.00 |
| 466 | Norm Cash (AS) | 7.00 |
| 467 | Chuck Schilling (AS) | 5.00 |
| 468 | Brooks Robinson (AS) | 15.00 |
| 469 | Luis Aparicio (AS) | 9.00 |
| 470 | Al Kaline (AS) | 15.00 |
| 471 | Mickey Mantle (AS) | 100.00 |
| 472 | Rocky Colavito (AS) | 7.00 |
| 473 | Elston Howard (AS) | 8.00 |
| 474 | Frank Lary (AS) | 5.00 |
| 475 | Whitey Ford (AS) | 12.00 |
| 476 | Baltimore Orioles | 8.00 |
| 477 | Andre Rodgers | 5.00 |
| 478 | Don Zimmer | 7.00 |
| 479 | Joel Horlen | 5.00 |

| NO. | PLAYER | NR. MT. |
|-----|--------|---------|
| 480 | Harvey Kuenn | 6.00 |
| 481 | Vic Wertz | 5.00 |
| 482 | Sam Mele | 5.00 |
| 483 | Don McMahon | 5.00 |
| 484 | Dick Schofield | 5.00 |
| 485 | Pedro Ramos | 5.00 |
| 486 | Jim Gilliam | 7.00 |
| 487 | Jerry Lynch | 5.00 |
| 488 | Hal Brown | 5.00 |
| 489 | Julio Gotay | 5.00 |
| 490 | Clete Boyer | 6.00 |
| 491 | Leon Wagner | 5.00 |
| 492 | Hal Smith | 5.00 |
| 493 | Danny McDevitt | 5.00 |
| 494 | Sammy White | 5.00 |
| 495 | Don Cardwell | 5.00 |
| 496 | Wayne Causey | 5.00 |
| 497 | Ed Bouchee | 5.00 |
| 498 | Jim Donohue | 5.00 |
| 499 | Zoilo Versalles | 5.00 |
| 500 | Duke Snider | 50.00 |
| 501 | Claude Osteen | 5.00 |
| 502 | Hector Lopez | 5.00 |
| 503 | Danny Murtaugh (Mgr.) | 5.00 |
| 504 | Eddie Bressoud | 5.00 |
| 505 | Juan Marichal | 40.00 |
| 506 | Charley Maxwell | 5.00 |
| 507 | Ernie Broglio | 5.00 |
| 508 | Gordy Coleman | 5.00 |
| 509 | Dave Giusti | 5.00 |
| 510 | Jim Lemon | 5.00 |
| 511 | Bubba Phillips | 5.00 |
| 512 | Mike Fornieles | 5.00 |
| 513 | Whitey Herzog | 6.00 |
| 514 | Sherm Lollar | 5.00 |
| 515 | Stan Williams | 5.00 |
| 516 | Checklist No. 7 | 12.00 |
| 517 | Dave Wickersham | 5.00 |
| 518 | Lee Maye | 5.00 |
| 519 | Bob Johnson | 5.00 |
| 520 | Bob Friend | 5.00 |
| 521 | Jacke Davis | 5.00 |
| 522 | Lindy McDaniel | 5.00 |
| 523 | Russ Nixon | 12.00 |
| 524 | Howie Nunn | 12.00 |
| 525 | George Thomas | 12.00 |
| 526 | Hal Woodeschick | 12.00 |

| NO. | PLAYER | NR. MT. |
|-----|--------|---------|
| 527 | Dick McAuliffe | 12.00 |
| 528 | Turk Lown | 12.00 |
| 529 | John Schaive | 12.00 |
| 530 | Bob Gibson | 150.00 |
| 531 | Bobby G. Smith | 12.00 |
| 532 | Dick Stigman | 12.00 |
| 533 | Charley Lau | 12.00 |
| 534 | Tony Gonzalez | 12.00 |
| 535 | Ed Roebuck | 12.00 |
| 536 | Dick Gernert | 12.00 |
| 537 | Cleveland Indians | 35.00 |
| 538 | Jack Sanford | 12.00 |
| 539 | Billy Moran | 12.00 |
| 540 | Jim Landis | 12.00 |
| 541 | Don Nottebart | 12.00 |
| 542 | Dave Philley | 12.00 |
| 543 | Bob Allen | 12.00 |
| 544 | Willie McCovey | 160.00 |
| 545 | Hoyt Wilhelm | 55.00 |
| 546 | Moe Thacker | 12.00 |
| 547 | Don Ferrarese | 12.00 |
| 548 | Bobby Del Greco | 12.00 |
| 549 | Bill Rigney (Mgr.) | 12.00 |
| 550 | Art Mahaffey | 12.00 |
| 551 | Harry Bright | 12.00 |
| 552 | Chicago Cubs | 40.00 |
| 553 | Jim Coates | 13.00 |
| 554 | Bubba Morton | 12.00 |
| 555 | John Buzhardt | 12.00 |
| 556 | Al Spangler | 12.00 |
| 557 | Bob Anderson | 12.00 |
| 558 | John Goryl | 12.00 |
| 559 | Mike Higgins (Mgr.) | 12.00 |
| 560 | Chuck Estrada | 12.00 |
| 561 | Gene Oliver | 12.00 |
| 562 | Bill Henry | 12.00 |
| 563 | Ken Aspromonte | 12.00 |
| 564 | Bob Grim | 12.00 |
| 565 | Jose Pagan | 12.00 |
| 566 | Marty Kutyna | 12.00 |
| 567 | Tracy Stallard | 12.00 |
| 568 | Jim Golden | 12.00 |
| 569 | Ed Sadowski | 12.00 |
| 570 | Bill Stafford | 12.00 |
| 571 | Billy Klaus | 12.00 |
| 572 | Bob Miller | 12.00 |
| 573 | Johnny Logan | 12.00 |

| NO. | PLAYER | NR. MT. |
|-----|--------|---------|
| 574 | Dean Stone | 12.00 |
| 575 | Red Schoendienst | 50.00 |
| 576 | Russ Kemmerer | 12.00 |
| 577 | Dave Nicholson | 12.00 |
| 578 | Jim Duffalo | 12.00 |
| 579 | Jim Schaffer | 12.00 |
| 580 | Bill Monbouquette | 12.00 |
| 581 | Mel Roach | 12.00 |
| 582 | Ron Piche | 12.00 |
| 583 | Larry Osborne | 12.00 |
| 584 | Minnesota Twins | 40.00 |
| 585 | Glen Hobbie | 12.00 |
| 586 | Sammy Esposito | 12.00 |
| 587 | Frank Funk | 12.00 |
| 588 | Birdie Tebbetts (Mgr.) | 12.00 |
| 589 | Bob Turley | 15.00 |
| 590 | Curt Flood | 20.00 |
| 591 | Rookie Pitchers: Sam McDowell, D. Radatz, Ron Taylor, Ron Nischwitz, Art Quirk | 55.00 |
| 592 | Rookie Pitchers: D. Stenhouse, Dan Pfister, Bo Belinsky, Jim Bouton, Joe Bonikowski | 75.00 |
| 593 | Rookie Pitchers: Bob Moorhead, Jack Lamabe, Jack Hamilton, Bob Veale, Craig Anderson | 25.00 |
| 594 | Rookie Catchers: Bob Uecker, Doc Edwards, Ken Retzer, Doug Camilli, Don Pavletich | 120.00 |
| 595 | Rookie Infielders: Bob Sadowski, Marlan Coughtry, Ed Charles, Felix Torres | 25.00 |
| 596 | Rookie Infielders: Bernie Allen, Phil Linz, Rich Rollins, Joe Pepitone | 60.00 |
| 597 | Rookie Infielders: Denis Menke, Jim McKnight, Rod Kanehl, Amado Samuel | 30.00 |
| 598 | Rookie Outfielders: Al Luplow, Danny Jimenez, Ed Olivares, Howie Gross, Jim Hickman | 75.00 |

## 1963 Topps . . . Complete Set of 576 Cards—Value $1800.00 (Exc.) $4750.00 (Near Mint)

Pete Rose's rookie card is in this set. Cards 507 to 576 are the high numbers. Also includes the rookie cards of Willie Stargell, Tony Oliva, and Rusty Staub. Cards 29 and 54 exist with the error "1962 Rookie Stars" instead of "1963 Rookie Stars"—worth $5.00 each.

| NO. | PLAYER | NR. MT. |
|-----|--------|---------|
| 1 | NL Bat Ldrs.: (exc. $9.00) Frank Robinson, Stan Musial, Tommy Davis, Bill White, Hank Aaron | 30.00 |
| 2 | AL Batting Leaders: Norm Siebern, Pete Runnels, Floyd Robinson, C. Hinton, Mickey Mantle | 13.00 |

| NO. | PLAYER | NR. MT. |
|-----|--------|---------|
| 3 | NL Home Run Leaders: O. Cepeda, Hank Aaron, Ernie Banks, Frank Robinson, Willie Mays | 12.00 |
| 4 | AL Home Run Leaders: Roger Maris, R. Colavito, Harmon Killebrew, Norm Cash, J. Gentile, L. Wagner | 4.00 |

| NO. | PLAYER | NR. MT. |
|-----|--------|---------|
| 5 | NL ERA Leaders: Bob Purkey, Bob Shaw, Sandy Koufax, Bob Gibson, Don Drysdale | 5.00 |
| 6 | AL ERA Leaders: Whitey Ford, Robin Roberts, Eddie Fisher, Hank Aguirre, Dean Chance | 3.00 |

| NO. | PLAYER | NR. MT. |
|-----|--------|---------|
| 7 | NL Pitching Leaders: Don Drysdale, Billy O'Dell, Jack Sanford, Bob Purkey, Art Mahaffey, Joe Jay | 3.00 |
| 8 | AL Pitching Leaders: Dick Donovan, Ray Herbert, Ralph Terry, Jim Bunning, Camilo Pascual | 3.00 |

| NO. PLAYER | NR. MT. |
|---|---|
| 9 NL Strikeout Leaders: | 6.00 |
| Sandy Koufax, Bob Gibson, | |
| Don Drysdale, Billy O'Dell, | |
| Dick Farrell | |
| 10 AL Strikeout Leaders: | 3.00 |
| Ralph Terry, Juan Pizarro, | |
| Camilo Pascual, Jim | |
| Bunning, Jim Kaat | |
| 11 Lee Walls | 1.50 |
| 12 Steve Barber | 1.50 |
| 13 Philadelphia Phillies | 3.00 |
| 14 Pedro Ramos | 1.50 |
| 15 Ken Hubbs | 4.00 |
| 16 Al Smith | 1.50 |
| 17 Ryne Duren | 1.50 |
| 18 Buc Blasters: | 10.00 |
| Smoky Burgess, Dick Stuart, | |
| Bob Clemente, Bob Skinner | |
| 19 Pete Burnside | 1.50 |
| 20 Tony Kubek | 4.00 |
| 21 Marty Keough | 1.50 |
| 22 Curt Simmons | 1.50 |
| 23 Ed Lopat (Mgr.) | 2.00 |
| 24 Bob Bruce | 1.50 |
| 25 A. Kaline | 30.00 |
| 26 Ray Moore | 1.50 |
| 27 Choo Choo Coleman | 1.50 |
| 28 Mike Fornieles* | 1.50 |
| 29 Rookie Stars:* | 3.00 |
| Sammy Ellis, Jesse Gonder, | |
| Ray Culp, John Boozer | |
| 30 Harvey Kuenn | 2.00 |
| 31 Cal Koonce | 1.50 |
| 32 Tony Gonzalez | 1.50 |
| 33 Bo Belinsky | 1.50 |
| 34 Dick Schofield | 1.50 |
| 35 John Buzhardt | 1.50 |
| 36 Jerry Kindall | 1.50 |
| 37 Jerry Lynch | 1.50 |
| 38 Bud Daley | 1.50 |
| 39 Los Angeles Angels | 3.00 |
| 40 Vic Power | 1.50 |
| 41 Charlie Lau | 1.50 |
| 42 Stan Williams | 1.50 |
| 43 Veteran Masters: | 5.00 |
| C. Stengel, G. Woodling | |
| 44 Terry Fox | 1.50 |
| 45 Bob Aspromonte | 1.50 |
| 46 Tommie Aaron | 1.50 |
| 47 Don Lock | 1.50 |
| 48 Birdie Tebbetts (Mgr.) | 1.50 |
| 49 Dal Maxvill | 1.50 |
| 50 Bill Pierce | 2.00 |
| 51 George Alusik | 1.50 |
| 52 Chuck Schilling | 1.50 |
| 53 Joe Moeller | 1.50 |
| 54 Rookie Stars: | 5.00 |
| N. Mathews, D. DeBusschere, | |
| Harry Fanok, J. Cullen | |
| 55 Bill Virdon | 2.00 |
| 56 Dennis Bennett | 1.50 |
| 57 Billy Moran | 1.50 |
| 58 Bob Will | 1.50 |
| 59 Craig Anderson | 1.50 |
| 60 Elston Howard | 6.00 |
| 61 Ernie Bowman | 1.50 |
| 62 Bob Hendley | 1.50 |
| 63 Cincinnati Reds | 3.00 |
| 64 Dick McAuliffe | 1.50 |
| 65 Jackie Brandt | 1.50 |
| 66 Mike Joyce | 1.50 |
| 67 Ed Charles | 1.50 |
| 68 Friendly Foes: | 10.00 |
| Duke Snider, Gil Hodges | |
| 69 Bud Zipfel | 1.50 |
| 70 Jim O'Toole | 1.50 |
| 71 Bobby Wine | 1.50 |
| 72 Johnny Romano | 1.50 |
| 73 Bob Bragan (Mgr.) | 1.50 |
| 74 Denver Lemaster | 1.50 |
| 75 Bobby Allison | 1.50 |
| 76 Earl Wilson | 1.50 |

| NO. PLAYER | NR. MT. |
|---|---|
| 77 Al Spangler | 1.50 |
| 78 Marv Throneberry | 2.50 |
| 79 Checklist No. 1 | 6.00 |
| 80 Jim Gilliam | 2.50 |
| 81 Jim Schaffer | 1.50 |
| 82 Ed Rakow | 1.50 |
| 83 Charley James | 1.50 |
| 84 Ron Kline | 1.50 |
| 85 Tom Haller | 1.50 |
| 86 Charley Maxwell | 1.50 |
| 87 Bob Veale | 1.50 |
| 88 Ron Hansen | 1.50 |
| 89 Dick Stigman | 1.50 |
| 90 Gordy Coleman | 1.50 |
| 91 Dallas Green | 3.00 |
| 92 Hector Lopez | 1.50 |
| 93 Galen Cisco | 1.50 |
| 94 Bob Schmidt | 1.50 |
| 95 Larry Jackson | 1.50 |
| 96 Lou Clinton | 1.50 |
| 97 Bob Duliba | 1.50 |
| 98 George Thomas | 1.50 |
| 99 Jim Umbricht | 1.50 |
| 100 Joe Cunningham | 1.50 |
| 101 Joe Gibbon | 1.50 |
| 102 Checklist No. 2 | 6.00 |
| 103 Chuck Essegian | 1.50 |
| 104 Lew Krausse | 1.50 |
| 105 Ron Fairly | 1.50 |
| 106 Bob Bolin | 1.50 |
| 107 Jim Hickman | 1.50 |
| 108 Hoyt Wilhelm | 9.00 |
| 109 Lee Maye | 1.50 |
| 110 Rich Rollins | 2.00 |
| 111 Al Jackson | 2.00 |
| 112 Dick Brown | 2.00 |
| 113 Don Landrum | 2.00 |
| (photo of Ron Santo) | |
| 114 Dan Osinski | 2.00 |
| 115 Carl Yastrzemski | 85.00 |
| 116 Jim Brosnan | 2.00 |
| 117 Jacke Davis | 2.00 |
| 118 Sherm Lollar | 2.00 |
| 119 Bob Lillis | 2.00 |
| 120 Roger Maris | 60.00 |
| 121 Jim Hannan | 2.00 |
| 122 Julio Gotay | 2.00 |
| 123 Frank Howard | 3.00 |
| 124 Dick Howser | 2.00 |
| 125 Robin Roberts | 11.00 |
| 126 Bob Uecker | 36.00 |
| 127 Bill Tuttle | 2.00 |
| 128 Matty Alou | 2.00 |
| 129 Gary Bell | 2.00 |
| 130 Dick Groat | 2.00 |
| 131 Washington Senators | 3.00 |
| 132 Jack Hamilton | 2.00 |
| 133 Gene Freese | 2.00 |
| 134 Bob Scheffing (Mgr.) | 2.00 |
| 135 Richie Ashburn | 8.00 |
| 136 Ike Delock | 2.00 |
| 137 Mack Jones | 2.00 |
| 138 Pride Of N.L.: | 30.00 |
| Willie Mays, Stan Musial | |
| 139 Earl Averill | 2.00 |
| 140 Frank Lary | 2.00 |
| 141 Manny Mota (R) | 6.00 |
| 142 World Series Game 1 | 5.00 |
| Ford Wins Opener | |
| 143 World Series Game 2 | 4.00 |
| Sanford Shutout | |
| 144 World Series Game 3 | 8.00 |
| Maris Sparks Rally | |
| 145 World Series Game 4 | 4.00 |
| Hiller Grand Slam | |
| 146 World Series Game 5 | 4.00 |
| Tresh's Homer | |
| 147 World Series Game 6 | 4.00 |
| Pierce Victory | |
| 148 World Series Game 7 | 5.00 |
| Yanks Celebrate | |
| 149 Marv Breeding | 2.00 |

| NO. PLAYER | NR. MT. |
|---|---|
| 150 Johnny Podres | 2.50 |
| 151 Pittsburgh Pirates | 3.00 |
| 152 Ron Nischwitz | 2.00 |
| 153 Hal Smith | 2.00 |
| 154 Walt Alston (Mgr.) | 5.00 |
| 155 Bill Stafford | 2.00 |
| 156 Roy McMillan | 2.00 |
| 157 Diego Segui | 2.00 |
| 158 Rookie Stars: | 2.00 |
| Bob Saverine, Rogelio | |
| Alvarez, Dave Roberts, | |
| Tommy Harper | |
| 159 Jim Pagliaroni | 2.00 |
| 160 Juan Pizarro | 2.00 |
| 161 Frank Torre | 2.00 |
| 162 Minnesota Twins | 3.00 |
| 163 Don Larsen | 2.50 |
| 164 Bubba Morton | 2.00 |
| 165 Jim Kaat | 5.00 |
| 166 Johnny Keane (Mgr.) | 2.00 |
| 167 Jim Fregosi | 2.50 |
| 168 Russ Nixon | 2.00 |
| 169 Rookie Stars: | 30.00 |
| Gaylord Perry, Dick Egan, | |
| Julio Navarro, Tommie Sisk | |
| 170 Joe Adcock | 2.00 |
| 171 Steve Hamilton | 2.00 |
| 172 Gene Oliver | 2.00 |
| 173 Bombers' Best: | 50.00 |
| Tom Tresh, Mickey Mantle, | |
| Bobby Richardson | |
| 174 Larry Burright | 2.00 |
| 175 Bob Buhl | 2.00 |
| 176 Jim King | 2.00 |
| 177 Bubba Phillips | 2.00 |
| 178 Johnny Edwards | 2.00 |
| 179 Ron Pich | 2.00 |
| 180 Bill Skowron | 3.00 |
| 181 Sammy Esposito | 2.00 |
| 182 Albie Pearson | 2.00 |
| 183 Joe Pepitone | 3.00 |
| 184 Vern Law | 2.00 |
| 185 Chuck Hiller | 2.00 |
| 186 Jerry Zimmerman | 2.00 |
| 187 Willie Kirkland | 2.00 |
| 188 Eddie Bressoud | 2.00 |
| 189 Dave Giusti | 2.00 |
| 190 Minnie Minoso | 3.00 |
| 191 Checklist No. 3 | 6.00 |
| 192 Clay Dalrymple | 2.00 |
| 193 Andre Rodgers | 2.00 |
| 194 Joe Nuxhall | 2.00 |
| 195 Manny Jimenez | 2.00 |
| 196 Doug Camilli | 2.00 |
| 197 Roger Craig | 2.25 |
| 198 Lenny Green | 2.25 |
| 199 Joe Amalfitano | 2.50 |
| 200 Mickey Mantle | 350.00 |
| 201 Cecil Butler | 2.25 |
| 202 Boston Red Sox | 3.00 |
| 203 Chico Cardenas | 2.25 |
| 204 Don Nottebart | 2.25 |
| 205 Luis Aparicio | 12.00 |
| 206 Ray Washburn | 2.25 |
| 207 Ken Hunt | 2.25 |
| 208 Rookie Stars: | 2.25 |
| Ron Herbel, John Miller, | |
| Ron Taylor, Wally Wolf | |
| 209 Hobie Landrith | 2.25 |
| 210 Sandy Koufax | 125.00 |
| 211 Fred Whitfield | 2.25 |
| 212 Glen Hobbie | 2.25 |
| 213 Billy Hitchcock (Mgr.) | 2.25 |
| 214 Orlando Pena | 2.25 |
| 215 Bob Skinner | 2.25 |
| 216 Gene Conley | 2.25 |
| 217 Joe Christopher | 2.25 |
| 218 Tiger Twirlers: | 2.50 |
| Frank Lary, Don Mossi, | |
| Jim Bunning | |
| 219 Chuck Cottier | 2.25 |
| 220 Camilo Pascual | 2.25 |

| NO. PLAYER | NR. MT. |
|---|---|
| 221 Cookie Rojas | 3.00 |
| 222 Chicago Cubs | 2.25 |
| 223 Eddie Fisher | 2.25 |
| 224 Mike Roarke | 2.25 |
| 225 Joe Jay | 2.25 |
| 226 Julian Javier | 2.25 |
| 227 Jim Grant | 2.25 |
| 228 Rookie Stars: | 40.00 |
| Max Alvis, Bob Bailey, | |
| Pedro Oliva, Ed Kranepool | |
| 229 Willie Davis | 2.25 |
| 230 Pete Runnels | 2.25 |
| 231 Eli Grba | 2.25 |
| (photo of Ryne Duren) | |
| 232 Frank Malzone | 2.25 |
| 233 Casey Stengel (Mgr.) | 15.00 |
| 234 Dave Nicholson | 2.25 |
| 235 Bill O'Dell | 2.25 |
| 236 Bill Bryan | 2.25 |
| 237 Jim Coates | 2.25 |
| 238 Lou Johnson | 2.25 |
| 239 Harvey Haddix | 2.25 |
| 240 Rocky Colavito | 7.00 |
| 241 Billy Smith | 2.25 |
| 242 Power Plus: | 25.00 |
| Ernie Banks, Hank Aaron | |
| 243 Don Leppert | 2.25 |
| 244 John Tsitouris | 2.25 |
| 245 Gil Hodges | 15.00 |
| 246 Lee Stange | 2.25 |
| 247 New York Yankees | 12.00 |
| 248 Tito Francona | 2.25 |
| 249 Leo Burke | 2.25 |
| 250 Stan Musial | 110.00 |
| 251 Jack Lamabe | 2.25 |
| 252 Ron Santo | 5.00 |
| 253 Rookie Stars: | 2.25 |
| Len Gabrielson, Pete | |
| Jernigan, Deacon Jones, | |
| John Wojcik | |
| 254 Mike Hershberger | 2.25 |
| 255 Bob Shaw | 2.25 |
| 256 Jerry Lumpe | 2.25 |
| 257 Hank Aguirre | 2.25 |
| 258 Alvin Dark (Mgr.) | 2.25 |
| 259 Johnny Logan | 2.25 |
| 260 Jim Gentile | 2.25 |
| 261 Bob Miller | 2.25 |
| 262 Ellis Burton | 2.25 |
| 263 Dave Stenhouse | 2.25 |
| 264 Phil Linz | 2.25 |
| 265 Vada Pinson | 4.00 |
| 266 Bob Allen | 2.25 |
| 267 Carl Sawatski | 2.25 |
| 268 Don Demter | 2.25 |
| 269 Don Mincher | 2.25 |
| 270 Felipe Alou | 2.25 |
| 271 Dean Stone | 2.25 |
| 272 Danny Murphy | 2.25 |
| 273 Sammy Taylor | 2.25 |
| 274 Checklist No. 4 | 6.00 |
| 275 Ed Mathews | 20.00 |
| 276 Barry Shetrone | 2.25 |
| 277 Dick Farrell | 2.25 |
| 278 Chico Fernandez | 2.25 |
| 279 Wally Moon | 2.25 |
| 280 Bob Rodgers | 3.00 |
| 281 Tom Sturdivant | 2.25 |
| 282 Bob Del Greco | 2.25 |
| 283 Roy Sievers | 2.25 |
| 284 Dave Sisler | 3.00 |
| 285 Dick Stuart | 3.00 |
| 286 Stu Miller | 3.00 |
| 287 Dick Bertell | 3.00 |
| 288 Chicago White Sox | 3.00 |
| 289 Hal Brown | 3.00 |
| 290 Bill White | 4.00 |
| 291 Don Rudolph | 3.00 |
| 292 Pumpsie Green | 3.00 |
| 293 Bill Pleis | 3.00 |
| 294 Bill Rigney (Mgr.) | 3.00 |
| 295 Ed Roebuck | 3.00 |

| NO. PLAYER | NR. MT. |
|---|---|
| 296 Doc Edwards | 3.00 |
| 297 Jim Golden | 3.00 |
| 298 Don Dillard | 3.00 |
| 299 Rookie Stars: | 3.00 |
| Dave Morehead, Bob Dustal, | |
| Dan Schenider, Tom Butters | |
| 300 Willie Mays | 125.00 |
| 301 Bill Fischer | 3.00 |
| 302 Whitey Herzog | 4.00 |
| 303 Earl Francis | 3.00 |
| 304 Harry Bright | 3.00 |
| 305 Don Hoak | 3.00 |
| 306 Star Receivers: | 3.50 |
| Earl Battey, Elston Howard | |
| 307 Chet Nichols | 3.00 |
| 308 Camilo Carreon | 3.00 |
| 309 Jim Brewer | 3.00 |
| 310 Tommy Davis | 4.00 |
| 311 Joe McClain | 3.00 |
| 312 Houston Colts | 10.00 |
| 313 Ernie Broglio | 3.00 |
| 314 John Goryl | 3.00 |
| 315 Ralph Terry | 3.00 |
| 316 Norm Sherry | 3.00 |
| 317 Sam McDowell | 3.00 |
| 318 Gene Mauch (Mgr.) | 3.00 |
| 319 Joe Gaines | 3.00 |
| 320 Warren Spahn | 35.00 |
| 321 Gino Cimoli | 3.00 |
| 322 Bob Turley | 3.00 |
| 323 Bill Mazeroski | 4.00 |
| 324 Rookie Stars: | 4.00 |
| G. Williams, Vic Davalillo, | |
| P. Ward, Phil Roof | |
| 325 Jack Sanford | 3.00 |
| 326 Hank Foiles | 3.00 |
| 327 Paul Foytack | 3.00 |
| 328 Dick Williams | 3.00 |
| 329 Lindy McDaniel | 3.00 |
| 330 Chuck Hinton | 3.00 |
| 331 Series Foes: | 3.00 |
| Bill Stafford, Bill Pierce | |
| 332 Joel Horlen | 3.00 |
| 333 Carl Warwick | 3.00 |
| 334 Wynn Hawkins | 3.00 |
| 335 Leon Wagner | 3.00 |
| 336 Ed Bauta | 3.00 |
| 337 Los Angeles Dodgers | 10.00 |
| 338 Russ Kemmerer | 3.00 |
| 339 Ted Bowsfield | 3.00 |
| 340 Yogi Berra | 65.00 |
| 341 Jack Baldschun | 3.00 |
| 342 Gene Woodling | 3.00 |
| 343 Johnny Pesky (Mgr.) | 3.00 |
| 344 Don Schwall | 3.00 |
| 345 Brooks Robinson | 40.00 |
| 346 Billy Hoeft | 3.00 |
| 347 Joe Torre | 7.00 |
| 348 Vic Wertz | 3.00 |
| 349 Zoilo Versalles | 3.00 |
| 350 Bob Purkey | 3.00 |
| 351 Al Luplow | 3.00 |
| 352 Ken Johnson | 3.00 |
| 353 Billy Williams | 25.00 |
| 354 Dom Zanni | 3.00 |
| 355 Dean Chance | 3.00 |
| 356 John Schaive | 3.00 |
| 357 George Altman | 3.00 |
| 358 Milt Pappas | 3.00 |
| 359 Haywood Sullivan | 3.00 |
| 360 Don Drysdale | 30.00 |
| 361 Clete Boyer | 4.00 |
| 362 Checklist No. 5 | 6.00 |
| 363 Dick Radatz | 3.00 |
| 364 Howie Goss | 3.00 |
| 365 Jim Bunning | 7.00 |
| 366 Tony Taylor | 3.00 |
| 367 Tony Cloninger | 3.00 |
| 368 Ed Bailey | 3.00 |

| NO. PLAYER | NR. MT. |
|---|---|
| 369 Jim Lemon | 3.00 |
| 370 Dick Donovan | 3.00 |
| 371 Rod Kanehl | 3.50 |
| 372 Don Lee | 3.50 |
| 373 Jim Campbell | 3.50 |
| 374 Claude Osteen | 3.50 |
| 375 Ken Boyer | 6.00 |
| 376 John Wyatt | 3.00 |
| 377 Baltimore Orioles | 5.00 |
| 378 Bill Henry | 3.50 |
| 379 Bob Anderson | 3.50 |
| 380 Ernie Banks | 50.00 |
| 381 Frank Baumann | 3.50 |
| 382 Ralph Houk (Mgr.) | 3.50 |
| 383 Pete Richert | 3.50 |
| 384 Bob Tillman | 3.50 |
| 385 Art Mahaffey | 3.50 |
| 386 Rookie Stars: | 4.00 |
| Ed Kirkpatrick, J. Bateman, | |
| G. Roggenburk, L. Bearnarth | |
| 387 Al McBean | 3.50 |
| 388 Jim Davenport | 3.50 |
| 389 Frank Sullivan | 3.50 |
| 390 Hank Aaron | 125.00 |
| 391 Bill Dailey | 3.50 |
| 392 Tribe Thumpers: | 3.50 |
| Johnny Romano, | |
| Tito Francona | |
| 393 Ken MacKenzie | 3.50 |
| 394 Tim McCarver | 10.00 |
| 395 Don McMahon | 3.50 |
| 396 Joe Koppe | 3.50 |
| 397 Kansas C. Athletics | 5.00 |
| 398 Boog Powell | 15.00 |
| 399 Dick Ellsworth | 3.50 |
| 400 Frank Robinson | 40.00 |
| 401 Jim Bouton | 6.00 |
| 402 Mickey Vernon (Mgr.) | 3.50 |
| 403 Ron Perranoski | 3.50 |
| 404 Bob Oldis | 3.50 |
| 405 Floyd Robinson | 3.50 |
| 406 Howie Koplitz | 3.50 |
| 407 Rookie Stars: | 3.50 |
| Dick Simpson, Frank Kostro, | |
| Chico Ruiz, Larry Elliot | |
| 408 Billy Gardner | 3.50 |
| 409 Roy Face | 3.50 |
| 410 Earl Battey | 3.50 |
| 411 Jim Constable | 3.50 |
| 412 Dodger Big Three: | 35.00 |
| Sandy Koufax, Johnny | |
| Podres, Don Drysdale | |
| 413 Jerry Walker | 3.00 |
| 414 Ty Cline | 3.00 |
| 415 Bob Gibson | 40.00 |
| 416 Alex Grammas | 3.00 |
| 417 San F. Giants | 6.00 |
| 418 Johnny Orsino | 3.00 |
| 419 Tracy Stallard | 3.00 |
| 420 Bobby Richardson | 6.00 |
| 421 Tom Morgan | 3.50 |
| 422 Fred Hutchinson (Mgr.) | 3.50 |
| 423 Ed Hobaugh | 3.50 |
| 424 Charley Smith | 3.50 |
| 425 Smokey Burgess | 3.50 |
| 426 Barry Latman | 3.50 |
| 427 Bernie Allen | 3.50 |
| 428 Carl Boles | 3.50 |
| 429 Lou Burdette | 4.00 |
| 430 Norm Siebern | 3.50 |
| 431 Checklist No. 6 | 6.00 |
| 432 Roman Mejias | 3.50 |
| 433 Denis Menke | 3.50 |
| 434 Johnny Callison | 3.50 |
| 435 Woody Held | 3.50 |
| 436 Tim Harkness | 3.50 |
| 437 Bill Bruton | 3.50 |
| 438 Wes Stock | 3.50 |
| 439 Don Zimmer | 4.00 |

| NO. PLAYER | NR. MT. |
|---|---|
| 440 Juan Marichal | 25.00 |
| 441 Lee Thomas | 3.50 |
| 442 J.C. Hartman | 3.50 |
| 443 Jim Piersall | 4.00 |
| 444 Jim Maloney | 4.00 |
| 445 Norm Cash | 5.00 |
| 446 Whitey Ford | 40.00 |
| 447 Felix Mantilla | 12.00 |
| 448 Jack Kralick | 12.00 |
| 449 Jose Tartabull | 12.00 |
| 450 Bob Friend | 12.00 |
| 451 Cleveland Indians | 12.00 |
| 452 Barney Schultz | 12.00 |
| 453 Jake Wood | 12.00 |
| 454 Art Fowler | 12.00 |
| 455 Ruben Amaro | 12.00 |
| 456 Jim Coker | 12.00 |
| 457 Tex Clevenger | 12.00 |
| 458 Al Lopez (Mgr.) | 16.00 |
| 459 Dick LeMay | 12.00 |
| 460 Del Crandall | 12.00 |
| 461 Norm Bass | 12.00 |
| 462 Wally Post | 12.00 |
| 463 Joe Schaffernoth | 12.00 |
| 464 Ken Aspromonte | 12.00 |
| 465 Chuck Estrada | 12.00 |
| 466 Rookie Stars: | 35.00 |
| Tony Martinez, Bill Freehan, | |
| Jerry Robinson, Nate Oliver | |
| 467 Phil Ortega | 12.00 |
| 468 Carroll Hardy | 12.00 |
| 469 Jay Hook | 12.00 |
| 470 Tom Tresh | 35.00 |
| 471 Ken Retzer | 12.00 |
| 472 Lou Brock | 140.00 |
| 473 New York Mets | 85.00 |
| 474 Jack Fisher | 12.00 |
| 475 Gus Triandos | 12.00 |
| 476 Frank Funk | 12.00 |
| 477 Donn Clendenon | 12.00 |
| 478 Paul Brown | 12.00 |
| 479 Ed Brinkman | 12.00 |
| 480 Bill Monbouquette | 12.00 |
| 481 Bob Taylor | 12.00 |
| 482 Felix Torres | 12.00 |
| 483 Jim Owens | 12.00 |
| 484 Dale Long | 15.00 |
| 485 Jim Landis | 12.00 |
| 486 Ray Sadecki | 12.00 |
| 487 John Roseboro | 12.00 |
| 488 Jerry Adair | 12.00 |
| 489 Paul Toth | 12.00 |
| 490 Willie McCovey | 125.00 |
| 491 Harry Craft (Mgr.) | 12.00 |
| 492 Dave Wickersham | 12.00 |
| 493 Walt Bond | 12.00 |
| 494 Phil Regan | 12.00 |
| 495 Frank Thomas | 12.00 |
| 496 Rookie Stars: | 12.00 |
| Steve Dalkowski, Carl | |
| Bouldin, Fred Newman, | |
| Jack Smith | |
| 497 Bennie Daniels | 12.00 |
| 498 Eddie Kasko | 12.00 |
| 499 J.C. Martin | 12.00 |
| 500 Harmon Killebrew | 100.00 |
| 501 Joe Azcue | 12.00 |
| 502 Daryl Spencer | 12.00 |
| 503 Milwaukee Braves | 30.00 |
| 504 Bob Johnson | 12.00 |
| 505 Curt Flood | 16.00 |
| 506 Gene Green | 12.00 |
| 507 Roland Sheldon | 12.00 |
| 508 Ted Savage | 12.00 |
| 509 Checklist No. 7 | 20.00 |
| 510 Ken McBride | 12.00 |
| 511 Charlie Neal | 12.00 |
| 512 Cal McLish | 12.00 |
| 513 Gary Geiger | 12.00 |

| NO. PLAYER | NR. MT. |
|---|---|
| 514 Larry Osborne | 12.00 |
| 515 Don Elston | 12.00 |
| 516 Purnal Goldy | 12.00 |
| 517 Hal Woodeschick | 12.00 |
| 518 Don Blasingame | 12.00 |
| 519 Claude Raymond | 12.00 |
| 520 Orlando Cepeda | 20.00 |
| 521 Dan Pfister | 12.00 |
| 522 Rookie Stars: | 12.00 |
| Mel Nelson, Gary Peters, | |
| Art Quirk, Jim Roland | |
| 523 Bill Kunkel | 7.50 |
| 524 St. Louis Cards | 15.00 |
| 525 Nellie Fox | 16.00 |
| 526 Dick Hall | 7.50 |
| 527 Ed Sadowski | 7.50 |
| 528 Carl Willey | 7.50 |
| 529 Wes Covington | 7.50 |
| 530 Don Mossi | 7.50 |
| 531 Sam Mele (Mgr.) | 7.50 |
| 532 Steve Boros | 7.50 |
| 533 Bobby Shantz | 7.50 |
| 534 Ken Walters | 7.50 |
| 535 Jim Perry | 7.50 |
| 536 Norm Larker | 7.50 |
| 537 Rookie Stars: | 600.00 |
| Pedro Gonzalez, Pete Rose, | |
| Ken McMullen, Al Weis | |
| 538 George Brunet | 7.50 |
| 539 Wayne Causey | 7.50 |
| 540 Bob Clemente | 180.00 |
| 541 Ron Moeller | 7.50 |
| 542 Lou Klimchock | 7.50 |
| 543 Russ Snyder | 7.50 |
| 544 Rookie Stars: | 40.00 |
| Rusty Staub, Duke Carmel, | |
| Bill Haas, Dick Phillips | |
| 545 Jose Pagan | 7.50 |
| 546 Hal Reniff | 7.50 |
| 547 Gus Bell | 7.50 |
| 548 Tom Satriano | 7.50 |
| 549 Rookie Stars: | 7.50 |
| Paul Ratliff, Marcelino | |
| Lopez, Pete Lovrich, | |
| Elmo Plaskett | |
| 550 Duke Snider | 75.00 |
| 551 Billy Klaus | 7.50 |
| 552 Detroit Tigers | 25.00 |
| 553 Rookie Stars: | 275.00 |
| Brock Davis, Jim Gosger, | |
| W. Stargell, J. Herrnstein | |
| 554 Hank Fischer | 7.50 |
| 555 John Blanchard | 7.50 |
| 556 Al Worthington | 7.50 |
| 557 Cuno Barragan | 7.50 |
| 558 Rookie Stars: | 7.50 |
| Bill Faul, Ron Hunt, | |
| Bob Lipski, Al Moran | |
| 559 Danny Murtaugh (Mgr.) | 7.50 |
| 560 Ray Herbert | 7.50 |
| 561 Mike De La Hoz | 7.50 |
| 562 Rookie Stars: | 15.00 |
| Don Rowe, Randy Cardinal, | |
| Dave McNally, Ken Rowe | |
| 563 Mike McCormick | 12.00 |
| 564 George Banks | 12.00 |
| 565 Larry Sherry | 12.00 |
| 566 Clif Cook | 12.00 |
| 567 Jim Duffalo | 12.00 |
| 568 Bob Sadowski | 12.00 |
| 569 Luis Arroyo | 12.00 |
| 570 Frank Bolling | 12.00 |
| 571 Johnny Klippstein | 12.00 |
| 572 Jack Spring | 12.00 |
| 573 Coot Veal | 12.00 |
| 574 Hal Kolstad | 12.00 |
| 575 Don Cardwell | 12.00 |
| 576 Johnny Temple | 15.00 |

# 1964 Topps . . . Complete Set of 587 Cards—Value $1150.00 (Exc.); $3000.00 (Near Mint)

Phil Niekro's rookie card is in this set. The high numbers are 523 to 587. For the first time a card was issued for a deceased player—Ken Hubbs.

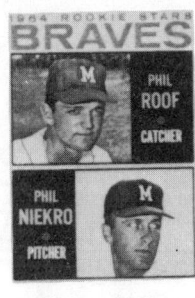

| NO. | PLAYER | NR. MT. |
|---|---|---|
| 1 | NL ERA Ldrs.. (exc. $5.00) Sandy Koufax, Dick Ellsworth, Bob Friend | 20.00 |
| 2 | AL ERA Leaders: Gary Peters, Juan Pizarro, Camilo Pascual | 3.00 |
| 3 | NL Pitching Leaders: S. Koufax, Juan Marichal, W. Spahn, Jim Maloney | 7.50 |
| 4 | AL Pitching Leaders: Whitey Ford, Camilo Pascual, Jim Bouton | 3.50 |
| 5 | NL Strikeout Leaders: Sandy Koufax, Jim Maloney, Don Drysdale | 7.50 |
| 6 | AL Strikeout Leaders: Camilo Pascual, Jim Bunning, Dick Stigman | 3.00 |
| 7 | NL Batting Leaders: T. Davis, Bob Clemente, D. Groat, Hank Aaron | 6.00 |
| 8 | AL Batting Leaders: Carl Yastrzemski, Al Kaline, Rich Rollins | 5.00 |
| 9 | NL Home Run Leaders: Hank Aaron, W. McCovey, W. Mays, Orlando Cepeda | 11.00 |
| 10 | AL Home Run Leaders: Harmon Killebrew, Dick Stuart, Bob Allison | 4.00 |
| 11 | NL RBI Leaders: Hank Aaron, Ken Boyer, Bill White | 4.00 |
| 12 | AL RBI Leaders: Dick Stuart, Al Kaline, Harmon Killebrew | 3.00 |
| 13 | Hoyt Wilhelm | 8.00 |
| 14 | Dodgers Rookies: Dick Nen, Nick Willhite | 1.50 |
| 15 | Zoilo Versalles | 1.50 |
| 16 | John Boozer | 1.50 |
| 17 | Willie Kirkland | 1.50 |
| 18 | Bill O'Dell | 1.50 |
| 19 | Don Wert | 1.50 |
| 20 | Bob Friend | 1.50 |
| 21 | Yogi Berra (Mgr.) | 35.00 |
| 22 | Jerry Adair | 1.50 |
| 23 | Chris Zachary | 1.50 |
| 24 | Carl Sawatski | 1.50 |
| 25 | Bill Monbouquett | 1.50 |
| 26 | Gino Cimoli | 1.50 |
| 27 | New York Mets | 6.00 |
| 28 | Claude Osteen | 1.50 |
| 29 | Lou Brock | 35.00 |
| 30 | Ron Perranoski | 1.50 |
| 31 | Dave Nicholson | 1.50 |
| 32 | Dean Chance | 2.00 |
| 33 | Reds Rookies: Sammy Ellis, Mel Queen | 1.50 |
| 34 | Jim Perry | 1.50 |
| 35 | Ed Mathews | 17.00 |
| 36 | Hal Reniff | 1.50 |
| 37 | Smoky Burgess | 1.50 |
| 38 | Jim Wynn (R) | 4.00 |
| 39 | Hank Aguirre | 1.50 |
| 40 | Dick Groat | 2.00 |

| NO. | PLAYER | NR. MT. |
|---|---|---|
| 41 | Friendly Foes: W. McCovey, Leon Wagner | 4.00 |
| 42 | Moe Drabowski | 1.50 |
| 43 | Roy Sievers | 1.50 |
| 44 | Duke Carmel | 1.50 |
| 45 | Milt Pappas | 1.50 |
| 46 | Ed Brinkman | 1.50 |
| 47 | Giants Rookies: Jesus Alou, Ron Herbel | 2.00 |
| 48 | Bob Perry | 1.50 |
| 49 | Bill Henry | 1.50 |
| 50 | M. Mantle | 225.00 |
| 51 | Pete Richert | 1.50 |
| 52 | Chuck Hinton | 1.50 |
| 53 | Denis Menke | 1.50 |
| 54 | Sam Mele | 1.50 |
| 55 | Ernie Banks | 27.00 |
| 56 | Hal Brown | 1.50 |
| 57 | Tim Harkness | 1.50 |
| 58 | Don Demeter | 1.50 |
| 59 | Ernie Broglio | 1.50 |
| 60 | Frank Malzone | 1.50 |
| 61 | Angel Backstops: Bob Rodgers, Ed Sadowski | 1.50 |
| 62 | Ted Savage | 1.50 |
| 63 | Johnny Orsino | 1.50 |
| 64 | Ted Abernathy | 1.50 |
| 65 | Felipe Alou | 1.50 |
| 66 | Eddie Fisher | 1.50 |
| 67 | Detroit Tigers | 3.00 |
| 68 | Willie Davis | 1.50 |
| 69 | Clete Boyer | 2.00 |
| 70 | Joe Torre | 4.00 |
| 71 | Jack Spring | 1.50 |
| 72 | Chico Cardenas | 1.50 |
| 73 | Jimmie Hall | 1.50 |
| 74 | Pirates Rookies: Bob Priddy, Tom Butters | 1.50 |
| 75 | Wayne Causey | 1.50 |
| 76 | Checklist No. 1 | 6.00 |
| 77 | Jerry Walker | 1.50 |
| 78 | Merritt Ranew | 1.50 |
| 79 | Bob Heffner | 1.50 |
| 80 | Vada Pinson | 3.00 |
| 81 | All-Star Vets: Nellie Fox, H. Killebrew | 5.00 |
| 82 | Jim Davenport | 1.50 |
| 83 | Gus Triandos | 1.50 |
| 84 | Carl Willey | 1.50 |
| 85 | Pete Ward | 1.50 |
| 86 | Al Doning | 1.50 |
| 87 | St. Louis Cardinals | 3.00 |
| 88 | John Roseboro | 1.50 |
| 89 | Boog Powell | 4.00 |
| 90 | Earl Battey | 1.50 |
| 91 | Bob Bailey | 1.50 |
| 92 | Steve Ridzik | 1.50 |
| 93 | Gary Geiger | 1.50 |
| 94 | Braves Rookies: Jim Britton, Larry Maxie | 1.50 |
| 95 | George Altman | 1.50 |
| 96 | Bob Buhl | 1.50 |
| 97 | Jim Fregosi | 1.50 |
| 98 | Bill Bruton | 1.50 |
| 99 | Al Stanek | 1.50 |
| 100 | Elston Howard | 5.00 |

| NO. | PLAYER | NR. MT. |
|---|---|---|
| 101 | Walt Alston (Mgr.) | 4.00 |
| 102 | Checklist No. 2 | 6.00 |
| 103 | Curt Flood | 3.00 |
| 104 | Art Mahaffey | 1.50 |
| 105 | Woody Held | 1.50 |
| 106 | Joe Nuxhall | 1.50 |
| 107 | White Sox Rookies: B. Howard, F. Kreutzer | 1.50 |
| 108 | John Wyatt | 1.50 |
| 109 | Rusty Staub | 7.00 |
| 110 | Albie Pearson | 1.50 |
| 111 | Don Elston | 1.50 |
| 112 | Bob Tillman | 1.50 |
| 113 | Grover Powell | 1.50 |
| 114 | Don Lock | 1.50 |
| 115 | Frank Bolling | 1.50 |
| 116 | Twins Rookies: Jay Ward, Tony Oliva | 12.00 |
| 117 | Earl Francis | 1.50 |
| 118 | John Blanchard | 1.50 |
| 119 | Gary Kolb | 1.50 |
| 120 | Don Drysdale | 18.00 |
| 121 | Pete Runnels | 1.50 |
| 122 | Don McMahon | 1.50 |
| 123 | Jose Pagan | 1.50 |
| 124 | Orlando Pena | 1.50 |
| 125 | Pete Rose | 175.00 |
| 126 | Russ Snyder | 1.50 |
| 127 | Angels Rookies: Dick Simpson, Aubrey Gatewood | 1.50 |
| 128 | Mickey Lolich (R) | 12.00 |
| 129 | Amado Samuel | 1.50 |
| 130 | Gary Peters | 1.50 |
| 131 | Steve Boros | 1.50 |
| 132 | Milwaukee Braves | 3.00 |
| 133 | Jim Grant | 1.50 |
| 134 | Don Zimmer | 2.00 |
| 135 | Johnny Callison | 1.50 |
| 136 | World Series Game 1 Koufax Strikes Out 15 | 11.00 |
| 137 | World Series Game 2 Davis Sparks Rally | 4.00 |
| 138 | World Series Game 3 LA Takes 3 Straight | 4.00 |
| 139 | World Series Game 4 Sealing Yanks' Doom | 4.00 |
| 140 | World Series Dodgers Celebrate | 4.00 |
| 141 | Danny Murtaugh (Mgr.) | 1.50 |
| 142 | John Bateman | 1.50 |
| 143 | Bubba Phillips | 1.50 |
| 144 | Al Worthington | 1.50 |
| 145 | Norm Siebern | 1.50 |
| 146 | Indians Rookies: Tommy John, Bob Chance | 50.00 |
| 147 | Ray Sadecki | 1.50 |
| 148 | J.C. Martin | 1.50 |
| 149 | Paul Foytack | 1.50 |
| 150 | Willie Mays | 85.00 |
| 151 | K.C. Athletics | 3.00 |
| 152 | Denver LeMaster | 1.50 |
| 153 | Dick Williams | 1.50 |
| 154 | Dick Tracewski | 1.50 |
| 155 | Duke Snider | 30.00 |
| 156 | Bill Dailey | 1.50 |

| NO. | PLAYER | NR. MT. |
|---|---|---|
| 157 | Gene Mauch | 1.50 |
| 158 | Ken Johnson | 1.50 |
| 159 | Charlie Dees | 1.50 |
| 160 | Ken Boyer | 5.00 |
| 161 | Dave McNally | 1.50 |
| 162 | Hitting Area: Dick Sisler, Vada Pinson | 1.50 |
| 163 | Donn Clendenon | 1.50 |
| 164 | Bud Daley | 1.50 |
| 165 | Jerry Lumpe | 1.50 |
| 166 | Marty Keough | 1.50 |
| 167 | Senators Rookies: Mike Brumley, Lou Piniella | 25.00 |
| 168 | Al Weis | 1.50 |
| 169 | Del Crandall | 1.50 |
| 170 | Dick Radatz | 1.50 |
| 171 | Ty Cline | 1.50 |
| 172 | Cleveland Indians | 3.00 |
| 173 | Ryne Duren | 1.50 |
| 174 | Doc Edwards | 1.50 |
| 175 | Billy Williams | 15.00 |
| 176 | Tracy Stallard | 1.50 |
| 177 | Harmon Killebrew | 17.00 |
| 178 | Hank Bauer (Mgr.) | 1.50 |
| 179 | Carl Warwick | 1.50 |
| 180 | Tommy Davis | 1.50 |
| 181 | Dave Wickersham | 1.50 |
| 182 | Sox Sockers: C. Schilling, C. Yastrzemski | 10.00 |
| 183 | Ron Taylor | 1.50 |
| 184 | Al Luplow | 1.50 |
| 185 | Jim O'Toole | 1.50 |
| 186 | Roman Mejias | 1.50 |
| 187 | Ed Roebuck | 1.50 |
| 188 | Checklist No. 3 | 5.00 |
| 189 | Bob Hendley | 1.50 |
| 190 | Bobby Richardson | 5.00 |
| 191 | Clay Dalrymple | 1.50 |
| 192 | Cubs Rookies: J. Boccabella, B. Cowan | 1.50 |
| 193 | Jerry Lynch | 1.50 |
| 194 | John Goryl | 1.50 |
| 195 | Floyd Robinson | 1.50 |
| 196 | Jim Gentile | 1.50 |
| 197 | Frank Lary | 2.50 |
| 198 | Len Gabrielson | 2.50 |
| 199 | Joe Azcue | 2.50 |
| 200 | Sandy Koufax | 85.00 |
| 201 | Orioles Rookies: Wally Bunker, Sam Bowens | 2.50 |
| 202 | Galen Cisco | 2.50 |
| 203 | John Kennedy | 2.50 |
| 204 | Matty Alou | 2.50 |
| 205 | Nellie Fox | 4.00 |
| 206 | Steve Hamilton | 2.50 |
| 207 | Fred Hutchinson (Mgr.) | 2.50 |
| 208 | Wes Covington | 2.50 |
| 209 | Bob Allen | 2.50 |
| 210 | Carl Yastrzemski | 80.00 |
| 211 | Jim Coker | 2.50 |
| 212 | Pete Lovrich | 2.50 |
| 213 | L.A. Angels | 4.00 |
| 214 | Ken McMullen | 2.50 |
| 215 | Ray Herbert | 2.50 |
| 216 | Mike De La Hoz | 2.50 |
| 217 | Jim King | 2.50 |

| NO. | PLAYER | NR. MT. |
|---|---|---|
| 218 | Hank Fischer | 2.50 |
| 219 | Young Aces: | 3.00 |
|  | Al Downing, Jim Bouton | |
| 220 | Dick Ellsworth | 2.50 |
| 221 | Bob Saverine | 2.50 |
| 222 | Bill Pierce | 3.00 |
| 223 | George Banks | 2.50 |
| 224 | Tommie Sisk | 2.50 |
| 225 | Roger Maris | 60.00 |
| 226 | Colts Rookies: | 3.00 |
|  | Gerald Grote, Larry Yellen | |
| 227 | Barry Latman | 2.50 |
| 228 | Felix Mantilla | 2.50 |
| 229 | Charley Lau | 2.50 |
| 230 | Brooks Robinson | 30.00 |
| 231 | Dick Calmus | 2.50 |
| 232 | Al Lopez (Mgr.) | 3.00 |
| 233 | Hal Smith | 2.50 |
| 234 | Gary Bell | 2.50 |
| 235 | Ron Hunt | 2.50 |
| 236 | Bill Faul | 2.50 |
| 237 | Chicago Cubs | 3.50 |
| 238 | Roy McMillan | 2.50 |
| 239 | Herm Starrette | 2.50 |
| 240 | Bill White | 3.00 |
| 241 | Jim Owens | 2.50 |
| 242 | Harvey Kuenn | 2.50 |
| 243 | Phillies Rookies (R) | 12.00 |
|  | Richie Allen, J. Herrnstein | |
| 244 | Tony LaRussa (R) | 15.00 |
| 245 | Dick Stigman | 2.50 |
| 246 | Manny Mota | 3.00 |
| 247 | Dave DeBusschere | 3.50 |
| 248 | Johnny Pesky | 2.50 |
| 249 | Doug Camilli | 2.50 |
| 250 | Al Kaline | 25.00 |
| 251 | Choo Choo Coleman | 2.50 |
| 252 | Ken Aspromonte | 2.50 |
| 253 | Wally Post | 2.50 |
| 254 | Don Hoak | 2.50 |
| 255 | Lee Thomas | 2.50 |
| 256 | Johnny Weekly | 2.50 |
| 257 | San F. Giants | 4.00 |
| 258 | Garry Roggenburk | 2.50 |
| 259 | Harry Bright | 2.50 |
| 260 | Frank Robinson | 25.00 |
| 261 | Jim Hannan | 2.50 |
| 262 | Cardinals Rookies: | 5.00 |
|  | Harry Fanok, Mike Shannon | |
| 263 | Chuck Estrada | 2.50 |
| 264 | Jim Lndis | 2.50 |
| 265 | Jim Bunning | 5.00 |
| 266 | Gene Freese | 2.50 |
| 267 | Wilbur Wood | 2.50 |
| 268 | Bill's Got It: | 2.50 |
|  | Bill Virdon, D. Murtaugh | |
| 269 | Ellis Burton | 2.50 |
| 270 | Rich Rollins | 2.50 |
| 271 | Bob Sadowski | 2.50 |
| 272 | Jake Wood | 2.50 |
| 273 | Mel Nelson | 2.50 |
| 274 | Checklist No. 4 | 5.00 |
| 275 | John Tsitouris | 2.50 |
| 276 | Jose Tartabull | 2.50 |
| 277 | Ken Retzer | 2.50 |
| 278 | Bobby Shantz | 2.50 |
| 279 | Joe Koppe | 2.50 |
| 280 | Juan Marichal | 11.00 |
| 281 | Yankees Rookies: | 2.50 |
|  | Jake Gibbs, Tom Metcalf | |
| 282 | Bob Bruce | 2.50 |
| 283 | Tommy McCraw | 2.50 |
| 284 | Dick Schofield | 2.50 |
| 285 | Robin Roberts | 9.00 |
| 286 | Don Landrum | 2.50 |
| 287 | Red Sox Rookies: | 20.00 |
|  | T. Conigliaro, B. Spanswick | |
| 288 | Al Moran | 2.50 |
| 289 | Frank Funk | 2.50 |
| 290 | Bob Allison | 2.50 |
| 291 | Phil Ortega | 2.50 |
| 292 | Mike Roarke | 2.50 |
| 293 | Philadelphia Phillies | 4.00 |
| 294 | Ken Hunt | 2.50 |
| 295 | Roger Craig | 2.50 |
| 296 | Ed Kirkpatrick | 2.50 |
| 297 | Ken MacKenzie | 2.50 |
| 298 | Harry Craft (Mgr.) | 2.50 |
| 299 | Bill Stafford | 2.50 |
| 300 | Hank Aaron | 90.00 |
| 301 | Larry Brown | 2.50 |
| 302 | Dan Pfister | 2.50 |
| 303 | Jim Campbell | 2.50 |
| 304 | Bob Johnson | 2.50 |
| 305 | Jack Lamabe | 2.50 |
| 306 | Giant Gunners: | 17.50 |
|  | Willie Mays, O. Cepeda | |
| 307 | Joe Gibbon | 2.50 |
| 308 | Gene Stephens | 2.50 |
| 309 | Paul Toth | 2.50 |
| 310 | Jim Gilliam | 3.00 |
| 311 | Tom Brown | 2.50 |
| 312 | Tigers Rookies: | 2.50 |
|  | Fred Gladding, Fritz Fisher | |
| 313 | Chuck Hiller | 2.50 |
| 314 | Jerry Buchek | 2.50 |
| 315 | Bo Belinsky | 2.50 |
| 316 | Gene Oliver | 2.50 |
| 317 | Al Smith | 2.50 |
| 318 | Minnesota Twins | 4.00 |
| 319 | Paul Brown | 2.50 |
| 320 | Rocky Colavito | 6.00 |
| 321 | Bob Lillis | 2.50 |
| 322 | George Brunet | 2.50 |
| 323 | John Buzhardt | 2.50 |
| 324 | Casey Stengel (Mgr.) | 12.00 |
| 325 | Hector Lopez | 2.50 |
| 326 | Ron Brand | 2.50 |
| 327 | Don Blasingame | 2.50 |
| 328 | Bob Shaw | 2.50 |
| 329 | Russ Nixon | 2.50 |
| 330 | Tommy Harper | 2.50 |
| 331 | AL Bombers: | 85.00 |
|  | Mickey Mantle, R. Maris, | |
|  | Norm Cash, Al Kaline | |
| 332 | Ray Washburn | 2.50 |
| 333 | Billy Moran | 2.50 |
| 334 | Lew Krausse | 2.50 |
| 335 | Don Mossi | 2.50 |
| 336 | Andre Rodgers | 2.50 |
| 337 | Dodgers Rookies: | 6.00 |
|  | Al Ferrara, Jeff Torborg | |
| 338 | Jack Kralick | 2.50 |
| 339 | Walt Bond | 2.50 |
| 340 | Joe Cunningham | 2.50 |
| 341 | Jim Roland | 2.50 |
| 342 | Willie Stargell | 45.00 |
| 343 | Washington Senators | 3.00 |
| 344 | Phil Linz | 2.50 |
| 345 | Frank Thomas | 2.50 |
| 346 | Joe Jay | 2.50 |
| 347 | Bobby Wine | 2.50 |
| 348 | Ed Lopat | 3.00 |
| 349 | Art Fowler | 2.50 |
| 350 | Willie McCovey | 25.00 |
| 351 | Dan Schneider | 2.50 |
| 352 | Eddie Bressoud | 2.50 |
| 353 | Wally Moon | 2.50 |
| 354 | Dave Giusti | 2.50 |
| 355 | Vic Power | 2.50 |
| 356 | Reds Rookies: | 2.50 |
|  | Bill McCool, Chico Ruiz | |
| 357 | Charley James | 2.50 |
| 358 | Ron Kline | 2.50 |
| 359 | Jim Schaffer | 2.50 |
| 360 | Joe Pepitone | 3.00 |
| 361 | Jay Hook | 2.50 |
| 362 | Checklist No. 5 | 5.00 |
| 363 | Dick McAuliffe | 2.50 |
| 364 | Joe Gaines | 2.50 |
| 365 | Cal McLish | 2.50 |
| 366 | Nelson Mathews | 2.50 |
| 367 | Fred Whitfield | 2.50 |
| 368 | White Sox Rookies: | 2.50 |
|  | Fritz Ackley, Don Buford | |
| 369 | Jerry Zimmerman | 2.50 |
| 370 | Hal Woodeschick | 2.50 |
| 371 | Frank Howard | 4.00 |
| 372 | Howie Koplitz | 4.00 |
| 373 | Pittsburgh Pirates | 6.00 |
| 374 | Bobby Bolin | 4.00 |
| 375 | Ron Santo | 6.00 |
| 376 | Dave Morehead | 4.00 |
| 377 | Bob Skinner | 4.00 |
| 378 | Braves Rookies: | 4.00 |
|  | W. Woodward, Jack Smith | |
| 379 | Tony Gonzalez | 4.00 |
| 380 | Whitey Ford | 28.00 |
| 381 | Bob Taylor | 4.00 |
| 382 | Wes Stock | 4.00 |
| 383 | Bill Rigney (Mgr.) | 4.00 |
| 384 | Ron Hansen | 4.00 |
| 385 | Curt Simmons | 4.00 |
| 386 | Lenny Green | 4.00 |
| 387 | Terry Fox | 4.00 |
| 388 | A's Rookies: | 4.00 |
|  | G. Williams, J. O'Donoghue | |
| 389 | Jim Umbricht | 4.00 |
| 390 | Orlando Cepeda | 7.00 |
| 391 | Sam McDowell | 4.00 |
| 392 | Jim Pagliaroni | 5.00 |
| 393 | Casey Teaches: | 4.00 |
|  | C. Stengel, Ed Kranepool | |
| 394 | Bob Miller | 4.00 |
| 395 | Tom Tresh | 4.00 |
| 396 | Dennis Bennett | 4.00 |
| 397 | Chuck Cottier | 4.00 |
| 398 | Mets Rookies: | 4.00 |
|  | Bill Haas, Dick Smith | |
| 399 | Jackie Brandt | 4.00 |
| 400 | Warren Spahn | 25.00 |
| 401 | Charlie Maxwell | 4.00 |
| 402 | Tom Sturdivant | 4.00 |
| 403 | Cincinnati Reds | 6.00 |
| 404 | Tony Martinez | 4.00 |
| 405 | Ken McBride | 4.00 |
| 406 | Al Spangler | 4.00 |
| 407 | Bill Freehan | 5.00 |
| 408 | Cubs Rookies: | 4.00 |
|  | Jim Stewart, Fred Burdette | |
| 409 | Bill Fischer | 4.00 |
| 410 | Dick Stuart | 4.00 |
| 411 | Lee Walls | 4.00 |
| 412 | Ray Culp | 4.00 |
| 413 | Johnny Keane (Mgr.) | 4.00 |
| 414 | Jack Sanford | 4.00 |
| 415 | Tony Kubek | 7.00 |
| 416 | Lee Maye | 4.00 |
| 417 | Don Cardwell | 4.00 |
| 418 | Orioles Rookies: | 4.00 |
|  | Les Narum, D. Knowles | |
| 419 | Ken Harrelson (R) | 7.00 |
| 420 | Jim Maloney | 4.00 |
| 421 | Camilo Carreon | 4.00 |
| 422 | Jack Fisher | 4.00 |
| 423 | Tops in N.L.: | 75.00 |
|  | Hank Aaron, Willie Mays | |
| 424 | Dick Bertell | 4.00 |
| 425 | Norm Cash | 5.00 |
| 426 | Bob Rodgers | 4.00 |
| 427 | Don Rudolph | 4.00 |
| 428 | Red Sox Rookies: | 4.00 |
|  | Archie Skeen, Pete Smith | |
| 429 | Tim McCarver | 8.00 |
| 430 | Juan Pizarro | 4.00 |
| 431 | George Alusik | 4.00 |
| 432 | Ruben Amaro | 4.00 |
| 433 | New York Yankees | 12.00 |
| 434 | Don Nottebart | 4.00 |
| 435 | Vic Davalillo | 4.00 |
| 436 | Charlie Neal | 4.00 |
| 437 | Ed Bailey | 4.00 |
| 438 | Checklist No. 6 | 6.00 |
| 439 | Harvey Haddix | 4.50 |
| 440 | Bob Clemente | 120.00 |
| 441 | Bob Duliba | 4.00 |
| 442 | Pumpsie Green | 4.00 |
| 443 | Chuck Dressen (Mgr.) | 4.00 |
| 444 | Larry Jackson | 4.00 |
| 445 | Bill Skowron | 5.00 |
| 446 | Julian Javier | 4.00 |
| 447 | Ted Bowsfield | 4.00 |
| 448 | Cookie Rojas | 4.00 |
| 449 | Deron Johnson | 4.00 |
| 450 | Steve Barber | 4.00 |
| 451 | Joe Amalfitano | 4.00 |
| 452 | Giants Rookies: | 5.00 |
|  | Gil Garrido, Jim Hart | |
| 453 | Frank Baumann | 4.00 |
| 454 | Tommie Aaron | 4.00 |
| 455 | Bernie Allen | 4.00 |
| 456 | Dodgers Rookies: | 5.00 |
|  | John Werhas, Wes Parker | |
| 457 | Jesse Gonder | 4.00 |
| 458 | Ralph Terry | 4.00 |
| 459 | Red Sox Rookies: | 4.00 |
|  | Pete Charton, D. Jones | |
| 460 | Bob Gibson | 30.00 |
| 461 | George Thomas | 4.00 |
| 462 | Birdie Tebbetts | 4.00 |
| 463 | Don Leppert | 4.00 |
| 464 | Dallas Green | 5.00 |
| 465 | Mike Hershberger | 4.00 |
| 466 | A's Rookies: | 4.00 |
|  | D. Green, A. Monteagudo | |
| 467 | Bob Aspromonte | 4.00 |
| 468 | Gaylord Perry | 40.00 |
| 469 | Cubs Rookies: | 4.00 |
|  | S. Slaughter, Fred Norman | |
| 470 | Jim Bouton | 5.00 |
| 471 | Gates Brown (R) | 5.00 |
| 472 | Vern Law | 5.00 |
| 473 | Baltimore Orioles | 6.00 |
| 474 | Larry Sherry | 4.00 |
| 475 | Ed Charles | 4.00 |
| 476 | Braves Rookies: | 8.00 |
|  | Rico Carty, Dick Kelley | |
| 477 | Mike Joyce | 4.00 |
| 478 | Dick Howser | 5.00 |
| 479 | Cardinals Rookies: | 4.00 |
|  | D. Bakenhaster, J. Lewis | |
| 480 | Bob Purkey | 4.00 |
| 481 | Chuck Schilling | 4.00 |
| 482 | Phillies Rookies: | 4.00 |
|  | John Briggs, Danny Cater | |
| 483 | Fred Valentine | 4.00 |
| 484 | Bill Pleis | 4.00 |
| 485 | Tom Haller | 4.00 |
| 486 | Bob Kennedy | 4.00 |
| 487 | Mike McCormick | 4.00 |
| 488 | Yankees Rookies: | 4.00 |
|  | Pete Mikkelsen, Bob Meyer | |
| 489 | Julio Navarro | 4.00 |
| 490 | Ron Fairly | 4.00 |
| 491 | Ed Rakow | 4.00 |
| 492 | Colts Rookies: | 4.00 |
|  | Jim Beauchamp, M. White | |
| 493 | Don Lee | 4.00 |
| 494 | Al Jackson | 4.00 |
| 495 | Bill Virdon | 2.50 |
| 496 | Chicago White Sox | 6.00 |
| 497 | Jeoff Long | 4.00 |
| 498 | Dave Stenhouse | 4.00 |
| 499 | Indians Rookies: | 4.00 |
|  | Chico Salmon, G. Seyfried | |
| 500 | Camilo Pascual | 4.00 |
| 501 | Bob Veale | 4.00 |
| 502 | Angels Rookies: | 4.00 |
|  | Bobby Knoop, Bob Lee | |
| 503 | Earl Wilson | 4.00 |
| 504 | Claude Raymond | 4.00 |
| 505 | Stan Williams | 4.00 |
| 506 | Bobby Bragan (Mgr.) | 4.00 |
| 507 | John Edwards | 4.00 |

| NO. PLAYER | NR. MT. | NO. PLAYER | NR. MT. | NO. PLAYER | NR. MT. | NO. PLAYER | NR. MT. |
|---|---|---|---|---|---|---|---|
| 508 Diego Segui | 4.00 | 529 Al Dark | 8.00 | 549 Joe Moeller | 8.00 | 568 NL Rookies: | 8.00 |
| 509 Pirates Rookies: | 5.00 | 530 Leon Wagner | 8.00 | 550 Ken Hubbs | 20.00 | Phil Gagliano, Cap Peterson | |
| Gene Alley, O. McFarlane | | 531 L.A. Dodgers | 18.00 | (In Memoriam) | | 569 Fred Newman | 8.00 |
| 510 Lindy McDaniel | 4.00 | 532 Twins Rookies: | 8.00 | 551 Billy Hoeft | 8.00 | 570 Bill Mazeroski | 10.00 |
| 511 Lou Jackson | 4.00 | Bud Bloomfield (wrong | | 552 Indians Rookies: | 8.00 | 571 Gene Conley | 8.00 |
| 512 Tigers Rookies: | 9.00 | photo), Joe Nossek | | Tom Kelley, Sonny Siebert | | 572 AL Rookies: | 8.00 |
| Joe Sparma, Willie Horton | | 533 John Klippstein | 8.00 | 553 Jim Brewer | 8.00 | Dave Gray, Dick Egan | |
| 513 Don Larsen | 5.00 | 534 Gus Bell | 8.00 | 554 Hank Foiles | 8.00 | 573 Jim Duffalo | 8.00 |
| 514 Jim Hickman | 4.00 | 535 Phil Regan | 8.00 | 555 Lee Stange | 8.00 | 574 Manny Jimenez | 8.00 |
| 515 Johnny Romano | 4.00 | 536 Mets Rookies: | 8.00 | 556 Mets Rookies: | 8.00 | 575 Tony Cloninger | 8.00 |
| 516 Twins Rookies: | 4.00 | Larry Elliot, J. Stephenson | | Steve Dillon, Ron Locke | | 576 Mets Rookies: | 8.00 |
| Dwight Siebler, Jerry Arrigo | | 537 Dan Osinski | 8.00 | 557 Leo Burke | 8.00 | J. Hinsley, Bill Wakefield | |
| 517 Checklist No. 7 | 10.00 | 538 Minnie Minoso | 10.00 | 558 Don Schwall | 8.00 | 577 Gordy Coleman | 8.00 |
| 518 Carl Bouldin | 4.00 | 539 Roy Face | 8.00 | 559 Dick Phillips | 8.00 | 578 Glen Hobbie | 8.00 |
| 519 Charlie Smith | 4.00 | 540 Luis Aparicio | 20.00 | 560 Dick Farrell | 8.00 | 579 Boston Red Sox | 15.00 |
| 520 Jack Baldschun | 4.00 | 541 Braves Rookies: | 175.00 | 561 Phillies Rookies: | 10.00 | 580 Johnny Podres | 10.00 |
| 521 Tom Satriano | 4.00 | Phil Niekro, Phil Roof | | Dave Bennett, Rick Wise | | 581 Yankees Rookies: | 8.00 |
| 522 Bobby Tiefenauer | 4.00 | 542 Don Mincher | 8.00 | 562 Pedro Ramos | 8.00 | P. Gonzalez, Archie Moore | |
| 523 Lou Burdette | 9.00 | 543 Bob Uecker | 55.00 | 563 Dal Maxvill | 8.00 | 582 Rod Kanehl | 8.00 |
| 524 Reds Rookies: | 8.00 | 544 Colts Rookies: | 8.00 | 564 AL Rookies: | 8.00 | 583 Tito Francona | 8.00 |
| Jim Dickson, Bobby Klaus | | Steve Hertz, Joe Hoerner | | Joe McCabe, J. McNertney | | 584 Joel Horlen | 8.00 |
| 525 Al McBean | 8.00 | 545 Max Alvis | 8.00 | 565 Stu Miller | 8.00 | 585 Tony Taylor | 8.00 |
| 526 Lou Clinton | 8.00 | 546 Joe Christopher | 8.00 | 566 Ed Kranepool | 8.00 | 586 Jim Piersall | 10.00 |
| 527 Larry Bearnarth | 8.00 | 547 Gil Hodges (Mgr.) | 15.00 | 567 Jim Kaat | 11.00 | 587 Bennie Daniels (exc. $3.00) | 12.00 |
| 528 A's Rookies: | 8.00 | 548 NL Rookies: | 8.00 | | | | |
| D. Duncan, Tom Reynolds | | W. Schurr, P. Speckenbach | | | | | |

## 1965 Topps . . . Complete Set of 598 Cards—Value $1450.00 (Exc.); $3250.00 (Near Mint)

This set includes the rookie cards of Steve Carlton, Joe Morgan, Tony Perez and "Catfish" Hunter. Cards 523 to 598 are the high numbers. Semi-high numbers are 447 to 522.

| NO. PLAYER | NR. MT. | NO. PLAYER | NR. MT. | NO. PLAYER | NR. MT. | NO. PLAYER | NR. MT. |
|---|---|---|---|---|---|---|---|
| 1 AL Bat Ldrs.: (exc. $1.50) | 15.00 | 11 AL Strikeout Leaders: | 2.00 | 37 Fred Gladding | 1.25 | 66 Bill Rigney | 1.25 |
| Elston Howard, Tony Oliva, | | A. Downing, D. Chance, | | 38 Jim King | 1.25 | 67 Harvey Haddix | 1.25 |
| Brooks Robinson | | C. Pascual | | 39 Gerry Arrigo | 1.25 | 68 Del Crandall | 1.25 |
| 2 NL Batting Leaders: | 7.00 | 12 NL Strikeout Leaders: | 3.00 | 40 Frank Howard | 2.50 | 69 Bill Virdon | 1.50 |
| Hank Aaron, Bob Clemente, | | Bob Gibson, B. Veale, | | 41 White Sox Rookies: | 1.25 | 70 Bill Skowron | 2.00 |
| Rico Carty | | Don Drysdale | | Bruce Howard, Marv Staehle | | 71 John O'Donoghue | 1.25 |
| 3 AL Home Run Leaders: | 12.00 | 13 Pedro Ramos | 1.25 | 42 Earl Wilson | 1.25 | 72 Tony Gonzalez | 1.25 |
| Boog Powell, Harmon | | 14 Len Gabrielson | 1.25 | 43 Mike Shannon | 1.25 | 73 Dennis Ribant | 1.25 |
| Killebrew, Mickey Mantle | | 15 Robin Roberts | 7.50 | 44 Wade Blasingame | 1.25 | 74 Red Sox Rookies: | 5.00 |
| 4 NL Home Run Leaders: | 6.00 | 16 Houston Rookies: | 175.00 | 45 Roy McMillan | 1.25 | R. Petrocelli, J. Stephenson | |
| Willie Mays, Billy Williams, | | Joe Morgan, Sonny Jackson | | 46 Bob Lee | 1.25 | 75 Deron Johnson | 1.25 |
| Johnny Callison, Jim Hart, | | 17 John Romano | 1.25 | 47 Tommy Harper | 1.25 | 76 Sam McDowell | 1.50 |
| Orlando Cepeda | | 18 Bill McCool | 1.25 | 48 Claude Raymond | 1.25 | 77 Doug Camilli | 1.25 |
| 5 AL RBI Leaders: | 10.00 | 19 Gates Brown | 1.25 | 49 Orioles Rookies: | 3.00 | 78 Dal Maxvill | 1.25 |
| Brooks Robinson, Dick | | 20 Jim Bunning | 4.00 | John Miller, Curt Blefary | | 79 Checklist No. 1 | 5.00 |
| Stuart, Harmon Killebrew, | | 21 Don Blasingame | 1.25 | 50 Juan Marical | 10.00 | 80 Turk Farrell | 1.25 |
| Mickey Mantle | | 22 Charlie Smith | 1.25 | 51 Billy Bryan | 1.25 | 81 Don Buford | 1.25 |
| 6 NL RBI Leaders: | 4.00 | 23 Bob Tiefenauer | 1.25 | 52 Ed Roebuck | 1.25 | 82 Braves Rookies: | 1.25 |
| Ken Boyer, Willie Mays, | | 24 Twins—6th Place | 3.00 | 53 Dick McAuliffe | 1.25 | Santos Alomar, John Braun | |
| Ron Santo | | 25 Al McBeane | 1.25 | 54 Joe Gibbon | 1.25 | 83 George Thomas | 1.25 |
| 7 AL ERA Leaders: | 2.50 | 26 Bob Knoop | 1.25 | 55 Tony Conigliaro | 7.00 | 84 Ron Herbel | 1.25 |
| Dean Chance, Joel Horlen | | 27 Dick Bertell | 1.25 | 56 Ron Kline | 1.25 | 85 Willie Smith | 1.25 |
| 8 NL ERA Leaders: | 6.00 | 28 Barney Schultz | 1.25 | 57 Cardinals—1st Place | 3.00 | 86 Les Narum | 1.25 |
| S. Koufax, Don Drysdale | | 29 Felix Mantilla | 1.25 | 58 Fred Talbot | 1.25 | 87 Nelson Mathews | 1.25 |
| 9 AL Pitching Leaders: | 2.00 | 30 Jim Bouton | 2.50 | 59 Nate Oiver | 1.25 | 88 Jack Lamabe | 1.25 |
| D. Chance, G. Peters, | | 31 Mike White | 1.25 | 60 Jim O'Toole | 1.25 | 89 Mike Hershberger | 1.25 |
| J. Pizarro, W. Bunker, | | 32 Herman Franks | 1.25 | 61 Chris Cannizzaro | 1.25 | 90 Rich Rollins | 1.25 |
| D. Wickersham | | 33 Jackie Brandt | 1.25 | 62 Jim Kaat | 5.00 | 91 Cubs—8th Place | 3.00 |
| 10 NL Pitching Leaders: | 2.00 | 34 Cal Koonce | 1.25 | 63 Ty Cline | 1.25 | 92 Dick Howser | 2.00 |
| L. Jackson, Juan Marichal, | | 35 Ed Charles | 1.25 | 64 Lou Burdette | 2.50 | 93 Jack Fisher | 1.25 |
| Ray Sadecki | | 36 Bobby Wine | 1.25 | 65 Tony Kubek | 3.50 | 94 Charlie Lau | 1.25 |

| NO. PLAYER | NR. MT. |
|---|---|
| 95 Bill Mazeroski | 3.00 |
| 96 Sonny Siebert | 1.25 |
| 97 Pedro Gonzalez | 1.25 |
| 98 Bob Miller | 1.25 |
| 99 Gil Hodges | 6.00 |
| 100 Ken Boyer | 3.00 |
| 101 Fred Newman | 1.25 |
| 102 Steve Boros | 1.25 |
| 103 Harvey Kuenn | 1.50 |
| 104 Checklist No. 2 | 5.00 |
| 105 Chico Salmon | 1.25 |
| 106 Gene Oliver | 1.25 |
| 107 Phillies Rookies: | 2.00 |
| C. Shockley, Pat Corrales | |
| 108 Don Mincher | 1.25 |
| 109 Walt Bond | 1.25 |
| 110 Ron Santo | 3.00 |
| 111 Lee Thomas | 1.25 |
| 112 Derrell Griffith | 1.25 |
| 113 Steve Barber | 1.25 |
| 114 Jim Hickman | 1.25 |
| 115 Bob Richardson | 3.00 |
| 116 Cardinals Rookies: | 2.00 |
| Dave Dowling, Bob Tolan | |
| 117 Wes Stock | 1.25 |
| 118 Hal Lanier (R) | 1.50 |
| 119 John Kennedy | 1.25 |
| 120 Frank Robinson | 22.00 |
| 121 Gene Alley | 1.25 |
| 122 Bill Pleis | 1.25 |
| 123 Frank Thomas | 1.25 |
| 124 Tom Satriano | 1.25 |
| 125 Juan Pizarro | 1.25 |
| 126 Dodgers—6th Place | 4.00 |
| 127 Frank Lary | 1.25 |
| 128 Vic Davalillo | 1.25 |
| 129 Bennie Daniels | 1.25 |
| 130 Al Kaline | 25.00 |
| 131 Johnny Keane (Mgr.) | .75 |
| 132 World Series Game 1 | 3.00 |
| Cards Take Opener | |
| 133 World Series Game 2 | 3.00 |
| Stottlemyre Wins | |
| 134 World Series Game 3 | 25.00 |
| Mantle's Clutch Homer | |
| 135 World Series Game 4 | 3.00 |
| Boyer's Grand-Slam | |
| 136 World Series Game 5 | 3.00 |
| 10th Inning Triumph | |
| 137 World Series Game 6 | 3.00 |
| Bouton Wins Again | |
| 138 World Series Game 7 | 7.00 |
| Gibson Wins Finale | |
| 139 World Series | 4.00 |
| The Cards Celebrate | |
| 140 Dean Chance | 1.25 |
| 141 Charlie James | 1.25 |
| 142 Bill Monouquette | 1.25 |
| 143 Pirates Rookies: | 1.25 |
| John Gelnar, Jerry Ma | |
| 144 Ed Kranepool | 1.25 |
| 145 Luis Tiant (R) | 10.00 |
| 146 Ron Hansen | 1.25 |
| 147 Dennis Bennett | 1.25 |
| 148 Willie Kirkland | 1.25 |
| 149 Wayne Schurr | 1.25 |
| 150 Brooks Robinson | 25.00 |
| 151 Athletics—10th Place | 3.00 |
| 152 Phil Ortega | 1.25 |
| 153 Norm Cash | 3.00 |
| 154 Bob Humphreys | 1.25 |
| 155 Roger Maris | 50.00 |
| 156 Bob Sadowski | 1.25 |
| 157 Zoilo Versalles | 2.00 |
| 158 Dick Sisler (Mgr.) | 1.25 |
| 159 Jim Duffalo | 1.25 |
| 160 Bob Clemente | 75.00 |
| 161 Frank Baumann | 1.25 |
| 162 Russ Nixon | 1.25 |
| 163 John Briggs | 1.25 |
| 164 Al Spangler | 1.25 |
| 165 Dick Ellsworth | 1.25 |
| 166 Indians Rookies: | 2.00 |
| G. Culver, Tommie Age | |
| 167 Bill Wakefield | 1.25 |

| NO. PLAYER | NR. MT. |
|---|---|
| 168 Dick Green | 1.25 |
| 169 Dave Vineyard | 1.25 |
| 170 Hank Aaron | 80.00 |
| 171 Jim Roland | 1.25 |
| 172 Jim Piersall | 2.00 |
| 173 Tigers—4th Place | 3.00 |
| 174 Joe Jay | 1.25 |
| 175 Bob Aspromonte | 1.25 |
| 176 Willie McCovey | 18.00 |
| 177 Pete Mikkelsen | 1.25 |
| 178 Dalton Jones | 1.25 |
| 179 Hal Woodeschick | 1.25 |
| 180 Bob Allison | 1.50 |
| 181 Senators Rookies: | 1.25 |
| Don Loun, Joe McCabe | |
| 182 Mike De La Hoz | 1.25 |
| 183 Dave Nicholson | 1.25 |
| 184 John Boozer | 1.25 |
| 185 Max Alvis | 1.25 |
| 186 Bill Cowan | 1.25 |
| 187 Casey Stengel (Mgr.) | 12.00 |
| 188 Sam Bowens | 1.25 |
| 189 Checklist No. 3 | 5.00 |
| 190 Bill White | 3.00 |
| 191 Phil Regan | 1.25 |
| 192 Jim Coker | 1.25 |
| 193 Gaylord Perry | 16.00 |
| 194 Angels Rookies: | 1.25 |
| Rick Reichardt, Bill Kelso | |
| 195 Bob Veale | 1.25 |
| 196 Ron Fairly | 1.25 |
| 197 Diego Segui | 1.50 |
| 198 Smoky Burgess | 1.50 |
| 199 Bob Heffner | 1.50 |
| 200 Joe Torre | 3.00 |
| 201 Twins Rookies: | 2.00 |
| S. Valdespino, Cesar Tovar | |
| 202 Leo Burke | 1.50 |
| 203 Dallas Green | 2.50 |
| 204 Russ Snyder | 1.50 |
| 205 Warren Spahn | 20.00 |
| 206 Willie Horton | 2.00 |
| 207 Pete Rose | 160.00 |
| 208 Tommy John | 11.00 |
| 209 Pirates—6th Place | 3.00 |
| 210 Jim Fregosi | 2.00 |
| 211 Steve Ridzik | 1.50 |
| 212 Ron Brand | 1.50 |
| 213 Jim Davenport | 1.50 |
| 214 Bob Purkey | 1.50 |
| 215 Pete Ward | 1.50 |
| 216 Al Worthington | 1.50 |
| 217 Walt Alston (Mgr.) | 4.00 |
| 218 Dick Schofield | 1.50 |
| 219 Bob Meyer | 1.50 |
| 220 Billy Williams | 11.00 |
| 221 John Tsitouris | 1.50 |
| 222 Bob Tillman | 1.50 |
| 223 Dan Osinski | 1.50 |
| 224 Bob Chance | 1.50 |
| 225 Bo Belinsky | 1.50 |
| 226 Yankees Rookies: | 2.00 |
| Elvio Jimenez, Jake Gibbs | |
| 227 Bobby Klaus | 1.50 |
| 228 Jack Sanford | 1.50 |
| 229 Lou Clinton | 1.50 |
| 230 Ray Sadecki | 1.50 |
| 231 Jerry Adair | 1.50 |
| 232 Steve Blass (R) | 2.00 |
| 233 Don Zimmer | 2.00 |
| 234 White Sox—2nd Place | 3.00 |
| 235 Chuck Hinton | 1.50 |
| 236 Dennis McLain (R) | 16.00 |
| 237 Bernie Allen | 1.50 |
| 238 Joe Moeller | 1.50 |
| 239 Doc Edwards | 1.50 |
| 240 Bob Bruce | 1.50 |
| 241 Mack Jones | 1.50 |
| 242 George Brunet | 1.50 |
| 243 Reds Rookies: | 2.00 |
| T. Helms, Ted Davidson | |
| 244 Lindy McDaniel | 1.50 |
| 245 Joe Pepitone | 2.00 |
| 246 Tom Butters | 1.50 |
| 247 Wally Moon | 1.50 |

| NO. PLAYER | NR. MT. |
|---|---|
| 248 Gus Triandos | 1.50 |
| 249 Dave McNally | 1.50 |
| 250 Willie Mays | 100.00 |
| 251 Billy Herman (Mgr.) | 2.50 |
| 252 Pete Richert | 1.50 |
| 253 Danny Cater | 1.50 |
| 254 Roland Sheldon | 1.50 |
| 255 Camilo Pascual | 1.50 |
| 256 Tito Francona | 1.50 |
| 257 Jim Wynn | 1.50 |
| 258 Larry Bearnarth | 1.50 |
| 259 Tigers Rookies: | 3.00 |
| Jim Northrup, Ray Oyler | |
| 260 Don Drysdale | 18.00 |
| 261 Duke Carmel | 1.50 |
| 262 Bud Daley | 1.50 |
| 263 Marty Keough | 1.50 |
| 264 Bob Buhl | 1.50 |
| 265 Jim Pagliaroni | 1.50 |
| 266 Bert Campaneris | 5.00 |
| 267 Senators—9th Place | 3.00 |
| 268 Ken McBride | 1.50 |
| 269 Frank Bolling | 1.50 |
| 270 Milt Pappas | 1.50 |
| 271 Don Wert | 1.50 |
| 272 Chuck Schilling | 1.50 |
| 273 Checklist No. 4 | 4.00 |
| 274 Lum Harris (Mgr.) | 1.50 |
| 275 Dick Groat | 1.50 |
| 276 Hoyt Wilhelm | 8.00 |
| 277 Johnny Lewis | 1.50 |
| 278 Ken Retzer | 1.50 |
| 279 Dick Tracewski | 1.50 |
| 280 Dick Stuart | 1.50 |
| 281 Bill Stafford | 1.50 |
| 282 Giants Rookies: | 3.00 |
| Dick Estelle, M. Murakami | |
| 283 Fred Whitfield | 1.50 |
| 284 Nick Willhite | 3.00 |
| 285 Ron Hunt | 3.00 |
| 286 Athletics Rookies: | 3.00 |
| J. Dickson, A. Monteagudo | |
| 287 Gary Kolb | 3.00 |
| 288 Jack Hamilton | 3.00 |
| 289 Gordy Coleman | 3.00 |
| 290 Wally Bunker | 3.00 |
| 291 Jerry Lynch | 3.00 |
| 292 Larry Yellen | 3.00 |
| 293 Angels—5th Place | 4.00 |
| 294 Tim McCarver | 5.00 |
| 295 Dick Radatz | 3.00 |
| 296 Tony Taylor | 3.00 |
| 297 Dave Debusschere | 3.50 |
| 298 Jim Stewart | 3.00 |
| 299 Jerry Zimmerman | 3.00 |
| 300 Sandy Koufax | 110.00 |
| 301 Birdie Tebbetts | 3.00 |
| 302 Al Stanek | 3.00 |
| 303 John Orsino | 3.00 |
| 304 Dave Stenhouse | 3.00 |
| 305 Rico Carty | 3.50 |
| 306 Bubba Phillips | 3.00 |
| 307 Barry Latman | 3.00 |
| 308 Mets Rookies: | 4.00 |
| Tom Parsons, Cleon Jones | |
| 309 Steve Hamilton | 3.00 |
| 310 Johnny Callison | 3.00 |
| 311 Orlando Pena | 3.00 |
| 312 Joe Nuxhall | 3.00 |
| 313 Jim Schaffer | 3.00 |
| 314 Sterling Slaughter | 3.00 |
| 315 Frank Malzone | 3.00 |
| 316 Reds—2nd Place | 5.00 |
| 317 Don McMahon | 3.00 |
| 318 Matty Alou | 3.00 |
| 319 Ken McMullen | 3.00 |
| 320 Bob Bruce | 25.00 |
| 321 Rusty Staub | 4.00 |
| 322 Rick Wise | 3.00 |
| 323 Hank Bauer (Mgr.) | 3.00 |
| 324 Bobby Locke | 3.00 |
| 325 Donn Clendenon | 3.00 |
| 326 Dwight Siebler | 3.00 |
| 327 Dennis Menke | 3.00 |
| 328 Eddie Fisher | 3.00 |

| NO. PLAYER | NR. MT. |
|---|---|
| 329 Hawk Taylor | 3.00 |
| 330 Whitey Ford | 25.00 |
| 331 Dodgers Rookies: | 3.50 |
| Al Ferrara, John Purdin | |
| 332 Ted Abernathy | 3.00 |
| 333 Tommie Reynolds | 3.00 |
| 334 Vic Roznovsky | 3.00 |
| 335 Mickey Lolich | 5.00 |
| 336 Woody Held | 3.00 |
| 337 Mike Cuellar | 3.00 |
| 338 Phillies—2nd Place | 4.00 |
| 339 Ryne Duren | 3.00 |
| 340 Tony Oliva | 8.00 |
| 341 Bobby Bolin | 3.00 |
| 342 Bob Rodgers | 3.00 |
| 343 Mike McCormick | 3.00 |
| 344 Wes Parker | 3.00 |
| 345 Floyd Robinson | 3.00 |
| 346 Bob Bragan (Mgr.) | 3.00 |
| 347 Roy Face | 3.50 |
| 348 George Banks | 3.00 |
| 349 Larry Miller | 3.00 |
| 350 Mickey Mantle | 400.00 |
| 351 Jim Perry | 4.00 |
| 352 Alex Johnson | 3.00 |
| 353 Jerry Lumpe | 3.00 |
| 354 Cubs Rookies: | 3.00 |
| Billy Ott, Jack Warner | |
| 355 Vada Pinson | 3.00 |
| 356 Bill Spanswick | 3.00 |
| 357 Carl Warwick | 3.00 |
| 358 Albie Pearson | 3.00 |
| 359 Ken Johnson | 3.00 |
| 360 Orlando Cepeda | 7.00 |
| 361 Checklist No. 5 | 4.00 |
| 362 Don Schwall | 3.00 |
| 363 Bob Johnson | 3.00 |
| 364 Galen Cisco | 3.00 |
| 365 Jim Gentile | 3.00 |
| 366 Dan Schneider | 3.00 |
| 367 Leon Wagner | 3.00 |
| 368 White Sox Rookies: | 3.50 |
| Ken Berry, Joel Gibson | |
| 369 Phil Linz | 3.00 |
| 370 Tommy Davis | 3.50 |
| 371 Frank Kreutzer | 3.50 |
| 372 Clay Dalrymple | 3.50 |
| 373 Curt Simmons | 3.50 |
| 374 Angels Rookies: | 4.00 |
| J. Cardenal, D. Simpson | |
| 375 Dave Wickersham | 3.50 |
| 376 Jim Landis | 3.50 |
| 377 Willie Stargell | 25.00 |
| 378 Chuck Estrada | 3.50 |
| 379 Giants—4th Place | 6.00 |
| 380 Rocky Colavito | 6.00 |
| 381 Al Jackson | 3.50 |
| 382 J.C. Martin | 3.50 |
| 383 Felipe Alou | 4.00 |
| 384 Johnny Klippstein | 3.50 |
| 385 Carl Yastrzemski | 90.00 |
| 386 Cubs Rookies: | 4.00 |
| Paul Jaeckel, Fred Norman | |
| 387 Johnny Podres | 4.00 |
| 388 John Blanchard | 3.50 |
| 389 Don Larsen | 4.00 |
| 390 Bill Freehan | 4.00 |
| 391 Mel McGaha | 3.50 |
| 392 Bob Friend | 3.50 |
| 393 Ed Kirkpatrck | 3.50 |
| 394 Jim Hannan | 3.50 |
| 395 Jim Hart | 4.00 |
| 396 Frank Bertaina | 3.50 |
| 397 Jerry Buchek | 3.50 |
| 398 Reds Rookies: | 3.50 |
| Art Shamsky, Dan Neville | |
| 399 Ray Herbert | 3.50 |
| 400 Harmon Killebrew | 28.00 |
| 401 Carl Willey | 3.50 |
| 402 Joe Amalfitano | 3.50 |
| 403 Red Sox—8th Place | 6.00 |
| 404 Stan Williams | 3.50 |
| 405 John Roseboro | 3.50 |
| 406 Ralph Terry | 3.50 |
| 407 Lee Maye | 3.50 |

| NO. PLAYER | NR. MT. |
|---|---|
| 408 Larry Sherry | 3.50 |
| 409 Astros Rookies: | 3.50 |
|     Jim Beauchamp, L. Dierker | |
| 410 Luis Aparicio | 10.00 |
| 411 Roger Craig | 4.00 |
| 412 Bob Bailey | 3.50 |
| 413 Hal Reniff | 3.50 |
| 414 Al Lopez | 4.00 |
| 415 Curt Flood | 5.00 |
| 416 Jim Brewer | 3.50 |
| 417 Ed Brinkman | 3.50 |
| 418 Johnny Edwards | 3.50 |
| 419 Ruben Amaro | 3.50 |
| 420 Larry Jackson | 3.50 |
| 421 Twins Rookies: | 3.50 |
|     Gary Dotter, Jay Ward | |
| 422 Aubrey Gatewood | 3.50 |
| 423 Jesse Gonder | 3.50 |
| 424 Gary Bell | 3.50 |
| 425 Wayne Causey | 3.50 |
| 426 Braves—5th Place | 6.00 |
| 427 Bob Saverine | 3.50 |
| 428 Bob Shaw | 3.50 |
| 429 Don Demeter | 3.50 |
| 430 Gary Peters | 3.50 |
| 431 Cards Rookies: | 3.50 |
|     Nelson Briles, W. Spiezio | |
| 432 Jim Grant | 3.50 |
| 433 John Bateman | 3.50 |
| 434 Dave Morehead | 3.50 |
| 435 Willie Davis | 4.00 |
| 436 Don Elston | 3.50 |
| 437 Chico Cardenas | 3.50 |
| 438 Harry Walker (Mgr.) | 3.50 |
| 439 Moe Drabowsky | 3.50 |
| 440 Tom Tresh | 4.00 |
| 441 Denver LeMaster | 3.50 |
| 442 Vic Power | 3.50 |
| 443 Checklist No. 6 | 5.00 |
| 444 Bob Hendley | 3.50 |
| 445 Don Lock | 3.50 |
| 446 Art Mahaffey | 3.50 |
| 447 Julian Javier | 5.00 |
| 448 Lee Stange | 5.00 |
| 449 Mets Rookies: | 5.00 |
|     Jerry Hinsley, Gary Kroll | |
| 450 Elston Howard | 7.00 |
| 451 Jim Owens | 5.00 |
| 452 Gary Geiger | 5.00 |
| 453 Dodgers Rookies: | 6.00 |
|     W. Crawford, J. Werhas | |
| 454 Ed Rakow | 5.00 |
| 455 Norm Siebern | 5.00 |
| 456 Bill Henry | 5.00 |
| 457 Bob Kennedy—Coach | 5.00 |
| 458 John Buzhardt | 5.00 |
| 459 Frank Kostro | 5.00 |
| 460 Richie Allen | 15.00 |

| NO. PLAYER | NR. MT. |
|---|---|
| 461 Braves Rookies: | 50.00 |
|     Clay Carroll, Phil Niekro | |
| 462 Lew Krausse | 5.00 |
|     (photo of Pete Lovrich) | |
| 463 Manny Mota | 5.00 |
| 464 Ron Piche | 5.00 |
| 465 Tom Haller | 5.00 |
| 466 Senators Rookies: | 5.00 |
|     Pete Craig, Dick Nen | |
| 467 Ray Washburn | 5.00 |
| 468 Larry Brown | 5.00 |
| 469 Don Nottebart | 5.00 |
| 470 Yogi Berra | 50.00 |
| 471 Billy Hoeft | 5.00 |
| 472 Don Pavletich | 5.00 |
| 473 Orioles Rookies: | 12.00 |
|     Paul Blair, Dave Johnson | |
| 474 Cookie Rojas | 5.00 |
| 475 Clete Boyer | 6.00 |
| 476 Billy O'Dell | 5.00 |
| 477 Cards Rookies: | 500.00 |
|     Fritz Ackley, Steve Carlton | |
| 478 Wilbur Wood | 5.00 |
| 479 Ken Harrelson | 6.00 |
| 480 Joel Horlen | 5.00 |
| 481 Indians—7th Place | 10.00 |
| 482 Bob Priddy | 5.00 |
| 483 George Smith | 5.00 |
| 484 Ron Perranoski | 6.00 |
| 485 Nellie Fox | 10.00 |
| 486 Angels Rookies: | 5.00 |
|     Pat Rogan Tom Egan | |
| 487 Woody Woodward | 5.00 |
| 488 Ted Wills | 5.00 |
| 489 Gene Mauch (Mgr.) | 5.00 |
| 490 Earl Battey | 5.00 |
| 491 Tracy Stallard | 5.00 |
| 492 Gene Freese | 5.00 |
| 493 Tigers Rookies: | 5.00 |
|     Bill Roman, Bruce Brubaker | |
| 494 Jay Ritchie | 5.00 |
| 495 Joe Christopher | 5.00 |
| 496 Joe Cunningham | 5.00 |
| 497 Giants Rookies: | 5.00 |
|     Ken Henderson, Jack Hiatt | |
| 498 Gene Stephens | 5.00 |
| 499 Stu Miller | 5.00 |
| 500 Ed Mathews | 30.00 |
| 501 Indians Rookies: | 5.00 |
|     Jim Rittwage, R. Gagliano | |
| 502 Don Cardwell | 5.00 |
| 503 Phil Gagliano | 5.00 |
| 504 Jerry Grote | 5.00 |
| 505 Ray Culp | 5.00 |
| 506 Sam Mele | 5.00 |
| 507 Sammy Ellis | 5.00 |
| 508 Checklist No. 7 | 5.00 |
| 509 Red Sox Rookies: | 5.00 |
|     Bob Guindon, G. Vezendy | |

| NO. PLAYER | NR. MT. |
|---|---|
| 510 Ernie Banks | 60.00 |
| 511 Ron Locke | 5.00 |
| 512 Cap Peterson | 5.00 |
| 513 Yankees—1st Place | 12.00 |
| 514 Joe Azcue | 5.00 |
| 515 Vern Law | 5.00 |
| 516 Al Weis | 5.00 |
| 517 Angels Rookies: | 5.00 |
|     Paul Schaal, Jack Warner | |
| 518 Ken Rowe | 5.00 |
| 519 Bob Uecker | 45.00 |
| 520 Tony Cloninger | 5.00 |
| 521 Phillies Rookies: | 5.00 |
|     Dave Bennett, M. Steevens | |
| 522 Hank Aguirre | 5.00 |
| 523 Mike Brumley | 9.00 |
| 524 Dave Giusti | 9.00 |
| 525 Ed Bressoud | 6.00 |
| 526 Athletics Rookies: | 175.00 |
|     S. Lockwood, R. Lachemann, | |
|     Johnny Odom, Jim Hunter | |
| 527 Jeff Torborg | 11.00 |
| 528 George Altman | 6.00 |
| 529 Jerry Fosnow | 9.00 |
| 530 Jim Maloney | 9.00 |
| 531 Chuck Hiller | 9.00 |
| 532 Hector Lopez | 9.00 |
| 533 Mets Rookies: | 25.00 |
|     Dan Napoleon, Ron | |
|     Swoboda, Jim Bethke, | |
|     Tug McGraw | |
| 534 John Herrnstein | 6.00 |
| 535 Jack Kralick | 9.00 |
| 536 Andre Rodgers | 9.00 |
| 537 Angels Rookies: | 6.00 |
|     Marcelino Lopez, Rudy | |
|     May, Phil Roof | |
| 538 Chuck Dressen (Mgr.) | 9.00 |
| 539 Herm Starrette | 6.00 |
| 540 Lou Brock | 50.00 |
| 541 White Sox Rookies: | 6.00 |
|     Bob Locker, Greg Bollo | |
| 542 Lou Klimchock | 6.00 |
| 543 Ed Connolly | 9.00 |
| 544 Howie Reed | 6.00 |
| 545 Jesus Alou | 9.00 |
| 546 Indians Rookies: | 6.00 |
|     Floyd Weaver, Bill Davis, | |
|     Mike Hedlund, Ray Barker | |
| 547 Jake Wood | 9.00 |
| 548 Dick Stigman | 6.00 |
| 549 Cubs Rookies: | 15.00 |
|     R. Pena, Glenn Beckert | |
| 550 Mel Stottlemyre (R) | 25.00 |
| 551 Mets—10th Place | 20.00 |
| 552 Julio Gotay | 6.00 |
| 553 Astros Rookies: | 6.00 |
|     Gene Ratliff, Dan Coombs, | |
|     Jack McClure | |

| NO. PLAYER | NR. MT. |
|---|---|
| 554 Chico Ruiz | 9.00 |
| 555 Jack Baldschun | 9.00 |
| 556 Red Schoendienst | 15.00 |
| 557 Jose Santiago | 6.00 |
| 558 Tommie Sisk | 6.00 |
| 559 Ed Bailey | 9.00 |
| 560 Boog Powell | 12.00 |
| 561 Dodgers Rookies: | 12.00 |
|     D. Daboll, Mike Kekich, | |
|     H. Valle, Jim Lefebvre | |
| 562 Billy Moran | 6.00 |
| 563 Julio Navarro | 6.00 |
| 564 Mel Nelson | 6.00 |
| 565 Ernie Broglio | 9.00 |
| 566 Yankees Rookies: | 9.00 |
|     Art Lopez, Gil Blanco, | |
|     Ross Moschitto | |
| 567 Tommie Aaron | 6.00 |
| 568 Ron Taylor | 9.00 |
| 569 Gino Cimoli | 9.00 |
| 570 Claude Osteen | 9.00 |
| 571 Ossie Virgil | 9.00 |
| 572 Orioles—3rd Place | 16.00 |
| 573 Red Sox Rookies: | 17.50 |
|     Jim Lonborg, Mike Ryan, | |
|     G. Moses, Bill Schlesinger | |
| 574 Roy Sievers | 6.00 |
| 575 Jose Pagan | 6.00 |
| 576 Terry Fox | 9.00 |
| 577 AL Rookie Stars: | 9.00 |
|     D. Knowles, R. Scheinblum, | |
|     Don Buschhorn | |
| 578 Camilo Carreon | 9.00 |
| 579 Dick Smith | 9.00 |
| 580 Jimmie Hall | 9.00 |
| 581 NL Rookie Stars: | 135.00 |
|     Tony Perez, Dave Ricketts, | |
|     Kevin Collins | |
| 582 Bob Schmidt | 9.00 |
| 583 Wes Covington | 9.00 |
| 584 Harry Bright | 6.00 |
| 585 Hank Fischer | 9.00 |
| 586 Tommy McCraw | 9.00 |
| 587 Joe Sparma | 6.00 |
| 588 Lenny Green | 6.00 |
| 589 Giants Rookies: | 9.00 |
|     Frank Linzy, B. Schroder | |
| 590 Johnnie Wyatt | 6.00 |
| 591 Bob Skinner | 9.00 |
| 592 Frank Bork | 9.00 |
| 593 Tigers Rookies: | 9.00 |
|     Jackie Moore, John Sullivan | |
| 594 Joe Gaines | 6.00 |
| 595 Don Lee | 6.00 |
| 596 Don Landrum | 9.00 |
| 597 Twins Rookies: | 6.00 |
|     Dick Reese, Joe Noss, | |
|     John Sevcik | |
| 598 Al Downing . (exc. $4.00) | 16.00 |

## 1966 Topps . . . Complete Set of 598 Cards—Value $1400.00 (Exc.); $4000.00 (Near Mint)

Features the rookies cards of Jim Palmer and Don Sutton. The high no's. are 523 to 598. Cards 62, 103 and 104 (worth $30.00) and card 91 (worth $60.00) exist without a *traded* or *sold* line. Card 101 (checklist) exists identifying card 115 as either Bill Henry—worth $5.00 or Warren Spahn—worth $12.00.

| NO. PLAYER | NR. MT. |
|---|---|
| 1 Willie Mays (exc. $30.00) | 150.00 |
| 2 Ted Abernathy | 1.25 |
| 3 Sam Mele (Mgr.) | 1.25 |
| 4 Ray Culp | 1.25 |
| 5 Jim Fregosi | 2.50 |
| 6 Chuck Schilling | 1.25 |
| 7 Tracy Stallard | 1.25 |
| 8 Floyd Robinson | 1.25 |
| 9 Clete Boyer | 2.50 |
| 10 Tony Cloninger | 1.25 |
| 11 Senators Rookies: | 1.25 |
| Brant Alyea, Pete Craig | |
| 12 John Tsitouris | 1.25 |
| 13 Lou Johnson | 1.25 |
| 14 Norm Siebern | 1.25 |
| 15 Vern Law | 2.00 |
| 16 Larry Brown | 1.25 |
| 17 John Stephenson | 1.25 |
| 18 Roland Sheldon | 1.25 |
| 19 Giants—2nd Place | 3.00 |
| 20 Willie Horton | 2.50 |
| 21 Don Nottebart | 1.25 |
| 22 Joe Nossek | 1.25 |
| 23 Jack Sanford | 1.25 |
| 24 Don Kessinger (R) | 3.00 |
| 25 Joe Ward | 1.25 |
| 26 Ray Sadecki | 1.25 |
| 27 Orioles Rookies: | 1.50 |
| D. Knowles, A. Etchebarren | |
| 28 Phil Niekro | 15.00 |
| 29 Mike Brumley | 1.75 |
| 30 Pete Rose | 45.00 |
| 31 Jack Cullen | 1.25 |
| 32 Adolfo Phillips | 1.25 |
| 33 Jim Pagliaroni | 1.25 |
| 34 Checklist No. 1 | 5.00 |
| 35 Ron Swoboda | 1.75 |
| 36 Jim Hunter | 27.00 |
| 37 Billy Herman | 2.50 |
| 38 Ron Nischwitz | 1.25 |
| 39 Ken Henderson | 1.25 |
| 40 Jim Grant | 1.25 |
| 41 Don LeJohn | 1.25 |
| 42 Aubrey Gatewood | 1.25 |
| 43 Don Landrum | 1.25 |
| 44 Indians Rookies: | 1.25 |
| Bill Davis, Tom Kelley | |
| 45 Jim Gentile | 1.50 |
| 46 Howie Koplitz | 1.25 |
| 47 J.C. Martin | 1.25 |
| 48 Paul Blair | 1.75 |
| 49 Woody Woodward | 1.25 |
| 50 Mick Mantle | 175.00 |
| 51 Gordon Richardson | 1.25 |
| 52 Power Plus: | 1.50 |
| W. Covington, J. Callison | |
| 53 Bob Duliba | 1.25 |
| 54 Jose Pagan | 1.25 |
| 55 Ken Harrelson | 1.50 |
| 56 Sandy Valdespino | 1.25 |
| 57 Jim Lefebvre | 1.50 |
| 58 Dave Wickersham | 1.25 |
| 59 Reds—4th Place | 3.00 |
| 60 Curt Flood | 2.00 |
| 61 Bob Bolin | 1.25 |
| 62 Merritt Ranew* | 1.25 |
| 63 Jim Stewart | 1.25 |
| 64 Bob Bruce | 1.25 |
| 65 Leon Wagner | 1.25 |
| 66 Al Weis | 1.25 |
| 67 Mets Rookies: | 2.00 |
| Cleon Jones, Dick Selma | |
| 68 Hal Reniff | 1.25 |
| 69 Ken Hamlin | 1.25 |
| 70 Carl Yastrzemski | 50.00 |
| 71 Frank Carpin | 1.25 |
| 72 Tony Perez | 25.00 |
| 73 Jerry Zimmerman | 1.25 |
| 74 Don Mossi | 1.50 |
| 75 Tommy Davis | 1.50 |
| 76 R. Schoendienst (Mgr.) | 4.00 |
| 77 Johnny Orsino | 1.25 |
| 78 Frank Linzy | 1.25 |
| 79 Joe Pepitone | 2.00 |
| 80 Richie Allen | 4.00 |

| NO. PLAYER | NR. MT. |
|---|---|
| 81 Ray Oyler | 1.25 |
| 82 Bob Hendley | 1.25 |
| 83 Albie Pearson | 1.25 |
| 84 Braves Rookies: | 1.25 |
| J. Beauchamp, D. Kelley | |
| 85 Eddie Fisher | 1.25 |
| 86 John Bateman | 1.25 |
| 87 Dan Napoleon | 1.25 |
| 88 Fred Whitfield | 1.25 |
| 89 Ted Davidson | 1.25 |
| 90 Luis Aparicio | 7.00 |
| 91 Bob Uecker* | 20.00 |
| 92 Yankees—6th Place | 4.00 |
| 93 Jim Lonborg | 2.00 |
| 94 Matty Alou | 1.75 |
| 95 Pete Richert | 1.25 |
| 96 Felipe Alou | 1.50 |
| 97 Jim Merritt | 1.25 |
| 98 Don Demeter | 1.25 |
| 99 Buc Belters: | 3.50 |
| W. Stargell, D. Clendenon | |
| 100 Sandy Koufax | 85.00 |
| 101 Checklist No. 2* | 5.00 |
| 102 Ed Kirkpatrick | 1.25 |
| 103 Dick Groat* | 1.50 |
| 104 Alex Johnson* | 1.50 |
| 105 Milt Pappas | 1.50 |
| 106 Rusty Staub | 3.00 |
| 107 A's Rookies: | 1.25 |
| L. Stahl, Ron Tompkins | |
| 108 Bobby Klaus | 1.25 |
| 109 Ralph Terry | 1.25 |
| 110 Ernie Banks | 20.00 |
| 111 Gary Peters | 1.25 |
| 112 Manny Mota | 1.75 |
| 113 Hank Aguirre | 1.25 |
| 114 Jim Gosger | 1.25 |
| 115 Bill Henry* | 1.25 |
| 116 Walt Alston (Mgr.) | 3.50 |
| 117 Jake Gibbs | 1.25 |
| 118 Mike McCormick | 1.25 |
| 119 Art Shamsky | 1.25 |
| 120 Harmon Killebrew | 17.00 |
| 121 Ray Herbert | 1.25 |
| 122 Joe Gaines | 1.25 |
| 123 Pirates Rookies: | 1.25 |
| Frank Bork, Jerry May | |
| 124 Tug McGraw | 4.00 |
| 125 Lou Brock | 20.00 |
| 126 Jim Palmer (R) | 225.00 |
| 127 Ken Berry | 1.25 |
| 128 Jim Landis | 1.25 |
| 129 Jack Kralick | 1.25 |
| 130 Joe Torre | 2.50 |
| 131 Angels—7th Place | 3.00 |
| 132 Orlando Cepeda | 5.00 |
| 133 Don McMahon | 1.25 |
| 134 Wes Parker | 1.25 |
| 135 Dave Morehead | 1.25 |
| 136 Woody Held | 1.25 |
| 137 Pat Corrales | 1.50 |
| 138 Roger Repoz | 1.25 |
| 139 Cubs Rookies: | 1.25 |
| Byron Browne, Don Young | |
| 140 Jim Maloney | 1.50 |
| 141 Tom McCraw | 1.25 |
| 142 Don Dennis | 1.25 |
| 143 Jose Tartabull | 1.25 |
| 144 Don Schwall | 1.25 |
| 145 Bill Freehan | 1.50 |
| 146 George Altman | 1.25 |
| 147 Lum Harris (Mgr.) | 1.25 |
| 148 Bob Johnson | 1.25 |
| 149 Dick Nen | 1.25 |
| 150 Rocky Colavito | 4.00 |
| 151 Gary Wagner | 1.25 |
| 152 Frank Malzone | 1.25 |
| 153 Rico Carty | 1.75 |
| 154 Chuck Hiller | 1.25 |
| 155 Marcelino Lopez | 1.25 |
| 156 Double Play Combo: | 1.50 |
| Dick Schofield, Hal Lanier | |
| 157 Rene Lachemann | 1.25 |
| 158 Jim Brewer | 1.25 |
| 159 Chico Ruiz | 1.25 |

| NO. PLAYER | NR. MT. |
|---|---|
| 160 Whitey Ford | 20.00 |
| 161 Jerry Lumpe | 1.25 |
| 162 Lee Maye | 1.25 |
| 163 Tito Francona | 1.25 |
| 164 White Sox Rookies: | 1.50 |
| Tommie Agee, M. Staehle | |
| 165 Don Lock | 1.25 |
| 166 Chris Krug | 1.25 |
| 167 Boog Powell | 3.50 |
| 168 Dan Osinski | 1.25 |
| 169 Duke Sims | 1.25 |
| 170 Cookie Rojas | 1.25 |
| 171 Nick Willhite | 1.25 |
| 172 Mets—10th Place | 3.00 |
| 173 Al Spangler | 1.25 |
| 174 Ron Taylor | 1.25 |
| 175 Bert Campaneris | 2.00 |
| 176 Jim Davenport | 1.25 |
| 177 Hector Lopez | 1.25 |
| 178 Bob Tillman | 1.25 |
| 179 Cards Rookies: | 1.50 |
| Dennis Aust, Bob Tolan | |
| 180 Vada Pinson | 2.50 |
| 181 Al Worthington | 1.25 |
| 182 Jerry Lynch | 1.25 |
| 183 Checklist No. 3 | 5.00 |
| 184 Denis Menke | 1.25 |
| 185 Bob Buhl | 1.25 |
| 186 Ruben Amaro | 1.25 |
| 187 Chuck Dressen (Mgr.) | 1.50 |
| 188 Al Luplow | 1.25 |
| 189 John Roseboro | 1.25 |
| 190 Jimmie Hall | 1.25 |
| 191 Darrell Sutherland | 1.25 |
| 192 Vic Power | 1.25 |
| 193 Dave McNally | 1.50 |
| 194 Senators—8th Place | 3.00 |
| 195 Joe Morgan | 40.00 |
| 196 Don Pavletich | 1.50 |
| 197 Sonny Siebert | 1.50 |
| 198 Mickey Stanley | 2.00 |
| 199 Chisox Clubbers: | 2.00 |
| Bill Skowron, Johnny | |
| Romano, Floyd Robinson | |
| 200 Ed Mathews | 12.00 |
| 201 Jim Dickson | 1.50 |
| 202 Clay Dalrymple | 1.50 |
| 203 Jose Santiago | 1.50 |
| 204 Cubs—8th Place | 3.00 |
| 205 Tom Tresh | 2.50 |
| 206 Alvin Jackson | 1.50 |
| 207 Frank Quilici | 1.50 |
| 208 Bob Miller | 1.50 |
| 209 Tigers Rookies: | 3.00 |
| Fritz Fisher, John Hiller | |
| 210 Bill Mazeroski | 3.00 |
| 211 Frank Kreutzer | 1.50 |
| 212 Ed Kranepool | 2.00 |
| 213 Fred Newman | 1.50 |
| 214 Tommy Harper | 1.50 |
| 215 NL Batting Leaders: | 16.00 |
| Willie Mays, Bob | |
| Clemente, Hank Aaron | |
| 216 AL Batting Leaders: | 5.00 |
| Tony Oliva, Carl | |
| Yastrzemski, Vic Davalillo | |
| 217 NL Home Run Leaders: | 10.00 |
| Willie McCovey, Willie | |
| Mays, Billy Williams | |
| 218 AL Home Run Leaders: | 3.00 |
| Norm Cash, Willie | |
| Horton, Tony Conigliaro | |
| 219 NL RBI Leaders: | 5.00 |
| Frank Robinson, Deron | |
| Johnson, Willie Mays | |
| 220 AL RBI Leaders: | 3.00 |
| Rocky Colavito, Willie | |
| Horton, Tony Oliva | |
| 221 NL ERA Leaders: | 5.00 |
| Sandy Koufax, Vern | |
| Law, Juan Marichal | |
| 222 AL ERA Leaders: | 3.00 |
| Sam McDowell, Sonny | |
| Siebert, Eddie Fisher | |
| 223 NL Pitching Leaders: | 5.00 |
| Sandy Koufax, Tony | |
| Cloninger, Don Drysdale | |

| NO. PLAYER | NR. MT. |
|---|---|
| 224 AL Pitching Leaders: | 3.00 |
| Mel Stottlemyre, | |
| Jim Grant, Jim Kaat | |
| 225 NL Strikeout Leaders: | 5.00 |
| Bob Gibson, Sandy Koufax, | |
| Bob Veale | |
| 226 AL Strikeout Leaders: | 4.00 |
| Sam McDowell, Mickey | |
| Lolich, Denny McLain, | |
| Sonny Siebert | |
| 227 Russ Nixon | 1.25 |
| 228 Larry Dierker | 1.25 |
| 229 Hank Bauer | 1.50 |
| 230 Johnny Callison | 1.50 |
| 231 F. Weaver | 1.25 |
| 232 Glenn Beckert | 1.50 |
| 233 Dom Zanni | 1.25 |
| 234 Yankees Rookies: | 5.00 |
| Roy White, Rich Beck | |
| 235 Don Cardwell | 1.25 |
| 236 Mike Hershberger | 1.25 |
| 237 Billy O'Dell | 1.25 |
| 238 Dodgers—1st Place | 4.00 |
| 239 Orlando Pena | 1.25 |
| 240 Earl Battey | 1.25 |
| 241 Dennis Ribant | 1.25 |
| 242 Jesus Alou | 1.25 |
| 243 Nelson Briles | 1.25 |
| 244 Astros Rookies: | 1.25 |
| C. Harrison, S. Jackson | |
| 245 John Buzhardt | 1.25 |
| 246 Ed Bailey | 1.25 |
| 247 Carl Warwick | 1.25 |
| 248 Pete Mikkelsen | 1.25 |
| 249 Bill Rigney (Mgr.) | 1.25 |
| 250 Sam Ellis | 1.25 |
| 251 Ed Brinkman | 1.25 |
| 252 Denver Lemaster | 1.25 |
| 253 Don Wert | 1.25 |
| 254 Phillies Rookies: | 120.00 |
| Ferguson Jenkins, | |
| Bill Sorrell | |
| 255 Willie Stargell | 18.00 |
| 256 Lew Krausse | 1.25 |
| 257 Jeff Torborg | 1.25 |
| 258 Dave Giusti | 1.25 |
| 259 Red Sox—9th Place | 3.00 |
| 260 Bob Shaw | 1.25 |
| 261 Ron Hansen | 1.25 |
| 262 Jack Hamilton | 1.25 |
| 263 Tom Egan | 1.25 |
| 264 Twins Rookies: | 1.25 |
| Ted Uhlaender, Andy Kosco | |
| 265 Stu Miller | 1.25 |
| 266 Pedro Gonzalez | 1.25 |
| 267 Joe Sparma | 1.25 |
| 268 John Blanchard | 1.25 |
| 269 Don Heffner (Mgr.) | 1.25 |
| 270 Claude Osteen | 1.50 |
| 271 Hal Lanier | 1.50 |
| 272 Jack Baldschun | 1.25 |
| 273 Astro Aces: | 2.00 |
| Bob Aspromonte, | |
| Rusty Staub | |
| 274 Buster Narum | 1.25 |
| 275 Tim McCarver | 3.50 |
| 276 Jim Bouton | 2.50 |
| 277 George Thomas | 1.25 |
| 278 Calvin Koonce | 1.25 |
| 279 Checklist No. 4 | 5.00 |
| 280 Bobby Knoop | 1.25 |
| 281 Bruce Howard | 1.25 |
| 282 Johnny Lewis | 1.25 |
| 283 Jim Perry | 1.75 |
| 284 Bobby Wine | 2.50 |
| 285 Luis Tiant | 2.50 |
| 286 Gary Geiger | 2.00 |
| 287 Jack Aker | 2.00 |
| 288 Dodgers Rookies: | 125.00 |
| Bill Singer, Don Sutton | |
| 289 Larry Sherry | 2.00 |
| 290 Ron Santo | 3.50 |
| 291 Moe Drabowsky | 2.00 |
| 292 Jim Coker | 2.00 |

| NO. PLAYER | NR. MT. | NO. PLAYER | NR. MT. | NO. PLAYER | NR. MT. | NO. PLAYER | NR. MT. |
|---|---|---|---|---|---|---|---|
| 293 Mike Shannon | 2.00 | 374 Bob Locker | 3.00 | 455 Mickey Lolich | 7.50 | 531 Joe Cunningham | 13.00 |
| 294 Steve Ridzik | 2.00 | 375 Donn Clendenon | 4.00 | 456 Red Sox Rookies: | 6.00 | 532 Aurelio Monteagudo | 20.00 |
| 295 Jim Hart | 2.00 | 376 Paul Schaal | 3.00 | Darrell Brandon, Joe Foy | | 533 Jerry Adair | 20.00 |
| 296 Johnny Keane (Mgr.) | 2.00 | 377 Turk Farrell | 3.00 | 457 Joe Gibbon | 6.00 | 534 Mets Rookies: | 13.00 |
| 297 Jim Owens | 2.00 | 378 Dick Tracewski | 3.00 | 458 Manny Jiminez | 6.00 | Dave Eilers, Rob Gardner | |
| 298 Rico Petrocelli | 2.50 | 379 Cardinal—7th Place | 4.00 | 459 Bill McCool | 6.00 | 535 Willie Davis | 35.00 |
| 299 Lou Burdette | 2.50 | 380 Tony Conigliaro | 6.00 | 460 Curt Blefary | 6.00 | 536 Dick Egan | 13.00 |
| 300 Bob Clemente | 75.00 | 381 Hank Fischer | 3.00 | 461 Roy Face | 7.00 | 537 Herman Franks (Mgr.) | 13.00 |
| 301 Greg Bollo | 2.00 | 382 Phil Roof | 3.00 | 462 Bob Rodgers | 7.00 | 538 Bob Allen | 20.00 |
| 302 Ernie Bowman | 2.00 | 383 Jack Brandt | 3.00 | 463 Phillies—6th Place | 10.00 | 539 Astros Rookies: | 13.00 |
| 303 Indians—5th Place | 4.00 | 384 Al Downing | 3.50 | 464 Larry Bearnarth | 6.00 | Bill Heath, Carroll Sembera | |
| 304 John Herrnstein | 2.00 | 385 Ken Boyer | 3.50 | 465 Don Buford | 6.00 | 540 Denny McLain | 50.00 |
| 305 Camilo Pascual | 2.50 | 386 Gil Hodges (Mgr.) | 5.00 | 466 Ken Johnson | 6.00 | 541 Gene Oliver | 20.00 |
| 306 Ty Cline | 2.00 | 387 Howie Reed | 3.00 | 467 Vic Roznovsky | 6.00 | 542 George Smith | 13.00 |
| 307 Clay Carroll | 2.00 | 388 Don Mincher | 3.00 | 468 Johnny Podres | 7.00 | 543 Roger Craig | 35.00 |
| 308 Tom Haller | 2.00 | 389 Jim O'Toole | 3.00 | 469 Yankees Rookies: | 20.00 | 544 Cardinals Rookies: | 30.00 |
| 309 Diego Segui | 2.00 | 390 Brooks Robinson | 25.00 | Bobby Murcer, | | J. Williams, J. Hoerner, | |
| 310 Frank Robinson | 35.00 | 391 Chuck Hinton | 3.00 | Dooley Womack | | George Kernek | |
| 311 Reds Rookies: | 2.00 | 392 Cubs Rookies: | 3.00 | 470 Sam McDowell | 7.00 | 545 Dick Green | 20.00 |
| D. Simpson, T. Helms | | Bill Hands, Randy Hundley | | 471 Bob Skinner | 6.00 | 546 Dwight Siebler | 13.00 |
| 312 Bob Saverine | 2.00 | 393 George Brunet | 3.00 | 472 Terry Fox | 6.00 | 547 Horace Clarke (R) | 50.00 |
| 313 Chris Zachary | 2.00 | 394 Ron Brand | 3.00 | 473 Rich Rollins | 6.00 | 548 Gary Kroll | 13.00 |
| 314 Hector Valle | 2.00 | 395 Len Gabrielson | 3.00 | 474 Dick Schofield | 6.00 | 549 Senators Rookies: | 13.00 |
| 315 Norm Cash | 3.50 | 396 Jerry Stephenson | 3.00 | 475 Dick Radatz | 6.00 | Al Closter, Casey Cox | |
| 316 Jack Fisher | 2.00 | 397 Bill White | 4.00 | 476 Bobby Bragan | 6.00 | 550 Willie McCovey | 120.00 |
| 317 Dalton Jones | 2.00 | 398 Danny Cater | 3.00 | 477 Steve Barber | 6.00 | 551 Bob Purkey | 20.00 |
| 318 Harry Walker | 2.00 | 399 Ray Washburn | 3.00 | 478 Tony Gonzalez | 6.00 | 552 Birdie Tebbetts | 20.00 |
| 319 Gene Freese | 2.00 | 400 Zoilo Versalles | 3.00 | 479 Jim Hannan | 6.00 | 553 Rookie Stars: | 13.00 |
| 320 Bob Gibson | 20.00 | 401 Ken McMullen | 3.00 | 480 Dick Stuart | 6.00 | Pat Garrett, Jackie Warner | |
| 321 Rick Reichardt | 2.00 | 402 Jim Hickman | 3.00 | 481 Bob Lee | 6.00 | 554 Jim Northrup | 20.00 |
| 322 Bill Faul | 2.00 | 403 Fred Talbot | 3.00 | 482 Cubs Rookies: | 6.00 | 555 Ron Perranoski | 20.00 |
| 323 Ray Barker | 2.00 | 404 Pirates—3rd Place | 4.00 | J. Boccabella, D. Dowling | | 556 Mel Queen | 20.00 |
| 324 John Boozer | 2.00 | 405 Elston Howard | 4.50 | 483 Joe Nuxhall | 7.00 | 557 Felix Mantilla | 20.00 |
| 325 Vic Davalillo | 2.50 | 406 Joe Jay | 3.00 | 484 Wes Covington | 6.00 | 558 Red Sox Rookies: | 25.00 |
| 326 Braves—5th Place | 4.00 | 407 John Kennedy | 3.00 | 485 Bob Bailey | 6.00 | Pete Magrini, Guido Grilli, | |
| 327 Bernie Allen | 2.00 | 408 Lee Thomas | 3.00 | 486 Tommy John | 11.00 | George Scott | |
| 328 Jerry Grote | 2.00 | 409 Billy Hoeft | 3.00 | 487 Al Ferrara | 6.00 | 559 Roberto Pena | 20.00 |
| 329 Pete Charton | 2.00 | 410 Al Kaline | 25.00 | 488 George Banks | 6.00 | 560 Joel Horlen | 13.00 |
| 330 Ron Fairly | 2.00 | 411 Gene Mauch (Mgr.) | 3.50 | 489 Curt Simmons | 6.00 | 561 Choo Choo Coleman | 40.00 |
| 331 Ron Herbel | 2.00 | 412 Sam Bowens | 3.00 | 490 Bobby Richardson | 10.00 | 562 Russ Snyder | 13.00 |
| 332 Billy Bryan | 2.00 | 413 John Romano | 3.00 | 491 Dennis Bennett | 6.00 | 563 Twins Rookies: | 13.00 |
| 333 Senators Rookies: | 2.00 | 414 Dan Coombs | 3.00 | 492 Athletics—10th Place | 10.00 | Pete Cimino, Cesar Tovar | |
| Joe Coleman, Jim French | | 415 Max Alvis | 3.00 | 493 John Klippstein | 6.00 | 564 Bob Chance | 20.00 |
| 334 Marty Keough | 2.00 | 416 Phil Ortega | 3.00 | 494 Gordon Coleman | 6.00 | 565 Jimmy Piersall | 35.00 |
| 335 Juan Pizarro | 2.00 | 417 Angels Rookies: | 3.00 | 495 Dick McAuliffe | 6.00 | 566 Mike Cuellar | 20.00 |
| 336 Gene Alley | 2.00 | Jim McGlothlin, Ed Sukla | | 496 Lindy McDaniel | 6.00 | 567 Dick Howser | 25.00 |
| 337 Fred Gladding | 2.00 | 418 Phil Gagliano | 3.00 | 497 Chris Cannizzaro | 6.00 | 568 Athletics Rookies: | 13.00 |
| 338 Dal Maxvill | 2.00 | 419 Mike Ryan | 3.00 | 498 Pirates Rookies: | 6.00 | Paul Lindblad, Ron Stone | |
| 339 Del Crandall | 2.00 | 420 Juan Marichal | 11.00 | Luke Walker, W. Fryman | | 569 Orlando McFarlane | 20.00 |
| 340 Dean Chance | 2.00 | 421 Roy McMillan | 3.00 | 499 Wally Bunker | 6.00 | 570 Art Mahaffey | 20.00 |
| 341 Wes Westrum | 2.00 | 422 Ed Charles | 3.00 | 500 Hank Aaron | 90.00 | 571 Dave Roberts | 20.00 |
| 342 Bob Humphreys | 2.00 | 423 Ernie Broglio | 3.00 | 501 John O'Donoghue | 6.00 | 572 Bob Priddy | 13.00 |
| 343 Joe Christopher | 2.00 | 424 Reds Rookies: | 6.00 | 502 Lenny Green | 6.00 | 573 Derrell Griffith | 13.00 |
| 344 Steve Blass | 2.00 | Lee May, Darrell Osteen | | 503 Steve Hamilton | 6.00 | 574 Mets Rookies: | 13.00 |
| 345 Bob Allison | 2.00 | 425 Bob Veale | 3.00 | 504 Grady Hatton | 6.00 | Billy Hepler, Bill Murphy | |
| 346 Mike De La Hoz | 2.00 | 426 White Sox—2nd Place | 4.00 | 505 Jose Cardenal | 6.00 | 575 Earl Wilson | 13.00 |
| 347 Phil Regan | 2.00 | 427 John Miller | 3.00 | 506 Bo Belinsky | 6.00 | 576 Dave Nicholson | 20.00 |
| 348 Orioles—3rd Place | 2.00 | 428 Sandy Alomar | 3.00 | 507 John Edwards | 6.00 | 577 Jack Lamabe | 20.00 |
| 349 Cap Peterson | 2.00 | 429 Bill Monbouquette | 3.00 | 508 Steve Hargan | 6.00 | 578 Chi Chi Olivo | 13.00 |
| 350 Mel Stottlemyre | 3.50 | 430 Don Drysdale | 17.00 | 509 Jake Wood | 6.00 | 579 Orioles Rookies: | 20.00 |
| 351 Fred Valentine | 2.00 | 431 Walt Bond | 3.00 | 510 Hoyt Wilhelm | 12.00 | F. Bertaina, G. Brabender, | |
| 352 Bob Aspromonte | 2.00 | 432 Bob Heffner | 3.00 | 511 Giants Rookies: | 6.00 | Dave Johnson | |
| 353 Al McBean | 2.00 | 433 Alvin Dark (Mgr.) | 3.50 | Bob Barton, Tito Fuentes | | 580 Billy Williams | 90.00 |
| 354 Smoky Burgess | 2.00 | 434 Willie Kirkland | 3.00 | 512 Dick Stigman | 6.00 | 581 Tony Martinez | 13.00 |
| 355 Wade Blasingame | 2.00 | 435 Jim Bunning | 6.00 | 513 Camilo Carreon | 6.00 | 582 Garry Roggenburk | 13.00 |
| 356 Red Sox Rookies: | 2.00 | 436 Julian Javier | 3.00 | 514 Hal Woodeschick | 6.00 | 583 Tigers—3rd Place | 125.00 |
| Owen Johnson, | | 437 Al Stanek | 3.00 | 515 Frank Howard | 7.00 | 584 Yankees Rookies: | 13.00 |
| Ken Sanders | | 438 Willie Smith | 3.00 | 516 Eddie Bressoud | 6.00 | F. Fernandez, F. Peterson | |
| 357 Gerry Arrigo | 2.00 | 439 Pedro Ramos | 3.00 | 517 Checklist No. 7 | 15.00 | 585 Tony Taylor | 13.00 |
| 358 Charlie Smith | 2.00 | 440 Deron Johnson | 3.00 | 518 Braves Rookies: | 6.00 | 586 Claude Raymond | 20.00 |
| 359 Johnny Briggs | 2.00 | 441 Tommie Sisk | 3.00 | Arnie Umbach, H. Hippauf | | 587 Dick Bertell | 13.00 |
| 360 Ron Hunt | 2.00 | 442 Orioles Rookies: | 3.00 | 519 Bob Friend | 6.00 | 588 Athletics Rookies: | 13.00 |
| 361 Tom Satriano | 2.00 | Ed Barnowski, Eddie Watt | | 520 Jim Wynn | 6.00 | Ken Suarez, Chuck Dobson | |
| 362 Gates Brown | 2.00 | 443 Bill Wakefield | 3.00 | 521 John Wyatt | 6.00 | 589 Lou Klimchock | 20.00 |
| 363 Checklist No. 5 | 5.00 | 444 Checklist No. 6 | 5.00 | 522 Phil Linz | 6.00 | 590 Bill Skowron | 40.00 |
| 364 Nate Oliver | 2.00 | 445 Jim Kaat | 6.00 | 523 Bob Sadowski | 13.00 | 591 NL Rookie Stars | 30.00 |
| 365 Roger Maris | 50.00 | 446 Mack Jones | 3.00 | 524 Giants Rookies: | 20.00 | Bart Shirley, Grant Jackson | |
| 366 Wayne Causey | 2.00 | 447 Dick Ellsworth | 6.00 | Ollie Brown, Don Mason | | 592 Andre Rodgers | 13.00 |
| 367 Mel Nelson | 2.00 | (photo of Ken Hubbs) | | 525 Gary Bell | 20.00 | 593 Doug Camilli | 20.00 |
| 368 Charlie Lau | 2.00 | 448 Eddie Stanky | 6.00 | 526 Twins—1st Place | 65.00 | 594 Chico Salmon | 13.00 |
| 369 Jim King | 2.00 | 449 Joe Moeller | 6.00 | 527 Julio Navarro | 13.00 | 595 Larry Jackson | 13.00 |
| 370 Chico Cardenas | 2.00 | 450 Tony Oliva | 8.00 | 528 Jesse Gonder | 20.00 | 596 John Sullivan | 20.00 |
| 371 Lee Stange | 3.00 | 451 Barry Latman | 6.00 | 529 White Sox Rookies: | 13.00 | 597 Astros Rookies: | 13.00 |
| 372 Harvey Kuenn | 4.00 | 452 Joe Azcue | 6.00 | Dennis Higgins, Lee Elia, | | Nate Colbert, Greg Sims | |
| 373 Giants Rookies: | 3.00 | 453 Ron Kline | 6.00 | Bill Voss | | 598 G. Perry (exc. $60.00) | 300.00 |
| Jack Hiatt, Dick Estelle | | 454 Jerry Buchek | 6.00 | 530 Robin Roberts | 40.00 | | |

# 1967 Topps . . . Complete Set of 609 Cards—Value $1850.00 (Exc.); $4800.00 (Mint)

Features the rookie cards of Tom Seaver and Rod Carew. Cards 534 to 609 are high numbers. Cards 458 to 533 are semi-high numbers. Cards 26 and 86 exist without the *traded* line—worth $25.00 each. Card 191 exists identifying card 214 as either Dick Kelley—worth $20.00 or Tom Kelley—worth $6

| NO. | PLAYER | NR. MT. |
|---|---|---|
| 1 | The Champs: (exc. $4.00) | 20.00 |
| | Frank Robinson, Hank | |
| | Bauer, Brooks Robinson | |
| 2 | Jack Hamilton | 1.25 |
| 3 | Duke Sims | 1.25 |
| 4 | Hal Lanier | 1.75 |
| 5 | Whitey Ford | 18.00 |
| 6 | Dick Simpson | 1.25 |
| 7 | Don McMahon | 1.25 |
| 8 | Chuck Harrison | 1.25 |
| 9 | Ron Hansen | 1.25 |
| 10 | Matty Alou | 1.75 |
| 11 | Barry Moore | 1.25 |
| 12 | Dodgers Rookies: | 1.75 |
| | J. Campanis, Bill Singer | |
| 13 | Joe Sparma | 1.25 |
| 14 | Phil Linz | 1.25 |
| 15 | Earl Battey | 1.50 |
| 16 | Bill Hands | 1.25 |
| 17 | Jim Gosger | 1.25 |
| 18 | Gene Oliver | 1.25 |
| 19 | Jim McGlothlin | 1.25 |
| 20 | Orlando Cepeda | 7.00 |
| 21 | Dave Bristol (Mgr.) | 1.25 |
| 22 | Gene Brabender | 1.25 |
| 23 | Larry Elliot | 1.25 |
| 24 | Bob Allen | 1.25 |
| 25 | Elstan Howard | 4.00 |
| 26 | Bob Priddy* | 1.25 |
| 27 | Bob Saverine | 1.25 |
| 28 | Barry Latman | 1.25 |
| 29 | Tom McCraw | 1.25 |
| 30 | Al Kaline | 16.00 |
| 31 | Jim Brewer | 1.25 |
| 32 | Bob Bailey | 1.25 |
| 33 | Athletic Rookies: | 3.00 |
| | Sal Bando, R. Schwartz | |
| 34 | Pete Cimino | 1.25 |
| 35 | Rico Carty | 2.00 |
| 36 | Bob Tillman | 1.25 |
| 37 | Rick Wise | 1.50 |
| 38 | Bob Johnson | 1.25 |
| 39 | Curt Simmons | 1.50 |
| 40 | Rick Reichardt | 1.25 |
| 41 | Joe Hoerner | 1.25 |
| 42 | Mets Team | 4.00 |
| 43 | Chico Salmon | 1.25 |
| 44 | Joe Nuxhall | 1.50 |
| 45 | Roger Maris | 40.00 |
| 46 | Lindy McDaniel | 1.25 |
| 47 | Ken McMullen | 1.25 |
| 48 | Bill Freehan | 1.75 |
| 49 | Roy Face | 2.00 |
| 50 | Tony Olava | 4.00 |
| 51 | Astros Rookies: | 1.25 |
| | Dave Adlesh, W. Bales | |
| 52 | Dennis Higgins | 1.25 |
| 53 | Clay Dalrymple | 1.25 |
| 54 | Dick Green | 1.25 |
| 55 | Don Drysdale | 12.00 |
| 56 | Jose Tartabull | 1.25 |
| 57 | Pat Jarvis | 1.25 |
| 58 | Paul Schaal | 1.25 |
| 59 | Ralph Terry | 1.25 |
| 60 | Luis Aparicio | 6.00 |
| 61 | Gordy Coleman | 1.25 |

| NO. | PLAYER | NR. MT. |
|---|---|---|
| 62 | Checklist No. 1 | 5.00 |
| 63 | Cards Clubbers | 6.00 |
| | Lou Brock, Curt Flood | |
| 64 | Fred Valentine | 1.25 |
| 65 | Tom Haller | 1.25 |
| 66 | Manny Mota | 2.50 |
| 67 | Ken Berry | 1.25 |
| 68 | Bob Buhl | 1.25 |
| 69 | Vic Davalillo | 1.25 |
| 70 | Ron Santo | 3.00 |
| 71 | Camilo Pascual | 1.25 |
| 72 | Tigers Rookies: | 1.75 |
| | George Korince (Photo of | |
| | John Brown), J. Matchick | |
| 73 | Rusty Staub | 2.50 |
| 74 | Wes Stock | 1.25 |
| 75 | George Scott | 2.00 |
| 76 | Jim Barbieri | 1.25 |
| 77 | Dooley Womack | 1.25 |
| 78 | Pat Corrales | 1.50 |
| 79 | Bubba Morton | 1.25 |
| 80 | Jim Maloney | 1.25 |
| 81 | Eddie Stanky (Mgr.) | 1.50 |
| 82 | Steve Barber | 1.25 |
| 83 | Ollie Brown | 1.25 |
| 84 | Tommie Sisk | 1.25 |
| 85 | Johnny Callison | 1.50 |
| 86 | Mike McCormick* | 1.50 |
| 87 | George Altman | 1.25 |
| 88 | Mickey Lolich | 2.50 |
| 89 | Felix Millan | 1.25 |
| 90 | Jim Nash | 1.25 |
| 91 | Johnny Lewis | 1.25 |
| 92 | Ray Washburn | 1.25 |
| 93 | Yankees Rookies: | 4.00 |
| | Stan Bahnsen, B. Murcer | |
| 94 | Ron Fairly | 1.50 |
| 95 | Sonny Siebert | 1.50 |
| 96 | Art Shamsky | 1.25 |
| 97 | Mike Cuellar | 1.50 |
| 98 | Rich Rollins | 1.25 |
| 99 | Lee Stange | 1.25 |
| 100 | Frank Robinson | 16.00 |
| 101 | Ken Johnson | 1.25 |
| 102 | Phillies Team | 3.00 |
| 103 | Checklist No. 2 | 7.00 |
| 104 | Minnie Rojas | 1.25 |
| 105 | Ken Boyer | 2.50 |
| 106 | Randy Hundley | 1.25 |
| 107 | Joel Horlen | 1.25 |
| 108 | Alex Johnson | 1.25 |
| 109 | Tribe Thumpers: | 2.00 |
| | R. Colavito, Leon Wagner | |
| 110 | Jack Aker | 1.50 |
| 111 | John Kennedy | 1.50 |
| 112 | Dave Wickersham | 1.50 |
| 113 | Dave Nicholson | 1.50 |
| 114 | Jack Baldschun | 1.50 |
| 115 | Paul Casanova | 1.50 |
| 116 | Herman Franks | 1.50 |
| 117 | Darrell Brandon | 1.50 |
| 118 | Bernie Allen | 1.50 |
| 119 | Wade Blasingame | 1.50 |
| 120 | Floyd Robinson | 1.50 |
| 121 | Ed Bressoud | 1.50 |
| 122 | George Brunet | 1.50 |

| NO. | PLAYER | NR. MT. |
|---|---|---|
| 123 | Pirates Rookies: | 1.50 |
| | Jim Price, L. Walker | |
| 124 | Jim Stewart | 1.50 |
| 125 | Moe Drabowsky | 1.50 |
| 126 | Tony Taylor | 1.50 |
| 127 | John O'Donoghue | 1.50 |
| 128 | Ed Spiezio | 1.50 |
| 129 | Phil Roof | 1.50 |
| 130 | Phil Regan | 1.50 |
| 131 | Yankees Team | 5.00 |
| 132 | Ozzie Virgil | 1.50 |
| 133 | Ron Kline | 1.50 |
| 134 | Gates Brown | 1.50 |
| 135 | Deron Johnson | 1.50 |
| 136 | Carroll Sembera | 1.50 |
| 137 | Twins Rookies: | 1.50 |
| | Ron Clark, Jim Ollum | |
| 138 | Dick Kelley | 1.50 |
| 139 | Dalton Jones | 1.50 |
| 140 | Willie Stargell | 18.00 |
| 141 | John Miller | 1.50 |
| 142 | Jackie Brandt | 1.50 |
| 143 | Sox Sockers: | 1.50 |
| | Don Buford, Pete Ward | |
| 144 | Bill Hepler | 1.50 |
| 145 | Larry Brown | 1.50 |
| 146 | Steve Carlton | 100.00 |
| 147 | Tom Egan | 1.50 |
| 148 | Adolfo Phillips | 1.50 |
| 149 | Joe Moeller | 1.50 |
| 150 | Mickey Mantle | 225.00 |
| 151 | World Series Game 1: | 3.00 |
| | Moe Mows Down 11 | |
| 152 | World Series Game 2: | 5.00 |
| | Palmer Blanks Dodgers | |
| 153 | World Series Game 3: | 3.00 |
| | Blair's Homer Defeats L.A. | |
| 154 | World Series Game 4: | 3.00 |
| | Orioles Win 4 Straight | |
| 155 | World Series: | 3.00 |
| | The Winners Celebrate | |
| 156 | Ron Herbel | 1.50 |
| 157 | Danny Cater | 1.50 |
| 158 | Jimmy Coker | 1.50 |
| 159 | Bruce Howard | 1.50 |
| 160 | Willie Davis | 1.75 |
| 161 | Dick Williams (Mgr.) | 1.75 |
| 162 | Billy O'Dell | 1.50 |
| 163 | Vic Roznovsky | 1.50 |
| 164 | Dwight Siebler | 1.50 |
| 165 | Cleon Jones | 1.50 |
| 166 | Ed Mathews | 10.00 |
| 167 | Senators Rookies: | 1.50 |
| | Joe Coleman, Tim Cullen | |
| 168 | Ray Culp | 1.50 |
| 169 | Horace Clarke | 1.50 |
| 170 | Dick McAuliffe | 1.50 |
| 171 | Calvin Koonce | 1.50 |
| 172 | Bill Heath | 1.50 |
| 173 | Cardinals Team | 3.00 |
| 174 | Dick Radatz | 1.50 |
| 175 | Bobby Knoop | 1.50 |
| 176 | Sammy Ellis | 1.50 |
| 177 | Tito Fuentes | 1.50 |
| 178 | John Buzhardt | 1.50 |
| 179 | Braves Rookies: | 1.50 |
| | C. Vaughan, Cecil Upshaw | |

| NO. | PLAYER | NR. MT. |
|---|---|---|
| 180 | Curt Blefary | 1.50 |
| 181 | Terry Fox | 1.50 |
| 182 | Ed Charles | 1.50 |
| 183 | Jim Pagliaroni | 1.50 |
| 184 | George Thomas | 1.50 |
| 185 | Ken Holtzman (R) | 2.50 |
| 186 | Mets Maulers | 1.75 |
| | Ed Kranepool, R. Swoboda | |
| 187 | Pedro Ramos | 1.50 |
| 188 | Ken Harrelson | 1.75 |
| 189 | Chuck Hinton | 1.50 |
| 190 | Turk Farrell | 1.50 |
| 191 | Checklist No. 3* | 6.00 |
| 192 | Fred Gladding | 1.50 |
| 193 | Jose Cardenal | 1.50 |
| 194 | Bob Allison | 1.50 |
| 195 | Al Jackson | 1.50 |
| 196 | Johnny Romano | 1.50 |
| 197 | Ron Perranoski | 1.50 |
| 198 | Chuck Hiller | 1.50 |
| 199 | Billy Hitchcock | 1.50 |
| 200 | Willie Mays | 75.00 |
| 201 | Hal Reniff | 1.50 |
| 202 | Johnny Edwards | 1.50 |
| 203 | Al McBean | 1.50 |
| 204 | Orioles Rookies: | 1.75 |
| | Mike Epstein, Tom Phoebus | |
| 205 | Dick Groat | 1.75 |
| 206 | Dennis Bennett | 1.50 |
| 207 | John Orsino | 1.50 |
| 208 | Jack Lamabe | 1.50 |
| 209 | Joe Nossek | 1.50 |
| 210 | Bob Gibson | 17.00 |
| 211 | Twins Team | 3.00 |
| 212 | Chris Zachary | 1.50 |
| 213 | Jay Johnstone | 1.75 |
| 214 | Tom Kelley | 1.50 |
| 215 | Ernie Banks | 18.00 |
| 216 | Bengal Belters: | 6.00 |
| | Norm Cash, Al Kaline | |
| 217 | Rob Gardner | 1.50 |
| 218 | Wes Parker | 1.50 |
| 219 | Clay Carroll | 1.50 |
| 220 | Jim Hart | 1.50 |
| 221 | Woody Fryman | 1.50 |
| 222 | Reds Rookies: | 2.00 |
| | Darrell Osteen, Lee May | |
| 223 | Mike Ryan | 1.50 |
| 224 | Walt Bond | 1.50 |
| 225 | Mel Stottlemyre | 2.50 |
| 226 | Julian Javier | 1.50 |
| 227 | Paul Lindblad | 1.50 |
| 228 | Gil Hodges (Mgr.) | 5.00 |
| 229 | Larry Jackson | 1.50 |
| 230 | Boog Powell | 3.00 |
| 231 | John Bateman | 1.50 |
| 232 | Don Buford | 1.50 |
| 233 | AL ERA Leaders: | 2.50 |
| | Joel Horlen, Gary Peters, | |
| | Steve Hargan | |
| 234 | NL ERA Leaders: | 6.00 |
| | Sandy Koufax, Mike | |
| | Cuellar, Juan Marichal | |
| 235 | AL Pitching Leaders: | 2.50 |
| | Earl Wilson, Jim Kaat, | |
| | Denny McLain | |

| NO. PLAYER | NR. MT. |
|---|---|
| 236 NL Pitching Leaders: Sandy Koufax, Juan Marichal, Gaylord Perry, Bob Gibson | 12.00 |
| 237 AL Strikeout Leaders: Jim Kaat, Earl Wilson, Sam McDowell | 2.50 |
| 238 NL Strikeout Leaders: Sandy Koufax, Jim Bunning, Bob Veale | 4.00 |
| 239 AL Batting Leaders: Al Kaline, Frank Robinson, Tony Oliva | 4.00 |
| 240 NL Batting Leaders: Matty Alou, Felipe Alou, Rico Carty | 2.50 |
| 241 AL RBI Leaders: Frank Robinson, Boog Powell, Harmon Killebrew | 4.50 |
| 242 NL RBI Leaders: Bob Clemente, Richie Allen, Hank Aaron | 6.00 |
| 243 AL Home Run Leaders: Frank Robinson, Harmon Killebrew, Boog Powell | 4.00 |
| 244 NL Home Run Leaders: Hank Aaron, Richie Allen, Willie Mays | 7.00 |
| 245 Curt Flood | 2.00 |
| 246 Jim Perry | 2.00 |
| 247 Jerry Lumpe | 1.50 |
| 248 Gene Mauch (Mgr.) | 1.75 |
| 249 Nick Willhite | 1.50 |
| 250 Hank Aaron | 75.00 |
| 251 Woody Held | 1.50 |
| 252 Bob Bolin | 1.50 |
| 253 Indians Rookies: Bill Davis, Gus Gil | 1.50 |
| 254 Milt Pappas | 1.50 |
| 255 Frank Howard | 2.00 |
| 256 Bob Hendley | 1.50 |
| 257 Charley Smith | 1.50 |
| 258 Lee Maye | 1.50 |
| 259 Don Dennis | 1.50 |
| 260 Jim Lefebvre | 1.75 |
| 261 John Wyatt | 1.50 |
| 262 Athletics Team | 3.00 |
| 263 Hank Aguirre | 1.50 |
| 264 Ron Swoboda | 1.75 |
| 265 Lou Burdette | 2.00 |
| 266 Pitt Power: W. Stargell, D. Clendenon | 4.00 |
| 267 Don Schwall | 1.50 |
| 268 John Briggs | 1.50 |
| 269 Don Nottebart | 1.50 |
| 270 Zoilo Versalles | 1.50 |
| 271 Eddie Watt | 1.50 |
| 272 Cubs Rookies: Bill Connors, Dave Dowling | 1.50 |
| 273 Dick Lines | 1.50 |
| 274 Bob Aspromonte | 1.50 |
| 275 Fred Whitfield | 1.50 |
| 276 Bruce Brubaker | 1.50 |
| 277 Steve Whitaker | 1.50 |
| 278 Checklist No. 4 | 4.00 |
| 279 Frank Linzy | 1.50 |
| 280 Tony Conigliaro | 5.00 |
| 281 Bob Rodgers | 1.50 |
| 282 Johnny Odom | 1.50 |
| 283 Gene Alley | 1.50 |
| 284 Johnny Podres | 2.00 |
| 285 Lou Brock | 20.00 |
| 286 Wayne Causey | 2.00 |
| 287 Mets Rookies: Greg Goossen, Bart Shirley | 2.50 |
| 288 Denver Lemaster | 2.00 |
| 289 Tom Tresh | 2.50 |
| 290 Bill White | 3.00 |
| 291 Jim Hannan | 2.50 |
| 292 Don Pavletich | 2.50 |
| 293 Ed Kirkpatrick | 2.50 |
| 294 Walt Alston (Mgr.) | 2.50 |
| 295 Sam McDowell | 3.00 |
| 296 Glenn Beckert | 2.00 |
| 297 Dave Morehead | 2.00 |

| NO. PLAYER | NR. MT. |
|---|---|
| 298 Ron Davis | 2.00 |
| 299 Norm Siebern | 2.00 |
| 300 Jim Kaat | 4.00 |
| 301 Jesse Gonder | 2.00 |
| 302 Orioles Team | 3.00 |
| 303 Gil Blanco | 2.00 |
| 304 Phil Gagliano | 2.00 |
| 305 Earl Wilson | 2.00 |
| 306 Bud Harrelson | 3.00 |
| 307 Jim Beauchamp | 2.00 |
| 308 Al Downing | 2.50 |
| 309 Hurlers Beware: J. Callison, Richie Allen | 3.00 |
| 310 Gary Peters | 2.00 |
| 311 Ed Brinkman | 2.00 |
| 312 Don Mincher | 2.00 |
| 313 Bob Lee | 2.00 |
| 314 Red Sox Rookies: Mike Andrews, R. Smith | 6.00 |
| 315 Billy Williams | 10.00 |
| 316 Jack Kralick | 2.00 |
| 317 Cesar Tovar | 2.00 |
| 318 Dave Giusti | 2.00 |
| 319 Paul Blair | 2.00 |
| 320 Gaylord Perry | 12.00 |
| 321 Mayo Smith (Mgr.) | 2.00 |
| 322 Jose Pagan | 2.00 |
| 323 Mike Hershberger | 2.00 |
| 324 Hal Woodeschick | 2.00 |
| 325 Chico Cardenas | 2.00 |
| 326 Bob Uecker | 20.00 |
| 327 Angels Team | 3.00 |
| 328 Clete Boyer | 2.50 |
| 329 Charlie Lau | 2.50 |
| 330 Claude Osteen | 2.00 |
| 331 Joe Foy | 2.00 |
| 332 Jesus Alou | 2.00 |
| 333 Ferguson Jenkins | 30.00 |
| 334 Twin Terrors: Bob Allison, H. Killebrew | 4.00 |
| 335 Bob Veale | 2.00 |
| 336 Joe Azcue | 2.00 |
| 337 Joe Morgan | 24.00 |
| 338 Bob Locker | 2.00 |
| 339 Chico Ruiz | 2.00 |
| 340 Joe Pepitone | 2.50 |
| 341 Giants Rookies: Dick Dietz, Bill Sorrell | 2.50 |
| 342 Hank Fischer | 2.00 |
| 343 Tom Satriano | 2.00 |
| 344 Ossie Chavarria | 2.00 |
| 345 Stu Miller | 2.00 |
| 346 Jim Hickman | 2.00 |
| 347 Grady Hatton (Mgr.) | 2.00 |
| 348 Tug McGraw | 3.00 |
| 349 Bob Chance | 2.00 |
| 350 Joe Torre | 3.00 |
| 351 Vern Law | 2.00 |
| 352 Ray Oyler | 2.00 |
| 353 Bill McCool | 2.00 |
| 354 Cubs Team | 3.00 |
| 355 Carl Yastrzemski | 95.00 |
| 356 Larry Jaster | 2.00 |
| 357 Bill Skowron | 2.50 |
| 358 Ruben Amaro | 2.00 |
| 359 Dick Ellsworth | 2.00 |
| 360 Leon Wagner | 2.00 |
| 361 Checklist No. 5 | 4.00 |
| 362 Darold Knowles | 2.00 |
| 363 Dave Johnson | 2.50 |
| 364 Claude Raymond | 2.00 |
| 365 John Roseboro | 2.00 |
| 366 Andy Kosco | 2.00 |
| 367 Angels Rookies: Bill Kelso, Don Wallace | 2.00 |
| 368 Jack Hiatt | 2.00 |
| 369 Jim Hunter | 20.00 |
| 370 Tommy Davis | 2.00 |
| 371 Jim Lonborg | 4.00 |
| 372 Mike De La Hoz | 2.50 |
| 373 White Sox Rookies: D. Josephson, F. Klages | 2.50 |
| 374 Mel Queen | 2.50 |
| 375 Jake Gibbs | 2.50 |
| 376 Don Lock | 2.50 |

| NO. PLAYER | NR. MT. |
|---|---|
| 377 Luis Tiant | 3.50 |
| 378 Tigers Team | 4.00 |
| 379 Jerry May | 2.50 |
| 380 Dean Chance | 2.50 |
| 381 Dick Schofield | 2.50 |
| 382 Dave McNally | 3.00 |
| 383 Ken Henderson | 2.50 |
| 384 Cardinals Rookies: Dick Hughes, Jim Cosman | 2.50 |
| 385 Jim Fregosi | 3.00 |
| 386 Dick Selma | 2.50 |
| 387 Cap Peterson | 2.50 |
| 388 Arnold Earley | 2.50 |
| 389 Al Dark (Mgr.) | 3.00 |
| 390 Jim Wynn | 3.00 |
| 391 Wilbur Wood | 2.50 |
| 392 Tommy Harper | 2.50 |
| 393 Jim Bouton | 3.00 |
| 394 Jake Wood | 2.50 |
| 395 Chris Short | 2.50 |
| 396 Atlanta Aces: D. Meke, T. Cloninger | 2.50 |
| 397 Willie Smith | 2.50 |
| 398 Jeff Torborg | 2.75 |
| 399 Al Worthington | 2.50 |
| 400 Bob Clemente | 60.00 |
| 401 Jim Coates | 2.50 |
| 402 Phillies Rookies: Grant Jackson, Billy Wilson | 2.50 |
| 403 Dick Nen | 2.50 |
| 404 Nelson Briles | 2.50 |
| 405 Russ Snyder | 2.50 |
| 406 Lee Elia | 2.50 |
| 407 Reds Team | 5.00 |
| 408 Jim Northrup | 2.50 |
| 409 Ray Sadecki | 2.50 |
| 410 Lou Johnson | 2.50 |
| 411 Dick Howser | 3.00 |
| 412 Astros Rookies: Norm Miller, Doug Rader | 3.50 |
| 413 Jerry Grote | 2.50 |
| 414 Casey Cox | 2.50 |
| 415 Sonny Jackson | 2.50 |
| 416 Roger Repoz | 2.50 |
| 417 Bob Bruce | 2.50 |
| 418 Sam Mele (Mgr.) | 2.50 |
| 419 Don Kessinger | 2.50 |
| 420 Denny McLain | 5.00 |
| 421 Dal Maxvill | 2.50 |
| 422 Hoyt Wilhelm | 7.00 |
| 423 Fence Busters: Willie Mays, Willie McCovey | 20.00 |
| 424 Pedro Gonzalez | 2.50 |
| 425 Pete Mikkelsen | 2.50 |
| 426 Lou Clinton | 2.50 |
| 427 Ruben Gomez | 2.50 |
| 428 Dodgers Rookies: Tom Hutton, Gene Michael | 3.00 |
| 429 Garry Roggenburk | 2.50 |
| 430 Pete Rose | 70.00 |
| 431 Ted Uhlaender | 3.00 |
| 432 Jimmie Hall | 3.00 |
| 433 Al Luplow | 3.00 |
| 434 Eddie Fisher | 3.00 |
| 435 Mack Jones | 3.00 |
| 436 Pete Ward | 3.00 |
| 437 Senators Team | 4.00 |
| 438 Chuck Dobson | 3.00 |
| 439 Byron Browne | 3.00 |
| 440 Steve Hargan | 3.00 |
| 441 Jim Davenport | 3.00 |
| 442 Yankees Rookies: Bill Robinson, Joe Verbanic | 4.00 |
| 443 Tito Francona | 3.00 |
| 444 George Smith | 3.00 |
| 445 Don Sutton | 25.00 |
| 446 Russ Nixon | 2.50 |
| 447 Bo Belinsky | 2.50 |
| 448 Harry Walker (Mgr.) | 2.50 |
| 449 Orlando Pena | 2.50 |
| 450 Richie Allen | 5.00 |
| 451 Fred Newman | 2.50 |
| 452 Ed Kranepool | 3.00 |
| 453 Aurelio Monteagudo | 2.50 |
| 454 Checklist No. 6 | 5.00 |

| NO. PLAYER | NR. MT. |
|---|---|
| 455 Tommy Agee | 2.50 |
| 456 Phil Niekro | 12.00 |
| 457 Andy Etchebarren | 2.50 |
| 458 Lee Thomas | 6.00 |
| 459 Senators Rookies: Dick Bosman, Pete Craig | 6.00 |
| 460 Harmon Killebrew | 45.00 |
| 461 Bob Miller | 5.00 |
| 462 Bob Barton | 5.00 |
| 463 Hill Aces: Sam McDowell, S. Siebert | 5.00 |
| 464 Dan Coombs | 5.00 |
| 465 Willie Horton | 5.00 |
| 466 Bobby Wine | 5.00 |
| 467 Jim O'Toole | 5.00 |
| 468 Ralph Houk (Mgr.) | 7.50 |
| 469 Len Gabrielson | 6.00 |
| 470 Bob Shaw | 6.00 |
| 471 Rene Lachemann | 6.00 |
| 472 Rookies Pirates: John Gelnar, G. Spriggs | 6.00 |
| 473 Jose Santiago | 6.00 |
| 474 Bob Tolan | 6.00 |
| 475 Jim Palmer | 100.00 |
| 476 Tony Perez | 80.00 |
| 477 Braves Team | 12.00 |
| 478 Bob Humphreys | 6.00 |
| 479 Gary Bell | 6.00 |
| 480 Willie McCovey | 30.00 |
| 481 Leo Durocher (Mgr.) | 10.00 |
| 482 Bill Monbouquette | 6.00 |
| 483 Jim Landis | 6.00 |
| 484 Jerry Adair | 6.00 |
| 485 Tim McCarver | 20.00 |
| 486 Twins Rookies: Rich Reese, Bill Whitby | 6.00 |
| 487 Tom Reynolds | 6.00 |
| 488 Gerry Arrigo | 6.00 |
| 489 Doug Clemens | 6.00 |
| 490 Tony Cloninger | 6.00 |
| 491 Sam Bowens | 6.00 |
| 492 Pirates Team | 13.00 |
| 493 Phil Ortega | 6.00 |
| 494 Bill Rigney (Mgr.) | 6.00 |
| 495 Fritz Peterson | 6.00 |
| 496 Orlando McFarlane | 6.00 |
| 497 Ron Campbell | 6.00 |
| 498 Larry Dierker | 6.00 |
| 499 Indians Rookies: George Culver, Jose Vidal | 6.00 |
| 500 Juan Marichal | 22.00 |
| 501 Jerry Zimmerman | 6.00 |
| 502 Derrell Griffith | 6.00 |
| 503 Dodgers Team | 12.00 |
| 504 Orlando Martinez | 6.00 |
| 505 Tommy Helms | 6.00 |
| 506 Smoky Burgess | 6.00 |
| 507 Orioles Rookies: Ed Barnowski, Larry Haney | 6.00 |
| 508 Dick Hall | 6.00 |
| 509 Jim King | 6.00 |
| 510 Bill Mazeroski | 12.00 |
| 511 Don Wert | 6.00 |
| 512 R. Schoendienst (Mgr.) | 10.00 |
| 513 Marcelino Lopez | 6.00 |
| 514 John Werhas | 6.00 |
| 515 Bert Campaneris | 7.00 |
| 516 Giants Team | 13.00 |
| 517 Fred Talbot | 6.00 |
| 518 Denis Menke | 6.00 |
| 519 Ted Davidson | 6.00 |
| 520 Max Alvis | 6.00 |
| 521 Bird Bombers: Boog Powell, Curt Blefary | 7.00 |
| 522 John Stephenson | 6.00 |
| 523 Jim Merritt | 6.00 |
| 524 Felix Mantilla | 6.00 |
| 525 Ron Hunt | 6.00 |
| 526 Tigers Rookies: Pat Dobson, G. Korince | 7.00 |
| 527 Dennis Ribant | 6.00 |
| 528 Rico Petrocelli | 7.00 |
| 529 Gary Wagner | 6.00 |
| 530 Felipe Alou | 7.00 |
| 531 Checklist No. 7 | 10.00 |

| NO. PLAYER | NR. MT. |
|---|---|
| 532 Jim Hicks | 6.00 |
| 533 Jack Fisher | 6.00 |
| 534 Hank Bauer (Mgr.) | 18.00 |
| 535 Donn Clendenon | 18.00 |
| 536 Cubs Rookies: | 35.00 |
| Joe Niekro, Paul Popovich | |
| 537 Chuck Estrada | 18.00 |
| 538 J.C. Martin | 18.00 |
| 539 Dick Egan | 18.00 |
| 540 Norm Cash | 35.00 |
| 541 Joe Gibbon | 15.00 |
| 542 Athletics Rookies: | 11.00 |
| Tony Pierce, Rick Monday | |
| 543 Dan Schneider | 18.00 |
| 544 Indians Team | 30.00 |
| 545 Jim Grant | 18.00 |
| 546 Woody Woodward | 18.00 |
| 547 Red Sox Rookies: | 18.00 |
| Russ Gibson, Bill Rohr | |
| 548 Tony Gonzalez | 18.00 |
| 549 Jack Sanford | 18.00 |
| 550 Vada Pinson | 12.00 |
| 551 Doug Camilli | 18.00 |

| NO. PLAYER | NR. MT. |
|---|---|
| 552 Ted Savage | 18.00 |
| 553 Yankees Rookies: | 30.00 |
| Mike Hegan, Thad Tillotson | |
| 554 Andre Rodgers | 18.00 |
| 555 Don Cardwell | 18.00 |
| 556 Al Weis | 18.00 |
| 557 Al Ferrara | 18.00 |
| 558 Orioles Rookies: | 45.00 |
| Mark Belanger, Bill Dillman | |
| 559 Dick Tracewski | 18.00 |
| 560 Jim Bunning | 45.00 |
| 561 Sandy Alomar | 18.00 |
| 562 Steve Blass | 18.00 |
| 563 Joe Adcock (Mgr.) | 24.00 |
| 564 Astros Rookies: | 18.00 |
| Alonzo Harris, A. Pointer | |
| 565 Lew Krausse | 18.00 |
| 566 Gary Geiger | 18.00 |
| 567 Steve Hamilton | 18.00 |
| 568 John Sullivan | 18.00 |
| 569 AL Rookies: | 475.00 |
| Rod Carew, Hank Allen | |
| 570 Maury Wills | 100.00 |

| NO. PLAYER | NR. MT. |
|---|---|
| 571 Larry Sherry | 18.00 |
| 572 Don Demeter | 18.00 |
| 573 White Sox Team | 30.00 |
| 574 Jerry Buchek | 18.00 |
| 575 Dave Boswell | 18.00 |
| 576 NL Rookies: | 18.00 |
| R. Hernandez, Norm Gigon | |
| 577 Bill Short | 18.00 |
| 578 John Boccabella | 18.00 |
| 579 Bill Henry | 18.00 |
| 580 Rocky Colavito | 60.00 |
| 581 Mets Rookies: | 1150.00 |
| Bill Denehy, Tom Seaver | |
| 582 Jim Owens | 18.00 |
| 583 Ray Barker | 18.00 |
| 584 Jim Piersall | 22.00 |
| 585 Wally Bunker | 18.00 |
| 586 Manny Jimenez | 18.00 |
| 587 NL Rookies: | 20.00 |
| Don Shaw, Gary Sutherland | |
| 588 Johnny Klippstein | 18.00 |
| 589 Dave Ricketts | 18.00 |
| 590 Pete Richert | 18.00 |

| NO. PLAYER | NR. MT. |
|---|---|
| 591 Ty Cline | 18.00 |
| 592 NL Rookies: | 18.00 |
| Jim Shellenback, Ron Wi |
| 593 Wes Westrum (Mgr.) | 18.00 |
| 594 Dan Osinski | 18.00 |
| 595 Cookie Rojas | 18.00 |
| 596 Galen Cisco | 18.00 |
| 597 Ted Abernathy | 18.00 |
| 598 White Sox Rookies: | 18.00 |
| Ed Stroud, Walt Williams | |
| 599 Bob Duliba (Mgr.) | 18.00 |
| 600 Brooks Robinson | 225.00 |
| 601 Bill Bryan | 18.00 |
| 602 Juan Pizarro | 18.00 |
| 603 Athletics Rookies: | 18.00 |
| Tim Talton, Ramon Webster | |
| 604 Red Sox Team | 125.00 |
| 605 Mike Shannon | 40.00 |
| 606 Ron Taylor | 18.00 |
| 607 Mickey Stanley | 30.00 |
| 608 Cubs Rookies: | 18.00 |
| John Upham, Rich Nye | |
| 609 Tommy John (exc. $30.00) | 120.00 |

## 1968 Topps . . . Complete Set of 598 Cards—Value $1200.00 (Exc.); $3000.00 (Near Mint)

Features the rookie cards of Johnny Bench and Nolan Ryan. High numbers are 534 to 598. Card 66 exists with "Senators" in *white*—worth $1.50 and "Senators" in *yellow*—$90.00. Card 518 (checklist) exists identifying card 539 as "Maj. L. Rookies"—worth $3.00 or "Am. L. Rookies"—worth $12.00.

    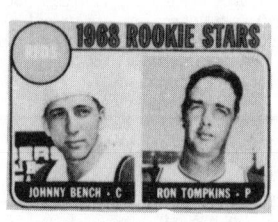

| NO. PLAYER | NR. MT. |
|---|---|
| 1 NL Ldrs.: (exc. $2.50) | 12.50 |
| Bob Clemente, Matty Alou, Tony Gonzalez | |
| 2 AL Batting Leaders: | 7.00 |
| Frank Robinson, Al Kaline, Carl Yastrzemski | |
| 3 NL RBI Leaders: | 4.50 |
| Hank Aaron, O. Cepeda, Bob Clemente | |
| 4 AL RBI Leaders: | 7.50 |
| C. Yastrzemski, H. Killebrew, F. Robinson | |
| 5 NL Home Run Leaders: | 4.00 |
| Ron Santo, Hank Aaron, Jim Wynn, Willie McCovey | |
| 6 AL Home Run Leaders: | 4.00 |
| C. Yastrzemski, H. Killebrew, F. Howard | |
| 7 NL ERA Leaders: | 2.50 |
| Jim Bunning, Chris Short, Phil Niekro | |
| 8 AL ERA Leaders: | 2.50 |
| Joe Horlen, Sonny Siebert, Gary Peters | |
| 9 NL Pitching Leaders: | 2.50 |
| C. Osteen, M. McCormick, F. Jenkins, J. Bunning | |
| 10 AL Pitching Leaders: | 2.50 |
| Jim Lonborg, Earl Wilson, Dean Chance | |
| 11 NL Strikeout Leaders: | 2.50 |
| Ferguson Jenkins, Gaylord Perry, Jim Bunning | |
| 12 AL Strikeout Leaders: | 2.50 |
| Jim Lonborg, Dean Chance, Sam McDowell | |

| NO. PLAYER | NR. MT. |
|---|---|
| 13 Chuck Hartenstein | 1.25 |
| 14 Jerry McNertney | 1.25 |
| 15 Ron Hunt | 1.25 |
| 16 Indians Rookies: | 1.25 |
| Lou Piniella, R. Schienblum | |
| 17 Dick Hall | 1.25 |
| 18 Mike Hershberger | 1.25 |
| 19 Juan Pizzaro | 1.25 |
| 20 Brooks Robinson | 17.00 |
| 21 Ron Davis | 1.25 |
| 22 Pat Dobson | 1.25 |
| 23 Chico Cardenas | 1.25 |
| 24 Bobby Locke | 1.25 |
| 25 Jan Javier | 1.25 |
| 26 Darrell Brandon | 1.25 |
| 27 Gil Hodges (Mgr.) | 6.00 |
| 28 Ted Uhlaender | 1.25 |
| 29 Joe Verbanic | 1.25 |
| 30 Joe Torre | 2.00 |
| 31 Ed Stroud | 1.25 |
| 32 Joe Gibbon | 1.25 |
| 33 Pete Ward | 1.25 |
| 34 Al Ferrara | 1.25 |
| 35 Steve Hargan | 1.25 |
| 36 Pirates Rookies: | 1.25 |
| Bob Moose, B. Robertson | |
| 37 Billy Williams | 9.00 |
| 38 Tony Pierce | 1.25 |
| 39 Cookie Rojas | 1.25 |
| 40 Denny McLain | 7.50 |
| 41 Julio Gotay | 1.25 |
| 42 Larry Haney | 1.25 |
| 43 Gary Bell | 1.25 |
| 44 Frank Kostro | 1.25 |
| 45 Tom Seaver | 200.00 |
| 46 Dave Ricketts | 1.25 |

| NO. PLAYER | NR. MT. |
|---|---|
| 47 Ralph Houk (Mgr.) | 1.50 |
| 48 Ted Davidson | 1.25 |
| 49 Ed Brinkman | 1.25 |
| 50 Willy Mays | 55.00 |
| 51 Bob Locker | 1.25 |
| 52 Hawk Taylor | 1.25 |
| 53 Gene Alley | 1.25 |
| 54 Stan Williams | 1.25 |
| 55 Felipe Alou | 1.50 |
| 56 Orioles Rookies: | 1.25 |
| Dave May, Dave Leonhard | |
| 57 Dan Schneider | 1.25 |
| 58 Ed Mathews | 8.00 |
| 59 Don Lock | 1.25 |
| 60 Ken Holtzman | 1.50 |
| 61 Reggie Smith | 1.75 |
| 62 Chuck Dobson | 1.25 |
| 63 Dick Kenworthy | 1.25 |
| 64 Jim Merritt | 1.25 |
| 65 John Roseboro | 1.25 |
| 66 Casey Cox* | 1.25 |
| 67 Checklist No. 1 | 4.00 |
| 68 Ron Willis | 1.25 |
| 69 Tom Tresh | 1.50 |
| 70 Bob Veale | 1.50 |
| 71 Vern Fuller | 1.25 |
| 72 Tommy John | 4.00 |
| 73 Jim Hart | 1.25 |
| 74 Milt Pappas | 1.50 |
| 75 Don Mincher | 1.25 |
| 76 Braves Rookies: | 1.75 |
| Jim Britton, Ron Reed | |
| 77 Don Wilson | 1.25 |
| 78 Jim Northrup | 1.50 |
| 79 Ted Kubiak | 1.25 |
| 80 Rod Carew | 135.00 |

| NO. PLAYER | NR. MT. |
|---|---|
| 81 Larry Jackson | 1.25 |
| 82 Sam Bowens | 1.25 |
| 83 John Stephenson | 1.25 |
| 84 Bob Tolan | 1.25 |
| 85 Gaylord Perry | 10.00 |
| 86 Willie Stargell | 11.00 |
| 87 Dick Williams (Mgr.) | 1.50 |
| 88 Phil Regan | 1.25 |
| 89 Jake Gibbs | 1.25 |
| 90 Vada Pinson | 2.00 |
| 91 Jim Ollom | 1.25 |
| 92 Ed Kranepool | 1.25 |
| 93 Tony Cloninger | 1.25 |
| 94 Lee Maye | 1.25 |
| 95 Bob Aspromonte | 1.25 |
| 96 Senator Rookies: | 1.25 |
| Frank Coggins, Dick Nold | |
| 97 Tom Phoebus | 1.25 |
| 98 Gary Sutherland | 1.25 |
| 99 Rocky Colavito | 3.00 |
| 100 Bob Gibson | 22.00 |
| 101 Glenn Beckert | 1.25 |
| 102 Jose Cardenal | 1.25 |
| 103 Don Sutton | 9.00 |
| 104 Dick Dietz | 1.25 |
| 105 Al Downing | 1.50 |
| 106 Dalton Jones | 1.25 |
| 107 Checklist No. 2 | 4.00 |
| 108 Don Pavletich | 1.25 |
| 109 Bert Campaneris | 1.50 |
| 110 Hank Aaron | 60.00 |
| 111 Rich Reese | 1.25 |
| 112 Woody Fryman | 1.25 |
| 113 Tigers Rookies: | 1.25 |
| T. Matchick, D. Patterson | |
| 114 Ron Swoboda | 1.50 |

| NO. PLAYER | NR. MT. |
|---|---|
| 115 Sam McDowell | 1.50 |
| 116 Ken McMullen | 1.25 |
| 117 Larry Jaster | 1.25 |
| 118 Mark Belanger | 1.75 |
| 119 Ted Savage | 1.25 |
| 120 Mel Stottlemyre | 2.00 |
| 121 Jimmie Hall | 1.25 |
| 122 Gene Mauch (Mgr.) | 1.25 |
| 123 Jose Santiago | 1.25 |
| 124 Nate Oliver | 1.25 |
| 125 Joe Horlen | 1.25 |
| 126 Bobby Etheridge | 1.25 |
| 127 Paul Lindblad | 1.25 |
| 128 Astros Rookies: | 1.25 |
| Alonzo Harris, Tom Dukes | |
| 129 Mickey Stanley | 1.25 |
| 130 Tony Perez | 12.00 |
| 131 Frank Bertaina | 1.25 |
| 132 Bud Harrelson | 1.25 |
| 133 Fred Whitfield | 1.25 |
| 134 Pat Jarvis | 1.25 |
| 135 Paul Blair | 1.25 |
| 136 Randy Hundley | 1.25 |
| 137 Minnesota Twins | 3.00 |
| 138 Ruben Amaro | 1.25 |
| 139 Chris Short | 1.25 |
| 140 Tony Conigliaro | 4.00 |
| 141 Dal Maxvill | 1.25 |
| 142 White Sox Rookies: | 1.25 |
| Bill Voss, B. Bradford | |
| 143 Pete Cimino | 1.25 |
| 144 Joe Morgan | 15.00 |
| 145 Don Drysdale | 10.00 |
| 146 Sal Bando | 2.50 |
| 147 Frank Linzy | 1.25 |
| 148 Dave Bristol (Mgr.) | 1.25 |
| 149 Bob Saverine | 1.25 |
| 150 Bob Clemente | 45.00 |
| 151 World Series Game 1: | 6.00 |
| Brock Socks 4 Hits | |
| 152 World Series Game 2: | 8.00 |
| Yaz Smashes 2 Homers | |
| 153 World Series Game 3: | 3.00 |
| Briles Cools Off Boston | |
| 154 World Series Game 4: | 6.00 |
| Gibson Hurls Shutout | |
| 155 World Series Game 5: | 3.00 |
| Lonborg Wins Again | |
| 156 World Series Game 6: | 3.00 |
| Petrocelli 2 Homers | |
| 157 World Series Game 7: | 3.00 |
| St. Louis Wins It | |
| 158 World Series: | 3.00 |
| The Cardinal Celebrate | |
| 159 Don Kessinger | 1.50 |
| 160 Earl Wilson | 1.25 |
| 161 Norm Miller | 1.25 |
| 162 Cardinals Rookies: | 2.00 |
| Hal Gilson, Mike Torrez | |
| 163 Gene Brabender | 1.25 |
| 164 Ramon Webster | 1.25 |
| 165 Tony Oliva | 3.00 |
| 166 Claude Raymond | 1.25 |
| 167 Elston Howard | 2.50 |
| 168 Los Angeles Dodgers | 3.00 |
| 169 Bob Bolin | 1.25 |
| 170 Jim Fregosi | 2.00 |
| 171 Don Nottebart | 1.25 |
| 172 Walt Williams | 1.25 |
| 173 John Boozer | 1.25 |
| 174 Bob Tillman | 1.25 |
| 175 Maury Wills | 4.00 |
| 176 Bob Allen | 1.25 |
| 177 Mets Rookies: | 1500.00 |
| J. Koosman, Nolan Ryan | |
| 178 Don Wert | 1.25 |
| 179 Bill Stoneman | 1.25 |
| 180 Curt Flood | 1.50 |
| 181 Jerry Zimmerman | 1.25 |
| 182 Dave Guisti | 1.25 |
| 183 Bob Kennedy | 1.25 |
| 184 Lou Johnson | 1.25 |
| 185 Tom Haller | 1.25 |
| 186 Eddie Watt | 1.25 |
| 187 Sonny Jackson | 1.25 |

| NO. PLAYER | NR. MT. |
|---|---|
| 188 Cap Peterson | 1.25 |
| 189 Bill Landis | 1.25 |
| 190 Bill White | 2.50 |
| 191 Dan Frisella | 1.25 |
| 192 Checklist No. 3 | 6.00 |
| 193 Jack Hamilton | 1.25 |
| 194 Don Buford | 1.25 |
| 195 Joe Pepitone | 1.50 |
| 196 Gary Nolan | 1.25 |
| 197 Larry Brown | 1.25 |
| 198 Roy Face | 2.00 |
| 199 A's Rookies: | 1.25 |
| R. Rodriquez, D. Osteen | |
| 200 Orlando Cepeda | 4.00 |
| 201 Mike Marshall (R) | 2.50 |
| 202 Adolfo Phillips | 1.25 |
| 203 Dick Kelley | 1.25 |
| 204 Andy Etchebarren | 1.25 |
| 205 Juan Marichal | 7.50 |
| 206 Cal Ermer | 1.25 |
| 207 Carroll Sembera | 1.25 |
| 208 Willie Davis | 1.75 |
| 209 Tim Cullen | 1.25 |
| 210 Gary Peters | 1.25 |
| 211 J.C. Martin | 1.25 |
| 212 Dave Morehead | 1.25 |
| 213 Chico Ruiz | 1.25 |
| 214 Yankees Rookies: | 2.50 |
| S. Bahnsen, F. Fernandez | |
| 215 Jim Bunning | 4.00 |
| 216 Bubba Morton | 1.25 |
| 217 Turk Farrell | 1.25 |
| 218 Ken Suarez | 1.25 |
| 219 Rob Gardner | 1.25 |
| 220 Harmon Killebrew | 12.00 |
| 221 Atlanta Braves | 3.00 |
| 222 Jim Hardin | 1.25 |
| 223 Ollie Brown | 1.25 |
| 224 Jack Aker | 1.25 |
| 225 Richie Allen | 3.00 |
| 226 Jimmie Price | 1.25 |
| 227 Joe Hoerner | 1.25 |
| 228 Dodgers Rookies: | 1.25 |
| Jack Billingham, Jim Fairev | |
| 229 Fred Klages | 1.25 |
| 230 Pete Rose | 50.00 |
| 231 Dave Baldwin | 1.25 |
| 232 Denis Menke | 1.25 |
| 233 George Scott | 1.50 |
| 234 Bill Monbouquette | 1.25 |
| 235 Ron Santo | 2.50 |
| 236 Tug McGraw | 3.00 |
| 237 Alvin Dark (Mgr.) | 2.00 |
| 238 Tom Satriano | 1.25 |
| 239 Bill Henry | 1.25 |
| 240 Al Kaline | 20.00 |
| 241 Felix Millan | 1.25 |
| 242 Moe Drabowsky | 1.25 |
| 243 Rich Rollins | 1.25 |
| 244 John Donaldson | 1.25 |
| 245 Tony Gonzalez | 1.25 |
| 246 Fritz Peterson | 1.25 |
| 247 Reds Rookies: | 300.00 |
| Johnny Bench, R. Tompkins | |
| 248 Fred Valentine | 1.25 |
| 249 Bill Singer | 1.25 |
| 250 Carl Yastrzemski | 40.00 |
| 251 Manny Sanguillen (R) | 4.00 |
| 252 Angels Team | 3.00 |
| 253 Dick Hughes | 1.25 |
| 254 Cleon Jones | 1.25 |
| 255 Dean Chance | 1.25 |
| 256 Norm Cash | 4.00 |
| 257 Phil Niekro | 6.00 |
| 258 Cubs Rookies: | 1.75 |
| J. Arcia, B. Schlesinger | |
| 259 Ken Boyer | 2.00 |
| 260 Jim Wynn | 1.75 |
| 261 Dave Duncan | 1.25 |
| 262 Rick Wise | 1.25 |
| 263 Horace Clarke | 1.50 |
| 264 Ted Abernathy | 1.25 |
| 265 Tommy Davis | 1.50 |
| 266 Paul Popovich | 1.25 |
| 267 Herman Franks (Mgr.) | 1.25 |

| NO. PLAYER | NR. MT. |
|---|---|
| 268 Bob Humphreys | 1.25 |
| 269 Bob Tiefenauer | 1.25 |
| 270 Matty Alou | 2.00 |
| 271 Bobby Knoop | 1.25 |
| 272 Ray Culp | 1.25 |
| 273 Dave Johnson | 1.50 |
| 274 Mike Cuellar | 1.75 |
| 275 Tim McCarver | 2.50 |
| 276 Jim Roland | 1.25 |
| 277 Jerry Buchek | 1.25 |
| 278 Checklist No. 4 | 4.00 |
| 279 Bill Hands | 1.25 |
| 280 Mickey Mantle | 200.00 |
| 281 Jim Campanis | 1.25 |
| 282 Rick Monday | 1.50 |
| 283 Mel Queen | 1.25 |
| 284 John Briggs | 1.25 |
| 285 Dick McAuliffe | 1.25 |
| 286 Cecil Upshaw | 1.25 |
| 287 White Sox Rookies: | 1.50 |
| Mickey Abarbanel, | |
| Cisco Carlos | |
| 288 Dave Wickersham | 1.25 |
| 289 Woody Held | 1.25 |
| 290 Willie McCovey | 10.00 |
| 291 Dick Lines | 1.25 |
| 292 Art Shamsky | 1.25 |
| 293 Bruce Howard | 1.25 |
| 294 Red Schoendienst | 4.00 |
| 295 Sonny Siebert | 1.25 |
| 296 Byron Browne | 1.25 |
| 297 Russ Gibson | 1.25 |
| 298 Jim Brewer | 1.25 |
| 299 Gene Michael | 1.50 |
| 300 Rusty Staub | 2.00 |
| 301 Twins Rookies: | 2.00 |
| G. Mitterwald, R. Renick | |
| 302 Gerry Arrigo | 1.25 |
| 303 Dick Green | 1.25 |
| 304 Sandy Valdespino | 1.25 |
| 305 Minnie Rojas | 1.25 |
| 306 Mike Ryan | 1.25 |
| 307 John Hiller | 1.25 |
| 308 Pittsburgh Pirates | 3.00 |
| 309 Ken Henderson | 1.25 |
| 310 Luis Aparicio | 5.00 |
| 311 Jack Lamabe | 1.25 |
| 312 Curt Blefary | 1.25 |
| 313 Al Weis | 1.25 |
| 314 Red Sox Rookies: | 1.25 |
| Bill Rohr, George Spriggs | |
| 315 Zoilo Versalles | 1.25 |
| 316 Steve Barber | 1.25 |
| 317 Ron Brand | 1.25 |
| 318 Chico Salmon | 1.25 |
| 319 George Culver | 1.25 |
| 320 Frank Howard | 2.00 |
| 321 Leo Durocher (Mgr.) | 2.50 |
| 322 Dave Boswell | 1.25 |
| 323 Deron Johnson | 1.25 |
| 324 Jim Nash | 1.25 |
| 325 Manny Mota | 1.75 |
| 326 Denny Ribant | 1.25 |
| 327 Tony Taylor | 1.25 |
| 328 Angels Rookies: | 1.25 |
| Chuck Vinson, Jim Weaver | |
| 329 Duane Josephson | 1.25 |
| 330 Roger Maris | 32.00 |
| 331 Dan Osinski | 1.25 |
| 332 Doug Rader | 1.25 |
| 333 Ron Herbel | 1.25 |
| 334 Baltimore Orioles | 3.00 |
| 335 Bob Allison | 1.25 |
| 336 John Purdin | 1.25 |
| 337 Bill Robinson | 1.25 |
| 338 Bob Johnson | 1.25 |
| 339 Rich Nye | 1.25 |
| 340 Max Alvis | 1.25 |
| 341 Jim Lemon (Mgr.) | 1.25 |
| 342 Ken Johnson | 1.25 |
| 343 Jim Gosger | 1.25 |
| 344 Don Clendenon | 1.75 |
| 345 Bob Hendley | 1.25 |
| 346 Jerry Adair | 1.25 |
| 347 George Brunet | 1.25 |

| NO. PLAYER | NR. MT. |
|---|---|
| 348 Phillies Rookies: | 1.25 |
| Larry Colton, Dick Thoenen | |
| 349 Ed Spiezio | 1.25 |
| 350 Hoyt Wilhelm | 6.00 |
| 351 Bob Barton | 1.25 |
| 352 Jackie Hernandez | 1.25 |
| 353 Mack Jones | 1.25 |
| 354 Pete Richert | 1.25 |
| 355 Ernie Banks | 18.00 |
| 356 Checklist No. 5 | 4.00 |
| 357 Len Gabrielson | 1.25 |
| 358 Mike Epstein | 1.25 |
| 359 Joe Moeller | 1.25 |
| 360 Willie Horton | 1.75 |
| 361 Harmon Killebrew (AS) | 6.00 |
| 362 Orlando Cepeda (AS) | 3.00 |
| 363 Rod Carew (AS) | 12.00 |
| 364 Joe Morgan (AS) | 7.00 |
| 365 Brooks Robinson (AS) | 7.00 |
| 366 Ron Santo (AS) | 2.50 |
| 367 Jim Fregosi (AS) | 2.00 |
| 368 Gene Alley (AS) | 2.00 |
| 369 Carl Yastrzemski (AS) | 11.00 |
| 370 Hank Aaron (AS) | 12.00 |
| 371 Tony Oliva (AS) | 2.50 |
| 372 Lou Brock (AS) | 7.00 |
| 373 Frank Robinson (AS) | 7.00 |
| 374 Bob Clemente (AS) | 11.00 |
| 375 Bill Freehan (AS) | 2.00 |
| 376 Tim McCarver (AS) | 3.00 |
| 377 Joe Horlen (AS) | 2.00 |
| 378 Bob Gibson (AS) | 7.00 |
| 379 Gary Peters (AS) | 2.00 |
| 380 Ken Holtzman (AS) | 2.00 |
| 381 Boog Powell | 2.50 |
| 382 Ramon Hernandez | 1.25 |
| 383 Steve Whitaker | 1.25 |
| 384 Reds Rookies: | 7.50 |
| Bill Henry, Hal McRae | |
| 385 Jim Hunter | 12.00 |
| 386 Greg Goossen | 1.25 |
| 387 Joe Foy | 1.25 |
| 388 Ray Washburn | 1.25 |
| 389 Jay Johnstone | 1.25 |
| 390 Bill Mazeroski | 2.50 |
| 391 Bob Priddy | 1.25 |
| 392 Grady Hatton (Mgr.) | 1.25 |
| 393 Jim Perry | 1.50 |
| 394 Tommie Aaron | 1.50 |
| 395 Camilo Pascual | 1.50 |
| 396 Bobby Wine | 1.25 |
| 397 Vic Davalillo | 1.25 |
| 398 Jim Grant | 1.25 |
| 399 Ray Oyler | 1.25 |
| 400 Mike McCormick | 1.25 |
| 401 New York Mets | 3.00 |
| 402 Mike Hegan | 1.25 |
| 403 John Buzhardt | 1.25 |
| 404 Floyd Robinson | 1.25 |
| 405 Tommy Helms | 1.25 |
| 406 Dick Ellsworth | 1.25 |
| 407 Gary Kolb | 1.25 |
| 408 Steve Carlton | 50.00 |
| 409 Orioles Rookies: | 1.25 |
| Frank Peters, Don Stone | |
| 410 Ferguson Jenkins | 16.00 |
| 411 Ron Hansen | 1.25 |
| 412 Clay Carroll | 1.25 |
| 413 Tommy McCraw | 1.25 |
| 414 Mickey Lolich | 3.00 |
| 415 Johnny Callison | 1.25 |
| 416 Bill Rigney (Mgr.) | 1.25 |
| 417 Willie Crawford | 1.25 |
| 418 Eddie Fisher | 1.25 |
| 419 Jack Hiatt | 1.25 |
| 420 Cesar Tovar | 1.25 |
| 421 Ron Taylor | 1.25 |
| 422 Rene Lachemann | 1.25 |
| 423 Fred Gladding | 1.25 |
| 424 Chicago White Sox | 3.00 |
| 425 Jim Maloney | 1.25 |
| 426 Hank Allen | 1.25 |
| 427 Dick Calmus | 1.25 |
| 428 Vic Roznovsky | 1.25 |
| 429 Tommie Sisk | 1.25 |

| NO. | PLAYER | NR. MT. |
|---|---|---|
| 430 | Rico Petrocelli | 2.50 |
| 431 | Dooley Womack | 1.25 |
| 432 | Indians Rookies: | 1.25 |
| | Bill Davis, Jose Vidal | |
| 433 | Bob Rodgers | 1.25 |
| 434 | Ricardo Joseph | 1.25 |
| 435 | Ron Perranoski | 1.50 |
| 436 | Hal Lanier | 1.25 |
| 437 | Don Cardwell | 1.25 |
| 438 | Lee Thomas | 1.25 |
| 439 | Luman Harris (Mgr.) | 1.25 |
| 440 | Claude Osteen | 1.25 |
| 441 | Alex Johnson | 1.25 |
| 442 | Dick Bosman | 1.25 |
| 443 | Joe Azcue | 1.25 |
| 444 | Jack Fisher | 1.25 |
| 445 | Mike Shannon | 1.25 |
| 446 | Ron Kline | 1.25 |
| 447 | Tigers Rookies: | 1.25 |
| | G. Korince, F. Lasher | |
| 448 | Gary Wagner | 1.25 |
| 449 | Gene Oliver | 1.25 |
| 450 | Jim Kaat | 3.00 |
| 451 | Al Spangler | 1.25 |
| 452 | Jesus Alou | 1.25 |
| 453 | Sammy Ellis | 1.25 |
| 454 | Checklist No. 6 | 6.00 |
| 455 | Rico Carty | 2.50 |
| 456 | John O'Donoghue | 1.25 |
| 457 | Jim Lefebvre | 1.25 |
| 458 | Lew Krausse | 2.25 |
| 459 | Dick Simpson | 2.25 |
| 460 | Jim Lonborg | 2.25 |
| 461 | Chuck Hiller | 2.25 |
| 462 | Barry Moore | 2.25 |
| 463 | Jimmie Schaffer | 2.25 |
| 464 | Don McMahon | 2.25 |
| 465 | Tommie Agee | 2.25 |
| 466 | Bill Dillman | 2.25 |
| 467 | Dick Howser | 2.25 |
| 468 | Larry Sherry | 2.25 |
| 469 | Ty Cline | 2.25 |
| 470 | Bill Freehan | 2.50 |
| 471 | Orlando Pena | 2.50 |
| 472 | Walt Alston (Mgr.) | 3.00 |
| 473 | Al Worthington | 2.25 |

| NO. | PLAYER | NR. MT. |
|---|---|---|
| 474 | Paul Schaal | 2.25 |
| 475 | Joe Niekro | 3.00 |
| 476 | Woody Woodward | 2.25 |
| 477 | Philadelphia Phillies | 4.00 |
| 478 | Dave McNally | 2.25 |
| 479 | Phil Gagliano | 2.25 |
| 480 | Manager's Dream: | 25.00 |
| | Tony Oliva, Chico | |
| | Cardenas, Bob Clemente | |
| 481 | John Wyatt | 2.25 |
| 482 | Jose Pagan | 2.25 |
| 483 | Darold Knowles | 2.25 |
| 484 | Phil Roof | 2.25 |
| 485 | Ken Berry | 2.25 |
| 486 | Cal Koonce | 2.25 |
| 487 | Lee May | 2.25 |
| 488 | Dick Tracewski | 2.25 |
| 489 | Wally Bunker | 2.25 |
| 490 | Super Stars: | 80.00 |
| | Harmon Killebrew, Willie | |
| | Mays, Mickey Mantle | |
| 491 | Denny LeMaster | 2.25 |
| 492 | Jeff Torborg | 2.25 |
| 493 | Jim McGlothlin | 2.25 |
| 494 | Ray Sadecki | 2.25 |
| 495 | Leon Wagner | 2.25 |
| 496 | Steve Hamilton | 2.25 |
| 497 | St. Louis Cardinals | 4.00 |
| 498 | Bill Bryan | 2.25 |
| 499 | Steve Blass | 2.25 |
| 500 | Frank Robinson | 21.00 |
| 501 | John Odom | 2.25 |
| 502 | Mike Andrews | 2.25 |
| 503 | Al Jackson | 2.25 |
| 504 | Russ Snyder | 2.25 |
| 505 | Joe Sparma | 2.25 |
| 506 | Clarence Jones | 2.25 |
| 507 | Wade Blasingame | 2.25 |
| 508 | Duke Sims | 2.25 |
| 509 | Dennis Higgins | 2.25 |
| 510 | Ron Fairly | 2.25 |
| 511 | Bill Kelso | 2.25 |
| 512 | Grant Jackson | 2.25 |
| 513 | Hank Bauer (Mgr.) | 2.25 |
| 514 | Al McBean | 2.25 |
| 515 | Russ Nixon | 2.25 |

| NO. | PLAYER | NR. MT. |
|---|---|---|
| 516 | Pete Mikkelsen | 2.25 |
| 517 | Diego Segui | 2.25 |
| 518 | Checklist No. 7* | 5.00 |
| 519 | Jerry Stephenson | 2.25 |
| 520 | Lou Brock | 25.00 |
| 521 | Don Shaw | 2.25 |
| 522 | Wayne Causey | 2.25 |
| 523 | John Tsitouris | 2.25 |
| 524 | Andy Kosco | 2.25 |
| 525 | Jim Davenport | 2.25 |
| 526 | Bill Denehy | 2.25 |
| 527 | Tito Francona | 2.25 |
| 528 | Detroit Tigers | 50.00 |
| 529 | Bruce Von Hoff | 2.25 |
| 530 | Bird Belters: | 10.00 |
| | Frank Robinson, | |
| | Brooks Robinson | |
| 531 | Chuck Hinton | 2.25 |
| 532 | Luis Tiant | 3.00 |
| 533 | Wes Parker | 2.25 |
| 534 | Bob Miller | 2.25 |
| 535 | Danny Cater | 2.25 |
| 536 | Bill Short | 2.25 |
| 537 | Norm Siebern | 2.25 |
| 538 | Manny Jimenez | 2.25 |
| 539 | Major League Rookies: | 2.50 |
| | Jim Ray, Mike Ferraro | |
| 540 | Nelson Briles | 2.25 |
| 541 | Sandy Alomar | 2.25 |
| 542 | John Boccabella | 2.25 |
| 543 | Bob Lee | 2.25 |
| 544 | Mayo Smith (Mgr.) | 2.25 |
| 545 | Lindy McDaniel | 2.25 |
| 546 | Roy White | 2.50 |
| 547 | Dan Coombs | 2.25 |
| 548 | Bernie Allen | 2.25 |
| 549 | Orioles Rookies: | 2.25 |
| | Curt Motton, Roger Nelson | |
| 550 | Clete Boyer | 2.50 |
| 551 | Darrell Sutherland | 2.25 |
| 552 | Ed Kirkpatrick | 2.25 |
| 553 | Hank Aguirre | 2.25 |
| 554 | Oakland A's | 4.00 |
| 555 | Jose Tartabull | 2.25 |
| 556 | Dick Selma | 2.25 |
| 557 | Frank Quilici | 2.25 |

| NO. | PLAYER | NR. MT. |
|---|---|---|
| 558 | John Edwards | 2.25 |
| 559 | Pirates Rookies: | 2.25 |
| | Carl Taylor, Luke Walker | |
| 560 | Paul Casanova | 2.25 |
| 561 | Lee Elia | 2.25 |
| 562 | Jim Bouton | 3.00 |
| 563 | Ed Charles | 2.25 |
| 564 | Eddie Stanky | 2.25 |
| 565 | Larry Dierker | 2.25 |
| 566 | Ken Harrelson | 3.00 |
| 567 | Clay Dalrymple | 2.25 |
| 568 | Willie Smith | 2.25 |
| 569 | NL Rookies: | 2.25 |
| | Ivan Murrell, Les Rohr | |
| 570 | Rick Reichardt | 2.25 |
| 571 | Tony LaRussa | 3.00 |
| 572 | Don Bosch | 2.25 |
| 573 | Joe Coleman | 2.25 |
| 574 | Cincinnati Reds | 5.00 |
| 575 | Jim Palmer | 60.00 |
| 576 | Dave Adlesh | 2.25 |
| 577 | Fred Talbot | 2.25 |
| 578 | Orlando Martinez | 2.25 |
| 579 | NL Rookies: | 2.50 |
| | Larry Hisle, Mike Lum | |
| 580 | Bob Bailey | 2.25 |
| 581 | Garry Roggenburk | 2.25 |
| 582 | Jerry Grote | 2.25 |
| 583 | Gates Brown | 2.25 |
| 584 | Larry Shepard | 2.25 |
| 585 | Wilbur Wood | 2.25 |
| 586 | Jim Pagliaroni | 2.25 |
| 587 | Roger Repoz | 2.25 |
| 588 | Dick Schofield | 2.25 |
| 589 | Twins Rookies: | 2.25 |
| | Ron Clark, Moe Ogier | |
| 590 | Tommy Harper | 2.25 |
| 591 | Dick Nen | 2.25 |
| 592 | John Bateman | 2.25 |
| 593 | Lee Stange | 2.25 |
| 594 | Phil Linz | 2.25 |
| 595 | Phil Ortega | 2.25 |
| 596 | Charlie Smith | 2.25 |
| 597 | Bill McCool | 2.25 |
| 598 | Jerry May (Exc. $1.00) | 4.00 |

## 1969 Topps . . . Complete Set of 664 Cards—Value $1075.00 (Exc.); $2400.00 (Near Mint)

Includes the rookie cards of Reggie Jackson, Al Oliver and Rollie Fingers. The high numbers are 513 to 664. The values listed for the 23 cards with an *asterisk* are with the player's entire name in *yellow* letters. These cards also exist with the players name in *white* letters—worth $15.00 each, except card no. 440—$80.00, no. 485—$60.00 and no. 500—$500.00.

| NO. | PLAYER | NR. MT. |
|---|---|---|
| 1 | AL Bat Ldrs. (exc. $2.50) | 10.00 |
| | Carl Yastrzemski, Tony | |
| | Oliva, Danny Cater | |
| 2 | NL Batting Leaders: | 4.00 |
| | Matty Alou, Felipe Alou, | |
| | Pete Rose | |
| 3 | AL RBI Leaders: | 2.00 |
| | Frank Howard, Ken | |
| | Harrelson, Jim Northrup | |

| NO. | PLAYER | NR. MT. |
|---|---|---|
| 4 | NL RBI Leaders: | 3.50 |
| | Willie McCovey, Ron | |
| | Santo, Billy Williams | |
| 5 | AL Home Run Leaders: | 2.00 |
| | Frank Howard, Willie | |
| | Horton, Ken Harrelson | |
| 6 | NL Home Run Leaders: | 3.50 |
| | Willie McCovey, Richie | |
| | Allen, Ernie Banks | |

| NO. | PLAYER | NR. MT. |
|---|---|---|
| 7 | AL ERA Leaders: | 2.00 |
| | Luis Tiant, Sam | |
| | McDowell, Dave McNally | |
| 8 | NL ERA Leaders: | 2.00 |
| | Bobby Bolin, Bob Gibson, | |
| | Bob Veale | |
| 9 | AL Pitching Leaders: | 2.00 |
| | Mel Stottlemyre, Denny | |
| | McLain, Dave McNally, | |
| | Luis Tiant | |

| NO. | PLAYER | NR. MT. |
|---|---|---|
| 10 | NL Pitching Leaders: | 4.00 |
| | Juan Marichal, Bob | |
| | Gibson, Fergie Jenkins | |
| 11 | AL Strikeout Leaders: | 2.00 |
| | Sam McDowell, Denny | |
| | McLain, Luis Tiant | |
| 12 | NL Strikeout Leaders: | 2.50 |
| | Bob Gibson, Fergie | |
| | Jenkins, Bill Singer | |

| NO. PLAYER | NR. MT. |
|---|---|
| 13 Mickey Stanley | 1.25 |
| 14 Al McBean | 1.00 |
| 15 Boog Powell | 2.50 |
| 16 Giants Rookies: | 1.25 |
| C. Gutierrez, R. Robertson | |
| 17 Mike Marshall | 1.50 |
| 18 Dick Schofield | 1.00 |
| 19 Ken Suarez | 1.00 |
| 20 Ernie Banks | 16.00 |
| 21 Jose Santiago | 1.00 |
| 22 Jesus Alou | 1.00 |
| 23 Lew Krause | 1.00 |
| 24 Walt Alston (Mgr.) | 2.00 |
| 25 Ray White | 1.25 |
| 26 Clay Carroll | 1.00 |
| 27 Bernie Allen | 1.00 |
| 28 Mike Ryan | 1.00 |
| 29 Dave Morehead | 1.00 |
| 30 Bob Allison | 1.00 |
| 31 Mets Rookies: | 2.00 |
| Gary Gentry, Amos Otis | |
| 32 Sammy Ellis | 1.00 |
| 33 Wayne Causey | 1.00 |
| 34 Gary Peters | 1.00 |
| 35 Joe Morgan | 11.00 |
| 36 Luke Walker | 1.00 |
| 37 Curt Motton | 1.00 |
| 38 Zoilo Versalles | 1.00 |
| 39 Dick Hughes | 1.00 |
| 40 Mayo Smith (Mgr.) | 1.00 |
| 41 Bob Barton | 1.00 |
| 42 Tommy Harper | 1.00 |
| 43 Joe Niekro | 1.50 |
| 44 Danny Cater | 1.00 |
| 45 Maury Wills | 2.25 |
| 46 Fritz Peterson | 1.00 |
| 47 Paul Popovich | 1.00 |
| (without "C" on helmet) | |
| 47 Paul Popovich | 15.00 |
| (with "C" on helmet) | |
| 48 Brant Alyea | 1.00 |
| 49 Royals Rookies: | 1.00 |
| Steve Jones, E. Rodriguez | |
| 49 Royals Rookies: | 15.00 |
| Error—name misspelled | |
| "Rodriquez" | |
| 50 Bob Clemente | 45.00 |
| 51 Woody Fryman | 1.00 |
| 52 Mike Andrews | 1.00 |
| 53 Sonny Jackson | 1.00 |
| 54 Cisco Carlos | 1.00 |
| 55 Jerry Grote | 1.00 |
| 56 Rich Reese | 1.00 |
| 57 Checklist No. 1 | 4.00 |
| 58 Fred Gladding | 1.00 |
| 59 Jay Johnstone | 1.00 |
| 60 Nelson Briles | 1.00 |
| 61 Jimmie Hall | 1.00 |
| 62 Chico Salmon | 1.00 |
| 63 Jim Hickman | 1.00 |
| 64 Bill Monbouquette | 1.00 |
| 65 Willie Davis | 1.50 |
| 66 Orioles Rookies: | 1.00 |
| M. Adamson, M. Rettenmund | |
| 67 Bill Stoneman | 1.00 |
| 68 Dave Duncan | 1.00 |
| 69 Steve Hamilton | 1.00 |
| 70 Tommy Helms | 1.00 |
| 71 Steve Whitaker | 1.00 |
| 72 Ron Taylor | 1.00 |
| 73 Johnny Briggs | 1.00 |
| 74 Preston Gomez (Mgr.) | 1.00 |
| 75 Luis Aparicio | 5.00 |
| 76 Norm Miller | 1.00 |
| 77 Ron Perranoski | 1.00 |
| (no team logo on hat) | |
| 77 Ron Perranoski | 15.00 |
| (with team logo on hat) | |
| 78 Tom Satriano | 1.00 |
| 79 Milt Pappas | 1.00 |
| 80 Norm Cash | 2.50 |
| 81 Mel Queen | 1.00 |
| 82 Pirates Rookies: | 10.00 |
| Rich Hebner, Al Oliver | |
| 83 Mike Ferraro | 1.00 |

| NO. PLAYER | NR. MT. |
|---|---|
| 84 Bob Humphreys | 1.00 |
| 85 Lou Brock | 15.00 |
| 86 Pete Richert | 1.00 |
| 87 Horace Clarke | 1.00 |
| 88 Rich Nye | 1.00 |
| 89 Russ Gibson | 1.00 |
| 90 Jerry Koosman | 4.00 |
| 91 Al Dark (Mgr.) | 1.25 |
| 92 Jack Billingham | 1.00 |
| 93 Joe Foy | 1.00 |
| 94 Hank Aguirre | 1.00 |
| 95 Johnny Bench | 160.00 |
| 96 Denver LeMaster | 1.00 |
| 97 Buddy Bradford | 1.00 |
| 98 Dave Giusti | 1.00 |
| 99 Twins Rookies: | 15.00 |
| Danny Morris, Graig Nettles | |
| 100 Hank Aaron | 50.00 |
| 101 Daryl Patterson | 1.00 |
| 102 Jim Davenport | 1.00 |
| 103 Roger Repoz | 1.00 |
| 104 Steve Blass | 1.00 |
| 105 Rick Monday | 1.00 |
| 106 Jim Hannan | 1.00 |
| 107 Checklist No.2 | 5.00 |
| (error—#161 Jim Purdin) | |
| 107 Checklist No.2 | 13.00 |
| (correct—#161 John Purdin) | |
| 108 Tony Taylor | 1.00 |
| 109 Jim Lonborg | 1.00 |
| 110 Mike Shannon | 1.00 |
| 111 Johnny Morris | 1.00 |
| 112 J.C. Martin | 1.00 |
| 113 Dave May | 1.00 |
| 114 Yankees Rookies: | 1.00 |
| A. Closter, J. Cumberland | |
| 115 Bill Hands | 1.00 |
| 116 Chuck Harrison | 1.00 |
| 117 Jim Fairey | 1.00 |
| 118 Stan Williams (Mgr.) | 1.00 |
| 119 Doug Rader | 1.00 |
| 120 Pete Rose | 35.00 |
| 121 Joe Grzenda | 1.00 |
| 122 Ron Fairly | 1.00 |
| 123 Wilbur Wood | 1.00 |
| 124 Hank Bauer (Mgr.) | 1.00 |
| 125 Ray Sadecki | 1.00 |
| 126 Dick Tracewski | 1.00 |
| 127 Kevin Collins | 1.00 |
| 128 Tommie Aaron | 1.00 |
| 129 Bill McCool | 1.00 |
| 130 Carl Yastrzemski | 30.00 |
| 131 Chris Cannizzaro | 1.00 |
| 132 Dave Baldwin | 1.00 |
| 133 Johnny Callison | 1.00 |
| 134 Jim Weaver | 1.00 |
| 135 Tommy Davis | 1.50 |
| 136 Cards Rookies: | 1.25 |
| Steve Huntz, Mike Torrez | |
| 137 Wally Bunker | 1.00 |
| 138 John Bateman | 1.00 |
| 139 Andy Kosco | 1.00 |
| 140 Jim Lefebvre | 1.00 |
| 141 Bill Dillman | 1.00 |
| 142 Woody Woodward | 1.00 |
| 143 Joe Nossek | 1.00 |
| 144 Bob Hendley | 1.00 |
| 145 Max Alvis | 1.00 |
| 146 Jim Perry | 1.25 |
| 147 Leo Durocher (Mgr.) | 2.50 |
| 148 Lee Stange | 1.00 |
| 149 Ollie Brown | 1.00 |
| 150 Denny McLain | 4.00 |
| 151 Clay Dalrymple | 1.00 |
| (Orioles Team) | |
| 151 Clay Dalrymple | 14.00 |
| (Phillies Team) | |
| 152 Tommie Sisk | 1.00 |
| 153 Ed Brinkman | 1.00 |
| 154 Jim Britton | 1.00 |
| 155 Pete Ward | 1.00 |
| 156 Houston Rookies: | 1.00 |
| Hal Gilson, Leon McFadden | |
| 157 Bob Rodgers | 1.00 |
| 158 Joe Gibbon | 1.00 |

| NO. PLAYER | NR. MT. |
|---|---|
| 159 Jerry Adair | 1.00 |
| 160 Vada Pinson | 2.00 |
| 161 John Purdin | 1.00 |
| 162 World Series Game 1: | 5.00 |
| Gibson Fans 17 | |
| 163 World Series Game 2: | 3.00 |
| Tigers Deck Cards | |
| 164 World Series Game 3: | 3.00 |
| McCarver's Homer | |
| 165 World Series Game 4: | 5.00 |
| Brock Lead-Off HR | |
| 166 World Series Game 5: | 6.00 |
| Kaline's Key Hit | |
| 167 World Series Game 6: | 3.00 |
| Tigers 10-Run Inning | |
| 168 World Series Game 7: | 5.00 |
| Lolich Outduels Gibson | |
| 169 World Series: | 3.00 |
| Tigers Celebrate Victory | |
| 170 Frank Howard | 2.00 |
| 171 Glenn Beckert | 1.00 |
| 172 Jerry Stephenson | 1.00 |
| 173 White Sox Rookies: | 1.00 |
| B. Christian, G. Nyman | |
| 174 Grant Jackson | 1.00 |
| 175 Jim Bunning | 3.50 |
| 176 Joe Azcue | 1.00 |
| 177 Ron Reed | 1.00 |
| 178 Ray Oyler | 1.00 |
| 179 Don Pavletich | 1.00 |
| 180 Willie Horton | 1.25 |
| 181 Mel Nelson | 1.00 |
| 182 Bill Rigney (Mgr.) | 1.00 |
| 183 Don Shaw | 1.00 |
| 184 Roberto Pena | 1.00 |
| 185 Tom Phoebus | 1.00 |
| 186 John Edwards | 1.00 |
| 187 Leon Wagner | 1.00 |
| 188 Rick Wise | 1.00 |
| 189 Red Sox Rookies: | 1.25 |
| J. Lahoud, J. Thibadeau | |
| 190 Willie Mays | 55.00 |
| 191 Lindy McDaniel | 1.00 |
| 192 Jose Pagan | 1.00 |
| 193 Don Cardwell | 1.00 |
| 194 Ted Uhlaender | 1.00 |
| 195 John Odom | 1.00 |
| 196 Lum Harris (Mgr.) | 1.00 |
| 197 Dick Selma | 1.00 |
| 198 Willie Smith | 1.00 |
| 199 Jim French | 1.00 |
| 200 Bob Gibson | 12.00 |
| 201 Russ Snyder | 1.00 |
| 202 Don Wilson | 1.00 |
| 203 Dave Johnson | 1.50 |
| 204 Jack Hiatt | 1.00 |
| 205 Rick Reichardt | 1.00 |
| 206 Phillies Rookies: | 1.25 |
| Larry Hisle, Barry Lersch | |
| 207 Roy Face | 1.25 |
| 208 Donn Clendenon | 1.00 |
| (Astros Team) | |
| 208 Donn Clendenon | 15.00 |
| (Expos Team) | |
| 209 Larry Haney | 1.00 |
| (negative reversed) | |
| 210 Felix Millan | 1.00 |
| 211 Galen Cisco | 1.00 |
| 212 Tom Tresh | 1.25 |
| 213 Gerry Arrigo | 1.00 |
| 214 Checklist No. 3 | 4.00 |
| 215 Rico Petrocelli | 1.00 |
| 216 Don Sutton | 7.00 |
| 217 John Donaldson | 1.00 |
| 218 John Roseboro | 1.00 |
| 219 Freddie Patek | 1.50 |
| 220 Sam McDowell | 1.50 |
| 221 Art Shamsky | 1.50 |
| 222 Duane Josephson | 1.50 |
| 223 Tom Dukes | 1.50 |
| 224 Angels Rookies: | 1.50 |
| B. Harrelson, S. Kealey | |
| 225 Don Kessinger | 2.00 |
| 226 Bruce Howard | 1.50 |
| 227 Frank Johnson | 1.50 |

| NO. PLAYER | NR. MT. |
|---|---|
| 228 Dave Leonhard | 1.50 |
| 229 Don Lock | 1.50 |
| 230 Rusty Staub | 3.00 |
| 231 Pat Dobson | 1.50 |
| 232 Dave Ricketts | 1.50 |
| 233 Steve Barber | 1.50 |
| 234 Dave Bristol (Mgr.) | 1.50 |
| 235 Jim Hunter | 12.00 |
| 236 Manny Mota | 2.00 |
| 237 Bobby Cox | 2.50 |
| 238 Ken Johnson | 1.50 |
| 239 Bob Taylor | 1.50 |
| 240 Ken Harrelson | 1.75 |
| 241 Jim Brewer | 1.50 |
| 242 Frank Kostro | 1.50 |
| 243 Ron Kline | 1.50 |
| 244 Indians Rookies: | 1.75 |
| R. Fosse, G. Woodson | |
| 245 Ed Charles | 1.50 |
| 246 Joe Coleman | 1.50 |
| 247 Gene Oliver | 1.50 |
| 248 Bob Priddy | 1.50 |
| 249 Ed Spiezio | 1.50 |
| 250 Frank Robinson | 25.00 |
| 251 Ron Herbel | 1.50 |
| 252 Chuck Cottier | 1.50 |
| 253 Jerry Johnson | 1.50 |
| 254 Joe Schultz (Mgr.) | 1.50 |
| 255 Steve Carlton | 45.00 |
| 256 Gates Brown | 1.50 |
| 257 Jim Ray | 1.50 |
| 258 Jackie Hernandez | 1.50 |
| 259 Bill Short | 1.50 |
| 260 Reggie Jackson (R) | 550.00 |
| 261 Bob Johnson | 1.50 |
| 262 Mike Kekich | 1.50 |
| 263 Jerry May | 1.50 |
| 264 Bill Landis | 1.50 |
| 265 Chico Cardenas | 1.50 |
| 266 Dodger Rookies: | 1.75 |
| Tom Hutton, Alan Foster | |
| 267 Vicente Romo | 1.50 |
| 268 Al Spangler | 1.50 |
| 269 Al Weis | 1.50 |
| 270 Mickey Lolich | 3.00 |
| 271 Larry Stahl | 1.50 |
| 272 Ed Stroud | 1.50 |
| 273 Ron Willis | 1.50 |
| 274 Clyde King (Mgr.) | 1.50 |
| 275 Vic Davalillo | 1.50 |
| 276 Gary Wagner | 1.50 |
| 277 Ron Hendricks | 1.50 |
| 278 Gary Geiger | 1.50 |
| 279 Roger Nelson | 1.50 |
| 280 Alex Johnson | 1.50 |
| 281 Ted Kubiak | 1.50 |
| 282 Pat Jarvis | 1.50 |
| 283 Sandy Alomar | 1.50 |
| 284 Expos Rookies: | 1.50 |
| M. Wegener, J. Robertson | |
| 285 Don Mincher | 1.50 |
| 286 Dock Ellis | 1.75 |
| 287 Jose Tartabull | 1.50 |
| 288 Ken Holtzman | 1.75 |
| 289 Bart Shirley | 1.50 |
| 290 Jim Kaat | 4.00 |
| 291 Vern Fuller | 1.50 |
| 292 Al Downing | 1.75 |
| 293 Dick Dietz | 1.50 |
| 294 Jim Lemon | 1.50 |
| 295 Tony Perez | 10.00 |
| 296 Andy Messersmith (R) | 2.50 |
| 297 Deron Johnson | 1.50 |
| 298 Dave Nicholson | 1.50 |
| 299 Mark Belanger | 1.75 |
| 300 Felipe Alou | 1.75 |
| 301 Darrell Brandon | 1.50 |
| 302 Jim Pagliaroni | 1.50 |
| 303 Cal Koonce | 1.50 |
| 304 Padres Rookies: | 4.00 |
| Bill Davis, Clarence Gaston | |
| 305 Dick McAuliffe | 1.50 |
| 306 Jim Grant | 1.50 |
| 307 Gary Kolb | 1.50 |
| 308 Wade Blasingame | 1.50 |

| NO. PLAYER | NR. MT. |
|---|---|
| 309 Walt Williams | 1.50 |
| 310 Tom Haller | 1.50 |
| 311 Sparky Lyle (R) | 10.00 |
| 312 Lee Elia | 1.50 |
| 313 Bill Robinson | 1.75 |
| 314 Checklist No. 4 | 4.00 |
| 315 Eddie Fisher | 1.50 |
| 316 Hal Lanier | 1.75 |
| 317 Bruce Look | 1.50 |
| 318 Jack Fisher | 1.50 |
| 319 Ken McMullen | 1.50 |
| 320 Dal Maxvill | 1.50 |
| 321 Jim McAndrew | 1.50 |
| 322 Jose Vidal | 1.50 |
| 323 Larry Miller | 1.50 |
| 324 Tiger Rookies: | 2.00 |
| Les Cain, Dave Campbell | |
| 325 Jose Cardenal | 1.50 |
| 326 Gary Sutherland | 1.50 |
| 327 Willie Crawford | 1.50 |
| 328 Joe Horlen | 1.00 |
| 329 Rick Joseph | 1.00 |
| 330 Tony Conigliaro | 2.50 |
| 331 Braves Rookies: | 1.25 |
| Tom House, Gil Garrido | |
| 332 Fred Talbot | 1.00 |
| 333 Ivan Murrell | 1.00 |
| 334 Phil Roof | 1.00 |
| 335 Bill Mazeroski | 2.00 |
| 336 Jim Roland | 1.00 |
| 337 Marty Martinez | 1.00 |
| 338 Del Unser | 1.00 |
| 339 Reds Rookies: | 1.25 |
| Steve Mingori, Jose Pena | |
| 340 Dave McNally | 1.25 |
| 341 Dave Adlesh | 1.00 |
| 342 Bubba Morton | 1.00 |
| 343 Dan Frisella | 1.00 |
| 344 Tom Matchick | 1.00 |
| 345 Frank Linzy | 1.00 |
| 346 Wayne Comer | 1.00 |
| 347 Randy Hundley | 1.00 |
| 348 Steve Hargan | 1.00 |
| 349 Dick Williams (Mgr.) | 1.00 |
| 350 Richie Allen | 2.50 |
| 351 Carroll Sembera | 1.00 |
| 352 Paul Schaal | 1.00 |
| 353 Jeff Torborg | 1.00 |
| 354 Nate Oliver | 1.00 |
| 355 Phil Niekro | 5.00 |
| 356 Frank Quilici | 1.00 |
| 357 Carl Taylor | 1.00 |
| 358 Athletics Rookies: | 1.00 |
| George Lauzerique, | |
| Roberto Rodriguez | |
| 359 Dick Kelley | 1.00 |
| 360 Jim Wynn | 1.00 |
| 361 Gary Holman | 1.00 |
| 362 Jim Maloney | 1.00 |
| 363 Russ Nixon | 1.00 |
| 364 Tommie Agee | 1.00 |
| 365 Jim Fregosi | 1.50 |
| 366 Bo Belinsky | 1.00 |
| 367 Lou Johnson | 1.00 |
| 368 Vic Roznovsky | 1.00 |
| 369 Bob Skinner (Mgr.) | 1.00 |
| 370 Juan Marichal | 6.00 |
| 371 Sal Bando | 1.25 |
| 372 Adolfo Phillips | 1.00 |
| 373 Fred Lasher | 1.00 |
| 374 Bob Tillman | 1.00 |
| 375 Harmon Killebrew | 16.00 |
| 376 Royals Rookies: | 1.25 |
| Mike Fiore, Jim Rooker | |
| 377 Gary Bell | 1.00 |
| 378 Jose Herrera | 1.00 |
| 379 Ken Boyer | 2.00 |
| 380 Stan Bahnsen | 1.00 |
| 381 Ed Kranepool | 1.00 |
| 382 Pat Corrales | 1.00 |
| 383 Casey Cox | 1.00 |
| 384 Larry Shepard | 1.00 |
| 385 Orlando Cepeda | 3.00 |
| 386 Jim McGlothlin | 1.00 |

| NO. PLAYER | NR. MT. |
|---|---|
| 387 Bobby Klaus | 1.00 |
| 388 Tom McCraw | 1.00 |
| 389 Dan Coombs | 1.00 |
| 390 Bill Freehan | 1.25 |
| 391 Ray Culp | 1.00 |
| 392 Bob Burda | 1.00 |
| 393 Gene Brabender | 1.00 |
| 394 Pilots Rookies: | 4.00 |
| Lou Piniella, M. Staehle | |
| 395 Chris Short | 1.00 |
| 396 Jim Campanis | 1.00 |
| 397 Chuck Dobson | 1.00 |
| 398 Tito Francona | 1.00 |
| 399 Bob Bailey | 1.00 |
| 400 Don Drysdale | 10.00 |
| 401 Jake Gibbs | 1.00 |
| 402 Ken Boswell | 1.00 |
| 403 Bob Miller | 1.00 |
| 404 Cubs Rookies: | 1.25 |
| Vic LaRose, Gary Ross | |
| 405 Lee May | 1.25 |
| 406 Phil Ortega | 1.00 |
| 407 Tom Egan | 1.00 |
| 408 Nate Colbert | 1.00 |
| 409 Bob Moose | 1.00 |
| 410 Al Kaline | 15.00 |
| 411 Larry Dierker | 1.00 |
| 412 Checklist No. 5 | 7.50 |
| 413 Roland Sheldon | 1.00 |
| 414 Duke Sims | 1.00 |
| 415 Ray Washburn | 1.00 |
| 416 Willie McCovey (AS) | 6.00 |
| 417 Ken Harrelson (AS) | 2.00 |
| 418 Tommy Helms (AS) | 2.00 |
| 419 Rod Carew (AS) | 8.00 |
| 420 Ron Santo (AS) | 2.00 |
| 421 Brooks Robinson (AS) | 6.00 |
| 422 Don Kessinger (AS) | 2.00 |
| 423 Bert Campaneris (AS) | 2.00 |
| 424 Pete Rose (AS) | 11.00 |
| 425 Carl Yastrzemski (AS) | 10.00 |
| 426 Curt Flood (AS) | 2.00 |
| 427 Tony Oliva (AS) | 2.00 |
| 428 Lou Brock (AS) | 6.00 |
| 429 Willie Horton (AS) | 2.00 |
| 430 Johnny Bench (AS) | 14.00 |
| 431 Bill Freehan (AS) | 2.00 |
| 432 Bob Gibson (AS) | 5.00 |
| 433 Denny McLain (AS) | 2.00 |
| 434 Jerry Koosman (AS) | 2.00 |
| 435 Sam McDowell (AS) | 2.00 |
| 436 Gene Alley | 1.00 |
| 437 Luis Alcaraz | 1.00 |
| 438 Gary Waslewski | 1.00 |
| 439 White Sox Rookies: | 1.00 |
| Ed Herrmann, Dan Lazar | |
| 440 Willie McCovey* | 15.00 |
| 441 Dennis Higgins* | 1.00 |
| 442 Ty Cline | 1.00 |
| 443 Don Wert | 1.00 |
| 444 Joe Moeller* | 1.00 |
| 445 Bobby Knoop | 1.00 |
| 446 Claude Raymond | 1.00 |
| 447 Ralph Houk (Mgr.)* | 1.25 |
| 448 Bob Tolan | 1.00 |
| 449 Paul Lindblad | 1.00 |
| 450 Billy Williams | 7.00 |
| 451 Rich Rollins | 1.00 |
| 452 Al Ferrara* | 1.00 |
| 453 Mike Cuellar | 1.50 |
| 454 Phillies Rookies:* | 1.25 |
| Larry Colton, Don Money | |
| 455 Sonny Siebert | 1.00 |
| 456 Bud Harrelson | 1.00 |
| 457 Dalton Jones | 1.00 |
| 458 Curt Blefary | 1.00 |
| 459 Dave Boswell | 1.00 |
| 460 Joe Torre | 2.00 |
| 461 Mike Epstein* | 1.00 |
| 462 Red Schoendienst | 3.00 |
| 463 Dennis Ribant | 1.00 |
| 464 Dave Marshall* | 1.00 |
| 465 Tommy John | 4.00 |
| 466 John Boccabella | 1.00 |

| NO. PLAYER | NR. MT. |
|---|---|
| 467 Tom Reynolds | 1.00 |
| 468 Pirates Rookies:* | 1.25 |
| Bruce Del Canton, | |
| Bob Robertson | |
| 469 Chico Ruiz | 1.00 |
| 470 Mel Stottlemyre* | 2.00 |
| 471 Ted Savage* | 1.00 |
| 472 Jim Price | 1.00 |
| 473 Jose Arcia* | 1.00 |
| 474 Tom Murphy | 1.00 |
| 475 Tim McCarver | 2.50 |
| 476 Boston Rookies:* | 1.25 |
| Ken Brett, Gerry Moses | |
| 477 Jeff James | 1.00 |
| 478 Don Buford | 1.00 |
| 479 Richie Scheinblum | 1.00 |
| 480 Tom Seaver | 120.00 |
| 481 Bill Melton | 1.00 |
| 482 Jim Gosger* | 1.00 |
| 483 Ted Abernathy | 1.00 |
| 484 Joe Gordon | 1.25 |
| 485 Gaylord Perry* | 9.00 |
| 486 Paul Casanova* | 1.00 |
| 487 Denis Menke | 1.00 |
| 488 Joe Sparma | 1.00 |
| 489 Clete Boyer | 1.50 |
| 490 Matty Alou | 1.25 |
| 491 Twins Rookies:* | 1.25 |
| Jerry Crider, | |
| George Mitterwald | |
| 492 Tony Cloninger | 1.00 |
| 493 Wes Parker* | 1.00 |
| 494 Ken Berry | 1.00 |
| 495 Bert Campaneris | 1.25 |
| 496 Larry Jaster | 1.00 |
| 497 Julian Javier | 1.00 |
| 498 Juan Pizarro | 1.00 |
| 499 Astro Rookies: | 1.25 |
| Don Bryant, Steve Shea | |
| 500 Mickey Mantle* | 200.00 |
| 501 Tony Gonzalez* | 1.00 |
| 502 Minnie Rojas | 1.00 |
| 503 Larry Brown | 1.00 |
| 504 Checklist No. 6 | 4.00 |
| 505 Bobby Bolin* | 1.00 |
| 506 Paul Blair | 1.00 |
| 507 Cookie Rojas | 1.00 |
| 508 Moe Drabowsky | 1.00 |
| 509 Manny Sanguillen | 1.00 |
| 510 Rod Carew | 70.00 |
| 511 Diego Segui* | 1.00 |
| 512 Cleon Jones | 1.00 |
| 513 Camilo Pascual | 1.50 |
| 514 Mike Lum | 1.25 |
| 515 Dick Green | 1.25 |
| 516 Earl Weaver (Mgr.) | 7.00 |
| 517 Mike McCormick | 1.25 |
| 518 Fred Whitfield | 1.25 |
| 519 Yankees Rookies: | 1.50 |
| G. Kenney, Len Boehmer | |
| 520 Bob Veale | 1.50 |
| 521 George Thomas | 1.25 |
| 522 Joe Hoerner | 1.25 |
| 523 Bob Chance | 1.25 |
| 524 Expos Rookies: | 1.25 |
| Jose Laboy, Floyd Wicker | |
| 525 Earl Wilson | 1.25 |
| 526 Hector Torres | 1.25 |
| 527 Al Lopez (Mgr.) | 2.50 |
| 528 Claude Osteen | 1.25 |
| 529 Ed Kirkpatrick | 1.25 |
| 530 Cesar Tovar | 1.25 |
| 531 Dick Farrell | 1.25 |
| 532 Bird Hill Aces: | 1.50 |
| D. McNally, T. Phoebus, | |
| J. Hardin, M. Cuellar | |
| 533 Nolan Ryan | 400.00 |
| 534 Jerry McNertney | 1.25 |
| 535 Phil Regan | 1.25 |
| 536 Padres Rookies: | 1.50 |
| D. Breeden, Dave Roberts | |
| 537 Mike Paul | 1.25 |
| 538 Charlie Smith | 1.25 |
| 539 Ted Shows How: | 5.00 |
| Mike Epstein, Ted Williams | |

| NO. PLAYER | NR. MT. |
|---|---|
| 540 Curt Flood | 2.00 |
| 541 Joe Verbanic | 1.25 |
| 542 Bob Aspromonte | 1.25 |
| 543 Fred Newman | 1.25 |
| 544 Tigers Rookies: | 1.50 |
| Mike Kilkenny, Ron Woods | |
| 545 Willie Stargell | 12.00 |
| 546 Jim Nash | 1.25 |
| 547 Billy Martin (Mgr.) | 5.00 |
| 548 Bob Locker | 1.25 |
| 549 Ron Brand | 1.25 |
| 550 Brooks Robinson | 15.00 |
| 551 Wayne Granger | 1.25 |
| 552 Dodgers Rookies: | 1.50 |
| Ted Sizemore, Bill Sudakis | |
| 553 Ron Davis | 1.25 |
| 554 Frank Bertaina | 1.25 |
| 555 Jim Hart | 1.25 |
| 556 A's Stars: | 1.50 |
| Bert Campaneris, Sal | |
| Bando, Danny Cater | |
| 557 Frank Fernandez | 1.25 |
| 558 Tom Burgmeier | 1.25 |
| 559 Cardinals Rookies: | 1.25 |
| Joe Hague, Jim Hicks | |
| 560 Luis Tiant | 2.00 |
| 561 Ron Clark | 1.25 |
| 562 Bob Watson (R) | 3.00 |
| 563 Marty Pattin | 1.25 |
| 564 Gil Hodges (Mgr.) | 6.00 |
| 565 Hoyt Wilhelm | 6.00 |
| 566 Ron Hansen | 1.25 |
| 567 Pirates Rookies: | 1.25 |
| Elvio Jimenez, | |
| Jim Shellenback | |
| 568 Cecil Upshaw | 1.25 |
| 569 Billy Harris | 1.25 |
| 570 Ron Santo | 4.00 |
| 571 Cap Peterson | 1.25 |
| 572 Giants Heroes: | 10.00 |
| Willie McCovey, | |
| Juan Marichal | |
| 573 Jim Palmer | 35.00 |
| 574 George Scott | 1.25 |
| 575 Bill Singer | 1.25 |
| 576 Phillies Rookies: | 1.25 |
| Ron Stone, Bill Wilson | |
| 577 Mike Hegan | 1.25 |
| 578 Don Bosch | 1.25 |
| 579 Dave Nelson | 1.25 |
| 580 Jim Northrup | 1.25 |
| 581 Gary Nolan | 1.25 |
| 582 Checklist No. 7 | 4.00 |
| 583 Clyde Wright | 1.25 |
| 584 Don Mason | 1.25 |
| 585 Ron Swoboda | 1.25 |
| 586 Tim Cullen | 1.25 |
| 587 Joe Rudi (R) | 3.00 |
| 588 Bill White | 2.50 |
| 589 Joe Pepitone | 2.00 |
| 590 Rico Carty | 1.50 |
| 591 Mike Hedlund | 1.50 |
| 592 Padres Rookies: | 1.50 |
| R. Robles, Al Santorini | |
| 593 Don Nottebart | 1.50 |
| 594 Dooley Womack | 1.50 |
| 595 Lee Maye | 1.50 |
| 596 Chuck Hartenstein | 1.50 |
| 597 AL Rookies: | 100.00 |
| Bob Floyd, Larry Burchart, | |
| Rollie Fingers | |
| 598 Ruben Amaro | 1.50 |
| 599 John Boozer | 1.50 |
| 600 Tony Oliva | 4.00 |
| 601 Tug McGraw | 3.00 |
| 602 Cubs Rookies: | 1.50 |
| Alec Distaso, Jim Qualls, | |
| Don Young | |
| 603 Joe Keough | 1.50 |
| 604 Bobby Etheridge | 1.50 |
| 605 Dick Ellsworth | 1.50 |
| 606 Gene Mauch (Mgr.) | 1.50 |
| 607 Dick Bosman | 1.50 |
| 608 Dick Simpson | 1.50 |

# 1969 Topps (Continued)

| NO. PLAYER | NR. MT. | NO. PLAYER | NR. MT. | NO. PLAYER | NR. MT. | NO. PLAYER | NR. MT. |
|---|---|---|---|---|---|---|---|
| 609 Phil Gagliano | 1.50 | 624 NL Rookies: | 1.50 | 638 Ed Sprague | 1.50 | 654 White Sox Rookies: | 2.00 |
| 610 Jim Hardin | 1.50 | Darrel Chaney, Duffy Dyer, | | 639 Barry Moore | 1.50 | Carlos May, Don Secrist, | |
| 611 Braves Rookies: | 1.50 | Terry Harmon | | 640 Fergie Jenkins | 15.00 | Rich Morales | |
| Bob Didier, Walt Hriniak, | | 625 Mack Jones | 1.50 | 641 NL Rookies: | 1.50 | 655 Mike Hershberger | 1.50 |
| Gary Neibauer | | 626 Gene Michael | 1.50 | Bobby Darwin, John Miller, | | 656 Dan Schneider | 1.50 |
| 612 Jack Aker | 1.50 | 627 George Stone | 1.50 | Tommy Dean | | 657 Bobby Murcer | 3.00 |
| 613 Jim Beauchamp | 1.50 | 628 Red Sox Rookies: | 2.50 | 642 John Hiller | 1.50 | 658 AL Rookies: | 1.50 |
| 614 Houston Rookies: | 1.50 | Bill Conigliaro, Syd | | 643 Billy Cowan | 1.50 | Tom Hall, Bill Burbach, | |
| Tom Griffin, Skip Guinn | | O'Brien, Fred Wenz | | 644 Chuck Hinton | 1.50 | Jim Miles | |
| 615 Len Gabrielson | 1.50 | 629 Jack Hamilton | 1.50 | 645 George Brunet | 1.50 | 659 Johnny Podres | 2.00 |
| 616 Don McMahon | 1.50 | 630 Bobby Bonds (R) | 25.00 | 646 Expos Rookies: | 1.50 | 660 Reggie Smith | 3.00 |
| 617 Jesse Gonder | 1.50 | 631 John Kennedy | 1.50 | Carl Morton, Dan McGinn | | 661 Jim Merritt | 1.50 |
| 618 Ramon Webster | 1.50 | 632 Jon Warden | 1.50 | 647 Dave Wickersham | 1.50 | 662 Royals Rookies: | 2.00 |
| 619 Royals Rookies: | 1.25 | 633 Harry Walker (Mgr.) | 1.50 | 648 Bobby Wine | 1.50 | Dick Drago, Bob Oliver, | |
| Pat Kelly, Juan Rios, | | 634 Andy Etchebarren | 1.50 | 649 Al Jackson | 1.50 | George Spriggs | |
| Bill Butler | | 635 George Culver | 1.50 | 650 Ted Williams (Mgr.) | 9.00 | 663 Dick Radatz | 1.50 |
| 620 Dean Chance | 1.50 | 636 Woodie Held | 1.50 | 651 Gus Gil | 1.50 | 664 Ron Hunt (exc. $1.00) | 4.00 |
| 621 Bill Voss | 1.50 | 637 Padres Rookies: | 1.50 | 652 Eddie Watt | 1.50 | | |
| 622 Dan Osinski | 1.50 | Jerry DaVanon, Frank | | 653 Aurelio Rodriguez | 2.50 | | |
| 623 Hank Allen | 1.50 | Reberger, Clay Kirby | | (Photo of Angels Batboy) | | | |

# 1970 Topps . . . Complete Set of 720 Cards—Value $1125.00 (Exc.); $2000.00 (Near Mint)

Features the rookie cards of Thurman Munson, Darrell Evans, Vida Blue, and Bill Buckner. The high numbers are 634 to 720. Card 588 (checklist) exists with *Adolpho* misspelled *Adolfo*—worth $7.00

  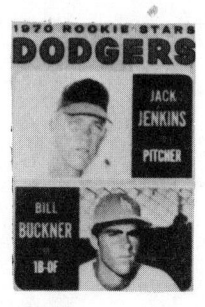  

| NO. PLAYER | NR. MT. | NO. PLAYER | NR. MT. | NO. PLAYER | NR. MT. | NO. PLAYER | NR. MT. |
|---|---|---|---|---|---|---|---|
| 1 Champ Mets (exc. $2.50) | 12.00 | 36 Red Rookies: | .50 | 64 AL RBI Leaders: | 3.00 | 80 Don Kessinger | .50 |
| 2 Diego Segui | .50 | D. Breeden, B. Carbo | | Harmon Killebrew, Boog | | 81 Dave May | .50 |
| 3 Darrel Chaney | .50 | 37 Dick Drago | .50 | Powell, Reggie Jackson | | 82 Frank Fernandez | .50 |
| 4 Tom Egan | .50 | 38 Mack Jones | .50 | 65 NL Home Run Leaders: | 3.50 | 83 Don Cardwell | .50 |
| 5 Wes Parker | .50 | 39 Mike Nagy | .50 | Hank Aaron, Willie | | 84 Paul Casanova | .50 |
| 6 Grant Jackson | .50 | 40 Rich Allen | 1.50 | McCovey, Lee May | | 85 Max Alvis | .50 |
| 7 Indians Rookies: | .50 | 41 George Lauzerique | .50 | 66 AL Home Run Leaders: | 3.00 | 86 Lum Harris (Mgr.) | .50 |
| Gary Boyd, Russ Nagelson | | 42 Tito Fuentes | .50 | Harmon Killebrew, Frank | | 87 Steve Renko | .50 |
| 8 Jose Martinez | .50 | 43 Jack Aker | .50 | Howard, Reggie Jackson | | 88 Pilots Rookies: | .50 |
| 9 Checklist No. 1 | 4.00 | 44 Roberto Pena | .50 | 67 NL ERA Leaders: | 4.00 | Miguel Fuentes, Dick Baney | |
| 10 Carl Yastrzemski | 30.00 | 45 Dave Johnson | 1.00 | Bob Gibson, Juan | | 89 Juan Rios | .50 |
| 11 Nate Colbert | .50 | 46 Ken Rudolph | .50 | Marichal, Steve Carlton | | 90 Tim McCarver | 2.00 |
| 12 John Hiller | .50 | 47 Bob Miller | .50 | 68 AL ERA Leaders: | 2.00 | 91 Rich Morales | .50 |
| 13 Jack Hiatt | .50 | 48 Gil Garrido | .50 | Dick Bosman, Jim Palmer, | | 92 George Culver | .50 |
| 14 Hank Allen | .50 | 49 Tim Cullen | .50 | Mike Cuellar | | 93 Rick Renick | .50 |
| 15 Larry Dierker | .50 | 50 Tommy Agee | .75 | 69 NL Pitching Leaders: | 4.00 | 94 Fred Patek | .50 |
| 16 Charlie Metro | .50 | 51 Bob Christian | .50 | Phil Niekro, Tom Seaver, | | 95 Earl Wilson | .50 |
| 17 Hoyt Wilhelm | 4.00 | 52 Bruce Dal Canton | .50 | F. Jenkins, Juan Marichal | | 96 Cardinals Rookies: | 2.00 |
| 18 Carlos May | .50 | 53 John Kennedy | .50 | 70 AL Pitching Leaders: | 2.00 | Leron Lee, Jerry Reuss | |
| 19 John Boccabella | .50 | 54 Jeff Torborg | .75 | Dennis McLain, Mike | | 97 Joe Moeller | .50 |
| 20 Dave McNally | .75 | 55 John Odom | .50 | Cuellar, Dave McNally, | | 98 Gates Brown | .50 |
| 21 A's Rookies: | .50 | 56 Phillies Rookies: | .50 | Jim Perry, Dave Boswell, | | 99 Bobby Pfeil | .50 |
| Gene Tenace, Vida Blue | | Joe Lis, Scott Reid | | Mel Stottlemyre | | 100 Mel Stottlemyre | 1.00 |
| 22 Ray Washburn | .50 | 57 Pat Kelly | .50 | 71 NL Strikeout Leaders: | 2.00 | 101 Bobby Floyd | .50 |
| 23 Bill Robinson | .75 | 58 Dave Marshall | .50 | Fergie Jenkins, Bob | | 102 Joe Rudi | 1.00 |
| 24 Dick Selma | .50 | 59 Dick Ellsworth | .50 | Gibson, Bill Singer | | 103 Frank Reberger | .50 |
| 25 Cesaer Tovar | .50 | 60 Jim Wynn | .75 | 72 AL Strikeout Leaders: | 2.00 | 104 Gerry Moses | .50 |
| 26 Tug McGraw | 1.50 | 61 NL Batting Leaders: | 4.00 | Andy Messersmith, Sam | | 105 Tony Gonzalez | .50 |
| 27 Chuck Hinton | .50 | Cleon Jones, Pete Rose, | | McDowell, Mickey Lolich | | 106 Darold Knowles | .50 |
| 28 Billy Wilson | .50 | Bob Clemente | | 73 Wayne Granger | .50 | 107 Bobby Etheridge | .50 |
| 29 Sandy Alomar | .50 | 62 AL Batting Leaders: | 2.00 | 74 Angels Rookies: | .75 | 108 Tom Burgmeier | .50 |
| 30 Matty Alou | .75 | Rod Carew, Reggie Smith, | | Greg Washburn, Wally Wolf | | 109 Expos Rookies: | .75 |
| 31 Marty Pattin | .50 | Tony Oliva | | 75 Jim Kaat | 2.00 | Garry Jestadt, Carl Morton | |
| 32 Harry Walker | .50 | 63 NL RBI Leaders: | 2.00 | 76 Carl Taylor | .50 | 110 Bob Moose | .50 |
| 33 Don Wert | .50 | Ron Santo, Tony Perez, | | 77 Frank Linzy | .50 | 111 Mike Hegan | .50 |
| 34 Willie Crawford | .50 | Willie McCovey | | 78 Joe Lahoud | .50 | 112 Dave Nelson | .50 |
| 35 Joe Horlen | .50 | | | 79 Clay Kirby | .50 | 113 Jim Ray | .50 |

43

| NO. | PLAYER | NR. MT. |
|---|---|---|
| 114 | Gene Michael | .50 |
| 115 | Alex Johnson | .50 |
| 116 | Sparky Lyle | 1.25 |
| 117 | Don Young | .50 |
| 118 | George Mitterwald | .50 |
| 119 | Chuck Taylor | .50 |
| 120 | Sal Bando | .75 |
| 121 | Orioles Rookies: | .75 |
|  | Fred Beene, Terry Crowley | |
| 122 | George Stone | .50 |
| 123 | Don Gutteridge (Mgr.) | .50 |
| 124 | Larry Jaster | .50 |
| 125 | Deron Johnson | .50 |
| 126 | Marty Martinez | .50 |
| 127 | Joe Coleman | .50 |
| 128 | Checklist No. 2 | 4.00 |
| 129 | Jimmie Price | .50 |
| 130 | Ollie Brown | .50 |
| 131 | Dodgers Rookies: | .75 |
|  | Ray Lamb, Bob Stinson | |
| 132 | Jim McGlothlin | .50 |
| 133 | Clay Carroll | .75 |
| 134 | Danny Walton | .75 |
| 135 | Dick Dietz | .75 |
| 136 | Steve Hargan | .75 |
| 137 | Art Shamsky | .75 |
| 138 | Joe Foy | .75 |
| 139 | Rich Nye | .75 |
| 140 | Reggie Jackson | 135.00 |
| 141 | Pirates Rookies: | .90 |
|  | Dave Cash, Johnny Jeter | |
| 142 | Fritz Peterson | .75 |
| 143 | Phil Gagliano | .75 |
| 144 | Ray Culp | .75 |
| 145 | Rico Carty | 1.00 |
| 146 | Danny Murphy | .75 |
| 147 | Angel Hermoso | .75 |
| 148 | Earl Weaver (Mgr.) | 2.00 |
| 149 | Billy Champion | .75 |
| 150 | Harmon Killebrew | 7.00 |
| 151 | Dave Roberts | .75 |
| 152 | Ike Brown | .75 |
| 153 | Gary Gentry | .75 |
| 154 | Senators Rookies: | .90 |
|  | Jim Miles, Jan Dukes | |
| 155 | Denis Menke | .75 |
| 156 | Eddie Fisher | .75 |
| 157 | Manny Mota | .90 |
| 158 | Jerry McNertney | .75 |
| 159 | Tommy Helms | .90 |
| 160 | Phil Niekro | 4.00 |
| 161 | Richie Scheinblum | .75 |
| 162 | Jerry Johnson | .75 |
| 163 | Syd O'Brien | .75 |
| 164 | Ty Cline | .75 |
| 165 | Ed Kirkpatrick | .75 |
| 166 | Al Oliver | 2.50 |
| 167 | Bill Burbach | .75 |
| 168 | Dave Watkins | .75 |
| 169 | Tom Hall | .75 |
| 170 | Billy Williams | 6.00 |
| 171 | Jim Nash | .75 |
| 172 | Braves Rookies: | 2.00 |
|  | Garry Hill, Ralph Garr | |
| 173 | Jim Hicks | .75 |
| 174 | Ted Sizemore | .75 |
| 175 | Dick Bosman | .75 |
| 176 | Jim Hart | .90 |
| 177 | Jim Northrup | .75 |
| 178 | Denny Lemaster | .75 |
| 179 | Ivan Murrell | .75 |
| 180 | Tommy John | 2.50 |
| 181 | Sparky Anderson | 1.25 |
| 182 | Dick Hall | .75 |
| 183 | Jerry Grote | .75 |
| 184 | Ray Fosse | .75 |
| 185 | Don Mincher | .75 |
| 186 | Rick Joseph | .75 |
| 187 | Mike Hedlund | .75 |
| 188 | Manny Sanguillen | .75 |
| 189 | Yankees Rookies: | 100.00 |
|  | Thurman Munson, | |
|  | Dave McDonald | |
| 190 | Joe Torre | 1.50 |
| 191 | Vicente Romo | .75 |

| NO. | PLAYER | NR. MT. |
|---|---|---|
| 192 | Jim Qualls | .75 |
| 193 | Mike Wegener | .75 |
| 194 | Chuck Manuel | .75 |
| 195 | NL Playoff Game 1: | 5.00 |
|  | Seaver Wins Opener | |
| 196 | NL Playoff Game 2: | 2.50 |
|  | Mets Show Muscle | |
| 197 | NL Playoff Game 3: | 12.00 |
|  | Ryan Saves the Day | |
| 198 | We're Number One | 3.00 |
|  | Mets Celebrate | |
| 199 | AL Playoff Game 1: | 2.50 |
|  | Orioles Win Squeaker | |
| 200 | AL Playoff Game 2: | 2.50 |
|  | Powell Scores Winning Run | |
| 201 | AL Playoff Game 3: | 2.50 |
|  | Birds Wrap it Up | |
| 202 | Sweep Twins in Three! | 2.50 |
|  | Orioles Celebrate | |
| 203 | Rudy May | .75 |
| 204 | Len Gabrielson | .75 |
| 205 | Bert Campaneris | .90 |
| 206 | Clete Boyer | .75 |
| 207 | Tigers Rookies: | .90 |
|  | Norman McRae, Bob Reed | |
| 208 | Fred Gladding | .75 |
| 209 | Ken Suarez | .75 |
| 210 | Juan Marichal | 6.00 |
| 211 | Ted Williams (Mgr.) | 7.00 |
| 212 | Al Santorini | .75 |
| 213 | Andy Etchebarren | .75 |
| 214 | Ken Boswell | .75 |
| 215 | Reggie Smith | 1.25 |
| 216 | Chuck Hartenstein | .75 |
| 217 | Ron Hansen | .75 |
| 218 | Ron Stone | .75 |
| 219 | Jerry Kenney | .75 |
| 220 | Steve Carlton | 25.00 |
| 221 | Ron Brand | .75 |
| 222 | Jim Rooker | .75 |
| 223 | Nate Oliver | .75 |
| 224 | Steve Barber | .75 |
| 225 | Lee May | .90 |
| 226 | Ron Perranoski | .75 |
| 227 | Astros Rookies: | 1.25 |
|  | J. Mayberry, B. Watkins | |
| 228 | Aurelio Rodriguez | .75 |
| 229 | Rich Robertson | .75 |
| 230 | Brooks Robinson | 10.00 |
| 231 | Luis Tiant | 1.25 |
| 232 | Bob Didier | .75 |
| 233 | Lew Krausse | .75 |
| 234 | Tommy Dean | .75 |
| 235 | Mike Epstein | .75 |
| 236 | Bob Veale | .75 |
| 237 | Russ Gibson | .75 |
| 238 | Jose Laboy | .75 |
| 239 | Ken Berry | .75 |
| 240 | Fergie Jenkins | 7.00 |
| 241 | Royals Rookies: | .75 |
|  | A. Fitzmorris, S. Northey | |
| 242 | Walter Alston (Mgr.) | 1.50 |
| 243 | Joe Sparma | .75 |
| 244 | Checklist No. 3 | 4.00 |
| 245 | Leo Cardenas | .75 |
| 246 | Jim McAndrew | .75 |
| 247 | Lou Klimchock | .75 |
| 248 | Jesus Alou | .75 |
| 249 | Bob Locker | .75 |
| 250 | Willie McCovey | 8.00 |
| 251 | Dick Schofield | .75 |
| 252 | Lowell Palmer | .75 |
| 253 | Ron Woods | .75 |
| 254 | Camilo Pascual | .75 |
| 255 | Jim Spencer | .75 |
| 256 | Vic Davalillo | .75 |
| 257 | Dennis Higgins | .75 |
| 258 | Paul Popovich | .75 |
| 259 | Tommie Reynolds | .75 |
| 260 | Claude Osteen | .75 |
| 261 | Curt Motton | .75 |
| 262 | Twins Rookies: | .90 |
|  | Jerry Morales, Jim Williams | |
| 263 | Duane Josephson | .75 |
| 264 | Rich Hebner | .90 |

| NO. | PLAYER | NR. MT. |
|---|---|---|
| 265 | Randy Hundley | .75 |
| 266 | Wally Bunker | .75 |
| 267 | Twins Rookies: | .90 |
|  | Paul Ratliff, Herman Hill | |
| 268 | Claude Raymond | .75 |
| 269 | Cesar Gutierrez | .75 |
| 270 | Chris Short | .75 |
| 271 | Greg Goossen | .75 |
| 272 | Hector Torres | .75 |
| 273 | Ralph Houk (Mgr.) | .90 |
| 274 | Gerry Arrigo | .75 |
| 275 | Duke Sims | .75 |
| 276 | Ron Hunt | .75 |
| 277 | Paul Doyle | .75 |
| 278 | Tommie Aaron | .90 |
| 279 | Bill Lee | .90 |
| 280 | Donn Clendenon | .90 |
| 281 | Casey Cox | .75 |
| 282 | Steve Huntz | .75 |
| 283 | Angel Bravo | .75 |
| 284 | Jack Baldschun | .75 |
| 285 | Paul Blair | .75 |
| 286 | Dodgers Rookies: | 8.00 |
|  | Bill Buckner, Jack Jenkins | |
| 287 | Fred Talbot | .75 |
| 288 | Larry Hisle | .90 |
| 289 | Gene Brabender | .75 |
| 290 | Rod Carew | 50.00 |
| 291 | Leo Durocher (Mgr.) | 1.50 |
| 292 | Eddie Leon | .75 |
| 293 | Bob Bailey | .75 |
| 294 | Jose Azcue | .75 |
| 295 | Cecil Upshaw | .75 |
| 296 | Woody Woodward | .75 |
| 297 | Curt Blefary | .75 |
| 298 | Ken Henderson | .75 |
| 299 | Buddy Bradford | .75 |
| 300 | Tom Seaver | 80.00 |
| 301 | Chico Salmon | .75 |
| 302 | Jeff James | .75 |
| 303 | Brant Alyea | .75 |
| 304 | Bill Russell (R) | 2.50 |
| 305 | World Series Game 1 | 2.50 |
|  | Buford's Leadoff Homer | |
| 306 | World Series Game 2 | 2.50 |
|  | Clendenon's Homer | |
| 307 | World Series Game 3 | 2.50 |
|  | Agee's Catch | |
| 308 | World Series Game 4 | 2.50 |
|  | Martin's Bunt | |
| 309 | World Series Game 5 | 2.50 |
|  | Koosman Shuts Door | |
| 310 | World Series Celebration | 2.50 |
|  | Mets Whoop it Up | |
| 311 | Dick Green | .75 |
| 312 | Mike Torrez | .90 |
| 313 | Mayo Smith (Mgr.) | .75 |
| 314 | Bill McCool | .75 |
| 315 | Luis Aparicio | 4.00 |
| 316 | Skip Guinn | .75 |
| 317 | Red Sox Rookies: | .90 |
|  | B. Conigliaro, L. Alvarado | |
| 318 | Willie Smith | .75 |
| 319 | Clay Dalrymple | .75 |
| 320 | Jim Maloney | .75 |
| 321 | Lou Piniella | 2.00 |
| 322 | Luke Walker | .75 |
| 323 | Wayne Comer | .75 |
| 324 | Tony Taylor | .75 |
| 325 | Dave Boswell | .75 |
| 326 | Bill Voss | .75 |
| 327 | Hal King | .75 |
| 328 | George Brunet | .75 |
| 329 | Chris Cannizzaro | .75 |
| 330 | Lou Brock | 8.00 |
| 331 | Chuck Dobson | .75 |
| 332 | Bobby Wine | .75 |
| 333 | Bobby Murcer | 1.50 |
| 334 | Phil Regan | .75 |
| 335 | Bill Freehan | 1.00 |
| 336 | Del Unser | .75 |
| 337 | Mike McCormick | .75 |
| 338 | Paul Schaal | .75 |
| 339 | Johnny Edwards | .75 |
| 340 | Tony Conigliaro | 1.50 |

| NO. | PLAYER | NR. MT. |
|---|---|---|
| 341 | Bill Sudakis | .75 |
| 342 | Wilbur Wood | .75 |
| 343 | Checklist No. 4 | 4.00 |
| 344 | Marcelino Lopez | .75 |
| 345 | Al Ferrara | .75 |
| 346 | Red Schoendienst | 2.25 |
| 347 | Russ Snyder | .75 |
| 348 | Mets Rookies: | .90 |
|  | M. Jorgensen, J. Hudson | |
| 349 | Steve Hamilton | .75 |
| 350 | Roberto Clemente | 40.00 |
| 351 | Tom Murphy | .75 |
| 352 | Bob Barton | .75 |
| 353 | Stan Williams | .75 |
| 354 | Amos Otis | .75 |
| 355 | Doug Rader | .75 |
| 356 | Fred Lasher | .75 |
| 357 | Bob Burda | .75 |
| 358 | Pedro Borbon | .75 |
| 359 | Phil Roof | .75 |
| 360 | Curt Flood | .90 |
| 361 | Ray Jarvis | .75 |
| 362 | Joe Hague | .75 |
| 363 | Tom Shopay | .75 |
| 364 | Dan McGinn | .75 |
| 365 | Zoilo Versalles | .75 |
| 366 | Barry Moore | .75 |
| 367 | Mike Lum | .75 |
| 368 | Ed Herrmann | .75 |
| 369 | Alan Foster | .75 |
| 370 | Tommy Harper | .75 |
| 371 | Rod Gaspar | .75 |
| 372 | Dave Guisti | .75 |
| 373 | Roy White | .90 |
| 374 | Tommie Sisk | .75 |
| 375 | Johnny Callison | .75 |
| 376 | Lefty Phillips (Mgr.) | .75 |
| 377 | Bill Butler | .75 |
| 378 | Jim Davenport | .75 |
| 379 | Tom Tischinski | .75 |
| 380 | Tony Perez | 8.00 |
| 381 | Athletics Rookies: | .90 |
|  | Bobby Brooks, Mike Olivo | |
| 382 | Jack DiLauro | .75 |
| 383 | Mickey Stanley | .90 |
| 384 | Gary Neibauer | .75 |
| 385 | George Scott | .90 |
| 386 | Bill Dillman | .75 |
| 387 | Baltimore Orioles | 2.50 |
| 388 | Byron Browne | .75 |
| 389 | Jim Shellenback | .75 |
| 390 | Willie Davis | .90 |
| 391 | Larry Brown | .75 |
| 392 | Walt Hriniak | .75 |
| 393 | John Gelnar | .75 |
| 394 | Gil Hodges (Mgr.) | 4.00 |
| 395 | Walt Williams | .75 |
| 396 | Steve Blass | .75 |
| 397 | Roger Repoz | .75 |
| 398 | Bill Stoneman | .75 |
| 399 | New York Yankees | 3.00 |
| 400 | Denny McLain | 3.00 |
| 401 | Giants Rookies: | .90 |
|  | John Harrell, B. Williams | |
| 402 | Ellie Rodriguez | .75 |
| 403 | Jim Bunning | 2.50 |
| 404 | Rich Reese | .75 |
| 405 | Bill Hands | .75 |
| 406 | Mike Andrews | .75 |
| 407 | Bob Watson | .90 |
| 408 | Paul Lindblad | .75 |
| 409 | Bob Tolan | .75 |
| 410 | Boog Powell | 3.00 |
| 411 | L.A. Dodgers | 2.50 |
| 412 | Larry Burchart | .75 |
| 413 | Sonny Jackson | .75 |
| 414 | Paul Edmondson | .75 |
| 415 | Julian Javier | .75 |
| 416 | Joe Verbanic | .75 |
| 417 | John Bateman | .75 |
| 418 | John Donaldson | .75 |
| 419 | Ron Taylor | .75 |
| 420 | Ken McMullen | .75 |
| 421 | Pat Dobson | .75 |
| 422 | Kansas City Royals | 2.50 |

| NO. PLAYER | NR. MT. |
|---|---|
| 423 Jerry May | .75 |
| 424 Mike Kilkenny | .75 |
| 425 Bobby Bonds | 6.00 |
| 426 Bill Rigney (Mgr.) | .75 |
| 427 Fred Norman | .75 |
| 428 Don Buford | .75 |
| 429 Cubs Rookies: | .90 |
|     Randy Bobb, Jim Cosman | |
| 430 Andy Messersmith | 1.25 |
| 431 Ron Swoboda | 1.25 |
| 432 Checklist No. 5 | 4.00 |
| 433 Ron Bryant | .75 |
| 434 Felipe Alou | .90 |
| 435 Nelson Briles | .75 |
| 436 Philadelphia Phillies | 2.50 |
| 437 Danny Cater | .75 |
| 438 Pat Jarvis | .75 |
| 439 Lee Maye | .75 |
| 440 Bill Mazeroski | 1.25 |
| 441 John O'Donoghue | .75 |
| 442 Gene Mauch (Mgr.) | .90 |
| 443 Al Jackson | .75 |
| 444 White Sox Rookies: | .90 |
|     Billy Farmer, John Matias | |
| 445 Vada Pinson | 1.50 |
| 446 B. Grabarkewitz | .75 |
| 447 Lee Stange | .75 |
| 448 Houston Astros | 2.50 |
| 449 Jim Palmer | 20.00 |
| 450 Willie McCovey (AS) | 4.00 |
| 451 Boog Powell (AS) | 1.50 |
| 452 Felix Millan (AS) | 1.25 |
| 453 Rod Carew (AS) | 6.00 |
| 454 Ron Santo (AS) | 1.50 |
| 455 Brooks Robinson (AS) | 4.00 |
| 456 Don Kessinger (AS) | 1.50 |
| 457 Rico Petrocelli (AS) | 1.50 |
| 458 Pete Rose (AS) | 12.00 |
| 459 Reggie Jackson (AS) | 16.00 |
| 460 Matty Alou (AS) | 1.25 |
| 461 Carl Yastrzemski (AS) | 10.00 |
| 462 Hank Aaron (AS) | 11.00 |
| 463 Frank Robinson (AS) | 5.00 |
| 464 Johnny Bench (AS) | 10.00 |
| 465 Bill Freehan (AS) | 1.25 |
| 466 Juan Marichal (AS) | 4.00 |
| 467 Denny McLain (AS) | 1.50 |
| 468 Jerry Koosman (AS) | 2.00 |
| 469 Sam McDowell (AS) | 1.25 |
| 470 Willie Stargell | 9.00 |
| 471 Chris Zachary | 1.25 |
| 472 Atlanta Braves | 2.50 |
| 473 Don Bryant | 1.25 |
| 474 Dick Kelley | 1.25 |
| 475 Dick McAuliffe | 1.25 |
| 476 Don Shaw | 1.25 |
| 477 Orioles Rookies: | 1.50 |
|     Roger Freed, Al Severinsen | |
| 478 Bob Heise | 1.25 |
| 479 Dick Woodson | 1.25 |
| 480 Glen Beckert | 1.25 |
| 481 Jose Tartabull | 1.25 |
| 482 Tom Hilgendorf | 1.25 |
| 483 Gail Hopkins | 1.25 |
| 484 Gary Nolan | 1.25 |
| 485 Jay Johnstone | 1.50 |
| 486 Terry Harmon | 1.25 |
| 487 Cisco Carlos | 1.25 |
| 488 J.C. Martin | 1.25 |
| 489 Eddie Kasko (Mgr.) | 1.25 |
| 490 Bill Singer | 1.25 |
| 491 Graig Nettles | 4.00 |
| 492 Astros Rookies: | 1.25 |
|     K. Lampard, S. Spinks | |
| 493 Lindy McDaniel | 1.25 |
| 494 Larry Stahl | 1.25 |
| 495 Dave Morehead | 1.25 |
| 496 Steve Whitaker | 1.25 |
| 497 Eddie Watt | 1.25 |
| 498 Al Weis | 1.25 |
| 499 Skip Lockwood | 1.25 |

| NO. PLAYER | NR. MT. |
|---|---|
| 500 Hank Aaron | 40.00 |
| 501 Chicago White Sox | 2.50 |
| 502 Rollie Fingers | 20.00 |
| 503 Dal Maxvill | 1.25 |
| 504 Don Pavletich | 1.25 |
| 505 Ken Holtzman | 1.25 |
| 506 Ed Stroud | 1.25 |
| 507 Pat Corrales | 1.25 |
| 508 Joe Niekro | 2.00 |
| 509 Montreal Expos | 2.50 |
| 510 Tony Oliva | 2.50 |
| 511 Joe Hoerner | 1.25 |
| 512 Billy Harris | 1.25 |
| 513 Preston Gomez (Mgr.) | 1.25 |
| 514 Steve Hovley | 1.25 |
| 515 Don Wilson | 1.25 |
| 516 Yankees Rookies: | 1.75 |
|     John Ellis, Jim Lyttle | |
| 517 Joe Gibbon | 1.25 |
| 518 Bill Melton | 1.25 |
| 519 Don McMahon | 1.25 |
| 520 Willie Horton | 1.50 |
| 521 Cal Koonce | 1.25 |
| 522 California Angels | 2.50 |
| 523 Jose Pena | 1.25 |
| 524 Alvin Dark (Mgr.) | 2.00 |
| 525 Jerry Adair | 1.25 |
| 526 Ron Herbel | 1.25 |
| 527 Don Bosch | 1.25 |
| 528 Elrod Hendricks | 1.25 |
| 529 Bob Aspromonte | 1.25 |
| 530 Bob Gibson | 10.00 |
| 531 Ron Clark | 1.25 |
| 532 Danny Murtaugh (Mgr.) | 1.25 |
| 533 Buzz Stephen | 1.25 |
| 534 Minnesota Twins | 2.50 |
| 535 Andy Kosco | 1.25 |
| 536 Mike Kekich | 1.25 |
| 537 Joe Morgan | 11.00 |
| 538 Bob Humphreys | 1.25 |
| 539 Phillies Rookies: | 4.00 |
|     Larry Bowa, Dennis Doyle | |
| 540 Gary Peters | 1.25 |
| 541 Bill Heath | 1.25 |
| 542 Checklist No. 6 | 4.00 |
| 543 Clyde Wright | 1.25 |
| 544 Cincinnati Reds | 3.00 |
| 545 Ken Harrelson | 1.50 |
| 546 Ron Reed | 1.25 |
| 547 Rick Monday | 3.00 |
| 548 Howie Reed | 2.50 |
| 549 St. Louis Cardinals | 4.00 |
| 550 Frank Howard | 3.00 |
| 551 Dock Ellis | 2.50 |
| 552 Royals Rookies: | 2.50 |
|     Dennis Paepke, Fred Rico, | |
|     Don O'Riley | |
| 553 Jim LeFebvre | 2.50 |
| 554 Tom Timmermann | 2.50 |
| 555 Orlando Cepeda | 5.00 |
| 556 Dave Bristol | 2.50 |
| 557 Ed Kranepool | 2.50 |
| 558 Vern Fuller | 2.50 |
| 559 Tommy Davis | 2.50 |
| 560 Gaylord Perry | 10.00 |
| 561 Tom McCraw | 2.50 |
| 562 Ted Abernathy | 2.50 |
| 563 Boston Red Sox | 4.00 |
| 564 Johnny Briggs | 2.50 |
| 565 Jim Hunter | 11.00 |
| 566 Gene Alley | 2.50 |
| 567 Bob Oliver | 2.50 |
| 568 Stan Bahnsen | 2.50 |
| 569 Cookie Rojas | 2.50 |
| 570 Jim Fregosi | 3.00 |
| 571 Jim Brewer | 2.50 |
| 572 Frank Quilici | 2.50 |
| 573 Padres Rookies: | 2.50 |
|     Mike Corkins, Rafael | |
|     Robles, Ron Slocum | |
| 574 Bobby Bolin | 2.50 |

| NO. PLAYER | NR. MT. |
|---|---|
| 575 Cleon Jones | 2.50 |
| 576 Milt Pappas | 2.50 |
| 577 Bernie Allen | 2.50 |
| 578 Tom Griffin | 2.50 |
| 579 Detroit Tigers | 4.00 |
| 580 Pete Rose | 75.00 |
| 581 Tom Satriano | 2.50 |
| 582 Mike Paul | 2.50 |
| 583 Hal Lanier | 2.50 |
| 584 Al Downing | 2.50 |
| 585 Rusty Staub | 3.00 |
| 586 Rickey Clark | 2.50 |
| 587 Jose Arcia | 2.50 |
| 588 Checklist No. 7* | 4.00 |
| 589 Joe Keough | 2.50 |
| 590 Mike Cuellar | 2.50 |
| 591 Mike Ryan | 2.50 |
| 592 Daryl Patterson | 2.50 |
| 593 Chicago Cubs | 4.00 |
| 594 Jake Gibbs | 2.50 |
| 595 Maury Wills | 3.50 |
| 596 Mike Hershberger | 2.50 |
| 597 Sonny Siebert | 2.50 |
| 598 Joe Pepitone | 3.50 |
| 599 Senators Rookies: | 2.50 |
|     Dick Such, Gene Martin, | |
|     Dick Stelmaszek, | |
| 600 Willie Mays | 60.00 |
| 601 Pete Richert | 2.50 |
| 602 Ted Savage | 2.50 |
| 603 Ray Oyler | 2.50 |
| 604 Clarence Gaston | 2.50 |
| 605 Rick Wise | 2.50 |
| 606 Chico Ruiz | 2.50 |
| 607 Gary Waslewski | 2.50 |
| 608 Pittsburgh Pirates | 4.00 |
| 609 Buck Martinez | 2.50 |
| 610 Jerry Koosman | 3.00 |
| 611 Norm Cash | 3.00 |
| 612 Jim Hickman | 2.50 |
| 613 Dave Baldwin | 2.50 |
| 614 Mike Shannon | 2.50 |
| 615 Mark Belanger | 2.50 |
| 616 Jim Merritt | 2.50 |
| 617 Jim French | 2.50 |
| 618 Billy Wynne | 2.50 |
| 619 Norm Miller | 2.50 |
| 620 Jim Perry | 3.00 |
| 621 Braves Rookies: | 20.00 |
|     Darrell Evans, Mike | |
|     McQueen, Rick Kester | |
| 622 Don Sutton | 13.00 |
| 623 Horace Clarke | 2.50 |
| 624 Clyde King | 2.50 |
| 625 Dean Chance | 2.50 |
| 626 Dave Ricketts | 2.50 |
| 627 Gary Wagner | 2.50 |
| 628 Wayne Garrett | 2.50 |
| 629 Merv Rettenmund | 2.50 |
| 630 Ernie Banks | 27.00 |
| 631 Oakland Athletics | 4.00 |
| 632 Gary Sutherland | 2.50 |
| 633 Roger Nelson | 2.50 |
| 634 Bud Harrelson | 5.00 |
| 635 Bob Allison | 4.00 |
| 636 Jim Stewart | 4.00 |
| 637 Cleveland Indians | 8.00 |
| 638 Frank Bertaina | 4.00 |
| 639 Dave Campbell | 4.00 |
| 640 Al Kaline | 40.00 |
| 641 Al McBean | 4.00 |
| 642 Angels Rookies: | 4.00 |
|     Greg Garrett, Jarvis Tatum, | |
|     Gordon Lund | |
| 643 Jose Pagan | 4.00 |
| 644 Gerry Nyman | 4.00 |
| 645 Don Money | 4.00 |
| 646 Jim Britton | 4.00 |
| 647 Tom Matchick | 4.00 |
| 648 Larry Haney | 4.00 |
| 649 Jimmie Hall | 4.00 |

| NO. PLAYER | NR. MT. |
|---|---|
| 650 Sam McDowell | 4.00 |
| 651 Jim Gosger | 4.00 |
| 652 Rich Rollins | 4.00 |
| 653 Moe Drabowsky | 4.00 |
| 654 NL Rookies: | 5.00 |
|     Oscar Gamble, Boots Day, | |
|     Angel Mangual | |
| 655 John Roseboro | 4.00 |
| 656 Jim Hardin | 4.00 |
| 657 San Diego Padres | 8.00 |
| 658 Ken Tatum | 4.00 |
| 659 Pete Ward | 4.00 |
| 660 Johnny Bench | 160.00 |
| 661 Jerry Robertson | 4.00 |
| 662 Frank Lucchesi | 4.00 |
| 663 Tito Francona | 4.00 |
| 664 Bob Robertson | 4.00 |
| 665 Jim Lonborg | 4.00 |
| 666 Adolfo Phillips | 4.00 |
| 667 Bob Meyer | 4.00 |
| 668 Bob Tillman | 4.00 |
| 669 White Sox Rookies: | 4.00 |
|     Bart Johnson, Dan Lazar, | |
|     Mickey Scott | |
| 670 Ron Santo | 6.00 |
| 671 Jim Campanis | 4.00 |
| 672 Leon McFadden | 4.00 |
| 673 Ted Uhlaender | 4.00 |
| 674 Dave Leonhard | 4.00 |
| 675 Jose Cardenal | 4.00 |
| 676 Washington Senators | 8.00 |
| 677 Woodie Fryman | 4.00 |
| 678 Dave Duncan | 4.00 |
| 679 Ray Sadecki | 4.00 |
| 680 Rico Petrocelli | 4.00 |
| 681 Bob Garibaldi | 4.00 |
| 682 Dalton Jones | 4.00 |
| 683 Reds Rookies: | 5.00 |
|     Wayne Simpson, Vern | |
|     Geishert, Hal McRae | |
| 684 Jack Fisher | 4.00 |
| 685 Tom Haller | 4.00 |
| 686 Jackie Hernandez | 4.00 |
| 687 Bob Priddy | 4.00 |
| 688 Ted Kubiak | 4.00 |
| 689 Frank Tepedino | 4.00 |
| 690 Ron Fairly | 4.00 |
| 691 Joe Grzenda | 4.00 |
| 692 Duffy Dyer | 4.00 |
| 693 Bob Johnson | 4.00 |
| 694 Gary Ross | 4.00 |
| 695 Bobby Knoop | 4.00 |
| 696 S.F. Giants | 8.00 |
| 697 Jim Hannan | 4.00 |
| 698 Tom Tresh | 5.00 |
| 699 Hank Aguirre | 4.00 |
| 700 Frank Robinson | 40.00 |
| 701 Jack Billingham | 4.00 |
| 702 AL Rookies: | 4.00 |
|     Bob Johnson, Ron | |
|     Klimkowski, Bill Zepp | |
| 703 Lou Marone | 4.00 |
| 704 Frank Baker | 4.00 |
| 705 Tony Cloninger | 4.00 |
| 706 John McNamara (R) | 7.00 |
| 707 Kevin Collins | 4.00 |
| 708 Jose Santiago | 4.00 |
| 709 Mike Fiore | 4.00 |
| 710 Felix Millan | 4.00 |
| 711 Ed Brinkman | 4.00 |
| 712 Nolan Ryan | 400.00 |
| 713 Seattle Pilots | 15.00 |
| 714 Al Spangler | 4.00 |
| 715 Mickey Lolich | 5.00 |
| 716 Cardinals Rookies: | 4.00 |
|     Sal Campisi, R. Cleveland, | |
|     Santiago Guzman | |
| 717 Tom Phoebus | 4.00 |
| 718 Ed Spiezio | 4.00 |
| 719 Jim Roland | 4.00 |
| 720 R. Reichardt (Exc. $1.00) | 6.00 |

# 1971 Topps . . . Complete Set of 752 Cards—Value $850.00 (Exc.); $2000.00 (Near Mint)

Features the rookie cards of Steve Garvey, Don Baylor and George Foster. The high numbers are 644 to 752. Semi-high numbers are 524 to 643. The cards in this set are more difficult to find in *mint* condition because the black border scratches easily.

| NO. PLAYER | NR. MT. |
|---|---|
| 1 World Champs (exc. $3.00) | 12.00 |
| 2 Dock Ellis | .75 |
| 3 Dick McAuliffe | .75 |
| 4 Vic Davalillo | .75 |
| 5 Thurman Munson | 35.00 |
| 6 Ed Spiezio | .75 |
| 7 Jim Holt | .75 |
| 8 Mike McQueen | .75 |
| 9 George Scott | .75 |
| 10 Claude Osteen | .75 |
| 11 Elliott Maddox | .75 |
| 12 Johnny Callison | .75 |
| 13 White Sox Rookies: | .90 |
| C. Brinkman, D. Moloney | |
| 14 Dave Concepcion (R) | 12.00 |
| 15 Andy Messersmith | .75 |
| 16 Ken Singleton (R) | 3.00 |
| 17 Billy Sorrell | .75 |
| 18 Norm Miller | .75 |
| 19 Skip Pitlock | .75 |
| 20 Reggie Jackson | 80.00 |
| 21 Dan McGinn | .75 |
| 22 Phil Roof | .75 |
| 23 Oscar Gamble | 1.00 |
| 24 Rich Hand | .75 |
| 25 Clarence Caston | .75 |
| 26 Bert Blyleven (R) | 50.00 |
| 27 Pirates Rookies | .90 |
| Fred Cambria, Gene Clines | |
| 28 Ron Klimkowski | .75 |
| 29 Don Buford | .75 |
| 30 Phil Niekro | 4.00 |
| 31 Eddie Kasko | .75 |
| 32 Jerry Da Vanon | .75 |
| 33 Del Unser | .75 |
| 34 Sandy Vance | .75 |
| 35 Lou Piniella | 1.25 |
| 36 Dean Chance | .75 |
| 37 Rich McKinney | .75 |
| 38 Jim Colborn | .75 |
| 39 Tiger Rookies: | .90 |
| L. LaGrow, Gene Lamont | |
| 40 Lee May | .75 |
| 41 Rick Austin | .75 |
| 42 Boots Day | .75 |
| 43 Steve Kealey | .75 |
| 44 Johnny Edwards | .75 |
| 45 Jim Hunter | 7.00 |
| 46 Dave Campbell | .75 |
| 47 Johnny Jeter | .75 |
| 48 Dave Baldwin | .75 |
| 49 Don Money | .75 |
| 50 Willy McCovey | 9.00 |
| 51 Steve Kline | .75 |
| 52 Braves Rookies: | 1.00 |
| Oscar Brown, Earl Williams | |
| 53 Paul Blair | .75 |
| 54 Checklist No. 1 | 4.00 |
| 55 Steve Carlton | 25.00 |
| 56 Duane Josephson | .75 |
| 57 Von Joshua | .75 |
| 58 Bill Lee | .75 |
| 59 Gene Mauch (Mgr.) | .75 |
| 60 Dick Bosman | .75 |
| 61 AL Batting Leaders: | 2.50 |
| Alex Johnson, Carl Yastrzemski, Tony Oliva | |

| NO. PLAYER | NR. MT. |
|---|---|
| 62 NL Batting Leaders: | 2.00 |
| Joe Torre, Rico Carty, Manny Sanguillen | |
| 63 AL RBI Leaders: | 2.50 |
| Boog Powell, Frank Robinson, Tony Conigliaro | |
| 64 NL RBI Leaders: | 2.50 |
| Johnny Bench, Billy Williams, Tony Perez | |
| 65 AL HR Leaders: | 2.50 |
| Frank Howard, Harmon Killebrew, C. Yastrzemski | |
| 66 NL HR Leaders: | 3.00 |
| Johnny Bench, Billy Williams, Tony Perez | |
| 67 AL ERA Leaders: | 2.00 |
| Clyde Wright, Diego Segui, Jim Palmer | |
| 68 NL ERA Leaders: | 2.50 |
| Wayne Simpson, Luke Walker, Tom Seaver | |
| 69 AL Pitching Leaders: | 2.25 |
| Mike Cuellar, Dave McNally, Jim Perry | |
| 70 NL Pitching Leaders: | 3.00 |
| Gaylord Perry, Bob Gibson, Fergie Jenkins | |
| 71 AL Strikeout Leaders: | 2.00 |
| Sam McDowell, Mickey Lolich, Bob Johnson | |
| 72 NL Strikeout Leaders: | 4.00 |
| Bob Gibson, Tom Seaver, Fergie Jenkins | |
| 73 George Brunet | .75 |
| 74 Twins Rookies: | .90 |
| Pete Hamm, Jim Nettles | |
| 75 Gary Nolan | .75 |
| 76 Ted Savage | .75 |
| 77 Mike Compton | .75 |
| 78 Jim Spencer | .75 |
| 79 Wade Blasingame | .75 |
| 80 Bill Melton | .75 |
| 81 Felix Millan | .75 |
| 82 Casey Cox | .75 |
| 83 Met Rookies: | .90 |
| Tim Foli, Randy Bobb | |
| 84 Marcel Lachemann | .75 |
| 85 Bill Grabarkewitz | .75 |
| 86 Mike Kilkenny | .75 |
| 87 Jack Heidemann | .75 |
| 88 Hal King | .75 |
| 89 Ken Brett | .75 |
| 90 Joe Pepitone | 1.00 |
| 91 Bob Lemon (Mgr.) | 2.00 |
| 92 Fred Wenz | 1.00 |
| 93 Senators Rookies: | 1.00 |
| Norm McRae, Denny Riddleberger | |
| 94 Don Hahn | .75 |
| 95 Luis Tiant | 1.25 |
| 96 Joe Hague | .75 |
| 97 Floyd Wicker | .75 |
| 98 Joe Decker | .75 |
| 99 Mark Belanger | 1.00 |
| 100 Pete Rose | 45.00 |
| 101 Les Cain | .75 |

| NO. PLAYER | NR. MT. |
|---|---|
| 102 Astros Rookies: | 1.50 |
| Ken Forsch, Larry Howard | |
| 103 Rich Severson | 1.00 |
| 104 Dan Frisella | 1.00 |
| 105 Tony Conigliaro | 1.25 |
| 106 Tom Dukes | .75 |
| 107 Roy Foster | .75 |
| 108 John Cumberland | .75 |
| 109 Steve Hovley | .75 |
| 110 Bill Mazeroski | 1.25 |
| 111 Yankee Rookies: | .90 |
| L. Colson, B. Mitchell | |
| 112 Manny Mota | 1.00 |
| 113 Jerry Crider | .75 |
| 114 Billy Conigliaro | .75 |
| 115 Donn Clendenon | .75 |
| 116 Ken Sanders | .75 |
| 117 Ted Simmons (R) | 10.00 |
| 118 Cookie Rojas | .75 |
| 119 Frank Lucchesi (Mgr.) | .75 |
| 120 Willie Horton | .90 |
| 121 Cubs Rookies: | .90 |
| J. Dunegan, R. Skidmore | |
| 122 Eddie Watt | .75 |
| 123 Checklist No. 2 | 4.00 |
| 124 Don Gullett | .75 |
| 125 Ray Fosse | .75 |
| 126 Danny Coombs | .75 |
| 127 Danny Thompson | .75 |
| 128 Frank Johnson | .75 |
| 129 Aurelio Monteagudo | .75 |
| 130 Denis Menke | .75 |
| 131 Curt Blefary | .75 |
| 132 Jose Laboy | .75 |
| 133 Mickey Lolich | 1.25 |
| 134 Jose Arcia | .75 |
| 135 Rick Monday | 1.00 |
| 136 Duffy Dyer | .75 |
| 137 Marcelino Lopez | .75 |
| 138 Phillies Rookies: | .90 |
| Joe Lis, W. Montanez | |
| 139 Paul Casanova | .75 |
| 140 Gaylord Perry | 7.00 |
| 141 Frank Quilici | .75 |
| 142 Mack Jones | .75 |
| 143 Steve Blass | .75 |
| 144 Jackie Hernandez | .75 |
| 145 Bill Singer | .75 |
| 146 Ralph Houk (Mgr.) | .90 |
| 147 Bob Priddy | .75 |
| 148 John Mayberry | .75 |
| 149 Mike Hershberger | .75 |
| 150 Sam McDowell | 1.00 |
| 151 Tommy Davis | .90 |
| 152 Angels Rookies: | .75 |
| Lloyd Allen, Winston Llenas | |
| 153 Gary Ross | .75 |
| 154 Cesar Gutierrez | .75 |
| 155 Ken Henderson | .75 |
| 156 Bart Johnson | .75 |
| 157 Bob Bailey | .75 |
| 158 Jerry Reuss | 1.00 |
| 159 Jarvis Tatum | .75 |
| 160 Tom Seaver | 50.00 |
| 161 Coins Checklist | 2.50 |
| 162 Jack Billingham | .75 |

| NO. PLAYER | NR. MT. |
|---|---|
| 163 Buck Martinez | .75 |
| 164 Reds Rookies: | 1.00 |
| Frank Duffy, Milt Wilcox | |
| 165 Cesar Tovar | .75 |
| 166 Joe Hoerner | .75 |
| 167 Tom Grieve | 1.25 |
| 168 Bruce Dal Canton | .75 |
| 169 Ed Herrmann | .75 |
| 170 Mike Cuellar | 1.25 |
| 171 Bobby Wine | .75 |
| 172 Duke Sims | .75 |
| 173 Gil Garrido | .75 |
| 174 Dave LaRoche | .75 |
| 175 Jim Hickman | .75 |
| 176 Red Sox Rookies: | .90 |
| Bob Montgomery, Doug Griffin | |
| 177 Hal McRae | 1.50 |
| 178 Dave Duncan | .75 |
| 179 Mike Corkins | .75 |
| 180 Al Kaline | 15.00 |
| 181 Hal Lanier | 1.00 |
| 182 Al Downing | .75 |
| 183 Gil Hodges (Mgr.) | 4.00 |
| 184 Stan Bahnsen | .75 |
| 185 Julian Javier | .75 |
| 186 Bob Spence | .75 |
| 187 Ted Abernathy | .75 |
| 188 Dodgers Rookies: | 3.00 |
| Mike Strahler, Bob Valentine | |
| 189 George Mitterwald | .75 |
| 190 Bob Tolan | .75 |
| 191 Mike Andrews | .75 |
| 192 Billy Wilson | .75 |
| 193 Bob Grich (R) | 3.00 |
| 194 Mike Lum | .75 |
| 195 AL Playoff Game 1 | 2.50 |
| Powell Muscles Twins | |
| 196 AL Playoff Game 2 | 2.50 |
| McNally's Two Straight | |
| 197 AL Playoff Game 3 | 3.00 |
| Palmer Mows 'Em Down | |
| 198 Orioles Celebrate | 2.50 |
| A Team Effort | |
| 199 NL Playoff Game 1 | 2.50 |
| Cline Pinch-Triple | |
| 200 NL Playoff Game 2 | 2.50 |
| Tolan Scores Third Time | |
| 201 NL Playoff Game 3 | 2.50 |
| Cline Scores Winning Run | |
| 202 Reds Celebrate | 2.50 |
| World Series Bound | |
| 203 Larry Gura (R) | 1.25 |
| 204 Brewers Rookies: | 1.00 |
| B. Smith, G. Kopacz | |
| 205 Gerry Moses | .75 |
| 206 Checklist No. 3 | 4.00 |
| 207 Alan Foster | .75 |
| 208 Billy Martin | 3.00 |
| 209 Steve Renko | .75 |
| 210 Rod Carew | 35.00 |
| 211 Phil Hennigan | .75 |
| 212 Rich Hebner | .75 |
| 213 Frank Baker | .75 |
| 214 Al Ferrara | .75 |
| 215 Diego Segui | .75 |

| NO. | PLAYER | NR. MT. |
|---|---|---|
| 216 | Cards Rookies: Reggie Cleveland, Luis Melendez | .90 |
| 217 | Ed Stroud | .75 |
| 218 | Tony Cloninger | .75 |
| 219 | Elrod Hendricks | .75 |
| 220 | Ron Santo | 2.00 |
| 221 | Dave Morehead | .75 |
| 222 | Bob Watson | 1.00 |
| 223 | Cecil Upshaw | .75 |
| 224 | Alan Gallagher | .75 |
| 225 | Gary Peters | .75 |
| 226 | Bill Russell | 1.25 |
| 227 | Floyd Weaver | .75 |
| 228 | Wayne Garrett | .75 |
| 229 | Jim Hannan | .75 |
| 230 | Willie Stargell | 9.00 |
| 231 | Indians Rookies: Vince Colbert, John Lowenstein | .90 |
| 232 | John Strohmayer | .75 |
| 233 | Larry Bowa | 2.00 |
| 234 | Jim Lyttle | .75 |
| 235 | Nate Colbert | .75 |
| 236 | Bob Humphreys | .75 |
| 237 | Cesar Cedeno (R) | 3.00 |
| 238 | Chuck Dobson | .75 |
| 239 | R. Schoendienst (Mgr.) | 2.00 |
| 240 | Clyde Wright | .75 |
| 241 | Dave Nelson | .75 |
| 242 | Jim Ray | .75 |
| 243 | Carlos May | .75 |
| 244 | Bob Tillman | .75 |
| 245 | Jim Kaat | 2.00 |
| 246 | Tony Taylor | .75 |
| 247 | Royals Rookies: Jerry Cram, Paul Splittorff | 1.00 |
| 248 | Hoyt Wilhelm | 4.00 |
| 249 | Chico Salmon | .75 |
| 250 | Johnny Bench | 50.00 |
| 251 | Frank Reberger | .75 |
| 252 | Eddie Leon | .75 |
| 253 | Bill Sudakis | .75 |
| 254 | Cal Koonce | .75 |
| 255 | Bob Robertson | .75 |
| 256 | Tony Gonzalez | .75 |
| 257 | Nelson Briles | .75 |
| 258 | Dick Green | .75 |
| 259 | Dave Marshall | .75 |
| 260 | Tommy Harper | .75 |
| 261 | Darold Knowles | .75 |
| 262 | Padres Rookies: D. Robinson, J. Williams | .90 |
| 263 | John Ellis | .75 |
| 264 | Joe Morgan | 8.00 |
| 265 | Jim Northrup | 1.00 |
| 266 | Bill Stoneman | 1.00 |
| 267 | Rich Morales | 1.00 |
| 268 | Philadelphia Phillies | 2.50 |
| 269 | Gail Hopkins | 1.00 |
| 270 | Rico Carty | 1.25 |
| 271 | Bill Zepp | 1.00 |
| 272 | Tommy Helms | 1.00 |
| 273 | Pete Richert | 1.00 |
| 274 | Ron Slocum | 1.00 |
| 275 | Vada Pinson | 1.50 |
| 276 | Giants Rookies: M. Davison, George Foster | 7.00 |
| 277 | Gary Waslewski | 1.00 |
| 278 | Jerry Grote | 1.00 |
| 279 | Lefty Phillips (Mgr.) | 1.00 |
| 280 | Fergie Jenkins | 8.00 |
| 281 | Danny Walton | 1.00 |
| 282 | Jose Pagan | 1.00 |
| 283 | Dick Such | 1.00 |
| 284 | Jim Gosger | 1.00 |
| 285 | Sal Bando | 1.25 |
| 286 | Jerry McNertney | 1.00 |
| 287 | Mike Fiore | 1.00 |
| 288 | Joe Moeller | 1.00 |
| 289 | Chicago White Sox | 2.50 |
| 290 | Tony Oliva | 3.00 |
| 291 | George Culver | 1.00 |
| 292 | Jay Johnstone | 1.00 |
| 293 | Pat Corrales | 1.25 |
| 294 | Steve Dunning | 1.00 |
| 295 | Bobby Bonds | 4.00 |
| 296 | Tom Timmermann | 1.00 |
| 297 | Johnny Briggs | 1.00 |
| 298 | Jim Nelson | 1.00 |
| 299 | Ed Kirkpatrick | 1.00 |
| 300 | Brooks Robinson | 12.00 |
| 301 | Earl Wilson | 1.00 |
| 302 | Phil Gagliano | 1.00 |
| 303 | Lindy McDaniel | 1.00 |
| 304 | Ron Brand | 1.00 |
| 305 | Reggie Smith | 1.50 |
| 306 | Jim Nash | 1.00 |
| 307 | Don Wert | 1.00 |
| 308 | St. Louis Cardinals | 2.50 |
| 309 | Dick Ellsworth | 1.00 |
| 310 | Tommie Agee | 1.25 |
| 311 | Lee Stange | 1.00 |
| 312 | Harry Walker | 1.00 |
| 313 | Tom Hall | 1.00 |
| 314 | Jeff Torborg | 1.00 |
| 315 | Ron Fairly | 1.00 |
| 316 | Fred Scherman | 1.00 |
| 317 | Athletic Rookies: Angel Mangual, Jim Driscoll | 1.00 |
| 318 | Rudy May | 1.00 |
| 319 | Ty Cline | 1.00 |
| 320 | Dave McNally | 1.00 |
| 321 | Tom Matchick | 1.00 |
| 322 | Jim Beauchamp | 1.00 |
| 323 | Billy Champion | 1.00 |
| 324 | Graig Nettles | 2.50 |
| 325 | Juan Marichal | 5.00 |
| 326 | Richie Scheinblum | 1.00 |
| 327 | World Series Game 1 Powell Homers | 2.50 |
| 328 | World Series Game 2 Buford Goes 2 For 4 | 2.50 |
| 329 | World Series Game 3 F. Robinson Shows Muscle | 3.00 |
| 330 | World Series Game 4 Reds Stay Alive | 2.50 |
| 331 | World Series Game 5 B. Robinson Robbery | 3.00 |
| 332 | World Series Celebration Convincing Performance | 2.50 |
| 333 | Clay Kirby | 1.00 |
| 334 | Roberto Pena | 1.00 |
| 335 | Jerry Koosman | 2.00 |
| 336 | Detroit Tigers | 2.50 |
| 337 | Jesus Alou | 1.00 |
| 338 | Gene Tenace | 1.00 |
| 339 | Wayne Simpson | 1.00 |
| 340 | Rico Petrocelli | 1.25 |
| 341 | Steve Garvey (R) | 80.00 |
| 342 | Frank Tepedino | 1.00 |
| 343 | Pirates Rookies: Ed Acosta, M. May | 1.00 |
| 344 | Ellie Rodriguez | 1.00 |
| 345 | Joe Horlen | 1.00 |
| 346 | Lum Harris | 1.00 |
| 347 | Ted Uhlaender | 1.00 |
| 348 | Fred Norman | 1.00 |
| 349 | Rich Reese | 1.00 |
| 350 | Billy Williams | 5.00 |
| 351 | Jim Shellenback | 1.00 |
| 352 | Denny Doyle | 1.00 |
| 353 | Carl Taylor | 1.00 |
| 354 | Don McMahon | 1.00 |
| 355 | Bud Harrelson | 1.25 |
| 356 | Bob Locker | 1.00 |
| 357 | Cincinnati Reds | 2.50 |
| 358 | Danny Cater | 1.00 |
| 359 | Ron Reed | 1.00 |
| 360 | Jim Fregosi | 1.25 |
| 361 | Don Sutton | 6.00 |
| 362 | Orioles Rookies: Mike Adamson, R. Freed | 1.25 |
| 363 | Mike Nagy | 1.00 |
| 364 | Tommy Dean | 1.00 |
| 365 | Bob Johnson | 1.00 |
| 366 | Ron Stone | 1.00 |
| 367 | Dalton Jones | 1.00 |
| 368 | Bob Veale | 1.00 |
| 369 | Checklist No. 4 | 4.00 |
| 370 | Joe Torre | 3.00 |
| 371 | Jack Hiatt | 1.00 |
| 372 | Lew Krausse | 1.00 |
| 373 | Tom McCraw | 1.00 |
| 374 | Clete Boyer | 1.25 |
| 375 | Steve Hargan | 1.00 |
| 376 | Expos Rookies: C. Mashore, E. McAnally | 1.00 |
| 377 | Greg Garrett | 1.00 |
| 378 | Tito Fuentes | 1.00 |
| 379 | Wayne Granger | 1.00 |
| 380 | Ted Williams (Mgr.) | 6.00 |
| 381 | Fred Gladding | 1.00 |
| 382 | Jake Gibbs | 1.00 |
| 383 | Rod Gaspar | 1.00 |
| 384 | Rollie Fingers | 10.00 |
| 385 | Maury Wills | 2.50 |
| 386 | Boston Red Sox | 2.50 |
| 387 | Ron Herbel | 1.00 |
| 388 | Al Oliver | 2.50 |
| 389 | Ed Brinkman | 1.00 |
| 390 | Glenn Beckert | 1.00 |
| 391 | Twins Rookies: Steve Brye, Cotton Nash | 1.00 |
| 392 | Grant Jackson | 1.00 |
| 393 | Merv Rettenmund | 1.00 |
| 394 | Clay Carroll | 1.25 |
| 395 | Roy White | 1.75 |
| 396 | Dick Schofield | 1.25 |
| 397 | Alvin Dark (Mgr.) | 2.00 |
| 398 | Howie Reed | 1.25 |
| 399 | Jim French | 1.25 |
| 400 | Hank Aaron | 40.00 |
| 401 | Tom Murphy | 1.25 |
| 402 | Los Angeles Dodgers | 2.50 |
| 403 | Joe Coleman | 1.25 |
| 404 | Astros Rookies: B. Harris, R. Metzger | 1.25 |
| 405 | Leo Cardenas | 1.25 |
| 406 | Ray Sadecki | 1.25 |
| 407 | Joe Rudi | 1.50 |
| 408 | Rafael Robles | 1.25 |
| 409 | Don Pavletich | 1.25 |
| 410 | Ken Holtzman | 1.50 |
| 411 | George Spriggs | 1.25 |
| 412 | Jerry Johnson | 1.25 |
| 413 | Pat Kelly | 1.25 |
| 414 | Woodie Fryman | 1.25 |
| 415 | Mike Hegan | 1.25 |
| 416 | Gene Alley | 1.25 |
| 417 | Dick Hall | 1.25 |
| 418 | Adolfo Phillips | 1.25 |
| 419 | Ron Hansen | 1.25 |
| 420 | Jim Merritt | 1.25 |
| 421 | John Stephenson | 1.25 |
| 422 | Frank Bertaina | 1.25 |
| 423 | Tigers Rookies: T. Marting, D. Saunders | 1.50 |
| 424 | Roberto Rodriquez | 1.25 |
| 425 | Doug Rader | 1.50 |
| 426 | Chris Cannizzaro | 1.25 |
| 427 | Bernie Allen | 1.25 |
| 428 | Jim McAndrew | 1.25 |
| 429 | Chuck Hinton | 1.25 |
| 430 | Wes Parker | 1.50 |
| 431 | Tom Burgmeier | 1.25 |
| 432 | Bob Didier | 1.25 |
| 433 | Skip Lockwood | 1.25 |
| 434 | Gary Sutherland | 1.25 |
| 435 | Jose Cardenal | 1.25 |
| 436 | Wilbur Wood | 1.25 |
| 437 | Danny Murtaugh (Mgr.) | 1.25 |
| 438 | Mike McCormick | 1.25 |
| 439 | Phillies Rookies: Greg Luzinski, Scott Reid | 3.00 |
| 440 | Bert Campaneris | 1.50 |
| 441 | Milt Pappas | 1.25 |
| 442 | California Angels | 2.50 |
| 443 | Rich Robertson | 1.25 |
| 444 | Jimmie Price | 1.25 |
| 445 | Art Shamsky | 1.25 |
| 446 | Bobby Bolin | 1.25 |
| 447 | Cesar Geronimo | 1.25 |
| 448 | Dave Roberts | 1.25 |
| 449 | Brant Alyea | 1.25 |
| 450 | Bob Gibson | 13.00 |
| 451 | Joe Keough | 1.25 |
| 452 | John Boccabella | 1.25 |
| 453 | Terry Crowley | 1.25 |
| 454 | Mike Paul | 1.25 |
| 455 | Don Kessinger | 1.25 |
| 456 | Bob Meyer | 1.25 |
| 457 | Willie Smith | 1.25 |
| 458 | White Sox Rookies: Ron Lolich, Dave Lemonds | 1.50 |
| 459 | Jim LeFebvre | 1.25 |
| 460 | Fritz Peterson | 1.25 |
| 461 | Jim Hart | 1.50 |
| 462 | Senators Team | 2.50 |
| 463 | Tom Kelley | 1.25 |
| 464 | Aurelio Rodriguez | 1.25 |
| 465 | Tim McCarver | 2.00 |
| 466 | Ken Berry | 1.25 |
| 467 | Al Santorini | 1.25 |
| 468 | Frank Fernandez | 1.25 |
| 469 | Bob Aspromonte | 1.25 |
| 470 | Bob Oliver | 1.25 |
| 471 | Tom Griffin | 1.25 |
| 472 | Ken Rudolph | 1.25 |
| 473 | Gary Wagner | 1.25 |
| 474 | Jim Fairey | 1.25 |
| 475 | Ron Perranoski | 2.00 |
| 476 | Dal Maxvill | 1.25 |
| 477 | Earl Weaver (Mgr.) | 2.00 |
| 478 | Bernie Carbo | 1.25 |
| 479 | Dennis Higgins | 1.25 |
| 480 | Manny Sanguillen | 1.50 |
| 481 | Daryl Patterson | 1.25 |
| 482 | San Diego Padres | 2.50 |
| 483 | Gene Michael | 1.50 |
| 484 | Don Wilson | 1.25 |
| 485 | Ken McMullen | 1.25 |
| 486 | Steve Huntz | 1.25 |
| 487 | Paul Schaal | 1.25 |
| 488 | Jerry Stephenson | 1.25 |
| 489 | Luis Alvardao | 1.25 |
| 490 | Deron Johnson | 1.25 |
| 491 | Jim Hardin | 1.25 |
| 492 | Ken Boswell | 1.25 |
| 493 | Dave May | 1.25 |
| 494 | Braves Rookies: Ralph Garr, Rick Kester | 2.00 |
| 495 | Felipe Alou | 2.00 |
| 496 | Woody Woodward | 2.00 |
| 497 | Horacio Pina | 1.25 |
| 498 | John Kennedy | 1.25 |
| 499 | Checklist No. 5 | 4.00 |
| 500 | Jim Perry | 1.00 |
| 501 | Andy Etchebarren | 1.25 |
| 502 | Chicago Cubs | 2.50 |
| 503 | Gates Brown | 1.25 |
| 504 | Ken Wright | 1.25 |
| 505 | Ollie Brown | 1.25 |
| 506 | Bobby Knoop | 1.25 |
| 507 | George Stone | 1.25 |
| 508 | Roger Repoz | 1.25 |
| 509 | Jim Grant | 1.25 |
| 510 | Ken Harrelson | 1.75 |
| 511 | Chris Short | 1.25 |
| 512 | Red Sox Rookies: Dick Mills, Mike Garman | 1.50 |
| 513 | Nolan Ryan | 175.00 |
| 514 | Ron Woods | 1.25 |
| 515 | Carl Morton | 1.25 |
| 516 | Ted Kubiak | 1.25 |
| 517 | Charlie Fox (Mgr.) | 1.25 |
| 518 | Joe Grzenda | 1.25 |
| 519 | Willie Crawford | 1.25 |
| 520 | Tommy John | 3.00 |
| 521 | Leron Lee | 1.25 |
| 522 | Minnesota Twins | 2.50 |
| 523 | John Odom | 1.25 |
| 524 | Mickey Stanley | 3.00 |
| 525 | Ernie Banks | 27.00 |
| 526 | Ray Jarvis | 3.00 |
| 527 | Cleon Jones | 3.00 |
| 528 | Wally Bunker | 3.00 |
| 529 | NL Rookies: Enzo, Hernandez, Bill Buckner, Marty Perez | 5.00 |

| NO. | PLAYER | NR. MT. |
|---|---|---|
| 530 | Carl Yastrzemski | 40.00 |
| 531 | Mike Torrez | 3.00 |
| 532 | Bill Rigney (Mgr.) | 3.00 |
| 533 | Mike Ryan | 3.00 |
| 534 | Luke Walker | 3.00 |
| 535 | Curt Flood | 4.00 |
| 536 | Claude Raymond | 3.00 |
| 537 | Tom Egan | 3.00 |
| 538 | Angel Bravo | 3.00 |
| 539 | Larry Brown | 3.00 |
| 540 | Larry Dierker | 3.00 |
| 541 | Bob Burda | 3.00 |
| 542 | Bob Miller | 3.00 |
| 543 | New York Yankees | 5.00 |
| 544 | Vida Blue | 4.00 |
| 545 | Dick Dietz | 3.00 |
| 546 | John Matias | 3.00 |
| 547 | Pat Dobson | 3.00 |
| 548 | Don Mason | 3.00 |
| 549 | Jim Brewer | 3.00 |
| 550 | Harmon Killebrew | 20.00 |
| 551 | Frank Linzy | 3.00 |
| 552 | Buddy Bradford | 3.00 |
| 553 | Kevin Collins | 3.00 |
| 554 | Lowell Palmer | 3.00 |
| 555 | Walt Williams | 3.00 |
| 556 | Jim McGlothlin | 3.00 |
| 557 | Tom Satriano | 3.00 |
| 558 | Hector Torres | 3.00 |
| 559 | AL Rookies: | 3.00 |
|  | Gary Jones, Terry Cox, Bill Gogolewski | |
| 560 | Rusty Staub | 4.00 |
| 561 | Syd O'Brien | 3.00 |
| 562 | Dave Giusti | 3.00 |
| 563 | Giants Team | 5.00 |
| 564 | Al Fitzmorris | 3.00 |
| 565 | Jim Wynn | 3.00 |
| 566 | Tim Cullen | 3.00 |
| 567 | Walt Alston (Mgr.) | 4.00 |
| 568 | Sal Campisi | 3.00 |
| 569 | Ivan Murrell | 3.00 |
| 570 | Jim Palmer | 30.00 |
| 571 | Ted Sizemore | 3.00 |
| 572 | Jerry Kenney | 3.00 |
| 573 | Ed Kranepool | 3.00 |
| 574 | Jim Bunning | 4.00 |
| 575 | Bill Freehan | 3.00 |
| 576 | Cubs Rookies: | 3.00 |
|  | Brock Davis, Adrian Garrett, Garry Jestadt | |
| 577 | Jim Lonborg | 4.00 |
| 578 | Ron Hunt | 3.00 |
| 579 | Marty Pattin | 3.00 |
| 580 | Tony Perez | 10.00 |
| 581 | Roger Nelson | 3.00 |
| 582 | Dave Cash | 3.00 |
| 583 | Ron Cook | 3.00 |
| 584 | Cleveland Indians | 5.00 |
| 585 | Willie Davis | 3.00 |
| 586 | Dick Woodson | 3.00 |

| NO. | PLAYER | NR. MT. |
|---|---|---|
| 587 | Sonny Jackson | 3.00 |
| 588 | Tom Bradley | 3.00 |
| 589 | Bob Barton | 3.00 |
| 590 | Alex Johnson | 3.00 |
| 591 | Jackie Brown | 3.00 |
| 592 | Randy Hundley | 3.00 |
| 593 | Jack Aker | 3.00 |
| 594 | Cardinals Rookies: | 4.00 |
|  | Bob Chlupsa, Bob Stinson, Al Hrabosky | |
| 595 | Dave Johnson | 4.00 |
| 596 | Mike Jorgensen | 3.00 |
| 597 | Ken Suarez | 3.00 |
| 598 | Rick Wise | 3.00 |
| 599 | Norm Cash | 4.00 |
| 600 | Willie Mays | 75.00 |
| 601 | Ken Tatum | 3.00 |
| 602 | Marty Martinez | 3.00 |
| 603 | Pittsburgh Pirates | 5.00 |
| 604 | John Gelnar | 3.00 |
| 605 | Orlando Cepeda | 5.00 |
| 606 | Chuck Taylor | 3.00 |
| 607 | Paul Ratliff | 3.00 |
| 608 | Mike Wegener | 3.00 |
| 609 | Leo Durocher (Mgr.) | 4.00 |
| 610 | Amos Otis | 4.00 |
| 611 | Tom Phoebus | 3.00 |
| 612 | Indians Rookies: | 3.00 |
|  | Ted Ford, Steve Mingori, Lou Camilli | |
| 613 | Pedro Borbon | 3.00 |
| 614 | Billy Cowan | 3.00 |
| 615 | Mel Stottlemyre | 3.50 |
| 616 | Larry Hisle | 3.00 |
| 617 | Clay Dalrymple | 3.00 |
| 618 | Tug McGraw | 4.00 |
| 619 | Checklist No. 6 | 4.00 |
| 620 | Frank Howard | 4.00 |
| 621 | Ron Bryant | 3.00 |
| 622 | Joe LaHoud | 3.00 |
| 623 | Pat Jarvis | 3.00 |
| 624 | Oakland Athletics | 5.00 |
| 625 | Lou Brock | 25.00 |
| 626 | Freddie Patek | 3.00 |
| 627 | Steve Hamilton | 3.00 |
| 628 | John Bateman | 3.00 |
| 629 | John Hiller | 3.00 |
| 630 | Roberto Clemente | 50.00 |
| 631 | Eddie Fisher | 3.00 |
| 632 | Darrel Chaney | 3.00 |
| 633 | AL Rookies: | 3.00 |
|  | Pete Koegel, Bobby Brooks, Scott Northey | |
| 634 | Phil Regan | 3.00 |
| 635 | Bobby Murcer | 4.00 |
| 636 | Denny LeMaster | 3.00 |
| 637 | Dave Bristol (Mgr.) | 3.00 |
| 638 | Stan Williams | 3.00 |
| 639 | Tom Haller | 3.00 |
| 640 | Frank Robinson | 35.00 |
| 641 | New York Mets | 8.00 |

| NO. | PLAYER | NR. MT. |
|---|---|---|
| 642 | Jim Roland | 3.00 |
| 643 | Rick Reichardt | 3.00 |
| 644 | Jim Stewart | 5.00 |
| 645 | Jim Maloney | 5.00 |
| 646 | Bobby Floyd | 5.00 |
| 647 | Juan Pizarro | 5.00 |
| 648 | Mets Rookies: | 8.00 |
|  | Rich Folkers, Ted Martinez, John Matlack | |
| 649 | Sparky Lyle | 9.00 |
| 650 | Rich Allen | 15.00 |
| 651 | Jerry Robertson | 5.00 |
| 652 | Atlanta Braves | 10.00 |
| 653 | Russ Snyder | 5.00 |
| 654 | Don Shaw | 5.00 |
| 655 | Mike Epstein | 5.00 |
| 656 | Gerry Nyman | 5.00 |
| 657 | Jose Azcue | 5.00 |
| 658 | Paul Lindblad | 5.00 |
| 659 | Byron Browne | 5.00 |
| 660 | Ray Culp | 5.00 |
| 661 | Chuck Tanner (Mgr.) | 6.00 |
| 662 | Mike Hedlund | 5.00 |
| 663 | Marv Staehle | 5.00 |
| 664 | Rookies Pitchers: | 5.00 |
|  | Archie Reynolds, Bob Reynolds, K. Reynolds | |
| 665 | Ron Swoboda | 5.00 |
| 666 | Gene Brabender | 5.00 |
| 667 | Pete Ward | 5.00 |
| 668 | Gary Neibauer | 5.00 |
| 669 | Ike Brown | 5.00 |
| 670 | Bill Hands | 5.00 |
| 671 | Bill Voss | 5.00 |
| 672 | Ed Crosby | 5.00 |
| 673 | Gerry Janeski | 5.00 |
| 674 | Montreal Expos | 10.00 |
| 675 | Dave Boswell | 5.00 |
| 676 | Tommie Reynolds | 5.00 |
| 677 | Jack DiLauro | 5.00 |
| 678 | George Thomas | 5.00 |
| 679 | Don O'Riley | 5.00 |
| 680 | Don Mincher | 5.00 |
| 681 | Bill Butler | 5.00 |
| 682 | Terry Harmon | 5.00 |
| 683 | Bill Burbach | 5.00 |
| 684 | Curt Motton | 5.00 |
| 685 | Moe Drabowsky | 5.00 |
| 686 | Chico Ruiz | 5.00 |
| 687 | Ron Taylor | 5.00 |
| 688 | S. Anderson (Mgr.) | 12.00 |
| 689 | Frank Baker | 5.00 |
| 690 | Bob Moose | 5.00 |
| 691 | Bob Heise | 5.00 |
| 692 | AL Rookies Pitchers: | 5.00 |
|  | Hal Haydel, Rogelio Moret, Wayne Twitchell | |
| 693 | Jose Pena | 5.00 |
| 694 | Rick Renick | 5.00 |
| 695 | Joe Niekro | 6.00 |
| 696 | Jerry Morales | 5.00 |

| NO. | PLAYER | NR. MT. |
|---|---|---|
| 697 | Rickey Clark | 5.00 |
| 698 | Milwaukee Brewers | 10.00 |
| 699 | Jim Britton | 5.00 |
| 700 | Boog Powell | 12.00 |
| 701 | Bob Garibaldi | 5.00 |
| 702 | Milt Ramirez | 5.00 |
| 703 | Mike Kekich | 5.00 |
| 704 | J.C. Martin | 5.00 |
| 705 | Dick Selma | 5.00 |
| 706 | Joe Foy | 5.00 |
| 707 | Fred Lasher | 5.00 |
| 708 | Russ Nagelson | 5.00 |
| 709 | Rookie Outfielders: | 36.00 |
|  | Don Baylor, Tom Paciorek, Dusty Baker | |
| 710 | Sonny Siebert | 5.00 |
| 711 | Larry Stahl | 5.00 |
| 712 | Jose Martinez | 5.00 |
| 713 | Mike Marshall | 6.00 |
| 714 | Dick Williams (Mgr.) | 6.00 |
| 715 | Horace Clarke | 5.00 |
| 716 | Dave Leonhard | 5.00 |
| 717 | Tommie Aaron | 5.00 |
| 718 | Billy Wynne | 5.00 |
| 719 | Jerry May | 5.00 |
| 720 | Matty Alou | 5.00 |
| 721 | John Morris | 5.00 |
| 722 | Houston Astros | 10.00 |
| 723 | Vicente Romo | 5.00 |
| 724 | Tom Tischinski | 5.00 |
| 725 | Gary Gentry | 5.00 |
| 726 | Paul Popovich | 5.00 |
| 727 | Ray Lamb | 5.00 |
| 728 | NL Rookie Outfielders: | 5.00 |
|  | Wayne Redmond, Keith Lampard, Bernie Williams | |
| 729 | Dick Billings | 5.00 |
| 730 | Jim Rooker | 5.00 |
| 731 | Jim Qualls | 5.00 |
| 732 | Bob Reed | 5.00 |
| 733 | Lee Maye | 5.00 |
| 734 | Rob Gardner | 5.00 |
| 735 | Mike Shannon | 5.00 |
| 736 | Mel Queen | 5.00 |
| 737 | Preston Gomez (Mgr.) | 5.00 |
| 738 | Russ Gibson | 5.00 |
| 739 | Barry Lersch | 5.00 |
| 740 | Luis Aparicio | 18.00 |
| 741 | Skip Guinn | 5.00 |
| 742 | Kansas City Royals | 10.00 |
| 743 | John O'Donoghue | 5.00 |
| 744 | Chuck Manuel | 5.00 |
| 745 | Sandy Alomar | 5.00 |
| 746 | Andy Kosco | 5.00 |
| 747 | NL Rookie Pitchers: | 5.00 |
|  | Al Severinsen, Scipio Spinks, Balor Moore | |
| 748 | John Purdin | 5.00 |
| 749 | Ken Szotkiewicz | 5.00 |
| 750 | Denny McLain | 10.00 |
| 751 | Al Weis | 11.00 |
| 752 | Dick Drago (exc. $2.25) | 9.00 |

## 1972 Topps . . . Complete Set of 787 Cards—Value $775.00 (Exc.) $1800.00 (Near Mint)

Features the rookie cards of Carlton Fisk and Ben Oglivie. The high numbers are 657 to 787. Semi-high numbers are 526 to 656.

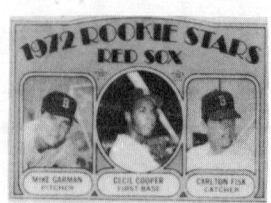

| NO. PLAYER | NR. MT. |
|---|---|
| 1 Pirates-Champs. (exc. $2.00) | 8.00 |
| 2 Ray Culp | .35 |
| 3 Bob Tolan | .35 |
| 4 Checklist No. 1 | 2.00 |
| 5 John Bateman | .35 |
| 6 Fred Scherman | .35 |
| 7 Enzo Hernandez | .35 |
| 8 Ron Swoboda | .35 |
| 9 Stan Williams | .35 |
| 10 Amos Otis | .50 |
| 11 Bobby Valentine | .75 |
| 12 Jose Cardenal | .35 |
| 13 Joe Grzenda | .35 |
| 14 Phillies Rookies: | .40 |
| Pete Koegel, Mike Anderson, W. Twitchell | |
| 15 Walt Williams | .35 |
| 16 Mike Jorgensen | .35 |
| 17 Dave Duncan | .35 |
| 18 Juan Pizarro | .35 |
| 19 Billy Cowan | .35 |
| 20 Don Wilson | .35 |
| 21 Atlanta Braves | 1.50 |
| 22 Rob Gardner | .35 |
| 23 Ted Kubiak | .35 |
| 24 Ted Ford | .35 |
| 25 Will Singer | .35 |
| 26 Andy Etchebarren | .35 |
| 27 Bob Johnson | .35 |
| 28 Twins Rookies: | .50 |
| Steve Brye, Bob Gebhard, Hal Haydel | |
| 29 Bill Bonham | .35 |
| 30 Rico Petrocelli | .50 |
| 31 Cleon Jones | .35 |
| 32 C. Jones (In Action) | .35 |
| 33 Billy Martin | 3.00 |
| 34 B. Martin (In Action) | 1.50 |
| 35 Jerry Johnson | .35 |
| 36 J. Johnson (In Action) | .35 |
| 37 Carl Yastrzemski | 16.00 |
| 38 Yastrzemski (In Action) | 8.00 |
| 39 Bob Barton | .35 |
| 40 B. Barton (In Action) | .35 |
| 41 Tommy Davis | .75 |
| 42 T. Davis (In Action) | .35 |
| 43 Rick Wise | .50 |
| 44 R. Wise (In Action) | .50 |
| 45 Glenn Beckert | .50 |
| 46 G. Beckert (In Action) | .50 |
| 47 John Ellis | .35 |
| 48 J. Ellis (In Action) | .35 |
| 49 Willie Mays | 25.00 |
| 50 W. Mays (All Action) | 12.50 |
| 51 Harmon Killebrew | 5.00 |
| 52 H. Killebrew (In Action) | 2.50 |
| 53 Bud Harrelson | .75 |
| 54 B. Harrelson (In Action) | .35 |
| 55 Clyde Wright | .35 |
| 56 Rich Chiles | .35 |
| 57 Bob Oliver | .35 |
| 58 Ernie McAnally | .35 |
| 59 Fred Stanley | .35 |
| 60 Manny Sanguillen | .50 |
| 61 Cubs Rookies: | 1.25 |
| Burt Hooton, Gene Hiser, Earl Stephenson | |
| 62 Angel Mangual | .35 |
| 63 Duke Sims | .35 |
| 64 Pete Broberg | .35 |
| 65 Cesar Cedeno | .75 |
| 66 Ray Corbin | .35 |
| 67 Red Schoendienst | 1.25 |
| 68 Jim York | .35 |
| 69 Roger Freed | .35 |
| 70 Mike Cuellar | .50 |
| 71 Angels Team | 1.25 |
| 72 Bruce Kison (R) | .75 |
| 73 Steve Huntz | .35 |
| 74 Cecil Upshaw | .35 |
| 75 Bert Campaneris | .75 |
| 76 Don Carrithers | .35 |
| 77 Ron Theobald | .35 |
| 78 Steve Arlin | .35 |

| NO. PLAYER | NR. MT. |
|---|---|
| 79 Red Sox Rookies: | 135.00 |
| Carlton Fisk, Mike Garman, Cecil Cooper | |
| 80 Tony Perez | 3.00 |
| 81 Mike Hedlund | .35 |
| 82 Ron Woods | .35 |
| 83 Dalton Jones | .35 |
| 84 Vince Colbert | .35 |
| 85 NL Batting Leaders: | 1.25 |
| Ralph Garr, Glenn Beckert, Joe Torre | |
| 86 AL Batting Leaders: | 1.25 |
| Tony Oliva, Bobby Murcer, Merv Rettenmund | |
| 87 NL RBI Leaders: | 2.25 |
| Joe Torre, Willie Stargell, Hank Aaron | |
| 88 AL RBI Leaders: | 2.00 |
| Harmon Killebrew, Frank Robinson, Reggie Smith | |
| 89 NL Home Run Leaders: | 2.25 |
| Willie Stargell, Lee May, Hank Aaron | |
| 90 AL Home Run Leaders: | 1.75 |
| Reggie Jackson, Bill Melton, Norm Cash | |
| 91 NL ERA Leaders: | 1.50 |
| Tom Seaver, Dave Roberts (wrong photo), D. Wilson | |
| 92 AL ERA Leaders: | 1.50 |
| Vida Blue, Wilbur Wood, Jim Palmer | |
| 93 NL Pitching Leaders: | 2.25 |
| Tom Seaver, Fergie Jenkins, Steve Carlton, Al Downing | |
| 94 AL Pitching Leaders: | 1.50 |
| Mickey Lolich, Vida Blue, Wilbur Wood | |
| 95 NL Strikeout Leaders: | 2.00 |
| Bill Stoneman, Tom Seaver, Fergie Jenkins | |
| 96 AL Strikeout Leaders: | 1.50 |
| Mickey Lolich, Vida Blue, Joe Coleman | |
| 97 Tom Kelley | .35 |
| 98 Chuck Tanner | .50 |
| 99 Ross Grimsley | .35 |
| 100 Frank Robinson | 5.00 |
| 101 Astros Rookies: | 2.00 |
| B. Greif, J.R. Richard, Ray Busse | |
| 102 Lloyd Allen | .35 |
| 103 Checklist No. 2 | 2.00 |
| 104 Toby Harrah (R) | 1.50 |
| 105 Gary Gentry | .35 |
| 106 Milwaukee Brewers | 1.25 |
| 107 Jose Cruz (R) | 2.00 |
| 108 Gary Waslewski | .35 |
| 109 Jerry May | .35 |
| 110 Ron Hunt | .35 |
| 111 Jim Grant | .35 |
| 112 Greg Luzinski | 1.00 |
| 113 Rogelio Moret | .35 |
| 114 Bill Buckner | 2.00 |
| 115 Jim Fregosi | .50 |
| 116 Ed Farmer | .35 |
| 117 Cleo James | .35 |
| 118 Skip Lockwood | .35 |
| 119 Marty Perez | .35 |
| 120 Bill Freehan | .50 |
| 121 Ed Sprague | .35 |
| 122 Larry Biittner | .35 |
| 123 Ed Acosta | .35 |
| 124 Yankees Rookies: | .60 |
| Alan Closter, Rusty Torres, R. Hambright | |
| 125 Dave Cash | .35 |
| 126 Bart Johnson | .35 |
| 127 Duffy Dyer | .35 |
| 128 Eddie Watt | .35 |
| 129 Charlie Fox | .35 |
| 130 Bob Gibson | 5.00 |
| 131 Jim Nettles | .35 |

| NO. PLAYER | NR. MT. |
|---|---|
| 132 Joe Morgan | 5.00 |
| 133 Joe Keough | .50 |
| 134 Carl Morton | .50 |
| 135 Vada Pinson | .75 |
| 136 Darrel Chaney | .50 |
| 137 Dick Williams | .50 |
| 138 Mike Kekich | .50 |
| 139 Tim McCarver | 1.00 |
| 140 Pat Dobson | .50 |
| 141 Mets Rookies: | .75 |
| Buzz Capra, Leroy Stanton, Jon Matlack | |
| 142 Chris Chambliss (R) | 2.00 |
| 143 Garry Jestadt | .50 |
| 144 Marty Pattin | .50 |
| 145 Don Kessinger | .50 |
| 146 Steve Kealey | .50 |
| 147 Dave Kingman (R) | 6.00 |
| 148 Dick Billings | .50 |
| 149 Gary Neibauer | .50 |
| 150 Norm Cash | .75 |
| 151 Jim Brewer | .50 |
| 152 Gene Clines | .50 |
| 153 Rick Auerbach | .50 |
| 154 Ted Simmons | 2.50 |
| 155 Larry Dierker | .50 |
| 156 Minnesota Twins | 1.25 |
| 157 Don Gullett | .50 |
| 158 Jerry Kenney | .50 |
| 159 John Boccabella | .50 |
| 160 Andy Messersmith | .50 |
| 161 Brock Davis | .50 |
| 162 Brewers Rookies: | 1.00 |
| Darrell Porter, Jerry Bell, Bob Reynolds (Bell and Porter photos switched) | |
| 163 Tug McGraw | .75 |
| 164 T. McGraw (In Action) | .60 |
| 165 Chris Speier | 1.00 |
| 166 C. Speier (In Action) | .50 |
| 167 Deron Johnson | .50 |
| 168 D. Johnson (In Action) | 1.00 |
| 169 Vida Blue | 1.00 |
| 170 V. Blue (In Action) | .50 |
| 171 Darrell Evans | 1.50 |
| 172 D. Evans (In Action) | .75 |
| 173 Clay Kirby | .50 |
| 174 C. Kirby (In Action) | .50 |
| 175 Tom Haller | .50 |
| 176 T. Haller (In Action) | .50 |
| 177 Paul Schaal | .50 |
| 178 P. Schaal (In Action) | .50 |
| 179 Dock Ellis | .50 |
| 180 D. Ellis (In Action) | .50 |
| 181 Ed Kranepool | .50 |
| 182 E. Kranepool (In Action) | .50 |
| 183 Bill Melton | .50 |
| 184 B. Melton (In Action) | .50 |
| 185 Ron Bryant | .50 |
| 186 R. Bryant (In Action) | .50 |
| 187 Gates Brown | .50 |
| 188 Frank Lucchesi | .50 |
| 189 Gene Tenace | .50 |
| 190 Dave Giusti | .50 |
| 191 Jeff Burroughs | .75 |
| 192 Chicago Cubs | 1.25 |
| 193 Kurt Bevacqua | .50 |
| 194 Fred Norman | .50 |
| 195 Orlando Cepeda | 2.50 |
| 196 Mel Queen | .50 |
| 197 Johnny Briggs | .50 |
| 198 Dodgers Rookies: | 3.00 |
| Charlie Hough, Bob O'Brien, Mike Strahler | |
| 199 Mike Fiore | .50 |
| 200 Lou Brock | 6.00 |
| 201 Phil Roof | .50 |
| 202 Scipio Spinks | .50 |
| 203 Ron Blomberg | .50 |
| 204 Tommy Helms | .50 |
| 205 Dick Drago | .50 |
| 206 Dal Maxvill | .50 |
| 207 Tom Egan | .50 |
| 208 Milt Pappas | .50 |

| NO. PLAYER | NR. MT. |
|---|---|
| 209 Joe Rudi | .50 |
| 210 Denny McLain | 1.25 |
| 211 Gary Sutherland | .50 |
| 212 Grant Jackson | .50 |
| 213 Angels Rookies: | .50 |
| Tom Silverio, Billy Parker, Art Kusnyer | |
| 214 Mike McQueen | .50 |
| 215 Alex Johnson | .50 |
| 216 Joe Niekro | .75 |
| 217 Roger Metzger | .50 |
| 218 Eddie Kasko | .50 |
| 219 Rennie Stennett | .50 |
| 220 Jim Perry | .50 |
| 221 NL Playoffs: | 1.25 |
| Bucs Champs | |
| 222 AL Playoffs: | 1.75 |
| Orioles Champs | |
| 223 World Series Game 1 | 1.25 |
| 224 World Series Game 2 | 1.25 |
| 225 World Series Game 3 | 1.25 |
| 226 World Series Game 4 | 2.50 |
| 227 World Series Game 5 | 1.25 |
| 228 World Series Game 6 | 1.25 |
| 229 World Series Game 7 | 1.25 |
| 230 World S. Celebration | 1.25 |
| 231 Casey Cox | .50 |
| 232 Giants Rookies: | .50 |
| Chris Arnold, Jim Barr, Dave Rader | |
| 233 Jay Johnstone | .50 |
| 234 Ron Taylor | .50 |
| 235 Merv Rettenmund | .50 |
| 236 Jim McGlothlin | .50 |
| 237 New York Yankees | 1.50 |
| 238 Leron Lee | .50 |
| 239 Tom Timmermann | .50 |
| 240 Rich Allen | 2.50 |
| 241 Rollie Fingers | 6.00 |
| 242 Don Mincher | .50 |
| 243 Frank Linzy | .50 |
| 244 Steve Braun | .50 |
| 245 Tommie Agee | .60 |
| 246 Tom Burgmeier | .50 |
| 247 Milt May | .50 |
| 248 Tom Bradley | .50 |
| 249 Garry Walker | .50 |
| 250 Boog Powell | 1.25 |
| 251 Checklist No. 3 | 2.00 |
| 252 Ken Reynolds | .50 |
| 253 Sandy Alomar | .50 |
| 254 Boots Day | .50 |
| 255 Jim Lonborg | .50 |
| 256 George Foster | 2.00 |
| 257 Tigers Rookies: | .50 |
| Paul Jata, Jim Foor, Tim Hosley | |
| 258 Randy Hundley | .50 |
| 259 Sparky Lyle | 1.25 |
| 260 Ralph Garr | .50 |
| 261 Steve Mingori | .50 |
| 262 San Diego Padres | 1.25 |
| 263 Felipe Alou | .50 |
| 264 Tommy John | 2.00 |
| 265 Wes Parker | .60 |
| 266 Bobby Bolin | .60 |
| 267 Dave Concepcion | 2.50 |
| 268 A's Rookies: | .60 |
| Dwain Anderson, C. Floethe | |
| 269 Don Hahn | .60 |
| 270 Jim Palmer | 12.00 |
| 271 Ken Rudolph | .60 |
| 272 Mickey Rivers | 1.00 |
| 273 Bobby Floyd | .60 |
| 274 Al Severinsen | .60 |
| 275 Cesar Tovar | .60 |
| 276 Gene Mauch | .60 |
| 277 Eliott Maddox | .60 |
| 278 Dennis Higgins | .60 |
| 279 Larry Brown | .60 |
| 280 Willie McCovey | 5.00 |
| 281 Bill Parsons | .60 |
| 282 Houston Astros | 1.25 |
| 283 Darrell Brandon | .60 |

| NO. | PLAYER | NR. MT. |
|---|---|---|
| 284 | Ike Brown | .60 |
| 285 | Gaylord Perry | 6.00 |
| 286 | Gene Alley | .60 |
| 287 | Jim Hardin | .60 |
| 288 | Johnny Jeter | .60 |
| 289 | Syd O'Brien | .60 |
| 290 | Sonny Siebert | .60 |
| 291 | Hal McRae | 1.00 |
| 292 | H. McRae (In Action) | .60 |
| 293 | Danny Frisella | .60 |
| 294 | D. Frisella (In Action) | .60 |
| 295 | Dick Dietz (In Action) | .60 |
| 296 | D. Dietz (In Action) | .60 |
| 297 | Claude Osteen | .60 |
| 298 | C. Osteen (In Action) | .60 |
| 299 | Hank Aaron | 30.00 |
| 300 | H. Aaron (In Action) | 12.00 |
| 301 | George Mitterwald | .60 |
| 302 | Mitterwald (In Action) | .60 |
| 303 | Joe Pepitone | .75 |
| 304 | J. Pepitone (In Action) | .60 |
| 305 | Ken Boswell | .60 |
| 306 | K. Boswell (In Action) | .60 |
| 307 | Steve Renko | .60 |
| 308 | S. Renko (In Action) | .60 |
| 309 | Roberto Clemente | 30.00 |
| 310 | Clemente (In Action) | 12.00 |
| 311 | Clay Carroll | .60 |
| 312 | C. Carroll (In Action) | .60 |
| 313 | Luis Aparicio | 3.00 |
| 314 | L. Aparicio (In Action) | 1.50 |
| 315 | Paul Splittorff | .60 |
| 316 | Cardinals Rookies: | .75 |
|  | Jim Bibby, Jorge Roque, |  |
|  | Santiago Guzman |  |
| 317 | Rich Hand | .60 |
| 318 | Sonny Jackson | .60 |
| 319 | Aurelio Rodriguez | .60 |
| 320 | Steve Blass | .60 |
| 321 | Joe LaHoud | .60 |
| 322 | Jose Pena | .60 |
| 323 | Earl Weaver | 1.00 |
| 324 | Mike Ryan | .60 |
| 325 | Mel Stottlemyre | .60 |
| 326 | Pat Kelly | .60 |
| 327 | Steve Stone (R) | 1.00 |
| 328 | Boston Red Sox | 1.50 |
| 329 | Roy Foster | .60 |
| 330 | Jim Hunter | 5.00 |
| 331 | Stan Swanson | .60 |
| 332 | Buck Martinez | .60 |
| 333 | Steve Barber | .60 |
| 334 | Rangers Rookies: | .60 |
|  | Bill Fahey, Jim Mason, |  |
|  | Tom Ragland |  |
| 335 | Bill Hands | .60 |
| 336 | Marty Martinez | .60 |
| 337 | Mike Kilkenny | .60 |
| 338 | Bob Grich | .75 |
| 339 | Ron Cook | .60 |
| 340 | Roy White | .60 |
| 341 | Joe Torre (Boyhood) | .75 |
| 342 | Wilbur Wood (Boyhood) | .75 |
| 343 | W. Stargell (Boyhood) | 1.25 |
| 344 | D. McNally (Boyhood) | .75 |
| 345 | Rick Wise (Boyhood) | .75 |
| 346 | Jim Fregosi (Boyhood) | .75 |
| 347 | Tom Seaver (Boyhood) | 2.50 |
| 348 | Sal Bando (Boyhood) | .75 |
| 349 | Al Fitzmorris | .60 |
| 350 | Frank Howard | 1.00 |
| 351 | Braves Rookies: | .60 |
|  | Tom House, Rick Kester, |  |
|  | Jimmy Britton |  |
| 352 | Dave LaRoche | .60 |
| 353 | Art Shamsky | .60 |
| 354 | Tom Murphy | .60 |
| 355 | Bob Watson | .60 |
| 356 | Gerry Moses | .60 |
| 357 | Woodie Fryman | .60 |
| 358 | Sparky Anderson | .60 |
| 359 | Don Pavletich | .60 |
| 360 | Dave Roberts | .60 |
| 361 | Mike Andrews | .60 |
| 362 | New York Mets | 1.50 |

| NO. | PLAYER | NR. MT. |
|---|---|---|
| 363 | Ron Klimkowski | .60 |
| 364 | Johnny Callison | .60 |
| 365 | Dick Bosman | .60 |
| 366 | Jimmy Rosario | .60 |
| 367 | Ron Perranoski | .60 |
| 368 | Danny Thompson | .60 |
| 369 | Jim LeFebvre | .60 |
| 370 | Don Buford | .60 |
| 371 | Denny LeMaster | .60 |
| 372 | Royals Rookies: | .60 |
|  | Lance Clemons, |  |
|  | Monty Montgomery |  |
| 373 | John Mayberry | .60 |
| 374 | Jack Heidemann | .60 |
| 375 | Reggie Cleveland | .60 |
| 376 | Andy Kosco | .60 |
| 377 | Terry Harmon | .60 |
| 378 | Checklist No. 4 | 2.00 |
| 379 | Ken Berry | .60 |
| 380 | Earl Williams | .60 |
| 381 | Chicago White Sox | 1.25 |
| 382 | Joe Gibbon | .60 |
| 383 | Brant Alyea | .60 |
| 384 | Dave Campbell | .60 |
| 385 | Mickey Stanley | .60 |
| 386 | Jim Colborn | .60 |
| 387 | Horace Clarke | .60 |
| 388 | Charlie Williams | .60 |
| 389 | Bill Rigney | .60 |
| 390 | Willie Davis | .60 |
| 391 | Kan Sanders | .60 |
| 392 | Pirates Rookies: | .75 |
|  | Fred Cambria, Richie Zisk |  |
| 393 | Curt Motton | .60 |
| 394 | Ken Forsch | .60 |
| 395 | Matty Alou | 1.00 |
| 396 | Paul Lindblad | .75 |
| 397 | Philadelphia Phillies | 2.50 |
| 398 | Larry Hisle | 1.00 |
| 399 | Milt Wilcox | 1.00 |
| 400 | Tony Oliva | 2.00 |
| 401 | Jim Nash | 1.00 |
| 402 | Bobby Heise | 1.00 |
| 403 | John Cumberland | 1.00 |
| 404 | Jeff Torborg | 1.00 |
| 405 | Ron Fairly | 1.00 |
| 406 | George Hendrick (R) | 1.25 |
| 407 | Chuck Taylor | 1.00 |
| 408 | Jim Northrup | 1.00 |
| 409 | Frank Baker | 1.00 |
| 410 | Fergie Jenkins | 5.00 |
| 411 | Bob Montgomery | 1.00 |
| 412 | Dick Kelley | 1.00 |
| 413 | White Sox Rookies: | 1.25 |
|  | Don Eddy, Dave Lemonds |  |
| 414 | Bob Miller | 1.00 |
| 415 | Cookie Rojas | 1.00 |
| 416 | Johnny Edwards | 1.00 |
| 417 | Tom Hall | 1.00 |
| 418 | Tom Shopay | 1.00 |
| 419 | Jim Spencer | 1.00 |
| 420 | Steve Carlton | 20.00 |
| 421 | Ellie Rodriguez | 1.00 |
| 422 | Ray Lamb | 1.00 |
| 423 | Oscar Gamble | 1.00 |
| 424 | Bill Gogolewski | 1.00 |
| 425 | Ken Singleton | 1.50 |
| 426 | K. Singleton (In Action) | 1.00 |
| 427 | Tito Fuentes | 1.00 |
| 428 | T. Fuentes (In Action) | 1.00 |
| 429 | Bob Robertson | 1.00 |
| 430 | B. Robertson (In Action) | 1.00 |
| 431 | Clarence Gaston | 1.00 |
| 432 | C. Gaston (In Action) | 1.00 |
| 433 | Johnny Bench | 40.00 |
| 434 | J. Bench (In Action) | 17.00 |
| 435 | Reggie Jackson | 40.00 |
| 436 | R. Jackson (In Action) | 18.00 |
| 437 | Maury Wills | 1.50 |
| 438 | M. Wills (In Action) | 1.00 |
| 439 | Billy Williams | 4.00 |
| 440 | B. Williams (In Action) | 2.00 |
| 441 | Thurman Munson | 16.00 |
| 442 | T. Munson (In Action) | 8.00 |
| 443 | Ken Henderson | 1.00 |

| NO. | PLAYER | NR. MT. |
|---|---|---|
| 444 | Henderson (In Action) | 1.00 |
| 445 | Tom Seaver | 30.00 |
| 446 | T. Seaver (In Action) | 15.00 |
| 447 | Willie Stargell | 5.00 |
| 448 | W. Stargell (In Action) | 2.50 |
| 449 | Bob Lemon | 1.25 |
| 450 | Mickey Lolich | 1.25 |
| 451 | Tony LaRussa | 1.25 |
| 452 | Ed Herrmann | 1.00 |
| 453 | Barry Lersch | 1.00 |
| 454 | Oakland A's | 2.50 |
| 455 | Tommy Harper | 1.00 |
| 456 | Mark Belanger | 1.25 |
| 457 | Padres Rookies: | 1.25 |
|  | Darcy Fast, Derrel Thomas, |  |
|  | Mike Ivie |  |
| 458 | Aurelio Monteagudo | 1.00 |
| 459 | Rick Renick | 1.00 |
| 460 | Al Downing | 1.00 |
| 461 | Tim Cullen | 1.00 |
| 462 | Rickey Clark | 1.00 |
| 463 | Bernie Carbo | 1.00 |
| 464 | Jim Roland | 1.00 |
| 465 | Gil Hodges | 3.00 |
| 466 | Norm Miller | 1.00 |
| 467 | Steve Kline | 1.00 |
| 468 | Richie Scheinblum | 1.00 |
| 469 | Ron Herbel | 1.00 |
| 470 | Ray Fosse | 1.00 |
| 471 | Luke Walker | 1.00 |
| 472 | Phil Gagliano | 1.00 |
| 473 | Dan McGinn | 1.00 |
| 474 | Orioles Rookies: | 4.00 |
|  | Johnny Oates, Don Baylor, |  |
|  | Roric Harrison |  |
| 475 | Gary Nolan | 1.00 |
| 476 | Lee Richard | 1.00 |
| 477 | Tom Phoebus | 1.00 |
| 478 | Checklist No. 5 | 2.00 |
| 479 | Don Shaw | 1.00 |
| 480 | Lee May | 1.25 |
| 481 | Billy Conigliaro | 1.00 |
| 482 | Joe Hoerner | 1.00 |
| 483 | Ken Suarez | 1.00 |
| 484 | Lum Harris | 1.00 |
| 485 | Phil Regan | 1.00 |
| 486 | John Lowenstein | 1.00 |
| 487 | Detroit Tigers | 2.50 |
| 488 | Mike Nagy | 1.00 |
| 489 | Rookies: | 1.00 |
|  | T. Humphrey, K. Lampard |  |
| 490 | Dave McNally | 1.00 |
| 491 | Lou Piniella (Boyhood) | 1.00 |
| 492 | M. Stottlemyre (Boyhood) | 1.00 |
| 493 | Bob Bailey (Boyhood) | 1.00 |
| 494 | Willie Horton (Boyhood) | 1.00 |
| 495 | Bill Melton (Boyhood) | 1.00 |
| 496 | B. Harrelson (Boyhood) | 1.00 |
| 497 | Jim Perry (Boyhood) | 1.00 |
| 498 | R. Robinson (Boyhood) | 1.50 |
| 499 | Vicente Romo | 1.00 |
| 500 | Joe Torre | 1.50 |
| 501 | Pete Hamm | 1.00 |
| 502 | Jackie Hernandez | 1.00 |
| 503 | Gary Peters | 1.00 |
| 504 | Ed Spiezio | 1.00 |
| 505 | Mike Marshall | 1.00 |
| 506 | Indians Rookies: | 1.00 |
|  | Terry Ley, Dick Tidrow, |  |
|  | Jim Moyer |  |
| 507 | Fred Gladding | 1.00 |
| 508 | Ellie Hendricks | 1.00 |
| 509 | Don McMahon | 1.00 |
| 510 | Ted Williams (Mgr.) | 5.00 |
| 511 | Tony Taylor | 1.00 |
| 512 | Paul Popovich | 1.00 |
| 513 | Lindy McDaniel | 1.00 |
| 514 | Ted Sizemore | 1.00 |
| 515 | Bert Blyleven | 11.00 |
| 516 | Oscar Brown | 1.00 |
| 517 | Ken Brett | 1.00 |
| 518 | Wayne Garrett | 1.00 |
| 519 | Ted Abernathy | 1.00 |
| 520 | Larry Bowa | 1.50 |
| 521 | Alan Foster | 1.00 |

| NO. | PLAYER | NR. MT. |
|---|---|---|
| 522 | Los Angeles Dodgers | 2.50 |
| 523 | Chuck Dobson | 1.00 |
| 524 | Reds Rookies: | 1.25 |
|  | Ed Armbrister, Mel Behney |  |
| 525 | Carlos May | 1.00 |
| 526 | Bob Bailey | 2.00 |
| 527 | Dave Leonhard | 2.00 |
| 528 | Ron Stone | 2.00 |
| 529 | Dave Nelson | 2.00 |
| 530 | Don Sutton | 5.00 |
| 531 | Freddie Patek | 2.00 |
| 532 | Fred Kendall | 2.00 |
| 533 | Ralph Houk (Mgr.) | 2.00 |
| 534 | Jim Hickman | 2.00 |
| 535 | Ed Brinkman | 2.00 |
| 536 | Doug Rader | 2.00 |
| 537 | Bob Locker | 2.00 |
| 538 | Charlie Sands | 2.00 |
| 539 | Terry Forster (R) | 2.50 |
| 540 | Felix Milan | 2.00 |
| 541 | Roger Repoz | 2.00 |
| 542 | Jack Billingham | 2.00 |
| 543 | Duane Josephson | 2.00 |
| 544 | Ted Martinez | 2.00 |
| 545 | Wayne Granger | 2.00 |
| 546 | Joe Hague | 2.00 |
| 547 | Cleveland Indians | 2.00 |
| 548 | Frank Reberger | 2.00 |
| 549 | Dave May | 2.00 |
| 550 | Brooks Robinson | 20.00 |
| 551 | Ollie Brown | 2.00 |
| 552 | O. Brown (In Action) | 2.00 |
| 553 | Wilbur Wood | 2.50 |
| 554 | W. Wood (In Action) | 2.00 |
| 555 | Ron Santo | 3.00 |
| 556 | R. Santo (In Action) | 2.00 |
| 557 | John Odom | 2.00 |
| 558 | J. Odom (In Action) | 2.00 |
| 559 | Pete Rose | 55.00 |
| 560 | P. Rose (In Action) | 27.00 |
| 561 | Leo Cardenas | 2.00 |
| 562 | L. Cardenas (In Action) | 2.00 |
| 563 | Ray Sadecki | 2.00 |
| 564 | R. Sadecki (In Action) | 2.00 |
| 565 | Reggie Smith | 2.50 |
| 566 | R. Smith (In Action) | 2.00 |
| 567 | Juan Marichal | 5.00 |
| 568 | J. Marichal (In Action) | 2.50 |
| 569 | Ed Kirkpatrick | 2.00 |
| 570 | Kirkpatrick (In Action) | 2.00 |
| 571 | Nate Colbert | 2.00 |
| 572 | N. Colbert (In Action) | 2.00 |
| 573 | Fritz Peterson | 2.00 |
| 574 | F. Peterson (In Action) | 2.00 |
| 575 | Al Oliver | 2.50 |
| 576 | Leo Durocher | 2.50 |
| 577 | Mike Paul | 2.00 |
| 578 | Billy Grabarkewitz | 2.00 |
| 579 | Doyle Alexander (R) | 3.00 |
| 580 | Lou Piniella | 3.00 |
| 581 | Wade Blasingame | 2.00 |
| 582 | Montreal Expos | 4.00 |
| 583 | Darold Knowles | 2.00 |
| 584 | Jerry McNertney | 2.00 |
| 585 | George Scott | 2.00 |
| 586 | Denis Menke | 2.00 |
| 587 | Billy Wilson | 2.00 |
| 588 | Jim Holt | 2.00 |
| 589 | Hal Lanier | 2.00 |
| 590 | Graig Nettles | 3.00 |
| 591 | Paul Casanova | 2.00 |
| 592 | Lew Krausse | 2.00 |
| 593 | Rich Morales | 2.00 |
| 594 | Jim Beauchamp | 2.00 |
| 595 | Nolan Ryan | 165.00 |
| 596 | Manny Mota | 2.50 |
| 597 | Jim Magnuson | 2.00 |
| 598 | Hal King | 2.00 |
| 599 | Billy Champion | 2.00 |
| 600 | Al Kaline | 20.00 |
| 601 | George Stone | 2.00 |
| 602 | Dave Bristol | 2.00 |
| 603 | Jim Ray | 2.00 |
| 604 | Checklist No. 6 | 4.00 |
| 605 | Nelson Briles | 2.00 |

| NO. PLAYER | NR. MT. | NO. PLAYER | NR. MT. | NO. PLAYER | NR. MT. | NO. PLAYER | NR. MT. |
|---|---|---|---|---|---|---|---|
| 606 Luis Melendez | 2.00 | 653 Jim Fairey | 2.00 | 700 B. Murcer (In Action) | 6.00 | 744 Jim Slaton | 4.00 |
| 607 Frank Duffy | 2.00 | 654 Horacio Pina | 2.00 | 701 Jose Pagan | 4.00 | 745 Julian Javier | 4.00 |
| 608 Mike Corkins | 2.00 | 655 Jerry Grote | 2.00 | 702 J. Pagan (In Action) | 4.00 | 746 Lowell Palmer | 4.00 |
| 609 Tom Grieve | 2.00 | 656 Rudy May | 2.00 | 703 Doug Griffin | 4.00 | 747 Jim Stewart | 4.00 |
| 610 Bill Stoneman | 2.00 | 657 Bobby Wine | 4.00 | 704 D. Griffin (In Action) | 4.00 | 748 Phil Hennigan | 4.00 |
| 611 Rich Reese | 2.00 | 658 Steve Dunning | 4.00 | 705 Pat Corrales | 4.00 | 749 Walter Alston (Mgr.) | 8.00 |
| 612 Joe Decker | 2.00 | 659 Bob Aspromonte | 4.00 | 706 P. Corrales (In Action) | 4.00 | 750 Willie Horton | 4.00 |
| 613 Mike Ferraro | 2.00 | 660 Paul Blair | 5.00 | 707 Tim Foli | 4.00 | 751 S. Carlton (Traded) | 45.00 |
| 614 Ted Uhlaender | 2.00 | 661 Bill Virdon | 5.00 | 708 T. Foli (In Action) | 4.00 | 752 Joe Morgan (Traded) | 35.00 |
| 615 Steve Hargan | 2.00 | 662 Stan Bahnsen | 4.00 | 709 Jim Kaat | 12.00 | 753 D. McLain (Traded) | 10.00 |
| 616 Joe Ferguson (R) | 2.00 | 663 Fran Healy | 4.00 | 710 J. Kaat (In Action) | 8.00 | 754 F. Robinson (Traded) | 30.00 |
| 617 Kansas City Royals | 4.00 | 664 Bobby Knoop | 4.00 | 711 Bobby Bonds | 12.00 | 755 Jim Fregosi (Traded) | 5.00 |
| 618 Rich Robertson | 2.00 | 665 Chris Short | 4.00 | 712 B. Bonds (In Action) | 8.00 | 756 Rick Wise (Traded) | 5.00 |
| 619 Rich McKinney | 2.00 | 666 Hector Torres | 4.00 | 713 Gene Michael | 4.00 | 757 J. Cardenal (Traded) | 5.00 |
| 620 Phil Niekro | 5.00 | 667 Ray Newman | 4.00 | 714 G. Michael (In Action) | 4.00 | 758 Gil Garrido | 4.00 |
| 621 Commissioners Award | 3.00 | 668 Texas Rangers | 8.00 | 715 Mike Epstein | 4.00 | 759 Chris Cannizzaro | 4.00 |
| 622 MVP Award | 3.00 | 669 Willie Crawford | 4.00 | 716 Jesus Alou | 4.00 | 760 Bill Mazeroski | 6.00 |
| 623 Cy Young Award | 3.00 | 670 Ken Holtzman | 5.00 | 717 Bruce Dal Canton | 4.00 | 761 Rookie Stars: | 15.00 |
| 624 Minor League Player | | 671 Donn Clendenon | 5.00 | 718 Del Rice | 4.00 | Bernie Williams, Ben |
| of the Year | 3.00 | 672 Archie Reynolds | 4.00 | 719 Cesar Geronimo | 4.00 | Oglivie, Ron Cey |
| 625 Rookie of the Year | 3.00 | 673 Dave Marshall | 4.00 | 720 Sam McDowell | 4.00 | 762 Wayne Simpson | 4.00 |
| 626 Babe Ruth Award | 3.00 | 674 John Kennedy | 4.00 | 721 Eddie Leon | 4.00 | 763 Ron Hansen | 4.00 |
| 627 Moe Drabowsky | 2.00 | 675 Pat Jarvis | 4.00 | 722 Bill Sudakis | 4.00 | 764 Dusty Baker | 6.00 |
| 628 Terry Crowley | 2.00 | 676 Danny Cater | 4.00 | 723 Al Santorini | 4.00 | 765 Ken McMullen | 4.00 |
| 629 Paul Doyle | 2.00 | 677 Ivan Murrell | 4.00 | 724 AL Rookie Pitchers: | 4.00 | 766 Steve Hamilton | 4.00 |
| 630 Rich Hebner | 2.00 | 678 Steve Luebber | 4.00 | John Curtis, Rich Hinton, | | 767 Tom McCraw | 4.00 |
| 631 John Strohmayer | 2.00 | 679 Astros Rookies: | 4.00 | Mickey Scott | | 768 Denny Doyle | 4.00 |
| 632 Mike Hegan | 2.00 | Bob Fenwick, Bob Stinson | | 725 Dick McAuliffe | 4.00 | 769 Jack Aker | 4.00 |
| 633 Jack Hiatt | 2.00 | 680 Dave Johnson | 5.00 | 726 Dick Selma | 4.00 | 770 Jim Wynn | 5.00 |
| 634 Dick Woodson | 2.00 | 681 Bobby Pfeil | 4.00 | 727 Jose LaBoy | 4.00 | 771 San Francisco Giants | 8.00 |
| 635 Don Money | 2.50 | 682 Mike McCormick | 4.00 | 728 Gail Hopkins | 4.00 | 772 Ken Tatum | 4.00 |
| 636 Bill Lee | 2.50 | 683 Steve Hovley | 4.00 | 729 Bob Veale | 4.00 | 773 Ron Brand | 4.00 |
| 637 Preston Gomez | 2.00 | 684 Hal Breeden | 4.00 | 730 Rick Monday | 5.00 | 774 Luis Alvarado | 4.00 |
| 638 Ken Wright | 2.00 | 685 Joe Horlen | 4.00 | 731 Baltimore Orioles | 7.50 | 775 Jerry Reuss | 5.00 |
| 639 J.C. Martin | 2.00 | 686 Steve Garvey | 80.00 | 732 George Culver | 4.00 | 776 Bill Voss | 4.00 |
| 640 Joe Coleman | 2.00 | 687 Del Unser | 4.00 | 733 Jim Hart | 4.00 | 777 Hoyt Wilhelm | 15.00 |
| 641 Mike Lum | 2.00 | 688 St. Louis Cardinals | 7.00 | 734 Bob Burda | 4.00 | 778 Twins Rookies: | 6.00 |
| 642 Dennis Riddleberger | 2.00 | 689 Eddie Fisher | 4.00 | 735 Diego Segui | 4.00 | Vic Albury, Rick Dempsey, |
| 643 Russ Gibson | 2.00 | 690 Willie Montanez | 4.00 | 736 Bill Russell | 6.00 | Jim Strickland |
| 644 Bernie Allen | 2.00 | 691 Curt Blefary | 4.00 | 737 Lenny Randle | 4.00 | 779 Tony Cloninger | 4.00 |
| 645 Jim Maloney | 2.50 | 692 C. Blefary (In Action) | 4.00 | 738 Jim Merritt | 4.00 | 780 Dick Green | 4.00 |
| 646 Chico Salmon | 2.00 | 693 Alan Gallagher | 4.00 | 739 Don Mason | 4.00 | 781 Jim McAndrew | 4.00 |
| 647 Bob Moose | 2.00 | 694 Gallagher (In Action) | 4.00 | 740 Rico Carty | 6.00 | 792 Larry Stahl | 4.00 |
| 648 Jim Lyttle | 2.00 | 695 Rod Carew | 100.00 | 741 Rookie Stars: | 6.00 | 783 Les Cain | 4.00 |
| 649 Pete Richert | 2.00 | 696 R. Carew (In Action) | 45.00 | Tom Hutton, John Milner, | | 784 Ken Aspromonte | 4.00 |
| 650 Sal Bando | 2.50 | 697 Jerry Koosman | 10.00 | Rick Miller | | 785 Vic Davalillo | 4.00 |
| 651 Cincinnati Reds | 4.00 | 698 J. Koosman (In Action) | 6.00 | 742 Jim Rooker | 4.00 | 786 Chuck Brinkman | 4.00 |
| 652 Marcelino Lopez | 2.00 | 699 Bobby Murcer | 10.00 | 743 Cesar Gutierrez | 4.00 | 787 Ron Reed (exc. $1.50) | 6.00 |

## 1973 Topps . . . Complete Set of 660 Cards—Value $425.00 (Exc.); $1050.00 (Near Mint)

Includes the rookie cards of Mike Schmidt, Darrell Evans and Davey Lopes. The high numbers are 529 to 660. This was the last Topps' set to be issued in *series*. Starting in 1974 the entire set was issued at one time.

| NO. PLAYER | NR. MT. | NO. PLAYER | NR. MT. | NO. PLAYER | NR. MT. | NO. PLAYER | NR. MT. |
|---|---|---|---|---|---|---|---|
| 1 All-Time HR Leaders | 20.00 | 10 Don Sutton | 2.50 | 21 Randy Hundley | .40 | 32 Fred Norman | .40 |
| Babe Ruth, Hank Aaron, | | 11 Chris Chambliss | .60 | 22 Ted Abernathy | .40 | 33 Jim Breazeale | .40 |
| Willie Mays (Exc. $6.00) | | 12 Don Zimmer (Mgr.) | .60 | 23 Dave Kingman | 1.50 | 34 Pat Dobson | .40 |
| 2 Rich Hebner | .40 | 13 George Hendrick | .75 | 24 Al Santorini | .40 | 35 Willie Davis | .50 |
| 3 Jim Lonborg | .40 | 14 Sonny Siebert | .40 | 25 Ray White | .50 | 36 Steve Barber | .40 |
| 4 John Milner | .40 | 15 Ralph Garr | .40 | 26 Pittsburgh Pirates | 1.00 | 37 Bill Robinson | .40 |
| 5 Ed Brinkman | .40 | 16 Steve Braun | .40 | 27 Bill Gogolewski | .40 | 38 Mike Epstein | .40 |
| 6 Mac Scarce | .40 | 17 Fred Gladding | .40 | 28 Hal McRae | .75 | 39 Dave Roberts | .40 |
| 7 Texas Rangers | .40 | 18 Leroy Stanton | .40 | 29 Tony Taylor | .40 | 40 Reggie Smith | .75 |
| 8 Tom Hall | .40 | 19 Tim Foli | .40 | 30 Tug McGraw | .75 | 41 Tom Walker | .40 |
| 9 Johnny Oates | .50 | 20 Stan Bahnsen | .40 | 31 Buddy Bell (R) | 4.00 | 42 Mike Andrews | .40 |

| NO. | PLAYER | NR. MT. |
|---|---|---|
| 43 | Randy Moffitt | .40 |
| 44 | Rick Monday | .50 |
| 45 | Ellie Rodriguez (wrong photo) | .40 |
| 46 | Lindy McDaniel | .40 |
| 47 | Luis Melendez | .40 |
| 48 | Paul Splittorff | .40 |
| 49 | Frank Quilici (Mgr.) | .60 |
| 50 | Roberto Clement | 25.00 |
| 51 | Chuck Seelbach | .40 |
| 52 | Denis Menke | .40 |
| 53 | Steve Dunning | .40 |
| 54 | Checklist No. 1 | 1.50 |
| 55 | Jon Matlack | .60 |
| 56 | Merv Rettenmund | .40 |
| 57 | Derrel Thomas | .40 |
| 58 | Mike Paul | .40 |
| 59 | Steve Yeager (R) | 1.00 |
| 60 | Ken Holtzman | .50 |
| 61 | Batting Leaders: Billy Williams, Rod Carew | 2.00 |
| 62 | Home Run Leaders: Johnny Bench, Dick Allen | 1.50 |
| 63 | RBI Leaders: Johnny Bench, Dick Allen | 1.50 |
| 64 | Stolen Base Leaders: B. Campaneris, L. Brock | 1.25 |
| 65 | ERA Leaders: Steve Carlton, Luis Tiant | 1.50 |
| 66 | Victory Leaders: Wilbur Wood, Steve Carlton, Gaylord Perry | 1.50 |
| 67 | Strikeout Leaders: Steve Carlton, Nolan Ryan | 5.00 |
| 68 | Leading Firemen: Clay Carroll, Sparky Lyle | 1.00 |
| 69 | Phil Gagliano | .40 |
| 70 | Milt Pappas | .40 |
| 71 | Johnny Briggs | .40 |
| 72 | Ron Reed | .40 |
| 73 | Ed Herrmann | .40 |
| 74 | Billy Champion | .40 |
| 75 | Vada Pinson | .50 |
| 76 | Doug Rader | .40 |
| 77 | Mike Torrez | .50 |
| 78 | Richie Scheinblum | .40 |
| 79 | Jim Willoughby | .40 |
| 80 | Tony Oliva | 1.25 |
| 81 | Whitey Lockman (Mgr.) | .60 |
| 82 | Fritz Peterson | .40 |
| 83 | Leron Lee | .40 |
| 84 | Rollie Fingers | 5.00 |
| 85 | Ted Simmons | 1.50 |
| 86 | Tom McCraw | .40 |
| 87 | Ken Boswell | .40 |
| 88 | Mickey Stanley | .40 |
| 89 | Jack Billingham | .40 |
| 90 | Brooks Robinson | 5.00 |
| 91 | Los Angeles Dodgers | 1.25 |
| 92 | Jerry Bell | .40 |
| 93 | Jesus Alou | .40 |
| 94 | Dick Billings | .40 |
| 95 | Steve Blass | .40 |
| 96 | Doug Griffin | .40 |
| 97 | Willie Montanez | .40 |
| 98 | Dick Woodson | .40 |
| 99 | Carl Taylor | .40 |
| 100 | Hank Aaron | 20.00 |
| 101 | Ken Henderson | .40 |
| 102 | Rudy May | .40 |
| 103 | Celerino Sanchez | .40 |
| 104 | Reggie Cleveland | .40 |
| 105 | Carlos May | .40 |
| 106 | Terry Humphrey | .40 |
| 107 | Phil Hennigan | .40 |
| 108 | Bill Russell | .40 |
| 109 | Doyle Alexander | .60 |
| 110 | Bob Watson | .60 |
| 111 | Dave Nelson | .40 |
| 112 | Gary Ross | .40 |
| 113 | Jerry Grote | .40 |
| 114 | Lynn McGlothen | .40 |
| 115 | Ron Santo | 1.00 |
| 116 | Ralph Houk (Mgr.) | .75 |
| 117 | Ramon Hernandez | .40 |
| 118 | John Mayberry | .60 |
| 119 | Larry Bowa | .75 |
| 120 | Joe Coleman | .40 |
| 121 | Dave Rader | .40 |
| 122 | Jim Strickland | .40 |
| 123 | Sandy Alomar | .40 |
| 124 | Jim Hardin | .40 |
| 125 | Ron Fairly | .40 |
| 126 | Jim Brewer | .40 |
| 127 | Milwaukee Brewers | 1.25 |
| 128 | Ted Sizemore | .40 |
| 129 | Terry Forster | .50 |
| 130 | Pete Rose | 18.00 |
| 131 | Eddie Kasko (Mgr.) | .75 |
| 132 | Matty Alou | .75 |
| 133 | Dave Roberts | .40 |
| 134 | Milt Wilcox | .50 |
| 135 | Lee May | .50 |
| 136 | Earl Weaver (Mgr.) | 1.00 |
| 137 | Jim Beauchamp | .40 |
| 138 | Horacio Pina | .40 |
| 139 | Carmen Fanzone | .40 |
| 140 | Lou Piniella | .75 |
| 141 | Bruce Kison | .50 |
| 142 | Thurman Munson | 9.00 |
| 143 | John Curtis | .40 |
| 144 | Marty Perez | .40 |
| 145 | Bobby Bonds | 1.25 |
| 146 | Woodie Fryman | .40 |
| 147 | Mike Anderson | .40 |
| 148 | Dave Goltz | .40 |
| 149 | Ron Hunt | .40 |
| 150 | Wilbur Wood | .40 |
| 151 | Wes Parker | .40 |
| 152 | Dave May | .40 |
| 153 | Al Hrabosky | .50 |
| 154 | Jeff Torborg | .40 |
| 155 | Sal Bando | .60 |
| 156 | Cesar Geronimo | .40 |
| 157 | Denny Riddleberger | .40 |
| 158 | Houston Astros | 1.25 |
| 159 | Clarence Gaston | .40 |
| 160 | Jim Palmer | 9.00 |
| 161 | Ted Martinez | .40 |
| 162 | Pete Broberg | .40 |
| 163 | Vic Davalillo | .40 |
| 164 | Monty Montgomery | .40 |
| 165 | Luis Aparicio | 2.50 |
| 166 | Terry Harmon | .40 |
| 167 | Steve Stone | .40 |
| 168 | Jim Northrup | .40 |
| 169 | Ron Schueler | .40 |
| 170 | Harmon Killebrew | 4.00 |
| 171 | Bernie Carbo | .40 |
| 172 | Steve Kline | .40 |
| 173 | Hal Breeden | .40 |
| 174 | Rich Gossage (R) | 14.00 |
| 175 | Frank Robinson | 5.00 |
| 176 | Chuck Taylor | .40 |
| 177 | Bill Plummer | .40 |
| 178 | Don Rose | .40 |
| 179 | Dick Williams (Mgr.) | .75 |
| 180 | Fergie Jenkins | 4.00 |
| 181 | Jack Brohamer | .40 |
| 182 | Mike Caldwell (R) | .75 |
| 183 | Don Buford | .40 |
| 184 | Jerry Koosman | .60 |
| 185 | Jim Wynn | .40 |
| 186 | Bill Fahey | .40 |
| 187 | Luke Walker | .40 |
| 188 | Cookie Rojas | .40 |
| 189 | Greg Luzinski | 1.00 |
| 190 | Bob Gibson | 4.00 |
| 191 | Detroit Tigers | 1.25 |
| 192 | Pat Jarvis | .40 |
| 193 | Carlton Fisk | 30.00 |
| 194 | Jorge Orta | .40 |
| 195 | Clay Carroll | .40 |
| 196 | Ken McMullen | .40 |
| 197 | Ed Goodson | .40 |
| 198 | Horace Clarke | .40 |
| 199 | Bert Blyleven | 4.00 |
| 200 | Billy Williams | 3.50 |
| 201 | AL Playoffs: Hendrick Scores | 1.00 |
| 202 | NL Playoffs: Foster's Run Decides It | 1.00 |
| 203 | World Series Game 1 Tenace the Menace | 1.00 |
| 204 | World Series Game 2 A's Make It Two Straight | 1.00 |
| 205 | World Series Game 3 Reds Win Squeaker | 1.00 |
| 206 | World Series Game 4 Tenace Singles In Ninth | 1.00 |
| 207 | World Series Game 5 Odom Out at Plate | 1.00 |
| 208 | World Series Game 6 Red's Ties Series | 1.00 |
| 209 | World Series Game 7 Campy Stars Rally | 1.00 |
| 210 | World Series A's— World Champions | 1.00 |
| 211 | Balor Moore | .40 |
| 212 | Joe LaHoud | .40 |
| 213 | Steve Garvey | 12.00 |
| 214 | Steve Hamilton | .40 |
| 215 | Dusty Baker | .75 |
| 216 | Toby Harrah | .40 |
| 217 | Don Wilson | .40 |
| 218 | Aurelio Rodriguez | .40 |
| 219 | St. Louis Cardinals | 1.25 |
| 220 | Nolan Ryan | 65.00 |
| 221 | Fred Kendall | .40 |
| 222 | Rob Gardner | .40 |
| 223 | Bud Harrelson | .40 |
| 224 | Bill Lee | .40 |
| 225 | Al Oliver | 1.25 |
| 226 | Ray Fosse | .40 |
| 227 | Wayne Twitchell | .40 |
| 228 | Bobby Darwin | .40 |
| 229 | Roric Harrison | .40 |
| 230 | Joe Morgan | 5.00 |
| 231 | Bill Parsons | .40 |
| 232 | Ken Singleton | .75 |
| 233 | Ed Kirkpatrick | .40 |
| 234 | Bill North | .40 |
| 235 | Jim Hunter | 4.00 |
| 236 | Tito Fuentes | .40 |
| 237 | Eddie Mathews (Mgr.) | 1.00 |
| 238 | Tony Muser | .40 |
| 239 | Pete Richert | .40 |
| 240 | Bobby Murcer | .75 |
| 241 | Dwain Anderson | .40 |
| 242 | George Culver | .40 |
| 243 | California Angels | 1.25 |
| 244 | Ed Acosta | .40 |
| 245 | Carl Yastrzemski | 13.00 |
| 246 | Ken Sanders | .40 |
| 247 | Del Unser | .40 |
| 248 | Jerry Johnson | .40 |
| 249 | Larry Biittner | .40 |
| 250 | Manny Sanguillen | .50 |
| 251 | Roger Nelson | .40 |
| 252 | Charlie Fox (Mgr.) | .75 |
| 253 | Mark Belanger | .40 |
| 254 | Bill Stoneman | .40 |
| 255 | Reggie Jackson | 25.00 |
| 256 | Chris Zachary | .40 |
| 257 | Yogi Berra (Mgr.) | 1.50 |
| 258 | Tommy John | 1.50 |
| 259 | Jim Holt | .40 |
| 260 | Gary Nolan | .40 |
| 261 | Pat Kelly | .40 |
| 262 | Jack Aker | .40 |
| 263 | George Scott | .40 |
| 264 | Checklist No. 2 | 1.50 |
| 265 | Gene Michael | .75 |
| 266 | Mike Lum | .40 |
| 267 | Lloyd Allen | .40 |
| 268 | Jerry Morales | .40 |
| 269 | Tim McCarver | 1.00 |
| 270 | Luis Tiant | .75 |
| 271 | Tom Hutton | .40 |
| 272 | Ed Farmer | .40 |
| 273 | Chris Speier | .50 |
| 274 | Darold Knowles | .40 |
| 275 | Tony Perez | 3.00 |
| 276 | Joe Lovitto | .40 |
| 277 | Bob Miller | .40 |
| 278 | Baltimore Orioles | 1.25 |
| 279 | Mike Strahler | .40 |
| 280 | Al Kaline | 5.00 |
| 281 | Mike Jorgensen | .40 |
| 282 | Steve Hovley | .40 |
| 283 | Ray Sadecki | .40 |
| 284 | Glenn Borgmann | .40 |
| 285 | Don Kessinger | .50 |
| 286 | Frank Linzy | .40 |
| 287 | Eddie Leon | .40 |
| 288 | Gary Gentry | .40 |
| 289 | Bob Oliver | .40 |
| 290 | Cesar Cedeno | .75 |
| 291 | Rogelio Moret | .40 |
| 292 | Jose Cruz | 1.00 |
| 293 | Bernie Allen | .40 |
| 294 | Steve Arlin | .40 |
| 295 | Bert Campaneris | .60 |
| 296 | Sparky Anderson (Mgr.) | .60 |
| 297 | Walt Williams | .40 |
| 298 | Ron Bryant | .40 |
| 299 | Ted Ford | .40 |
| 300 | Steve Carlton | 13.00 |
| 301 | Billy Grabarkewitz | .40 |
| 302 | Terry Crowley | .40 |
| 303 | Nelson Briles | .40 |
| 304 | Duke Sims | .40 |
| 305 | Willie Mays | 25.00 |
| 306 | Tom Burgmeier | .40 |
| 307 | Boots Day | .40 |
| 308 | Skip Lockwood | .40 |
| 309 | Paul Popovich | .40 |
| 310 | Dick Allen | .75 |
| 311 | Joe Decker | .40 |
| 312 | Oscar Brown | .40 |
| 313 | Jim Ray | .40 |
| 314 | Ron Swoboda | .40 |
| 315 | John Odom | .40 |
| 316 | San Diego Padres | 1.25 |
| 317 | Danny Cater | .40 |
| 318 | Jim McGlothlin | .40 |
| 319 | Jim Spencer | .40 |
| 320 | Lou Brock | 5.00 |
| 321 | Rich Hinton | .40 |
| 322 | Garry Maddox (R) | 1.00 |
| 323 | Billy Martin (Mgr.) | 1.00 |
| 324 | Al Downing | .60 |
| 325 | Boog Powell | 1.00 |
| 326 | Darrell Brandon | .40 |
| 327 | John Lowenstein | .40 |
| 328 | Bill Bonham | .40 |
| 329 | Ed Kranepool | .75 |
| 330 | Rod Carew | 13.00 |
| 331 | Carl Morton | .40 |
| 332 | John Felske | .40 |
| 333 | Gene Clines | .40 |
| 334 | Freddie Patek | .40 |
| 335 | Bob Tolan | .40 |
| 336 | Tom Bradley | .40 |
| 337 | Dave Duncan | .40 |
| 338 | Checklist No. 3 | 1.50 |
| 339 | Dick Tidrow | .40 |
| 340 | Nate Colbert | .40 |
| 341 | Jim Palmer (Boyhood) | 1.50 |
| 342 | S. McDowell (Boyhood) | .60 |
| 343 | B. Murcer (Boyhood) | .60 |
| 344 | Jim Hunter (Boyhood) | 1.25 |
| 345 | Chris Speier (Boyhood) | .60 |
| 346 | G. Perry (Boyhood) | 1.25 |
| 347 | Kansas City Royals | 1.25 |
| 348 | Rennie Stennett | .40 |
| 349 | Dick McAuliffe | .40 |
| 350 | Tom Seaver | 22.00 |
| 351 | Jimmy Stewart | .40 |
| 352 | Don Stanhouse | .40 |
| 353 | Steve Brye | .40 |
| 354 | Billy Parker | .40 |
| 355 | Mike Marshall | .75 |
| 356 | Chuck Tanner (Mgr.) | .75 |
| 357 | Ross Grimsley | .40 |
| 358 | Jim Nettles | .40 |
| 359 | Cecil Upshaw | .40 |
| 360 | Joe Rudi (photo of Gene Tenace) | .75 |
| 361 | Fran Healy | .40 |

| NO. PLAYER | NR. MT. |
|---|---|
| 362 Eddie Watt | .40 |
| 363 Jackie Hernandez | .40 |
| 364 Rick Wise | .40 |
| 365 Rico Petrocelli | .60 |
| 366 Brock Davis | .40 |
| 367 Burt Hooton | .40 |
| 368 Bill Buckner | 1.00 |
| 369 Lerrin LaGrow | .40 |
| 370 Willie Stargell | 4.00 |
| 371 Mike Kekich | .40 |
| 372 Oscar Gamble | .50 |
| 373 Clyde Wright | .40 |
| 374 Darrell Evans | .75 |
| 375 Larry Dierker | .50 |
| 376 Frank Duffy | .40 |
| 377 Gene Mauch (Mgr.) | .75 |
| 378 Lenny Randle | .40 |
| 379 Cy Acosta | .40 |
| 380 Johnny Bench | 22.00 |
| 381 Vicente Romo | .40 |
| 382 Mike Hegan | .40 |
| 383 Diego Segui | .40 |
| 384 Don Baylor | 1.50 |
| 385 Jim Perry | .50 |
| 386 Don Money | .40 |
| 387 Jim Barr | .40 |
| 388 Ben Oglivie | .60 |
| 389 New York Mets | 2.50 |
| 390 Mickey Lolich | .75 |
| 391 Lee Lacy (R) | 1.00 |
| 392 Dick Drago | .40 |
| 393 Jose Cardenal | .40 |
| 394 Sparky Lyle | .60 |
| 395 Roger Metzger | .40 |
| 396 Grant Jackson | .40 |
| 397 Dave Cash | .60 |
| 398 Rich Hand | .60 |
| 399 George Foster | 1.50 |
| 400 Gaylord Perry | 4.00 |
| 401 Clyde Mashore | 1.00 |
| 402 Jack Hiatt | 1.00 |
| 403 Sonny Jackson | 1.00 |
| 404 Chuck Brinkman | 1.00 |
| 405 Cesar Tovar | 1.00 |
| 406 Paul Lindblad | 1.00 |
| 407 Felix Millan | 1.00 |
| 408 Jim Colborn | 1.00 |
| 409 Ivan Murrell | 1.00 |
| 410 Willie McCovey | 5.00 |
| 411 Ray Corbin | 1.00 |
| 412 Manny Mota | 1.25 |
| 413 Tom Timmerman | 1.00 |
| 414 Ken Rudolph | 1.00 |
| 415 Marty Pattin | 1.00 |
| 416 Paul Schaal | 1.00 |
| 417 Scipio Spinks | 1.00 |
| 418 Bobby Grich | 1.25 |
| 419 Casey Cox | 1.00 |
| 420 Tommie Agee | 1.00 |
| 421 Bobby Winkles (Mgr.) | 1.25 |
| 422 Bob Robertson | 1.00 |
| 423 Johnny Jeter | 1.00 |
| 424 Denny Doyle | 1.00 |
| 425 Alex Johnson | 1.00 |
| 426 Dave LaRoche | 1.00 |
| 427 Rick Auerbach | 1.00 |
| 428 Wayne Simpson | 1.00 |
| 429 Jim Fairey | 1.00 |
| 430 Vida Blue | 1.25 |
| 431 Gerry Moses | 1.00 |
| 432 Dan Frisella | 1.00 |
| 433 Willie Horton | 1.25 |
| 434 San F. Giants | 1.50 |
| 435 Rico Carty | 1.25 |
| 436 Jim McAndrew | 1.00 |
| 437 John Kennedy | 1.00 |
| 438 Enzo Hernandez | 1.00 |
| 439 Eddie Fisher | 1.00 |
| 440 Glenn Beckert | 1.00 |
| 441 Gail Hopkins | 1.00 |
| 442 Dick Dietz | 1.00 |
| 443 Danny Thompson | 1.00 |
| 444 Ken Brett | 1.00 |
| 445 Ken Berry | 1.00 |
| 446 Jerry Reuss | 1.25 |

| NO. PLAYER | NR. MT. |
|---|---|
| 447 Joe Hague | 1.00 |
| 448 John Hiller | 1.00 |
| 449 Ken Aspromonte (Mgr.) | 1.25 |
| 450 Joe Torre | 1.25 |
| 451 John Vuckovich | 1.00 |
| 452 Paul Casanova | 1.00 |
| 453 Checklist No. 4 | 1.50 |
| 454 Tom Haller | 1.00 |
| 455 Bill Melton | 1.00 |
| 456 Dick Green | 1.00 |
| 457 John Strohmayer | 1.00 |
| 458 Jim Mason | 1.00 |
| 459 Jimmy Howarth | 1.00 |
| 460 Bill Freehan | 1.25 |
| 461 Mike Corkins | 1.00 |
| 462 Ron Blomberg | 1.00 |
| 463 Ken Tatum | 1.00 |
| 464 Chicago Cubs | 1.50 |
| 465 Dave Giusti | 1.00 |
| 466 Jose Arcia | 1.00 |
| 467 Mike Ryan | 1.00 |
| 468 Tom Griffin | 1.00 |
| 469 Dan Monzon | 1.00 |
| 470 Mike Cuellar | 1.25 |
| 471 All-Time Hits | 4.00 |
|   Ty Cobb (4,191) | |
| 472 All-Time Grand Slams: | 4.00 |
|   Lou Gehrig (23) | |
| 473 All-Time Total Bases | 4.00 |
|   hank Aaron (6,172) | |
| 474 All-Time RBI's | 6.00 |
|   Babe Ruth (2,209) | |
| 475 All-Time Batting | 4.00 |
|   Ty Cobb (.367) | |
| 476 All-Time Shutouts: | 1.50 |
|   Walter Johnson (113) | |
| 477 All-Time Victory Ldrs. | 1.50 |
|   Cy Young (511) | |
| 478 All-Time Strikeouts: | 1.50 |
|   Walter Johnson (3,508) | |
| 479 Hal Lanier | 1.00 |
| 480 Juan Marichal | 4.00 |
| 481 Chicago White Sox | 1.50 |
| 482 Rick Reuschel (R) | 6.00 |
| 483 Dal Maxvill | 1.00 |
| 484 Ernie McAnally | 1.00 |
| 485 Norm Cash | 1.25 |
| 486 Danny Ozark (Mgr.) | 1.25 |
| 487 Bruce Dal Canton | 1.00 |
| 488 Dave Campbell | 1.00 |
| 489 Jeff Burroughs | 1.00 |
| 490 Claude Osteen | 1.25 |
| 491 Bob Montgomery | 1.00 |
| 492 Pedro Borbon | 1.00 |
| 493 Duffy Dyer | 1.00 |
| 494 Rich Morales | 1.00 |
| 495 Tommy Helms | 1.00 |
| 496 Ray Lamb | 1.00 |
| 497 R. Schoendienst (Mgr.) | 1.25 |
| 498 Graig Nettles | 2.50 |
| 499 Bob Moose | 1.00 |
| 500 Oakland A's | 2.00 |
| 501 Larry Gura | 1.00 |
| 502 Bobby Valentine | 1.25 |
| 503 Phil Niekro | 4.00 |
| 504 Earl Williams | 1.00 |
| 505 Bob Bailey | 1.00 |
| 506 Bart Johnson | 1.00 |
| 507 Darrel Chaney | 1.00 |
| 508 Gates Brown | 1.00 |
| 509 Jim Nash | 1.00 |
| 510 Amos Otis | 1.25 |
| 511 Sam McDowell | 1.25 |
| 512 Dalton Jones | 1.00 |
| 513 Dave Marshall | 1.00 |
| 514 Jerry Kenney | 1.00 |
| 515 Andy Messersmith | 1.25 |
| 516 Danny Walton | 1.00 |
| 517 Bill Virdon (Mgr.) | 1.25 |
| 518 Bob Veale | 1.00 |
| 519 John Edwards | 1.00 |
| 520 Mel Stottlemyre | 1.00 |
| 521 Atlanta Braves | 1.50 |
| 522 Leo Cardenas | 1.00 |

| NO. PLAYER | NR. MT. |
|---|---|
| 523 Wayne Granger | 1.00 |
| 524 Gene Tenace | 1.25 |
| 525 Jim Fregosi | 1.25 |
| 526 Ollie Brown | 1.00 |
| 527 Dan McGinn | 1.00 |
| 528 Paul Blair | 1.00 |
| 529 Milt May | 2.50 |
| 530 Jim Kaat | 4.00 |
| 531 Ron Woods | 2.50 |
| 532 Steve Mingori | 2.50 |
| 533 Larry Stahl | 2.50 |
| 534 Dave Lemonds | 2.50 |
| 535 John Callison | 2.50 |
| 536 Philadelphia Phillies | 5.00 |
| 537 Bill Slayback | 3.00 |
| 538 Jim Hart | 3.00 |
| 539 Tom Murphy | 3.00 |
| 540 Cleon Jones | 3.50 |
| 541 Bob Bolin | 3.00 |
| 542 Pat Corrales | 3.50 |
| 543 Alan Foster | 3.00 |
| 544 Von Joshua | 3.00 |
| 545 Orlando Cepeda | 4.00 |
| 546 Jim York | 2.50 |
| 547 Bobby Heise | 2.50 |
| 548 Don Durham | 2.50 |
| 549 Whitey Herzog (Mgr.) | 3.00 |
| 550 Dave Johnson | 2.50 |
| 551 Mike Kilkenny | 2.50 |
| 552 J.C. Martin | 2.50 |
| 553 Mickey Scott | 2.50 |
| 554 Dave Concepcion | 4.00 |
| 555 Bill Hands | 2.50 |
| 556 New York Yankees | 6.00 |
| 557 Bernie Williams | 3.00 |
| 558 Jerry May | 3.00 |
| 559 Barry Lersch | 3.00 |
| 560 Frank Howard | 4.00 |
| 561 Jim Geddes | 3.00 |
| 562 Wayne Garrett | 3.00 |
| 563 Larry Haney | 3.00 |
| 564 Mike Thompson | 3.00 |
| 565 Jim Hickman | 3.00 |
| 566 Lew Krausse | 3.00 |
| 567 Bob Fenwick | 3.00 |
| 568 Ray Newman | 3.00 |
| 569 Walt Alston (Mgr.) | 4.00 |
| 570 Bill Singer | 2.50 |
| 571 Rusty Torres | 2.50 |
| 572 Gary Sutherland | 2.50 |
| 573 Fred Beene | 2.50 |
| 574 Bob Didier | 2.50 |
| 575 Dock Ellis | 2.50 |
| 576 Montreal Expos | 5.00 |
| 577 Eric Soderholm | 3.00 |
| 578 Ken Wright | 3.00 |
| 579 Tom Grieve | 3.00 |
| 580 Joe Pepitone | 3.00 |
| 581 Steve Kealey | 2.50 |
| 582 Darrell Porter | 3.00 |
| 583 Bill Grief | 2.50 |
| 584 Chris Arnold | 2.50 |
| 585 Joe Niekro | 4.00 |
| 586 Bill Sudakis | 3.00 |
| 587 Rich McKinney | 3.00 |
| 588 Checklist No. 5 | 15.00 |
| 589 Ken Forsch | 3.00 |
| 590 Deron Johnson | 3.00 |
| 591 Mike Hedlund | 3.00 |
| 592 John Boccabella | 3.00 |
| 593 Jack McKeon (Mgr.) | 3.00 |
| 594 Vic Harris | 3.00 |
| 595 Don Gullett | 3.50 |
| 596 Boston Red Sox | 5.00 |
| 597 Mickey Rivers | 3.00 |
| 598 Phil Roof | 2.50 |
| 599 Ed Crosby | 2.50 |
| 600 Dave McNally | 2.50 |
| 601 Rookie Catchers: | 3.50 |
|   George Pena, Sergio Robles, R. Stelmaszek | |
| 602 Rookie Pitchers: | 3.50 |
|   Doug Rau, Mel Behney, Ralph Garcia | |

| NO. PLAYER | NR. MT. |
|---|---|
| 603 Rookie 3rd Basemen: | 3.50 |
|   Billy McNulty, Ken Reitz, Terry Hughes | |
| 604 Rookie Pitchers: | 3.50 |
|   Jesse Jefferson, Dennis O'Toole, Bob Strampe | |
| 605 Rookie 1st Basemen: | 3.50 |
|   Pat Bourque, Enos Cabell, Gonzalo Marquez | |
| 606 Rookie Outfielders: | 4.00 |
|   Jorge Roque, Gary Matthews, T. Paciorek | |
| 607 Rookie Shortstops: | 3.50 |
|   Pepe Frias, Ray Busse, Mario Guerrero | |
| 608 Rookie Pitchers: | 3.50 |
|   S. Busby, G. Medich, Dick Colpaert | |
| 609 Rookie 2nd Basemen: | 5.00 |
|   Larvell Blanks, P. Garcia, Dave Lopes | |
| 610 Rookie Pitchers: | 3.50 |
|   Hank Webb, J. Freeman, Charlie Hough | |
| 611 Rookie Outfielders: | 3.00 |
|   Richie Zisk, Rich Coggins, J. Wohlford | |
| 612 Rookie Pitchers: | 3.00 |
|   Steve Lawson, Bob Reynolds, Brent Strom | |
| 613 Rookie Catchers: | 35.00 |
|   Bob Boone, S. Jutze, Mike Ivie | |
| 614 Rookie Outfielders: | 75.00 |
|   A. Bumbry, Dwight Evans, Charlie Spikes | |
| 615 Rookie 3rd Basemen: | 450.00 |
|   Ron Cey, Mike Schmidt, John Hilton | |
| 616 Rookie Pitchers: | 2.50 |
|   S. Blateric, Norm Angelini, Mike Garman | |
| 617 Rich Chiles | 2.50 |
| 618 Andy Etchebarren | 2.50 |
| 619 Billy Wilson | 2.50 |
| 620 Tommy Harper | 2.50 |
| 621 Joe Ferguson | 2.50 |
| 622 Larry Hisle | 2.50 |
| 623 Steve Renko | 2.50 |
| 624 Leo Durocher (Mgr.) | 3.50 |
| 625 Angel Mangual | 3.00 |
| 626 Bob Barton | 3.00 |
| 627 Luis Alvarado | 3.00 |
| 628 Jim Slaton | 3.00 |
| 629 Cleveland Indians | 5.00 |
| 630 Denny McLain | 4.00 |
| 631 Tom Matchick | 2.50 |
| 632 Dick Selma | 2.50 |
| 633 Ike Brown | 2.50 |
| 634 Alan Closter | 2.50 |
| 635 Gene Alley | 2.50 |
| 636 Rick Clark | 2.50 |
| 637 Norm Miller | 2.50 |
| 638 Ken Reynolds | 2.50 |
| 639 Willie Crawford | 2.50 |
| 640 Dick Bosman | 2.50 |
| 641 Cincinnati Reds | 5.00 |
| 642 Jose LaBoy | 2.50 |
| 643 Al Fitzmorris | 2.50 |
| 644 Jack Heidemann | 2.50 |
| 645 Bob Locker | 2.50 |
| 646 Del Crandall (Mgr.) | 3.00 |
| 647 George Stone | 2.50 |
| 648 Tom Egan | 2.50 |
| 649 Rich Folkers | 2.50 |
| 650 Felipe Alou | 3.00 |
| 651 Don Carrithers | 2.50 |
| 652 Ted Kubiak | 2.50 |
| 653 Joe Hoerner | 2.50 |
| 654 Minnesota Twins | 5.00 |
| 655 Clay Kirby | 2.50 |
| 656 John Ellis | 2.50 |
| 657 Bob Johnson | 2.50 |
| 658 Elliott Maddox | 2.50 |
| 659 Jose Pagan | 2.50 |
| 660 F. Scherman (Exc. $.60) | 3.00 |

# 1974 Topps . . . Complete Set of 660 Cards—Value $600.00 (Mint)

Features the rookie cards of Dave Parker and Dave Winfield. This was Topps' first card set to be released all at one time. Previous card sets were released in series, several weeks or months apart. Fifteen Padres cards were printed either "San Diego" or "Washington". Because of a false rumor that the Padres were moving, Topps printed "Washington" on the cards, but it was quickly corrected.

| NO. PLAYER | NR. MT. | NO. PLAYER | NR. MT. | NO. PLAYER | NR. MT. | NO. PLAYER | NR. MT. |
|---|---|---|---|---|---|---|---|
| 1 Hank Aaron (Exc. $8.00) . . | 25.00 | 64 Doug Rau | .35 | 127 Tom Paciorek | .35 | 191 Al Fitzmorris | .35 |
| Home Run King | | 65 Amos Otis | .50 | 128 John Ellis | .35 | 192 Mario Guerrero | .35 |
| 2 Aaron Special (1954-57) | 5.00 | 66 Sparky Lyle | .50 | 129 Chris Speier | .35 | 193 Tom Walker | .35 |
| 3 Aaron Special (1958-61) | 5.00 | 67 Tommy Helms | .35 | 130 Reggie Jackson | 17.50 | 194 Darrell Porter | .35 |
| 4 Aaron Special (1962-65) | 5.00 | 68 Grant Jackson | .35 | 131 Bob Boone | 3.00 | 195 Carlos May | .35 |
| 5 Aaron Special (1966-69) | 5.00 | 69 Del Unser | .35 | 132 Felix Milan | .35 | 196 Jim Fregosi | .50 |
| 6 Aaron Special (1970-73) | 5.00 | 70 Dick Allen | .60 | 133 David Clyde | .35 | 197 Vicente Romo (SD) | .40 |
| 7 Jim Hunter | 4.00 | 71 Dan Frisella | .35 | 134 Denis Menke | .35 | 197 Vicente Romo (Wash.) | 4.00 |
| 8 George Theodore | .35 | 72 Aurelio Rodriguez | .35 | 135 Roy White | .40 | 198 Dave Cash | .35 |
| 9 Mickey Lolich | .60 | 73 Mike Marshall | .75 | 136 Rick Reuschel | 1.50 | 199 Mike Kekich | .35 |
| 10 Johnny Bench | 13.00 | 74 Minnesota Twins | .60 | 137 Al Bumbry | .35 | 200 Cesar Cedeno | .75 |
| 11 Jim Bibby | .35 | 75 Jim Colborn | .35 | 138 Ed Brinkman | .35 | 201 Batting Leaders: | 4.00 |
| 12 Dave May | .35 | 76 Mickey Rivers | .35 | 139 Aurelio Monteagudo | .35 | Rod Carew, Pete Rose |
| 13 Tom Hilgendorf | .35 | 77 Rich Troedson (SD) | .35 | 140 Darrell Evans | .50 | 202 Home Run Leaders: | 2.50 |
| 14 Paul Popovich | .35 | 77 Rich Troedson (Wash.) | 4.00 | 141 Pat Bourque | .35 | R. Jackson, Willie Stargell |
| 15 Joe Torre | .75 | 78 Charlie Fox (Mgr.) | .35 | 142 Pedro Garcia | .35 | 203 RBI Leaders: | 2.50 |
| 16 Baltimore Orioles | .60 | 79 Gene Tenace | .35 | 143 Dick Woodson | .35 | R. Jackson, Willie Stargell |
| 17 Doug Bird | .35 | 80 Tom Seaver | 15.00 | 144 Walter Alston (Mgr.) | 1.00 | 204 Stolen Base Leaders: | 1.00 |
| 18 Gary Thomasson | .35 | 81 Frank Duffy | .35 | 145 Dock Ellis | .35 | Tommy Harper, Lou Brock |
| 19 Gerry Moses | .35 | 82 Dave Giusti | .35 | 146 Ron Fairly | .35 | 205 Victory Leaders: | 1.00 |
| 20 Nolan Ryan | 45.00 | 83 Orlando Cepeda | 1.00 | 147 Bart Johnson | .35 | Wilbur Wood, Ron Bryant |
| 21 Bob Gallagher | .35 | 84 Rick Wise | .35 | 148 Dave Hilton (SD) | .40 | 206 ERA Leaders: | 3.00 |
| 22 Cy Acosta | .35 | 85 Joe Morgan | 4.00 | 148 Dave Hilton (Wash.) | 4.00 | Jim Palmer, T. Seaver |
| 23 Craig Robinson | .35 | 86 Joe Ferguson | .35 | 149 Mac Scarce | .35 | 207 Strikeout Leaders: | 5.00 |
| 24 John Hiller | .35 | 87 Fergie Jenkins | 3.00 | 150 John Mayberry | .35 | Nolan Ryan, Tom Seaver |
| 25 Len Singleton | .50 | 88 Freddie Patek | .35 | 151 Diego Segui | .35 | 208 Leading Firemen: | 1.00 |
| 26 Bill Campbell (R) | .50 | 89 Jackie Brown | .35 | 152 Oscar Gamble | .35 | John Hiller, M. Marshall |
| 27 George Scott | .35 | 90 Bobby Murcer | .60 | 153 Jon Matlack | .35 | 209 Ted Sizemore | .35 |
| 28 Manny Sanguillen | .35 | 91 Ken Forsch | .35 | 154 Houston Astros | .60 | 210 Bill Singer | .35 |
| 29 Phil Niekro | 2.50 | 92 Paul Blair | .35 | 155 Bert Campaneris | .50 | 211 Chicago Cubs | .60 |
| 30 Bobby Bonds | 1.00 | 93 Rod Gilbreath | .35 | 156 Randy Moffitt | .35 | 212 Rollie Fingers | 3.50 |
| 31 Preston Gomez (Mgr.) | .35 | 94 Detroit Tigers | .75 | 157 Vic Harris | .35 | 213 Dave Rader | .35 |
| 32 John Grubb (SD) | .75 | 95 Steve Carlton | 8.00 | 158 Jack Billingham | .35 | 214 Bill Grabarkewitz | .35 |
| 32 John Grubb (Wash.) | 4.00 | 96 Jerry Hairston | .35 | 159 Jim Hart | .35 | 215 Al Kaline | 5.00 |
| 33 Don Newhauser | .35 | 97 Bob Bailey | .35 | 160 Brooks Robinson | 4.00 | 216 Ray Sadecki | .35 |
| 34 Andy Kosco | .35 | 98 Bert Blyleven | 2.50 | 161 Ray Burris (R) | .75 | 217 Tim Foli | .35 |
| 35 Gaylord Perry | 3.00 | 99 Del Crandall (Mgr.) | .50 | 162 Bill Freehan | .50 | 218 Johnny Briggs | .35 |
| 36 St. Louis Cardinals | .60 | 100 Willie Stargell | 3.50 | 163 Ken Berry | .35 | 219 Doug Griffin | .35 |
| 37 Dave Sells | .35 | 101 Bobby Valentine | .50 | 164 Tom House | .35 | 220 Don Sutton | 2.50 |
| 38 Don Kessinger | .35 | 102 Bill Greif (SD) | .50 | 165 Willie Davis | .35 | 221 Chuck Tanner (Mgr.) | .50 |
| 39 Ken Suarez | .35 | 102 Bill Greif (Wash.) | 4.00 | 166 Jack McKeon (Mgr.) | .35 | 222 Ramon Hernandez | .35 |
| 40 Jim Palmer | 7.00 | 103 Sal Bando | .60 | 167 Luis Tiant | .60 | 223 Jeff Burroughs | .50 |
| 41 Bobby Floyd | .35 | 104 Ron Bryant | .35 | 168 Danny Thompson | .35 | 224 Roger Metzger | .35 |
| 42 Claude Osteen | .35 | 105 Carlton Fisk | 20.00 | 169 Steve Rogers (R) | .60 | 225 Paul Splittorff | .50 |
| 43 Jim Wynn | .35 | 106 Harry Parker | .35 | 170 Bill Melton | .35 | 226 Padres Team (SD) | 1.00 |
| 44 Mel Stottlemyre | .50 | 107 Alex Johnson | .35 | 171 Eduardo Rodriguez | .35 | 226 Padres Team (Wash.) | 5.00 |
| 45 Dave Johnson | .75 | 108 Al Hrabosky | .50 | 172 Gene Clines | .35 | 227 Mike Lum | .35 |
| 46 Pat Kelly | .35 | 109 Bob Grich | .50 | 173 Randy Jones (SD) | .75 | 228 Ted Kubiak | .35 |
| 47 Dick Ruthven | .35 | 110 Billy Williams | 3.00 | 173 Randy Jones (Wash.) | 6.00 | 229 Fritz Peterson | .35 |
| 48 Dick Sharon | .35 | 111 Clay Carroll | .35 | 174 Bill Robinson | .35 | 230 Tony Perez | 2.50 |
| 49 Steve Renko | .35 | 112 Dave Lopes | .60 | 175 Reggie Cleveland | .35 | 231 Dick Tidrow | .35 |
| 50 R. Carew | 12.00 | 113 Dick Drago | .35 | 176 John Lowenstein | .35 | 232 Steve Brye | .35 |
| 51 Bob Heise | .35 | 114 California Angels | .60 | 177 Dave Roberts | .35 | 233 Jim Barr | .35 |
| 52 Al Oliver | 1.00 | 115 Willie Horton | .50 | 178 Garry Maddox | .35 | 234 John Milner | .35 |
| 53 Fred Kendall (SD) | .35 | 116 Jerry Reuss | .50 | 179 Yogi Berra (Mgr.) | 1.50 | 235 Dave McNally | .35 |
| 53 Fred Kendall (Wash.) | 4.00 | 117 Ron Blomberg | .35 | 180 Ken Holtzman | .35 | 236 R. Schoendienst (Mgr.) | .50 |
| 54 Elias Sosa | .35 | 118 Bill Lee | .35 | 181 Cesar Geronimo | .35 | 237 Ken Brett | .35 |
| 55 Frank Robinson | 4.00 | 119 Danny Ozark (Mgr.) | .35 | 182 Lindy McDaniel | .35 | 238 Fran Healy | .35 |
| 56 New York Mets | 1.00 | 120 Wilbur Wood | .35 | 183 Johnny Oates | .35 | 239 Bill Russell | .35 |
| 57 Darold Knowles | .35 | 121 Larry Lintz | .35 | 184 Texas Rangers | .60 | 240 Joe Coleman | .35 |
| 58 Charlie Spikes | .35 | 122 Jim Holt | .35 | 185 Jose Cardenal | .35 | 241 Glenn Beckert (SD) | .40 |
| 59 Ross Grimsley | .35 | 123 Nellie Briles | .35 | 186 Fred Scherman | .35 | 241 Glenn Beckert (Wash.) | 4.00 |
| 60 Lou Brock | 4.00 | 124 Bobby Coluccio | .35 | 187 Don Baylor | 1.25 | 242 Bill Gogolewski | .35 |
| 61 Luis Aparicio | 2.00 | 125 Nate Colbert (SD) | .40 | 188 Rudy Meoli | .35 | 243 Bob Oliver | .35 |
| 62 Bob Locker | .35 | 125 Nate Colbert (Wash.) | 4.00 | 189 Jim Brewer | .35 | 244 Carl Morton | .35 |
| 63 Bill Sudakis | .35 | 126 Checklist No. 1 | 1.50 | 190 Tony Oliva | 1.00 | 245 Cleon Jones | .35 |

| NO. | PLAYER | NR. MT. |
|---|---|---|
| 246 | Oakland Athletics | .75 |
| 247 | Rick Miller | .35 |
| 248 | Tom Hall | .35 |
| 249 | George Mitterwald | .35 |
| 250 | W. McCovey (SD) | 5.00 |
| 250 | W. McCovey (Wash.) | 20.00 |
| 251 | Graig Nettles | 2.00 |
| 252 | Dave Parker (R) | 45.00 |
| 253 | John Boccabella | .35 |
| 254 | Stan Bahnsen | .35 |
| 255 | Larry Bowa | .75 |
| 256 | Tom Griffin | .35 |
| 257 | Buddy Bell | 1.25 |
| 258 | Jerry Morales | .35 |
| 259 | Bob Reynolds | .25 |
| 260 | Ted Simmons | 1.25 |
| 261 | Jerry Bell | .35 |
| 262 | Ed Kirkpatrick | .35 |
| 263 | Checklist No. 2 | 1.50 |
| 264 | Joe Rudi | .35 |
| 265 | Tug McGraw | .50 |
| 266 | Jim Northrup | .35 |
| 267 | Andy Messersmith | .50 |
| 268 | Tom Grieve | .35 |
| 269 | Bob Johnson | .35 |
| 270 | Ron Santo | .75 |
| 271 | Bill Hands | .35 |
| 272 | Paul Casanova | .35 |
| 273 | Checklist No. 3 | 1.50 |
| 274 | Fred Beene | .35 |
| 275 | Ron Hunt | .35 |
| 276 | Bobby Winkles (Mgr.) | .50 |
| 277 | Gary Nolan | .35 |
| 278 | Cookie Rojas | .35 |
| 279 | Jim Crawford | .35 |
| 280 | Carl Yastrzemski | 12.00 |
| 281 | San F. Giants | .75 |
| 282 | Doyle Alexander | .35 |
| 283 | Mike Schmidt | 100.00 |
| 284 | Dave Duncan | .35 |
| 285 | Reggie Smith | .50 |
| 286 | Tony Muser | .35 |
| 287 | Clay Kirby | .35 |
| 288 | Gorman Thomas (R) | 2.00 |
| 289 | Rick Auerback | .35 |
| 290 | Vida Blue | .50 |
| 291 | Don Hahn | .35 |
| 292 | Chuck Seelbach | .35 |
| 293 | Milt May | .35 |
| 294 | Steve Foucault | .35 |
| 295 | Rick Monday | .50 |
| 296 | Ray Corbin | .35 |
| 297 | Hal Breeden | .35 |
| 298 | Roric Harrison | .35 |
| 299 | Gene Michael | .40 |
| 300 | Pete Rose | 15.00 |
| 301 | Bob Montgomery | .35 |
| 302 | Rudy May | .35 |
| 303 | George Hendrick | .50 |
| 304 | Don Wilson | .35 |
| 305 | Tito Fuentes | .35 |
| 306 | Earl Weaver (Mgr.) | .60 |
| 307 | Luis Melendez | .35 |
| 308 | Bruce Dal Canton | .35 |
| 309 | Dave Roberts (SD) | .40 |
| 309 | Dave Roberts (Wash.) | 4.00 |
| 310 | Terry Forster | .35 |
| 311 | Jerry Grote | .35 |
| 312 | Deron Johnson | .35 |
| 313 | Barry Lersch | .35 |
| 314 | Milwaukee Brewers | .75 |
| 315 | Ron Cey | 1.00 |
| 316 | Jim Perry | .35 |
| 317 | Richie Zisk | .35 |
| 318 | Jim Merritt | .35 |
| 319 | Randy Hundley | .35 |
| 320 | Dusty Baker | .60 |
| 321 | Steve Braun | .35 |
| 322 | Ernie McAnally | .35 |
| 323 | Richie Scheinblum | .35 |
| 324 | Steve Kline | .35 |
| 325 | Tommy Harper | .35 |
| 326 | Sparky Anderson (Mgr.) | .60 |
| 327 | Tom Timmermann | .35 |
| 328 | Skip Jutze | .35 |
| 329 | Mark Belanger | .35 |
| 330 | Juan Marichal | 2.50 |
| 331 | All-Star Catchers: Carlton Fisk, Johnny Bench | 4.00 |
| 332 | AS 1st Baseman: Dick Allen, Hank Aaron | 2.50 |
| 333 | AS 2nd Baseman: Rod Carew, Joe Morgan | 2.50 |
| 334 | AS 3rd Baseman: B. Robinson, Ron Santo | 1.25 |
| 335 | AS Shortstops: B. Campaneris, C. Speier | .75 |
| 336 | AS Left Fielders: Pete Rose, Bobby Mercer | 2.50 |
| 337 | AS Center Fielders: Amos Otis, Cesar Cedeno | .75 |
| 338 | AS Right Fielders: R. Jackson, B. Williams | 3.00 |
| 339 | AS Pitchers: Jim Hunter, Rick Wise | 1.00 |
| 340 | Thurman Munson | 7.00 |
| 341 | Dan Driessen | .75 |
| 342 | Jim Lonborg | .35 |
| 343 | Kansas City Royals | .75 |
| 344 | Mike Caldwell | .35 |
| 345 | Bill North | .35 |
| 346 | Ron Reed | .35 |
| 347 | Sandy Alomar | .35 |
| 348 | Pete Richert | .35 |
| 349 | John Vukovich | .35 |
| 350 | Bob Gibson | 4.00 |
| 351 | Dwight Evans | 15.00 |
| 352 | Bill Stoneman | .35 |
| 353 | Rich Coggins | .35 |
| 354 | Whitey Lockman (Mgr.) | .60 |
| 355 | Dave Nelson | .35 |
| 356 | Jerry Koosman | .60 |
| 357 | Buddy Bradford | .35 |
| 358 | Dal Maxvill | .35 |
| 359 | Brent Strom | .35 |
| 360 | Greg Luzinski | .75 |
| 361 | Don Carrithers | .35 |
| 362 | Hal King | .35 |
| 363 | New York Yankees | 1.25 |
| 364 | C. Gaston (SD) | .40 |
| 364 | C. Gaston (Wash.) | 4.00 |
| 365 | Steve Busby | .35 |
| 366 | Larry Hisle | .35 |
| 367 | Norm Cash | .50 |
| 368 | Manny Mota | .50 |
| 369 | Paul Lindblad | .35 |
| 370 | Bob Watson | .35 |
| 371 | Jim Slaton | .35 |
| 372 | Ken Reitz | .35 |
| 373 | John Curtis | .35 |
| 374 | Marty Perez | .35 |
| 375 | Earl Williams | .35 |
| 376 | Jorge Orta | .35 |
| 377 | Ron Woods | .35 |
| 378 | Burt Hooton | .35 |
| 379 | Billy Martin (Mgr.) | 1.00 |
| 380 | Bud Harrelson | .75 |
| 381 | Charlies Sands | .35 |
| 382 | Bob Moose | .35 |
| 383 | Phil. Phillies | .75 |
| 384 | Chris Chambliss | .50 |
| 385 | Don Gullett | .50 |
| 386 | Gary Matthews | .60 |
| 387 | Rich Morales (SD) | .40 |
| 387 | Rich Morales (Wash.) | 4.00 |
| 388 | Phil Roof | .35 |
| 389 | Gates Brown | .35 |
| 390 | Lou Piniella | .75 |
| 391 | Billy Champion | .35 |
| 392 | Dick Green | .35 |
| 393 | Orlando Pena | .35 |
| 394 | Ken Henderson | .35 |
| 395 | Doug Rader | .35 |
| 396 | Tommy Davis | .40 |
| 397 | George Stone | .35 |
| 398 | Duke Sims | .35 |
| 399 | Mike Paul | .35 |
| 400 | Harmon Killebrew | 4.00 |
| 401 | Elliott Maddox | .35 |
| 402 | Jim Rooker | .35 |
| 403 | Darrell Johnson (Mgr.) | .40 |
| 404 | Jim Howarth | .35 |
| 405 | Ellie Rodriguez | .35 |
| 406 | Steve Arlin | .35 |
| 407 | Jim Wohlford | .35 |
| 408 | Charlie Hough | .50 |
| 409 | Ike Brown | .35 |
| 410 | Pedro Borbon | .35 |
| 411 | Frank Baker | .35 |
| 412 | Chuck Taylor | .35 |
| 413 | Don Money | .50 |
| 414 | Checklist No. 4 | 1.50 |
| 415 | Gary Gentry | .35 |
| 416 | Chicago White Sox | .75 |
| 417 | Rich Folkers | .35 |
| 418 | Walt Williams | .35 |
| 419 | Wayne Twitchell | .35 |
| 420 | Ray Fosse | .35 |
| 421 | Dan Fife | .35 |
| 422 | Gonzalo Marquez | .35 |
| 423 | Fred Stanley | .35 |
| 424 | Jim Beauchamp | .35 |
| 425 | Pete Broberg | .35 |
| 426 | Rennie Stennett | .35 |
| 427 | Bobby Bolin | .35 |
| 428 | Gary Sutherland | .35 |
| 429 | Dick Lange | .35 |
| 430 | Matty Alou | .50 |
| 431 | Gene Garber | .35 |
| 432 | Chris Arnold | .35 |
| 433 | Lerrin LaGrow | .35 |
| 434 | Ken McMullen | .35 |
| 435 | Dave Concepcion | 1.00 |
| 436 | Don Hood | .35 |
| 437 | Jim Lyttle | .35 |
| 438 | Ed Herrmann | .35 |
| 439 | Norm Miller | .35 |
| 440 | Jim Kaat | 1.00 |
| 441 | Tom Ragland | .35 |
| 442 | Alan Foster | .35 |
| 443 | Tom Hutton | .35 |
| 444 | Vic Davalillo | .35 |
| 445 | George Medich | .35 |
| 446 | Len Randle | .35 |
| 447 | Frank Quilici (Mgr.) | .40 |
| 448 | Ron Hodges | .35 |
| 449 | Tom McCraw | .35 |
| 450 | Rich Hebner | .35 |
| 451 | Tommy John | 1.50 |
| 452 | Gene Hiser | .35 |
| 453 | Balor Moore | .35 |
| 454 | Kurt Bevacqua | .35 |
| 455 | Tom Bradley | .35 |
| 456 | Dave Winfield (R) | 75.00 |
| 457 | Chuck Goggin | .35 |
| 458 | Jim Ray | .35 |
| 459 | Cincinnati Reds | .75 |
| 460 | Boog Powell | .75 |
| 461 | John Odom | .35 |
| 462 | Luis Alvarado | .35 |
| 463 | Pat Dobson | .35 |
| 464 | Jose Cruz | .60 |
| 465 | Dick Bosman | .35 |
| 466 | Dick Billings | .35 |
| 467 | Winston Llenas | .35 |
| 468 | Pepe Frias | .35 |
| 469 | Joe Decker | .35 |
| 470 | A.L. Playoffs: A's Beat Orioles | 4.00 |
| 471 | N.L. Playoffs: Mets Beat Reds | .75 |
| 472 | World Series Game 1: Oakland 2, N.Y. 1 | .75 |
| 473 | World Series Game 2: N.Y. 10, Oakland 7 | 4.00 |
| 474 | World Series Game 3: Oakland 3, N.Y. 2 | .75 |
| 475 | World Series Game 4: N.Y. 6, Oakland 1 | .75 |
| 476 | World Series Game 5: N.Y. 2, Oakland 0 | .75 |
| 477 | World Series Game 6: Oakland 3, N.Y. 1 | 4.00 |
| 478 | World Series Game 7: Oakland 5, N.Y. 2 | .75 |
| 479 | World Series: A's Win | 1.00 |
| 480 | Willie Crawford | .35 |
| 481 | Jerry Terrell | .35 |
| 482 | Bob Didier | .35 |
| 483 | Atlanta Braves | .75 |
| 484 | Carmen Fanzone | .35 |
| 485 | Felipe Alou | .50 |
| 486 | Steve Stone | .40 |
| 487 | Ted Martinez | .35 |
| 488 | Andy Etchebarren | .35 |
| 489 | Danny Murtaugh (Mgr.) | .35 |
| 490 | Vada Pinson | .50 |
| 491 | Roger Nelson | .35 |
| 492 | Mike Rogodzinski | .35 |
| 493 | Joe Hoerner | .35 |
| 494 | Ed Goodson | .35 |
| 495 | Dick McAuliffe | .35 |
| 496 | Tom Murphy | .35 |
| 497 | Bobby Mitchell | .35 |
| 498 | Pat Corrales | .40 |
| 499 | Rusty Torres | .35 |
| 500 | Lee May | .50 |
| 501 | Eddie Leon | .35 |
| 502 | Dave LaRoche | .35 |
| 503 | Eric Soderholm | .35 |
| 504 | Joe Niekro | .60 |
| 505 | Bill Buckner | .75 |
| 506 | Ed Farmer | .35 |
| 507 | Larry Stahl | .35 |
| 508 | Montreal Expos | .75 |
| 509 | Jesse Jefferson | .35 |
| 510 | Wayne Garrett | .35 |
| 511 | Toby Harrah | .50 |
| 512 | Joe Lahoud | .35 |
| 513 | Jim Campanis | .35 |
| 514 | Paul Schaal | .35 |
| 515 | Willie Montanez | .35 |
| 516 | Horacio Pina | .35 |
| 517 | Mike Hegan | .35 |
| 518 | Derrel Thomas | .35 |
| 519 | Bill Sharp | .35 |
| 520 | Tim McCarver | .50 |
| 521 | Ken Aspromonte (Mgr.) | .40 |
| 522 | J.R. Richard | .35 |
| 523 | Cecil Cooper | 2.00 |
| 524 | Bill Plummer | .35 |
| 525 | Clyde Wright | .35 |
| 526 | Frank Tepedino | .35 |
| 527 | Bobby Darwin | .35 |
| 528 | Bill Bonham | .35 |
| 529 | Horace Clarke | .35 |
| 530 | Mickey Stanley | .35 |
| 531 | Gene Mauch (Mgr.) | .50 |
| 532 | Skip Lockwood | .35 |
| 533 | Mike Phillips | .35 |
| 534 | Eddie Watt | .35 |
| 535 | Bob Tolan | .35 |
| 536 | Duffy Dyer | .35 |
| 537 | Steve Mingori | .35 |
| 538 | Cesar Tovar | .35 |
| 539 | Lloyd Allen | .35 |
| 540 | Bob Robertson | .35 |
| 541 | Cleveland Indians | .75 |
| 542 | Rich Gossage | 3.00 |
| 543 | Danny Cater | .35 |
| 544 | Ron Schueler | .35 |
| 545 | Billy Conigliaro | .35 |
| 546 | Mike Corkins | .35 |
| 547 | Glenn Borgmann | .35 |
| 548 | Sonny Siebert | .35 |
| 549 | Mike Jorgensen | .35 |
| 550 | Sam McDowell | .50 |
| 551 | Von Joshua | .35 |
| 552 | Denny Doyle | .35 |
| 553 | Jim Willoughby | .35 |
| 554 | Tim Johnson | .35 |
| 555 | Woodie Fryman | .35 |
| 556 | Dave Campbell | .35 |
| 557 | Jim McGlothlin | .35 |
| 558 | Bill Fahey | .35 |
| 559 | Darrell Chaney | .35 |
| 560 | Mike Cuellar | .50 |
| 561 | Ed Kranepool | .50 |
| 562 | Jack Aker | .35 |

| NO. PLAYER | NR. MT. |
|---|---|
| 563 Hal McRae | .50 |
| 564 Mike Ryan | .35 |
| 565 Milt Wilcox | .35 |
| 566 Jackie Hernandez | .35 |
| 567 Boston Red Sox | .75 |
| 568 Mike Torrez | .50 |
| 569 Rick Dempsey | .35 |
| 570 Ralph Garr | .35 |
| 571 Rich Hand | .35 |
| 572 Enzo Hernandez | .35 |
| 573 Mike Adams | .35 |
| 574 Bill Parsons | .35 |
| 575 Steve Garvey | 12.00 |
| 576 Scipio Spinks | .35 |
| 577 Mike Sadek | .35 |
| 578 Ralph Houk (Mgr.) | .50 |
| 579 Cecil Upshaw | .35 |
| 580 Jim Spencer | .35 |
| 581 Fred Norman | .35 |
| 582 Bucky Dent (R) | 2.00 |
| 583 Marty Pattin | .35 |
| 584 Ken Rudolph | .35 |
| 585 Merv Rettenmund | .35 |
| 586 Jack Brohamer | .35 |
| 587 Larry Christenson | .35 |
| 588 Hal Lanier | .50 |
| 589 Boots Day | .35 |
| 590 Roger Moret | .35 |
| 591 Sonny Jackson | .35 |
| 592 Ed Bane | .35 |
| 593 Steve Yeager | .35 |
| 594 Leroy Stanton | .35 |
| 595 Steve Blass | .35 |
| 596 Rookie Pitchers: | .50 |
|   Wayne Garland, Fred | |
|   Holdsworth, Dick Pole, | |
|   Mark Littell | |

| NO. PLAYER | NR. MT. |
|---|---|
| 597 Rookie Shortstops: | 1.00 |
|   John Gamble, Pete | |
|   MacKanin, Dave Chalk, | |
|   Manny Trillo | |
| 598 Rookie Outfielders: | 20.00 |
|   Steve Ontiveros, Dave | |
|   Augustine, Ken Griffey, | |
|   Jim Tyrone | |
| 599 Rookie Pitchers | 5.00 |
|   "San Diego"—small type | |
|   Ron Diorio, D. Freisleben, | |
|   F. Riccelli, G. Shanahan | |
| 599 Rookie Pitchers | 2.50 |
|   "San Diego"—large type | |
| 599 Rookie Pitchers | 1.00 |
|   "Washington" | |
|   Ron Diorio, D. Freisleben, | |
|   F. Riccelli, G. Shanahan | |
| 600 Rookie Infielders: | 5.00 |
|   Ron Cash, Jim Cox, Bill | |
|   Madlock, Reggie Sanders | |
| 601 Rookie Outfielders: | 3.00 |
|   Ed Armbrister, Rich Bladt, | |
|   B. Downing, B. McBride | |
| 602 Rookie Pitchers: | .50 |
|   Glenn Abbott, Craig Swan | |
|   R. Henninger, D. Vossler | |
| 603 Rookie Catchers: | .40 |
|   B. Foote, T. Lundstedt, | |
|   C. Moore, S. Robles | |
| 604 Rookie Infielders: | 4.00 |
|   Terry Hughes, John Knox, | |
|   A. Thornton, F. White | |

| NO. PLAYER | NR. MT. |
|---|---|
| 605 Rookie Pitchers: | 3.00 |
|   Vic Albury, Ken Frailing, | |
|   Kevin Kobel, Frank Tanana | |
| 606 Rookie Outfielders: | .50 |
|   Jim Fuller, Wilbur Howard, | |
|   Tommy Smith, Otto Velez | |
| 607 Rookie Shortstops: | .50 |
|   Leo Foster, Dave Rosello, | |
|   T. Heintzelman, F. Taveras | |
| 608 Rookie Pitchers: | 2.50 |
|   Bob Apodaca, Mike Wallace | |
|   D. Baney, J. D'Acquisto | |
| 608 "Apodaca"—error | 2.00 |
|   misspelled "Apodoco" | |
| 609 Rico Petrocelli | .35 |
| 610 Dave Kingman | 1.00 |
| 611 Rich Stelmaszek | .35 |
| 612 Luke Walker | .35 |
| 613 Dan Monzon | .35 |
| 614 Adrian Devine | .35 |
| 615 John Jeter | .35 |
| 616 Larry Gura | .50 |
| 617 Ted Ford | .35 |
| 618 Jim Mason | .35 |
| 619 Mike Anderson | .35 |
| 620 Al Downing | .50 |
| 621 Bernie Carbo | .35 |
| 622 Phil Gagliano | .35 |
| 623 Celerino Sanchez | .35 |
| 624 Bob Miller | .35 |
| 625 Ollie Brown | .35 |
| 626 Pittsburgh Pirates | .75 |
| 627 Carl Taylor | .35 |
| 628 Ivan Murrell | .35 |

| NO. PLAYER | NR. MT. |
|---|---|
| 629 Rusty Staub | .75 |
| 630 Tommie Agee | .50 |
| 631 Steve Barber | .35 |
| 632 George Culver | .35 |
| 633 Dave Hamilton | .35 |
| 634 Eddie Mathews (Mgr.) | 1.00 |
| 635 John Edwards | .35 |
| 636 Dave Goltz | .35 |
| 637 Checklist No. 5 | 1.50 |
| 638 Ken Sanders | .35 |
| 639 Joe Lovitto | .35 |
| 640 Milt Pappas | .50 |
| 641 Chuck Brinkman | .35 |
| 642 Terry Harmon | .35 |
| 643 Los Angeles Dodgers | .75 |
| 644 Wayne Granger | .35 |
| 645 Ken Boswell | .35 |
| 646 George Foster | 1.25 |
| 647 Juan Beniquez | .75 |
| 648 Terry Crowley | .35 |
| 649 Fernando Gonzalez | .35 |
| 650 Mike Epstein | .35 |
| 651 Leron Lee | .35 |
| 652 Gail Hopkins | .35 |
| 653 Bob Stinson | .35 |
| 654 Jesus Alou | .35 |
| 654 Jesus Alou | 6.00 |
|   "outfield" deleted on front | |
| 655 Mike Tyson | .35 |
| 656 Adrian Garrett | .35 |
| 657 Jim Shellenback | .35 |
| 658 Lee Lacy | .35 |
| 659 Joe Lis | .35 |
| 660 Larry Dierker (Exc. .15) | .50 |

## 1974 Topps Traded.... Complete Set of 44 Cards—Value $10.00 (Near Mint)

Topps' first Traded set. Topps issued another in 1976, and beginning in 1981 issued a Traded set every year. The traded set features players who were traded after the main set was printed. This set uses the same numbers as the regular set, followed by a "T".

| NO. PLAYER | NR. MT. |
|---|---|
| 23 T Craig Robinson | .15 |
| 42 T Claude Osteen | .15 |
| 43 T Jim Wynn | .25 |
| 51 T Bobby Heise | .15 |
| 59 T Ross Grimsley | .15 |
| 62 T Bob Locker | .15 |
| 63 T Bill Sudakis | .15 |
| 73 T Mike Marshall | .25 |
| 123 T Nelson Briles | .15 |
| 139 T Aurelio Monteagudo | .15 |
| 151 T Diego Segui | .15 |

| NO. PLAYER | NR. MT. |
|---|---|
| 165 T Willie Davis | .25 |
| 175 T Reggie Cleveland | .15 |
| 182 T Lindy McDaniel | .15 |
| 186 T Fred Scherman | .15 |
| 249 T George Mitterwald | .15 |
| 262 T Ed Kirkpatrick | .15 |
| 269 T Bob Johnson | .15 |
| 270 T Ron Santo | .40 |
| 313 T Barry Lersch | .15 |
| 319 T Randy Hundley | .15 |
| 330 T Juan Marichal | 1.25 |

| NO. PLAYER | NR. MT. |
|---|---|
| 348 T Pete Richert | .15 |
| 373 T John Curtis | .15 |
| 390 T Lou Piniella | .60 |
| 428 T Gary Sutherland | .15 |
| 454 T Kurt Bevacqua | .15 |
| 458 T Jim Ray | .15 |
| 485 T Felipe Alou | .20 |
| 486 T Steve Stone | .15 |
| 496 T Tom Murphy | .15 |
| 516 T Horacio Pina | .15 |
| 534 T Eddie Watt | .15 |

| NO. PLAYER | NR. MT. |
|---|---|
| 538 T Cesar Tovar | .15 |
| 544 T Ron Schueler | .15 |
| 579 T Cecil Upshaw | .15 |
| 585 T Merv Rettenmund | .15 |
| 612 T Luke Walker | .15 |
| 616 T Larry Gura | .20 |
| 618 T Jim Mason | .15 |
| 630 T Tommie Agee | .15 |
| 648 T Terry Crowley | .15 |
| 649 T Fernando Gonzalez | .15 |
| — Traded Checklist | .75 |

# 1975 Topps . . . Complete Set of 660 Cards—Value $850.00 (Near Mint)

Features the rookie cards of Robin Yount, George Brett, Jim Rice, Gary Carter, Fred Lynn and Keith Hernandez. The set was also issued in a mini-size (2¼″ x 3⅛″) which was tested in a section of the country. The mini-size cards are worth 2 to 2½ times more than the regular size cards.

    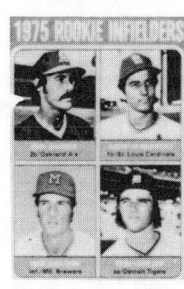

| NO. PLAYER | NR. MT. |
|---|---|
| Highlights: (exc. $5.00) .... | 25.00 |
| Aaron Sets Homer Mark | |
| 2 Highlights: ............. | 3.00 |
| Brock Steals 118 Bases | |
| 3 Highlights: ............. | 3.00 |
| Gibson's 3000th Strikeout | |
| 4 Highlights: ............. | 3.00 |
| Kaline's 3000th Hit | |
| 5 Highlights: ............. | 10.00 |
| Ryan Fans 300—3rd Year | |
| 6 Highlights: ............. | .75 |
| Marshall Hurls 106 Games | |
| 7 Highlights: ............. | 2.50 |
| No Hitters: Nolan Ryan, | |
| Dick Bosman, Steve Busby | |
| 8 Rogelio Moret .......... | .30 |
| 9 Frank Tepedino ........ | .30 |
| 10 Willie Davis .......... | .50 |
| 11 Bill Melton ............. | .30 |
| 12 David Clyde ........... | .30 |
| 13 Gene Locklear ......... | .30 |
| 14 Milt Wilcox............ | .30 |
| 15 Jose Cardenal ........ | .30 |
| 16 Frank Tanana ......... | .75 |
| 17 Dave Concepcion ...... | 1.00 |
| 18 Tigers/R. Houk (Mgr.) .. | 1.25 |
| 19 Jerry Koosman ........ | .75 |
| 20 Thurman Munson ...... | 7.00 |
| 21 Rollie Fingers ......... | 3.50 |
| 22 Dave Cash ............ | .30 |
| 23 Bill Russell .......... | .50 |
| 24 Al Fitzmorris ......... | .30 |
| 25 Lea May ............... | .50 |
| 26 Dave McNally ......... | .50 |
| 27 Ken Reitz ............. | .30 |
| 28 Tom Murphy .......... | .30 |
| 29 Dave Parker........... | 12.00 |
| 30 Bert Blyleven .......... | 2.00 |
| 31 Dave Rader ........... | .30 |
| 32 Reggie Cleveland ...... | .30 |
| 33 Dusty Baker .......... | 1.00 |
| 34 Steve Renko .......... | .30 |
| 35 Ron Santo ............. | .75 |
| 36 Joe Lovitto ........... | .30 |
| 37 Dave Freisleben ....... | .30 |
| 38 Buddy Bell ............ | .75 |
| 39 Andy Thornton ........ | .50 |
| 40 Bill Singer ........... | .30 |
| 41 Cesar Geronimo ....... | .30 |
| 42 Joe Coleman........... | .30 |
| 43 Cleon Jones .......... | .30 |
| 44 Pat Dobson ........... | .30 |
| 45 Joe Rudi .............. | .60 |
| 46 Phillies/D. Ozark (Mgr.) . | 1.25 |
| 47 Tommy John .......... | 1.25 |
| 48 Freddie Patek ......... | .30 |
| 49 Larry Dierker .......... | .30 |
| 50 Brook Robinson........ | 5.00 |
| 51 Bob Forsch .......... | 1.00 |
| 52 Darrell Porter ......... | .50 |
| 53 Dave Giusti ........... | .30 |
| 54 Eric Soderholm ........ | .30 |
| 55 Bobby Bonds ......... | 1.00 |
| 56 Rick Wise ............. | .30 |
| 57 Dave Johnson ......... | .75 |
| 58 Chuck Taylor ......... | .30 |

| NO. PLAYER | NR. MT. |
|---|---|
| 59 Ken Henderson ........ | .30 |
| 60 Fergie Jenkins ........ | 3.00 |
| 61 Dave Winfield .......... | 20.00 |
| 62 Fritz Peterson ......... | .30 |
| 63 Steve Swisher ......... | .30 |
| 64 Dave Chalk ........... | .30 |
| 65 Don Gullett ........... | .30 |
| 66 Willie Horton .......... | .50 |
| 67 Tug McGraw .......... | .60 |
| 68 Ron Blomberg ......... | .30 |
| 69 John Odom ........... | .30 |
| 70 Mike Schmidt ......... | 55.00 |
| 71 Charlie Hough ......... | .40 |
| 72 Royals/J. McKeon (Mgr.) | 1.25 |
| 73 J.R. Richard .......... | .50 |
| 74 Mark Belanger ........ | .50 |
| 75 Ted Simmons ......... | 1.25 |
| 76 Ed Sprague .......... | .30 |
| 77 Richie Zisk............ | .60 |
| 78 Ray Corbin ........... | .30 |
| 79 Gary Matthews ........ | .60 |
| 80 Carlton Fisk........... | 12.00 |
| 81 Ron Reed ............. | .30 |
| 82 Pat Kelly ............. | .30 |
| 83 Jim Merritt ........... | .30 |
| 84 Enzo Hernandez ....... | .30 |
| 85 Bill Bonham .......... | .30 |
| 86 Joe Lis ............... | .30 |
| 87 George Foster ........ | 1.00 |
| 88 Tom Egan ............ | .30 |
| 89 Jim Ray ............. | .30 |
| 90 Rusty Staub .......... | .75 |
| 91 Dick Green ........... | .30 |
| 92 Cecil Upshaw ......... | .30 |
| 93 Dave Lopes .......... | .50 |
| 94 Jim Lonborg .......... | .30 |
| 95 John Mayberry ........ | .50 |
| 96 Mike Cosgrove ........ | .30 |
| 97 Earl Williams .......... | .30 |
| 98 Rich Folkers .......... | .30 |
| 99 Mike Hegan .......... | .30 |
| 100 Willie Stargell ....... | 3.00 |
| 101 Expos/G. Mauch (Mgr.) . | 1.25 |
| 102 Joe Decker .......... | .30 |
| 103 Rick Miller .......... | .30 |
| 104 Bill Madlock ......... | 1.50 |
| 105 Buzz Capra .......... | .30 |
| 106 Mike Hargrove (R) ...... | .75 |
| 107 Jim Barr ............ | .30 |
| 108 Tom Hall ............ | .30 |
| 109 George Hendrick ...... | .50 |
| 110 Wilbur Wood ......... | .40 |
| 111 Wayne Garrett ........ | .30 |
| 112 Larry Hardy .......... | .30 |
| 113 Elliot Maddox ........ | .30 |
| 114 Dick Lange .......... | .30 |
| 115 Joe Ferguson ........ | .30 |
| 116 Lerrin LaGrow ........ | .30 |
| 117 Orioles/E. Weaver (Mgr.) . | 1.25 |
| 118 Mike Anderson ........ | .30 |
| 119 Tommy Helms ........ | .30 |
| 120 Steve Busby ......... | .50 |
| (photo of Fran Healy) | |
| 121 Bill North ............ | .30 |
| 122 Al Hrabosky.......... | .40 |
| 123 Johnny Briggs ........ | .30 |

| NO. PLAYER | NR. MT. |
|---|---|
| 124 Jerry Reuss ............ | .45 |
| 125 Ken Singleton ........ | .45 |
| 126 Checklist No.1 ....... | 1.50 |
| 127 Glenn Borgmann ...... | .30 |
| 128 Bill Lee ................ | .40 |
| 129 Rick Monday ......... | .30 |
| 130 Phil Niekro .......... | 2.50 |
| 131 Toby Harrah ......... | .35 |
| 132 Randy Moffitt ........ | .30 |
| 133 Dan Driessen ........ | .45 |
| 134 Ron Hodges ......... | .30 |
| 135 Charlie Spikes ........ | .30 |
| 136 Jim Mason ........... | .30 |
| 137 Terry Forster ......... | .45 |
| 138 Del Unser ............. | .30 |
| 139 Horacio Pina ......... | .30 |
| 140 Steve Garvey .......... | 7.00 |
| 141 Mickey Stanley ....... | .45 |
| 142 Bob Reynolds ......... | .30 |
| 143 Cliff Johnson ........ | .30 |
| 144 Jim Wohlford ........ | .30 |
| 145 Ken Holtzman ......... | .40 |
| 146 San Diego Padres | |
| J. McNamara (Mgr.) ... | 1.25 |
| 147 Pedro Garcia ........ | .30 |
| 148 Jim Rooker .......... | .30 |
| 149 Tim Foli ............. | .30 |
| 150 Bob Gibson .......... | 4.00 |
| 151 Steve Brye ........... | .30 |
| 152 Mario Guerrero ....... | .30 |
| 153 Rick Reuschel ........ | .75 |
| 154 Mike Lum ............ | .30 |
| 155 Jim Bibby ............ | .30 |
| 156 Dave Kingman........ | 1.00 |
| 157 Pedro Borbon ........ | .30 |
| 158 Jerry Grote .......... | .30 |
| 159 Steve Arlin .......... | .30 |
| 160 Graig Nettles.......... | 1.00 |
| 161 Stan Bahnsen ........ | .30 |
| 162 Willie Montanez ...... | .30 |
| 163 Jim Brewer .......... | .30 |
| 164 Mickey Rivers ........ | .45 |
| 165 Doug Rader .......... | .30 |
| 166 Woodie Fryman ...... | .30 |
| 167 Rich Coggins ........ | .30 |
| 168 Bill Greif ............. | .30 |
| 169 Cookie Rojas ........ | .30 |
| 170 Bert Campaneris ...... | .50 |
| 171 Ed Kirkpatrick ....... | .30 |
| 172 Boston Red Sox ....... | 1.25 |
| D. Johnson (Mgr.) | |
| 173 Steve Rogers ........ | .40 |
| 174 Bake McBride ........ | .30 |
| 175 Don Money .......... | .30 |
| 176 Burt Hooton ......... | .40 |
| 177 Vic Correll .......... | .30 |
| 178 Cesar Tovar ......... | .30 |
| 179 Tom Bradley ......... | .30 |
| 180 Joe Morgan .......... | 6.00 |
| 181 Fred Beene .......... | .30 |
| 182 Don Hahn ........... | .30 |
| 183 Mel Stottlemyre ...... | .45 |
| 184 Jorge Orta ........... | .30 |
| 185 Steve Carlton ........ | 7.50 |
| 186 Willie Crawford ...... | .30 |
| 187 Denny Doyle ......... | .30 |

| NO. PLAYER | NR. MT. |
|---|---|
| 188 Tom Griffin ........... | .30 |
| 189 1951 MVP's: .......... | 1.50 |
| Y. Berra, R. Campanella | |
| 190 1952 MVP': ........... | .75 |
| B. Shantz, Hank Bauer | |
| 191 1953 MVP's: .......... | 1.00 |
| Al Rosen, R. Campanella | |
| 192 1954 MVP's: .......... | 1.50 |
| Yogi Berra, Willie Mays | |
| 193 1955 MVP's: .......... | 1.75 |
| Y. Berra, R. Campanella | |
| 194 1956 MVP's: .......... | 5.00 |
| M. Mantle, D. Newcombe | |
| 195 1957 MVP's: .......... | 7.50 |
| Hank Aaron, M. Mantle | |
| 196 1958 MVP's: .......... | 1.00 |
| J. Jensen, Ernie Banks | |
| 197 1959 MVP's: .......... | 1.25 |
| Nellie Fox, Ernie Banks | |
| 198 1960 MVP's: .......... | 1.00 |
| Roger Maris, Dick Groat | |
| 199 1961 MVP's: .......... | 1.50 |
| F. Robinson, Roger Maris | |
| 200 1962 MVP's: .......... | 5.00 |
| M. Mantle, Maury Wills | |
| 201 1963 MVP's: .......... | 1.00 |
| Elston Howard, S. Koufax | |
| 202 1964 MVP's: .......... | 1.00 |
| Ken Boyer, B. Robinson | |
| 203 1965 MVP's: .......... | 1.25 |
| Zoilo Versalles, W. Mays | |
| 204 1966 MVP's: .......... | 1.50 |
| F. Robinson, Bob Clemente | |
| 205 1967 MVP's: .......... | 1.25 |
| C. Yastrzemski, O. Cepeda | |
| 206 1968 MVP's: .......... | 1.25 |
| D. McLain, Bob Gibson | |
| 207 1969 MVP's: .......... | 1.25 |
| W. McCovey, H. Killebrew | |
| 208 1970 MVP's: .......... | 1.00 |
| Boog Powell, J. Bench | |
| 209 1971 MVP's: .......... | 1.00 |
| Vida Blue, Joe Torre | |
| 210 1972 MVP's: .......... | 1.00 |
| Richie Allen, J. Bench | |
| 211 1973 MVP's: .......... | 5.00 |
| Pete Rose, R. Jackson | |
| 212 1974 MVP's: .......... | 1.00 |
| J. Burroughs, S. Garvey | |
| 213 Oscar Gamble ........ | .35 |
| 214 Harry Parker ......... | .30 |
| 215 Bobby Valentine ...... | .45 |
| 216 San Francisco Giants | |
| Wes Westrum (Mgr.) . | 1.25 |
| 217 Lou Piniella .......... | .60 |
| 218 Jerry Johnson ........ | .30 |
| 219 Ed Herrmann ......... | .30 |
| 220 Don Sutton .......... | 2.50 |
| 221 Aurelio Rodriguez ..... | .30 |
| 222 Dan Spillner ......... | .30 |
| 223 Robin Yount (R) .......| 175.00 |
| 224 Ramon Hernandez ..... | .30 |
| 225 Bob Grich .......... | .45 |
| 226 Bill Campbell ......... | .30 |
| 227 Bob Watson .......... | .40 |
| 228 George Brett (R) .... | 175.00 |

| NO. | PLAYER | NR. MT. |
|---|---|---|
| 229 | Barry Foote | .30 |
| 230 | Jim Hunter | 3.00 |
| 231 | Mike Tyson | .30 |
| 232 | Diego Segui | .30 |
| 233 | Billy Grabarkewitz | .30 |
| 234 | Tom Grieve | .30 |
| 235 | Jack Billingham | .30 |
| 236 | Angels/D. Williams (Mgr.) | 1.25 |
| 237 | Carl Morton | .30 |
| 238 | Dave Duncan | .30 |
| 239 | George Stone | .30 |
| 240 | Garry Maddox | .45 |
| 241 | Dick Tidrow | .30 |
| 242 | Jay Johnstone | .30 |
| 243 | Jim Kaat | 1.00 |
| 244 | Bill Buckner | .65 |
| 245 | Mickey Lolich | .50 |
| 246 | St. Louis Cardinals | 1.25 |
| | Red Schoendienst (Mgr.) | |
| 247 | Enos Cabell | .30 |
| 248 | Randy Jones | .30 |
| 249 | Danny Thompson | .30 |
| 250 | Ken Brett | .30 |
| 251 | Fran Healy | .30 |
| 252 | Fred Scherman | .30 |
| 253 | Jesus Alou | .30 |
| 254 | Mike Torrez | .45 |
| 255 | Dwight Evans | 6.00 |
| 256 | Billy Champion | .30 |
| 257 | Checklist No. 2 | 1.50 |
| 258 | Dave LaRoche | .30 |
| 259 | Len Randle | .30 |
| 260 | Johnny Bench | 12.00 |
| 261 | Andy Hassler | .30 |
| 262 | Rowland Office | .30 |
| 263 | Jim Perry | .30 |
| 264 | John Milner | .30 |
| 265 | Ron Bryant | .30 |
| 266 | Sandy Alomar | .30 |
| 267 | Dick Ruthven | .30 |
| 268 | Hal McRae | .60 |
| 269 | Doug Rau | .30 |
| 270 | Ron Fairly | .30 |
| 271 | Jerry Moses | .30 |
| 272 | Lynn McGlothen | .30 |
| 273 | Steve Braun | .30 |
| 274 | Vincente Romo | .30 |
| 275 | Paul Blair | .30 |
| 276 | Chicago White Sox | 1.25 |
| | Chuck Tanner (Mgr.) | |
| 277 | Frank Taveras | .50 |
| 278 | Paul Lindblad | .30 |
| 279 | Milt May | .30 |
| 280 | Carl Yastrzemski | 10.00 |
| 281 | Jim Slaton | .30 |
| 282 | Jerry Morales | .30 |
| 283 | Steve Foucault | .30 |
| 284 | Ken Griffey | 3.00 |
| 285 | Ellie Rodriguez | .30 |
| 286 | Mike Jorgensen | .30 |
| 287 | Roric Harrison | .30 |
| 288 | Bruce Ellingsen | .30 |
| 289 | Ken Rudolph | .30 |
| 290 | Jon Matlack | .40 |
| 291 | Bill Sudakis | .30 |
| 292 | Ron Schueler | .30 |
| 293 | Dick Sharon | .30 |
| 294 | Geoff Zahn | .30 |
| 295 | Vada Pinson | .50 |
| 296 | Alan Foster | .30 |
| 297 | Craig Kusick | .30 |
| 298 | Johnny Grubb | .30 |
| 299 | Bucky Dent | .60 |
| 300 | Reggie Jackson | 15.00 |
| 301 | Dave Roberts | .30 |
| 302 | Rick Burleson (R) | .75 |
| 303 | Grant Jackson | .30 |
| 304 | Pittsburgh Pirates | .75 |
| | Danny Murtaugh (Mgr.) | |
| 305 | Jim Colborn | .30 |
| 306 | Batting Leaders: | 1.00 |
| | Rod Carew, Ralph Garr | |
| 307 | Home Run Leaders: | 2.50 |
| | Dick Allen, Mike Schmidt | |
| 308 | RBI Leaders: | 1.00 |
| | J. Burroughs, J. Bench | |
| 309 | Stolen Base Leaders: | .75 |
| | Bill North, Lou Brock | |
| 310 | Victory Leaders: | 1.00 |
| | Andy Messersmith, | |
| | Jim Hunter, Fergie | |
| | Jenkins, Phil Niekro | |
| 311 | ERA Leaders: | .75 |
| | Jim Hunter, Buzz Capra | |
| 312 | Strikeout Leaders: | 5.00 |
| | Nolan Ryan, Steve Carlton | |
| 313 | Leading Firemen: | .75 |
| | Mike Marshall, | |
| | Terry Forster | |
| 314 | Buck Martinez | .30 |
| 315 | Don Kessinger | .40 |
| 316 | Jackie Brown | .30 |
| 317 | Joe LaHoud | .30 |
| 318 | Ernie McAnally | .30 |
| 319 | Johnny Oates | .30 |
| 320 | Pete Rose | 14.00 |
| 321 | Rudy May | .30 |
| 322 | Ed Goodson | .30 |
| 323 | Fred Holdsworth | .30 |
| 324 | Ed Kranepool | .45 |
| 325 | Tony Oliva | .75 |
| 326 | Wayne Twitchell | .30 |
| 327 | Jerry Hairston | .30 |
| 328 | Sonny Siebert | .30 |
| 329 | Ted Kubiak | .30 |
| 330 | Mike Marshall | .40 |
| 331 | Cleveland Indians | 1.25 |
| | Frank Robinson (Mgr.) | |
| 332 | Fred Kendall | .30 |
| 333 | Dick Drago | .30 |
| 334 | Greg Gross | .30 |
| 335 | Jim Palmer | 7.00 |
| 336 | Rennie Stennett | .30 |
| 337 | Kevin Kobel | .30 |
| 338 | Rick Stelmaszek | .30 |
| 339 | Jim Fregosi | .40 |
| 340 | Paul Splittorff | .30 |
| 341 | Hal Breeden | .30 |
| 342 | Leroy Stanton | .30 |
| 343 | Danny Frisella | .30 |
| 344 | Ben Oglivie | .40 |
| 345 | Clay Carroll | .30 |
| 346 | Bobby Darwin | .30 |
| 347 | Mike Caldwell | .30 |
| 348 | Tony Muser | .30 |
| 349 | Ray Sadecki | .30 |
| 350 | Bobby Murcer | .75 |
| 351 | Bob Boone | 1.00 |
| 352 | Darold Knowles | .30 |
| 353 | Luis Melendez | .30 |
| 354 | Dick Bosman | .30 |
| 355 | Chris Cannizzaro | .30 |
| 356 | Rico Petrocelli | .40 |
| 357 | Ken Frosch | .30 |
| 358 | Al Bumbry | .30 |
| 359 | Paul Popovich | .30 |
| 360 | George Scott | .30 |
| 361 | Los Angeles Dodgers | 1.25 |
| | Walter Alston (Mgr.) | |
| 362 | Steve Hargan | .30 |
| 363 | Carmen Fanzone | .30 |
| 364 | Doug Bird | .30 |
| 365 | Bob Bailey | .30 |
| 366 | Ken Sanders | .30 |
| 367 | Craig Robinson | .30 |
| 368 | Vic Albury | .30 |
| 369 | Merv Rettenmund | .30 |
| 370 | Tom Seaver | 12.50 |
| 371 | Gates Brown | .30 |
| 372 | John D'Acquisto | .30 |
| 373 | Bill Sharp | .30 |
| 374 | Eddie Watt | .30 |
| 375 | Roy White | .45 |
| 376 | Steve Yeager | .30 |
| 377 | Tom Hilgendorf | .30 |
| 378 | Derrel Thomas | .30 |
| 379 | Bernie Carbo | .30 |
| 380 | Sal Bando | .45 |
| 381 | John Curtis | .30 |
| 382 | Don Baylor | 1.25 |
| 383 | Jim York | .30 |
| 384 | Milwaukee Brewers | .60 |
| | Del Crandall (Mgr.) | |
| 385 | Dock Ellis | .30 |
| 386 | Checklist: No. 3 | 1.50 |
| 387 | Jim Spencer | .30 |
| 388 | Steve Stone | .30 |
| 389 | Tony Solaita | .30 |
| 390 | Ron Cey | 1.00 |
| 391 | Don DeMola | .30 |
| 392 | Bruce Bochte (R) | .60 |
| 393 | Gary Gentry | .30 |
| 394 | Larvell Blanks | .30 |
| 395 | Bud Harrelson | .50 |
| 396 | Fred Norman | .30 |
| 397 | Bill Freehan | .40 |
| 398 | Elias Sosa | .30 |
| 399 | Terry Harmon | .30 |
| 400 | Dick Allen | .75 |
| 401 | Mike Wallace | .30 |
| 402 | Bob Tolan | .30 |
| 403 | Tom Buskey | |
| 404 | Ted Sizemore | .75 |
| 405 | John Montague | .30 |
| 406 | Bob Gallagher | .30 |
| 407 | Herb Washington | .30 |
| 408 | Clyde Wright | .30 |
| 409 | Bob Robertson | .30 |
| 410 | Mike Cueller | .40 |
| 411 | George Mitterwald | .30 |
| 412 | Bill Hands | .30 |
| 413 | Marty Pattin | .30 |
| 414 | Manny Mota | .45 |
| 415 | John Hiller | .30 |
| 416 | Larry Lintz | .30 |
| 417 | Skip Lockwood | .30 |
| 418 | Leo Foster | .30 |
| 419 | Dave Goltz | .30 |
| 420 | Larry Bowa | .60 |
| 421 | Mets/Y. Berra (Mgr.) | .75 |
| 422 | Brian Downing | .75 |
| 423 | Clay Kirby | .30 |
| 424 | John Lowenstein | .30 |
| 425 | Tito Fuentes | .30 |
| 426 | George Medich | .30 |
| 427 | Clarence Gaston | .30 |
| 428 | Dave Hamilton | .30 |
| 429 | Jim Dwyer | .30 |
| 430 | Luis Tiant | .45 |
| 431 | Rod Gilbreath | .30 |
| 432 | Ken Berry | .30 |
| 433 | Larry Demery | .30 |
| 434 | Bob Locker | .30 |
| 435 | Dave Nelson | .30 |
| 436 | Ken Frailing | .30 |
| 437 | Al Cowens (R) | .65 |
| 438 | Don Carrithers | .30 |
| 439 | Ed Brinkman | .30 |
| 440 | Andy Messersmith | .40 |
| 441 | Bobby Heise | .30 |
| 442 | Maximino Leon | .30 |
| 443 | Twins/F. Quilici (Mgr.) | 1.25 |
| 444 | Gene Garber | .30 |
| 445 | Felix Millan | .30 |
| 446 | Bart Johnson | .30 |
| 447 | Terry Crowley | .30 |
| 448 | Frank Duffy | .30 |
| 449 | Charlie Williams | .30 |
| 450 | Willie McCovey | 3.50 |
| 451 | Rick Dempsey | .40 |
| 452 | Angel Mangual | .30 |
| 453 | Claude Osteen | .30 |
| 454 | Doug Griffin | .30 |
| 455 | Don Wilson | .30 |
| 456 | Bob Coluccio | .30 |
| 457 | Mario Mendoza | .30 |
| 458 | Ross Grimsley | .30 |
| 459 | 1974 AL Champs: | .50 |
| | A's over Orioles | |
| 460 | 1974 NL Champs: | .75 |
| | Dodgers over Pirates | |
| 461 | World Series Game 1: | 2.00 |
| | Oakland 3, Los Angeles 2 | |
| 462 | World Series Game 2: | .75 |
| | Los Angeles 3, Oakland 2 | |
| 463 | World Series Game 3: | 1.00 |
| | Oakland 3, Los Angeles 2 | |
| 464 | World Series Game 4: | .75 |
| | Oakland 5, Los Angeles 2 | |
| 465 | World Series Game 5 | .75 |
| | Oakland 3, Los Angeles 2 | |
| 466 | A's Win 3rd World Series | 1.00 |
| 467 | Ed Halicki | .30 |
| 468 | Bobby Mitchell | .30 |
| 469 | Tom Dettore | .30 |
| 470 | Jeff Burroughs | .40 |
| 471 | Bob Stinson | .30 |
| 472 | Bruce Dal Canton | .30 |
| 473 | Ken McMullen | .30 |
| 474 | Luke Walker | .30 |
| 475 | Darrell Evans | .65 |
| 476 | Eduardo Figueroa | .30 |
| 477 | Tom Hutton | .30 |
| 478 | Tom Burgmeier | .30 |
| 479 | Ken Boswell | .30 |
| 480 | Carlos May | .30 |
| 481 | Will McEnaney | .30 |
| 482 | Tom McCraw | .30 |
| 483 | Steve Ontiveros | .30 |
| 484 | Glenn Beckert | .30 |
| 485 | Sparky Lyle | .45 |
| 486 | Ray Fosse | .30 |
| 487 | Astros/P. Gomez (Mgr.) | .75 |
| 488 | Bill Travers | .30 |
| 489 | Cecil Cooper | 1.50 |
| 490 | Reggie Smith | .40 |
| 491 | Doyle Alexander | .30 |
| 492 | Rich Hebner | .30 |
| 493 | Don Stanhouse | .30 |
| 494 | Pete LaCock | .30 |
| 495 | Nelson Briles | .30 |
| 496 | Pepe Frias | .30 |
| 497 | Jim Nettles | .30 |
| 498 | Al Downing | .30 |
| 499 | Marty Perez | .30 |
| 500 | Nolan Ryan | 45.00 |
| 501 | Bill Robinson | .30 |
| 502 | Pat Bourque | .30 |
| 503 | Fred Stanley | .30 |
| 504 | Buddy Bradford | .30 |
| 505 | Chris Speier | .30 |
| 506 | Leron Lee | .30 |
| 507 | Tom Carroll | .30 |
| 508 | Bob Hansen | .30 |
| 509 | Dave Hilton | .30 |
| 510 | Vida Blue | .45 |
| 511 | Rangers/B. Martin (Mgr.) | 1.25 |
| 512 | Larry Milbourne | .30 |
| 513 | Dick Pole | .30 |
| 514 | Jose Cruz | .60 |
| 515 | Manny Sanguillen | .30 |
| 516 | Don Hood | .30 |
| 517 | Checklist: No. 4 | 1.50 |
| 518 | Leo Cardenas | .30 |
| 519 | Jim Todd | .30 |
| 520 | Amos Otis | .50 |
| 521 | Dennis Blair | .30 |
| 522 | Gary Sutherland | .30 |
| 523 | Tom Paciorek | .30 |
| 524 | John Doherty | .30 |
| 525 | Tom House | .30 |
| 526 | Larry Hisle | .30 |
| 527 | Mac Scarce | .30 |
| 528 | Eddie Leon | .30 |
| 529 | Gary Thomasson | .30 |
| 530 | Gaylord Perry | 2.50 |
| 531 | Cincinnati Reds | .75 |
| | Sparky Anderson (Mgr.) | |
| 532 | Gorman Thomas | .60 |
| 533 | Rudy Meoli | .30 |
| 534 | Alex Johnson | .30 |
| 535 | Gene Tenace | .30 |
| 536 | Bob Moose | .30 |
| 537 | Tommy Harper | .30 |
| 538 | Duffy Dyer | .30 |
| 539 | Jesse Jefferson | .30 |
| 540 | Lou Brock | 4.00 |

| NO. | PLAYER | NR. MT. |
|-----|--------|---------|
| 541 | Roger Metzger | .30 |
| 542 | Pete Broberg | .30 |
| 543 | Larry Biittner | .30 |
| 544 | Steve Mingori | .30 |
| 545 | Billy Williams | 3.00 |
| 546 | John Knox | .30 |
| 547 | Von Joshua | .30 |
| 548 | Charlie Sands | .30 |
| 549 | Bill Butler | .30 |
| 550 | Ralph Garr | .30 |
| 551 | Larry Christenson | .30 |
| 552 | Jack Brohamer | .30 |
| 553 | John Boccabella | .30 |
| 554 | Rich Gossage | 1.50 |
| 555 | Al Oliver | .75 |
| 556 | Tim Johnson | .30 |
| 557 | Larry Gura | .30 |
| 558 | Dave Roberts | .30 |
| 559 | Bob Montgomery | .30 |
| 560 | Tony Perez | 2.00 |
| 561 | A's/Alvin Dark (Mgr.) | .60 |
| 562 | Gary Nolan | .30 |
| 563 | Wilbur Howard | .30 |
| 564 | Tommy Davis | .40 |
| 565 | Joe Torre | .75 |
| 566 | Ray Burris | .30 |
| 567 | Jim Sundberg (R) | .75 |
| 568 | Dale Murray | .30 |
| 569 | Frank White | .75 |
| 570 | Jim Wynn | .40 |
| 571 | Dave Lemanczyk | .30 |
| 572 | Roger Nelson | .30 |
| 573 | Orlando Pena | .30 |
| 574 | Tony Taylor | .30 |
| 575 | Gene Clines | .30 |
| 576 | Phil Roof | .30 |
| 577 | John Morris | .30 |
| 578 | Dave Tomlin | .30 |

| NO. | PLAYER | NR. MT. |
|-----|--------|---------|
| 579 | Skip Pitlock | .30 |
| 580 | Frank Robinson | 4.00 |
| 581 | Darrel Chaney | .30 |
| 582 | Eduardo Rodriguez | .30 |
| 583 | Andy Etchebarren | .30 |
| 584 | Mike Garman | .30 |
| 585 | Chris Chambliss | .50 |
| 586 | Tim McCarver | .75 |
| 587 | Chris Ward | .30 |
| 588 | Rick Auerbach | .30 |
| 589 | Braves/C. King (Mgr.) | 1.25 |
| 590 | Cesar Cedeno | .65 |
| 591 | Glenn Abbott | .30 |
| 592 | Balor Moore | .30 |
| 593 | Gene Lamont | .30 |
| 594 | Jim Fuller | .30 |
| 595 | Joe Niekro | .75 |
| 596 | Ollie Brown | .30 |
| 597 | Winston Llenas | .30 |
| 598 | Bruce Kison | .30 |
| 599 | Nate Colbert | .30 |
| 600 | Rod Carew | 10.00 |
| 601 | Juan Beniquez | .30 |
| 602 | John Vukovich | .30 |
| 603 | Lew Krausse | .30 |
| 604 | Oscar Zamora | .30 |
| 605 | John Ellis | .30 |
| 606 | Bruce Miller | .30 |
| 607 | Jim Holt | .30 |
| 608 | Gene Michael | .30 |
| 609 | Ellie Hendricks | .30 |
| 610 | Ron Hunt | .30 |
| 611 | Yankees/B. Virdon (Mgr.) | 1.25 |
| 612 | Terry Hughes | .30 |
| 613 | Bill Parsons | .30 |
| 614 | Rookie Pitchers: | .45 |
|     | Jack Kucek, Dyar Miller, | |
|     | Paul Siebert, Vern Ruhle | |

| NO. | PLAYER | NR. MT. |
|-----|--------|---------|
| 615 | Rookie Pitchers: | 1.00 |
|     | Dennis Leonard, Tom | |
|     | Underwood, Hank Webb, | |
|     | Pat Darcy | |
| 616 | Rookie Outfielders | 30.00 |
|     | Jim Rice, D. Augustine, | |
|     | Pepe Mangual, J. Scott | |
| 617 | Rookie Infielders: | 2.00 |
|     | Mike Cubbage, Reggie | |
|     | Sanders, Manny Trillo, | |
|     | Doug DeCinces | |
| 618 | Rookie Pitchers: | 2.00 |
|     | Tom Johnson, Jamie | |
|     | Easterly, Scott McGregor, | |
|     | Rick Rhoden | |
| 619 | Rookie Outfielders: | .40 |
|     | Benny Ayala, Nyls Nyman, | |
|     | Tommy Smith, Jerry Turner | |
| 620 | Rookie Catchers/OF's | 35.00 |
|     | Gary Carter, Marc Hill, | |
|     | Danny Meyer, Leon Roberts | |
| 621 | Rookie Pitchers: | .75 |
|     | John Denny, Rawly | |
|     | Eastwick, Jim Kern, | |
|     | Juan Veintidos | |
| 622 | Rookie Outfielders: | 12.00 |
|     | Ed Armbrister, Fred Lynn, | |
|     | T. Whitfield, Tom Poquette | |
| 623 | Rookie Infielders: | 24.00 |
|     | Phil Garner, Bob Sheldon, | |
|     | K. Hernandez, T. Veryzer | |
| 624 | Rookie Pitchers: | .40 |
|     | Doug Konieczny, Gary | |
|     | Lavelle, Jim Otten, | |
|     | Eddie Solomon | |
| 625 | Boog Powell | .50 |
| 626 | Larry Haney | .30 |
|     | (Photo of Dave Duncan) | |

| NO. | PLAYER | NR. MT. |
|-----|--------|---------|
| 627 | Tom Walker | .30 |
| 628 | Ron LeFlore (R) | .60 |
| 629 | Joe Hoerner | .30 |
| 630 | Greg Luzinski | .50 |
| 631 | Lee Lacy | .30 |
| 632 | Morris Nettles | .30 |
| 633 | Paul Casanova | .30 |
| 634 | Cy Acosta | .30 |
| 635 | Chuck Dobson | .30 |
| 636 | Charlie Moore | .30 |
| 637 | Ted Martinez | .30 |
| 638 | Cubs/J. Marshall (Mgr.) | 1.25 |
| 639 | Steve Kline | .30 |
| 640 | Harmon Killebrew | 4.00 |
| 641 | Jim Northrup | .30 |
| 642 | Mike Phillips | .30 |
| 643 | Brent Strom | .30 |
| 644 | Bill Fahey | .30 |
| 645 | Danny Cater | .30 |
| 646 | Checklist No. 5 | 1.00 |
| 647 | Claudell Washington | 2.00 |
| 648 | Dave Pagan | .30 |
| 649 | Jack Heidemann | .30 |
| 650 | Dave May | .30 |
| 651 | John Morlan | .30 |
| 652 | Lindy McDaniel | .30 |
| 653 | Lee Richards | .30 |
| 654 | Jerry Terrell | .30 |
| 655 | Rico Carty | .50 |
| 656 | Bill Plummer | .30 |
| 657 | Bob Oliver | .30 |
| 658 | Vic Harris | .30 |
| 659 | Bob Apodaca | .30 |
| 660 | Hank Aaron | 20.00 |

## 1976 Topps . . . Complete Set of 660 Cards—Value-$400.00 (Near Mint)

Features the rookie card of Ron Guidry. This set includes the only card ever issued for the Joe Garagiola and Bazooka "Bubble Gum Blowing Champ". Topps added a 44-card Traded set later in the season.

| NO. | PLAYER | NR. MT. |
|-----|--------|---------|
| 1 | Record—Aaron (Exc. $3.50) | 13.00 |
|   | Most RBI's—2,262 | |
| 2 | Record—Bonds | .60 |
|   | Most Lead-Off Homers—32; | |
|   | Most Seasons of 30 HR's; | |
|   | and 30 Stolen Bases | |
| 3 | Record—Lolich | .40 |
|   | Most Strikeouts | |
|   | Lefthander—2,679 | |
| 4 | Record—Lopes | .40 |
|   | Most Consecutive Steal | |
|   | Attempts—38 | |
| 5 | Record—Seaver | 2.50 |
|   | Most Consecutive Seasons | |
|   | of 200 Strikeouts—8 | |
| 6 | Record—Stennett | .40 |
|   | Most Hits in a Nine | |
|   | Inning Game—7 | |
| 7 | Jim Umbarger | .20 |
| 8 | Tito Fuentes | .20 |

| NO. | PLAYER | NR. MT. |
|-----|--------|---------|
| 9 | Paul Lindblad | .20 |
| 10 | Lou Brock | 4.00 |
| 11 | Jim Hughes | .20 |
| 12 | Richie Zisk | .30 |
| 13 | Johnny Wockenfuss | .20 |
| 14 | Gene Garber | .20 |
| 15 | George Scott | .25 |
| 16 | Bob Apodaca | .20 |
| 17 | New York Yankees | 1.00 |
| 18 | Dale Murray | .20 |
| 19 | George Brett | 45.00 |
| 20 | Bob Watson | .20 |
| 21 | Dave LaRoche | .20 |
| 22 | Bill Russell | .20 |
| 23 | Brian Downing | .50 |
| 24 | Cesar Geronimo | .20 |
| 25 | Mick Torrez | .20 |
| 26 | Andy Thornton | .30 |
| 27 | Ed Figueroa | .20 |
| 28 | Dusty Baker | .35 |

| NO. | PLAYER | NR. MT. |
|-----|--------|---------|
| 29 | Rick Burleson | .30 |
| 30 | John Montefusco (R) | .35 |
| 31 | Len Randle | .20 |
| 32 | Danny Frisella | .20 |
| 33 | Bill North | .20 |
| 34 | Mike Garman | .20 |
| 35 | Tony Oliva | .75 |
| 36 | Frank Taveras | .20 |
| 37 | John Hiller | .20 |
| 38 | Garry Maddox | .20 |
| 39 | Pete Broberg | .20 |
| 40 | Dave Kingman | .75 |
| 41 | Tippy Martinez (R) | .35 |
| 42 | Barry Foote | .20 |
| 43 | Paul Splittorff | .30 |
| 44 | Doug Rader | .20 |
| 45 | Boog Powell | .40 |
| 46 | Los Angeles Dodgers | 1.00 |
| 47 | Jesse Jefferson | .20 |
| 48 | Dave Concepcion | .75 |

| NO. | PLAYER | NR. MT. |
|-----|--------|---------|
| 49 | Dave Duncan | .20 |
| 50 | F. Lynn | 2.00 |
| 51 | Ray Buris | .20 |
| 52 | Dave Chalk | .20 |
| 53 | Mike Beard | .20 |
| 54 | Dave Rader | .20 |
| 55 | Gaylord Perry | 2.00 |
| 56 | Bob Toaln | .20 |
| 57 | Phil Garner | .25 |
| 58 | Ron Reed | .20 |
| 59 | Larry Hisle | .20 |
| 60 | Jerry Reuss | .25 |
| 61 | Ron LeFlore | .25 |
| 62 | Johnny Oates | .20 |
| 63 | Bobby Darwin | .20 |
| 64 | Jerry Koosman | .30 |
| 65 | Chris Chambliss | .30 |
| 66 | Father & Son: | .40 |
|   | Gus Bell | |
|   | Buddy Bell | |

| NO. | PLAYER | NR. MT. |
|---|---|---|
| 67 | Father & Son: Ray Boone, Bob Boone | .25 |
| 68 | Father & Son: Joe Coleman, Joe Coleman, Jr. | .25 |
| 69 | Father & Son: Jim Hegan, Mike Hegan | .25 |
| 70 | Father & Son: Roy Smalley, Roy Smalley Jr. | .25 |
| 71 | Steve Rogers | .35 |
| 72 | Hal McRae | .50 |
| 73 | Baltimore Orioles | .75 |
| 74 | Oscar Gamble | .25 |
| 75 | Larry Dierker | .20 |
| 76 | Willie Crawford | .20 |
| 77 | Pedro Borbon | .20 |
| 78 | Cecil Cooper | 1.00 |
| 79 | Jerry Morales | .20 |
| 80 | Jim Kaat | .75 |
| 81 | Darrell Evans | .50 |
| 82 | Von Joshua | .20 |
| 83 | Jim Spencer | .20 |
| 84 | Brent Strom | .20 |
| 85 | Mickey Rivers | .30 |
| 86 | Mike Tyson | .20 |
| 87 | Tom Burgmeier | .20 |
| 88 | Duffy Dyer | .20 |
| 89 | Vern Ruhle | .20 |
| 90 | Sal Bando | .30 |
| 91 | Jim Hutton | .20 |
| 92 | Eduardo Rodriguez | .20 |
| 93 | Mike Phillips | .20 |
| 94 | Jim Dwyer | .20 |
| 95 | Brooks Robinson | 4.00 |
| 96 | Doug Bird | .20 |
| 97 | Wilbur Howard | .20 |
| 98 | Dennis Eckersley (R) | 35.00 |
| 99 | Lee Lacy | .25 |
| 100 | Jim Hunter | 2.50 |
| 101 | Pete LaCock | .20 |
| 102 | Jim Willoughby | .20 |
| 103 | Biff Pocoroba | .20 |
| 104 | Cincinnati Reds | 1.00 |
| 105 | Gary Lavelle | .20 |
| 106 | Tom Grieve | .20 |
| 107 | Dave Roberts | .20 |
| 108 | Don Kirkwood | .20 |
| 109 | Larry Lintz | .20 |
| 110 | Carlos May | .20 |
| 111 | Danny Thompson | .20 |
| 112 | Kent Tekulve (R) | .75 |
| 113 | Gary Sutherland | .20 |
| 114 | Jay Johstone | .20 |
| 115 | Ken Holtzman | .20 |
| 116 | Charlie Moore | .20 |
| 117 | Mike Jorgensen | .20 |
| 118 | Boston Red Sox | 1.00 |
| 119 | Checklist No. 1 | 1.50 |
| 120 | Rusty Staub | .35 |
| 121 | Tony Solaita | .20 |
| 122 | Mike Cosgrove | .20 |
| 123 | Walt Williams | .20 |
| 124 | Doug Rau | .20 |
| 125 | Don Baylor | .75 |
| 126 | Tom Dettore | .20 |
| 127 | Larvell Blanks | .20 |
| 128 | Ken Griffey | .75 |
| 129 | Andy Etchebarren | .20 |
| 130 | Luis Tiant | .35 |
| 131 | Bill Stein | .20 |
| 132 | Don Hood | .20 |
| 133 | Gary Matthews | .30 |
| 134 | Mike Ivie | .20 |
| 135 | Bake McBride | .20 |
| 136 | Dave Goltz | .20 |
| 137 | Bill Robinson | .20 |
| 138 | Lerrin LaGrow | .20 |
| 139 | Gorman Thomas | .50 |
| 140 | Vida Blue | .30 |
| 141 | Larry Parrish (R) | 1.25 |
| 142 | Dick Drago | .20 |
| 143 | Jerry Grote | .20 |
| 144 | Al Fitzmorris | .20 |
| 145 | Larry Bowa | .50 |
| 146 | George Medich | .20 |
| 147 | Houston Astros | .75 |
| 148 | Stan Thomas | .20 |
| 149 | Tommy Davis | .30 |
| 150 | Steve Garvey | 5.00 |
| 151 | Bill Bonham | .20 |
| 152 | Leroy Stanton | .20 |
| 153 | Buzz Capra | .20 |
| 154 | Bucky Dent | .50 |
| 155 | Jack Billingham | .20 |
| 156 | Rico Carty | .30 |
| 157 | Mike Caldwell | .20 |
| 158 | Ken Reitz | .20 |
| 159 | Jerry Terrell | .20 |
| 160 | Dave Winfield | 11.00 |
| 161 | Bruce Kison | .20 |
| 162 | Jack Pierce | .20 |
| 163 | Jim Staton | .20 |
| 164 | Pepe Mangual | .20 |
| 165 | Gene Tenace | .20 |
| 166 | Skip Lockwood | .20 |
| 167 | Freddie Patek | .20 |
| 168 | Tom Hilgendorf | .20 |
| 169 | Graig Nettles | 1.00 |
| 170 | Rick Wise | .30 |
| 171 | Greg Gross | .20 |
| 172 | Texas Rangers | .75 |
| 173 | Steve Swisher | .20 |
| 174 | Charlie Hough | .30 |
| 175 | Ken Singleton | .30 |
| 176 | Dick Lange | .20 |
| 177 | Marty Perez | .20 |
| 178 | Tom Buskey | .20 |
| 179 | George Foster | 1.00 |
| 180 | Rich Gossage | 1.25 |
| 181 | Willie Montanez | .20 |
| 182 | Harry Rasmussen | .20 |
| 183 | Steve Braun | .20 |
| 184 | Bill Greif | .20 |
| 185 | Dave Parker | 6.00 |
| 186 | Tom Walker | .20 |
| 187 | Pedro Garcia | .20 |
| 188 | Fred Scherman | .20 |
| 189 | Claudell Washington | .50 |
| 190 | Jon Matlack | .25 |
| 191 | NL Batting Leaders: Ted Simmons, Bill Madlock, Manny Sanguillen | .50 |
| 192 | AL Batting Leaders: Fred Lynn, Rod Carew, Thurman Munson | 1.50 |
| 193 | NL Home Run Leaders: Mike Schmidt, Greg Luzinski, Dave Kingman | 1.25 |
| 194 | AL Home Run Leaders: John Mayberry, Reggie Jackson, George Scott | 1.00 |
| 195 | NL RBI Leaders: Greg Luzinski, Johnny Bench, Tony Perez | 1.00 |
| 196 | AL RBI Leaders: John Mayberry, George Scott, Fred Lynn | .75 |
| 197 | NL Stolen Base Leaders: Dave Lopes, Lou Brock, Joe Morgan | 1.00 |
| 198 | AL Stolen Base Leaders: Mickey Rivers, Claudell Washington, Amos Otis | .75 |
| 199 | NL Victory Leaders: Tom Seaver, Randy Jones, Andy Messersmith | 1.00 |
| 200 | AL Victory Leaders: Jim Palmer, Jim Hunter, Vida Blue | 1.00 |
| 201 | NL ERA Leaders: Randy Jones, Andy Messersmith, Tom Seaver | .75 |
| 202 | AL ERA Leaders: Jim Hunter, Dennis Eckersley, Jim Palmer | 2.50 |
| 203 | NL Strikeout Leaders: John Montefusco, Andy Messersmith, Tom Seaver | .75 |
| 204 | AL Strikeout Leaders: Frank Tanana, Gaylord Perry, Bert Blyleven | .75 |
| 205 | Leading Firemen: Al Hrabosky, Rich Gossage | .75 |
| 206 | Manny Trillo | .30 |
| 207 | Andy Hassler | .20 |
| 208 | Mike Lum | .20 |
| 209 | Alan Ashby | .30 |
| 210 | Lee May | .30 |
| 211 | Clay Carroll | .20 |
| 212 | Pat Kelly | .20 |
| 213 | Dave Heaverlo | .20 |
| 214 | Eric Soderholm | .20 |
| 215 | Reggie Smith | .35 |
| 216 | Montreal Expos | .75 |
| 217 | Dave Freisleben | .20 |
| 218 | John Knox | .20 |
| 219 | Tom Murphy | .20 |
| 220 | Manny Sanguillen | .30 |
| 221 | Jim Todd | .20 |
| 222 | Wayne Garrett | .20 |
| 223 | Ollie Brown | .20 |
| 224 | Jim York | .20 |
| 225 | Roy White | .30 |
| 226 | Jim Sundberg | .25 |
| 227 | Oscar Zamora | .20 |
| 228 | John Hale | .20 |
| 229 | Jerry Remy (R) | .30 |
| 230 | Carl Yastrzemski | 8.00 |
| 231 | Tom House | .20 |
| 232 | Frank Duffy | .20 |
| 233 | Grant Jackson | .20 |
| 234 | Mike Sadek | .20 |
| 235 | Bert Blyleven | 1.25 |
| 236 | Kansas City Royals | .75 |
| 237 | Dave Hamilton | .20 |
| 238 | Larry Biittner | .20 |
| 239 | John Curtis | .20 |
| 240 | Pete Rose | 15.00 |
| 241 | Hector Torres | .20 |
| 242 | Dan Meyer | .20 |
| 243 | Jim Rooker | .20 |
| 244 | Bill Sharp | .20 |
| 245 | Felix Millan | .20 |
| 246 | Cesar Tovar | .20 |
| 247 | Terry Harmon | .20 |
| 248 | Dick Tidrow | .20 |
| 249 | Cliff Johnson | .20 |
| 250 | Fergie Jenkins | 1.00 |
| 251 | Rick Monday | .30 |
| 252 | Tim Nordbrook | .20 |
| 253 | Bill Buckner | .50 |
| 254 | Rudy Meoli | .20 |
| 255 | Fritz Peterson | .20 |
| 256 | Rowland Office | .20 |
| 257 | Ross Grimsley | .20 |
| 258 | Nyls Nyman | .20 |
| 259 | Darrel Chaney | .20 |
| 260 | Steve Busby | .30 |
| 261 | Gary Thomasson | .50 |
| 262 | Checklist No. 2 | 1.00 |
| 263 | Lyman Bostock (R) | .50 |
| 264 | Steve Renko | .20 |
| 265 | Willie Davis | .30 |
| 266 | Alan Foster | .20 |
| 267 | Aurelio Rodriguez | .20 |
| 268 | Del Unser | .20 |
| 269 | Rick Austin | .20 |
| 270 | Willie Stargell | 3.00 |
| 271 | Jim Lonborg | .20 |
| 272 | Rick Dempsey | .25 |
| 273 | Joe Niekro | .30 |
| 274 | Tommy Harper | .20 |
| 275 | Rick Manning (R) | .30 |
| 276 | Mickey Scott | .20 |
| 277 | Chicago Cubs | .75 |
| 278 | Bernie Carbo | .20 |
| 279 | Roy Howell | .20 |
| 280 | Burt Hooton | .30 |
| 281 | Dave May | .20 |
| 282 | Dan Osborn | .20 |
| 283 | Merv Rettenmund | .20 |
| 284 | Steve Ontiveros | .20 |
| 285 | Mike Cuellar | .25 |
| 286 | Jim Wohlford | .20 |
| 287 | Pete Mackanin | .20 |
| 288 | Bill Campbell | .20 |
| 289 | Enzo Hernandez | .20 |
| 290 | Ted Simmons | .75 |
| 291 | Ken Sanders | .20 |
| 292 | Leon Roberts | .20 |
| 293 | Bill Castro | .20 |
| 294 | Ed Kirkpatrick | .20 |
| 295 | Dave Cash | .20 |
| 296 | Pat Dobson | .20 |
| 297 | Roger Metzger | .20 |
| 298 | Dick Bosman | .20 |
| 299 | Champ Summers | .20 |
| 300 | Johnny Bench | 10.00 |
| 301 | Jackie Brown | .20 |
| 302 | Rick Miller | .20 |
| 303 | Steve Foucault | .20 |
| 304 | California Angels | .75 |
| 305 | Andy Messersmith | .30 |
| 306 | Rod Gilbreath | .20 |
| 307 | Al Bumbry | .20 |
| 308 | Jim Barr | .20 |
| 309 | Bill Melton | .20 |
| 310 | Randy Jones | .30 |
| 311 | Cookie Rojas | .20 |
| 312 | Don Carrithers | .20 |
| 313 | Dan Ford (R) | .35 |
| 314 | Ed Kranepool | .30 |
| 315 | Al Hrabosky | .20 |
| 316 | Robin Yount | 45.00 |
| 317 | John Candelaria (R) | 3.00 |
| 318 | Bob Boone | 1.00 |
| 319 | Larry Gura | .20 |
| 320 | Willie Horton | .30 |
| 321 | Jose Cruz | .40 |
| 322 | Glenn Abbott | .20 |
| 323 | Rob Sperring | .20 |
| 324 | Jim Bibby | .20 |
| 325 | Tony Perez | 1.50 |
| 326 | Dick Pole | .20 |
| 327 | Dave Moates | .20 |
| 328 | Carl Morton | .20 |
| 329 | Joe Ferguson | .20 |
| 330 | Nolan Ryan | 35.00 |
| 331 | San Diego Padres | .75 |
| 332 | Charlie Williams | .20 |
| 333 | Bob Coluccio | .20 |
| 334 | Dennis Leonard | .25 |
| 335 | Bob Grich | .25 |
| 336 | Vic Albury | .20 |
| 337 | Bud Harrelson | .20 |
| 338 | Bob Bailey | .20 |
| 339 | John Denny | .35 |
| 340 | Jim Rice | 7.00 |
| 341 | All-Time 1B: Lou Gehrig | 3.00 |
| 342 | All-Time 2B: Rogers Hornsby | 2.00 |
| 343 | All-Time 3B: Pie Traynor | 1.00 |
| 344 | All-Time SS: Honus Wagner | 2.00 |
| 345 | All-Time OF: Babe Ruth | 7.00 |
| 346 | All-Time OF: Ty Cobb | 4.00 |
| 347 | All-Time OF: Ted Williams | 4.00 |
| 348 | All-Time Catcher: Mickey Cochrane | 1.00 |
| 349 | All-Time Pitcher (Right) Walter Johnson | 1.50 |
| 350 | All-Time Pitcher (Left) Lefty Grove | .75 |
| 351 | Randy Hundley | .20 |
| 352 | Dave Giusti | .20 |
| 353 | Sixto Lezcano (R) | .40 |
| 354 | Ron Blomberg | .20 |
| 355 | Steve Carlton | 6.00 |
| 356 | Ted Martinez | .20 |
| 357 | Ken Forsch | .20 |
| 358 | Buddy Bell | .50 |
| 359 | Rick Reuschel | .75 |
| 360 | Jeff Burroughs | .20 |

| NO. | PLAYER | NR. MT. |
|---|---|---|
| 361 | Detroit Tigers | .75 |
| 362 | Will McEnaney | .20 |
| 363 | Dave Collins (R) | .75 |
| 364 | Elias Sosa | .20 |
| 365 | Carlton Fisk | 9.00 |
| 366 | Bobby Valentine | .30 |
| 367 | Bruce Miller | .20 |
| 368 | Wilbur Wood | .20 |
| 369 | Frank White | .35 |
| 370 | Ron Cey | .75 |
| 371 | Ellie Hendricks | .20 |
| 372 | Rick Baldwin | .20 |
| 373 | Johnny Briggs | .20 |
| 374 | Dan Warthen | .20 |
| 375 | Ron Fairly | .20 |
| 376 | Rich Hebner | .20 |
| 377 | Mike Hegan | .20 |
| 378 | Steve Stone | .20 |
| 379 | Ken Boswell | .20 |
| 380 | Bobby Bonds | .75 |
| 381 | Denny Doyle | .20 |
| 382 | Matt Alexander | .20 |
| 383 | John Ellis | .20 |
| 384 | Philadelphia Phillies | .75 |
| 385 | Mickey Lolich | .35 |
| 386 | Ed Goodson | .20 |
| 387 | Mike Miley | .20 |
| 388 | Stan Perzanowski | .20 |
| 389 | Glenn Adams | .20 |
| 390 | Don Gullett | .20 |
| 391 | Jerry Hairston | .20 |
| 392 | Checklist No. 3 | 1.00 |
| 393 | Paul Mitchell | .20 |
| 394 | Fran Healy | .20 |
| 395 | Jim Wynn | .25 |
| 396 | Bill Lee | .20 |
| 397 | Tim Foli | .20 |
| 398 | Dave Tomlin | .20 |
| 399 | Luis Melendez | .20 |
| 400 | Rod Carew | 7.00 |
| 401 | Ken Brett | .20 |
| 402 | Don Money | .20 |
| 403 | Geoff Zahn | .20 |
| 404 | Enos Cabell | .20 |
| 405 | Rollie Fingers | 2.50 |
| 406 | Ed Herrmann | .20 |
| 407 | Tom Underwood | .20 |
| 408 | Charlie Spikes | .20 |
| 409 | Dave Lemanczyk | .20 |
| 410 | Ralph Garr | .20 |
| 411 | Bill Singer | .20 |
| 412 | Toby Harrah | .30 |
| 413 | Pete Varney | .20 |
| 414 | Wayne Garland | .20 |
| 415 | Vada Pinson | .30 |
| 416 | Tommy John | 1.00 |
| 417 | Gene Clines | .20 |
| 418 | Jose Morales | .20 |
| 419 | Reggie Cleveland | .20 |
| 420 | Joe Morgan | 4.00 |
| 421 | Oakland A's | .40 |
| 422 | Johnny Grubb | .20 |
| 423 | Ed Halicki | .20 |
| 424 | Phil Roof | .20 |
| 425 | Rennie Stennett | .20 |
| 426 | Bob Forsch | .30 |
| 427 | Kurt Bevacqua | .20 |
| 428 | Jim Crawford | .20 |
| 429 | Fred Stanley | .20 |
| 430 | Jose Cardenal | .20 |
| 431 | Dick Ruthven | .20 |
| 432 | Tom Veryzer | .20 |
| 433 | Rick Waits | .20 |
| 434 | Morris Nettles | .20 |
| 435 | Phil Niekro | 2.00 |
| 436 | Bill Fahey | .20 |
| 437 | Terry Forster | .20 |
| 438 | Doug DeCinces | .60 |
| 439 | Rick Rhoden | .50 |
| 440 | John Mayberry | .30 |
| 441 | Gary Carter | 8.00 |
| 442 | Hank Webb | .20 |

| NO. | PLAYER | NR. MT. |
|---|---|---|
| 443 | S.F. Giants | .75 |
| 444 | Gary Nolan | .20 |
| 445 | Rico Petrocelli | .20 |
| 446 | Larry Haney | .20 |
| 447 | Gene Locklear | .20 |
| 448 | Tom Johnson | .20 |
| 449 | Bob Robertson | .20 |
| 450 | Jim Palmer | 6.00 |
| 451 | Buddy Bradford | .20 |
| 452 | Tom Hausman | .20 |
| 453 | Lou Piniella | .50 |
| 454 | Tom Griffin | .20 |
| 455 | Dick Allen | .40 |
| 456 | Joe Coleman | .20 |
| 457 | Ed Crosby | .20 |
| 458 | Earl Williams | .20 |
| 459 | Jim Brewer | .20 |
| 460 | Cesar Cedeno | .30 |
| 461 | Championships: | .50 |
|  | Reds Sweep Bucs, | |
|  | Bosox Surprise A's | |
| 462 | World Series: | .50 |
|  | Reds Champs! | |
| 463 | Steve Hargan | .20 |
| 464 | Ken Henderson | .20 |
| 465 | Mike Marshall | .30 |
| 466 | Bob Stinson | .20 |
| 467 | Woodie Fryman | .20 |
| 468 | Jesus Alou | .20 |
| 469 | Rawly Eastwick | .20 |
| 470 | Bobby Murcer | .40 |
| 471 | Jim Burton | .20 |
| 472 | Bob Davis | .20 |
| 473 | Paul Blair | .20 |
| 474 | Ray Corbin | .20 |
| 475 | Joe Rudi | .30 |
| 476 | Bob Moose | .20 |
| 477 | Cleveland Indians | .75 |
| 478 | Lynn McGlothen | .20 |
| 479 | Bobby Mitchell | .20 |
| 480 | Mike Schmidt | 30.00 |
| 481 | Rudy May | .20 |
| 482 | Tim Hosley | .20 |
| 483 | Mickey Stanley | .20 |
| 484 | Eric Raich | .20 |
| 485 | Mike Hargrove | .20 |
| 486 | Bruce Dal Canton | .20 |
| 487 | Leron Lee | .20 |
| 488 | Claude Osteen | .20 |
| 489 | Skip Jutze | .20 |
| 490 | Frank Tanana | .30 |
| 491 | Terry Crowley | .20 |
| 492 | Marty Pattin | .20 |
| 493 | Derrel Thomas | .20 |
| 494 | Craig Swan | .20 |
| 495 | Nate Colbert | .20 |
| 496 | Juan Beniquez | .20 |
| 497 | Joe McIntosh | .20 |
| 498 | Glenn Borgmann | .20 |
| 499 | Mario Guerrero | .20 |
| 500 | Reggie Jackson | 13.00 |
| 501 | Billy Champion | .20 |
| 502 | Tim McCarver | .40 |
| 503 | Elliott Maddox | .20 |
| 504 | Pittsburgh Pirates | .75 |
| 505 | Mark Belanger | .30 |
| 506 | George Mitterwald | .20 |
| 507 | Ray Bare | .20 |
| 508 | Duane Kuiper | .20 |
| 509 | Bill Hands | .20 |
| 510 | Amos Otis | .30 |
| 511 | Jamie Easterley | .20 |
| 512 | Ellie Rodriguez | .20 |
| 513 | Bart Johnson | .20 |
| 514 | Dan Driessen | .25 |
| 515 | Steve Yeager | .20 |
| 516 | Wayne Granger | .20 |
| 517 | John Milner | .20 |
| 518 | Doug Flynn | .20 |
| 519 | Steve Brye | .20 |
| 520 | Willie McCovey | 3.00 |

| NO. | PLAYER | NR. MT. |
|---|---|---|
| 521 | Jim Colborn | .20 |
| 522 | Ted Sizemore | .20 |
| 523 | Bob Montgomery | .20 |
| 524 | Pete Falcone | .20 |
| 525 | Billy Williams | 2.00 |
| 526 | Checklist No. 4 | 1.00 |
| 527 | Mike Anderson | .20 |
| 528 | Dock Ellis | .20 |
| 529 | Deron Johnson | .20 |
| 530 | Don Sutton | 1.50 |
| 531 | New York Mets | 1.00 |
| 532 | Milt May | .20 |
| 533 | Lee Richard | .20 |
| 534 | Stan Bahnsen | .20 |
| 535 | Dave Nelson | .20 |
| 536 | Mike Thompson | .20 |
| 537 | Tony Muser | .20 |
| 538 | Pat Darcy | .20 |
| 539 | John Balaz | .20 |
| 540 | Bill Freehan | .30 |
| 541 | Steve Mingori | .20 |
| 542 | Keith Hernandez | 6.00 |
| 543 | Wayne Twitchell | .20 |
| 544 | Pepe Frias | .20 |
| 545 | Sparky Lyle | .30 |
| 546 | Dave Rosello | .20 |
| 547 | Roric Harrison | .20 |
| 548 | Manny Mota | .30 |
| 549 | Randy Tate | .20 |
| 550 | Hank Aaron | 15.00 |
| 551 | Jerry DaVanon | .20 |
| 552 | Terry Humphrey | .20 |
| 553 | Randy Moffitt | .20 |
| 554 | Ray Fosse | .20 |
| 555 | Dyar Miller | .20 |
| 556 | Minnesota Twins | .75 |
| 557 | Dan Spillner | .20 |
| 558 | Clarence Gaston | .20 |
| 559 | Clyde Wright | .20 |
| 560 | Jorge Orta | .20 |
| 561 | Tom Carroll | .20 |
| 562 | Adrian Garrett | .20 |
| 563 | Larry Demery | .20 |
| 564 | Gum Blowing Champ: | .30 |
|  | Kurt Bevacqua | |
| 565 | Tug McGraw | .40 |
| 566 | Ken McMullen | .20 |
| 567 | George Stone | .20 |
| 568 | Rob Andrews | .20 |
| 569 | Nelson Briles | .20 |
| 570 | George Hendrick | .30 |
| 571 | Don DeMola | .20 |
| 572 | Rich Coggins | .20 |
| 573 | Bill Travers | .20 |
| 574 | Don Kessinger | .20 |
| 575 | Dwight Evans | 3.00 |
| 576 | Maximino Leon | .20 |
| 577 | Marc Hill | .20 |
| 578 | Ted Kubiak | .20 |
| 579 | Clay Kirby | .20 |
| 580 | Bert Campaneris | .30 |
| 581 | St. Louis Cardinals | .75 |
| 582 | Mike Kekich | .20 |
| 583 | Tommy Helms | .20 |
| 584 | Stan Wall | .20 |
| 585 | Joe Torre | .40 |
| 586 | Ron Schueler | .20 |
| 587 | Leo Cardenas | .20 |
| 588 | Kevin Kobel | .20 |
| 589 | Rookie Pitchers: | 2.00 |
|  | Joe Pactwa, Santo Alcala, | |
|  | Mike Flanagan, P. Torrealba | |
| 590 | Rookie Outfielders: | 1.25 |
|  | Henry Cruz, Ellis Valentine, | |
|  | Chet Lemon, T. Whitfield | |
| 591 | Rookie Pitchers: | .30 |
|  | Steve Grilli, C. Mitchell, | |
|  | Jose Sosa, George Throop | |
| 592 | Rookie Infielders: | 6.00 |
|  | W. Randolph, D. McKay, | |
|  | J. Royster, R. Staiger | |

| NO. | PLAYER | NR. MT. |
|---|---|---|
| 593 | Rookie Pitchers: | .40 |
|  | Larry Anderson, M. Littell, | |
|  | Butch Metzger, Ken Crosby | |
| 594 | Rookie Catchers & OF's | .40 |
|  | Andy Merchant, Ed Ott, | |
|  | R. Stillman, Jerry White | |
| 595 | Rookie Pitchers: | .40 |
|  | Art DeFillipis, R. Lerch, | |
|  | Sid Monge, Steve Barr | |
| 596 | Rookie Infielders: | .50 |
|  | C. Reynolds, L. Johnson, | |
|  | J. LeMaster, J. Manuel | |
| 597 | Rookie Pitchers: | .60 |
|  | D. Aase, Jack Kucek, | |
|  | Frank LaCorte, Mike Pazik | |
| 598 | Rookie Outfielders: | .40 |
|  | Hector Cruz, J. Quirk, | |
|  | Jerry Turner, Joe Wallis | |
| 599 | Rookie Pitchers: | 12.00 |
|  | Rob Dressler, Ron Guidry, | |
|  | Bob McClure, Pat Zachry | |
| 600 | Tom Seaver | 10.00 |
| 601 | Ken Rudolph | .20 |
| 602 | Doug Konieczny | .20 |
| 603 | Jim Holt | .20 |
| 604 | Joe Lovitto | .20 |
| 605 | Al Downing | .30 |
| 606 | Milwaukee Brewers | .75 |
| 607 | Rich Hinton | .20 |
| 608 | Vic Correll | .20 |
| 609 | Fred Norman | .20 |
| 610 | Greg Luzinski | .50 |
| 611 | Rich Folkers | .20 |
| 612 | Joe Lahoud | .20 |
| 613 | Tim Johnson | .20 |
| 614 | Fernando Arroyo | .20 |
| 615 | Mike Cubbage | .20 |
| 616 | Buck Martinez | .20 |
| 617 | Darold Knowles | .20 |
| 618 | Jack Brohamer | .20 |
| 619 | Bill Butler | .20 |
| 620 | Al Oliver | .50 |
| 621 | Tom Hall | .20 |
| 622 | Rick Auerbach | .20 |
| 623 | Bob Allietta | .20 |
| 624 | Tony Taylor | .20 |
| 625 | J.R. Richard | .25 |
| 626 | Bob Sheldon | .20 |
| 627 | Bill Plummer | .20 |
| 628 | John D'Acquisto | .20 |
| 629 | Sandy Alomar | .20 |
| 630 | Chris Speier | .20 |
| 631 | Atlanta Braves | .75 |
| 632 | Rogelio Moret | .20 |
| 633 | John Stearns (R) | .25 |
| 634 | Larry Christenson | .20 |
| 635 | Jim Fregosi | .25 |
| 636 | Joe Decker | .20 |
| 637 | Bruce Bochte | .20 |
| 638 | Doyle Alexander | .20 |
| 639 | Fred Kendall | .20 |
| 640 | Bill Madlock | 1.00 |
| 641 | Tom Paciorek | .20 |
| 642 | Dennis Blair | .20 |
| 643 | Checklist No. 5 | 1.00 |
| 644 | Tom Bradley | .20 |
| 645 | Darrell Porter | .20 |
| 646 | John Lowenstein | .20 |
| 647 | Ramon Hernandez | .20 |
| 648 | Al Cowens | .20 |
| 649 | Dave Roberts | .20 |
| 650 | Thurman Munson | 7.00 |
| 651 | John Odom | .20 |
| 652 | Ed Armbrister | .20 |
| 653 | Mike Norris (R) | .25 |
| 654 | Doug Griffin | .20 |
| 655 | Mike Vail | .20 |
| 656 | Chicago White Sox | .75 |
| 657 | Roy Smalley (R) | .50 |
| 658 | Jerry Johnson | .20 |
| 659 | Ben Oglivie | .30 |
| 660 | D. Lopes (Exc. .15) | .75 |

# 1976 Topps Traded.... Complete Set of 44 Cards—Value $10.00 (Near Mint)

This set features players who were traded after the regular 1976 set was printed. The card numbers are the same as the main set, with the addition of "T" after the number.

| NO. PLAYER | NR. MT. | NO. PLAYER | NR. MT. | NO. PLAYER | NR. MT. | NO. PLAYER | NR. MT. |
|---|---|---|---|---|---|---|---|
| 27 T Ed Figueroa | .15 | 146 T George Medich | .15 | 380 T Bobby Bonds | .45 | 527 T Mike Anderson | .15 |
| 28 T Dusty Baker | .35 | 158 T Ken Reitz | .15 | 383 T John Ellis | .15 | 528 T Dock Ellis | .15 |
| 44 T Doug Rader | .20 | 208 T Mike Lum | .15 | 385 T Mickey Lolich | .50 | 532 T Milt May | .15 |
| 58 T Ron Reed | .20 | 211 T Clay Carroll | .15 | 401 T Ken Brett | .20 | 554 T Ray Fosse | .15 |
| 74 T Oscar Gamble | .25 | 231 T Tom House | .15 | 410 T Ken Brett | .20 | 579 T Clay Kirby | .15 |
| 80 T Jim Kaat | .50 | 250 T Fergie Jenkins | 1.50 | 411 T Bill Singer | .15 | 583 T Tommy Helms | .15 |
| 83 T Jim Spencer | .15 | 259 T Darrel Chaney | .15 | 428 T Jim Crawford | .15 | 592 T Willie Randolph | 1.25 |
| 85 T Mickey Rivers | .25 | 292 T Leon Roberts | .15 | 434 T Morris Nettles | .15 | 618 T Jack Brohamer | .15 |
| 99 T Lee Lacy | .25 | 296 T Pat Dobson | .15 | 464 T Ken Henderson | .15 | 632 T Rogelio Moret | .15 |
| 120 T Rusty Staub | .75 | 309 T Bill Melton | .15 | 497 T Joe McIntosh | .15 | 649 T Dave Roberts | .15 |
| 127 T Larvell Blanks | .15 | 338 T Bob Bailey | .15 | 524 T Pete Falcone | .15 | —    Checklist | .75 |

# 1977 Topps . . . Complete Set of 660 Cards—Value $425.00 (Near Mint)

Dale Murphy, Tony Armas, and Andre Dawson's rookie cards are in this set. There is an error on card 634—the photos are switched.

  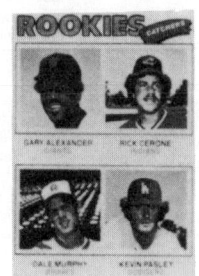  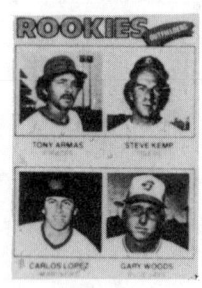

| NO. PLAYER | NR. MT. | NO. PLAYER | NR. MT. | NO. PLAYER | NR. MT. | NO. PLAYER | NR. MT. |
|---|---|---|---|---|---|---|---|
| 1 Batting Leaders: George Brett, Bill Madlock | 3.50 | 21 Ken Frosch | .18 | 50 R. Cey | .50 | 78 Bob Davis | .18 |
| 2 Home Run Leaders: Graig Nettles, Mike Schmidt | 1.00 | 22 Bill Freehan | .18 | 51 Milwaukee Brewers/ Alex Grammas (Mgr.) | .60 | 79 Don Money | .18 |
| 3 RBI Leaders: Lee May, George Foster | .40 | 23 Dan Driessen | .18 | 52 Ellis Valentine | .18 | 80 Andy Messersmith | .30 |
| 4 Stolen Base Leaders: B. North, Dave Lopes | .40 | 24 Carl Morton | .18 | 53 Paul Mitchell | .18 | 81 Juan Beniquez | .20 |
| 5 Victory Leaders: Jim Palmer, Randy Jones | .75 | 25 Dwight Evans | 2.50 | 54 Sandy Alomar | .18 | 82 Jim Rooker | .18 |
| 6 Strikeout Leaders: Nolan Ryan, Tom Seaver | 4.00 | 26 Ray Sadeki | .18 | 55 Jeff Burroughs | .25 | 83 Kevin Bell | .18 |
| 7 ERA Leaders: Mark Fidrych, J. Denny | .40 | 27 Bill Buckner | .40 | 56 Rudy May | .18 | 84 Ollie Brown | .18 |
| 8 Leading Firemen: B. Campbell, R. Eastwick | .40 | 28 Woodie Fryman | .18 | 57 Marc Hill | .18 | 85 Duane Kuiper | .18 |
| 9 Doug Rader | .18 | 29 Bucky Dent | .35 | 58 Chet Lemon | .40 | 86 Pat Zachry | .18 |
| 10 Reggie Jackson | 10.00 | 30 Greg Luzinski | .35 | 59 Larry Christenson | .18 | 87 Glenn Borgmann | .18 |
| 11 Rob Dressler | .18 | 31 Jim Todd | .18 | 60 Jim Rice | 4.00 | 88 Stan Wall | .18 |
| 12 Larry Haney | .18 | 32 Checklist No. 1 | .75 | 61 Manny Sanguillen | .18 | 89 Butch Hobson | .30 |
| 13 Luis Gomez | .18 | 33 Wayne Garland | .18 | 62 Eric Raich | .18 | 90 Cesar Cedeno | .35 |
| 14 Tommy Smith | .18 | 34 Angels/Norm Sherry (Mgr.) | .50 | 63 Tito Fuentes | .18 | 91 John Verhoeven | .18 |
| 15 Don Gullett | .18 | 35 Rennie Stennett | .18 | 64 Larry Biittner | .18 | 92 Dave Rosello | .18 |
| 16 Bob Jones | .18 | 36 John Ellis | .18 | 65 Skip Lockwood | .18 | 93 Tom Poquette | .18 |
| 17 Steve Stone | .18 | 37 Steve Hargan | .18 | 66 Roy Smalley | .18 | 94 Craig Swan | .18 |
| 18 Cleveland Indians/ Frank Robinson (Mgr.) | .60 | 38 Craig Kusick | .18 | 67 Joaquin Andujar (R) | .75 | 95 Keith Hernandez | 3.00 |
| 19 John D'Acquisto | .18 | 39 Tom Griffin | .18 | 68 Bruce Bochte | .18 | 96 Lou Piniella | .45 |
| 20 Graig Nettles | .75 | 40 Bobby Murcer | .50 | 69 Jim Crawford | .18 | 97 Dave Heaverlo | .18 |
|  |  | 41 Jim Kern | .18 | 70 Johnny Bench | 7.00 | 98 Milt May | .18 |
|  |  | 42 Jose Cruz | .30 | 71 Dock Ellis | .18 | 99 Tom Hausman | .18 |
|  |  | 43 Ray Bare | .18 | 72 Mike Anderson | .18 | 100 Joe Morgan | 2.50 |
|  |  | 44 Bud Harrelson | .18 | 73 Charlie Williams | .18 | 101 Dick Bosman | .18 |
|  |  | 45 Rawly Eastwick | .18 | 74 A's/J. McKeon (Mgr.) | .60 | 102 Jose Morales | .18 |
|  |  | 46 Buck Martinez | .18 | 75 Dennis Leonard | .18 | 103 Mike Bacsik | .18 |
|  |  | 47 Lynn McGlothen | .18 | 76 Tim Foli | .18 | 104 Omar Moreno (R) | .35 |
|  |  | 48 Tom Paciorek | .18 | 77 Dyar Miller | .18 | 105 Steve Yeager | .18 |
|  |  | 49 Grant Jackson | .18 |  |  | 106 Mike Flanagan | .40 |

| NO. PLAYER | NR. MT. |
|---|---|
| 107 Bill Melton | .18 |
| 108 Alan Foster | .18 |
| 109 Jorge Orta | .18 |
| 110 Steve Carlton | 5.00 |
| 111 Rico Petrocelli | .25 |
| 112 Bill Greif | .18 |
| 113 Toronto Blue Jays | .60 |
| Roy Hartsfield (Mgr.) | |
| 114 Bruce Dal Canton | .18 |
| 115 Rick Manning | .18 |
| 116 Joe Niekro | .40 |
| 117 Frank White | .40 |
| 118 Rick Jone | .18 |
| 119 John Stearns | .18 |
| 120 Rod Carew | 7.00 |
| 121 Gary Nolan | .18 |
| 122 Ben Oglivie | .25 |
| 123 Fred Stanley | .18 |
| 124 George Mitterwald | .18 |
| 125 Bill Travers | .18 |
| 126 Rod Gilbreath | .18 |
| 127 Ron Fairly | .18 |
| 128 Tommy John | 1.00 |
| 129 Mike Sadek | .18 |
| 130 Al Oliver | .50 |
| 131 Orlando Ramirez | .18 |
| 132 Chip Lang | .18 |
| 133 Ralph Garr | .18 |
| 134 San Diego Padres/ | .60 |
| John McNamara (Mgr.) | |
| 135 Mark Belanger | .30 |
| 136 Jerry Mumphrey (R) | .50 |
| 137 Jeff Terpko | .18 |
| 138 Bob Stinson | .18 |
| 139 Fred Norman | .18 |
| 140 Mike Schmidt | 20.00 |
| 141 Mark Littell | .18 |
| 142 Steve Dillard | .18 |
| 143 Ed Herrmann | .18 |
| 144 Bruce Sutter (R) | 3.00 |
| 145 Tom Veryzer | .18 |
| 146 Dusty Baker | .40 |
| 147 Jackie Brown | .18 |
| 148 Fran Healy | .18 |
| 149 Mike Cubbage | .18 |
| 150 Tom Seaver | 7.00 |
| 151 Johnnie LeMaster | .18 |
| 152 Gaylord Perry | 2.00 |
| 153 Ron Jackson | .18 |
| 154 Dave Guisti | .18 |
| 155 Joe Rudi | .25 |
| 156 Pete Mackanin | .18 |
| 157 Ken Brett | .18 |
| 158 Ted Kubiak | .18 |
| 159 Bernie Carbo | .18 |
| 160 Will McEnaney | .18 |
| 161 Garry Templeton (R) | 1.50 |
| 162 Mike Cuellar | .25 |
| 163 Dave Hilton | .18 |
| 164 Tug McGraw | .35 |
| 165 Jim Wynn | .18 |
| 166 Bill Campbell | .18 |
| 167 Rich Hebner | .18 |
| 168 Charlie Spikes | .18 |
| 169 Darold Knowles | .18 |
| 170 Thurman Munson | 5.00 |
| 171 Ken Sanders | .18 |
| 172 John Milner | .18 |
| 173 Chuck Scrivener | .18 |
| 174 Nelson Briles | .18 |
| 175 Butch Wynegar (R) | .75 |
| 176 Bob Robertson | .18 |
| 177 Bart Johnson | .18 |
| 178 Bombo Rivera | .18 |
| 179 Paul Hartzell | .18 |
| 180 Dave Lopes | .35 |
| 181 Ken McMullen | .18 |
| 182 Dan Spillner | .18 |
| 183 Cardinals/V. Rapp (Mgr.) | .60 |
| 184 Bo McLaughlin | .18 |
| 185 Sixto Lezcano | .18 |
| 186 Doug Flynn | .18 |
| 187 Dick Pole | .18 |
| 188 Bob Tolan | .18 |
| 189 Rick Dempsey | .20 |

| NO. PLAYER | NR. MT. |
|---|---|
| 190 Ray Burris | .18 |
| 191 Doug Griffin | .18 |
| 192 Clarence Gaston | .18 |
| 193 Larry Gura | .18 |
| 194 Gary Matthews | .35 |
| 195 Ed Figueroa | .18 |
| 196 Len Randle | .18 |
| 197 Ed Ott | .18 |
| 198 Wilbur Wood | .18 |
| 199 Pepe Frias | .18 |
| 200 Frank Tanana | .25 |
| 201 Ed Kranepool | .30 |
| 202 Tom Johnson | .18 |
| 203 Ed Armbrister | .18 |
| 204 Jeff Newman | .18 |
| 205 Pete Falcone | .18 |
| 206 Boog Powell | .40 |
| 207 Glenn Abott | .18 |
| 208 Checklist No. 2 | .75 |
| 209 Rob Andrews | .18 |
| 210 Fred Lynn | 1.50 |
| 211 San Francisco Giants/ | .60 |
| Joe Altobelli (Mgr.) | |
| 212 Jim Mason | .18 |
| 213 Maximino Leon | .18 |
| 214 Darrell Porter | .30 |
| 215 Butch Metzger | .30 |
| 216 Doug DeCinces | .50 |
| 217 Tom Underwood | .18 |
| 218 John Wathan | 1.25 |
| 219 Joe Coleman | .18 |
| 220 Chris Chambliss | .25 |
| 221 Bob Bailey | .18 |
| 222 Francisco Barrios | .18 |
| 223 Earl Williams | .18 |
| 224 Rusty Torres | .18 |
| 225 Bob Apodaca | .18 |
| 226 Leroy Stanton | .18 |
| 227 Joe Sambito | .40 |
| 228 Minnesota Twins/ | .60 |
| Gene Mauch (Mgr.) | |
| 229 Don Kessinger | .18 |
| 230 Vida Blue | .35 |
| 231 Record—Brett | 5.00 |
| Most Consecutive Games | |
| with 3 or More Hits | |
| 232 Record—Minoso | .40 |
| Oldest Player to Hit Safely | |
| 233 Record—Morales | .30 |
| Most Pinch-Hits for Season | |
| 234 Record—Ryan | 7.00 |
| Most Seasons 300 SO's | |
| 235 Cecil Cooper | .60 |
| 236 Tom Buskey | .18 |
| 237 Gene Clines | .18 |
| 238 Tippy Martinez | .18 |
| 239 Bill Plummer | .18 |
| 240 Ron LeFlore | .20 |
| 241 Dave Tomlin | .18 |
| 242 Ken Henderson | .18 |
| 243 Ron Reed | .18 |
| 244 John Mayberry | .35 |
| 245 Rick Rhoden | .30 |
| 246 Mike Vail | .18 |
| 247 Chris Knapp | .18 |
| 248 Wilbur Howard | .18 |
| 249 Pete Redfern | .18 |
| 250 Bill Madlock | .50 |
| 251 Tony Muser | .18 |
| 252 Dale Murray | .18 |
| 253 John Hale | .18 |
| 254 Doyle Alexander | .18 |
| 255 George Scott | .18 |
| 256 Joe Hoerner | .18 |
| 257 Mike Miley | .18 |
| 258 Luis Tiant | .20 |
| 259 Mets/J. Frazier (Mgr.) | .75 |
| 260 J.R. Richard | .25 |
| 261 Phil Garner | .25 |
| 262 Al Cowens | .25 |
| 263 Mike Marshall | .25 |
| 264 Tom Hutton | .18 |
| 265 Mark Fidrych (R) | .75 |
| 266 Derrel Thomas | .18 |
| 267 Ray Fosse | .18 |

| NO. PLAYER | NR. MT. |
|---|---|
| 268 Rick Sawyer | .18 |
| 269 Joe Lis | .18 |
| 270 Dave Parker | 4.00 |
| 271 Terry Forster | .25 |
| 272 Lee Lacy | .20 |
| 273 Eric Soderholm | .18 |
| 274 Don Stanhouse | .18 |
| 275 Mike Hargrove | .18 |
| 276 A.L. Championship: | .50 |
| Chambliss' Homer | |
| 277 N.L. Championship: | .60 |
| Reds Sweep Phillies in 3 | |
| 278 Danny Frisella | .18 |
| 279 Joe Wallis | .18 |
| 280 Jim Hunter | 2.00 |
| 281 Roy Staiger | .18 |
| 282 Sid Monge | .18 |
| 283 Jerry DaVanon | .18 |
| 284 Mike Norris | .18 |
| 285 Brooks Robinson | 3.00 |
| 286 Johnny Grubb | .18 |
| 287 Cincinnati Reds | .75 |
| Sparky Anderson (Mgr.) | |
| 288 Bob Montgomery | .18 |
| 289 Gene Garber | .18 |
| 290 Amos Otis | .35 |
| 291 Jason Thompson (R) | .60 |
| 292 Rogelio Moret | .18 |
| 293 Jack Brohamer | .18 |
| 294 George Medich | .18 |
| 295 Gary Carter | 5.00 |
| 296 Don Hood | .18 |
| 297 Ken Reitz | .18 |
| 298 Charlie Hough | .18 |
| 299 Otto Velez | .18 |
| 300 Jerry Koosman | .40 |
| 301 Toby Harrah | .20 |
| 302 Mike Garman | .18 |
| 303 Gene Tenace | .18 |
| 304 Jim Hughes | .18 |
| 305 Mickey Rivers | .30 |
| 306 Rick Waits | .18 |
| 307 Gary Sutherland | .18 |
| 308 Gene Pentz | .18 |
| 309 Boston Red Sox/ | .75 |
| Don Zimmer (Mgr.) | |
| 310 Larry Bowa | .30 |
| 311 Vern Ruhle | .18 |
| 312 Rob Belloir | .18 |
| 313 Paul Blair | .18 |
| 314 Steve Mingori | .18 |
| 315 Dave Chalk | .18 |
| 316 Steve Rogers | .25 |
| 317 Kurt Bevacqua | .18 |
| 318 Duffy Dyer | .18 |
| 319 Rich Gossage | .75 |
| 320 Ken Griffey | 1.25 |
| 321 Dave Goltz | .18 |
| 322 Bill Russell | .18 |
| 323 Larry Lintz | .18 |
| 324 John Curtis | .18 |
| 325 Mike Ivie | .18 |
| 326 Jesse Jefferson | .18 |
| 327 Astros/B. Virdon (Mgr.) | .60 |
| 328 Tommy Boggs | .18 |
| 329 Ron Hodges | .18 |
| 330 George Hendrick | .35 |
| 331 Jim Colborn | .18 |
| 332 Elliott Maddox | .18 |
| 333 Paul Reuschel | .18 |
| 334 Bill Stein | .18 |
| 335 Bill Robinson | .18 |
| 336 Denny Doyle | .18 |
| 337 Ron Schueler | .18 |
| 338 Dave Duncan | .18 |
| 339 Adrian Devine | .18 |
| 340 Hal McRae | .25 |
| 341 Joe Kerrigan | .18 |
| 342 Jerry Remy | .18 |
| 343 Ed Halicki | .18 |
| 344 Brian Downing | .30 |
| 345 Reggie Smith | .30 |
| 346 Bill Singer | .18 |
| 347 George Foster | 1.25 |
| 348 Brent Strom | .18 |

| NO. PLAYER | NR. MT. |
|---|---|
| 349 Jim Holt | .18 |
| 350 Larry Dierker | .18 |
| 351 Jim Sundberg | .18 |
| 352 Mike Phillips | .18 |
| 353 Stan Thomas | .18 |
| 354 Pirates/C. Tanner (Mgr.) | .50 |
| 355 Lou Brock | 3.00 |
| 356 Checklist No. 3 | .75 |
| 357 Tim McCarver | .45 |
| 358 Tom House | .18 |
| 359 Willie Randolph | 1.50 |
| 360 Rick Monday | .25 |
| 361 Eduardo Rodriguez | .18 |
| 362 Tommy Davis | .18 |
| 363 Dave Roberts | .18 |
| 364 Vic Correll | .18 |
| 365 Mike Torrez | .18 |
| 366 Ted Sizemore | .18 |
| 367 Dave Hamilton | .18 |
| 368 Mike Jorgensen | .18 |
| 369 Terry Humphrey | .18 |
| 370 John Montefusco | .18 |
| 371 Royals/W. Herzog (Mgr.) | .60 |
| 372 Rich Folkers | .18 |
| 373 Bert Campaneris | .25 |
| 374 Kent Tekulve | .20 |
| 375 Larry Hisle | .20 |
| 376 Nino Espinosa | .18 |
| 377 Dave McKay | .18 |
| 378 Jim Umbarger | .18 |
| 379 Larry Cox | .18 |
| 380 Lee May | .25 |
| 381 Bob Forsch | .25 |
| 382 Charlie Moore | .18 |
| 383 Stan Bahnsen | .18 |
| 384 Darrel Chaney | .18 |
| 385 Dave LaRoche | .18 |
| 386 Manny Mota | .30 |
| 387 New York Yankees/ | 1.00 |
| Billy Martin (Mgr.) | |
| 388 Terry Harmon | .30 |
| 389 Ken Kravec | .30 |
| 390 Dave Winfield | 7.00 |
| 391 Dan Warthen | .18 |
| 392 Phil Roof | .18 |
| 393 John Lowenstein | .18 |
| 394 Bill Laxton | .18 |
| 395 Manny Trillo | .25 |
| 396 Tom Murphy | .18 |
| 397 Larry Herndon (R) | .50 |
| 398 Tom Burgmeier | .18 |
| 399 Bruce Boisclair | .18 |
| 400 Steve Garvey | 3.00 |
| 401 Mickey Scott | .18 |
| 402 Tommy Helms | .18 |
| 403 Tom Grieve | .18 |
| 404 Eric Rasmussen | .18 |
| 405 Claudell Washington | .25 |
| 406 Tim Johnson | .18 |
| 407 Dave Freisleben | .18 |
| 408 Cesar Tovar | .18 |
| 409 Pete Broberg | .18 |
| 410 Willie Montanez | .18 |
| 411 World Series | .75 |
| Morgan Homers, | |
| Bench Stars for Reds | |
| 412 World Series # 1 & 2 | .75 |
| Reds' Defense, | |
| Bench's Two Homers | |
| 413 World Series # 3 & 4 | .60 |
| Cincy Wins | |
| 414 Tommy Harper | .18 |
| 415 Jay Johnstone | .18 |
| 416 Chuck Hartenstein | .18 |
| 417 Wayne Garrett | .18 |
| 418 Chicago White Sox/ | .60 |
| Bob Lemon (Mgr.) | |
| 419 Steve Swisher | .18 |
| 420 Rusty Staub | .35 |
| 421 Doug Rau | .18 |
| 422 Freddie Patek | .18 |
| 423 Gary Lavelle | .18 |
| 424 Steve Brye | .18 |
| 425 Joe Torre | .35 |
| 426 Dick Drago | .18 |

| NO. PLAYER | NR. MT. |
|---|---|
| 427 Dave Rader | .18 |
| 428 Texas Rangers/ Frank Lucchesi (Mgr.) | .60 |
| 429 Ken Boswell | .18 |
| 430 Fergie Jenkins | 1.50 |
| 431 Dave Collins (photo of Bobby Jones) | .30 |
| 432 Buzz Capra | .18 |
| 433 Turn Back Clock (1972) Colbert Hits 5 Homers | .30 |
| 434 Turn Back Clock (1967) Yaz Wins Triple Crown | 2.00 |
| 435 Turn Back Clock (1962) Wills 104 Steals | .60 |
| 436 Turn Back Clock (1957) Keegan No-Hitter | .30 |
| 437 Turn Back Clock (1952) Kiner Leads NL | .60 |
| 438 Marty Perez | .18 |
| 439 Gorman Thomas | .40 |
| 440 Jon Matlack | .18 |
| 441 Larvell Blanks | .18 |
| 442 Atlanta Braves/ Dave Bristol (Mgr.) | .60 |
| 443 Lamar Johnson | .18 |
| 444 Wayne Twitchell | .18 |
| 445 Ken Singleton | .40 |
| 446 Bill Bonham | .18 |
| 447 Jerry Turner | .18 |
| 448 Ellie Rodriguez | .18 |
| 449 Al Fitzmorris | .18 |
| 450 Pete Rose | 7.50 |
| 451 Checklist No. 4 | .75 |
| 452 Mike Caldwell | .18 |
| 453 Pedro Garcia | .18 |
| 454 Andy Etchebarren | .18 |
| 455 Rick Wise | .18 |
| 456 Leon Roberts | .18 |
| 457 Steve Luebber | .18 |
| 458 Leo Foster | .18 |
| 459 Steve Foucault | .18 |
| 460 Willie Stargell | 2.50 |
| 461 Dick Tidrow | .18 |
| 462 Don Baylor | .60 |
| 463 Jamie Quirk | .18 |
| 464 Randy Moffitt | .18 |
| 465 Rico Carty | .35 |
| 466 Fred Holdsworth | .18 |
| 467 Philadelphia Phillies/ Danny Ozark (Mgr.) | .60 |
| 468 Ramon Hernandez | .18 |
| 469 Pat Kelly | .18 |
| 470 Ted Simmons | .60 |
| 471 Del Unser | .18 |
| 472 Rookie Pitchers: Bob McClure, Don Aase, Gil Patterson, Dave Wehrmeister | .50 |
| 473 Rookie Outfielders: Gene Richards, John Scott, D. Walling, A. Dawson | 60.00 |
| 474 Rookie Shortstops: Bob Bailor, Kiko Garcia, C. Reynolds, A. Taveras | .40 |
| 475 Rookie Pitchers: Chris Batton, Rick Camp, S. McGregor, M. Sarmiento | .50 |
| 476 Rookie Catchers: Dale Murphy, Rick Cerone, G. Alexander, K. Pasley | 50.00 |
| 477 Rookie Infielders: R. Dauer, O. Gonzalez, D. Ault, P. Mankowski | .40 |

| NO. PLAYER | NR. MT. |
|---|---|
| 478 Rookie Pitchers: Leon Hooten, Jim Gideon, Mark Lemongello, Dave Johnson | .40 |
| 479 Rookie Outfielders: A. Woods, Wayne Gross, B. Asselstine, S. Mejias | .40 |
| 480 Carl Yastrzemski | 5.00 |
| 481 Roger Metzger | .18 |
| 482 Tony Solaita | .18 |
| 483 Richie Zisk | .30 |
| 484 Burt Hooton | .30 |
| 485 Roy White | .30 |
| 486 Ed Bane | .18 |
| 487 Rookie Pitchers: Joe Henderson, Ed Glynn, L. Anderson, G. Terlecky | .35 |
| 488 Rookie Outfielders: Lee Mazzilli, Jack Clark, R. Jones, D. Thomas | 15.00 |
| 489 Rookie Pitchers: Len Barker, Randy Lerch, Greg Minton, Mike Overy | .50 |
| 490 Rookie Shortstops: T. McMillan, B. Almon, M. Klutts, M. Wagner | .40 |
| 491 Rookie Pitchers: Mike Dupree, Bob Sykes, D. Martinez, C. Mitchell | 6.00 |
| 492 Rookie Outfielders: Tony Armas, Steve Kemp, C. Lopez, Gary Woods | .75 |
| 493 Rookie Pitchers: G. Wheelock, M. Krukow, Jim Otten, Mike Willis | .60 |
| 494 Rookie Infielders: Juan Bernhardt, J. Gantner, M. Champion, B. Wills | .60 |
| 495 Al Hrabosky | .18 |
| 496 Gary Thomasson | .18 |
| 497 Clay Carroll | .18 |
| 498 Sal Bando | .30 |
| 499 Pablo Torealba | .18 |
| 500 Dave Kingman | .50 |
| 501 Jim Bibby | .18 |
| 502 Randy Hundley | .18 |
| 503 Bill Lee | .18 |
| 504 Los Angeles Dodgers/ Tom Lasorda (Mgr.) | .75 |
| 505 Oscar Gamble | .25 |
| 506 Steve Grilli | .18 |
| 507 Mike Hegan | .18 |
| 508 Dave Pagan | .18 |
| 509 Cookie Rojas | .18 |
| 510 John Candelaria | .75 |
| 511 Bill Fahey | .18 |
| 512 Jack Billingham | .18 |
| 513 Jerry Terrell | .18 |
| 514 Cliff Johnson | .18 |
| 515 Chris Speier | .18 |
| 516 Bake McBride | .20 |
| 517 Pete Vuckovich (R) | .50 |
| 518 Chicago Cubs/ Herman Franks (Mgr.) | .60 |
| 519 Don Kirkwood | .18 |
| 520 Garry Maddox | .20 |
| 521 Bob Grich | .25 |
| 522 Enzo Hernandez | .18 |
| 523 Rollie Fingers | 2.00 |
| 524 Rowland Office | .12 |
| 525 Dennis Eckersley | 8.00 |
| 526 Larry Parrish | .30 |

| NO. PLAYER | NR. MT. |
|---|---|
| 527 Dan Meyer | .18 |
| 528 Bill Castro | .18 |
| 529 Jim Essian | .40 |
| 530 Rick Reuschel | .50 |
| 531 Lyman Bostock | .30 |
| 532 Jim Willoughby | .18 |
| 533 Mickey Stanley | .18 |
| 534 Paul Splittorff | .18 |
| 535 Cesar Geronimo | .18 |
| 536 Vic Albury | .18 |
| 537 Dave Roberts | .18 |
| 538 Frank Taveras | .18 |
| 539 Mike Wallace | .18 |
| 540 Bob Watson | .25 |
| 541 John Denny | .30 |
| 542 Frank Duffy | .18 |
| 543 Ron Blomberg | .18 |
| 544 Gary Ross | .18 |
| 545 Bob Boone | .50 |
| 546 Baltimore Orioles/ Earl Weaver (Mgr.) | .60 |
| 547 Willie McCovey | 2.50 |
| 548 Joel Youngblood | .18 |
| 549 Jerry Royster | .18 |
| 550 Randy Jones | .18 |
| 551 Bill North | .18 |
| 552 Pepe Mangual | .18 |
| 553 Jack Heidemann | .18 |
| 554 Bruce Kimm | .18 |
| 555 Dan Ford | .18 |
| 556 Doug Bird | .18 |
| 557 Jerry White | .18 |
| 558 Elias Sosa | .18 |
| 559 Alan Bannister | .18 |
| 560 Dave Concepcion | .50 |
| 561 Pete LaCock | .18 |
| 562 Checklist No. 5 | .75 |
| 563 Bruce Kison | .18 |
| 564 Alan Ashby | .20 |
| 565 Mickey Lolich | .25 |
| 566 Rick Miller | .18 |
| 567 Enos Cabell | .18 |
| 568 Carlos May | .18 |
| 569 Jim Lonborg | .18 |
| 570 Bobby Bonds | .50 |
| 571 Darrell Evans | .35 |
| 572 Ross Grimsley | .18 |
| 573 Joe Ferguson | .18 |
| 574 Aurelio Rodriguez | .18 |
| 575 Dick Ruthven | .18 |
| 576 Fred Kendall | .18 |
| 577 Jerry Augustine | .18 |
| 578 Bob Randall | .18 |
| 579 Don Carrithers | .18 |
| 580 George Brett | 24.00 |
| 581 Pedro Borbon | .18 |
| 582 Ed Kirkpatrick | .18 |
| 583 Paul Lindblad | .18 |
| 584 Ed Goodson | .18 |
| 585 Rick Burleson | .18 |
| 586 Steve Renko | .18 |
| 587 Rick Baldwin | .18 |
| 588 Dave Moates | .18 |
| 589 Mike Cosgrove | .18 |
| 590 Buddy Bell | .40 |
| 591 Chris Arnold | .18 |
| 592 Dan Briggs | .18 |
| 593 Dennis Blair | .18 |
| 594 Biff Pocoroba | .18 |
| 595 John Hiller | .18 |
| 596 Jerry Martin | .18 |

| NO. PLAYER | NR. MT. |
|---|---|
| 597 Seattle Mariners/ Darrell Johnson (Mgr.) | .50 |
| 598 Sparky Lyle | .40 |
| 599 Mike Tyson | .18 |
| 600 Jim Palmer | 4.00 |
| 601 Mike Lum | .18 |
| 602 Andy Hassler | .18 |
| 603 Willie Davis | .18 |
| 604 Jim Slaton | .18 |
| 605 Felix Millan | .18 |
| 606 Steve Braun | .18 |
| 607 Larry Demery | .18 |
| 608 Roy Howell | .18 |
| 609 Jim Barr | .18 |
| 610 Jose Cardenal | .18 |
| 611 Dave Lemanczyk | .18 |
| 612 Barry Foote | .18 |
| 613 Reggie Cleveland | .18 |
| 614 Greg Gross | .18 |
| 615 Phil Niekro | 1.50 |
| 616 Tommy Sandt | .18 |
| 617 Bobby Darwin | .18 |
| 618 Pat Dobson | .18 |
| 619 Johnny Oates | .18 |
| 620 Don Sutton | 1.50 |
| 621 Detroit Tigers/ Ralph Houk (Mgr.) | .60 |
| 622 Jim Wohlford | .18 |
| 623 Jack Kucek | .18 |
| 624 Hector Cruz | .18 |
| 625 Ken Holtzman | .18 |
| 626 Al Bumbry | .18 |
| 627 Bob Myrick | .18 |
| 628 Mario Guerrero | .18 |
| 629 Bobby Valentine | .30 |
| 630 Bert Blyleven | 1.00 |
| 631 Big League Brothers: George Brett, Ken Brett | 2.50 |
| 632 Big League Brothers: Ken Forsch, Bob Forsch | .30 |
| 633 Big League Brothers: Lee May, Carlos May | .30 |
| 634 Big League Brothers: Paul Reuschel, Rick Reuschel (photos switched) | .30 |
| 635 Robin Yount | 24.00 |
| 636 Santo Alcala | .18 |
| 637 Alex Johnson | .18 |
| 638 Jim Kaat | .60 |
| 639 Jerry Morales | .18 |
| 640 Carlton Fisk | 6.00 |
| 641 Dan Larson | .18 |
| 642 Willie Crawford | .18 |
| 643 Mike Pazik | .18 |
| 644 Matt Alexander | .18 |
| 645 Jerry Reuss | .20 |
| 646 Andres Mora | .18 |
| 647 Montreal Expos/ Dick Williams (Mgr.) | .50 |
| 648 Jim Spencer | .18 |
| 649 Dave Cash | .18 |
| 650 Nolan Ryan | 25.00 |
| 651 Von Joshua | .18 |
| 652 Tom Walker | .18 |
| 653 Diego Segui | .18 |
| 654 Ron Pruitt | .18 |
| 655 Tony Perez | 1.25 |
| 656 Ron Guidry | 2.50 |
| 657 Mick Kelleher | .18 |
| 658 Marty Pattin | .18 |
| 659 Merv Rettenmund | .18 |
| 660 W. Horton (Exc. .12) | .50 |

# 1978 Topps . . . Complete Set of 726 Cards—Value $350.00 (Near Mint)

After five consecutive years of issuing sets of 660 cards, Topps increased the size of its main set to 726 cards. 66 cards were double printed. Eddie Murray, Paul Molitor, and Lou Whitaker's rookie cards are in this set.

| NO. PLAYER | NR. MT. |
|---|---|
| 1 Record — L. Brock | 2.50 |
| Most Career Steals | |
| 2 Record — S. Lyle | .25 |
| Most Career Relief | |
| 3 Record — W. McCovey | 1.25 |
| Most 2 HR's in Inning | |
| 4 Record — B. Robinson | 1.00 |
| Most Seasons — Same Club | |
| 5 Record — P. Rose | 1.75 |
| Most Hits — Switch Hitter | |
| 6 Record — N. Ryan | 5.00 |
| Games 10 or More SO's | |
| 7 Record — R. Jackson | 2.50 |
| Most Homers — W. Series | |
| 8 Mike Sadek | .15 |
| 9 Doug DeCinces | .30 |
| 10 Phil Niekro | 1.25 |
| 11 Rick Manning | .15 |
| 12 Don Aase | .25 |
| 13 Art Howe | .30 |
| 14 Lerrin LaGrow | .15 |
| 15 Tony Perez | .50 |
| 16 Roy White | .25 |
| 17 Mike Krukow | .30 |
| 18 Bob Grich | .25 |
| 19 Darrell Porter | .25 |
| 20 Pete Rose | 3.50 |
| 21 Steve Kemp | .30 |
| 22 Charlie Hough | .15 |
| 23 Bump Wills | .15 |
| 24 Don Money | .15 |
| 25 Jon Matlack | .15 |
| 26 Rich Hebner | .15 |
| 27 Geoff Zahn | .15 |
| 28 Ed Ott | .15 |
| 29 Bob Lacey | .15 |
| 30 George Hendrick | .25 |
| 31 Glenn Abbott | .15 |
| 32 Garry Templeton | .30 |
| 33 Dave Lemanczyk | .15 |
| 34 Willie McCovey | 2.50 |
| 35 Sparky Lyle | .25 |
| 36 Eddie Murray (R) | 65.00 |
| 37 Rick Waits | .15 |
| 38 Willie Montanez | .15 |
| 39 Floyd Bannister (R) | .75 |
| 40 Carl Yastrzemski | 4.00 |
| 41 Burt Hooton | .15 |
| 42 Jorge Orta | .15 |
| 43 Bill Atkinson | .15 |
| 44 Toby Harrah | .15 |
| 45 Mark Fidrych | .35 |
| 46 Al Cowens | .20 |
| 47 Jack Billingham | .15 |
| 48 Don Baylor | .45 |
| 49 Ed Kranepool | .25 |
| 50 Rick Reuschel | .30 |
| 51 Charlie Moore | .15 |
| 52 Jim Lonborg | .15 |
| 53 Phil Garner | .15 |
| 54 Tom Johnson | .15 |
| 55 Mitchell Page | .15 |
| 56 Randy Jones | .15 |
| 57 Dan Meyer | .15 |
| 58 Bob Forsch | .20 |
| 59 Otto Velez | .15 |

| NO. PLAYER | NR. MT. |
|---|---|
| 60 Thurman Munson | 3.50 |
| 61 Larvell Blanks | .15 |
| 62 Jim Barr | .15 |
| 63 Don Zimmer (Mgr.) | .15 |
| 64 Gene Pentz | .15 |
| 65 Ken Singleton | .25 |
| 66 Chicago White Sox | .50 |
| 67 Claudell Washington | .20 |
| 68 Steve Foucault | .15 |
| 69 Mike Vail | .15 |
| 70 Rich Gossage | 1.00 |
| 71 Terry Humphrey | .15 |
| 72 Andre Dawson | 15.00 |
| 73 Andy Hassler | .15 |
| 74 Checklist No. 1 | .75 |
| 75 Dick Ruthven | .15 |
| 76 Steve Ontiveros | .15 |
| 77 Ed Kirkpatrick | .15 |
| 78 Pablo Torrealba | .15 |
| 79 Darrell Johnson (Mgr.) | .15 |
| 80 Ken Griffey | 1.00 |
| 81 Pete Redfern | .15 |
| 82 San Fran. Giants | .50 |
| 83 Bob Montgomery | .15 |
| 84 Kent Tekulve | .20 |
| 85 Ron Fairly | .15 |
| 86 Dave Tomlin | .15 |
| 87 John Lowenstein | .15 |
| 88 Mike Phillips | .15 |
| 89 Ken Clay | .15 |
| 90 Larry Bowa | .20 |
| 91 Oscar Zamora | .15 |
| 92 Adrian Devine | .15 |
| 93 Bobby Cox (Mgr.) | .15 |
| 94 Chuck Scrivener | .15 |
| 95 Jamie Quirk | .15 |
| 96 Baltimore Orioles | .40 |
| 97 Stan Bahnsen | .15 |
| 98 Jim Essian | .15 |
| 99 Willie Hernandez (R) | .60 |
| 100 George Brett | 15.00 |
| 101 Sid Monge | .15 |
| 102 Matt Alexander | .15 |
| 103 Tom Murphy | .15 |
| 104 Lee Lacy | .15 |
| 105 Reggie Cleveland | .15 |
| 106 Bill Plummer | .15 |
| 107 Ed Halicki | .15 |
| 108 Von Joshua | .15 |
| 109 Joe Torre (Mgr.) | .25 |
| 110 Richie Zisk | .25 |
| 111 Mike Tyson | .15 |
| 112 Houston Astros | .50 |
| 113 Don Carrithers | .15 |
| 114 Paul Blair | .15 |
| 115 Gary Nolan | .15 |
| 116 Tucker Ashford | .15 |
| 117 John Montague | .15 |
| 118 Terry Harmon | .15 |
| 119 Denny Martinez | 1.00 |
| 120 Gary Carter | 3.00 |
| 121 Alvis Woods | .15 |
| 122 Dennis Eckersley | 4.00 |
| 123 Manny Trillo | .20 |
| 124 Dave Rozema | .15 |
| 125 George Scott | .15 |

| NO. PLAYER | NR. MT. |
|---|---|
| 126 Paul Moskau | .15 |
| 127 Chet Lemon | .20 |
| 128 Bill Russell | .15 |
| 129 Jim Colborn | .15 |
| 130 Jeff Burroughs | .20 |
| 131 Bert Blyleven | 1.00 |
| 132 Enos Cabell | .15 |
| 133 Jerry Augustine | .15 |
| 134 Steve Henderson | .15 |
| 135 Ron Guidry | .60 |
| 136 Ted Sizemore | .15 |
| 137 Craig Kusick | .15 |
| 138 Larry Demery | .15 |
| 139 Wayne Gross | .15 |
| 140 Rollie Fingers | 1.50 |
| 141 Ruppert Jones | .15 |
| 142 John Montefusco | .15 |
| 143 Keith Hernandez | 2.00 |
| 144 Jesse Jefferson | .15 |
| 145 Rick Monday | .15 |
| 146 Doyle Alexander | .15 |
| 147 Lee Mazzilli | .20 |
| 148 Andre Thornton | .25 |
| 149 Dale Murray | .15 |
| 150 Bobby Bonds | .50 |
| 151 Milt Wilcox | .15 |
| 152 Ivan DeJesus | .15 |
| 153 Steve Stone | .15 |
| 154 Cecil Cooper | .30 |
| 155 Butch Hobson | .15 |
| 156 Andy Messersmith | .15 |
| 157 Pete LaCock | .15 |
| 158 Joaquin Andujar | .20 |
| 159 Lou Piniella | .40 |
| 160 Jim Palmer | 4.00 |
| 161 Bob Boone | .50 |
| 162 Paul Thormodsgard | .15 |
| 163 Bill North | .15 |
| 164 Bob Owchinko | .15 |
| 165 Rennie Stennett | .15 |
| 166 Carlos Lopez | .15 |
| 167 Tim Foli | .15 |
| 168 Reggie Smith | .25 |
| 169 Jerry Johnson | .15 |
| 170 Lou Brock | 2.25 |
| 171 Pat Zachry | .15 |
| 172 Mike Hargrove | .15 |
| 173 Robin Yount | 15.00 |
| 174 Wayne Garland | .15 |
| 175 Jerry Morales | .15 |
| 176 Milt May | .15 |
| 177 Gene Garber | .15 |
| 178 Dave Chalk | .15 |
| 179 Dick Tidrow | .15 |
| 180 Dave Concepcion | .50 |
| 181 Ken Forsch | .15 |
| 182 Jim Spencer | .15 |
| 183 Doug Bird | .15 |
| 184 Checklist No. 2 | .75 |
| 185 Ellis Valentine | .15 |
| 186 Bob Stanley (R) | .35 |
| 187 Jerry Royster | .15 |
| 188 Al Bumbry | .15 |
| 189 Tom Lasorda (Mgr.) | .20 |
| 190 John Candelaria | .20 |
| 191 Rodney Scott | .15 |

| NO. PLAYER | NR. MT. |
|---|---|
| 192 San Diego Padres | .50 |
| 193 Rich Chiles | .15 |
| 194 Derrel Thomas | .15 |
| 195 Larry Dierker | .15 |
| 196 Bob Bailor | .15 |
| 197 Nino Espinosa | .15 |
| 198 Ron Pruitt | .15 |
| 199 Craig Reynolds | .15 |
| 200 Reggie Jackson | 7.00 |
| 201 Batting Leaders: | 1.00 |
| Dave Parker, Rod Carew | |
| 202 Home Run Leaders: | .25 |
| George Foster, Jim Rice | |
| 203 RBI Leaders: | .25 |
| George Foster, Larry Hisle | |
| 204 Stolen Base Leaders: | .20 |
| F. Taveras, Freddie Patek | |
| 205 Victory Leaders: | .60 |
| Steve Carlton, D. Goltz, | |
| D. Leonard, J. Palmer | |
| 206 Strikeout Leaders: | 1.25 |
| Phil Niekro, Nolan Ryan | |
| 207 ERA Leaders: | .20 |
| J. Candelaria, F. Tanana | |
| 208 Leading Firemen: | .30 |
| R. Fingers, B. Campbell | |
| 209 Dock Ellis | .15 |
| 210 Jose Cardenal | .15 |
| 211 Earl Weaver (Mgr.) | .15 |
| 212 Mike Caldwell | .15 |
| 213 Alan Bannister | .15 |
| 214 California Angels | .50 |
| 215 Darrell Evans | .35 |
| 216 Mike Paxton | .15 |
| 217 Rod Gilbreath | .15 |
| 218 Marty Pattin | .15 |
| 219 Mike Cubbage | .15 |
| 220 Pedro Borbon | .15 |
| 221 Chris Speier | .15 |
| 222 Jerry Martin | .15 |
| 223 Bruce Kison | .15 |
| 224 Jerry Tabb | .15 |
| 225 Don Gullett | .15 |
| 226 Joe Ferguson | .15 |
| 227 Al Fitzmorris | .15 |
| 228 Manny Mota | .15 |
| 229 Leo Foster | .15 |
| 230 Al Hrabosky | .15 |
| 231 Wayne Nordhagen | .15 |
| 232 Mickey Stanley | .15 |
| 233 Dick Pole | .15 |
| 234 Herman Franks (Mgr.) | .15 |
| 235 Tim McCarver | .35 |
| 236 Terry Whitfield | .15 |
| 237 Rich Dauer | .15 |
| 238 Juan Beniquez | .15 |
| 239 Dyar Miller | .15 |
| 240 Gene Tenace | .15 |
| 241 Pete Vuckovich | .20 |
| 242 Barry Bonnell | .15 |
| 243 Bob McClure | .15 |
| 244 Montreal Expos | .40 |
| 245 Rick Burleson | .15 |
| 246 Dan Driessen | .15 |
| 247 Larry Christenson | .15 |
| 248 Frank White | .15 |

| NO. PLAYER | NR. MT. | NO. PLAYER | NR. MT. | NO. PLAYER | NR. MT. | NO. PLAYER | NR. MT. |
|---|---|---|---|---|---|---|---|
| 249 Dave Goltz | .15 | 334 John Stearns | .15 | 416 Jack Brohamer | .15 | 501 Dave Roberts | .15 |
| 250 Graig Nettles | .25 | 335 Bucky Dent | .30 | 417 Mike Garman | .15 | 502 Pat Rockett | .15 |
| 251 Don Kirkwood | .15 | 336 Steve Busby | .15 | 418 Tony Muser | .15 | 503 Ike Hampton | .15 |
| 252 Steve Swisher | .15 | 337 Tom Grieve | .15 | 419 Jerry Garvin | .15 | 504 Roger Freed | .15 |
| 253 Jim Kern | .15 | 338 Dave Heaverlo | .15 | 420 Greg Luzinski | .30 | 505 Felix Millan | .15 |
| 254 Dave Collins | .20 | 339 Mario Guerrero | .15 | 421 Junior Moore | .15 | 506 Ron Blomberg | .15 |
| 255 Jerry Reuss | .20 | 340 Bake McBride | .15 | 422 Steve Braun | .15 | 507 Willie Crawford | .15 |
| 256 Joe Altobelli (Mgr.) | .15 | 341 Mike Flanagan | .25 | 423 Dave Rosello | .15 | 508 Johnny Oates | .15 |
| 257 Hector Cruz | .15 | 342 Aurelio Rodriguez | .15 | 424 Boston Red Sox | .50 | 509 Brent Strom | .15 |
| 258 John Hiller | .15 | 343 John Wathan | .15 | 425 Steve Rogers | .15 | 510 Willie Stargell | 2.50 |
| 259 Los Angeles Dodgers | .50 | 344 Sam Ewing | .15 | 426 Fred Kendall | .15 | 511 Frank Duffy | .15 |
| 260 Bert Campaneris | .20 | 345 Luis Tiant | .25 | 427 Mario Soto (R) | .35 | 512 Larry Herndon | .20 |
| 261 Tim Hosely | .15 | 346 Larry Biittner | .15 | 428 Joel Youngblood | .15 | 513 Barry Foote | .15 |
| 262 Rudy May | .15 | 347 Terry Forster | .20 | 429 Mike Barlow | .15 | 514 Rob Sperring | .15 |
| 263 Danny Walton | .15 | 348 Del Unser | .15 | 430 Al Oliver | .40 | 515 Tim Corcoran | .15 |
| 264 Jamie Easterly | .15 | 349 Rick Camp | .15 | 431 Butch Metzger | .15 | 516 Gary Beare | .15 |
| 265 Sal Bando | .15 | 350 Steve Garvey | 3.00 | 432 Terry Bulling | .15 | 517 Andres Mora | .15 |
| 266 Bob Shirley | .15 | 351 Jeff Torborg (Mgr.) | .15 | 433 Fernando Gonzalez | .15 | 518 Tommy Boggs | .15 |
| 267 Doug Ault | .15 | 352 Tony Scott | .15 | 434 Mike Norris | .15 | 519 Brian Downing | .30 |
| 268 Gil Flores | .15 | 353 Doug Bair | .15 | 435 Checklist No. 4 | .75 | 520 Larry Hisle | .15 |
| 269 Wayne Twitchell | .15 | 354 Cesar Geronimo | .15 | 436 Vic Harris | .15 | 521 Steve Staggs | .15 |
| 270 Carlton Fisk | 4.00 | 355 Bill Travers | .15 | 437 Bo McLaughlin | .15 | 522 Dick Williams (Mgr.) | .20 |
| 271 Randy Lerch | .15 | 356 New York Mets | .50 | 438 John Ellis | .15 | 523 Donnie Moore (R) | .40 |
| 272 Royle Stillman | .15 | 357 Tom Poquette | .15 | 439 Ken Kravec | .15 | 524 Bernie Carbo | .15 |
| 273 Fred Norman | .15 | 358 Mark Lemongello | .15 | 440 Dave Lopes | .25 | 525 Jerry Terrell | .15 |
| 274 Freddie Patek | .15 | 359 Marc Hill | .15 | 441 Larry Gura | .20 | 526 Cincinnati Reds | .45 |
| 275 Dan Ford | .15 | 360 Mike Schmidt | 15.00 | 442 Elliott Maddox | .15 | 527 Vic Correll | .15 |
| 276 Bill Bonham | .15 | 361 Chris Knapp | .15 | 443 Darrell Chaney | .15 | 528 Rob Picciolo | .15 |
| 277 Bruce Boisclair | .15 | 362 Dave May | .15 | 444 Roy Hartsfield (Mgr.) | .15 | 529 Paul Hartzell | .15 |
| 278 Enrique Romo | .15 | 363 Bob Randall | .15 | 445 Mike Ivie | .15 | 530 Dave Winfield | 5.00 |
| 279 Bill Virdon (Mgr.) | .20 | 364 Jerry Turner | .15 | 446 Tug McGraw | .25 | 531 Tom Underwood | .15 |
| 280 Buddy Bell | .30 | 365 Ed Figueroa | .15 | 447 Leroy Stanton | .15 | 532 Skip Jutze | .15 |
| 281 Eric Rasmussen | .15 | 366 Larry Milbourne | .15 | 448 Bill Castro | .15 | 533 Sandy Alomar | .15 |
| 282 New York Yankees | .75 | 367 Rick Dempsey | .20 | 449 Tim Blackwell | .15 | 534 Wilbur Howard | .15 |
| 283 Omar Moreno | .20 | 368 Balor Moore | .15 | 450 Tom Seaver | 5.00 | 535 Checklist No. 5 | .75 |
| 284 Randy Moffitt | .15 | 369 Tim Nordbrook | .15 | 451 Minnesota Twins | .35 | 536 Roric Harrison | .15 |
| 285 Steve Yeager | .15 | 370 Rusty Staub | .25 | 452 Jerry Mumphrey | .15 | 537 Bruce Bochte | .15 |
| 286 Ben Oglivie | .20 | 371 Ray Burris | .15 | 453 Doug Flynn | .15 | 538 Johnnie LeMaster | .15 |
| 287 Kiko Garcia | .15 | 372 Brian Asselstine | .15 | 454 Dave LaRoche | .15 | 539 Vic Davalillo | .15 |
| 288 Dave Hamilton | .15 | 373 Jim Willoughby | .15 | 455 Bill Robinson | .15 | 540 Steve Carlton | 4.00 |
| 289 Checklist No. 3 | .75 | 374 Jose Morales | .15 | 456 Vern Ruhle | .15 | 541 Larry Cox | .15 |
| 290 Willie Horton | .20 | 375 Tommy John | .60 | 457 Bob Bailey | .15 | 542 Tim Johnson | .15 |
| 291 Gary Ross | .15 | 376 Jim Wohlford | .15 | 458 Jeff Newman | .15 | 543 Larry Harlow | .15 |
| 292 Gene Richards | .15 | 377 Manny Sarmiento | .15 | 459 Charlie Spikes | .15 | 544 Len Randle | .15 |
| 293 Mike Willis | .15 | 378 Bobby Winkles (Mgr.) | .15 | 460 Jim Hunter | 1.50 | 545 Bill Campbell | .15 |
| 294 Larry Parrish | .20 | 379 Skip Lockwood | .15 | 461 Rob Andrews | .15 | 546 Ted Martinez | .15 |
| 295 Bill Lee | .15 | 380 Ted Simmons | .40 | 462 Rogelio Moret | .15 | 547 John Scott | .15 |
| 296 Biff Pocoroba | .15 | 381 Philadelphia Phillies | .50 | 463 Kevin Bell | .15 | 548 Billy Hunter (Mgr.) | .15 |
| 297 Warren Brusstar | .15 | 382 Joe Lahoud | .15 | 464 Jerry Grote | .15 | 549 Joe Kerrigan | .15 |
| 298 Tony Armas | .40 | 383 Mario Mendoza | .15 | 465 Hal McRae | .20 | 550 John Mayberry | .20 |
| 299 Whitey Herzog (Mgr.) | .20 | 384 Jack Clark | 3.00 | 466 Dennis Blair | .15 | 551 Atlanta Braves | .35 |
| 300 Joe Morgan | 2.25 | 385 Tito Fuentes | .15 | 467 Alvin Dark (Mgr.) | .15 | 552 Francisco Barrios | .15 |
| 301 Buddy Schultz | .15 | 386 Bob Gorinski | .15 | 468 Warren Cromartie | .30 | 553 Terry Puhl (R) | .45 |
| 302 Chicago Cubs | .50 | 387 Ken Holtzman | .15 | 469 Rick Cerone | .15 | 554 Joe Coleman | .15 |
| 303 Sam Hinds | .15 | 388 Bill Fahey | .15 | 470 J.R. Richard | .20 | 555 Butch Wynegar | .20 |
| 304 John Milner | .15 | 389 Julio Gonzalez | .15 | 471 Roy Smalley | .15 | 556 Ed Armbrister | .15 |
| 305 Rico Carty | .25 | 390 Oscar Gamble | .15 | 472 Ron Reed | .15 | 557 Tony Solaita | .15 |
| 306 Joe Niekro | .25 | 391 Larry Haney | .15 | 473 Bill Buckner | .25 | 558 Paul Mitchell | .15 |
| 307 Glenn Borgmann | .15 | 392 Billy Almon | .15 | 474 Jim Slaton | .15 | 559 Phil Mankowski | .15 |
| 308 Jim Rooker | .15 | 393 Tippy Martinez | .15 | 475 Gary Matthews | .25 | 560 Dave Parker | 4.00 |
| 309 Cliff Johnson | .15 | 394 Roy Howell | .15 | 476 Bill Stein | .15 | 561 Charlie Williams | .15 |
| 310 Don Sutton | 1.50 | 395 Jim Hughes | .15 | 477 Doug Capilla | .15 | 562 Glenn Burke | .15 |
| 311 Jose Baez | 1.25 | 396 Bob Stinson | .15 | 478 Jerry Remy | .15 | 563 Dave Rader | .15 |
| 312 Greg Minton | .15 | 397 Greg Gross | .15 | 479 St. Louis Cardinals | .50 | 564 Mick Kelleher | .15 |
| 313 Andy Etchebarren | .15 | 398 Don Hood | .15 | 480 Ron LeFlore | .20 | 565 Jerry Koosman | .25 |
| 314 Paul Lindblad | .15 | 399 Pete Mackanin | .15 | 481 Jackson Todd | .15 | 566 Merv Rettenmund | .15 |
| 315 Mark Belanger | .15 | 400 Nolan Ryan | 20.00 | 482 Rick Miller | .15 | 567 Dick Drago | .15 |
| 316 Henry Cruz | .15 | 401 Sparky Anderson (Mgr.) | .20 | 483 Ken Macha | .15 | 568 Tom Hutton | .15 |
| 317 Dave Johnson | .30 | 402 Dave Campbell | .15 | 484 Jim Norris | .15 | 569 Lary Sorensen | .15 |
| 318 Tom Griffin | .15 | 403 Bud Harrelson | .15 | 485 Chris Chambliss | .20 | 570 Dave Kingman | .50 |
| 319 Alan Ashby | .15 | 404 Detroit Tigers | .60 | 486 John Curtis | .15 | 571 Buck Martinez | .15 |
| 320 Fred Lynn | 1.00 | 405 Rawly Eastwick | .15 | 487 Jim Tyrone | .15 | 572 Rick Wise | .15 |
| 321 Santo Alcala | .15 | 406 Mike Jorgensen | .15 | 488 Dan Spillner | .15 | 573 Luis Gomez | .15 |
| 322 Tom Paciorek | .15 | 407 Odell Jones | .15 | 489 Rudy Meoli | .15 | 574 Bob Lemon (Mgr.) | .25 |
| 323 Jim Fregosi | .15 | 408 Joe Zdeb | .15 | 490 Amos Otis | .20 | 575 Pat Dobson | .15 |
| 324 Vern Rapp (Mgr.) | .15 | 409 Ron Schueler | .15 | 491 Scott McGregor | .20 | 576 Sam Mejias | .15 |
| 325 Bruce Sutter | .75 | 410 Bill Madlock | .50 | 492 Jim Sundberg | .15 | 577 Oakland A's | .30 |
| 326 Mike Lum | .15 | 411 AL Championships: | .75 | 493 Steve Renko | .15 | 578 Buzz Capra | .15 |
| 327 Rick Langford | .15 | Yankees Defeat Royals | | 494 Chuck Tanner (Mgr.) | .15 | 579 Rance Mulliniks | .15 |
| 328 Milwaukee Brewers | .50 | 412 NL Championships: | .75 | 495 Dave Cash | .15 | 580 Rod Carew | 4.00 |
| 329 John Verhoeven | .15 | Dodgers Defeat Phillies | | 496 Jim Clancy | .20 | 581 Lynn McGlothen | .15 |
| 330 Bob Watson | .15 | 413 World Series: | 1.50 | 497 Glenn Adams | .15 | 582 Fran Healy | .15 |
| 331 Mark Littell | .15 | Yankees Reign Supreme | | 498 Joe Sambito | .15 | 583 George Medich | .15 |
| 332 Duane Kuiper | .15 | 414 Darold Knowles | .15 | 499 Seattle Mariners | .40 | 584 John Hale | .15 |
| 333 Jim Todd | .15 | 415 Ray Fosse | .15 | 500 George Foster | .75 | 585 Woodie Fryman | .15 |

| NO. PLAYER | NR. MT. |
|---|---|
| 586 Ed Goodson | .15 |
| 587 John Urrea | .15 |
| 588 Jim Mason | .15 |
| 589 Bob Knepper (R) | .75 |
| 590 Bobby Murcer | .30 |
| 591 George Zeber | .15 |
| 592 Bob Apodaca | .15 |
| 593 Dave Skaggs | .15 |
| 594 Dave Freisleben | .15 |
| 595 Sixto Lezcano | .15 |
| 596 Gary Wheelock | .15 |
| 597 Steve Dillard | .15 |
| 598 Eddie Solomon | .15 |
| 599 Gary Woods | .15 |
| 600 Frank Tanana | .25 |
| 601 Gene Mauch (Mgr.) | .20 |
| 602 Eric Soderholm | .15 |
| 603 Will McEnaney | .15 |
| 604 Earl Williams | .15 |
| 605 Rick Rhoden | .25 |
| 606 Pittsburgh Pirates | .50 |
| 607 Fernando Arroyo | .15 |
| 608 Johnny Grubb | .15 |
| 609 John Denny | .25 |
| 610 Garry Maddox | .20 |
| 611 Pat Scanlon | .15 |
| 612 Ken Henderson | .15 |
| 613 Marty Perez | .15 |
| 614 Joe Wallis | .15 |
| 615 Clay Carroll | .15 |
| 616 Pat Kelly | .15 |
| 617 Joe Nolan | .15 |
| 618 Tommy Helms | .15 |
| 619 Thad Bosley | .15 |
| 620 Willie Randolph | .50 |
| 621 Craig Swan | .15 |
| 622 Champ Summers | .15 |
| 623 Eduardo Rodriguez | .15 |
| 624 Gary Alexander | .15 |
| 625 Jose Cruz | .35 |
| 626 Toronto Blue Jays | .40 |
| 627 Dave Johnson | .15 |

| NO. PLAYER | NR. MT. |
|---|---|
| 628 Ralph Garr | .15 |
| 629 Don Stanhouse | .15 |
| 630 Ron Cey | .40 |
| 631 Danny Ozark (Mgr.) | .20 |
| 632 Rowland Office | .15 |
| 633 Tom Veryzer | .15 |
| 634 Len Barker | .15 |
| 635 Joe Rudi | .15 |
| 636 Jim Bibby | .15 |
| 637 Duffy Dyer | .15 |
| 638 Paul Splittorff | .15 |
| 639 Gene Clines | .15 |
| 640 Lee May | .15 |
| 641 Doug Rau | .15 |
| 642 Denny Doyle | .15 |
| 643 Tom House | .15 |
| 644 Jim Dwyer | .15 |
| 645 Mike Torrez | .15 |
| 646 Rick Auerbach | .15 |
| 647 Steve Dunning | .15 |
| 648 Gary Thomasson | .15 |
| 649 Moose Haas (R) | .30 |
| 650 Cesar Cedeno | .25 |
| 651 Doug Rader | .15 |
| 652 Checklist No. 6 | .50 |
| 653 Ron Hodges | .15 |
| 654 Pepe Frias | .15 |
| 655 Lyman Bostock | .20 |
| 656 Dave Garcia (Mgr.) | .15 |
| 657 Bombo Rivera | .15 |
| 658 Manny Sanguillen | .15 |
| 659 Texas Rangers | .35 |
| 660 Jason Thompson | .25 |
| 661 Grant Jackson | .15 |
| 662 Paul Dade | .15 |
| 663 Paul Reuschel | .15 |
| 664 Fred Stanley | .15 |
| 665 Dennis Leonard | .20 |
| 666 Billy Smith | .15 |
| 667 Jeff Byrd | .15 |
| 668 Dusty Baker | .25 |

| NO. PLAYER | NR. MT. |
|---|---|
| 669 Pete Falcone | .15 |
| 670 Jim Rice | 3.50 |
| 671 Gary Lavelle | .15 |
| 672 Don Kessinger | .15 |
| 673 Steve Brye | .15 |
| 674 Ray Knight (R) | 1.00 |
| 675 Jay Johnstone | .15 |
| 676 Bob Myrick | .15 |
| 677 Ed Herrmann | .15 |
| 678 Tom Burgmeier | .15 |
| 679 Wayne Garrett | .15 |
| 680 Vida Blue | .20 |
| 681 Rob Belloir | .15 |
| 682 Ken Brett | .15 |
| 683 Mike Champion | .15 |
| 684 Ralph Houk (Mgr.) | .20 |
| 685 Frank Taveras | .15 |
| 686 Gaylord Perry | 1.50 |
| 687 Julio Cruz (R) | .30 |
| 688 George Mitterwald | .15 |
| 689 Cleveland Indians | .50 |
| 690 Mickey Rivers | .20 |
| 691 Ross Grimsley | .15 |
| 692 Ken Reitz | .15 |
| 693 Lamar Johnson | .15 |
| 694 Elias Sosa | .15 |
| 695 Dwight Evans | 1.50 |
| 696 Steve Mingori | .15 |
| 697 Roger Metzger | .15 |
| 698 Juan Bernhardt | .15 |
| 699 Jackie Brown | .15 |
| 700 Johnny Bench | 4.00 |
| 701 Rookie Pitchers: | .40 |
| Larry Landreth, Tom Hume, | |
| Steve McCatty, B. Taylor | |
| 702 Rookie Catchers: | .25 |
| Rick Sweet, Bill Nahordony | |
| Kevin Pasley, Don Werner | |
| 703 Rookie Pitchers: | 10.00 |
| Jack Morris, L. Andersen, | |
| Tim Jones, M. Mahler | |

| NO. PLAYER | NR. MT. |
|---|---|
| 704 Rookie 2nd Basemen: | 12.00 |
| Garth Iorg, Sam Perlozzo, | |
| Dave Oliver, Lou Whitaker | |
| 705 Rookie Outfielders: | .50 |
| D. Bergman, W. Norwood, | |
| M. Dilone, C. Hurdle | |
| 706 Rookie 1st Basemen: | .40 |
| Wayne Cage, Ted Cox, | |
| P. Putnam, D. Revering | |
| 707 Rookie Shortstops: | 50.00 |
| Mickey Klutts, Paul Molitor, | |
| Alan Trammell, | |
| U.L. Washington | |
| 708 Rookie Catchers: | 20.00 |
| Bo Diaz, Dale Murphy, | |
| Ernie Whitt, Lance Parrish | |
| 709 Rookie Pitchers: | .40 |
| Steve Burke, Lance | |
| Rautzhan, Matt Keough, | |
| Dan Schatzeder | |
| 710 Rookie Outfielders: | .75 |
| Dell Alston, Rick Bosetti, | |
| Mike Easler, Keith Smith | |
| 711 Rookie Pitchers: | .35 |
| C. Camper, D. Lamp, | |
| R. Thomas, C. Mitchell | |
| 712 Bobby Valentine | .25 |
| 713 Bob Davis | .15 |
| 714 Mike Anderson | .15 |
| 715 Jim Kaat | .40 |
| 716 Clarence Gaston | .15 |
| 717 Nelson Briles | .15 |
| 718 Ron Jackson | .15 |
| 719 Randy Elliott | .15 |
| 720 Fergie Jenkins | 1.50 |
| 721 Billy Martin (Mgr.) | .50 |
| 722 Pete Broberg | .15 |
| 723 John Wockenfuss | .15 |
| 724 K.C. Royals | .50 |
| 725 Kurt Bevacqua | .15 |
| 726 W. Wood (Exc. .10) | .40 |

## 1979 Topps. . . . Complete Set of 726 Cards—Value $250.00

Features the rookie cards of Pedro Guerrero and Bob Horner. 66 cards were double printed. Card 369 (Bump Wills) was originally issued in error as a "Blue Jay". A corrected card was issued showing Wills as a "Ranger".

| NO. PLAYER | MINT |
|---|---|
| 1 Batting Leaders: | 2.00 |
| Rod Carew, Dave Parker | |
| 2 Home Run Leaders: | .50 |
| Jim Rice, George Foster | |
| 3 RBI Leaders: | .50 |
| Jim Rice, George Foster | |
| 4 Stolen Base Leaders: | .35 |
| Ron LeFlore, Omar Moreno | |
| 5 Victory Leaders: | .40 |
| Ron Guidry, Gaylord Perry | |
| 6 Stikeout Leaders: | 2.50 |
| Nolan Ryan, J.R. Richard | |
| 7 ERA Leaders: | .35 |
| Ron Guidry, Craig Swan | |
| 8 Leading Firemen: | .45 |
| R. Gossage, R. Fingers | |

| NO. PLAYER | MINT |
|---|---|
| 9 Dave Campbell | .10 |
| 10 Lee May | .10 |
| 11 Marc Hill | .10 |
| 12 Dick Drago | .10 |
| 13 Paul Dade | .10 |
| 14 Rafael Landestoy | .10 |
| 15 Ross Grimsley | .10 |
| 16 Fred Stanley | .10 |
| 17 Donnie Moore | .15 |
| 18 Tony Solaita | .10 |
| 19 Larry Gura | .10 |
| 20 Joe Morgan | 1.00 |
| 21 Kevin Kobel | .10 |
| 22 Mike Jorgensen | .10 |
| 23 Terry Forster | .15 |
| 24 Paul Molitor | 4.00 |

| NO. PLAYER | MINT |
|---|---|
| 25 Steve Carlton | 3.00 |
| 26 Jamie Quirk | .10 |
| 27 Dave Goltz | .10 |
| 28 Steve Brye | .10 |
| 29 Rick Langford | .10 |
| 30 Dave Winfield | 4.00 |
| 31 Tom House | .10 |
| 32 Jerry Mumphrey | .15 |
| 33 Dave Rozema | .10 |
| 34 Rob Andrews | .10 |
| 35 Ed Figueroa | .10 |
| 36 Alan Ashby | .10 |
| 37 Joe Kerrigan | .10 |
| 38 Bernie Carbo | .10 |
| 39 Dale Murphy | 8.00 |
| 40 Dennis Eckersley | 3.00 |

| NO. PLAYER | MINT |
|---|---|
| 41 Minnesota Twins/ | .40 |
| Gene Mauch (Mgr.) | |
| 42 Ron Blomberg | .10 |
| 43 Wayne Twitchell | .10 |
| 44 Kurt Bevacqua | .10 |
| 45 Al Hrabosky | .10 |
| 46 Ron Hodges | .10 |
| 47 Fred Norman | .10 |
| 48 Merv Rettenmund | .10 |
| 49 Vern Ruhle | .10 |
| 50 Steve Garvey | 1.25 |
| 51 Ray Fosse | .10 |
| 52 Randy Lerch | .10 |
| 53 Mick Kelleher | .10 |
| 54 Del Alston | .10 |
| 55 Wllie Stargell | 2.50 |

| NO. | PLAYER | MINT |
|---|---|---|
| 56 | John Hale | .10 |
| 57 | Eric Rasmussen | .10 |
| 58 | Bob Randall | .10 |
| 59 | John Denny | .10 |
| 60 | Mickey Rivers | .15 |
| 61 | Bo Diaz | .25 |
| 62 | Randy Moffitt | .10 |
| 63 | Jack Brohamer | .10 |
| 64 | Tom Underwood | .10 |
| 65 | Mark Belanger | .10 |
| 66 | Tigers/L. Moss (Mgr.) | .50 |
| 67 | Jim Mason | .10 |
| 68 | Joe Niekro | .10 |
| 69 | Elliott Maddox | .10 |
| 70 | John Candelaria | .15 |
| 71 | Brian Downing | .30 |
| 72 | Steve Mingori | .10 |
| 73 | Ken Henderson | .10 |
| 74 | Shane Rawley (R) | .40 |
| 75 | Steve Yeager | .10 |
| 76 | Warren Cromartie | .10 |
| 77 | Dan Briggs | .10 |
| 78 | Elias Sosa | .10 |
| 79 | Ted Cox | .10 |
| 80 | Jason Thompson | .15 |
| 81 | Roger Erickson | .10 |
| 82 | Mets/J. Torre (Mgr.) | .40 |
| 83 | Fred Kendall | .10 |
| 84 | Greg Minton | .10 |
| 85 | Gary Matthews | .20 |
| 86 | Rodney Scott | .10 |
| 87 | Pete Falcone | .10 |
| 88 | Bob Molinaro | .10 |
| 89 | Dick Tidrow | .10 |
| 90 | Bob Boone | .35 |
| 91 | Terry Crowley | .10 |
| 92 | Jim Bibby | .10 |
| 93 | Phil Mankowski | .10 |
| 94 | Len Barker | .15 |
| 95 | Robin Yount | 9.00 |
| 96 | Cleveland Indians/ Jeff Torborg (Mgr.) | .25 |
| 97 | Sam Mejias | .10 |
| 98 | Ray Burris | .10 |
| 99 | John Wathan | .10 |
| 100 | Tom Seaver | 2.50 |
| 101 | Roy Howell | .10 |
| 102 | Mike Anderson | .10 |
| 103 | Jim Todd | .10 |
| 104 | Johnny Oates | .10 |
| 105 | Rick Camp | .10 |
| 106 | Frank Duffy | .10 |
| 107 | Jesus Alou | .10 |
| 108 | Eduardo Rodriguez | .10 |
| 109 | Joel Youngblood | .10 |
| 110 | Vida Blue | .15 |
| 111 | Roger Freed | .10 |
| 112 | Philadelphia Phillies/ Danny Ozark (Mgr.) | .35 |
| 113 | Pete Redfern | .10 |
| 114 | Cliff Johnson | .10 |
| 115 | Nolan Ryan | 16.00 |
| 116 | Ozzie Smith (R) | 60.00 |
| 117 | Grant Jackson | .10 |
| 118 | Bud Harrelson | .10 |
| 119 | Don Stanhouse | .10 |
| 120 | Jim Sundberg | .10 |
| 121 | Checklist No. 1 | .20 |
| 122 | Mike Paxton | .10 |
| 123 | Lou Whitaker | 4.00 |
| 124 | Dan Schatzeder | .10 |
| 125 | Rick Burleson | .10 |
| 126 | Doug Bair | .10 |
| 127 | Thad Bosley | .10 |
| 128 | Ted Martinez | .10 |
| 129 | Marty Pattin | .10 |
| 130 | Bob Watson | .10 |
| 131 | Jim Clancy | .10 |
| 132 | Rowland Office | .10 |
| 133 | Bill Castro | .10 |
| 134 | Alan Bannister | .10 |
| 135 | Bobby Murcer | .25 |
| 136 | Jim Kaat | .45 |
| 137 | Larry Wolfe | .10 |
| 138 | Mark Lee | .10 |
| 139 | Luis Pujols | .10 |
| 140 | Don Gullett | .10 |
| 141 | Tom Paciorek | .10 |
| 142 | Charlie Williams | .10 |
| 143 | Tony Scott | .10 |
| 144 | Sandy Alomar | .10 |
| 145 | Rick Rhoden | .20 |
| 146 | Duane Kuiper | .10 |
| 147 | Dave Hamilton | .10 |
| 148 | Bruce Boisclair | .10 |
| 149 | Manny Sarmiento | .10 |
| 150 | Wayne Cage | .10 |
| 151 | John Hiller | .10 |
| 152 | Rick Cerone | .15 |
| 153 | Dennis Lamp | .10 |
| 154 | Jim Gantner | .10 |
| 155 | Dwight Evans | 1.25 |
| 156 | Buddy Solomon | .10 |
| 157 | U.L. Washington | .10 |
| 158 | Joe Sambito | .10 |
| 159 | Roy White | .10 |
| 160 | Mike Flanagan | .35 |
| 161 | Barry Foote | .10 |
| 162 | Tom Johnson | .10 |
| 163 | Glenn Burke | .10 |
| 164 | Mickey Lolich | .15 |
| 165 | Frank Taveras | .10 |
| 166 | Leon Roberts | .10 |
| 167 | Roger Metzger | .10 |
| 168 | Dave Freisleben | .10 |
| 169 | Bill Nahorodny | .10 |
| 170 | Don Sutton | 1.25 |
| 171 | Gene Clines | .10 |
| 172 | Mike Bruhert | .10 |
| 173 | John Lowenstein | .10 |
| 174 | Rick Auerbach | .10 |
| 175 | George Hendrick | .15 |
| 176 | Aurelio Rodriguez | .10 |
| 177 | Ron Reed | .10 |
| 178 | Alvis Woods | .10 |
| 179 | Jim Beattie | .10 |
| 180 | Larry Hisle | .10 |
| 181 | Mike Garman | .10 |
| 182 | Tim Johnson | .10 |
| 183 | Paul Splittorff | .10 |
| 184 | Darrel Chaney | .10 |
| 185 | Mike Torrez | .10 |
| 186 | Eric Soderholm | .10 |
| 187 | Mark Lemongello | .10 |
| 188 | Pat Kelly | .10 |
| 189 | Eddie Whitson (R) | .75 |
| 190 | Ron Cey | .40 |
| 191 | Mike Norris | .10 |
| 192 | St. Louis Cardinals/ Ken Boyer (Mgr.) | .35 |
| 193 | Glenn Adams | .10 |
| 194 | Randy Jones | .10 |
| 195 | Bill Madlock | .40 |
| 196 | Steve Kemp | .10 |
| 197 | Bob Apodaca | .10 |
| 198 | Johnny Grubb | .10 |
| 199 | Larry Milbourne | .10 |
| 200 | Johnny Bench | 2.00 |
| 201 | Record — M. Edwards Most Unassisted DP's by 2nd Baseman | .15 |
| 202 | Record — R. Guidry Most Strikeouts, Lefthander, 9 Inning Game | .25 |
| 203 | Record — J.R. Richard Most Season Stikeouts, Righthander | .25 |
| 204 | Record — P. Rose Most Consecutive Games Batting Safely | 1.25 |
| 205 | Record — J. Stearns Most Steals by Catcher, Season | .20 |
| 206 | Record — S. Stewart 7 Straight Stikeouts, First Major League Game | .20 |
| 207 | Dave Lemanczyk | .10 |
| 208 | Clarence Gaston | .10 |
| 209 | Reggie Cleveland | .10 |
| 210 | Larry Bowa | .20 |
| 211 | Denny Martinez | .50 |
| 212 | Carney Lansford (R) | 4.50 |
| 213 | Bill Travers | .10 |
| 214 | Boston Red Sox/ Don Zimmer (Mgr.) | .45 |
| 215 | Willie McCovey | 2.00 |
| 216 | Wilbur Wood | .10 |
| 217 | Steve Dillard | .10 |
| 218 | Dennis Leonard | .15 |
| 219 | Roy Smalley | .10 |
| 220 | Cesar Geronimo | .10 |
| 221 | Jesse Jefferson | .10 |
| 222 | Bob Beall | .10 |
| 223 | Kent Tekulve | .15 |
| 224 | Dave Revering | .10 |
| 225 | Rich Gossage | .50 |
| 226 | Ron Pruitt | .10 |
| 227 | Steve Stone | .10 |
| 228 | Vic Davalillo | .10 |
| 229 | Doug Flynn | .10 |
| 230 | Bob Forsch | .10 |
| 231 | Johnny Wockenfuss | .10 |
| 232 | Jimmy Sexton | .10 |
| 233 | Paul Mitchell | .10 |
| 234 | Toby Harrah | .10 |
| 235 | Steve Rogers | .15 |
| 236 | Jim Dwyer | .10 |
| 237 | Billy Smith | .10 |
| 238 | Balor Moore | .10 |
| 239 | Willie Horton | .10 |
| 240 | Rick Reuschel | .30 |
| 241 | Checklist No. 2 | .20 |
| 242 | Pablo Torrealba | .10 |
| 243 | Buck Martinez | .10 |
| 244 | Pittsburgh Pirates/ Chuck Tanner (Mgr.) | .35 |
| 245 | Jeff Burroughs | .10 |
| 246 | Darrell Jackson | .10 |
| 247 | Tucker Ashford | .10 |
| 248 | Pete LaCock | .10 |
| 249 | Paul Thormodsgard | .10 |
| 250 | Willie Randolph | .35 |
| 251 | Jack Morris | 4.00 |
| 252 | Bob Stinson | .10 |
| 253 | Rick Wise | .10 |
| 254 | Luis Gomez | .10 |
| 255 | Tommy John | .75 |
| 256 | Mike Sadek | .10 |
| 257 | Adrian Devine | .10 |
| 258 | Mike Phillips | .10 |
| 259 | Cincinnati Reds/ Sparky Anderson (Mgr.) | .40 |
| 260 | Richie Zisk | .10 |
| 261 | Mario Guerrero | .10 |
| 262 | Nelson Briles | .10 |
| 263 | Oscar Gamble | .10 |
| 264 | Don Robinson (R) | .75 |
| 265 | Don Money | .10 |
| 266 | Jim Willoughby | .10 |
| 267 | Joe Rudi | .10 |
| 268 | Julio Gonzalez | .10 |
| 269 | Woodie Fryman | .10 |
| 270 | Butch Hobson | .10 |
| 271 | Rawly Eastwick | .10 |
| 272 | Tim Corcoran | .10 |
| 273 | Jerry Terrell | .10 |
| 274 | Willie Norwood | .10 |
| 275 | Junior Moore | .10 |
| 276 | Jim Colborn | .10 |
| 277 | Tom Grieve | .10 |
| 278 | Andy Messersmith | .20 |
| 279 | Jerry Grote | .10 |
| 280 | Andre Thornton | .15 |
| 281 | Vic Correll | .10 |
| 282 | Toronto Blue Jays/ Roy Hartsfield (Mgr.) | .20 |
| 283 | Ken Kravec | .10 |
| 284 | Johnnie LeMaster | .10 |
| 285 | Bobby Bonds | .40 |
| 286 | Duffy Dyer | .10 |
| 287 | Andres Mora | .10 |
| 288 | Milt Wilcox | .10 |
| 289 | Jose Cruz | .25 |
| 290 | Dave Lopes | .20 |
| 291 | Tom Griffin | .10 |
| 292 | Don Reynolds | .10 |
| 293 | Jerry Garvin | .10 |
| 294 | Pepe Frias | .10 |
| 295 | Mitchell Page | .10 |
| 296 | Preston Hanna | .10 |
| 297 | Ted Sizemore | .10 |
| 298 | Rich Gale | .10 |
| 299 | Steve Ontiveros | .10 |
| 300 | Rod Carew | 3.00 |
| 301 | Tom Hume | .10 |
| 302 | Atlanta Braves/ Bobby Cox (Mgr.) | .35 |
| 303 | Lary Sorensen | .10 |
| 304 | Steve Swisher | .10 |
| 305 | Willie Montanez | .10 |
| 306 | Floyd Bannister | .15 |
| 307 | Larvell Blanks | .10 |
| 308 | Bert Blyleven | .75 |
| 309 | Ralph Garr | .10 |
| 310 | Thurman Munson | 2.50 |
| 311 | Gary Lavelle | .10 |
| 312 | Bob Robertson | .10 |
| 313 | Dyar Miller | .10 |
| 314 | Larry Harlow | .10 |
| 315 | John Matlack | .10 |
| 316 | Milt May | .10 |
| 317 | Jose Cardenal | .10 |
| 318 | Bob Welch (R) | 12.00 |
| 319 | Wayne Garrett | .10 |
| 320 | Carl Yastrzemski | 3.00 |
| 321 | Gaylord Perry | 1.50 |
| 322 | Danny Goodwin | .10 |
| 323 | Lynn McGlothen | .10 |
| 324 | Mike Tyson | .10 |
| 325 | Cecil Cooper | .50 |
| 326 | Pedro Borbon | .10 |
| 327 | Art Howe | .10 |
| 328 | Oakland A's/ Jack McKeon (Mgr.) | .20 |
| 329 | Joe Coleman | .10 |
| 330 | George Brett | 10.00 |
| 331 | Mickey Mahler | .10 |
| 332 | Gary Alexander | .10 |
| 333 | Chet Lemon | .35 |
| 334 | Craig Swan | .10 |
| 335 | Chris Chambliss | .15 |
| 336 | Bobby Thompson | .10 |
| 337 | John Montague | .10 |
| 338 | Vic Harris | .10 |
| 339 | Ron Jackson | .10 |
| 340 | Jim Palmer | 3.00 |
| 341 | Willie Upshaw (R) | .25 |
| 342 | Dave Roberts | .10 |
| 343 | Ed Glynn | .10 |
| 344 | Jerry Royster | .10 |
| 345 | Tug McGraw | .20 |
| 346 | Bill Buckner | .20 |
| 347 | Doug Rau | .10 |
| 348 | Andre Dawson | 8.00 |
| 349 | Jim Wright | .10 |
| 350 | Garry Templeton | .30 |
| 351 | Wayne Nordhagen | .10 |
| 352 | Steve Renko | .10 |
| 353 | Checklist No. 3 | .50 |
| 354 | Bill Bonham | .10 |
| 355 | Lee Mazzilli | .15 |
| 356 | San Francisco Giants/ Joe Altobelli (Mgr.) | .40 |
| 357 | Jerry Augustine | .10 |
| 358 | Alan Trammell | 12.00 |
| 359 | Dan Spillner | .15 |
| 360 | Amos Otis | .15 |
| 361 | Tom Dixon | .10 |
| 362 | Mike Cubbage | .10 |
| 363 | Craig Skok | .10 |
| 364 | Gene Richards | .10 |
| 365 | Sparky Lyle | .15 |
| 366 | Juan Bernhardt | .10 |
| 367 | Dave Skaggs | .10 |
| 368 | Don Aase | .10 |
| 369 | Bump Wills (error) (Blue Jays) | 3.00 |
| 369 | Bump Wills (correct) (Rangers) | 4.00 |
| 370 | Dave Kingman | .40 |

| NO. | PLAYER | MINT |
|---|---|---|
| 371 | Jeff Holly | .10 |
| 372 | Lamar Johnson | .10 |
| 373 | Lance Rautzhan | .10 |
| 374 | Ed Herrmann | .10 |
| 375 | Bill Campbell | .10 |
| 376 | Gorman Thomas | .35 |
| 377 | Paul Moskau | .10 |
| 378 | Rob Picciolo | .10 |
| 379 | Dale Murray | .10 |
| 380 | John Mayberry | .15 |
| 381 | Houston Astros/ Bill Virdon (Mgr.) | .25 |
| 382 | Jerry Martin | .10 |
| 383 | Phil Garner | .10 |
| 384 | Tommy Boggs | .10 |
| 385 | Dan Ford | .10 |
| 386 | Francisco Barrios | .10 |
| 387 | Gary Thomasson | .10 |
| 388 | Jack Billingham | .10 |
| 389 | Joe Zdeb | .10 |
| 390 | Rollie Fingers | 1.25 |
| 391 | Al Oliver | .35 |
| 392 | Doug Ault | .10 |
| 393 | Scott McGregor | .15 |
| 394 | Randy Stein | .10 |
| 395 | Dave Cash | .10 |
| 396 | Bill Plummer | .10 |
| 397 | Sergio Ferrer | .10 |
| 398 | Ivan DeJesus | .10 |
| 399 | David Clyde | .10 |
| 400 | Jim Rice | 2.50 |
| 401 | Ray Knight | .15 |
| 402 | Paul Hartzell | .10 |
| 403 | Tim Foli | .10 |
| 404 | Chicago White Sox/ Don Kessinger (Mgr.) | .25 |
| 405 | Butch Wynegar | .10 |
| 406 | Joe Wallis | .10 |
| 407 | Pete Vuckovich | .10 |
| 408 | Charlie Moore | .10 |
| 409 | Willie Wilson (R) | 1.75 |
| 410 | Darrell Evans | .30 |
| 411 | All-Time Hits: Season — George Sisler, Career — Ty Cobb | .50 |
| 412 | All-Time RBI's: Season — Hack Wilson Career — Hank Aaron | .50 |
| 413 | All-Time Home Runs: Season — Roger Maris Career — Hank Aaron | .50 |
| 414 | All-Time Batting Avg.: Career — Ty Cobb Season — R. Hornsby | .50 |
| 415 | All-Time Stolen Bases: Career — Lou Brock Season — Lou Brock | .50 |
| 416 | All-Time Wins: Career: Cy Young Season: J. Chesbro | .25 |
| 417 | All-Time Strikeouts: Career: Walter Johnson Season: Nolan Ryan | .25 |
| 418 | All-Time ERA: Career: W. Johnson Season: Dutch Leonard | .25 |
| 419 | Dick Ruthven | .10 |
| 420 | Ken Griffey | .75 |
| 421 | Doug DeCinces | .20 |
| 422 | Ruppert Jones | .15 |
| 423 | Bob Montgomery | .10 |
| 424 | California Angels/ Jim Fregosi (Mgr.) | .30 |
| 425 | Rick Manning | .10 |
| 426 | Chris Speier | .10 |
| 427 | Andy Replogle | .10 |
| 428 | Bobby Valentine | .10 |
| 429 | John Urrea | .10 |
| 430 | Dave Parker | 2.50 |
| 431 | Glenn Borgmann | .10 |
| 432 | Dave Heaverlo | .10 |
| 433 | Larry Biittner | .10 |
| 434 | Ken Clay | .10 |
| 435 | Gene Tenace | .10 |
| 436 | Hector Cruz | .10 |
| 437 | Rick Williams | .10 |
| 438 | Horace Speed | .10 |
| 439 | Frank White | .15 |
| 440 | Rusty Staub | .20 |
| 441 | Lee Lacy | .15 |
| 442 | Doyle Alexander | .10 |
| 443 | Bruce Bochte | .10 |
| 444 | Aurelio Lopez (R) | .25 |
| 445 | Steve Henderson | .10 |
| 446 | Jim Lonborg | .10 |
| 447 | Manny Sanguillen | .10 |
| 448 | Moose Haas | .10 |
| 449 | Bombo Rivera | .10 |
| 450 | Dave Concepcion | .40 |
| 451 | Kansas City Royals/ Whitey Herzog (Mgr.) | .25 |
| 452 | Jerry Morales | .10 |
| 453 | Chris Knapp | .10 |
| 454 | Len Randle | .10 |
| 455 | Bill Lee | .10 |
| 456 | Chuck Baker | .10 |
| 457 | Bruce Sutter | .75 |
| 458 | Jim Essian | .10 |
| 459 | Sid Monge | .10 |
| 460 | Graig Nettles | .40 |
| 461 | Jim Barr | .10 |
| 462 | Otto Velez | .10 |
| 463 | Steve Comer | .10 |
| 464 | Joe Nolan | .10 |
| 465 | Reggie Smith | .20 |
| 466 | Mark Littell | .10 |
| 467 | Don Kessinger | .10 |
| 468 | Stan Bahnsen | .10 |
| 469 | Lance Parrish | 3.00 |
| 470 | Garry Maddox | .10 |
| 471 | Joaquin Andujar | .30 |
| 472 | Craig Kusick | .10 |
| 473 | Dave Roberts | .10 |
| 474 | Dick Davis | .10 |
| 475 | Dan Driessen | .10 |
| 476 | Tom Poquette | .10 |
| 477 | Bob Grich | .15 |
| 478 | Juan Beniquez | .10 |
| 479 | San Diego Padres/ Roger Craig (Mgr.) | .25 |
| 480 | Fred Lynn | .75 |
| 481 | Skip Lockwood | .10 |
| 482 | Craig Reynolds | .10 |
| 483 | Checklist No. 4 | .20 |
| 484 | Rick Waits | .10 |
| 485 | Bucky Dent | .15 |
| 486 | Bob Knepper | .25 |
| 487 | Miguel Dilone | .10 |
| 488 | Bob Owchinko | .10 |
| 489 | Larry Cox (photo of Dave Rader) | .10 |
| 490 | Al Cowens | .10 |
| 491 | Tippy Martinez | .10 |
| 492 | Bob Bailor | .10 |
| 493 | Larry Christenson | .10 |
| 494 | Jerry White | .10 |
| 495 | Tony Perez | 1.00 |
| 496 | Barry Bonnell | .10 |
| 497 | Glenn Abbott | .10 |
| 498 | Rich Chiles | .10 |
| 499 | Texas Rangers/ Pat Corrales (Mgr.) | .25 |
| 500 | Ron Guidry | 1.00 |
| 501 | Junior Kennedy | .10 |
| 502 | Steve Braun | .10 |
| 503 | Terry Humphrey | .10 |
| 504 | Larry McWilliams (R) | .40 |
| 505 | Ed Kranepool | .10 |
| 506 | John D'Acquisto | .10 |
| 507 | Tony Armas | .35 |
| 508 | Charlie Hough | .10 |
| 509 | Mario Mendoza | .10 |
| 510 | Ted Simmons | .35 |
| 511 | Paul Reuschel | .10 |
| 512 | Jack Clark | 2.00 |
| 513 | Dave Johnson | .25 |
| 514 | Mike Proly | .10 |
| 515 | Enos Cabell | .10 |
| 516 | Champ Summers | .10 |
| 517 | Al Bumbry | .10 |
| 518 | Jim Umbarger | .10 |
| 519 | Ben Oglivie | .15 |
| 520 | Gary Carter | 2.50 |
| 521 | Sam Ewing | .10 |
| 522 | Ken Holtzman | .10 |
| 523 | John Milner | .10 |
| 524 | Tom Burgmeier | .10 |
| 525 | Freddie Patek | .10 |
| 526 | Los Angeles Dodgers/ Tom Lasorda (Mgr.) | .50 |
| 527 | Lerrin LaGrow | .10 |
| 528 | Wayne Gross | .10 |
| 529 | Brian Asselstine | .10 |
| 530 | Frank Tanana | .15 |
| 531 | Fernando Gonzalez | .10 |
| 532 | Buddy Schultz | .10 |
| 533 | Leroy Stanton | .10 |
| 534 | Ken Forsch | .10 |
| 535 | Ellis Valentine | .10 |
| 536 | Jerry Reuss | .15 |
| 537 | Tom Veryzer | .10 |
| 538 | Mike Ivie | .10 |
| 539 | John Ellis | .10 |
| 540 | Greg Luzinski | .25 |
| 541 | Jim Slaton | .10 |
| 542 | Rick Bosetti | .10 |
| 543 | Kiko Garcia | .10 |
| 544 | Fergie Jenkins | 1.25 |
| 545 | John Stearns | .10 |
| 546 | Bill Russell | .10 |
| 547 | Clint Hurdle | .10 |
| 548 | Enrique Romo | .10 |
| 549 | Bob Bailey | .10 |
| 550 | Sal Bando | .10 |
| 551 | Chicago Cubs/ Herman Franks (Mgr.) | .35 |
| 552 | Jose Morales | .10 |
| 553 | Denny Walling | .10 |
| 554 | Matt Keough | .10 |
| 555 | Biff Pocoroba | .10 |
| 556 | Mike Lum | .10 |
| 557 | Ken Brett | .10 |
| 558 | Jay Johnstone | .10 |
| 559 | Greg Pryor | .10 |
| 560 | John Montefusco | .10 |
| 561 | Ed Ott | .10 |
| 562 | Dusty Baker | .20 |
| 563 | Roy Thomas | .10 |
| 564 | Jerry Turner | .10 |
| 565 | Rico Carty | .10 |
| 566 | Nino Espinosa | .10 |
| 567 | Rich Hebner | .10 |
| 568 | Carlos Lopez | .10 |
| 569 | Bob Sykes | .10 |
| 570 | Cesar Cedeno | .20 |
| 571 | Darrell Porter | .15 |
| 572 | Rod Gilbreath | .10 |
| 573 | Jim Kern | .10 |
| 574 | Claudell Washington | .15 |
| 575 | Luis Tiant | .20 |
| 576 | Mike Parrott | .10 |
| 577 | Milwaukee Brewers/ George Bamberger (Mgr.) | .30 |
| 578 | Pete Broberg | .10 |
| 579 | Greg Gross | .10 |
| 580 | Ron Fairly | .10 |
| 581 | Darold Knowles | .10 |
| 582 | Paul Blair | .10 |
| 583 | Julio Cruz | .10 |
| 584 | Jim Rooker | .10 |
| 585 | Hal McRae | .15 |
| 586 | Bob Horner (R) | 1.00 |
| 587 | Ken Reitz | .10 |
| 588 | Tom Murphy | .10 |
| 589 | Terry Whitfield | .10 |
| 590 | J.R. Richard | .15 |
| 591 | Mike Hargrove | .10 |
| 592 | Mike Krukow | .10 |
| 593 | Rick Dempsey | .10 |
| 594 | Bob Shirley | .10 |
| 595 | Phil Niekro | 1.25 |
| 596 | Jim Wohlford | .10 |
| 597 | Bob Stanley | .15 |
| 598 | Mark Wagner | .10 |
| 599 | Jim Spencer | .10 |
| 600 | George Foster | .50 |
| 601 | Dave LaRoche | .10 |
| 602 | Checklist No. 5 | .50 |
| 603 | Rudy May | .10 |
| 604 | Jeff Newman | .10 |
| 605 | Rick Monday | .10 |
| 606 | Montreal Expos/ Dick Williams (Mgr.) | .25 |
| 607 | Omar Moreno | .10 |
| 608 | Dave McKay | .10 |
| 609 | Silvio Martinez | .10 |
| 610 | Mike Schmidt | 9.00 |
| 611 | Jim Norris | .10 |
| 612 | Rick Honeycutt (R) | .60 |
| 613 | Mike Edwards | .10 |
| 614 | Willie Hernandez | .25 |
| 615 | Ken Singleton | .15 |
| 616 | Billy Almon | .10 |
| 617 | Terry Puhl | .10 |
| 618 | Jerry Remy | .10 |
| 619 | Ken Landreaux | .20 |
| 620 | Bert Campaneris | .15 |
| 621 | Pat Zachry | .10 |
| 622 | Dave Collins | .15 |
| 623 | Bob McClure | .10 |
| 624 | Larry Herndon | .10 |
| 625 | Mark Fidrych | .15 |
| 626 | New York Yankees/ Bob Lemon (Mgr.) | .40 |
| 627 | Gary Serum | .10 |
| 628 | Del Unser | .10 |
| 629 | Gene Garber | .10 |
| 630 | Bake McBride | .10 |
| 631 | Jorge Orta | .10 |
| 632 | Don Kirkwood | .10 |
| 633 | Rob Wilfong | .10 |
| 634 | Paul Lindblad | .10 |
| 635 | Don Baylor | .75 |
| 636 | Wayne Garland | .10 |
| 637 | Bill Robinson | .10 |
| 638 | Al Fitzmorris | .10 |
| 639 | Manny Trillo | .10 |
| 640 | Eddie Murray | 15.00 |
| 641 | Bobby Castillo | .10 |
| 642 | Wilbur Howard | .10 |
| 643 | Tom Hausman | .10 |
| 644 | Manny Mota | .10 |
| 645 | George Scott | .10 |
| 646 | Rick Sweet | .10 |
| 647 | Bob Lacey | .10 |
| 648 | Lou Piniella | .30 |
| 649 | John Curtis | .10 |
| 650 | Pete Rose | 4.00 |
| 651 | Mike Caldwell | .10 |
| 652 | Stan Papi | .10 |
| 653 | Warren Brusstar | .10 |
| 654 | Rick Miller | .10 |
| 655 | Jerry Koosman | .20 |
| 656 | Hosken Powell | .10 |
| 657 | George Medich | .10 |
| 658 | Taylor Duncan | .10 |
| 659 | Seattle Mariners/ Darrell Johnson (Mgr.) | .20 |
| 660 | Ron LeFlore | .10 |
| 661 | Bruce Kison | .10 |
| 662 | Kevin Bell | .10 |
| 663 | Mike Vail | .10 |
| 664 | Doug Bird | .10 |
| 665 | Lou Brock | 2.00 |
| 666 | Rich Dauer | .10 |
| 667 | Don Hood | .10 |
| 668 | Bill North | .10 |
| 669 | Checklist No. 6 | .50 |
| 670 | Jim Hunter | .75 |
| 671 | Joe Ferguson | .10 |
| 672 | Ed Halicki | .10 |
| 673 | Tom Hutton | .10 |
| 674 | Dave Tomlin | .10 |
| 675 | Tim McCarver | .25 |
| 676 | Johnny Sutton | .10 |
| 677 | Larry Parrish | .10 |
| 678 | Geoff Zahn | .10 |
| 679 | Derrel Thomas | .10 |
| 680 | Carlton Fisk | 3.00 |
| 681 | John Johnson | .10 |
| 682 | Dave Chalk | .10 |

| NO. PLAYER | MINT | NO. PLAYER | MINT | NO. PLAYER | MINT | NO. PLAYER | MINT |
|---|---|---|---|---|---|---|---|
| 683 Dan Meyer | .10 | 703 Angels Prospects: | .15 | 711 A's Prospects: | .45 | 719 Dodgers Prospects: | 8.00 |
| 684 Jamie Easterly | .10 | Bob Slater, J. Anderson, | | Dwayne Murphy, Bruce | | Pedro Guerrero, Rudy Law, | |
| 685 Sixto Lezcano | .10 | Dave Frost | | Robinson, Alan Wirth | | Joe Simpson | |
| 686 Ron Schueler | .10 | 704 White Sox Prospects: | .15 | 712 Mariners Prospects: | .15 | 720 Expos Prospects: | 1.25 |
| 687 Rennie Stennett | .10 | Ross Baumgarten, Mike | | Greg Biercevicz, | | Jerry Fry, Jerry Pirtle, | |
| 688 Mike Willis | .10 | Colbern, Mike Squires | | B. McLaughlin, B. Anderson | | Scott Sanderson | |
| 689 Baltimore Orioles/ | .35 | 705 Indians Prospects: | 1.00 | 713 Rangers Prospects: | 1.00 | 721 Mets Prospects: | .25 |
| Earl Weaver (Mgr.) | | Tim Norrid, D. Oliver, | | Danny Darwin, Pat Putnam, | | Dwight Bernard, Juan | |
| 690 Buddy Bell | .10 | Alfredo Griffin | | Billy Sample | | Berenguer, Dan Norman | |
| 691 Dock Ellis | .10 | 706 Tigers Prospects: | .20 | 714 Blue Jays Prospects: | .15 | 722 Phillies Prospects: | 2.50 |
| 692 Mickey Stanley | .10 | Dave Stegman, Dave Tobik, | | Victor Cruz, Pat Kelly, | | Jim Morrison, Lonnie | |
| 693 Dave Rader | .10 | Kip Young | | Ernie Whitt | | Smith, Jim Wright | |
| 694 Burt Hooton | .10 | 707 Royals Prospects: | .15 | 715 Braves Prospects: | .40 | 723 Pirates Prospects: | .35 |
| 695 Keith Hernandez | 2.00 | Randy Bass, Jim Gaudet, | | Larry Whisenton, Bruce | | Eugenio Cotes, | |
| 696 Andy Hassler | .10 | R. McGilberry | | Benedict, Glenn Hubbard | | B. Wiltbank, Dale Berra | |
| 697 Dave Bergman | .10 | 708 Brewers Prospects: | 1.50 | 716 Cubs Prospects: | .20 | 724 Cardinals Prospects: | .50 |
| 698 Bill Stein | .10 | Kevin Bass, Ned Yost, | | S. Thompson, Dave Geisel, | | Tom Bruno, George | |
| 699 Hal Dues | .10 | Eddie Romero | | Karl Pagel | | Frazier, Terry Kennedy | |
| 700 Reggie Jackson | 3.00 | 709 Twins Prospects: | .15 | 717 Reds Prospects: | .45 | 725 Padres Prospects: | .15 |
| 701 Orioles Prospects: | .35 | R. Sofield, Kevin Stanfield, | | M. LaCoss, Ron Oester, | | Jim Beswick, Broderick | |
| Mark Corey, John Flinn, | | Sam Perlozzo | | Harry Spilman | | Perkins, Steve Mura | |
| Sammy Stewart | | 710 Yankees Prospects: | .40 | 718 Astros Prospects: | .15 | 726 Giants Prospects: | .20 |
| 702 Red Sox Prospects: | .20 | Mike Heath, D. Rajsich, | | Mike Fischlin, Bruce Bochy, | | J. Tamargo, Greg | |
| Garry Hancock, Joel Finch, | | Brian Doyle | | Don Pisker | | Johnston, Joe Strain | |
| Allen Ripton | | | | | | | |

# 1980 Topps. . . . Complete Set of 726 Cards—Value $275.00

Features the rookie cards of Rickey Henderson, Dan Quisenberry, Mike Scott and Dave Stieb. 66 cards were double printed.

| NO. PLAYER | MINT | NO. PLAYER | MINT | NO. PLAYER | MINT | NO. PLAYER | MINT |
|---|---|---|---|---|---|---|---|
| 1 Highlights: Brock and | 2.00 | 30 Vida Blue | .15 | 64 Joe Nolan | .08 | 96 Oakland A's/ | .35 |
| Yaz Get 3000 Hits (exc. .40) | | 31 Jay Johnstone | .08 | 65 Al Bumbry | .08 | Jim Marshall (Mgr.) | |
| 2 Highlights: McCovey | .75 | 32 Julio Cruz | .08 | 66 Kansas City Royals/ | .35 | 97 Bill Lee | .15 |
| 512 Home Runs | | 33 Tony Scott | .08 | Jim Frey (Mgr.) | | 98 Jerry Terrell | .08 |
| 3 Highlights: Manny Mota | .15 | 34 Jeff Newman | .08 | 67 Doyle Alexander | .08 | 99 Victor Cruz | .08 |
| 145 Pinch Hits | | 35 Luis Tiant | .12 | 68 Larry Harlow | .08 | 100 Johnny Bench | 3.00 |
| 4 Highlights: Pete Rose | 2.00 | 36 Rusty Torres | .08 | 69 Rick Williams | .08 | 101 Aurelio Lopez | .08 |
| 10th 200 Hit Season | | 37 Kiko Garcia | .08 | 70 Gary Carter | 2.00 | 102 Rich Dauer | .08 |
| 5 Highlights: G. Templeton | .25 | 38 Dan Spillner | .08 | 71 John Milner | .08 | 103 Bill Caudill (R) | .40 |
| 100 Lefty and Righty Hits | | 39 Rowland Office | .08 | 72 Fred Howard | .08 | 104 Manny Mota | .15 |
| 6 Highlights: Del Unser | .15 | 40 Carlton Fisk | 3.50 | 73 Dave Collins | .08 | 105 Frank Tanana | .15 |
| 3rd Consec. Pinch Homer | | 41 Texas Rangers/ | .30 | 74 Sid Monge | .08 | 106 Jeff Leonard (R) | .75 |
| 7 Mike Lum | .08 | Pat Corrales (Mgr.) | | 75 Bill Russell | .08 | 107 Francisco Barrios | .08 |
| 8 Craig Swan | .08 | 42 Dave Palmer (R) | .40 | 76 John Stearns | .08 | 108 Bob Horner | .30 |
| 9 Steve Braun | .08 | 43 Bombo Rivera | .08 | 77 Dave Stieb (R) | 7.00 | 109 Bill Travers | .08 |
| 10 Denny Martinez | .40 | 44 Bill Fahey | .08 | 78 Ruppert Jones | .08 | 110 Fred Lynn | .25 |
| 11 Jimmy Sexton | .08 | 45 Frank White | .15 | 79 Bob Owchinko | .08 | 111 Bob Knepper | .20 |
| 12 John Curtis | .08 | 46 Rico Carty | .15 | 80 Ron LeFlore | .12 | 112 Chicago White Sox/ | .35 |
| 13 Ron Pruitt | .08 | 47 Bill Bonham | .08 | 81 Ted Sizemore | .08 | Tony LaRussa (Mgr.) | |
| 14 Dave Cash | .08 | 48 Rick Miller | .08 | 82 Houston Astros/ | .35 | 113 Geoff Zahn | .08 |
| 15 Bill Campbell | .08 | 49 Mario Guerrero | .08 | Bill Virdon (Mgr.) | | 114 Juan Beniquez | .12 |
| 16 Jerry Narron | .08 | 50 J. Richard | .12 | 83 Steve Trout (R) | .30 | 115 Sparky Lyle | .15 |
| 17 Bruce Sutter | .50 | 51 Joe Ferguson | .08 | 84 Gary Lavelle | .08 | 116 Larry Cox | .08 |
| 18 Ron Jackson | .08 | 52 Warren Brusstar | .08 | 85 Ted Simmons | .30 | 117 Dock Ellis | .08 |
| 19 Balor Moore | .08 | 53 Ben Oglivie | .12 | 86 Dave Hamilton | .08 | 118 Phil Garner | .08 |
| 20 Dan Ford | .08 | 54 Dennis Lamp | .08 | 87 Pepe Frias | .08 | 119 Sammy Stewart | .08 |
| 21 Manny Sarmiento | .08 | 55 Bill Madlock | .40 | 88 Ken Landreaux | .12 | 120 Greg Luzinski | .25 |
| 22 Pat Putnam | .08 | 56 Bobby Valentine | .12 | 89 Don Hood | .08 | 121 Checklist No. 1 | .25 |
| 23 Derrel Thomas | .08 | 57 Pete Vuckovich | .12 | 90 Manny Trillo | .08 | 122 Dave Rosello | .08 |
| 24 Jim Slaton | .08 | 58 Doug Flynn | .08 | 91 Rick Dempsey | .08 | 123 Lynn Jones | .08 |
| 25 Lee Mazzilli | .12 | 59 Eddy Putman | .08 | 92 Rick Rhoden | .12 | 124 Dave Lemanczyk | .08 |
| 26 Marty Pattin | .08 | 60 Bucky Dent | .12 | 93 Dave Roberts | .08 | 125 Tony Perez | .75 |
| 27 Del Unser | .08 | 61 Gary Serum | .08 | 94 Neil Allen (R) | .25 | 126 Dave Tomlin | .08 |
| 28 Bruce Kison | .08 | 62 Mike Ivie | .08 | 95 Cecil Cooper | .20 | 127 Gary Thomasson | .08 |
| 29 Mark Wagner | .08 | 63 Bob Stanley | .12 | | | 128 Tom Burgmeier | .08 |

| NO. | PLAYER | MINT |
|---|---|---|
| 129 | Craig Reynolds | .08 |
| 130 | Amos Otis | .15 |
| 131 | Paul Mitchell | .08 |
| 132 | Biff Pocoroba | .08 |
| 133 | Jerry Turner | .08 |
| 134 | Matt Keough | .08 |
| 135 | Bill Buckner | .20 |
| 136 | Dick Ruthven | .08 |
| 137 | John Castino | .20 |
| 138 | Ross Baumgarten | .08 |
| 139 | Dane Iorg | .20 |
| 140 | Rich Gossage | .50 |
| 141 | Gary Alexander | .08 |
| 142 | Phil Huffman | .08 |
| 143 | Bruce Bochte | .08 |
| 144 | Steve Comer | .08 |
| 145 | Darrell Evans | .30 |
| 146 | Bob Welch | 1.50 |
| 147 | Terry Puhl | .08 |
| 148 | Manny Sanguillen | .15 |
| 149 | Tom Hume | .08 |
| 150 | Jason Thompson | .15 |
| 151 | Tom Hausman | .12 |
| 152 | John Fulgham | .08 |
| 153 | Tim Blackwell | .08 |
| 154 | Lary Sorensen | .08 |
| 155 | Jerry Remy | .08 |
| 156 | Tony Brizzolara | .08 |
| 157 | Willie Wilson | .25 |
| 158 | Rob Picciolo | .08 |
| 159 | Ken Clay | .08 |
| 160 | Eddie Murray | 7.50 |
| 161 | Larry Christenson | .08 |
| 162 | Bob Randall | .08 |
| 163 | Steve Swisher | .08 |
| 164 | Greg Pryor | .08 |
| 165 | Omar Moreno | .08 |
| 166 | Glenn Abbott | .08 |
| 167 | Jack Clark | 1.50 |
| 168 | Rick Waits | .08 |
| 169 | Luis Gomez | .08 |
| 170 | Burt Hooton | .08 |
| 171 | Fernando Gonzalez | .08 |
| 172 | Ron Hodges | .08 |
| 173 | John Henry Johnson | .08 |
| 174 | Ray Knight | .20 |
| 175 | Rick Reuschel | .20 |
| 176 | Champ Summers | .08 |
| 177 | Dave Heaverlo | .08 |
| 178 | Tim McCarver | .20 |
| 179 | Ron Davis (R) | .25 |
| 180 | Warren Cromartie | .08 |
| 181 | Moose Haas | .08 |
| 182 | Ken Reitz | .08 |
| 183 | Jim Anderson | .08 |
| 184 | Steve Renko | .08 |
| 185 | Hal McRae | .12 |
| 186 | Junior Moore | .08 |
| 187 | Alan Ashby | .08 |
| 188 | Terry Crowley | .08 |
| 189 | Kevin Kobel | .08 |
| 190 | Buddy Bell | .25 |
| 191 | Ted Martinez | .08 |
| 192 | Atlanta Braves/ Bobby Cox (Mgr.) | .35 |
| 193 | Dave Goltz | .08 |
| 194 | Mike Easler | .25 |
| 195 | Jim Montefusco | .15 |
| 196 | Lance Parrish | 1.50 |
| 197 | Byron McLaughlin | .08 |
| 198 | Dell Alston | .08 |
| 199 | Mike LaCoss | .15 |
| 200 | Jim Rice | 1.50 |
| 201 | Batting Leaders: K. Hernandez, Fred Lynn | .30 |
| 202 | Home Run Leaders: Dave Kingman, G. Thomas | .30 |
| 203 | RBI Leaders: Don Baylor, Dave Winfield | .30 |
| 204 | Stolen Base Leaders: Omar Moreno, Willie Wilson | .15 |
| 205 | Victory Leaders: Phil Niekro, Joe Niekro, Mike Flanagan | .25 |
| 206 | Strikeout Leaders: J.R. Richard, Nolan Ryan | 1.50 |
| 207 | ERA Leaders: J.R. Richard, Ron Guidry | .20 |
| 208 | Wayne Cage | .08 |
| 209 | Von Joshua | .08 |
| 210 | Steve Carlton | 2.00 |
| 211 | Dave Skaggs | .08 |
| 212 | Dave Roberts | .08 |
| 213 | Mike Jorgensen | .08 |
| 214 | California Angels/ Jim Fregosi (Mgr.) | .35 |
| 215 | Sixto Lezcano | .08 |
| 216 | Phil Mankowski | .08 |
| 217 | Ed Halicki | .08 |
| 218 | Jose Morales | .08 |
| 219 | Steve Mingori | .08 |
| 220 | Dave Concepcion | .35 |
| 221 | Joe Cannon | .08 |
| 222 | Ron Hassey | .25 |
| 223 | Bob Sykes | .08 |
| 224 | Willie Montanez | .08 |
| 225 | Lou Piniella | .25 |
| 226 | Bill Stein | .08 |
| 227 | Len Barker | .08 |
| 228 | Johnny Oates | .08 |
| 229 | Jim Bibby | .08 |
| 230 | Dave Winfield | 4.00 |
| 231 | Steve McCatty | .08 |
| 232 | Alan Trammell | 4.00 |
| 233 | LaRue Washington | .08 |
| 234 | Vern Ruhle | .08 |
| 235 | Andre Dawson | 6.00 |
| 236 | Marc Hill | .08 |
| 237 | Scott McGregor | .12 |
| 238 | Rob Wilfong | .08 |
| 239 | Don Aase | .08 |
| 240 | Dave Kingman | .35 |
| 241 | Checklist No. 2 | .25 |
| 242 | Lamar Johnson | .08 |
| 243 | Jerry Augustine | .08 |
| 244 | St. Louis Cardinals/ Ken Boyer (Mgr.) | .40 |
| 245 | Phil Niekro | 1.00 |
| 246 | Tim Foli | .08 |
| 247 | Frank Riccelli | .08 |
| 248 | Jamie Quirk | .08 |
| 249 | Jim Clancy | .08 |
| 250 | Jim Kaat | .40 |
| 251 | Kip Young | .08 |
| 252 | Ted Cox | .08 |
| 253 | John Montague | .08 |
| 254 | Paul Dade | .08 |
| 255 | Dusty Baker | .08 |
| 256 | Roger Erickson | .08 |
| 257 | Larry Herndon | .08 |
| 258 | Paul Moskau | .08 |
| 259 | New York Mets/ Joe Torre (Mgr.) | .50 |
| 260 | Al Oliver | .35 |
| 261 | Dave Chalk | .08 |
| 262 | Benny Ayala | .08 |
| 263 | Dave LaRoche | .08 |
| 264 | Bill Robinson | .08 |
| 265 | Robin Yount | 6.00 |
| 266 | Bernie Carbo | .08 |
| 267 | Dan Schatzeder | .08 |
| 268 | Rafael Landestoy | .08 |
| 269 | Dave Tobik | .08 |
| 270 | Mike Schmidt | 4.00 |
| 271 | Dick Drago | .08 |
| 272 | Ralph Garr | .08 |
| 273 | Eduardo Rodriguez | .08 |
| 274 | Dale Murphy | 5.00 |
| 275 | Jerry Koosman | .20 |
| 276 | Tom Veryzer | .08 |
| 277 | Rick Bosetti | .08 |
| 278 | Jim Spencer | .08 |
| 279 | Rob Andrews | .08 |
| 280 | Gaylord Perry | 1.00 |
| 281 | Paul Blair | .08 |
| 282 | Seattle Mariners/ Darrell Johnson (Mgr.) | .35 |
| 283 | John Ellis | .08 |
| 284 | Larry Murray | .08 |
| 285 | Don Baylor | .50 |
| 286 | Darold Knowles | .08 |
| 287 | John Lowenstein | .08 |
| 288 | Dave Rozema | .08 |
| 289 | Bruce Bochy | .08 |
| 290 | Steve Garvey | 2.00 |
| 291 | Randy Scarberry | .08 |
| 292 | Dale Berra | .08 |
| 293 | Elias Sosa | .08 |
| 294 | Charlie Spikes | .08 |
| 295 | Larry Gura | .08 |
| 296 | Dave Rader | .08 |
| 297 | Tim Johnson | .08 |
| 298 | Ken Holtzman | .08 |
| 299 | Steve Henderson | .08 |
| 300 | Ron Guidry | .75 |
| 301 | Mike Edwards | .08 |
| 302 | Los Angeles Dodgers/ Tom Lasorda (Mgr.) | .50 |
| 303 | Bill Castro | .08 |
| 304 | Butch Wynegar | .08 |
| 305 | Randy Jones | .08 |
| 306 | Denny Walling | .08 |
| 307 | Rick Honeycutt | .12 |
| 308 | Mike Hargrove | .08 |
| 309 | Larry McWilliams | .12 |
| 310 | Dave Parker | 2.00 |
| 311 | Roger Metzger | .08 |
| 312 | Mike Barlow | .08 |
| 313 | Johnny Grubb | .08 |
| 314 | Tim Stoddard | .20 |
| 315 | Steve Kemp | .15 |
| 316 | Bob Lacey | .08 |
| 317 | Mike Anderson | .08 |
| 318 | Jerry Reuss | .12 |
| 319 | Chris Speier | .08 |
| 320 | Dennis Eckersley | 1.50 |
| 321 | Keith Hernandez | 1.25 |
| 322 | Claudell Washington | .15 |
| 323 | Mick Kelleher | .08 |
| 324 | Tom Underwood | .08 |
| 325 | Dan Driessen | .08 |
| 326 | Bo McLaughlin | .08 |
| 327 | Ray Fosse | .08 |
| 328 | Minnesota Twins/ Gene Mauch (Mgr.) | .35 |
| 329 | Bert Roberge | .08 |
| 330 | Al Cowens | .08 |
| 331 | Rich Hebner | .08 |
| 332 | Enrique Romo | .08 |
| 333 | Jim Norris | .08 |
| 334 | Jim Beattie | .08 |
| 335 | Willie McCovey | 1.50 |
| 336 | George Medich | .08 |
| 337 | Carney Lansford | 1.00 |
| 338 | Johnny Wockenfuss | .08 |
| 339 | John D'Acquisto | .08 |
| 340 | Ken Singleton | .15 |
| 341 | Jim Essian | .08 |
| 342 | Odell Jones | .08 |
| 343 | Mike Vail | .08 |
| 344 | Randy Lerch | .08 |
| 345 | Larry Parrish | .12 |
| 346 | Buddy Solomon | .08 |
| 347 | Harry Chappas | .08 |
| 348 | Checklist No. 3 | .25 |
| 349 | Jack Brohamer | .08 |
| 350 | George Hendrick | .15 |
| 351 | Bob Davis | .08 |
| 352 | Dan Briggs | .08 |
| 353 | Andy Hassler | .08 |
| 354 | Rick Auerbach | .08 |
| 355 | Gary Matthews | .15 |
| 356 | San Diego Padres/ Jerry Coleman (Mgr.) | .35 |
| 357 | Bob McClure | .08 |
| 358 | Lou Whitaker | 1.50 |
| 359 | Randy Moffitt | .08 |
| 360 | Darrell Porter | .08 |
| 361 | Wayne Garland | .08 |
| 362 | Danny Goodwin | .08 |
| 363 | Wayne Gross | .08 |
| 364 | Ray Burris | .08 |
| 365 | Bobby Murcer | .20 |
| 366 | Rob Dressler | .08 |
| 367 | Billy Smith | .08 |
| 368 | Willie Aikens (R) | .25 |
| 369 | Jim Kern | .08 |
| 370 | Cesar Cedeno | .15 |
| 371 | Jack Morris | 2.00 |
| 372 | Joel Youngblood | .08 |
| 373 | Dan Petry (R) | .50 |
| 374 | Jim Gantner | .08 |
| 375 | Ross Grimsley | .08 |
| 376 | Gary Allenson | .08 |
| 377 | Junior Kennedy | .08 |
| 378 | Jerry Mumphrey | .08 |
| 379 | Kevin Bell | .08 |
| 380 | Garry Maddox | .09 |
| 381 | Chicago Cubs/ Preston Gomez (Mgr.) | .35 |
| 382 | Dave Freisleben | .08 |
| 383 | Ed Ott | .08 |
| 384 | Joey McLaughlin | .08 |
| 385 | Enos Cabell | .08 |
| 386 | Darrell Jackson | .08 |
| 387 | Fred Stanley | .08 |
| 388 | Mike Paxton | .08 |
| 389 | Pete LaCock | .08 |
| 390 | Fergie Jenkins | 1.00 |
| 391 | Tony Armas | .12 |
| 392 | Milt Wilcox | .08 |
| 393 | Ozzie Smith | 10.00 |
| 394 | Reggie Cleveland | .08 |
| 395 | Ellis Valentine | .08 |
| 396 | Dan Meyer | .08 |
| 397 | Roy Thomas | .08 |
| 398 | Barry Foote | .08 |
| 399 | Mike Proly | .08 |
| 400 | George Foster | .50 |
| 401 | Pete Falcone | .08 |
| 402 | Merv Rettenmund | .08 |
| 403 | Pete Redfern | .08 |
| 404 | Baltimore Orioles/ Earl Weaver (Mgr.) | .45 |
| 405 | Dwight Evans | 1.00 |
| 406 | Paul Molitor | 2.50 |
| 407 | Tony Solaita | .08 |
| 408 | Bill North | .08 |
| 409 | Paul Splittorff | .08 |
| 410 | Bobby Bonds | .12 |
| 411 | Frank LaCorte | .08 |
| 412 | Thad Bosley | .08 |
| 413 | Allen Ripley | .08 |
| 414 | George Scott | .12 |
| 415 | Bill Atkinson | .08 |
| 416 | Tom Brookens | .08 |
| 417 | Carig Chamberlain | .08 |
| 418 | Roger Freed | .08 |
| 419 | Vic Correll | .08 |
| 420 | Butch Hobson | .08 |
| 421 | Doug Bird | .08 |
| 422 | Larry Milbourne | .08 |
| 423 | Dave Frost | .08 |
| 424 | New York Yankees/ Dick Howser (Mgr.) | .60 |
| 425 | Mark Belanger | .15 |
| 426 | Grant Jackson | .08 |
| 427 | Tom Hutton | .08 |
| 428 | Pat Zachry | .08 |
| 429 | Duane Kuiper | .08 |
| 430 | Larry Hisle | .08 |
| 431 | Mike Krukow | .12 |
| 432 | Willie Norwood | .08 |
| 433 | Rich Gale | .08 |
| 434 | Johnnie LeMaster | .08 |
| 435 | Don Gullett | .08 |
| 436 | Billy Almon | .08 |
| 437 | Joe Niekro | .15 |
| 438 | Dave Revering | .08 |
| 439 | Mike Phillips | .08 |
| 440 | Don Sutton | 1.00 |
| 441 | Eric Soderholm | .08 |
| 442 | Jorge Orta | .08 |
| 443 | Mike Parrott | .08 |
| 444 | Alvis Woods | .08 |
| 445 | Mark Fidrych | .15 |

| NO. | PLAYER | MINT |
|---|---|---|
| 446 | Duffy Dyer | .08 |
| 447 | Nino Espinosa | .08 |
| 448 | Jim Wohlford | .08 |
| 449 | Doug Bair | .08 |
| 450 | George Brett | 7.50 |
| 451 | Cleveland Indians/ Dave Garcia (Mgr.) | .35 |
| 452 | Steve Dillard | .08 |
| 453 | Mike Bacsik | .08 |
| 454 | Tom Donohue | .08 |
| 455 | Mike Torrez | .08 |
| 456 | Frank Taveras | .08 |
| 457 | Bert Blyleven | .50 |
| 458 | Billy Sample | .08 |
| 459 | Mickey Lolich | .08 |
| 460 | Willie Randolph | .20 |
| 461 | Dwayne Murphy | .15 |
| 462 | Mike Sadek | .08 |
| 463 | Jerry Royster | .08 |
| 464 | John Denny | .15 |
| 465 | Rick Monday | .15 |
| 466 | Mike Squires | .08 |
| 467 | Jesse Jefferson | .08 |
| 468 | Aurelio Rodriguez | .08 |
| 469 | Randy Niemann | .08 |
| 470 | Bob Boone | .30 |
| 471 | Hosken Powell | .08 |
| 472 | Willie Hernandez | .30 |
| 473 | Bump Wills | .08 |
| 474 | Steve Busby | .08 |
| 475 | Cesar Geronimo | .08 |
| 476 | Bob Shirley | .08 |
| 477 | Buck Martinez | .08 |
| 478 | Gil Flores | .08 |
| 479 | Montreal Expos/ Dick Williams (Mgr.) | .35 |
| 480 | Bob Watson | .08 |
| 481 | Tom Paciorek | .08 |
| 482 | R. Henderson (R) | 150.00 |
| 483 | Bo Diaz | .08 |
| 484 | Checklist No. 4 | .25 |
| 485 | Mickey Rivers | .15 |
| 486 | Mike Tyson | .08 |
| 487 | Wayne Nordhagen | .08 |
| 488 | Roy Howell | .08 |
| 489 | Preston Hanna | .08 |
| 490 | Lee May | .15 |
| 491 | Steve Mura | .08 |
| 492 | Todd Cruz | .08 |
| 493 | Jerry Martin | .08 |
| 494 | Craig Minetto | .08 |
| 495 | Bake McBride | .08 |
| 496 | Silvio Martinez | .08 |
| 497 | Jim Mason | .08 |
| 498 | Danny Darwin | .08 |
| 499 | San Francisco Giants/ Dave Bristol (Mgr.) | .35 |
| 500 | Tom Seaver | 3.00 |
| 501 | Rennie Stennett | .08 |
| 502 | Rich Wortham | .08 |
| 503 | Mike Cubbage | .08 |
| 504 | Gene Garber | .08 |
| 505 | Bert Campaneris | .15 |
| 506 | Tom Buskey | .08 |
| 507 | Leon Roberts | .08 |
| 508 | U.L. Washington | .08 |
| 509 | Ed Glynn | .08 |
| 510 | Ron Cey | .35 |
| 511 | Eric Wilkins | .08 |
| 512 | Jose Cardenal | .08 |
| 513 | Tom Dixon | .08 |
| 514 | Steve Ontiveros | .08 |
| 515 | Mike Caldwell | .08 |
| 516 | Hector Cruz | .08 |
| 517 | Don Stanhouse | .08 |
| 518 | Nelson Norman | .08 |
| 519 | Steve Nicosia | .08 |
| 520 | Steve Rogers | .08 |
| 521 | Ken Brett | .08 |
| 522 | Jim Morrison | .08 |
| 523 | Ken Henderson | .08 |
| 524 | Jim Wright | .08 |
| 525 | Clint Hurdle | .08 |
| 526 | Philadelphia Phillies/ Dallas Green (Mgr.) | .35 |
| 527 | Doug Rau | .08 |
| 528 | Adrian Devine | .08 |
| 529 | Jim Barr | .08 |
| 530 | Jim Sundberg | .08 |
| 531 | Eric Rasmussen | .08 |
| 532 | Willie Horton | .12 |
| 533 | Checklist No. 5 | .25 |
| 534 | Andre Thornton | .15 |
| 535 | Bob Forsch | .12 |
| 536 | Lee Lacy | .12 |
| 537 | Alex Trevino | .12 |
| 538 | Joe Strain | .08 |
| 539 | Rudy May | .08 |
| 540 | Pete Rose | 4.00 |
| 541 | Miguel Dilone | .08 |
| 542 | Joe Coleman | .08 |
| 543 | Pat Kelly | .08 |
| 544 | Rick Sutcliffe (R) | 2.50 |
| 545 | Jeff Burroughs | .08 |
| 546 | Rick Langford | .08 |
| 547 | John Wathan | .08 |
| 548 | Dave Rajsich | .08 |
| 549 | Larry Wolfe | .08 |
| 550 | Ken Griffey | .50 |
| 551 | Pittsburgh Pirates/ Chuck Tanner (Mgr.) | .35 |
| 552 | Bill Nahorodny | .08 |
| 553 | Dick Davis | .08 |
| 554 | Art Howe | .08 |
| 555 | Ed Figueroa | .08 |
| 556 | Joe Rudi | .15 |
| 557 | Mark Lee | .08 |
| 558 | Alfredo Griffin | .15 |
| 559 | Dale Murray | .08 |
| 560 | Dave Lopes | .15 |
| 561 | Eddie Whitson | .12 |
| 562 | Joe Wallis | .08 |
| 563 | Will McEnaney | .08 |
| 564 | Rick Manning | .08 |
| 565 | Dennis Leonard | .12 |
| 566 | Bud Harrelson | .08 |
| 567 | Skip Lockwood | .08 |
| 568 | Gary Roenicke (R) | .30 |
| 569 | Terry Kennedy | .30 |
| 570 | Roy Smalley | .08 |
| 571 | Joe Sambito | .08 |
| 572 | Jerry Morales | .08 |
| 573 | Kent Tekulve | .12 |
| 574 | Scot Thompson | .08 |
| 575 | Ken Kravec | .08 |
| 576 | Jim Dwyer | .08 |
| 577 | Toronto Blue Jays/ Bobby Mattick (Mgr.) | .30 |
| 578 | Scott Sanderson | .25 |
| 579 | Charlie Moore | .08 |
| 580 | Nolan Ryan | 15.00 |
| 581 | Bob Bailor | .08 |
| 582 | Brian Doyle | .08 |
| 583 | Bob Stinson | .08 |
| 584 | Kurt Bevacqua | .08 |
| 585 | Al Hrabosky | .08 |
| 586 | Mitchell Page | .08 |
| 587 | Garry Templeton | .25 |
| 588 | Greg Minton | .08 |
| 589 | Chet Lemon | .15 |
| 590 | Jim Palmer | 2.50 |
| 591 | Rick Cerone | .08 |
| 592 | Jon Matlack | .08 |
| 593 | Jesus Alou | .08 |
| 594 | Dick Tidrow | .08 |
| 595 | Don Money | .08 |
| 596 | Rick Matula | .08 |
| 597 | Tom Poquette | .08 |
| 598 | Fred Kendall | .08 |
| 599 | Mike Norris | .08 |
| 600 | Reggie Jackson | 4.50 |
| 601 | Buddy Schultz | .08 |
| 602 | Brian Downing | .08 |
| 603 | Jack Billingham | .08 |
| 604 | Glenn Adams | .08 |
| 605 | Terry Forster | .12 |
| 606 | Cincinnati Reds/ John McNamara (Mgr.) | .30 |
| 607 | Woodie Fryman | .08 |
| 608 | Alan Bannister | .08 |
| 609 | Ron Reed | .08 |
| 610 | Willie Stargell | 1.50 |
| 611 | Jerry Garvin | .08 |
| 612 | Cliff Johnson | .08 |
| 613 | Randy Stein | .08 |
| 614 | John Hiller | .08 |
| 615 | Doug DeCinces | .20 |
| 616 | Gene Richards | .08 |
| 617 | Joaquin Andujar | .30 |
| 618 | Bob Montgomery | .08 |
| 619 | Sergio Ferrer | .08 |
| 620 | Richie Zisk | .15 |
| 621 | Bob Grich | .12 |
| 622 | Mario Soto | .20 |
| 623 | Gorman Thomas | .25 |
| 624 | Lerrin LaGrow | .08 |
| 625 | Chris Chambliss | .12 |
| 626 | Detroit Tigers/ S. Anderson (Mgr.) | .50 |
| 627 | Pedro Borbon | .08 |
| 628 | Doug Capilla | .08 |
| 629 | Jim Todd | .08 |
| 630 | Larry Bowa | .15 |
| 631 | Mark Littell | .08 |
| 632 | Barry Bonnell | .08 |
| 633 | Bob Apodaca | .08 |
| 634 | Glenn Borgmann | .08 |
| 635 | John Candelaria | .12 |
| 636 | Toby Harrah | .08 |
| 637 | Joe Simpson | .08 |
| 638 | Mark Clear (R) | .30 |
| 639 | Larry Biittner | .08 |
| 640 | Mike Flanagan | .12 |
| 641 | Ed Kranepool | .15 |
| 642 | Ken Forsch | .08 |
| 643 | John Mayberry | .15 |
| 644 | Charlie Hough | .12 |
| 645 | Rick Burleson | .12 |
| 646 | Checklist No. 6 | .25 |
| 647 | Milt May | .08 |
| 648 | Roy White | .12 |
| 649 | Tom Griffin | .08 |
| 650 | Joe Morgan | 2.00 |
| 651 | Rollie Fingers | 1.50 |
| 652 | Mario Mendoza | .08 |
| 653 | Stan Bahnsen | .08 |
| 654 | Bruce Boisclair | .08 |
| 655 | Tug McGraw | .15 |
| 656 | Larvell Blanks | .08 |
| 657 | Dave Edwards | .08 |
| 658 | Chris Knapp | .08 |
| 659 | Milwaukee Brewers/ George Bamberger (Mgr.) | .25 |
| 660 | Rusty Staub | .25 |
| 661 | Orioles Rookies: Wayne Krenchicki, Mark Corey, D. Ford | .15 |
| 662 | Red Sox Rookies: J. Finch, Mike O'Berry, Chuck Rainey | .15 |
| 663 | Angels Rookies: Ralph Botting, Bob Clark, Dickey Thon | .50 |
| 664 | White Sox Rookies: Guy Hoffman, M. Colbern, Dewey Robinson | .15 |
| 665 | Indians Rookies: Larry Anderson, Bobby Cuellar, Randy Wihtol | .15 |
| 666 | Tigers Rookies: M. Chris, Bruce Robbins, Al Greene | .25 |
| 667 | Royals Rookies: R. Martin, Bill Paschall, Dan Quisenberry | 1.50 |
| 668 | Brewers Rookies: Danny Boitano, W. Mueller, Lenn Sakata | .15 |
| 669 | Twin Rookies: Rick Sofield, Dan Graham, Gary Ward | .25 |
| 670 | Yankee Rookies: B. Brown, Brad Gulden, Darryl Jones | .25 |
| 671 | A's Rookies: Derek Bryant, B. Kingman, Mike Morgan | 1.00 |
| 672 | Mariners Rookies: Rodney Craig, Charlie Beamon, Rafael Vasquez | .15 |
| 673 | Rangers Rookies: Brian Allard, Jerry Don Gleaton, Greg Mahlberg | .15 |
| 674 | Blue Jays Rookies: Butch Edge, Pat Kelly, Ted Wilborn | .15 |
| 675 | Braves Rookies: Bruce Benedict, Eddie Miller, Larry Bradford | .20 |
| 676 | Cubs Rookies: Steve Macko, Dave Geisel, Karl Pagel | .20 |
| 677 | Reds Rookies: Art DeFreites, Harry Spilman, Frank Pastore | .15 |
| 678 | Astros Rookies: Reggie Baldwin, A. Knicely, Pete Ladd | .20 |
| 679 | Dodgers Rookies: Joe Beckwith, Mickey Hatcher, Dave Patterson | .30 |
| 680 | Expos Rookies: Randy Miller, Bernazard, John Tamargo | .20 |
| 681 | Mets Rookies: Dan Norman, J. Orosco, Mike Scott | 5.00 |
| 682 | Phillies Rookies: Kevin Saucier, Ramon Aviles, Dickie Noles | .25 |
| 683 | Pirates Rookies: D. Boyland, Alberto Lois, Harry Saferight | .15 |
| 684 | Cardinals Rookies: George Frazier, Tom Herr, Dan O'Brien | 1.00 |
| 685 | Padres Rookies: Brian Greer, Tim Flannery, Jim Wilhelm | .15 |
| 686 | Giants Rookies: Greg Johnston, D. Littlejohn, Phil Nastu | .15 |
| 687 | Mike Heath | .08 |
| 688 | Steve Stone | .15 |
| 689 | Boston Red Sox/ Don Zimmer (Mgr.) | .40 |
| 690 | Tommy John | .50 |
| 691 | Ivan DeJesus | .08 |
| 692 | Rawly Eastwick | .08 |
| 693 | Craig Kusick | .08 |
| 694 | Jim Rooker | .08 |
| 695 | Reggie Smith | .15 |
| 696 | Julio Gonzalez | .08 |
| 697 | David Clyde | .08 |
| 698 | Oscar Gamble | .15 |
| 699 | Floyd Bannister | .15 |
| 700 | Rod Carew | 1.50 |
| 701 | Ken Oberkfell | .30 |
| 702 | Ed Farmer | .08 |
| 703 | Otto Velez | .08 |
| 704 | Gene Tenace | .08 |
| 705 | Freddie Patek | .08 |
| 706 | Tippy Martinez | .08 |
| 707 | Elliott Maddox | .08 |
| 708 | Bob Tolan | .08 |
| 709 | Pat Underwood | .08 |
| 710 | Graig Nettles | .25 |
| 711 | Bob Galasso | .08 |
| 712 | Rodney Scott | .08 |
| 713 | Terry Whitfield | .08 |
| 714 | Fred Norman | .08 |
| 715 | Sal Bando | .15 |
| 716 | Lynn McGlothen | .08 |
| 717 | Mickey Klutts | .08 |
| 718 | Greg Gross | .08 |
| 719 | Don Robinson | .12 |
| 720 | Carl Yastrzemski | 1.50 |
| 721 | Paul Hartzell | .08 |
| 722 | Jose Cruz | .25 |
| 723 | Shane Rawley | .12 |
| 724 | Jerry White | .08 |
| 725 | Rick Wise | .08 |
| 726 | Steve Yeager | .12 |

# 1981 Topps.... Complete Set of 726 Cards— Value $125.00

Features the rookie cards of Fernando Valenzuela, Kirk Gibson, Harold Baines and Tim Raines. 66 cards were double printed. In 1981 Topps began getting competition from two other card manufacturers—Donruss and Fleer.

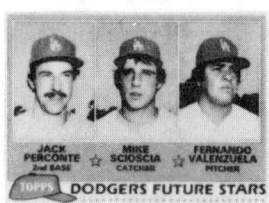    

| NO. | PLAYER | MINT |
|---|---|---|
| 1 | Batting Leaders: | 1.25 |
| | Bill Buckner, George Brett | |
| 2 | Home Run Leaders: | .50 |
| | Reggie Jackson, Ben | |
| | Oglivie, M. Schmidt | |
| 3 | RBI Leaders: | .35 |
| | Cecil Cooper, Mike | |
| | Schmidt | |
| 4 | Stolen Base Leaders: | 1.25 |
| | Rickey Henderson, | |
| | Ron LeFlore | |
| 5 | Victory Leaders: | .15 |
| | Steve Carlton, Steve Stone | |
| 6 | Strikeout Leaders: | .15 |
| | Len Barker, Steve Carlton | |
| 7 | ERA Leaders: | .10 |
| | Don Sutton, Rudy May | |
| 8 | Leading Firemen: | .15 |
| | Dan Quisenberry, Tom | |
| | Hume, Rollie Fingers | |
| 9 | Pete LaCock | .07 |
| 10 | Mike Flanagan | .12 |
| 11 | Jim Wohlford | .07 |
| 12 | Mark Clear | .07 |
| 13 | Joe Charboneau | .12 |
| 14 | John Tudor (R) | 1.00 |
| 15 | Larry Parrish | .10 |
| 16 | Ron Davis | .10 |
| 17 | Cliff Johnson | .07 |
| 18 | Glenn Adams | .07 |
| 19 | Jim Clancy | .07 |
| 20 | Jeff Burroughs | .07 |
| 21 | Ron Oester | .07 |
| 22 | Danny Darwin | .07 |
| 23 | Alex Trevino | .07 |
| 24 | Don Stanhouse | .07 |
| 25 | Sicto Lezcano | .07 |
| 26 | U.L. Washington | .07 |
| 27 | Champ Summers | .07 |
| 28 | Enrique Romo | .07 |
| 29 | Gene Tenace | .07 |
| 30 | Jack Clark | .60 |
| 31 | Checklist No. 1 | .15 |
| 32 | Ken Oberkfell | .07 |
| 33 | Rick Honeycutt | .07 |
| 34 | Aurelio Rodriquez | .07 |
| 35 | Mitchell Page | .07 |
| 36 | Ed Farmer | .07 |
| 37 | Gary Roenicke | .07 |
| 38 | Win Remmerswaal | .07 |
| 39 | Tom Veryzer | .07 |
| 40 | Tug McGraw | .12 |
| 41 | Ranger Rookies: | .20 |
| | Bob Babcock, J. Butcher, | |
| | Jerry Don Gleaton | |
| 42 | Jerry White | .07 |
| 43 | Jose Morales | .07 |
| 44 | Larry McWilliams | .07 |
| 45 | Enos Cabell | .07 |
| 46 | Rick Bosetti | .07 |
| 47 | Ken Brett | .07 |
| 48 | Dave Skaggs | .07 |
| 49 | Bob Shirley | .07 |
| 50 | Dave Lope | .12 |
| 51 | Bill Robinson | .07 |
| 52 | Hector Cruz | .07 |

| NO. | PLAYER | MINT |
|---|---|---|
| 53 | Kevin Saucier | .07 |
| 54 | Ivan DeJesus | .07 |
| 55 | Mike Norris | .07 |
| 56 | Buck Martinez | .07 |
| 57 | Dave Roberts | .07 |
| 58 | Joel Youngblood | .07 |
| 59 | Dan Petry | .25 |
| 60 | Willie Randolph | .25 |
| 61 | Butch Wynegar | .10 |
| 62 | Joe Pettini | .07 |
| 63 | Steve Renko | .07 |
| 64 | Brian Asselstine | .07 |
| 65 | Scott McGregor | .10 |
| 66 | Royals Rookies: | .15 |
| | Tim Ireland, Manny | |
| | Castillo, Mike Jones | |
| 67 | Ken Kravec | .07 |
| 68 | Matt Alexander | .07 |
| 69 | Ed Halicki | .07 |
| 70 | Al Oliver | .12 |
| 71 | Hal Dues | .07 |
| 72 | Barry Evans | .07 |
| 73 | Doug Bair | .07 |
| 74 | Mike Hargrove | .07 |
| 75 | Reggie Smith | .12 |
| 76 | Mario Mendoza | .07 |
| 77 | Mike Barlow | .07 |
| 78 | Steve Dillard | .07 |
| 79 | Bruce Robbins | .07 |
| 80 | Rusty Staub | .15 |
| 81 | Dave Stapleton | .15 |
| 82 | Astros Rookies: | .10 |
| | Bobby Sprowl, Danny | |
| | Heep, Alan Knicely | |
| 83 | Mike Proly | .07 |
| 84 | Johnnie LeMaster | .07 |
| 85 | Mike Caldwell | .07 |
| 86 | Wayne Gross | .07 |
| 87 | Rick Camp | .07 |
| 88 | Joe LeFebvre | .15 |
| 89 | Darrell Jackson | .07 |
| 90 | Bake McBride | .07 |
| 91 | Tim Stoddard | .07 |
| 92 | Mike Easler | .12 |
| 93 | Ed Glynn | .07 |
| 94 | Harry Spilman | .07 |
| 95 | Jim Sundberg | .07 |
| 96 | A's Rookies: | .12 |
| | Dave Beard, Pat Dempsey, | |
| | E. Camacho | |
| 97 | Chris Speier | .07 |
| 98 | Clint Hurdle | .07 |
| 99 | Eric Wilkins | .07 |
| 100 | Rod Carew | 2.00 |
| 101 | Benny Ayala | .07 |
| 102 | Dave Tobik | .07 |
| 103 | Jerry Martin | .07 |
| 104 | Terry Forster | .12 |
| 105 | Jose Cruz | .20 |
| 106 | Don Money | .07 |
| 107 | Rich Wortham | .07 |
| 108 | Bruce Benedict | .07 |
| 109 | Mike Scott | .75 |
| 110 | Carl Yastrzemski | 2.00 |
| 111 | Greg Minton | .07 |

| NO. | PLAYER | MINT |
|---|---|---|
| 112 | White Sox Rookies: | .15 |
| | Rusty Kuntz, F. Mullin, | |
| | Leo Sutherland | |
| 113 | Mike Phillips | .07 |
| 114 | Tom Underwood | .07 |
| 115 | Roy Smalley | .07 |
| 116 | Joe Simpson | .07 |
| 117 | Pete Falcone | .07 |
| 118 | Kurt Bevacqua | .07 |
| 119 | Tippy Martinez | .07 |
| 120 | Larry Bowa | .12 |
| 121 | Larry Harlow | .07 |
| 122 | John Denny | .15 |
| 123 | Al Cowens | .07 |
| 124 | Jerry Garvin | .07 |
| 125 | Andre Dawson | 3.00 |
| 126 | Charlie Leibrandt (R) | .50 |
| 127 | Rudy Law | .07 |
| 128 | Garry Allenson | .07 |
| 129 | Art Howe | .07 |
| 130 | Larry Gura | .07 |
| 131 | Keith Moreland (R) | .30 |
| 132 | Tommy Boggs | .07 |
| 133 | Jeff Cox | .07 |
| 134 | Steve Mura | .07 |
| 135 | Gorman Thomas | .20 |
| 136 | Doug Capilla | .07 |
| 137 | Hosken Powell | .07 |
| 138 | Rich Dotson (R) | .30 |
| 139 | Oscar Gamble | .07 |
| 140 | Bob Forsch | .07 |
| 141 | Miguel Dilone | .07 |
| 142 | Jackson Todd | .07 |
| 143 | Dan Meyer | .07 |
| 144 | Allen Ripley | .07 |
| 145 | Mickey Rivers | .10 |
| 146 | Bobby Castillo | .07 |
| 147 | Dale Berra | .07 |
| 148 | Randy Niemann | .07 |
| 149 | Joe Nolan | .07 |
| 150 | Mark Fidrych | .10 |
| 151 | Claudell Washington | .10 |
| 152 | John Urrea | .07 |
| 153 | Tom Poquette | .07 |
| 154 | Rick Langford | .07 |
| 155 | Chris Chambliss | .10 |
| 156 | Bob McClure | .07 |
| 157 | John Wathan | .07 |
| 158 | Fergie Jenkins | .75 |
| 159 | Brian Doyle | .07 |
| 160 | Garry Maddox | .07 |
| 161 | Dan Graham | .07 |
| 162 | Doug Corbett | .12 |
| 163 | Billy Almon | .07 |
| 164 | LaMarr Hoyt (R) | .20 |
| 165 | Tony Scott | .07 |
| 166 | Floyd Bannister | .07 |
| 167 | Terry Whitfield | .07 |
| 168 | Don Robinson | .07 |
| 169 | John Mayberry | .07 |
| 170 | Ross Grimsley | .07 |
| 171 | Gene Richards | .07 |
| 172 | Gary Woods | .07 |
| 173 | Bump Wills | .07 |
| 174 | Doug Rau | .07 |
| 175 | Dave Collins | .07 |

| NO. | PLAYER | MINT |
|---|---|---|
| 176 | Mike Krukow | .07 |
| 177 | Rick Peters | .12 |
| 178 | Jim Essian | .07 |
| 179 | Rudy May | .07 |
| 180 | Pete Rose | 3.00 |
| 181 | Elias Sosa | .07 |
| 182 | Bob Grich | .12 |
| 183 | Dick Davis | .07 |
| 184 | Jim Dwyer | .07 |
| 185 | Dennis Leonard | .07 |
| 186 | Wayne Nordhagen | .07 |
| 187 | Mike Parrott | .07 |
| 188 | Doug DeCinces | .15 |
| 189 | Craig Swan | .07 |
| 190 | Cesar Cedeno | .15 |
| 191 | Rick Sutcliffe | .35 |
| 192 | Braves Rookies: | .35 |
| | Terry Harper, Rafael | |
| | Ramirez, Ed Miller | |
| 193 | Pete Vuckovich | .12 |
| 194 | Rod Scurry | .10 |
| 195 | Rich Murray | .07 |
| 196 | Duffy Dyer | .07 |
| 197 | Jim Kern | .07 |
| 198 | Jerry Dybzinski | .07 |
| 199 | Chuck Rainey | .07 |
| 200 | George Foster | .30 |
| 201 | Record—J. Bench | .45 |
| | Most HR's, Catcher, Career | |
| 202 | Record—S. Carlton | .35 |
| | Strikeouts, Lefty, Career | |
| 203 | Record—B. Gullickson | .12 |
| | Strikeouts, Game, Rookie | |
| 204 | Rec.—LeFlore, Scott | .12 |
| | SB's, Teammates, Season | |
| 205 | Record—P. Rose | .75 |
| | Most Consecutive Seasons, | |
| | 600 or More At-Bats | |
| 206 | Record—M. Schmidt | 1.00 |
| | Homers, 3B, Season | |
| 207 | Record—O. Smith | .75 |
| | Assists, SS, Season | |
| 208 | Record—W. Wilson | .15 |
| | Most At-Bats, Season | |
| 209 | Dickie Thon | .07 |
| 210 | Jim Palmer | 1.25 |
| 211 | Derrel Thomas | .07 |
| 212 | Steve Nicosia | .07 |
| 213 | Al Holland (R) | .20 |
| 214 | Angels Rookies: | .15 |
| | John Harris, Ralph Botting, | |
| | Jim Dorsey | |
| 215 | Larry Hisle | .07 |
| 216 | John Henry Johnson | .07 |
| 217 | Rich Hebner | .07 |
| 218 | Paul Splittorff | .07 |
| 219 | Ken Landreaux | .07 |
| 220 | Tom Seaver | 2.00 |
| 221 | Bob Davis | .07 |
| 222 | Jorge Orta | .07 |
| 223 | Roy Lee Jackson | .10 |
| 224 | Pat Zachry | .07 |
| 225 | Ruppert Jones | .07 |
| 226 | Manny Sanguillen | .07 |
| 227 | Fred Martinez | .07 |
| 228 | Tom Paciorek | .07 |

| NO. | PLAYER | MINT |
|---|---|---|
| 229 | Rollie Fingers | 1.00 |
| 230 | George Hendrick | .12 |
| 231 | Joe Beckwith | .07 |
| 232 | Mickey Klutts | .07 |
| 233 | Skip Lockwood | .07 |
| 234 | Lou Whitaker | .75 |
| 235 | Scott Sanderson | .07 |
| 236 | Mike Ivie | .07 |
| 237 | Charlie Moore | .07 |
| 238 | Willie Hernandez | .20 |
| 239 | Rick Miller | .07 |
| 240 | Nolan Ryan | 7.50 |
| 241 | Checklist No. 2 | .15 |
| 242 | Chet Lemon | .12 |
| 243 | Sal Butera | .07 |
| 244 | Cardinals Rookies: Andy Rincon, T. Landrum, Al Olmsted | .20 |
| 245 | Ed Figueroa | .07 |
| 246 | Ed Ott | .07 |
| 247 | Glenn Hubbard | .07 |
| 248 | Joey McLaughlin | .07 |
| 249 | Larry Cox | .07 |
| 250 | Ron Guidry | .50 |
| 251 | Tom Brookens | .07 |
| 252 | Victor Cruz | .07 |
| 253 | Dave Bergman | .07 |
| 254 | Ozzie Smith | 4.00 |
| 255 | Mark Littell | .07 |
| 256 | Bombo Rivera | .07 |
| 257 | Rennie Stennett | .07 |
| 258 | Joe Price | .07 |
| 259 | Mets Rookies: Juan Berenguer, H. Brooks, Mookie Wilson | 2.50 |
| 260 | Ron Cey | .30 |
| 261 | Ricky Henderson | 25.00 |
| 262 | Sammy Stewart | .07 |
| 263 | Brian Downing | .07 |
| 264 | Jim Norris | .07 |
| 265 | John Candelaria | .10 |
| 266 | Tom Herr | .20 |
| 267 | Stan Bahnsen | .07 |
| 268 | Jerry Royster | .07 |
| 269 | Ken Forsch | .07 |
| 270 | Greg Luzinski | .15 |
| 271 | Bill Castro | .07 |
| 272 | Bruce Kimm | .07 |
| 273 | Stan Papi | .07 |
| 274 | Craig Chamberlain | .07 |
| 275 | Dwight Evans | .50 |
| 276 | Dan Spillner | .07 |
| 277 | Alfredo Griffin | .10 |
| 278 | Rick Sofield | .07 |
| 279 | Bob Knepper | .12 |
| 280 | Ken Griffey | .30 |
| 281 | Fred Stanley | .07 |
| 282 | Mariners Rookies: Rick Anderson, Rodney Craig, Greg Biercevicz | .15 |
| 283 | Billy Sample | .07 |
| 284 | Brian Kingman | .07 |
| 285 | Jerry Turner | .07 |
| 286 | Dave Frost | .07 |
| 287 | Lenn Sakata | .07 |
| 288 | Bob Clark | .07 |
| 289 | Mickey Hatcher | .07 |
| 290 | Bob Boone | .07 |
| 291 | Aurelio Lopez | .07 |
| 292 | Mike Squires | .07 |
| 293 | Charlie Lea (R) | .20 |
| 294 | Mike Tyson | .07 |
| 295 | Hal McRae | .10 |
| 296 | Bill Nahorodny | .07 |
| 297 | Bob Bailor | .07 |
| 298 | Buddy Solomon | .07 |
| 299 | Elliott Maddox | .07 |
| 300 | Paul Molitor | 1.00 |
| 301 | Matt Keough | .07 |
| 302 | Dodgers Rookies: Mike Scioscia, Jack Perconte, F. Valenzuela | 5.00 |
| 303 | Johnny Oates | .07 |
| 304 | John Castino | .07 |
| 305 | Ken Clay | .07 |
| 306 | Juan Beniquez | .07 |
| 307 | Gene Garber | .07 |
| 308 | Rick Manning | .07 |
| 309 | Luis Salazar | .15 |
| 310 | Vida Blue | .07 |
| 311 | Freddie Patek | .07 |
| 312 | Rick Rhoden | .12 |
| 313 | Luis Pujols | .07 |
| 314 | Rich Dauer | .07 |
| 315 | Kirk Gibson (R) | 6.00 |
| 316 | Craig Minetto | .07 |
| 317 | Lonnie Smith | .50 |
| 318 | Steve Yeager | .07 |
| 319 | Rowland Office | .07 |
| 320 | Tom Burgmeier | .07 |
| 321 | Leon Durham (R) | .40 |
| 322 | Neil Allen | .07 |
| 323 | Jim Morrison | .07 |
| 324 | Mike Willis | .07 |
| 325 | Ray Knight | .15 |
| 326 | Biff Pocoroba | .07 |
| 327 | Moose Haas | .07 |
| 328 | Twins Rookies: Dave Engle, G. Johnston, Gary Ward | .15 |
| 329 | Joaquin Andujar | .15 |
| 330 | Frank White | .12 |
| 331 | Dennis Lamp | .07 |
| 332 | Lee Lacy | .07 |
| 333 | Sid Monge | .07 |
| 334 | Dane Iorg | .07 |
| 335 | Rick Cerone | .07 |
| 336 | Eddie Whitson | .10 |
| 337 | Lynn Jones | .05 |
| 338 | Checklist No.3 | .15 |
| 339 | John Ellis | .07 |
| 340 | Bruce Kison | .07 |
| 341 | Dwayne Murphy | .12 |
| 342 | Eric Rasmussen | .07 |
| 343 | Frank Taveras | .07 |
| 344 | Byron McLaughlin | .07 |
| 345 | Warren Cromartie | .07 |
| 346 | Larry Christenson | .07 |
| 347 | Harold Baines (R) | 4.00 |
| 348 | Bob Sykes | .12 |
| 349 | Glenn Hoffman | .15 |
| 350 | J.R. Richard | .12 |
| 351 | Otto Velez | .07 |
| 352 | Dick Tidrow | .07 |
| 353 | Terry Kennedy | .15 |
| 354 | Mario Soto | .15 |
| 355 | Bob Horner | .20 |
| 356 | Padres Rookies: George Stablein, C. Stimac, Tom Tellmann | .15 |
| 357 | Jim Slaton | .07 |
| 358 | Mark Wagner | .07 |
| 359 | Tom Hausman | .07 |
| 360 | Willie Wilson | .25 |
| 361 | Joe Strain | .07 |
| 362 | Bo Diaz | .07 |
| 363 | Geoff Zahn | .07 |
| 364 | Mike Davis (R) | .30 |
| 365 | Graig Nettles | .07 |
| 366 | Mike Ramsey | .07 |
| 367 | Denny Martinez | .30 |
| 368 | Leon Roberts | .07 |
| 369 | Frank Tanana | .15 |
| 370 | Dave Winfield | 2.00 |
| 371 | Charlie Hough | .07 |
| 372 | Jay Johnstone | .07 |
| 373 | Pat Underwood | .07 |
| 374 | Tom Hutton | .07 |
| 375 | Dave Concepcion | .15 |
| 376 | Ron Reed | .07 |
| 377 | Jerry Morales | .07 |
| 378 | Dave Rader | .07 |
| 379 | Lary Sorensen | .07 |
| 380 | Willie Stargell | 1.00 |
| 381 | Cubs Rookies: Carlos Lezcano, Steve Macko, Randy Martz | .20 |
| 382 | Paul Mirabella | .07 |
| 383 | Eric Soderholm | .07 |
| 384 | Mike Sadek | .07 |
| 385 | Joe Sambito | .07 |
| 386 | Dave Edwards | .07 |
| 387 | Phil Niekro | .75 |
| 388 | Andre Thornton | .15 |
| 389 | Marty Pattin | .07 |
| 390 | Cesar Geronimo | .07 |
| 391 | Dave Lemanczyk | .07 |
| 392 | Lance Parrish | .75 |
| 393 | Broderick Perkins | .07 |
| 394 | Woodie Fryman | .07 |
| 395 | Scot Thompson | .07 |
| 396 | Bill Campbell | .07 |
| 397 | Julio Cruz | .07 |
| 398 | Ross Baumgarten | .07 |
| 399 | Orioles Rookies: Mike Boddicker, Mark Corey, Floyd Rayford | 1.25 |
| 400 | Reggie Jackson | 3.00 |
| 401 | A.L. Championships: Royals Sweep Yanks | .50 |
| 402 | N.L. Championships: Phillies Beat Astros | .25 |
| 403 | 1980 World Series: Phillies Beat Royals | .25 |
| 404 | 1980 World Series: Phillies Win | .25 |
| 405 | Nino Espinosa | .07 |
| 406 | Dickie Noles | .07 |
| 407 | Ernie Whitt | .07 |
| 408 | Fernando Arroyo | .07 |
| 409 | Larry Herndon | .07 |
| 410 | Bert Campaneris | .07 |
| 411 | Terry Puhl | .07 |
| 412 | Britt Burns (R) | .15 |
| 413 | Tony Bernazard | .07 |
| 414 | John Pacella | .07 |
| 415 | Ben Oglivie | .12 |
| 416 | Gary Alexander | .07 |
| 417 | Dan Schatzeder | .07 |
| 418 | Bobby Brown | .07 |
| 419 | Tom Hume | .07 |
| 420 | Keith Hernandez | .75 |
| 421 | Bob Stanley | .07 |
| 422 | Dan Ford | .07 |
| 423 | Shane Rawley | .12 |
| 424 | Yankees Rookies: Tim Lollar, Bruce Robinson, Dennis Werth | .20 |
| 425 | Al Bumbry | .07 |
| 426 | Warren Brusstar | .07 |
| 427 | Jonn D'Acquisto | .07 |
| 428 | John Stearns | .07 |
| 429 | Mick Kelleher | .07 |
| 430 | Jim Bibby | .07 |
| 431 | Dave Roberts | .07 |
| 432 | Len Barker | .12 |
| 433 | Rance Mulliniks | .07 |
| 434 | Roger Erickson | .07 |
| 435 | Jim Spencer | .07 |
| 436 | Gary Lucas | .12 |
| 437 | Mike Heath | .07 |
| 438 | John Montefusco | .07 |
| 439 | Denny Walling | .07 |
| 440 | Jerry Reuss | .12 |
| 441 | Ken Reitz | .07 |
| 442 | Ron Pruitt | .07 |
| 443 | Jim Beattie | .07 |
| 444 | Garth Iorg | .07 |
| 445 | Ellis Valentine | .07 |
| 446 | Checklist No. 4 | .15 |
| 447 | Junior Kennedy | .07 |
| 448 | Tim Corcoran | .07 |
| 449 | Paul Mitchell | .07 |
| 450 | Dave Kingman | .15 |
| 451 | Indians Rookies: Chris Bando, Tom Brennan, Sandy Wihtol | .20 |
| 452 | Renie Martin | .07 |
| 453 | Rob Wilfong | .07 |
| 454 | Andy Hassler | .07 |
| 455 | Rick Burleson | .12 |
| 456 | Jeff Reardon (R) | 6.00 |
| 457 | Mike Lum | .07 |
| 458 | Randy Jones | .07 |
| 459 | Greg Gross | .07 |
| 460 | Rich Gossage | .35 |
| 461 | Dave McKay | .07 |
| 462 | Jack Brohamer | .07 |
| 463 | Milt May | .07 |
| 464 | Adrian Devine | .07 |
| 465 | Bill Russell | .07 |
| 466 | Bob Molinaro | .07 |
| 467 | Dave Stieb | 1.50 |
| 468 | Johnny Wockenfuss | .07 |
| 469 | Jeff Leonard | .30 |
| 470 | Manny Trillo | .07 |
| 471 | Mike Vail | .07 |
| 472 | Dyar Miller | .07 |
| 473 | Jose Cardenal | .07 |
| 474 | Mike LaCoss | .07 |
| 475 | Buddy Bell | .20 |
| 476 | Jerry Koosman | .15 |
| 477 | Luis Gomez | .07 |
| 478 | Juan Eichelberger | .07 |
| 479 | Expos Rookies: B. Pate, Tim Raines, Roberto Ramos | 9.00 |
| 480 | Carlton Fisk | 2.00 |
| 481 | Bob Lacey | .07 |
| 482 | Jim Gantner | .07 |
| 483 | Mike Griffin | .07 |
| 484 | Max Venable | .07 |
| 485 | Garry Templeton | .20 |
| 486 | Marc Hill | .07 |
| 487 | Dewey Robinson | .07 |
| 488 | Damaso Garcia (R) | .20 |
| 489 | John Littlefield | .07 |
| 490 | Eddie Murray | 2.50 |
| 491 | Gordy Pladson | .07 |
| 492 | Barry Foote | .07 |
| 493 | Dan Quisenberry | .35 |
| 494 | Bob Walk | .25 |
| 495 | Dusty Baker | .12 |
| 496 | Paul Dade | .07 |
| 497 | Fred Norman | .07 |
| 498 | Pat Putnam | .07 |
| 499 | Frank Pastore | .07 |
| 500 | Jim Rice | .75 |
| 501 | Tim Foli | .07 |
| 502 | Giants Rookies: Chris Bourjos, Mike Rowland, A. Hargesheimer | .15 |
| 503 | Steve McCatty | .07 |
| 504 | Dale Murphy | 2.00 |
| 505 | Jason Thompson | .12 |
| 506 | Phil Huffman | .07 |
| 507 | Jamie Quirk | .07 |
| 508 | Rob Dressler | .07 |
| 509 | Pete Mackanin | .07 |
| 510 | Lee Mazzilli | .07 |
| 511 | Wayne Garland | .07 |
| 512 | Gary Thomasson | .07 |
| 513 | Frank LaCorte | .07 |
| 514 | George Riley | .07 |
| 515 | Robin Yount | 4.00 |
| 516 | Doug Bird | .07 |
| 517 | Richie Zisk | .07 |
| 518 | Grant Jackson | .07 |
| 519 | John Tamargo | .07 |
| 520 | Steve Stone | .07 |
| 521 | Sam Mejias | .07 |
| 522 | Mike Colbern | .07 |
| 523 | John Fulgham | .07 |
| 524 | Willie Aikens | .10 |
| 525 | Mike Torrez | .07 |
| 526 | Phillies Rookies: Marty Bystrom, Jay Loviglio, J. Wright | .20 |
| 527 | Danny Goodwin | .07 |
| 528 | Gary Matthews | .12 |
| 529 | Dave LaRoche | .07 |
| 530 | Steve Garvey | 1.00 |
| 531 | John Curtis | .07 |
| 532 | Bill Stein | .07 |
| 533 | Jesus Figueroa | .07 |
| 534 | Dave Smith | .40 |
| 535 | Omar Moreno | .12 |
| 536 | Bob Owchinko | .07 |
| 537 | Ron Hodges | .07 |
| 538 | Tom Griffin | .07 |

| NO. | PLAYER | MINT |
|---|---|---|
| 539 | Rodney Scott | .07 |
| 540 | Mike Schmidt | 2.00 |
| 541 | Steve Swisher | .07 |
| 542 | Larry Bradford | .07 |
| 543 | Terry Crowley | .07 |
| 544 | Rich Gale | .07 |
| 545 | Johnny Grubb | .07 |
| 546 | Paul Moskau | .07 |
| 547 | Mario Guerrero | .40 |
| 548 | Dave Goltz | .07 |
| 549 | Jerry Remy | .07 |
| 550 | Tommy John | .30 |
| 551 | Pirates Rookies: Vance Law, Pascual Perez Tony Pena | 2.00 |
| 552 | Steve Trout | .07 |
| 553 | Tim Blackwell | .07 |
| 554 | Bert Blyleven | .40 |
| 555 | Cecil Cooper | .30 |
| 556 | Jerry Mumphrey | .07 |
| 557 | Chris Knapp | .07 |
| 558 | Barry Bonnell | .07 |
| 559 | Willie Montanez | .07 |
| 560 | Joe Morgan | 1.25 |
| 561 | Dennis Littlejohn | .07 |
| 562 | Checklist No. 5 | .15 |
| 563 | Jim Kaat | .25 |
| 564 | Ron Hassey | .07 |
| 565 | Burt Hooton | .07 |
| 566 | Del Unser | .07 |
| 567 | Mark Bomback | .07 |
| 568 | Dave Revering | .07 |
| 569 | Al Williams | .07 |
| 570 | Ken Singleton | .12 |
| 571 | Todd Cruz | .07 |
| 572 | Jack Morris | 1.00 |
| 573 | Phil Garner | .07 |
| 574 | Bill Caudill | .15 |
| 575 | Tony Perez | .35 |
| 576 | Reggie Cleveland | .07 |
| 577 | Blue Jays Rookies: Luis Leal, Brian Miller, Ken Schrom | .20 |
| 578 | Bill Gullickson (R) | .60 |
| 579 | Tim Flannery | .07 |
| 580 | Don Baylor | .30 |
| 581 | Roy Howell | .07 |
| 582 | Gaylord Perry | .60 |
| 583 | Larry Milbourne | .07 |
| 584 | Randy Lerch | .07 |

| NO. | PLAYER | MINT |
|---|---|---|
| 585 | Amos Otis | .12 |
| 586 | Silvio Martinez | .07 |
| 587 | Jeff Newman | .07 |
| 588 | Gary Lavelle | .07 |
| 589 | Lamar Johnson | .07 |
| 590 | Bruce Sutter | .30 |
| 591 | John Lowenstein | .07 |
| 592 | Steve Comer | .07 |
| 593 | Steve Kemp | .15 |
| 594 | Preston Hanna | .07 |
| 595 | Butch Hobson | .07 |
| 596 | Jerry Augustine | .07 |
| 597 | Rafael Landestoy | .07 |
| 598 | George Vukovich | .07 |
| 599 | Dennis Kinney | .07 |
| 600 | Johnny Bench | 2.00 |
| 601 | Don Aase | .07 |
| 602 | Bobby Murcer | .15 |
| 603 | John Verhoeven | .07 |
| 604 | Rob Picciolo | .07 |
| 605 | Don Sutton | .75 |
| 606 | Reds Rookies: Bruce Berenyi, Geoff Combe, P. Householder | .15 |
| 607 | Dave Palmer | .07 |
| 608 | Greg Pryor | .07 |
| 609 | Lynn McGlothen | .07 |
| 610 | Darrell Porter | .07 |
| 611 | Rick Matula | .07 |
| 612 | Duane Kuiper | .07 |
| 613 | Jim Anderson | .07 |
| 614 | Dave Rozema | .07 |
| 615 | Rick Dempsey | .07 |
| 616 | Rick Wise | .07 |
| 617 | Craig Reynolds | .07 |
| 618 | John Milner | .07 |
| 619 | Steve Henderson | .07 |
| 620 | Dennis Eckersley | 1.00 |
| 621 | Tom Donohue | .07 |
| 622 | Randy Moffitt | .07 |
| 623 | Sal Bando | .07 |
| 624 | Bob Welch | .60 |
| 625 | Bill Buckner | .15 |
| 626 | Tigers Rookies: D. Steffen, Jerry Ujdur, Roger Weaver | .20 |
| 627 | Luis Tiant | .12 |
| 628 | Vic Correll | .07 |
| 629 | Tony Armas | .20 |
| 630 | Steve Carlton | 1.50 |

| NO. | PLAYER | MINT |
|---|---|---|
| 631 | Ron Jackson | .07 |
| 632 | Alan Bannister | .07 |
| 633 | Bill Lee | .07 |
| 634 | Doug Flynn | .07 |
| 635 | Bobby Bonds | .12 |
| 636 | Al Hrabosky | .07 |
| 637 | Jerry Narron | .07 |
| 638 | Checklist No. 6 | .15 |
| 639 | Carney Lansford | .40 |
| 640 | Dave Parker | 1.00 |
| 641 | Mark Belanger | .07 |
| 642 | Vern Ruhle | .07 |
| 643 | Lloyd Moseby (R) | .75 |
| 644 | Ramon Aviles | .07 |
| 645 | Rick Reuschel | .15 |
| 646 | Marvis Foley | .07 |
| 647 | Dick Drago | .07 |
| 648 | Darrell Evans | .20 |
| 649 | Manny Sarmiento | .07 |
| 650 | Bucky Dent | .12 |
| 651 | Pedro Guerrero | 1.50 |
| 652 | John Montague | .07 |
| 653 | Bill Fahey | .07 |
| 654 | Ray Burris | .07 |
| 655 | Dan Driessen | .07 |
| 656 | Jon Matlack | .07 |
| 657 | Mike Cubbage | .07 |
| 658 | Milt Wilcox | .07 |
| 659 | Brewers Rookies: Ned Yost, J. Flinn, Ed Romero | .07 |
| 660 | Gary Carter | 1.25 |
| 661 | Orioles Team | .20 |
| 662 | Red Sox Team | .20 |
| 663 | Angels Team | .20 |
| 664 | White Sox Team | .20 |
| 665 | Indians Team | .20 |
| 666 | Tigers Team | .25 |
| 667 | Royals Team | .20 |
| 668 | Brewers Team | .20 |
| 669 | Twins Team | .20 |
| 670 | Yankees Team | .25 |
| 671 | A's Team | .20 |
| 672 | Mariners Team | .15 |
| 673 | Rangers Team | .20 |
| 674 | Blue Jays Team | .20 |
| 675 | Braves Team | .20 |
| 676 | Cubs Team | .20 |
| 677 | Reds Team | .20 |
| 678 | Astros Team | .20 |

| NO. | PLAYER | MINT |
|---|---|---|
| 679 | Dodgers Team | .25 |
| 680 | Expos Team | .15 |
| 681 | Mets Team | .20 |
| 682 | Phillies Team | .20 |
| 683 | Pirates Team | .20 |
| 684 | Cardinals Team | .20 |
| 685 | Padres Team | .20 |
| 686 | Giants Team | .20 |
| 687 | Jeff Jones | .10 |
| 688 | Kiko Garcia | .07 |
| 689 | Red Sox Rookies: Bruce Hurst, Reid Nichols, Keith MacWhorter | 2.00 |
| 690 | Bob Watson | .07 |
| 691 | Dick Ruthven | .07 |
| 692 | Lenny Randle | .07 |
| 693 | Steve Howe (R) | .20 |
| 694 | Bud Harrelson | .07 |
| 695 | Kent Tekulve | .07 |
| 696 | Alan Ashby | .07 |
| 697 | Rick Waits | .07 |
| 698 | Mike Jorgensen | .07 |
| 699 | Glenn Abbott | .07 |
| 700 | George Brett | 4.00 |
| 701 | Joe Rudi | .07 |
| 702 | George Medich | .07 |
| 703 | Alvis Woods | .07 |
| 704 | Bill Travers | .07 |
| 705 | Ted Simmons | .25 |
| 706 | Dave Ford | .07 |
| 707 | Dave Cash | .07 |
| 708 | Doyle Alexander | .07 |
| 709 | Alan Trammell | .60 |
| 710 | Ron LeFlore | .07 |
| 711 | Joe Ferguson | .07 |
| 712 | Bill Bonham | .07 |
| 713 | Bill North | .07 |
| 714 | Pete Redfern | .07 |
| 715 | Bill Madlock | .20 |
| 716 | Glenn Borgmann | .07 |
| 717 | Jim Barr | .07 |
| 718 | Larry Biittner | .07 |
| 719 | Sparky Lyle | .12 |
| 720 | Fred Lynn | .30 |
| 721 | Toby Harrah | .07 |
| 722 | Joe Niekro | .12 |
| 723 | Bruce Bochte | .07 |
| 724 | Lou Piniella | .15 |
| 725 | Steve Rogers | .12 |
| 726 | Rick Monday | .15 |

## 1981 Topps Traded. . . . Complete Set of 132 Cards—Value $30.00

This was the first Topps "traded" set issued since 1976. It updates the main 1981 card set with players who had changed teams during the season and rookies who joined their teams early in the season. The first card in the traded set is numbered 727. It begins where the main set ends. The complete set was packaged in a printed box and only distributed through card hobby dealers.

| NO. | PLAYER | MINT |
|---|---|---|
| 727 | Danny Ainge (RR) | 1.25 |
| 728 | Doyle Alexander | .15 |
| 729 | Gary Alexander | .08 |
| 730 | Billy Almon | .08 |
| 731 | Joaquin Andujar | .15 |
| 732 | Bob Bailor | .08 |
| 733 | Juan Beniquez | .12 |

| NO. | PLAYER | MINT |
|---|---|---|
| 734 | Dave Bergman | .08 |
| 735 | Tony Bernazard | .08 |
| 736 | Larry Biittner | .08 |
| 737 | Doug Bird | .08 |
| 738 | Bert Blyleven | 1.25 |
| 739 | Mark Bomback | .08 |
| 740 | Bobby Bonds | .12 |

| NO. | PLAYER | MINT |
|---|---|---|
| 741 | Rick Bosetti | .08 |
| 742 | Hubie Brooks | 2.00 |
| 743 | Rick Burleson | .10 |
| 744 | Ray Burris | .08 |
| 745 | Jeff Burroughs | .10 |
| 746 | Enos Cabell | .08 |
| 747 | Ken Clay | .08 |

| NO. | PLAYER | MINT |
|---|---|---|
| 748 | Mark Clear | .08 |
| 749 | Larry Cox | .08 |
| 750 | Hector Cruz | .08 |
| 751 | Victor Cruz | .08 |
| 752 | Mike Cubbage | .08 |
| 753 | Dick Davis | .08 |
| 754 | Brian Doyle | .08 |

| NO. | PLAYER | MINT |
|-----|--------|------|
| 755 | Dick Drago | .08 |
| 756 | Leon Durham | .40 |
| 757 | Jim Dwyer | .08 |
| 758 | Dave Edwards | .08 |
| 759 | Jim Essian | .08 |
| 760 | Bill Fahey | .08 |
| 761 | Rollie Ringers | 2.00 |
| 762 | Carlton Fisk | 5.00 |
| 763 | Barry Foote | .08 |
| 764 | Ken Forsch | .12 |
| 765 | Kiko Garcia | .08 |
| 766 | Cesar Geronimo | .08 |
| 767 | Gary Gray | .08 |
| 768 | Mickey Hatcher | .08 |
| 769 | Steve Henderson | .12 |
| 770 | Marc Hill | .08 |
| 771 | Butch Hobson | .08 |
| 772 | Rick Honeycutt | .12 |
| 773 | Roy Howell | .08 |
| 774 | Mike Ivie | .08 |
| 775 | Roy Lee Jackson | .08 |
| 776 | Cliff Johnson | .08 |
| 777 | Randy Jones | .10 |
| 778 | Ruppert Jones | .08 |
| 779 | Mick Kelleher | .08 |
| 780 | Terry Kennedy | .20 |

| NO. | PLAYER | MINT |
|-----|--------|------|
| 781 | Dave Kingman | .30 |
| 782 | Bob Knepper | .12 |
| 783 | Ken Kravec | .08 |
| 784 | Bob Lacey | .08 |
| 785 | Dennis Lamp | .08 |
| 786 | Rafael Landestoy | .08 |
| 787 | Ken Landreaux | .12 |
| 788 | Carney Lansford | .75 |
| 789 | Dave LaRoche | .08 |
| 790 | Joe LeFebvre | .08 |
| 791 | Ron LeFlore | .12 |
| 792 | Randy Lerch | .08 |
| 793 | Sixto Lezcano | .12 |
| 794 | John Littlefield | .08 |
| 795 | Mike Lum | .08 |
| 796 | Greg Luzinski | .25 |
| 797 | Fred Lynn | .50 |
| 798 | Jerry Martin | .08 |
| 799 | Buck Martinez | .08 |
| 800 | Gary Matthews | .12 |
| 801 | Mario Mendoza | .08 |
| 802 | Larry Milbourne | .08 |
| 803 | Rick Miller | .08 |
| 804 | John Montefusco | .12 |
| 805 | Jerry Morales | .08 |
| 806 | Jose Morales | .08 |

| NO. | PLAYER | MINT |
|-----|--------|------|
| 807 | Joe Morgan | 2.00 |
| 808 | Jerry Mumphrey | .12 |
| 809 | Gene Nelson | .15 |
| 810 | Ed Ott | .08 |
| 811 | Bob Owchinko | .08 |
| 812 | Gaylord Perry | 1.50 |
| 813 | Mike Phillips | .08 |
| 814 | Darrell Porter | .12 |
| 815 | Mike Proly | .08 |
| 816 | Tim Raines | 12.00 |
| 817 | Lenny Randle | .08 |
| 818 | Doug Rau | .08 |
| 819 | Jeff Reardon | 5.00 |
| 820 | Ken Reitz | .08 |
| 821 | Steve Renko | .08 |
| 822 | Rick Reuschel | .20 |
| 823 | Dave Revering | .08 |
| 824 | Dave Roberts | .08 |
| 825 | Leon Roberts | .08 |
| 826 | Joe Rudi | .12 |
| 827 | Kevin Saucier | .08 |
| 828 | Tony Scott | .08 |
| 829 | Bob Shirley | .08 |
| 830 | Ted Simmons | .40 |
| 831 | Lary Sorensen | .08 |
| 832 | Jim Spencer | .08 |

| NO. | PLAYER | MINT |
|-----|--------|------|
| 833 | Harry Spilman | .08 |
| 834 | Fred Stanley | .08 |
| 835 | Rusty Staub | .25 |
| 836 | Bill Stein | .08 |
| 837 | Joe Strain | .08 |
| 838 | Bruce Sutter | .50 |
| 839 | Don Sutton | 1.00 |
| 840 | Steve Swisher | .08 |
| 841 | Frank Tanana | .08 |
| 842 | Gene Tenace | .08 |
| 843 | Jason Thompson | .15 |
| 844 | Dickie Thon | .25 |
| 845 | Bill Travers | .08 |
| 846 | Tom Underwood | .08 |
| 847 | John Urrea | .08 |
| 848 | Mike Vail | .08 |
| 849 | Ellis Valentine | .12 |
| 850 | Fernando Valenzuela | 5.00 |
| 851 | Pete Vuckovich | .12 |
| 852 | Mark Wagner | .08 |
| 853 | Bob Walk | .20 |
| 854 | Claudell Washington | .12 |
| 855 | Dave Winfield | 4.00 |
| 856 | Geoff Zahn | .08 |
| 857 | Richie Zisk | .12 |
| 858 | Traded Checklist | .20 |

## 1982 Topps . . . Complete Set of 792 Cards—Value $150.00

The complete set was increased to 792 cards. Double printed cards were eliminated (66 double prints were in each set from 1978 to 1981). Includes the rookie cards of Cal Ripken, Jesse Barfield, Kent Hrbek and Steve Sax. Card 342 exists with the *autograph* deleted.

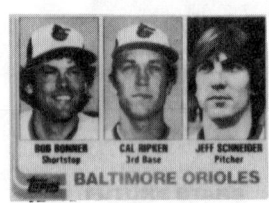

| NO. | PLAYER | MINT |
|-----|--------|------|
| 1 | Highlights—Carlton Sets NL Strikeout Record | .50 |
| 2 | Highlights—Davis Fans 8 Straight | .10 |
| 3 | Highlights—Raines Swipes 71 Bases, Rookie | .30 |
| 4 | Highlights—Rose Sets NL Career Hit Mark | .60 |
| 5 | Highlights—Ryan 5th Career No-Hitter | 2.00 |
| 6 | Highlights—Valenzuela 8 Rookie Shutouts | .25 |
| 7 | Scott Sanderson | .07 |
| 8 | Rich Dauer | .07 |
| 9 | Ron Guidry | .30 |
| 10 | Guidry (Action) | .15 |
| 11 | Gary Alexander | .07 |
| 12 | Moose Haas | .07 |
| 13 | Lamar Johnson | .07 |
| 14 | Steve Howe | .07 |
| 15 | Ellis Valentine | .07 |
| 16 | Steve Comer | .07 |
| 17 | Darrell Evans | .15 |
| 18 | Fernando Arroyo | .07 |
| 19 | Ernie Whitt | .07 |
| 20 | Garry Maddox | .07 |
| 21 | Orioles Rookies: Bob Bonner, Cal Ripken, Jeff Schneider | 50.00 |
| 22 | Jim Beattie | .07 |
| 23 | Willie Hernandez | .20 |
| 24 | Dave Frost | .07 |
| 25 | Jerry Remy | .07 |
| 26 | George Orta | .07 |

| NO. | PLAYER | MINT |
|-----|--------|------|
| 27 | Tom Herr | .15 |
| 28 | John Urrea | .07 |
| 29 | Dwayne Murphy | .07 |
| 30 | Tom Seaver | 1.50 |
| 31 | Seaver (Action) | .75 |
| 32 | Gene Garber | .07 |
| 33 | Jerry Morales | .07 |
| 34 | Joe Sambito | .07 |
| 35 | Willie Aikens | .10 |
| 36 | Rangers Leaders: Al Oliver, George Medich | .15 |
| 37 | Dan Graham | .07 |
| 38 | Charlie Lea | .07 |
| 39 | Lou Whitaker | .50 |
| 40 | Dave Parker | .60 |
| 41 | Parker (Action) | .30 |
| 42 | Rick Sofield | .07 |
| 43 | Mike Cubbage | .07 |
| 44 | Britt Burns | .10 |
| 45 | Rick Cerone | .07 |
| 46 | Jerry Augustine | .07 |
| 47 | Jeff Leonard | .15 |
| 48 | Bobby Castillo | .07 |
| 49 | Alvis Woods | .07 |
| 50 | Buddy Bell | .15 |
| 51 | Cubs Rookies: Jay Howell, C. Lezcano, Ty Waler | .40 |
| 52 | Larry Andersen | .07 |
| 53 | Greg Gross | .07 |
| 54 | Ron Hassey | .07 |
| 55 | Rick Burleson | .07 |
| 56 | Mark Littell | .07 |
| 57 | Craig Reynolds | .07 |

| NO. | PLAYER | MINT |
|-----|--------|------|
| 58 | John D'Acquisto | .07 |
| 59 | Rich Gedman (R) | .40 |
| 60 | Tony Armas | .20 |
| 61 | Tommy Boggs | .07 |
| 62 | Mike Tyson | .07 |
| 63 | Mario Soto | .15 |
| 64 | Lynn Jones | .07 |
| 65 | Terry Kennedy | .15 |
| 66 | Astros Leaders: Art Howe, Nolan Ryan | .35 |
| 67 | Rich Gale | .07 |
| 68 | Roy Howell | .07 |
| 69 | Al Williams | .07 |
| 70 | Tim Raines | 2.00 |
| 71 | Roy Lee Jackson | .07 |
| 72 | Rick Auerbach | .07 |
| 73 | Buddy Solomon | .07 |
| 74 | Bob Clark | .07 |
| 75 | Tommy John | .25 |
| 76 | Greg Pryor | .07 |
| 77 | Miguel Dilone | .07 |
| 78 | George Medich | .07 |
| 79 | Bob Bailor | .07 |
| 80 | Jim Palmer | 1.50 |
| 81 | Palmer (Action) | .75 |
| 82 | Bob Welch | .50 |
| 83 | Yankees Rookies: S. Balboni, A. Robertson, A. McGaffigan | .20 |
| 84 | Rennie Stennett | .07 |
| 85 | Lynn McGlothen | .07 |
| 86 | Dane Iorg | .07 |
| 87 | Matt Keough | .07 |
| 88 | Biff Pocoroba | .07 |

| NO. | PLAYER | MINT |
|-----|--------|------|
| 89 | Steve Henderson | .07 |
| 90 | Nolan Ryan | 7.50 |
| 91 | Carney Lansford | .25 |
| 92 | Brad Havens | .10 |
| 93 | Larry Hisle | .07 |
| 94 | Andy Hassler | .75 |
| 95 | Ozzie Smith | 2.00 |
| 96 | Royals Leaders: G. Brett, L. Gura | .35 |
| 97 | Paul Moskau | .07 |
| 98 | Terry Bulling | .07 |
| 99 | Barry Bonnell | .07 |
| 100 | Mike Schmidt | 3.00 |
| 101 | Schmidt (Action) | 1.50 |
| 102 | Dan Briggs | .07 |
| 103 | Bob Lacey | .07 |
| 104 | Rance Mulliniks | .07 |
| 105 | Kirk Gibson | 1.25 |
| 106 | Enrique Romo | .07 |
| 107 | Wayne Krenchicki | .07 |
| 108 | Bob Sykes | .07 |
| 109 | Dave Revering | .07 |
| 110 | Carlton Fisk | 1.50 |
| 111 | Fisk (Action) | .75 |
| 112 | Billy Sample | .07 |
| 113 | Steve McCatty | .07 |
| 114 | Ken Landreaux | .07 |
| 115 | Gaylord Perry | .50 |
| 116 | Jim Wohlford | .07 |
| 117 | Rawly Eastwick | .07 |
| 118 | Expos Rookies: Brad Mills, Terry Francona, Bryn Smith | .50 |
| 119 | Joe Pittman | .07 |

| NO. | PLAYER | MINT |
|---|---|---|
| 120 | Gary Lucas | .07 |
| 121 | Ed Lynch | .12 |
| 122 | Jamie Easterly | .07 |
| 123 | Danny Goodwin | .07 |
| 124 | Reid Nichols | .07 |
| 125 | Danny Ainge | .50 |
| 126 | Braves Leaders: | .15 |
| | C. Washington, Rick Mahler | |
| 127 | Lonnie Smith | .25 |
| 128 | Frank Pastore | .07 |
| 129 | Checklist No. 1 | .15 |
| 130 | Julio Cruz | .07 |
| 131 | Stan Bahnsen | .07 |
| 132 | Lee May | .07 |
| 133 | Pat Underwood | .07 |
| 134 | Dan Ford | .07 |
| 135 | Adny Rincon | .07 |
| 136 | Lenn Sakata | .07 |
| 137 | George Cappuzzello | .07 |
| 138 | Tony Pena | .30 |
| 139 | Jeff Jones | .07 |
| 140 | Ron Leflore | .07 |
| 141 | Indians Rookies: | 1.00 |
| | Chris Bando, Von Hayes, Tom Brennan | |
| 142 | Dave LaRoche | .07 |
| 143 | Mookie Wilson | .15 |
| 144 | Fred Breining | .12 |
| 145 | Bob Horner | .20 |
| 146 | Mike Griffin | .07 |
| 147 | Denny Walling | .07 |
| 148 | Mickey Klutts | .07 |
| 149 | Pat Putnam | .07 |
| 150 | Ted Simmons | .15 |
| 151 | Dave Edwards | .07 |
| 152 | Ramon Aviles | .07 |
| 153 | Roger Erickson | .07 |
| 154 | Dennis Werth | .07 |
| 155 | Otto Velez | .07 |
| 156 | A's Leaders: | .60 |
| | Rickey Henderson, Steve McCatty | |
| 157 | Steve Crawford | .10 |
| 158 | Brian Downing | .07 |
| 159 | Larry Biittner | .07 |
| 160 | Luis Tiant | .10 |
| 161 | Batting Leaders: | .15 |
| | B. Madlock, C. Lansford | |
| 162 | Home Run Leaders: | .25 |
| | Bobby Grich, Mike Schmidt, T. Armas, Dwight Evans, Eddie Murray | |
| 163 | RBI Leaders: | .50 |
| | M. Schmidt, E. Murray | |
| 164 | Stolen Base Leaders: | 1.25 |
| | R. Henderson, T. Raines | |
| 165 | Victory Leaders: | .25 |
| | Tom Seaver, D. Martinez, Steve McCatty, Pete Vuckovich, Jack Morris | |
| 166 | Strikeout Leaders: | .20 |
| | F. Valenzuela, L. Barker | |
| 167 | ERA Leaders: | .75 |
| | Steve McCatty, Nolan Ryan | |
| 168 | Leading Relievers: | .25 |
| | Bruce Sutter, Rollie Fingers | |
| 169 | Charlie Leibrandt | .10 |
| 170 | Jim Bibby | .07 |
| 171 | Giants Rookies: | 2.00 |
| | Bob Tufts, Bob Brenly, Chili Davis | |
| 172 | Bill Gullickson | .15 |
| 173 | Jamie Quirk | .07 |
| 174 | Dave Ford | .07 |
| 175 | Jerry Mumphrey | .07 |
| 176 | Dewey Robinson | .07 |
| 177 | John Ellis | .07 |
| 178 | Dyar Miller | .07 |
| 179 | Steve Garvey | .75 |
| 180 | Garvey (Action) | .35 |
| 181 | Silvio Martinez | .07 |
| 182 | Larry Herndon | .07 |
| 183 | Mike Proly | .07 |
| 184 | Mick Kelleher | .07 |
| 185 | Phil Niekro | .50 |

| NO. | PLAYER | MINT |
|---|---|---|
| 186 | Cardinals Leaders: | .15 |
| | K. Hernandez, B. Forsch | |
| 187 | Jeff Newman | .07 |
| 188 | Randy Martz | .07 |
| 189 | Glenn Hoffman | .07 |
| 190 | J.R. Richard | .10 |
| 191 | Tim Wallach (R) | 2.00 |
| 192 | Broderick Perkins | .07 |
| 193 | Darrell Jackson | .07 |
| 194 | Mike Vail | .07 |
| 195 | Paul Molitor | .75 |
| 196 | Willie Upshaw | .25 |
| 197 | Shane Rawley | .07 |
| 198 | Chris Speier | .07 |
| 199 | Don Aase | .07 |
| 200 | George Brett | 2.00 |
| 201 | Brett (Action) | 1.00 |
| 202 | Rick Manning | .07 |
| 203 | Blue Jays Rookies: | 1.75 |
| | Jesse Barfield, Brian Milner, Boomer Wells | |
| 204 | Gray Roenicke | .07 |
| 205 | Neil Allen | .07 |
| 206 | Tony Bernazard | .07 |
| 207 | Rod Scurry | .07 |
| 208 | Bobby Murcer | .15 |
| 209 | Gary Lavelle | .07 |
| 210 | Keith Hernandez | .50 |
| 211 | Dan Petry | .25 |
| 212 | Mario Mendoza | .07 |
| 213 | Dave Steward (R) | 8.00 |
| 214 | Brian Asselstine | .07 |
| 215 | Mike Krukow | .07 |
| 216 | White Sox Leaders: | .15 |
| | Chet Lemon, Dennis Lamp | |
| 217 | Bo McLaughlin | .07 |
| 218 | Dave Roberts | .07 |
| 219 | John Curtis | .07 |
| 220 | Manny Trillo | .07 |
| 221 | Jim Slaton | .07 |
| 222 | Butch Wynegar | .07 |
| 223 | Lloyd Moseby | .25 |
| 224 | Bruce Bochte | .07 |
| 225 | Mike Torrez | .07 |
| 226 | Checklist No. 2 | .15 |
| 227 | Ray Burris | .07 |
| 228 | Sam Mejias | .07 |
| 229 | Geoff Zahn | .07 |
| 230 | Willie Wilson | .20 |
| 231 | Phillies Rookies: | .50 |
| | Ozzie Virgil, Bob Dernier, Mark Davis | |
| 232 | Terry Crowley | .07 |
| 233 | Duane Kuiper | .07 |
| 234 | Ron Hodges | .07 |
| 235 | Mike Easler | .10 |
| 236 | John Martin | .07 |
| 237 | Rusty Kuntz | .07 |
| 238 | Kevin Saucier | .07 |
| 239 | Jon Matlack | .07 |
| 240 | Bucky Dent | .10 |
| 241 | Dent (Action) | .07 |
| 242 | Milt May | .07 |
| 243 | Bob Owchinko | .07 |
| 244 | Rufino Linares | .07 |
| 245 | Ken Reitz | .07 |
| 246 | Mets Leaders: | .07 |
| | Hubie Brooks, Mike Scott | |
| 247 | Pedro Guerrero | .75 |
| 248 | Frank LaCorte | .07 |
| 249 | Tim Flannery | .07 |
| 250 | Tug McGraw | .10 |
| 251 | Fred Lynn | .30 |
| 252 | Lynn (Action) | .20 |
| 253 | Chuck Baker | .07 |
| 254 | Jorge Bell (R) | 12.00 |
| 255 | Tony Perez | .30 |
| 256 | Perez (Action) | .15 |
| 257 | Larry Harlow | .07 |
| 258 | Bo Diaz | .10 |
| 259 | Rodney Scott | .07 |
| 260 | Bruce Sutter | .25 |
| 261 | Tigers Rookies: | .20 |
| | Howard Bailey, M. Castillo, Dave Rucker | |

| NO. | PLAYER | MINT |
|---|---|---|
| 262 | Doug Bair | .07 |
| 263 | Victor Cruz | .07 |
| 264 | Dan Quisenberry | .20 |
| 265 | Al Bumbry | .07 |
| 266 | Rick Leach | .12 |
| 267 | Kurt Bevacqua | .07 |
| 268 | Rickey Keeton | .07 |
| 269 | Jim Essian | .07 |
| 270 | Rusty Staub | .20 |
| 271 | Larry Bradford | .07 |
| 272 | Bump Wills | .07 |
| 273 | Doug Bird | .07 |
| 274 | Bob Ojeda (R) | .75 |
| 275 | Bob Watson | .07 |
| 276 | Angels Leaders: | .20 |
| | Ken Forsch, Rod Carew | |
| 277 | Terry Puhl | .07 |
| 278 | John Littlefield | .07 |
| 279 | Bill Russell | .07 |
| 280 | Ben Oglivie | .10 |
| 281 | John Verhoeven | .07 |
| 282 | Ken Macha | .07 |
| 283 | Brian Allard | .07 |
| 284 | Bob Grich | .10 |
| 285 | Sparky Lyle | .10 |
| 286 | Bill Fahey | .07 |
| 287 | Alan Bannister | .07 |
| 288 | Garry Templeton | .15 |
| 289 | Bob Stanley | .07 |
| 290 | Ken Singleton | .15 |
| 291 | Pirates Rookies: | .35 |
| | Vance Law, Bob Long, Johnny Ray | |
| 292 | David Palmer | .07 |
| 293 | Rob Picciolo | .07 |
| 294 | Mike LaCoss | .07 |
| 295 | Jason Thompson | .10 |
| 296 | Bob Walk | .07 |
| 297 | Clint Hurdle | .07 |
| 298 | Danny Darwin | .07 |
| 299 | Steve Trout | .07 |
| 300 | Reggie Jackson | 2.00 |
| 301 | Jackson (Action) | 1.00 |
| 302 | Doug Flynn | .07 |
| 303 | Bill Caudill | .10 |
| 304 | Johnnie LeMaster | .07 |
| 305 | Don Sutton | .50 |
| 306 | Sutton (Action) | .25 |
| 307 | Randy Bass | .07 |
| 308 | Charlie Moore | .07 |
| 309 | Pete Redfern | .07 |
| 310 | Mike Hargrove | .10 |
| 311 | Dodgers Leaders: | .15 |
| | Dusty Baker, Burt Hooton | |
| 312 | Lenny Randle | .07 |
| 313 | John Harris | .07 |
| 314 | Buck Martinez | .07 |
| 315 | Burt Hooten | .07 |
| 316 | Steve Braun | .07 |
| 317 | Dick Ruthven | .07 |
| 318 | Mike Heath | .07 |
| 319 | Dave Rozema | .07 |
| 320 | Chris Chambliss | .10 |
| 321 | Chambliss (Action) | .07 |
| 322 | Garry Hancock | .07 |
| 323 | Bill Lee | .07 |
| 324 | Steve Dillard | .07 |
| 325 | Jose Cruz | .15 |
| 326 | Pete Falcone | .07 |
| 327 | Joe Nolan | .07 |
| 328 | Ed Farmer | .07 |
| 329 | U.L. Washington | .07 |
| 330 | Rick Wise | .07 |
| 331 | Benny Ayala | .07 |
| 332 | Don Robinson | .07 |
| 333 | Brewers Rookies: | .20 |
| | Frank DiPino, M. Edwards, Chuck Porter | |
| 334 | Aurelio Rodriguez | .07 |
| 335 | Jim Sundberg | .07 |
| 336 | Mariners Leaders: | .15 |
| | G. Abbott, T. Paciorek | |
| 337 | Pete Rose (AS) | .75 |
| 338 | Dave Lopes (AS) | .10 |
| 339 | Mike Schmidt (AS) | .60 |

| NO. | PLAYER | MINT |
|---|---|---|
| 340 | Dave Concepcion (AS) | .15 |
| 341 | Andre Dawson (AS) | .50 |
| 342 | George Foster (AS) | .25 |
| 342 | George Foster (AS) | 2.00 |
| | (autograph deleted) | |
| 343 | Dave Parker (AS) | .25 |
| 344 | Gary Carter (AS) | .25 |
| 345 | F. Valenzuela (AS) | .25 |
| 346 | Tom Seaver (AS) | .50 |
| 347 | Bruce Sutter (AS) | .15 |
| 348 | Derrel Thomas | .07 |
| 349 | George Frazier | .07 |
| 350 | Thad Bosley | .07 |
| 351 | Reds Rookies: | .15 |
| | Geoff Coumbe, Scott Brown, P. Householder | |
| 352 | Dick Davis | .07 |
| 353 | Jack O'Connor | .07 |
| 354 | Roberto Ramos | .07 |
| 355 | Dwight Evans | .25 |
| 356 | Denny Lewallyn | .07 |
| 357 | Butch Hobson | .07 |
| 358 | Mike Parrott | .07 |
| 359 | Jim Dwyer | .07 |
| 360 | Len Barker | .07 |
| 361 | Rafael Landestoy | .07 |
| 362 | Jim Wright | .07 |
| | (wrong autograph) | |
| 363 | Bob Molinaro | .07 |
| 364 | Doyle Alexander | .07 |
| 365 | Bill Madlock | .20 |
| 366 | Padres Leaders: | .15 |
| | L. Salazar, J. Eichelberger | |
| 367 | Jim Kaat | .15 |
| 368 | Alex Trevino | .07 |
| 369 | Champ Summers | .07 |
| 370 | Mike Norris | .07 |
| 371 | Jerry Don Gleaton | .07 |
| 372 | Luis Gomez | .07 |
| 373 | Gene Nelson | .10 |
| 374 | Tim Blackwell | .07 |
| 375 | Dusty Baker | .12 |
| 376 | Chris Welsh | .10 |
| 377 | Kiko Garcia | .07 |
| 378 | Mike Caldwell | .07 |
| 379 | Rob Wilfong | .07 |
| 380 | Dave Stieb | .75 |
| 381 | Red Sox Rookies: | .75 |
| | D. Schmidt, Julio Valdez, Bruce Hurst | |
| 382 | Joe Simpson | .07 |
| 383 | Pascual Perez | .20 |
| 383 | P. Perez (error) | 30.00 |
| | No position on front | |
| 384 | Keith Moreland | .07 |
| 385 | Ken Forsch | .07 |
| 386 | Jerry White | .07 |
| 387 | Tom Veryzer | .07 |
| 388 | Joe Rudi | .07 |
| 389 | George Vukovich | .07 |
| 390 | Eddie Murray | 2.00 |
| 391 | Dave Tobik | .07 |
| 392 | Rick Bosetti | .07 |
| 393 | Al Hrabosky | .07 |
| 394 | Checklist No. 3 | .12 |
| 395 | Omar Moreno | .10 |
| 396 | Twins Leaders: | .15 |
| | John Castino, F. Arroyo | |
| 397 | Ken Brett | .07 |
| 398 | Mike Squires | .07 |
| 399 | Pat Zachry | .07 |
| 400 | Johnny Bench | 1.50 |
| 401 | Bench (Action) | .75 |
| 402 | Bill Stein | .07 |
| 403 | Jim Tracy | .07 |
| 404 | Dickie Thon | .10 |
| 405 | Rick Reuschel | .07 |
| 406 | Al Holland | .07 |
| 407 | Danny Boone | .07 |
| 408 | Ed Romero | .07 |
| 409 | Don Cooper | .07 |
| 410 | Ron Cey | .15 |
| 411 | Cey (Action) | .10 |
| 412 | Luis Leal | .07 |
| 413 | Dan Meyer | .07 |
| 414 | Elias Sosa | .07 |
| 415 | Don Baylor | .15 |

| NO. PLAYER | MINT |
|---|---|
| 416 Marty Bystrom | .07 |
| 417 Pat Kelly | .07 |
| 418 Rangers Rookies: | .25 |
| John Butcher, B. Johnson, Dave Schmidt | |
| 419 Steve Stone | .10 |
| 420 George Hendrick | .10 |
| 421 Mark Clear | .07 |
| 422 Cliff Johnson | .07 |
| 423 Stan Papi | .07 |
| 424 Bruce Benedict | .07 |
| 425 John Candelaria | .10 |
| 426 Orioles Leaders: | .15 |
| Eddie Murray, S. Stewart | |
| 427 Ron Oester | .07 |
| 428 LaMarr Hoyt | .15 |
| 429 John Wathan | .07 |
| 430 Vida Blue | .10 |
| 431 Blue (Action) | .07 |
| 432 Mike Scott | .50 |
| 433 Alan Ashby | .07 |
| 434 Joe LeFebvre | .07 |
| 435 Robin Yount | 4.00 |
| 436 Joe Strain | .07 |
| 437 Juan Berenguer | .07 |
| 438 Pete Mackanin | .07 |
| 439 Dave Righetti (R) | 2.00 |
| 440 Jeff Burroughs | .07 |
| 441 Astros Rookies: | .15 |
| Danny Heep, Billy Smith, Bobby Sprowl | |
| 442 Bruce Kison | .07 |
| 443 Mark Wagner | .07 |
| 444 Terry Forster | .10 |
| 445 Larry Parrish | .10 |
| 446 Wayne Garland | .07 |
| 447 Darrell Porter | .12 |
| 448 Porter (Action) | .07 |
| 449 Luis Aguayo | .07 |
| 450 Jack Morris | 1.00 |
| 451 Ed Miller | .07 |
| 452 Lee Smith (R) | 4.00 |
| 453 Art Howe | .07 |
| 454 Rick Langford | .07 |
| 455 Tom Burgmeier | .07 |
| 456 Cubs Leaders: | .15 |
| R. Martz, Bill Buckner | |
| 457 Tim Stoddard | .07 |
| 458 Willie Montanez | .07 |
| 459 Bruce Berenyi | .07 |
| 460 Jack Clark | .50 |
| 461 Rich Dotson | .10 |
| 462 Dave Chalk | .07 |
| 463 Jim Kern | .07 |
| 464 Juan Bonilla | .10 |
| 465 Lee Mazzilli | .07 |
| 466 Randy Lerch | .07 |
| 467 Mickey Hatcher | .07 |
| 468 Floyd Bannister | .10 |
| 469 Ed Ott | .07 |
| 470 John Mayberry | .07 |
| 471 Royals Rookies: | .25 |
| Mike Jones, Atlee Hammaker, Darryl Motley | |
| 472 Oscar Gamble | .07 |
| 473 Mike Stanton | .07 |
| 474 Ken Oberkfell | .07 |
| 475 Alan Trammell | .75 |
| 476 Brian Kingman | .07 |
| 477 Steve Yeager | .10 |
| 478 Ray Searage | .10 |
| 479 Rowland Office | .07 |
| 480 Steve Carlton | 1.25 |
| 481 Carlton (Action) | .30 |
| 482 Glenn Hubbard | .07 |
| 483 Gary Woods | .07 |
| 484 Ivan DeJesus | .07 |
| 485 Kent Tekulve | .10 |
| 486 Yankees Leaders: | .20 |
| J. Mumphrey, Tommy John | |
| 487 Bob McClure | .07 |
| 488 Ron Jackson | .07 |
| 489 Rick Dempsey | .07 |
| 490 Dennis Eckersley | .75 |
| 491 Checklist No. 4 | .15 |

| NO. PLAYER | MINT |
|---|---|
| 492 Joe Price | .07 |
| 493 Chet Lemon | .10 |
| 494 Hubie Brooks | .50 |
| 495 Dennis Leonard | .07 |
| 496 Johnny Grubb | .07 |
| 497 Jim Anderson | .07 |
| 498 Dave Bergman | .07 |
| 499 Paul Mirabella | .07 |
| 500 Rod Carew | 1.25 |
| 501 Carew (Action) | .60 |
| 502 Braves Rookies: | 2.50 |
| Steve Bedrosian, B. Butler, Larry Owen | |
| 503 Julio Gonzalez | .07 |
| 504 Rick Peters | .07 |
| 505 Graig Nettles | .20 |
| 506 Nettles (Action) | .15 |
| 507 Terry Harper | .07 |
| 508 Jody Davis (R) | .15 |
| 509 Harry Spilman | .07 |
| 510 Fernando Valenzuela | .75 |
| 511 Ruppert Jones | .07 |
| 512 Jerry Dybzinski | .07 |
| 513 Rick Rhoden | .07 |
| 514 Joe Ferguson | .07 |
| 515 Larry Bowa | .10 |
| 516 Bowa (Action) | .07 |
| 517 Mark Brouhard | .10 |
| 518 Garth Iorg | .07 |
| 519 Glenn Adams | .07 |
| 520 Mike Flanagan | .10 |
| 521 Billy Almon | .07 |
| 522 Chuck Rainey | .07 |
| 523 Gary Gray | .07 |
| 524 Tom Hausman | .07 |
| 525 Ray Knight | .10 |
| 526 Expos Leaders: | .15 |
| W. Cromartie, Bill Gullickson | |
| 527 John Henry Johnson | .07 |
| 528 Matt Alexander | .07 |
| 529 Allen Ripley | .07 |
| 530 Dickie Noles | .07 |
| 531 A's Rookies: | .12 |
| Rich Bordi, M. Budaska, Kelvin Moore | |
| 532 Toby Harrah | .07 |
| 533 Joaquin Andujar | .15 |
| 534 Dave McKay | .07 |
| 535 Lance Parrish | .50 |
| 536 Rafael Ramirez | .07 |
| 537 Doug Capilla | .07 |
| 538 Lou Piniella | .15 |
| 539 Vern Ruhle | .07 |
| 540 Andre Dawson | 2.00 |
| 541 Barry Evans | .07 |
| 542 Ned Yost | .07 |
| 543 Bill Robinson | .07 |
| 544 Larry Christenson | .07 |
| 545 Reggie Smith | .10 |
| 546 Smith (Action) | .07 |
| 547 Rod Carew (AS) | .35 |
| 548 Willie Randolph (AS) | .12 |
| 549 George Brett (AS) | .50 |
| 550 Bucky Dent (AS) | .12 |
| 551 Reggie Jackson (AS) | .50 |
| 552 Ken Singleton (AS) | .12 |
| 553 Dave Winfield (AS) | .35 |
| 554 Carlton Fisk (AS) | .40 |
| 555 Scott McGregor (AS) | .12 |
| 556 Jack Morris (AS) | .25 |
| 557 Rich Gossage (AS) | .20 |
| 558 John Tudor | .25 |
| 559 Indians Leaders: | .15 |
| M. Hargrove, B. Blyleven | |
| 560 Doug Corbett | .07 |
| 561 Cardinals Rookies: | .20 |
| Glenn Brummer, Luis DeLeon, Gene Roof | |
| 562 Mike O'Berry | .07 |
| 563 Ross Baumgarten | .07 |
| 564 Doug DeCinces | .15 |
| 565 Jackson Todd | .07 |
| 566 Mike Jorgensen | .07 |
| 567 Bob Babcock | .07 |

| NO. PLAYER | MINT |
|---|---|
| 568 Joe Pettini | .07 |
| 569 Willie Randolph | .10 |
| 570 Randolph (Action) | .07 |
| 571 Glenn Abbott | .07 |
| 572 Juan Beniquez | .07 |
| 573 Rick Waits | .07 |
| 574 Mike Ramsey | .07 |
| 575 Al Cowens | .07 |
| 576 Giants Leaders: | .12 |
| Milt May, Vida Blue | |
| 577 Rick Monday | .07 |
| 578 Shooty Babitt | .07 |
| 579 Rick Mahler (R) | .30 |
| 580 Bobby Bonds | .10 |
| 581 Ron Reed | .07 |
| 582 Luis Pujols | .07 |
| 583 Tippy Martinez | .07 |
| 584 Hosken Powell | .07 |
| 585 Rollie Fingers | .50 |
| 586 Fingers (Action) | .25 |
| 587 Tim Lollar | .07 |
| 588 Dale Berra | .07 |
| 589 Dave Stapleton | .07 |
| 590 Al Oliver | .25 |
| 591 Oliver (Action) | .15 |
| 592 Craig Swan | .07 |
| 593 Billy Smith | .07 |
| 594 Renie Martin | .07 |
| 595 Dave Collins | .07 |
| 596 Damaso Garcia | .12 |
| 597 Wayne Nordhagen | .07 |
| 598 Bob Galasso | .07 |
| 599 White Sox Rookies: | .12 |
| Jay Loviglio, R. Patterson, Leo Sutherland | |
| 600 Dave Winfield | 1.25 |
| 601 Sid Monge | .07 |
| 602 Freddie Patek | .07 |
| 603 Rich Hebner | .07 |
| 604 Orlando Sanchez | .10 |
| 605 Steve Rogers | .10 |
| 606 Blue Jays Leaders: | .10 |
| John Mayberry, Dave Stieb | |
| 607 Leon Durham | .30 |
| 608 Jerry Royster | .07 |
| 609 Rick Sutcliffe | .25 |
| 610 Rickey Henderson | 10.00 |
| 611 Joe Niekro | .12 |
| 612 Gary Ward | .07 |
| 613 Jim Gantner | .07 |
| 614 Juan Eichelberger | .07 |
| 615 Bob Boone | .07 |
| 616 Boone (Action) | .07 |
| 617 Scott McGregor | .10 |
| 618 Tim Foli | .07 |
| 619 Bill Campbell | .07 |
| 620 Ken Griffey | .30 |
| 621 Griffey (Action) | .15 |
| 622 Dennis Lamp | .07 |
| 623 Mets Rookies: | .50 |
| Ron Gardenhire, T. Leach, Tim Leary | |
| 624 Fergie Jenkins | .50 |
| 625 Hal McRae | .10 |
| 626 Randy Jones | .07 |
| 627 Enos Cabell | .07 |
| 628 Bill Travers | .07 |
| 629 Johnny Wockenfuss | .07 |
| 630 Joe Charboneau | .07 |
| 631 Gene Tenace | .07 |
| 632 Bryan Clark | .10 |
| 633 Mitchell Page | .07 |
| 634 Checklist No. 5 | .15 |
| 635 Ron Davis | .07 |
| 636 Phillies Leaders: | .35 |
| Pete Rose, Steve Carlton | |
| 637 Rick Camp | .07 |
| 638 John Milner | .07 |
| 639 Ken Kravec | .07 |
| 640 Cesar Cedeno | .10 |
| 641 Steve Mura | .07 |
| 642 Mike Scioscia | .30 |
| 643 Pete Vuckovich | .12 |
| 644 John Castino | .07 |
| 645 Frank White | .10 |

| NO. PLAYER | MINT |
|---|---|
| 646 White (Action) | .07 |
| 647 Warren Brusstar | .07 |
| 648 Jose Morales | .07 |
| 649 Ken Clay | .07 |
| 650 Carl Yastrzemski | 1.25 |
| 651 Yastrzemski (Action) | .75 |
| 652 Steve Nicosia | .07 |
| 653 Angels Rookies: | 1.50 |
| Luis Sanchez, Tom Brunansky, Daryl Sconiers | |
| 654 Jim Morrison | .07 |
| 655 Joel Youngblood | .07 |
| 656 Eddie Whitson | .10 |
| 657 Tom Poquette | .07 |
| 658 Tito Landrum | .07 |
| 659 Fred Martinez | .07 |
| 660 Dave Concepcion | .12 |
| 661 Concepcion (Action) | .07 |
| 662 Luis Salazar | .07 |
| 663 Hector Cruz | .07 |
| 664 Dan Spillner | .07 |
| 665 Jim Clancy | .07 |
| 666 Tigers Leaders: | .20 |
| Steve Kemp, Dan Petry | |
| 667 Jeff Reardon | 1.00 |
| 668 Dale Murphy | 1.50 |
| 669 Larry Milbourne | .07 |
| 670 Steve Kemp | .10 |
| 671 Mike Davis | .15 |
| 672 Bob Knepper | .07 |
| 673 Keith Drumright | .07 |
| 674 Dave Goltz | .07 |
| 675 Cecil Cooper | .25 |
| 676 Sal Butera | .07 |
| 677 Alfredo Griffin | .10 |
| 678 Tom Paciorek | .07 |
| 679 Sammy Stewart | .07 |
| 680 Gary Matthews | .10 |
| 681 Dodgers Rookies: | 5.00 |
| Steve Sax, Mike Marshall, Ron Roenicke | |
| 682 Jesse Jefferson | .07 |
| 683 Phil Garner | .07 |
| 684 Harold Baines | .75 |
| 685 Bert Blyleven | .25 |
| 686 Gary Allenson | .07 |
| 687 Greg Minton | .07 |
| 688 Leon Roberts | .07 |
| 689 Lary Sorensen | .07 |
| 690 Dave Kingman | .20 |
| 691 Dan Schatzeder | .07 |
| 692 Wayne Gross | .07 |
| 693 Cesar Geronimo | .07 |
| 694 Dave Wehrmeister | .07 |
| 695 Warren Cromartie | .07 |
| 696 Pirates Leaders: | .15 |
| Bill Madlock, B. Solomon | |
| 697 John Montefusco | .07 |
| 698 Tony Scott | .07 |
| 699 Dick Tidrow | .07 |
| 700 George Foster | .25 |
| 701 Foster (Action) | .15 |
| 702 Steve Renko | .07 |
| 703 Brewers Leaders: | .15 |
| Cecil Cooper, P. Vuckovich | |
| 704 Mickey Rivers | .07 |
| 705 Rivers (Action) | .07 |
| 706 Barry Foote | .07 |
| 707 Mark Bomback | .07 |
| 708 Gene Richards | .07 |
| 709 Don Money | .07 |
| 710 Jerry Reuss | .07 |
| 711 Mariners Rookies: | 4.00 |
| Dave Edler, Reggie Walton, Dave Henderson | |
| 712 Denny Martinez | .25 |
| 713 Del Unser | .07 |
| 714 Jerry Koosman | .10 |
| 715 Willie Stargell | .75 |
| 716 Stargell (Action) | .35 |
| 717 Rick Miller | .07 |
| 718 Charlie Hough | .07 |
| 719 Jerry Narron | .07 |
| 720 Greg Luzinski | .15 |
| 721 Luzinski (Action) | .10 |

# 1982 Topps (Continued)

| NO. | PLAYER | MINT |
|---|---|---|
| 722 | Jerry Martin | .07 |
| 723 | Junior Kennedy | .07 |
| 724 | Dave Rosello | .07 |
| 725 | Amos Otis | .10 |
| 726 | Otis (Action) | .07 |
| 727 | Sixto Lezcano | .07 |
| 728 | Aurelio Lopez | .07 |
| 729 | Jim Spencer | .07 |
| 730 | Gary Carter | .75 |
| 731 | Padres Rookies: | .15 |
|  | Doug Gwosdz, Mike |  |
|  | Armstrong, Fred Kuhaulua |  |
| 732 | Mike Lum | .07 |
| 733 | Larry McWilliams | .10 |
| 734 | Mike Ivie | .07 |
| 735 | Rudy May | .07 |
| 736 | Jerry Turner | .07 |
| 737 | Reggie Cleveland | .07 |
| 738 | Dave Engle | .07 |
| 739 | Joey McLaughlin | .07 |

| NO. | PLAYER | MINT |
|---|---|---|
| 740 | Dave Lopes | .10 |
| 741 | Lopes (Action) | .07 |
| 742 | Dick Drago | .07 |
| 743 | John Stearns | .07 |
| 744 | Mike Witt (R) | .50 |
| 745 | Bake McBride | .07 |
| 746 | Andre Thornton | .12 |
| 747 | John Lowenstein | .07 |
| 748 | Marc Hill | .07 |
| 749 | Bob Shirley | .07 |
| 750 | Jim Rice | .60 |
| 751 | Rick Honeycutt | .07 |
| 752 | Lee Lacy | .07 |
| 753 | Tom Brookens | .07 |
| 754 | Joe Morgan | .75 |
| 755 | Morgan (Action) | .20 |
| 756 | Reds Leaders: | .20 |
|  | Ken Griffey, Tom Seaver |  |
| 757 | Tom Underwood | .07 |

| NO. | PLAYER | MINT |
|---|---|---|
| 758 | Claudell Washington | .12 |
| 759 | Paul Splittorff | .07 |
| 760 | Bill Buckner | .15 |
| 761 | Dave Smith | .07 |
| 762 | Mike Phillips | .07 |
| 763 | Tom Hume | .07 |
| 764 | Steve Swisher | .07 |
| 765 | Gorman Thomas | .12 |
| 766 | Twins Rookies: | 5.00 |
|  | Lenny Faedo, Kent Hrbek, |  |
|  | Tim Laudner |  |
| 767 | Roy Smalley | .07 |
| 768 | Jerry Garvin | .07 |
| 769 | Richie Zisk | .07 |
| 770 | Rich Gossage | .25 |
| 771 | Gossage (Action) | .15 |
| 772 | Bert Campaneris | .07 |
| 773 | John Denny | .10 |
| 774 | Jay Johnstone | .07 |

| NO. | PLAYER | MINT |
|---|---|---|
| 775 | Bob Forsch | .07 |
| 776 | Mark Belanger | .07 |
| 777 | Tom Griffin | .07 |
| 778 | Kevin Hickey | .07 |
| 779 | Grant Jackson | .07 |
| 780 | Pete Rose | 2.00 |
| 781 | Rose (Action) | .85 |
| 782 | Frank Taveras | .07 |
| 783 | Greg Harris | .30 |
| 784 | Milt Wilcox | .07 |
| 785 | Dan Driessen | .07 |
| 786 | Red Sox Leaders: | .20 |
|  | C. Lansford, M. Torrez |  |
| 787 | Fred Stanley | .07 |
| 788 | Woodie Fryman | .07 |
| 789 | Checklist No. 6 | .15 |
| 790 | Larry Gura | .07 |
| 791 | Bobby Brown | .07 |
| 792 | Frank Tanana | .15 |

# 1982 Topps Traded . . . Complete Set of 132 Cards—Value $200.00

Updates the main 1982 card set with players who changed teams during the season and rookies. Unlike the 1981 Traded set, the cards are numbered from 1T to 132T. The complete set was packaged in a printed box and only distributed through card hobby dealers.

| NO. |  | PLAYER | MINT |
|---|---|---|---|
| 1 | T | Doyle Alexander | .15 |
| 2 | T | Jesse Barfield | 3.00 |
| 3 | T | Ross Baumgarten | .10 |
| 4 | T | Steve Bedrosian | .75 |
| 5 | T | Mark Belanger | .10 |
| 6 | T | Kurt Bevacqua | .10 |
| 7 | T | Tim Blackwell | .10 |
| 8 | T | Vida Blue | .15 |
| 9 | T | Bob Boone | .10 |
| 10 | T | Larry Bowa | .20 |
| 11 | T | Dan Briggs | .10 |
| 12 | T | Bobby Brown | .10 |
| 13 | T | Tom Brunansky | 2.25 |
| 14 | T | Jeff Burroughs | .12 |
| 15 | T | Enos Cabell | .10 |
| 16 | T | Bill Campbell | .10 |
| 17 | T | Bobby Castillo | .10 |
| 18 | T | Bill Caudill | .15 |
| 19 | T | Cesar Cedeno | .15 |
| 20 | T | Dave Collins | .12 |
| 21 | T | Doug Corbett | .10 |
| 22 | T | Al Cowens | .15 |
| 23 | T | Chili Davis | 2.50 |
| 24 | T | Dick Davis | .10 |
| 25 | T | Ron Davis | .10 |
| 26 | T | Doug DeCince | .25 |
| 27 | T | Ivan DeJesus | .12 |
| 28 | T | Bob Dernier | .20 |
| 29 | T | Bo Diaz | .10 |
| 30 | T | Roger Erickson | .10 |
| 31 | T | Jim Essian | .10 |
| 32 | T | Ed Farmer | .10 |
| 33 | T | Doug Flynn | .10 |

| NO. |  | PLAYER | MINT |
|---|---|---|---|
| 34 | T | Tim Foli | .10 |
| 35 | T | Dan Ford | .10 |
| 36 | T | George Foster | .50 |
| 37 | T | Dave Frost | .10 |
| 38 | T | Rich Gale | .10 |
| 39 | T | Ron Gardenhire | .10 |
| 40 | T | Ken Griffey | .75 |
| 41 | T | Greg Harris | .10 |
| 42 | T | Von Hayes | 1.50 |
| 43 | T | Larry Herndon | .10 |
| 44 | T | Kent Hrbek | 5.00 |
| 45 | T | Mike Ivie | .10 |
| 46 | T | Grant Jackson | .10 |
| 47 | T | Reggie Jackson | 6.00 |
| 48 | T | Ron Jackson | .10 |
| 49 | T | Fergie Jenkins | 1.25 |
| 50 | T | Lamar Johnson | .10 |
| 51 | T | Ray Johnson | .10 |
| 52 | T | Jay Johnstone | .10 |
| 53 | T | Mick Kelleher | .10 |
| 54 | T | Steve Kemp | .12 |
| 55 | T | Junior Kennedy | .10 |
| 56 | T | Jim Kern | .10 |
| 57 | T | Ray Knight | .20 |
| 58 | T | Wayne Krenchicki | .10 |
| 59 | T | Mike Krukow | .10 |
| 60 | T | Duane Kuiper | .10 |
| 61 | T | Mike LaCoss | .10 |
| 62 | T | Chet Lemon | .15 |
| 63 | T | Sixto Lezcano | .10 |
| 64 | T | Dave Lopes | .15 |
| 65 | T | Jerry Martin | .10 |
| 66 | T | Renie Martin | .10 |

| NO. |  | PLAYER | MINT |
|---|---|---|---|
| 67 | T | John Mayberry | .10 |
| 68 | T | Lee Mazzilli | .10 |
| 69 | T | Bake McBride | .15 |
| 70 | T | Dan Meyer | .10 |
| 71 | T | Larry Milbourne | .10 |
| 72 | T | Eddie Milner | .25 |
| 73 | T | Sid Monge | .10 |
| 74 | T | John Montefusco | .10 |
| 75 | T | Jose Morales | .10 |
| 76 | T | Keith Moreland | .15 |
| 77 | T | Jim Morrison | .10 |
| 78 | T | Rance Mulliniks | .10 |
| 79 | T | Steve Mura | .10 |
| 80 | T | Gene Nelson | .10 |
| 81 | T | Joe Nolan | .10 |
| 82 | T | Dickie Noles | .10 |
| 83 | T | Al Oliver | .20 |
| 84 | T | Jorge Orta | .10 |
| 85 | T | Tom Paciorek | .10 |
| 86 | T | Larry Parrish | .20 |
| 87 | T | Jack Perconte | .10 |
| 88 | T | Gaylord Perry | 1.25 |
| 89 | T | Rob Picciolo | .10 |
| 90 | T | Joe Pittman | .10 |
| 91 | T | Hosken Powell | .10 |
| 92 | T | Mike Proly | .10 |
| 93 | T | Greg Pryor | .10 |
| 94 | T | Charlie Puleo | .10 |
| 95 | T | Shane Rawley | .12 |
| 96 | T | Johnny Ray | .50 |
| 97 | T | Dave Revering | .10 |
| 98 | T | Cal Ripken | 135.00 |
| 99 | T | Allen Ripley | .10 |

| NO. |  | PLAYER | MINT |
|---|---|---|---|
| 100 | T | Bill Robinson | .10 |
| 101 | T | Aurelio Rodriquez | .10 |
| 102 | T | Joe Rudi | .10 |
| 103 | T | Steve Sax | 6.00 |
| 104 | T | Dan Schatzeder | .10 |
| 105 | T | Bob Shirley | .10 |
| 106 | T | Eric Show (RR) | .35 |
| 107 | T | Roy Smalley | .10 |
| 108 | T | Lonnie Smith | .30 |
| 109 | T | Ozzie Smith | 10.00 |
| 110 | T | Reggie Smith | .20 |
| 111 | T | Lary Sorensen | .10 |
| 112 | T | Elias Sosa | .10 |
| 113 | T | Mike Stanton | .10 |
| 114 | T | Steve Stroughter | .10 |
| 115 | T | Champ Summers | .10 |
| 116 | T | Rick Sutcliffe | .50 |
| 117 | T | Frank Tanana | .10 |
| 118 | T | Frank Taveras | .10 |
| 119 | T | Garry Templeton | .20 |
| 120 | T | Alex Trevino | .10 |
| 121 | T | Jerry Turner | .10 |
| 122 | T | Ed VandeBerg (RR) | .25 |
| 123 | T | Tom Veryzer | .10 |
| 124 | T | Ron Washington | .10 |
| 125 | T | Bob Watson | .10 |
| 126 | T | Dennis Werth | .10 |
| 127 | T | Eddie Whitson | .10 |
| 128 | T | Rob Wilfong | .10 |
| 129 | T | Bump Wills | .10 |
| 130 | T | Gary Woods | .10 |
| 131 | T | Butch Wynegar | .10 |
| 132 | T | Traded Checklist | .25 |

# 1983 Topps . . . Complete Set of 792 Cards—Value $175.00

Features the rookie cards of Willie McGee, Ryne Sandberg, Wade Boggs, Tony Gwynn, Frank Viola and Gary Gaetti.

| NO. | PLAYER | MINT |
|---|---|---|
| 1 | Record—T. Armas | .20 |
| | 11 Rightfield Putouts | |
| 2 | Record—R. Henderson | 1.50 |
| | Stolen Base Record | |
| 3 | Record—G. Minton | .08 |
| | No HR's in 269⅓ Innings | |
| 4 | Record—L. Parrish | .15 |
| | Threw Out 3 in AS Game | |
| 5 | Record—Trillo | .08 |
| | 479 Errorless Chances | |
| 6 | Record—J. Wathan | .08 |
| | 31st Stolen Base, Catcher | |
| 7 | Gene Richards | .06 |
| 8 | Steve Balboni | .10 |
| 9 | Joey McLaughlin | .06 |
| 10 | Gorman Thomas | .15 |
| 11 | Billy Gardner (Mgr.) | .06 |
| 12 | Paul Mirabella | .06 |
| 13 | Larry Herndon | .08 |
| 14 | Frank LaCorte | .06 |
| 15 | Ron Cey | .15 |
| 16 | George Vukovich | .06 |
| 17 | Kent Tekulve | .06 |
| 18 | Tekulve (Veteran) | .06 |
| 19 | Oscar Gamble | .08 |
| 20 | Carlton Fisk | 1.25 |
| 21 | Orioles Leaders: | .20 |
| | Eddie Murray, Jim Palmer | |
| 22 | Randy Martz | .06 |
| 23 | Mike Heath | .50 |
| 24 | Steve Mura | .25 |
| 25 | Hal McRae | .06 |
| 26 | Jerry Roystar | .06 |
| 27 | Doug Corbett | .06 |
| 28 | Bruce Bochte | .06 |
| 29 | Randy Jones | .06 |
| 30 | Jim Rice | .40 |
| 31 | Bill Gullickson | .08 |
| 32 | Dave Bergman | .06 |
| 33 | Jack O'Connor | .06 |
| 34 | Paul Householder | .06 |
| 35 | Rollie Fingers | .30 |
| 36 | Fingers (Veteran) | .15 |
| 37 | Darrell Johnson (Mgr.) | .06 |
| 38 | Tim Flannery | .06 |
| 39 | Terry Puhl | .06 |
| 40 | Fernando Valenzuela | .50 |
| 41 | Jerry Turner | .06 |
| 42 | Dale Murray | .06 |
| 43 | Bob Dernier | .08 |
| 44 | Don Robinson | .06 |
| 45 | John Mayberry | .06 |
| 46 | Richard Dotson | .08 |
| 47 | Dave McKay | .06 |
| 48 | Lary Sorensen | .06 |
| 49 | Willie McGee (R) | 5.00 |
| 50 | Bob Horner | .15 |
| 51 | Cubs Leaders: | .20 |
| | Leon Durham, F. Jenkins | |
| 52 | Onix Concepcion | .15 |
| 53 | Mike Witt | .20 |
| 54 | Jim Maler | .10 |
| 55 | Mookie Wilson | .08 |
| 56 | Chuck Rainey | .06 |
| 57 | Tim Blackwell | .06 |
| 58 | Al Holland | .06 |

| NO. | PLAYER | MINT |
|---|---|---|
| 59 | Benny Ayala | .06 |
| 60 | Johnny Bench | 1.50 |
| 61 | Bench (Veteran) | .75 |
| 62 | Bob McClure | .06 |
| 63 | Rick Monday | .06 |
| 64 | Bill Stein | .06 |
| 65 | Jack Morris | .75 |
| 66 | Bob Lillis (Mgr.) | .06 |
| 67 | Sal Butera | .06 |
| 68 | Eric Show (R) | .30 |
| 69 | Lee Lacy | .08 |
| 70 | Steve Carlton | 1.25 |
| 71 | Carlton (Veteran) | .60 |
| 72 | Tom Paciorek | .06 |
| 73 | Allen Ripley | .06 |
| 74 | Julio Gonzalez | .06 |
| 75 | Amos Otis | .06 |
| 76 | Rick Mahler | .06 |
| 77 | Hosken Powell | .06 |
| 78 | Bill Caudill | .08 |
| 79 | Mick Kelleher | .06 |
| 80 | George Foster | .25 |
| 81 | Yankees Leaders: | .20 |
| | J. Mumphrey, D. Righetti | |
| 82 | Bruce Hurst | .06 |
| 83 | Ryne Sandberg (R) | 50.00 |
| 84 | Milt May | .06 |
| 85 | Ken Singleton | .08 |
| 86 | Tom Hume | .06 |
| 87 | Joe Rudi | .06 |
| 88 | Jim Gantner | .06 |
| 89 | Leon Roberts | .06 |
| 90 | Jerry Reuss | .08 |
| 91 | Larry Milbourne | .06 |
| 92 | Mike LaCoss | .06 |
| 93 | John Castino | .06 |
| 94 | Dave Edwards | .06 |
| 95 | Alan Trammell | .75 |
| 96 | Dick Howser (Mgr.) | .06 |
| 97 | Ross Baumgarten | .06 |
| 98 | Vance Law | .06 |
| 99 | Dickie Noles | .06 |
| 100 | Pete Rose | 2.00 |
| 101 | Rose (Veteran) | .75 |
| 102 | Dave Beard | .06 |
| 103 | Darrell Porter | .08 |
| 104 | Bob Walk | .06 |
| 105 | Don Baylor | .20 |
| 106 | Gene Nelson | .06 |
| 107 | Mike Jorgensen | .06 |
| 108 | Glenn Hoffman | .06 |
| 109 | Luis Leal | .06 |
| 110 | Ken Griffey | .25 |
| 111 | Expos Leaders: | .15 |
| | Al Oliver, Steve Rogers | |
| 112 | Bob Shirley | .06 |
| 113 | Ron Roenicke | .06 |
| 114 | Jim Slaton | .06 |
| 115 | Chili Davis | .50 |
| 116 | Dave Schmidt | .06 |
| 117 | Alan Knicely | .06 |
| 118 | Chris Welsh | .06 |
| 119 | Tom Brookens | .06 |
| 120 | Len Barker | .06 |
| 121 | Mickey Hatcher | .06 |
| 122 | Jimmy Smith | .10 |

| NO. | PLAYER | MINT |
|---|---|---|
| 123 | George Frazier | .06 |
| 124 | Marc Hill | .06 |
| 125 | Leon Durham | .25 |
| 126 | Joe Torre (Mgr.) | .08 |
| 127 | Preston Hanna | .06 |
| 128 | Mike Ramsey | .06 |
| 129 | Checklist No. 1 | .12 |
| 130 | Dave Stieb | .50 |
| 131 | Ed Ott | .06 |
| 132 | Todd Cruz | .06 |
| 133 | Jim Barr | .06 |
| 134 | Hubie Brooks | .35 |
| 135 | Dwight Evans | .35 |
| 136 | Willie Aikens | .06 |
| 137 | Woodie Fryman | .06 |
| 138 | Rick Dempsey | .08 |
| 139 | Bruce Berenyi | .06 |
| 140 | Willie Randolph | .10 |
| 141 | Indians Leaders: | .12 |
| | Toby Harrah, Rick Sutcliffe | |
| 142 | Mike Caldwell | .06 |
| 143 | Joe Pettini | .06 |
| 144 | Mark Wagner | .06 |
| 145 | Don Sutton | .40 |
| 146 | Don Sutton (Veteran) | .15 |
| 147 | Rick Leach | .06 |
| 148 | Dave Roberts | .06 |
| 149 | Johnny Ray | .15 |
| 150 | Bruce Sutter | .20 |
| 151 | B. Sutter (Veteran) | .15 |
| 152 | Jay Johnstone | .06 |
| 153 | Jerry Koosman | .06 |
| 154 | Johnnie LeMaster | .06 |
| 155 | Dan Quisenberry | .20 |
| 156 | Billy Martin (Mgr.) | .15 |
| 157 | Steve Bedrosian | .20 |
| 158 | Rob Wilfong | .06 |
| 159 | Mike Stanton | .06 |
| 160 | Dave Kingman | .15 |
| 161 | D. Kingman (Veteran) | .10 |
| 162 | Mark Clear | .06 |
| 163 | Cal Ripken | 15.00 |
| 164 | David Palmer | .06 |
| 165 | Dan Driessen | .06 |
| 166 | John Pacella | .06 |
| 167 | Mark Brouhard | .06 |
| 168 | Juan Eichelberger | .06 |
| 169 | Doug Flynn | .06 |
| 170 | Steve Howe | .06 |
| 171 | Giants Leaders: | .12 |
| | Bill Laskey, Joe Morgan | |
| 172 | Vern Ruhle | .06 |
| 173 | Jim Morrison | .06 |
| 174 | Jerry Ujdur | .06 |
| 175 | Bo Diaz | .06 |
| 176 | Dave Righetti | .35 |
| 177 | Harold Baines | .60 |
| 178 | Luis Tiant | .08 |
| 179 | Luis Tiant (Veteran) | .06 |
| 180 | Rickey Henderson | 7.50 |
| 181 | Terry Felton | .12 |
| 182 | Mike Fischlin | .06 |
| 183 | Ed VandeBerg (R) | .25 |
| 184 | Bob Clark | .06 |
| 185 | Tim Lollar | .06 |
| 186 | Whitey Herzog (Mgr.) | .06 |

| NO. | PLAYER | MINT |
|---|---|---|
| 187 | Terry Leach | .06 |
| 188 | Rick Miller | .06 |
| 189 | Dan Schatzeder | .06 |
| 190 | Cecil Cooper | .20 |
| 191 | Joe Price | .06 |
| 192 | Floyd Rayford | .06 |
| 193 | Harry Spilman | .06 |
| 194 | Cesar Geronimo | .06 |
| 195 | Bob Stoddard | .10 |
| 196 | Bill Fahey | .06 |
| 197 | Jim Eisenreich | .60 |
| 198 | Kiko Garcia | .06 |
| 199 | Marty Bystrom | .06 |
| 200 | Rod Carew | 1.25 |
| 201 | Rod Carew (Veteran) | .60 |
| 202 | Blue Jays Leaders: | .12 |
| | Damaso Garcia, Dave Stieb | |
| 203 | Mike Morgan | .06 |
| 204 | Junior Kennedy | .06 |
| 205 | Dave Parker | .50 |
| 206 | Ken Oberkfell | .06 |
| 207 | Rick Camp | .06 |
| 208 | Dan Meyer | .06 |
| 209 | Mike Moore (R) | 1.50 |
| 210 | Jack Clark | .40 |
| 211 | John Denny | .15 |
| 212 | John Stearns | .06 |
| 213 | Tom Burgmeier | .06 |
| 214 | Jerry White | .06 |
| 215 | Mario Soto | .10 |
| 216 | Tony LaRussa (Mgr.) | .08 |
| 217 | Tim Stoddard | .06 |
| 218 | Roy Howell | .06 |
| 219 | Mike Armstrong | .06 |
| 220 | Dusty Baker | .12 |
| 221 | Joe Niekro | .08 |
| 222 | Damaso Garcia | .15 |
| 223 | John Montefusco | .06 |
| 224 | Mickey Rivers | .06 |
| 225 | Enos Cabell | .06 |
| 226 | Enrique Romo | .06 |
| 227 | Chris Bando | .06 |
| 228 | Joaquin Andujar | .12 |
| 229 | Phillies Leaders: | .12 |
| | Bo Diaz, Steve Carlton | |
| 230 | Fergie Jenkins | .30 |
| 231 | F. Jenkins (Veteran) | .15 |
| 232 | Tom Brunansky | .50 |
| 233 | Wayne Gross | .06 |
| 234 | Larry Andersen | .06 |
| 235 | Claudell Washington | .15 |
| 236 | Steve Renko | .06 |
| 237 | Dan Norman | .06 |
| 238 | Bud Black (R) | .75 |
| 239 | Dave Stapleton | .06 |
| 240 | Rich Gossage | .25 |
| 241 | Gossage (Veteran) | .15 |
| 242 | Joe Nolan | .06 |
| 243 | Duane Walker | .12 |
| 244 | Dwight Bernard | .06 |
| 245 | Steve Sax | .75 |
| 246 | G. Bamberger (Mgr.) | .06 |
| 247 | Dave Smith | .06 |
| 248 | Bake McBride | .06 |
| 249 | Checklist No. 2 | .12 |
| 250 | Bill Buckner | .15 |

| NO. | PLAYER | MINT |
|-----|--------|------|
| 251 | Alan Wiggins (R) | .15 |
| 252 | Luis Aguayo | .06 |
| 253 | Larry McWilliams | .06 |
| 254 | Rick Cerone | .06 |
| 255 | Gene Garber | .06 |
| 256 | G. Garber (Veteran) | .06 |
| 257 | Jesse Barfield | .60 |
| 258 | Manny Castillo | .06 |
| 259 | Jeff Jones | .06 |
| 260 | Steve Kemp | .08 |
| 261 | Tigers Leaders: | .12 |
|     | L. Herndon, Dan Petry | |
| 262 | Ron Jackson | .06 |
| 263 | Renie Martin | .06 |
| 264 | Jamie Quirk | .06 |
| 265 | Joel Youngblood | .06 |
| 266 | Paul Boris | .08 |
| 267 | Terry Francona | .06 |
| 268 | Storm Davis (R) | .35 |
| 269 | Ron Oester | .06 |
| 270 | Dennis Eckersley | .50 |
| 271 | Ed Romero | .06 |
| 272 | Frank Tanana | .06 |
| 273 | Mark Belanger | .06 |
| 274 | Terry Kennedy | .10 |
| 275 | Ray Knight | .06 |
| 276 | Gene Mauch (Mgr.) | .06 |
| 277 | Rance Mulliniks | .06 |
| 278 | Kevin Hickey | .06 |
| 279 | Greg Gross | .06 |
| 280 | Bert Blyleven | .25 |
| 281 | Andre Robertson | .06 |
| 282 | Reggie Smith | .10 |
| 283 | R. Smith (Veteran) | .08 |
| 284 | Jeff Lahti | .15 |
| 285 | Lance Parrish | .35 |
| 286 | Rick Langford | .06 |
| 287 | Bobby Brown | .06 |
| 288 | Joe Cowley (R) | .30 |
| 289 | Jerry Dybzinski | .06 |
| 290 | Jeff Reardon | .75 |
| 291 | Pirates Leaders: | .12 |
|     | B. Madlock, J. Candelaria | |
| 292 | Craig Swan | .06 |
| 293 | Glen Gulliver | .08 |
| 294 | Dave Engle | .06 |
| 295 | Jerry Remy | .06 |
| 296 | Greg Harris | .06 |
| 297 | Ned Yost | .06 |
| 298 | Floyd Chiffer | .10 |
| 299 | George Wright | .15 |
| 300 | Mike Schmidt | 3.00 |
| 301 | M. Schmidt (Veteran) | 1.50 |
| 302 | Ernie Whitt | .06 |
| 303 | Miguel Dilone | .06 |
| 304 | Dave Rucker | .06 |
| 305 | Larry Bowa | .10 |
| 306 | Tom Lasorda (Mgr.) | .10 |
| 307 | Lou Piniella | .12 |
| 308 | Jesus Vega | .08 |
| 309 | Jeff Leonard | .15 |
| 310 | Greg Luzinski | .15 |
| 311 | Glenn Brummer | .06 |
| 312 | Brian Kingman | .06 |
| 313 | Gary Gray | .06 |
| 314 | Ken Dayley | .06 |
| 315 | Rick Burleson | .06 |
| 316 | Paul Splittorff | .06 |
| 317 | Gary Rajsich | .10 |
| 318 | John Tudor | .15 |
| 319 | Lenn Sakata | .06 |
| 320 | Steve Rogers | .08 |
| 321 | Brewers Leaders: | .15 |
|     | P. Vuckovich, R. Yount | |
| 322 | Dave Van Gorder | .10 |
| 323 | Luis DeLeon | .06 |
| 324 | Mike Marshall | .20 |
| 325 | Von Hayes | .30 |
| 326 | Garth Iorg | .05 |
| 327 | Bobby Castillo | .06 |
| 328 | Craig Reynolds | .06 |
| 329 | Randy Niemann | .06 |
| 330 | Buddy Bell | .15 |
| 331 | Mike Krukow | .06 |
| 332 | Glenn Wilson (R) | .35 |

| NO. | PLAYER | MINT |
|-----|--------|------|
| 333 | Dave LaRoche | .06 |
| 334 | D. LaRoche (Veteran) | .06 |
| 335 | Steve Henderson | .06 |
| 336 | R. Lachemann (Mgr.) | .06 |
| 337 | Tito Landrum | .06 |
| 338 | Bob Owchinko | .06 |
| 339 | Terry Harper | .06 |
| 340 | Larry Gura | .06 |
| 341 | Doug DeCinces | .15 |
| 342 | Atlee Hammaker | .08 |
| 343 | Bob Bailor | .06 |
| 344 | Roger LaFrancois | .08 |
| 345 | Jim Clancy | .06 |
| 346 | Joe Pittman | .06 |
| 347 | Sammy Stewart | .06 |
| 348 | Alan Bannister | .06 |
| 349 | Checklist No. 3 | .12 |
| 350 | Robin Yount | 2.00 |
| 351 | Reds Leaders: | .12 |
|     | Cesar Cedeno, Mario Soto | |
| 352 | Mike Scioscia | .06 |
| 353 | Steve Comer | .06 |
| 354 | Randy Johnson | .06 |
| 355 | Jim Bibby | .06 |
| 356 | Gary Woods | .06 |
| 357 | Len Matuszek | .15 |
| 358 | Jerry Garvin | .06 |
| 359 | Dave Collins | .08 |
| 360 | Nolan Ryan | 6.00 |
| 361 | N. Ryan (Veteran) | 3.00 |
| 362 | Bill Almon | .06 |
| 363 | John Stuper | .15 |
| 364 | Bret Butler | .50 |
| 365 | Dave Lopes | .07 |
| 366 | Dick Williams (Mgr.) | .06 |
| 367 | Bud Anderson | .06 |
| 368 | Richie Zisk | .06 |
| 369 | Jesse Orosco | .10 |
| 370 | Gary Carter | .50 |
| 371 | Mike Richardt | .08 |
| 372 | Terry Crowley | .06 |
| 373 | Kevin Saucier | .06 |
| 374 | Wayne Krenchicki | .06 |
| 375 | Pete Vuckovich | .06 |
| 376 | Ken Landreaux | .06 |
| 377 | Lee May | .06 |
| 378 | Lee May (Veteran) | .06 |
| 379 | Guy Sularz | .10 |
| 380 | Ron Davis | .06 |
| 381 | Red Sox Leaders: | .15 |
|     | Bob Stanley, Jim Rice | |
| 382 | Bob Knepper | .06 |
| 383 | Ozzie Virgil | .06 |
| 384 | Dave Dravecky (R) | .75 |
| 385 | Mike Easler | .06 |
| 386 | Rod Carew (AS) | .35 |
| 387 | Bob Grich (AS) | .08 |
| 388 | George Brett (AS) | .50 |
| 389 | Robin Yount (AS) | .50 |
| 390 | Reggie Jackson (AS) | .50 |
| 391 | Rickey Henderson (AS) | 1.50 |
| 392 | Fred Lynn (AS) | .15 |
| 393 | Carlton Fisk (AS) | .30 |
| 394 | Pete Vuckovich (AS) | .08 |
| 395 | Larry Gura (AS) | .06 |
| 396 | Dan Quisenberry (AS) | .12 |
| 397 | Pete Rose (AS) | .60 |
| 398 | Manny Trillo (AS) | .08 |
| 399 | Mike Schmidt (AS) | .75 |
| 400 | Dave Concepcion (AS) | .10 |
| 401 | Dale Murphy (AS) | .30 |
| 402 | Andre Dawson (AS) | .35 |
| 403 | Tim Raines (AS) | .25 |
| 404 | Gary Carter (AS) | .25 |
| 405 | Steve Rogers (AS) | .08 |
| 406 | Steve Carlton (AS) | .40 |
| 407 | Bruce Sutter (AS) | .20 |
| 408 | Rudy May | .06 |
| 409 | Marvis Foley | .06 |
| 410 | Phil Niekro | .50 |
| 411 | P. Niekro (Veteran) | .25 |
| 412 | Rangers Leaders: | .10 |
|     | Buddy Bell, Charlie Hough | |
| 413 | Matt Keough | .06 |
| 414 | Julio Cruz | .06 |

| NO. | PLAYER | MINT |
|-----|--------|------|
| 415 | Bob Forsch | .06 |
| 416 | Joe Ferguson | .06 |
| 417 | Tom Hausman | .06 |
| 418 | Greg Pryor | .06 |
| 419 | Steve Crawford | .06 |
| 420 | Al Oliver | .15 |
| 421 | Al Oliver (Veteran) | .08 |
| 422 | George Cappuzzello | .06 |
| 423 | Tom Lawless | .12 |
| 424 | Jerry Augustine | .06 |
| 425 | Pedro Guerrero | .50 |
| 426 | Earl Weaver (Mgr.) | .12 |
| 427 | Roy Lee Jackson | .06 |
| 428 | Champ Summers | .06 |
| 429 | Eddie Whitson | .08 |
| 430 | Kirk Gibson | .40 |
| 431 | Gary Gaetti (R) | 2.00 |
| 432 | Porfirio Altamirano | .10 |
| 433 | Dale Berra | .06 |
| 434 | Dennis Lamp | .06 |
| 435 | Tony Armas | .15 |
| 436 | Bill Campbell | .06 |
| 437 | Rick Sweet | .06 |
| 438 | Dave LaPoint (R) | .20 |
| 439 | Rafael Ramirez | .06 |
| 440 | Ron Guidry | .25 |
| 441 | Astros Leaders: | .12 |
|     | Joe Niekro, Ray Knight | |
| 442 | Brian Downing | .06 |
| 443 | Don Hood | .06 |
| 444 | Wally Backman | .20 |
| 445 | Mike Flanagan | .08 |
| 446 | Reid Nichols | .06 |
| 447 | Bryn Smith | .06 |
| 448 | Darrell Evans | .12 |
| 449 | Eddie Milner | .12 |
| 450 | Ted Simmons | .15 |
| 451 | Ted Simmons (Veteran) | .10 |
| 452 | Lloyd Moseby | .15 |
| 453 | Lamar Johnson | .06 |
| 454 | Bob Welch | .35 |
| 455 | Sixto Lezcano | .06 |
| 456 | Lee Elia (Mgr.) | .06 |
| 457 | Milt Wilcox | .06 |
| 458 | Ron Washington | .12 |
| 459 | Ed Farmer | .06 |
| 460 | Roy Smalley | .06 |
| 461 | Steve Trout | .06 |
| 462 | Steve Nicosia | .06 |
| 463 | Gaylord Perry | .50 |
| 464 | G. Perry (Veteran) | .25 |
| 465 | Lonnie Smith | .25 |
| 466 | Tom Underwood | .06 |
| 467 | Rufino Linares | .06 |
| 468 | Dave Goltz | .06 |
| 469 | Ron Gardenhire | .06 |
| 470 | Greg Minton | .06 |
| 471 | Royals Leaders: | .12 |
|     | Willie Wilson, Vida Blue | |
| 472 | Gary Allenson | .06 |
| 473 | John Lowenstein | .06 |
| 474 | Ray Burris | .06 |
| 475 | Cesar Cedeno | .12 |
| 476 | Rob Picciolo | .06 |
| 477 | Tom Niedenfuer | .12 |
| 478 | Phil Garner | .06 |
| 479 | Charlie Hough | .06 |
| 480 | Toby Harrah | .06 |
| 481 | Scot Thompson | .06 |
| 482 | Tony Gwynn (R) | 30.00 |
| 483 | Lynn Jones | .06 |
| 484 | Dick Ruthven | .06 |
| 485 | Omar Moreno | .06 |
| 486 | Clyde King (Mgr.) | .06 |
| 487 | Jerry Hairston | .06 |
| 488 | Alfredo Griffin | .06 |
| 489 | Tom Herr | .15 |
| 490 | Jim Palmer | 1.25 |
| 491 | Jim Palmer (Veteran) | .60 |
| 492 | Paul Serna | .06 |
| 493 | Steve McCatty | .06 |
| 494 | Bob Brenly | .08 |
| 495 | Warren Cromartie | .06 |
| 496 | Tom Veryzer | .06 |
| 497 | Rick Sutcliffe | .20 |

| NO. | PLAYER | MINT |
|-----|--------|------|
| 498 | Wade Boggs (R) | 32.00 |
| 499 | Jeff Little | .10 |
| 500 | Reggie Jackson | 1.50 |
| 501 | R. Jackson (Veteran) | .75 |
| 502 | Braves Leaders: | .15 |
|     | Dale Murphy, Phil Niekro | |
| 503 | Moose Haas | .06 |
| 504 | Don Werner | .06 |
| 505 | Garry Templeton | .15 |
| 506 | Jim Gott | .35 |
| 507 | Tony Scott | .06 |
| 508 | Tom Filer (R) | .30 |
| 509 | Lou Whitaker | .30 |
| 510 | Tug McGraw | .08 |
| 511 | Tug McGraw (Veteran) | .06 |
| 512 | Doyle Alexander | .06 |
| 513 | Fred Stanley | .06 |
| 514 | Rudy Law | .06 |
| 515 | Gene Tenace | .06 |
| 516 | Bill Virdon (Mgr.) | .06 |
| 517 | Gary Ward | .06 |
| 518 | Bill Laskey (R) | .20 |
| 519 | Terry Bulling | .06 |
| 520 | Fred Lynn | .25 |
| 521 | Bruce Benedict | .06 |
| 522 | Pat Zachry | .06 |
| 523 | Carney Lansford | .25 |
| 524 | Tom Brennan | .06 |
| 525 | Frank White | .06 |
| 526 | Checklist No. 4 | .12 |
| 527 | Larry Biittner | .06 |
| 528 | Jamie Easterly | .06 |
| 529 | Tim Laudner | .06 |
| 530 | Eddie Murray | 2.00 |
| 531 | A's Leaders: | .35 |
|     | R. Henderson, R. Langford | |
| 532 | Dave Stewart | 1.50 |
| 533 | Luis Salazar | .06 |
| 534 | John Butcher | .06 |
| 535 | Manny Trillo | .08 |
| 536 | Johnny Wockenfuss | .06 |
| 537 | Rod Scurry | .06 |
| 538 | Danny Heep | .06 |
| 539 | Roger Erickson | .06 |
| 540 | Ozzie Smith | 1.50 |
| 541 | Britt Burns | .08 |
| 542 | Jody Davis | .10 |
| 543 | Alan Fowlkes | .10 |
| 544 | Larry Whisenton | .06 |
| 545 | Floyd Bannister | .06 |
| 546 | Dave Garcia (Mgr.) | .06 |
| 547 | Geoff Zahn | .06 |
| 548 | Brian Giles | .12 |
| 549 | Charlie Puleo | .09 |
| 550 | Carl Yastrzemski | 1.25 |
| 551 | Yastrzemski (Veteran) | .60 |
| 552 | Tim Wallach | .35 |
| 553 | Denny Martinez | .06 |
| 554 | Mike Vail | .06 |
| 555 | Steve Yeager | .06 |
| 556 | Willie Upshaw | .15 |
| 557 | Rick Honeycutt | .06 |
| 558 | Dickie Thon | .08 |
| 559 | Peter Redfern | .06 |
| 560 | Ron LeFlore | .08 |
| 561 | Cardinals Leaders: | .12 |
|     | L. Smith, J. Andujar | |
| 562 | Dave Rozema | .06 |
| 563 | Juan Bonilla | .06 |
| 564 | Sid Monge | .06 |
| 565 | Bucky Dent | .06 |
| 566 | Manny Sarmiento | .06 |
| 567 | Joe Simpson | .06 |
| 568 | Willie Hernandez | .20 |
| 569 | Jack Perconte | .06 |
| 570 | Vida Blue | .08 |
| 571 | Mickey Klutts | .06 |
| 572 | Bob Watson | .06 |
| 573 | Andy Hassler | .06 |
| 574 | Glenn Adams | .06 |
| 575 | Neil Allen | .06 |
| 576 | Frank Robinson (Mgr.) | .15 |
| 577 | Luis Aponte | .08 |
| 578 | David Green | .15 |
| 579 | Rich Dauer | .06 |

| NO. | PLAYER | MINT |
|---|---|---|
| 580 | Tom Seaver | 1.25 |
| 581 | T. Seaver (Veteran) | .60 |
| 582 | Marshall Edwards | .06 |
| 583 | Terry Forster | .08 |
| 584 | Dave Hostetler | .12 |
| 585 | Jose Cruz | .12 |
| 586 | Frank Viola (R) | 7.50 |
| 587 | Ivan DeJesus | .06 |
| 588 | Pat Underwood | .06 |
| 589 | Alvis Woods | .06 |
| 590 | Tony Pena | .25 |
| 591 | White Sox Leaders: | .12 |
| | Greg Luzinski, LaMarr Hoyt | |
| 592 | Shane Rawley | .06 |
| 593 | Broderick Perkins | .06 |
| 594 | Eric Rasmussen | .06 |
| 595 | Tim Raines | 1.00 |
| 596 | Randy Johnson | .10 |
| 597 | Mike Proly | .06 |
| 598 | Dwayne Murphy | .06 |
| 599 | Don Aase | .06 |
| 600 | George Brett | 2.00 |
| 601 | Ed Lynch | .06 |
| 602 | Rich Gedman | .15 |
| 603 | Joe Morgan | .75 |
| 604 | Joe Morgan (Veteran) | .40 |
| 605 | Gary Roenicke | .06 |
| 606 | Bobby Cox (Mgr.) | .06 |
| 607 | Charlie Leibrandt | .08 |
| 608 | Don Money | .06 |
| 609 | Danny Darwin | .06 |
| 610 | Steve Garvey | .60 |
| 611 | Bert Roberge | .06 |
| 612 | Steve Swisher | .06 |
| 613 | Mike Ivie | .06 |
| 614 | Ed Glynn | .08 |
| 615 | Garry Maddox | .06 |
| 616 | Bill Nahorodny | .06 |
| 617 | Butch Wynegar | .06 |
| 618 | LaMarr Hoyt | .15 |
| 619 | Keith Moreland | .08 |
| 620 | Mike Norris | .06 |
| 621 | Mets Leaders: | .12 |
| | Mookie Wilson, Craig Swan | |
| 622 | Dave Edler | .06 |
| 623 | Luis Sanchez | .06 |
| 624 | Glenn Hubbard | .06 |
| 625 | Ken Forsch | .06 |
| 626 | Jerry Martin | .06 |
| 627 | Doug Bair | .06 |
| 628 | Julio Valdez | .06 |
| 629 | Charlie Lea | .06 |
| 630 | Paul Molitor | .50 |
| 631 | Tippy Martinez | .06 |
| 632 | Alex Trevino | .06 |
| 633 | Vicente Romo | .06 |
| 634 | Max Venable | .06 |
| 635 | Graig Nettles | .15 |

| NO. | PLAYER | MINT |
|---|---|---|
| 636 | G. Nettles (Veteran) | .10 |
| 637 | Pat Corrales (Mgr.) | .06 |
| 638 | Dan Petry | .15 |
| 639 | Art Howe | .06 |
| 640 | Andre Thornton | .10 |
| 641 | Billy Sample | .06 |
| 642 | Checklist: No. 5 | .12 |
| 643 | Bump Wills | .06 |
| 644 | Joe LeFebvre | .06 |
| 645 | Bill Madlock | .15 |
| 646 | Jim Essian | .06 |
| 647 | Bobby Mitchell | .06 |
| 648 | Jeff Burroughs | .06 |
| 649 | Tommy Boggs | .06 |
| 650 | George Hendrick | .10 |
| 651 | Angels Leaders: | .20 |
| | Rod Carew, Mike Witt | |
| 652 | Butch Hobson | .06 |
| 653 | Ellis Valentine | .06 |
| 654 | Bob Ojeda | .12 |
| 655 | Al Bumbry | .06 |
| 656 | Dave Frost | .06 |
| 657 | Mike Gates | .08 |
| 658 | Frank Pastore | .06 |
| 659 | Charlie Moore | .06 |
| 660 | Mike Hargrove | .06 |
| 661 | Bill Russell | .06 |
| 662 | Joe Sambito | .06 |
| 663 | Tom O'Malley (R) | .12 |
| 664 | Bob Molinaro | .06 |
| 665 | Jim Sundberg | .06 |
| 666 | Sparky Anderson (Mgr.) | .06 |
| 667 | Dick Davis | .06 |
| 668 | Larry Christenson | .06 |
| 669 | Mike Squires | .06 |
| 670 | Jerry Mumphrey | .06 |
| 671 | Lenny Faedo | .06 |
| 672 | Jim Kaat | .10 |
| 673 | Jim Kaat (Veteran) | .06 |
| 674 | Kurt Bevacqua | .06 |
| 675 | Jim Beattie | .06 |
| 676 | Biff Pocoroba | .06 |
| 677 | Dave Revering | .06 |
| 678 | Juan Beniquez | .06 |
| 679 | Mike Scott | .25 |
| 680 | Andre Dawson | 1.50 |
| 681 | Dodgers Leaders: | .15 |
| | Fernando Valenzuela, Pedro Guerrero | |
| 682 | Bob Stanley | .06 |
| 683 | Dan Ford | .06 |
| 684 | Rafael Landestoy | .06 |
| 685 | Lee Mazzilli | .06 |
| 686 | Randy Lerch | .06 |
| 687 | U.L. Washington | .06 |
| 688 | Jim Wohlford | .06 |
| 689 | Ron Hassey | .06 |
| 690 | Kent Hrbek | .75 |

| NO. | PLAYER | MINT |
|---|---|---|
| 691 | Dave Tobik | .06 |
| 692 | Denny Walling | .06 |
| 693 | Sparky Lyle | .08 |
| 694 | S. Lyle (Veteran) | .06 |
| 695 | Ruppert Jones | .06 |
| 696 | Chuck Tanner (Mgr.) | .06 |
| 697 | Barry Foote | .06 |
| 698 | Tony Bernazard | .06 |
| 699 | Lee Smith | .75 |
| 700 | Keith Hernandez | .40 |
| 701 | Batting Leaders: | .15 |
| | Willie Wilson, Al Oliver | |
| 702 | Home Run Leaders: | .15 |
| | Gorman Thomas, Reggie Jackson, Dave Kingman | |
| 703 | RBI Leaders: | .15 |
| | Hal McRae, Al Oliver Dale Murphy | |
| 704 | Stolen Base Leaders: | .75 |
| | R. Henderson, T. Raines | |
| 705 | Victory Leaders: | .15 |
| | LaMarr Hoyt, Steve Carlton | |
| 706 | Strikeout Leaders: | .15 |
| | F. Bannister, Steve Carlton | |
| 707 | ERA Leaders: | .12 |
| | Rick Sutcliffe, Steve Rogers | |
| 708 | Leading Firemen: | .12 |
| | D. Quisenberry, B. Sutter | |
| 709 | Jimmy Sexton | .06 |
| 710 | Willie Wilson | .20 |
| 711 | Mariners Leaders: | .10 |
| | Bruce Bochte, Jim Beattie | |
| 712 | Bruce Kison | .06 |
| 713 | Ron Hodges | .06 |
| 714 | Wayne Nordhagen | .06 |
| 715 | Tony Perez | .35 |
| 716 | T. Perez (Veteran) | .20 |
| 717 | Scott Sanderson | .06 |
| 718 | Jim Dwyer | .06 |
| 719 | Rich Gale | .06 |
| 720 | Dave Concepcion | .12 |
| 721 | John Martin | .06 |
| 722 | Jorge Orta | .06 |
| 723 | Randy Moffitt | .06 |
| 724 | Johnny Grubb | .06 |
| 725 | Dan Spillner | .06 |
| 726 | Harvey Kuenn (Mgr.) | .06 |
| 727 | Chet Lemon | .10 |
| 728 | Ron Reed | .06 |
| 729 | Jerry Morales | .06 |
| 730 | Jason Thompson | .12 |
| 731 | Al Williams | .06 |
| 732 | Dave Henderson | 1.00 |
| 733 | Buck Martinez | .06 |
| 734 | Steve Braun | .06 |
| 735 | Tommy John | .20 |
| 736 | T. John (Veteran) | .10 |
| 737 | Mitchell Page | .06 |

| NO. | PLAYER | MINT |
|---|---|---|
| 738 | Tim Foli | .06 |
| 739 | Rick Ownbey | .08 |
| 740 | Rusty Staub | .12 |
| 741 | R. Staub (Veteran) | .08 |
| 742 | Padres Leaders: | .10 |
| | Terry Kennedy, Tim Lollar | |
| 743 | Mike Torrez | .06 |
| 744 | Brad Mills | .06 |
| 745 | Scott McGregor | .18 |
| 746 | John Wathan | .06 |
| 747 | Fred Breining | .06 |
| 748 | Derrel Thomas | .06 |
| 749 | Jon Matlack | .06 |
| 750 | Ben Oglivie | .10 |
| 751 | Brad Havens | .06 |
| 752 | Luis Pujols | .06 |
| 753 | Elias Sosa | .06 |
| 754 | Bill Robinson | .06 |
| 755 | John Candelaria | .06 |
| 756 | Russ Nixon (Mgr.) | .06 |
| 757 | Rick Manning | .06 |
| 758 | Aurelio Rodriguez | .06 |
| 759 | Doug Bird | .06 |
| 760 | Dale Murphy | 1.50 |
| 761 | Gary Lucas | .06 |
| 762 | Cliff Johnson | .06 |
| 763 | Al Cowens | .06 |
| 764 | Pete Falcone | .06 |
| 765 | Bob Boone | .06 |
| 766 | Barry Bonnell | .06 |
| 767 | Duane Kuiper | .06 |
| 768 | Chris Speier | .06 |
| 769 | Checklist No. 6 | .12 |
| 770 | Dave Winfield | 1.00 |
| 771 | Twins Leaders: | .10 |
| | Kent Hrbek, Bobby Castillo | |
| 772 | Jim Kern | .06 |
| 773 | Larry Hisle | .06 |
| 774 | Alan Ashby | .06 |
| 775 | Burt Hooton | .06 |
| 776 | Larry Parrish | .06 |
| 777 | John Curtis | .06 |
| 778 | Rich Hebner | .06 |
| 779 | Rick Waits | .06 |
| 780 | Gary Matthews | .10 |
| 781 | Rick Rhoden | .06 |
| 782 | Bobby Murcer | .08 |
| 783 | B. Murcer (Veteran) | .06 |
| 784 | Jeff Newman | .06 |
| 785 | Dennis Leonard | .06 |
| 786 | Ralph Houk (Mgr.) | .06 |
| 787 | Dick Tidrow | .06 |
| 788 | Dane Iorg | .06 |
| 789 | Bryan Clark | .06 |
| 790 | Bob Grich | .06 |
| 791 | Gary Lavelle | .06 |
| 792 | Chris Chambliss | .15 |

## 1983 Topps Traded . . . Complete Set of 132 Cards—Value $125.00

Updates the main 1983 card set with players who changed teams during the season, and rookies. Features the first Topps card of Darryl Strawberry. The complete set was packaged in a printed box and only distributed through card hobby dealers.

# 1983 Topps Traded (Continued)

| NO. PLAYER | MINT |
|---|---|
| 1 T Neil Allen | .12 |
| 2 T Bill Almon | .09 |
| 3 T Joe Altobelli (Mgr.) | .09 |
| 4 T Tony Armas | .10 |
| 5 T Doug Bair | .09 |
| 6 T Steve Baker | .12 |
| 7 T Floyd Bannister | .12 |
| 8 T Don Baylor | .10 |
| 9 T Tony Bernazard | .09 |
| 10 T Larry Biittner | .09 |
| 11 T Dann Bilardello | .09 |
| 12 T Doug Bird | .09 |
| 13 T Steve Boros (Mgr.) | .09 |
| 14 T Greg Brock | .30 |
| 15 T Mike Brown | .12 |
| 16 T Tom Burgmeier | .09 |
| 17 T Randy Bush | .25 |
| 18 T Bert Campaneris | .15 |
| 19 T Ron Cey | .20 |
| 20 T Chris Codiroli | .12 |
| 21 T Dave Collins | .15 |
| 22 T Terry Crowley | .09 |
| 23 T Julio Cruz | .09 |
| 24 T Mike Davis | .15 |
| 25 T Frank DiPino (RR) | .12 |
| 26 T Bill Doran (RR) | 1.00 |
| 27 T Jerry Dybzinski | .09 |
| 28 T Jamie Easterly | .09 |
| 29 T Juan Eichelberger | .09 |
| 30 T Jim Essian | .09 |
| 31 T Pete Falcone | .09 |
| 32 T Mike Ferraro (Mgr.) | .09 |
| 33 T Terry Forster | .12 |

| NO. PLAYER | MINT |
|---|---|
| 34 T Julio Franco (RR) | 9.00 |
| 35 T Rich Gale | .09 |
| 36 T Kiko Garcia | .09 |
| 37 T Steve Garvey | 1.25 |
| 38 T Johnny Grubb | .09 |
| 39 T Mel Hall | 1.25 |
| 40 T Von Hayes | .50 |
| 41 T Danny Heep | .09 |
| 42 T Steve Henderson | .09 |
| 43 T Keith Hernandez | .75 |
| 44 T Leo Hernandez | .15 |
| 45 T Willie Hernandez | .25 |
| 46 T Al Holland | .12 |
| 47 F Howard (Mgr.) | .09 |
| 48 T Bobby Johnson | .09 |
| 49 T Cliff Johnson | .09 |
| 50 T Odell Jones | .09 |
| 51 T Mike Jorgensen | .09 |
| 52 T Bob Kearney | .09 |
| 53 T Steve Kemp | .12 |
| 54 T Matt Keough | .09 |
| 55 T Ron Kittle (RR) | .50 |
| 56 T Mickey Klutts | .09 |
| 57 T Alan Knicely | .09 |
| 58 T Mike Krukow | .09 |
| 59 T Rafael Landestoy | .09 |
| 60 T Carney Lansford | .40 |
| 61 T Joe Lefebvre | .09 |
| 62 T Bryan Little | .12 |
| 63 T Aurelio Lopez | .15 |
| 64 T Mike Madden | .20 |
| 65 T Rick Manning | .09 |
| 66 T Billy Martin (Mgr.) | .15 |

| NO. PLAYER | MINT |
|---|---|
| 67 T Lee Mazzilli | .12 |
| 68 T Andy McGaffigan | .09 |
| 69 T Craig McMurtry | .20 |
| 70 T J. McNamara (Mgr.) | .09 |
| 71 T Orlando Mercado | .09 |
| 72 T Larry Milbourne | .09 |
| 73 T Randy Moffitt | .09 |
| 74 T Sid Monge | .09 |
| 75 T Jose Morales | .09 |
| 76 T Omar Moreno | .12 |
| 77 T Joe Morgan | 2.00 |
| 78 T Mike Morgan | .09 |
| 79 T Dale Murray | .09 |
| 80 T Jeff Newman | .09 |
| 81 T Pete O'Brien (RR) | 1.00 |
| 82 T Jorge Orta | .09 |
| 83 T Alejandro Pena | .75 |
| 84 T Pascual Perez | .12 |
| 85 T Tony Perez | .75 |
| 86 T Broderick Perkins | .09 |
| 87 T Tony Phillips | 1.00 |
| 88 T Charlie Puleo | .09 |
| 89 T Pat Putnam | .09 |
| 90 T Jamie Quirk | .09 |
| 91 T Doug Rader (Mgr.) | .12 |
| 92 T Chuck Rainey | .09 |
| 93 T Bobby Ramos | .09 |
| 94 T Gary Redus | .50 |
| 95 T Steve Renko | .09 |
| 96 T Leon Roberts | .09 |
| 97 T Aurelio Rodriquez | .09 |
| 98 T Dick Ruthven | .09 |
| 99 T Daryl Sconiers | .09 |

| NO. PLAYER | MINT |
|---|---|
| 100 T Mike Scott | .50 |
| 101 T Tom Seaver | 6.00 |
| 102 T John Shelby | .20 |
| 103 T Bob Shirley | .08 |
| 104 T Joe Simpson | .08 |
| 105 T Doug Sisk | .15 |
| 106 T Mike Smithson | .15 |
| 107 T Elias Sosa | .06 |
| 108 T D. Strawberry (RR) | 100.00 |
| 109 T Tom Tellmann | .08 |
| 110 T Gene Tenace | .08 |
| 111 T Gorman Thomas | .20 |
| 112 T Dick Tidrow | .08 |
| 113 T Dave Tobik | .08 |
| 114 T Wayne Tolleson | .12 |
| 115 T Mike Torrez | .10 |
| 116 T Manny Trillo | .12 |
| 117 T Steve Trout | .10 |
| 118 T Lee Tunnell | .12 |
| 119 T Mike Vail | .08 |
| 120 T Ellis Valentine | .15 |
| 121 T Tom Veryzer | .08 |
| 122 T George Vukovich | .08 |
| 123 T Rick Waits | .08 |
| 124 T Greg Walker | .20 |
| 125 T Chris Welsh | .08 |
| 126 T Len Whitehouse | .08 |
| 127 T Eddie Whitson | .10 |
| 128 T Jim Wohlford | .08 |
| 129 T Matt Young | .20 |
| 130 T Joel Youngblood | .08 |
| 131 T Pat Zachry | .08 |
| 132 T Traded Checklist | .25 |

## 1984 Topps . . . Complete Set of 792 Cards—Value $110.00

Features the rookie cards of Don Mattingly and Darryl Strawberry. Topps also introduced a "Tiffany" version of the set—printed on white stock, high gloss finish, and production limited to 10,000 sets.

| NO. PLAYER | MINT |
|---|---|
| 1 Highlight—S. Carlton 300th Win and SO King | .35 |
| 2 Highlight—Henderson 100 SB's, 3 Seasons | 1.00 |
| 3 Highlight—Quisenberry Save Record | .15 |
| 4 Highlight—N. Ryan, G. Perry, S. Carlton— Surpass Walter Johnson | .45 |
| 5 Highlight—D. Righetti, B. Forsch, B. Warren— No Hitters | .15 |
| 6 Highlight—Bench, Yaz, Perry,—All Retire | .35 |
| 7 Gary Lucas | .06 |
| 8 Don Mattingly (R) | 20.00 |
| 9 Jim Gott | .06 |
| 10 Robin Yount | 1.50 |
| 11 Twins Leaders: Kent Hrbek, Ken Schrom | .10 |
| 12 Billy Sample | .06 |
| 13 Scott Holman | .06 |
| 14 Tom Brookens | .06 |
| 15 Burt Hooton | .06 |
| 16 Omar Moreno | .08 |
| 17 John Denny | .08 |

| NO. PLAYER | MINT |
|---|---|
| 18 Dale Berra | .06 |
| 19 Ray Fontenot | .15 |
| 20 Greg Luzinski | .12 |
| 21 Joe Altobelli (Mgr.) | .06 |
| 22 Bryan Clark | .06 |
| 23 Keith Moreland | .08 |
| 24 John Martin | .06 |
| 25 Glenn Hubbard | .08 |
| 26 Bill Black | .06 |
| 27 Daryl Sconiers | .06 |
| 28 Frank Viola | .75 |
| 29 Danny Heep | .06 |
| 30 Wade Boggs | 5.00 |
| 31 Andy McGaffigan | .06 |
| 32 Bobby Ramos | .06 |
| 33 Tom Burgmeier | .06 |
| 34 Eddie Milner | .06 |
| 35 Don Sutton | .30 |
| 36 Denny Walling | .06 |
| 37 Rangers Leaders: Buddy Bell, Rick Honeycutt | .10 |
| 38 Luis DeLeon | .06 |
| 39 Garth Iorg | .06 |
| 40 Dusty Baker | .10 |
| 41 Tony Bernazard | .06 |
| 42 Johnny Grubb | .06 |

| NO. PLAYER | MINT |
|---|---|
| 43 Ron Reed | .06 |
| 44 Jim Morrison | .06 |
| 45 Jerry Mumphrey | .06 |
| 46 Ray Smith | .08 |
| 47 Rudy Law | .06 |
| 48 Julio Franco | 2.00 |
| 49 John Stuper | .06 |
| 50 Chris Chambliss | .08 |
| 51 Jim Fray (Mgr.) | .06 |
| 52 Paul Splittorff | .06 |
| 53 Juan Beniquez | .08 |
| 54 Jesse Orosco | .10 |
| 55 Dave Concepcion | .15 |
| 56 Gary Allenson | .06 |
| 57 Dan Schatzeder | .06 |
| 58 Max Venable | .06 |
| 59 Sammy Stewart | .06 |
| 60 Paul Molitor | .35 |
| 61 Chris Codiroli | .15 |
| 62 Dave Hostetler | .06 |
| 63 Ed VandeBerg | .08 |
| 64 Mike Scioscia | .06 |
| 65 Kirk Gibson | .40 |
| 66 Astros Leaders: Nolan Ryan, Jose Cruz | .35 |
| 67 Gary Ward | .06 |

| NO. PLAYER | MINT |
|---|---|
| 68 Luis Salazar | .06 |
| 69 Rod Scurry | .06 |
| 70 Gary Matthews | .08 |
| 71 Leo Hernandez | .15 |
| 72 Mike Squires | .06 |
| 73 Jody Davis | .10 |
| 74 Jerry Martin | .06 |
| 75 Bob Forsch | .06 |
| 76 Alfredo Griffin | .06 |
| 77 Brett Butler | .35 |
| 78 Mike Torrez | .06 |
| 79 Rob Wilfong | .06 |
| 80 Steve Rogers | .08 |
| 81 Billy Martin (Mgr.) | .15 |
| 82 Doug Bird | .06 |
| 83 Richie Zisk | .08 |
| 84 Lenny Faedo | .06 |
| 85 Atlee Hammaker | .06 |
| 86 John Shelby | .20 |
| 87 Frank Pastore | .06 |
| 88 Rob Picciolo | .06 |
| 89 Mike Smithson | .15 |
| 90 Pedro Guerrero | .40 |
| 91 Dan Spillner | .06 |
| 92 Lloyd Moseby | .20 |
| 93 Bob Knepper | .06 |

| NO. | PLAYER | MINT |
|---|---|---|
| 94 | Mario Ramirez | .08 |
| 95 | Aurelio Lopez | .06 |
| 96 | Royals Leaders: | .10 |
|  | Hal McRae, Larry Gura | |
| 97 | LaMarr Hoyt | .15 |
| 98 | Steve Nicosia | .06 |
| 99 | Craig Lefferts (R) | .25 |
| 100 | Reggie Jackson | 1.00 |
| 101 | Porfirio Altamirano | .06 |
| 102 | Ken Oberkfell | .06 |
| 103 | Dwayne Murphy | .08 |
| 104 | Ken Dayley | .06 |
| 105 | Tony Armas | .15 |
| 106 | Tim Stoddard | .06 |
| 107 | Ned Yost | .06 |
| 108 | Randy Moffitt | .06 |
| 109 | Brad Wellman | .08 |
| 110 | Ron Guidry | .20 |
| 111 | Bill Virdon (Mgr.) | .06 |
| 112 | Tom Niedenfuer | .08 |
| 113 | Kelly Paris | .12 |
| 114 | Checklist No. 1 | .08 |
| 115 | Andre Thornton | .08 |
| 116 | George Bjorkman | .06 |
| 117 | Tom Veryzer | .06 |
| 118 | Charlie Hough | .06 |
| 119 | Johnny Wockenfuss | .06 |
| 120 | Keith Hernandez | .35 |
| 121 | Pat Sheridan | .15 |
| 122 | Cecilio Guante | .06 |
| 123 | Butch Wynegar | .06 |
| 124 | Damaso Garcia | .10 |
| 125 | Britt Burns | .08 |
| 126 | Braves Leaders: | .10 |
|  | Dale Murphy, C. McMurtry | |
| 127 | Mike Madden | .15 |
| 128 | Rick Manning | .06 |
| 129 | Bill Laskey | .06 |
| 130 | Ozzie Smith | 1.00 |
| 131 | Batting Leaders: | .50 |
|  | Bill Madlock, Wade Boggs | |
| 132 | Home Run Leaders: | .30 |
|  | Mike Schmidt, Jim Rice | |
| 133 | RBI Leaders: | .25 |
|  | Dale Murphy, C. Cooper, Jim Rice | |
| 134 | Stolen Base Leaders: | .60 |
|  | T. Raines, R. Henderson | |
| 135 | Victory Leaders: | .15 |
|  | John Denny, LaMarr Hoyt | |
| 136 | Stikeout Leaders: | .25 |
|  | Steve Carlton, Jack Morris | |
| 137 | ERA Leaders: | .08 |
|  | A. Hammaker, R. Honeycutt | |
| 138 | Leading Firemen: | .10 |
|  | A. Holland, D. Quisenberry | |
| 139 | Bert Campaneris | .06 |
| 140 | Storm Davis | .12 |
| 141 | Pat Corrales (Mgr.) | .06 |
| 142 | Rich Gale | .06 |
| 143 | Jose Morales | .06 |
| 144 | Brian Harper | .50 |
| 145 | Gary Lavelle | .06 |
| 146 | Ed Romero | .06 |
| 147 | Dan Petry | .15 |
| 148 | Joe Lefebvre | .06 |
| 149 | Jon Matlack | .06 |
| 150 | Dale Murphy | .75 |
| 151 | Steve Trout | .06 |
| 152 | Glenn Brummer | .06 |
| 153 | Dick Tidrow | .06 |
| 154 | Dave Henderson | .50 |
| 155 | Frank White | .06 |
| 156 | A's Leaders: | .10 |
|  | R. Henderson, T. Conroy | |
| 157 | Gary Gaetti | .20 |
| 158 | John Curtis | .06 |
| 159 | Darryl Cias | .08 |
| 160 | Mario Soto | .08 |
| 161 | Junior Ortiz | .10 |
| 162 | Bob Ojeda | .06 |
| 163 | Lorenzo Gray | .08 |
| 164 | Scott Sanderson | .06 |
| 165 | Ken Singleton | .08 |
| 166 | Jamie Nelson | .12 |
| 167 | Marshall Edwards | .06 |
| 168 | Juan Bonilla | .06 |
| 169 | Larry Parrish | .06 |
| 170 | Jerry Reuss | .08 |
| 171 | Frank Robinson (Mgr.) | .12 |
| 172 | Frank DiPino | .06 |
| 173 | Marvell Wynne | .15 |
| 174 | Juan Berenguer | .06 |
| 175 | Graig Nettles | .15 |
| 176 | Lee Smith | .30 |
| 177 | Jerry Hairston | .06 |
| 178 | Bill Krueger | .12 |
| 179 | Buck Martinez | .06 |
| 180 | Manny Trillo | .08 |
| 181 | Roy Thomas | .06 |
| 182 | Darryl Strawberry (R) | 20.00 |
| 183 | Al Williams | .06 |
| 184 | Mike O'Berry | .06 |
| 185 | Sixto Lezcano | .06 |
| 186 | Cardinal Leaders: | .10 |
|  | Lonnie Smith, John Stuper | |
| 187 | Luis Aponte | .06 |
| 188 | Bryan Little | .08 |
| 189 | Tim Conroy | .12 |
| 190 | Ben Oglivie | .08 |
| 191 | Mike Boddicker | .15 |
| 192 | Nick Esasky (R) | .25 |
| 193 | Darrell Brown | .08 |
| 194 | Domingo Ramos | .08 |
| 195 | Jack Morris | .40 |
| 196 | Don Slaught | .06 |
| 197 | Garry Hancock | .06 |
| 198 | Bill Doran (R) | .30 |
| 199 | Willie Hernandez | .20 |
| 200 | Andre Dawson | .75 |
| 201 | Bruce Kison | .06 |
| 202 | Bobby Cox (Mgr.) | .06 |
| 203 | Matt Keough | .06 |
| 204 | Bobby Meacham | .20 |
| 205 | Greg Minton | .06 |
| 206 | Andy Van Slyke (R) | 2.50 |
| 207 | Donnie Moore | .08 |
| 208 | Jose Oquendo (R) | .30 |
| 209 | Manny Sarmiento | .06 |
| 210 | Joe Morgan | .35 |
| 211 | Rick Sweet | .06 |
| 212 | Broderick Perkins | .06 |
| 213 | Bruce Hurst | .06 |
| 214 | Paul Householder | .06 |
| 215 | Tippy Martinez | .06 |
| 216 | White Sox Leaders: | .10 |
|  | C. Fisk, R. Dotson | |
| 217 | Alan Ashby | .06 |
| 218 | Rick Waits | .06 |
| 219 | Joe Simpson | .06 |
| 220 | Fernando Valenzuela | .25 |
| 221 | Cliff Johnson | .06 |
| 222 | Rick Honeycutt | .08 |
| 223 | Wayne Krenchicki | .06 |
| 224 | Sid Monge | .06 |
| 225 | Lee Mazzilli | .06 |
| 226 | Juan Eichelberger | .06 |
| 227 | Steve Braun | .06 |
| 228 | John Rabb | .15 |
| 229 | Paul Owens (Mgr.) | .06 |
| 230 | Rickey Henderson | 5.00 |
| 231 | Gary Woods | .06 |
| 232 | Tim Wallach | .20 |
| 233 | Checklist No. 2 | .08 |
| 234 | Rafael Ramirez | .06 |
| 235 | Matt Young | .15 |
| 236 | Ellis Valentine | .06 |
| 237 | John Castino | .06 |
| 238 | Reid Nichols | .06 |
| 239 | Jay Howell | .06 |
| 240 | Eddie Murray | 1.25 |
| 241 | Billy Almon | .06 |
| 242 | Alex Trevino | .06 |
| 243 | Pete Ladd | .06 |
| 244 | Candy Maldonado | .25 |
| 245 | Rick Sutcliffe | .20 |
| 246 | Mets Leaders: | .12 |
|  | M. Wilson, Tom Seaver | |
| 247 | Onix Concepcion | .06 |
| 248 | Bill Dawley | .20 |
| 249 | Jay Johnstone | .06 |
| 250 | Bill Madlock | .15 |
| 251 | Tony Gwynn | 3.50 |
| 252 | Larry Christenson | .06 |
| 253 | Jim Wohlford | .06 |
| 254 | Shane Rawley | .06 |
| 255 | Bruce Benedict | .06 |
| 256 | Dave Geisel | .06 |
| 257 | Julio Cruz | .06 |
| 258 | Luis Sanchez | .06 |
| 259 | Sparky Anderson (Mgr.) | .08 |
| 260 | Scott McGregor | .08 |
| 261 | Bobby Brown | .06 |
| 262 | Tom Candiotti | .30 |
| 263 | Jack Fimple | .08 |
| 264 | Doug Frobel | .12 |
| 265 | Donnie Hill | .15 |
| 266 | Steve Lubratich | .06 |
| 267 | Carmelo Martinez (R) | .15 |
| 268 | Jack O'Connor | .06 |
| 269 | Aurelio Rodriquez | .06 |
| 270 | Jeff Russell (R) | .30 |
| 271 | Moose Haas | .06 |
| 272 | Rick Dempsey | .06 |
| 273 | Charlie Puleo | .06 |
| 274 | Rick Monday | .06 |
| 275 | Len Matuszek | .06 |
| 276 | Angels Leaders: | .10 |
|  | Rod Carew, Geoff Zahn | |
| 277 | Eddie Whitson | .06 |
| 278 | Jorge Bell | 1.00 |
| 279 | Ivan DeJesus | .06 |
| 280 | Floyd Bannister | .10 |
| 281 | Larry Milbourne | .06 |
| 282 | Jim Barr | .06 |
| 283 | Larry Biittner | .06 |
| 284 | Howard Bailey | .06 |
| 285 | Darrell Porter | .06 |
| 286 | Lary Sorensen | .06 |
| 287 | Warren Cromartie | .06 |
| 288 | Jim Beattie | .06 |
| 289 | Randy Johnson | .06 |
| 290 | Dave Dravecky | .08 |
| 291 | Chuck Tanner (Mgr.) | .06 |
| 292 | Tony Scott | .06 |
| 293 | Ed Lynch | .06 |
| 294 | U.L. Washington | .06 |
| 295 | Mike Flanagan | .08 |
| 296 | Jeff Newman | .06 |
| 297 | Bruce Berenyi | .06 |
| 298 | Jim Gantner | .06 |
| 299 | John Butcher | .06 |
| 300 | Pete Rose | 1.25 |
| 301 | Frank LaCorte | .06 |
| 302 | Barry Bonnell | .06 |
| 303 | Marty Castillo | .06 |
| 304 | Warren Brusstar | .06 |
| 305 | Roy Smalley | .06 |
| 306 | Dodgers Leaders: | .12 |
|  | Pedro Guerrero, Bob Welch | |
| 307 | Bobby Mitchell | .06 |
| 308 | Ron Hassey | .06 |
| 309 | Tony Phillips | .20 |
| 310 | Willie McGee | .40 |
| 311 | Jerry Koosman | .06 |
| 312 | Jorge Orta | .06 |
| 313 | Mike Jorgensen | .06 |
| 314 | Orlando Mercado | .08 |
| 315 | Bob Grich | .06 |
| 316 | Mark Bradley | .08 |
| 317 | Greg Pryor | .06 |
| 318 | Bill Gullickson | .08 |
| 319 | Al Bumbry | .06 |
| 320 | Bob Stanley | .06 |
| 321 | Harvey Kuenn (Mgr.) | .06 |
| 322 | Ken Schrom | .06 |
| 323 | Alan Knicely | .06 |
| 324 | Alejandro Pena (R) | .30 |
| 325 | Darrell Evans | .12 |
| 326 | Bob Kearney | .06 |
| 327 | Ruppert Jones | .06 |
| 328 | Vern Ruhle | .06 |
| 329 | Pat Tabler | .20 |
| 330 | John Candelaria | .06 |
| 331 | Bucky Dent | .06 |
| 332 | Kevin Gross (R) | .30 |
| 333 | Larry Herndon | .06 |
| 334 | Chuck Rainey | .06 |
| 335 | Don Baylor | .12 |
| 336 | Mariners Leaders: | .10 |
|  | Pat Putnam, M. Young | |
| 337 | Kevin Hagen | .08 |
| 338 | Mike Warren | .12 |
| 339 | Roy Lee Jackson | .06 |
| 340 | Hal McRae | .06 |
| 341 | Dave Tobik | .06 |
| 342 | Tim Foli | .06 |
| 343 | Mark Davis | .15 |
| 344 | Rick Miller | .06 |
| 345 | Kent Hrbek | .40 |
| 346 | Kurt Bevacqua | .06 |
| 347 | Allan Ramirez | .08 |
| 348 | Toby Harrah | .06 |
| 349 | Bob Gibson | .12 |
| 350 | George Foster | .20 |
| 351 | Russ Nixon (Mgr.) | .06 |
| 352 | Dave Stewart | .50 |
| 353 | Jim Anderson | .06 |
| 354 | Jeff Burroughs | .06 |
| 355 | Jason Thompson | .08 |
| 356 | Glenn Abbott | .06 |
| 357 | Ron Cey | .15 |
| 358 | Bob Dernier | .08 |
| 359 | Jim Acker (R) | .15 |
| 360 | Willie Randolph | .08 |
| 361 | Dave Smith | .06 |
| 362 | David Green | .06 |
| 363 | Tim Laudner | .06 |
| 364 | Scott Fletcher | .12 |
| 365 | Steve Bedrosian | .12 |
| 366 | Padres Leaders: | .10 |
|  | T. Kennedy, D. Dravecky | |
| 367 | Jamie Easterly | .06 |
| 368 | Hubie Brooks | .15 |
| 369 | Steve McCatty | .06 |
| 370 | Tim Raines | .50 |
| 371 | Dave Gumpert | .08 |
| 372 | Gary Roenicke | .06 |
| 373 | Bill Scherrer | .08 |
| 374 | Don Money | .06 |
| 375 | Dennis Leonard | .06 |
| 376 | Dave Anderson | .15 |
| 377 | Danny Darwin | .06 |
| 378 | Bob Brenly | .06 |
| 379 | Checklist No.3 | .08 |
| 380 | Steve Garvey | .40 |
| 381 | Ralph Houk (Mgr.) | .06 |
| 382 | Chris Nyman | .08 |
| 383 | Terry Puhl | .06 |
| 384 | Lee Tunnell | .12 |
| 385 | Tony Perez | .15 |
| 386 | George Hendrick (AS) | .10 |
| 387 | Johnny Ray (AS) | .10 |
| 388 | Mike Schmidt (AS) | .60 |
| 389 | Ozzie Smith (AS) | .30 |
| 390 | Tim Raines (AS) | .20 |
| 391 | Dale Murphy (AS) | .30 |
| 392 | Andre Dawson (AS) | .30 |
| 393 | Gary Carter (AS) | .20 |
| 394 | Steve Rogers (AS) | .12 |
| 395 | Steve Carlton (AS) | .30 |
| 396 | Jesse Orosco (AS) | .08 |
| 397 | Eddie Murray (AS) | .30 |
| 398 | Lou Whitaker (AS) | .12 |
| 399 | George Brett (AS) | .40 |
| 400 | Cal Ripken (AS) | 1.00 |
| 401 | Jim Rice (AS) | .20 |
| 402 | Dave Winfield (AS) | .30 |
| 403 | Lloyd Moseby (AS) | .12 |
| 404 | Ted Simmons (AS) | .12 |
| 405 | LaMarr Hoyt (AS) | .12 |
| 406 | Ron Guidry (AS) | .15 |
| 407 | Dan Quisenberry (AS) | .15 |
| 408 | Lou Piniella | .10 |
| 409 | Juan Agosto | .15 |
| 410 | Claudell Washington | .08 |
| 411 | Houston Jimenez | .08 |
| 412 | Doug Rader (Mgr.) | .06 |
| 413 | Spike Owen (R) | .25 |
| 414 | Mitchell Page | .06 |

| NO. | PLAYER | MINT |
|-----|--------|------|
| 415 | Tommy John | .15 |
| 416 | Dane Iorg | .06 |
| 417 | Mike Armstrong | .06 |
| 418 | Ron Hodges | .06 |
| 419 | John Johnson | .06 |
| 420 | Cecil Cooper | .15 |
| 421 | Charlie Lea | .06 |
| 422 | Jose Cruz | .12 |
| 423 | Mike Morgan | .06 |
| 424 | Dann Bilardello | .08 |
| 425 | Steve Howe | .06 |
| 426 | Orioles Leaders: | .50 |
| | M. Boddicker, C. Ripken | |
| 427 | Rick Leach | .06 |
| 428 | Fred Breining | .06 |
| 429 | Randy Bush | .20 |
| 430 | Rusty Staub | .10 |
| 431 | Chris Bando | .06 |
| 432 | Charlie Hudson (R) | .15 |
| 433 | Rich Hebner | .06 |
| 434 | Harold Baines | .30 |
| 435 | Neil Allen | .06 |
| 436 | Rick Peters | .06 |
| 437 | Mike Proly | .06 |
| 438 | Biff Pocoroba | .06 |
| 439 | Bob Stoddard | .06 |
| 440 | Steve Kemp | .06 |
| 441 | Bob Lillis (Mgr.) | .06 |
| 442 | Byron McLaughlin | .06 |
| 443 | Benny Ayala | .06 |
| 444 | Steve Renko | .06 |
| 445 | Jerry Remy | .06 |
| 446 | Luis Pujols | .06 |
| 447 | Tom Brunansky | .15 |
| 448 | Ben Hayes | .06 |
| 449 | Joe Pettini | .06 |
| 450 | Gary Carter | .45 |
| 451 | Bob Jones | .06 |
| 452 | Chuck Porter | .06 |
| 453 | Willie Upshaw | .15 |
| 454 | Joe Beckwith | .06 |
| 455 | Terry Kennedy | .10 |
| 456 | Cubs Leaders: | .12 |
| | F. Jenkins, K. Moreland | |
| 457 | Dave Rozema | .06 |
| 458 | Kiko Garcia | .06 |
| 459 | Kevin Hickey | .06 |
| 460 | Dave Winfield | .75 |
| 461 | Jim Maler | .06 |
| 462 | Lee Lacy | .06 |
| 463 | Dave Engle | .06 |
| 464 | Jeff Jones | .06 |
| 465 | Mookie Wilson | .08 |
| 466 | Gene Garber | .06 |
| 467 | Mike Ramsey | .06 |
| 468 | Geoff Zahn | .06 |
| 469 | Tom O'Malley | .06 |
| 470 | Nolan Ryan | 5.00 |
| 471 | Dick Howser (Mgr.) | .06 |
| 472 | Mike Brown | .08 |
| 473 | Jim Dwyer | .06 |
| 474 | Greg Bargar | .09 |
| 475 | Gary Redus (R) | .30 |
| 476 | Tom Tellmann | .06 |
| 477 | Rafael Landestoy | .06 |
| 478 | Alan Bannister | .06 |
| 479 | Frank Tanana | .20 |
| 480 | Ron Kittle | .20 |
| 481 | Mark Thurmond | .06 |
| 482 | Enos Cabell | .30 |
| 483 | Fergie Jenkins | .06 |
| 484 | Ozzie Virgil | .06 |
| 485 | Rick Rhoden | .12 |
| 486 | Yankees Leaders: | .12 |
| | Don Baylor, Ron Guidry | |
| 487 | Ricky Adams | .08 |
| 488 | Jesse Barfield | .25 |
| 489 | Dave Von Ohlen | .09 |
| 490 | Cal Ripken | 6.00 |
| 491 | Bobby Castillo | .06 |
| 492 | Tucker Ashford | .06 |
| 493 | Mike Norris | .06 |
| 494 | Chili Davis | .15 |
| 495 | Rollie Fingers | .30 |
| 496 | Terry Francona | .06 |

| NO. | PLAYER | MINT |
|-----|--------|------|
| 497 | Bud Anderson | .06 |
| 498 | Rich Gedman | .06 |
| 499 | Mike Witt | .20 |
| 500 | George Brett | 1.00 |
| 501 | Steve Henderson | .06 |
| 502 | Joe Torre (Mgr.) | .08 |
| 503 | Elias Sosa | .06 |
| 504 | Mickey Rivers | .08 |
| 505 | Pete Vuckovich | .08 |
| 506 | Ernie Whitt | .06 |
| 507 | Mike LaCoss | .06 |
| 508 | Mel Hall | .50 |
| 509 | Brad Havens | .06 |
| 510 | Alan Trammell | .50 |
| 511 | Marty Bystrom | .06 |
| 512 | Oscar Gamble | .08 |
| 513 | Dave Beard | .06 |
| 514 | Floyd Rayford | .06 |
| 515 | Gorman Thomas | .15 |
| 516 | Expos Leaders: | .10 |
| | Al Oliver, Charlie Lea | |
| 517 | John Moses | .12 |
| 518 | Greg Walker (R) | .15 |
| 519 | Ron Davis | .06 |
| 520 | Bob Boone | .06 |
| 521 | Pete Falcone | .06 |
| 522 | Dave Bergman | .06 |
| 523 | Glenn Hoffman | .06 |
| 524 | Carlos Diaz | .06 |
| 525 | Willie Wilson | .20 |
| 526 | Ron Oester | .06 |
| 527 | Checklist No. 4 | .08 |
| 528 | Mark Brouhard | .06 |
| 529 | Keith Atherton | .08 |
| 530 | Dan Ford | .06 |
| 531 | Steve Boros (Mgr.) | .06 |
| 532 | Eric Show | .06 |
| 533 | Ken Landreaux | .06 |
| 534 | Pete O'Brien (R) | .35 |
| 535 | Bo Diaz | .06 |
| 536 | Doug Bair | .06 |
| 537 | Johnny Ray | .12 |
| 538 | Kevin Bass | .06 |
| 539 | George Frazier | .06 |
| 540 | George Hendrick | .08 |
| 541 | Dennis Lamp | .06 |
| 542 | Duane Kuiper | .06 |
| 543 | Craig McMurtry (R) | .15 |
| 544 | Cesar Geronimo | .06 |
| 545 | Bill Buckner | .10 |
| 546 | Indians Leaders: | |
| | Mike Hargrove, L. Sorensen | |
| 547 | Mike Moore | .15 |
| 548 | Ron Jackson | .06 |
| 549 | Walt Terrell (R) | .20 |
| 550 | Jim Rice | .25 |
| 551 | Scott Ullger | .08 |
| 552 | Ray Burris | .06 |
| 553 | Joe Nolan | .06 |
| 554 | Ted Power | .06 |
| 555 | Greg Brock | .15 |
| 556 | Joey McLaughlin | .06 |
| 557 | Wayne Tolleson | .10 |
| 558 | Mike Davis | .08 |
| 559 | Mike Scott | .25 |
| 560 | Carlton Fisk | .75 |
| 561 | Whitey Herzog (Mgr.) | .08 |
| 562 | Manny Castillo | .06 |
| 563 | Glenn Wilson | .12 |
| 564 | Al Holland | .06 |
| 565 | Leon Durham | .20 |
| 566 | Jim Bibby | .06 |
| 567 | Mike Heath | .06 |
| 568 | Pete Filson | .10 |
| 569 | Bake McBride | .06 |
| 570 | Dan Quisenberry | .20 |
| 571 | Bruce Bochy | .06 |
| 572 | Jerry Royster | .06 |
| 573 | Dave Kingman | .10 |
| 574 | Brian Downing | .06 |
| 575 | Jim Clancy | .06 |
| 576 | Giants Leaders: | .07 |
| | J. Leonard, A. Hammaker | |
| 577 | Mark Clear | .06 |
| 578 | Lenn Sakata | .06 |

| NO. | PLAYER | MINT |
|-----|--------|------|
| 579 | Bob James (R) | .15 |
| 580 | Lonnie Smith | .20 |
| 581 | Jose DeLeon (R) | .25 |
| 582 | Bob McClure | .06 |
| 583 | Derrel Thomas | .06 |
| 584 | Dave Schmidt | .06 |
| 585 | Dan Driessen | .06 |
| 586 | Joe Niekro | .08 |
| 587 | Von Hayes | .20 |
| 588 | Milt Wilcox | .06 |
| 589 | Mike Easler | .08 |
| 590 | Dave Stieb | .25 |
| 591 | Tony LaRussa (Mgr.) | .06 |
| 592 | Andre Robertson | .06 |
| 593 | Jeff Lahti | .06 |
| 594 | Gene Richards | .06 |
| 595 | Jeff Reardon | .25 |
| 596 | Ryne Sandberg | 8.00 |
| 597 | Rick Camp | .06 |
| 598 | Rusty Kuntz | .06 |
| 599 | Doug Sisk | .15 |
| 600 | Rod Carew | .75 |
| 601 | John Tudor | .15 |
| 602 | John Wathan | .06 |
| 603 | Renie Martin | .06 |
| 604 | John Lowenstein | .06 |
| 605 | Mike Caldwell | .06 |
| 606 | Blue Jays Leaders: | .10 |
| | Lloyd Moseby, Dave Stieb | |
| 607 | Tom Hume | .06 |
| 608 | Bobby Johnson | .06 |
| 609 | Dan Meyer | .06 |
| 610 | Steve Sax | .30 |
| 611 | Chet Lemon | .08 |
| 612 | Harry Spilman | .06 |
| 613 | Greg Gross | .06 |
| 614 | Len Barker | .06 |
| 615 | Garry Templeton | .12 |
| 616 | Don Robinson | .06 |
| 617 | Rick Cerone | .06 |
| 618 | Dickie Noles | .06 |
| 619 | Jerry Dybzinski | .06 |
| 620 | Al Oliver | .15 |
| 621 | Frank Howard (Mgr.) | .06 |
| 622 | Al Cowens | .06 |
| 623 | Ron Washington | .06 |
| 624 | Terry Harper | .06 |
| 625 | Larry Gura | .06 |
| 626 | Bob Clark | .06 |
| 627 | Dave LaPoint | .06 |
| 628 | Ed Jurak | .12 |
| 629 | Rick Langford | .06 |
| 630 | Ted Simmons | .12 |
| 631 | Denny Martinez | .06 |
| 632 | Tom Foley | .12 |
| 633 | Mike Krukow | .06 |
| 634 | Mike Marshall | .15 |
| 635 | Dave Righetti | .20 |
| 636 | Pat Putnam | .06 |
| 637 | Phillies Leaders: | .10 |
| | G. Matthews, J. Denny | |
| 638 | George Vuckovich | .06 |
| 639 | Rick Lysander | .08 |
| 640 | Lance Parrish | .25 |
| 641 | Mike Richardt | .06 |
| 642 | Tom Underwood | .06 |
| 643 | Mike Brown | .15 |
| 644 | Tim Lollar | .06 |
| 645 | Tony Pena | .12 |
| 646 | Checklist No.5 | .08 |
| 647 | Ron Roenicke | .06 |
| 648 | Len Whitehouse | .08 |
| 649 | Tom Herr | .12 |
| 650 | Phil Niekro | .25 |
| 651 | J. McNamara (Mgr.) | .06 |
| 652 | Rudy May | .06 |
| 653 | Dave Stapleton | .06 |
| 654 | Bob Bailor | .06 |
| 655 | Amos Otis | .06 |
| 656 | Bryn Smith | .06 |
| 657 | Thad Bosley | .06 |
| 658 | Jerry Augustine | .06 |
| 659 | Duane Walker | .06 |
| 660 | Ray Knight | .12 |
| 661 | Steve Yeager | .06 |

| NO. | PLAYER | MINT |
|-----|--------|------|
| 662 | Tom Brennan | .06 |
| 663 | Johnnie LeMaster | .06 |
| 664 | Dave Stegman | .06 |
| 665 | Buddy Bell | .15 |
| 666 | Tigers Leaders: | .12 |
| | Lou Whitaker, J. Morris | |
| 667 | Vance Law | .06 |
| 668 | Larry McWilliams | .06 |
| 669 | Dave Lopes | .08 |
| 670 | Rich Gossage | .20 |
| 671 | Jamie Quirk | .06 |
| 672 | Ricky Nelson | .12 |
| 673 | Mike Walters | .12 |
| 674 | Tim Flannery | .06 |
| 675 | Pascual Perez | .08 |
| 676 | Brian Giles | .06 |
| 677 | Doyle Alexander | .06 |
| 678 | Chris Speier | .06 |
| 679 | Art Howe | .06 |
| 680 | Fred Lynn | .20 |
| 681 | Tom Lasorda (Mgr.) | .08 |
| 682 | Dan Morogiello | .08 |
| 683 | Marty Barrett (R) | .20 |
| 684 | Bob Shirley | .06 |
| 685 | Willie Aikens | .06 |
| 686 | Joe Price | .06 |
| 687 | Roy Howell | .06 |
| 688 | George Wright | .06 |
| 689 | Mike Fischlin | .06 |
| 690 | Jack Clark | .25 |
| 691 | Steve Lake | .12 |
| 692 | Dickie Thon | .06 |
| 693 | Alan Wiggins | .08 |
| 694 | Mike Stanton | .06 |
| 695 | Lou Whitaker | .30 |
| 696 | Pirates Leaders: | .08 |
| | Bill Madlock, Rick Rhoden | |
| 697 | Dale Murray | .06 |
| 698 | Marc Hill | .06 |
| 699 | Dave Rucker | .06 |
| 700 | Mike Schmidt | 2.00 |
| 701 | Batting Leaders: | .25 |
| | Bill Madlock, Dave Parker, Pete Rose | |
| 702 | Hit Leaders: | .25 |
| | Pete Rose, Rusty Staub, Tony Perez | |
| 703 | Home Run Leaders: | .25 |
| | Mike Schmidt, Tony Perez, D. Kingman | |
| 704 | RBI Leaders: | .15 |
| | Rusty Staub, Tony Perez, Al Oliver | |
| 705 | Stolen Bases Leaders: | .12 |
| | Larry Bowa, Joe Morgan, Cesar Cedeno | |
| 706 | Victory Leaders: | .15 |
| | Steve Carlton, F. Jenkins, Tom Seaver | |
| 707 | Strikeout Leaders: | .50 |
| | Tom Seaver, Steve Carlton, Nolan Ryan | |
| 708 | ERA Leaders: | .15 |
| | Tom Seaver, Steve Rogers, Steve Carlton | |
| 709 | Save Leaders: | .12 |
| | Bruce Sutter, Tug McGraw, G. Garber | |
| 710 | Batting Leaders: | .25 |
| | Rod Carew, Cecil Cooper, George Brett | |
| 711 | Hit Leaders: | .20 |
| | Reggie Jackson, Rod Carew, Bert Campaneris | |
| 712 | Home Run Leaders: | .20 |
| | Graig Nettles, Reggie Jackson, Greg Luzinski | |
| 713 | RBI Leaders: | .20 |
| | Reggie Jackson, Ted Simmons, Graig Nettles | |
| 714 | Stolen Bases Leaders: | .12 |
| | Bert Campaneris, D. Lopes, Omar Moreno | |
| 715 | Victory Leaders: | .15 |
| | Jim Palmer, Don Sutton, Tommy John | |

# 1984 Topps (Continued)

| NO. PLAYER | MINT | NO. PLAYER | MINT | NO. PLAYER | MINT | NO. PLAYER | MINT |
|---|---|---|---|---|---|---|---|
| 716 Strikeouts Leaders: | .12 | 731 Lynn Jones | .06 | 752 Phil Garner | .06 | 772 Jim Slaton | .06 |
| Don Sutton, Jerry | | 732 Terry Crowley | .06 | 753 Doug Gwosdz | .06 | 773 Todd Cruz | .06 |
| Koosman, Bert Blyleven | | 733 Dave Collins | .06 | 754 Kent Tekulve | .06 | 774 Tom Gorman | .12 |
| 717 ERA Leaders: | .15 | 734 Odell Jones | .06 | 755 Garry Maddox | .06 | 775 Dave Parker | .35 |
| Jim Palmer, R. Fingers, | | 735 Rick Burleson | .06 | 756 Reds Leaders: | .08 | 776 Craig Reynolds | .06 |
| Ron Guidry | | 736 Dick Ruthven | .06 | Ron Oester, Mario Soto | | 777 Tom Paciorek | .06 |
| 718 Save Leaders: | .15 | 737 Jim Essian | .06 | 757 Larry Bowa | .08 | 778 Andy Hawkins (R) | .25 |
| Rollie Fingers, R. Gossage, | | 738 Bill Schroeder (R) | .15 | 758 Bill Stein | .06 | 779 Jim Sundberg | .06 |
| Dan Quisenberry | | 739 Bob Watson | .06 | 759 Richard Dotson | .08 | 780 Steve Carlton | .75 |
| 719 Andy Hassler | .06 | 740 Tom Seaver | 1.00 | 760 Bob Horner | .25 | 781 Checklist No. 6 | .08 |
| 720 Dwight Evans | .25 | 741 Wayne Gross | .06 | 761 John Montefusco | .06 | 782 Steve Balboni | .06 |
| 721 Del Crandall (Mgr.) | .06 | 742 Dick Williams (Mgr.) | .06 | 762 Rance Mulliniks | .06 | 783 Luis Leal | .06 |
| 722 Bob Welch | .25 | 743 Don Hood | .06 | 763 Craig Swan | .06 | 784 Leon Roberts | .06 |
| 723 Rich Dauer | .06 | 744 Jamie Allen | .12 | 764 Mike Hargrove | .06 | 785 Joaquin Andujar | .12 |
| 724 Eric Rasmussen | .06 | 745 Dennis Eckersley | .50 | 765 Ken Forsch | .06 | 786 Red Sox Leaders: | .20 |
| 725 Cesar Cedeno | .08 | 746 Mickey Hatcher | .06 | 766 Mike Vail | .06 | Bob Ojeda, Wade Boggs | |
| 726 Brewers Leaders: | .06 | 747 Pat Zachry | .06 | 767 Carney Lansford | .12 | 787 Bill Campbell | .06 |
| Ted Simmons, Moose Haas | | 748 Jeff Leonard | .06 | 768 Champ Summers | .06 | 788 Milt May | .06 |
| 727 Joel Youngblood | .06 | 749 Doug Flynn | .06 | 769 Bill Caudill | .08 | 789 Bert Blyleven | .20 |
| 728 Tug McGraw | .08 | 750 Jim Palmer | .75 | 770 Ken Griffey | .15 | 790 Doug DeCinces | .08 |
| 729 Gene Tenace | .06 | 751 Charlie Moore | .06 | 771 Billy Gardner (Mgr.) | .06 | 791 Terry Forster | .06 |
| 730 Bruce Sutter | .20 | | | | | 792 Bill Russell | .12 |

## 1984 Topps Traded.... Complete Set of 132 Cards—Value $100.00

Updates the main 1984 card set with players who changed teams during the season and rookies. Features the first Topps card for Dwight Gooden and Bret Saberhagen. The complete set was packaged in a printed box and only distributed through card hobby dealers.

| NO. PLAYER | MINT | NO. PLAYER | MINT | NO. PLAYER | MINT | NO. PLAYER | MINT |
|---|---|---|---|---|---|---|---|
| 1 T Willie Aikens | .15 | 34 T Dennis Eckersley | 2.50 | 67 T R. Lachemann (Mgr.) | .10 | 100 T Jose Rijo (RR) | 5.00 |
| 2 T Luis Aponte | .10 | 35 T Jim Essian | .08 | 68 T Frank LaCorte | .10 | 101 T Jeff Robinson | .30 |
| 3 T Mike Armstrong | .10 | 36 T Darrell Evans | .25 | 69 T Dennis Lamp | .10 | 102 T Ron Romanick | .25 |
| 4 T Bob Bailor | .10 | 37 T Mike Fitzgerald | .15 | 70 T Mark Langston (RR) | 12.00 | 103 T Pete Rose | 7.00 |
| 5 T Dusty Baker | .12 | 38 T Tim Foli | .10 | 71 T Rich Leach | .10 | 104 T B. Saberhagen (RR) | 20.00 |
| 6 T Steve Balboni | .15 | 39 T George Frazier | .10 | 72 T Craig Lefferts | .10 | 105 T Juan Samuel (RR) | 3.00 |
| 7 T Alan Bannister | .10 | 40 T Rich Gale | .10 | 73 T Gary Lucas | .10 | 106 T Scott Sanderson | .12 |
| 8 T Dave Beard | .10 | 41 T Barbaro Garbey | .20 | 74 T Jerry Martin | .10 | 107 T Dick Schofield | .30 |
| 9 T Joe Beckwith | .10 | 42 T D. Gooden (RR) | 40.00 | 75 T Carmelo Martinez | .25 | 108 T Tom Seaver | 8.00 |
| 10 T Bruce Berenyi | .10 | 43 T Rich Gossage | .30 | 76 T Mike Mason | .20 | 109 T Jim Slaton | .08 |
| 11 T Dave Bergman | .10 | 44 T Wayne Gross | .10 | 77 T Gary Matthews | .15 | 110 T Mike Smithson | .08 |
| 12 T Tony Bernazard | .10 | 45 T Mark Gublcza (RR) | 2.00 | 78 T Andy McGaffigan | .10 | 111 T Lary Sorensen | .08 |
| 13 T Yogi Berra (Mgr.) | .50 | 46 T Jackie Gutierrez | .15 | 79 T Larry Milbourne | .10 | 112 T Tim Stoddard | .08 |
| 14 T Barry Bonnell | .10 | 47 T Mel Hall | .50 | 80 T Sid Monge | .10 | 113 T Champ Summers | .08 |
| 15 T Phil Bradley (RR) | 1.00 | 48 T Toby Harrah | .12 | 81 T Jackie Moore (Mgr.) | .10 | 114 T Jim Sundberg | .08 |
| 16 T Fred Breining | .10 | 49 T Ron Hassey | .10 | 82 T Joe Morgan | 2.00 | 115 T Rick Sutcliffe | .50 |
| 17 T Bill Buckner | .25 | 50 T Rich Hebner | .10 | 83 T Graig Nettles | .50 | 116 T Craig Swan | .10 |
| 18 T Ray Burris | .10 | 51 T Willie Hernandez | .25 | 84 T Phil Niekro | 1.50 | 117 T Tim Teufel | .40 |
| 19 T John Butcher | .10 | 52 T Ricky Horton | .25 | 85 T Ken Oberkfell | .12 | 118 T Derrel Thomas | .10 |
| 20 T Brett Butler | .50 | 53 T Art Howe | .10 | 86 T Mike O'Berry | .10 | 119 T Gorman Thomas | .15 |
| 21 T Enos Cabell | .10 | 54 T Dane Iorg | .10 | 87 T Al Oliver | .20 | 120 T Alex Trevino | .08 |
| 22 T Bill Campbell | .10 | 55 T Brook Jacoby (RR) | 1.00 | 88 T Jorge Orta | .10 | 121 T Manny Trillo | .12 |
| 23 T Bill Caudill | .15 | 56 T Mike Jeffcoat | .15 | 89 T Amos Otis | .15 | 122 T John Tudor | .30 |
| 24 T Bob Clark | .10 | 57 T D. Johnson (Mgr.) | .20 | 90 T Dave Parker | 2.00 | 123 T Tom Underwood | .10 |
| 25 T Bryan Clark | .10 | 58 T Lynn Jones | .10 | 91 T Tony Perez | .75 | 124 T Mike Vail | .10 |
| 26 T Jaimes Cocanower | .20 | 59 T Ruppert Jones | .10 | 92 T Gerald Perry | .50 | 125 T Tom Waddell | .20 |
| 27 T Ron Darling (RR) | 3.00 | 60 T Mike Jorgensen | .10 | 93 T Gary Pettis | .35 | 126 T Gary Ward | .20 |
| 28 T Alvin Davis (RR) | 5.00 | 61 T Bob Kearney | .10 | 94 T Rob Picciolo | .08 | 127 T Curt Wilkerson | .25 |
| 29 T Ken Dayley | .12 | 62 T Jimmy Key (RR) | 2.50 | 95 T Vern Rapp (Mgr.) | .08 | 128 T Frank Williams | .20 |
| 30 T Jeff Dedmon | .20 | 63 T Dave Kingman | .25 | 96 T Floyd Rayford | .08 | 129 T Glenn Wilson | .25 |
| 31 T Bob Dernier | .10 | 64 T Jerry Koosman | .40 | 97 T Randy Ready | .30 | 130 T Johnny Wockenfuss | .10 |
| 32 T Carlos Diaz | .10 | 65 T Wayne Krenchicki | .10 | 98 T Ron Reed | .10 | 131 T Ned Yost | .10 |
| 33 T Mike Easler | .12 | 66 T Rusty Kuntz | .10 | 99 T Gene Richards | .10 | 132 T Traded Checklist | .15 |

# 1985 Topps.... Complete Set of 792 Cards—Value $120.00

Features the rookie cards of Dwight Gooden, Roger Clemens, Eric Davis, Bret Saberhagen, Mark McGwire, Orel Hershiser, and Kirby Puckett.
Includes players and coaches of the 1984 USA Olympic Baseball Team, "#1 Draft Picks" and a revival of "Father & Son" cards.

| NO. PLAYER | MINT |
|---|---|
| 1 Record—C. Fisk | .30 |
| Longest Game, Catcher | |
| 2 Record—S. Garvey | .20 |
| Errorless Games, 18 | |
| 3 Record—D. Gooden | .75 |
| Most Strikeouts, Rookie | |
| 4 Record—C. Johnson | .08 |
| Most Pinch Homers | |
| 5 Record—J. Morgan | .15 |
| Most Homers, 2B | |
| 6 Record—P. Rose | .40 |
| Most Singles, Career | |
| 7 Record—N. Ryan | .75 |
| Most Strikeouts, Career | |
| 8 Record—J. Samuel | .15 |
| Stolen Bases, Rookie | |
| 9 Record—B. Sutter | .12 |
| Most Saves, Season | |
| 10 Record—D. Sutton | .12 |
| 100 Strikeout Seasons | |
| 11 Ralph Houk (Mgr.) | .05 |
| 12 Dave Lopes | .08 |
| 13 Tim Lollar | .05 |
| 14 Chris Bando | .05 |
| 15 Jerry Koosman | .15 |
| 16 Bobby Meacham | .05 |
| 17 Mike Scott | .20 |
| 18 Mickey Hatcher | .05 |
| 19 Geroge Frazier | .05 |
| 20 Chet Lemon | .08 |
| 21 Lee Tunnell | .05 |
| 22 Duane Kuiper | .05 |
| 23 Bret Saberhagen (R) | 4.00 |
| 24 Jesse Barfield | .20 |
| 25 Steve Bedrosian | .15 |
| 26 Ray Smalley | .05 |
| 27 Bruce Berenyi | .05 |
| 28 Dann Bilardello | .05 |
| 29 Odell Jones | .05 |
| 30 Cal Ripken | 3.00 |
| 31 Terry Whitfield | .05 |
| 32 Chuck Porter | .05 |
| 33 Tito Landrum | .05 |
| 34 Ed Nunez | .10 |
| 35 Graig Nettles | .12 |
| 36 Fred Breining | .05 |
| 37 Reid Nichols | .05 |
| 38 Jackie Moore (Mgr.) | .05 |
| 39 Johnny Wockenfuss | .05 |
| 40 Phil Niekro | .20 |
| 41 Mike Fischlin | .05 |
| 42 Luis Sanchez | .05 |
| 43 Andre David (R) | .12 |
| 44 Dickie Thon | .07 |
| 45 Greg Minton | .05 |
| 46 Gary Woods | .05 |
| 47 Dave Rozema | .05 |
| 48 Tony Fernandez | 1.00 |
| 49 Butch Davis | .08 |
| 50 John Candelaria | .08 |
| 51 Rob Watson | .05 |
| 52 Jerry Dybzinski | .05 |
| 53 Tom Gorman | .07 |
| 54 Cesar Cedeno | .08 |
| 55 Frank Tanana | .05 |
| 56 Jim Dwyer | .05 |

| NO. PLAYER | MINT |
|---|---|
| 57 Pat Zachry | .05 |
| 58 Orlando Mercado | .05 |
| 59 Rick Waits | .05 |
| 60 George Hendrick | .08 |
| 61 Curt Kaufman (R) | .12 |
| 62 Mike Ramsey | .05 |
| 63 Steve McCatty | .05 |
| 64 Mark Bailey (R) | .12 |
| 65 Bill Buckner | .10 |
| 66 Dick Williams (Mgr.) | .05 |
| 67 Rafael Santana (R) | .12 |
| 68 Von Hayes | .15 |
| 69 Jim Winn (R) | .12 |
| 70 Don Baylor | .10 |
| 71 Tim Laudner | .05 |
| 72 Rick Sutcliffe | .15 |
| 73 Rusty Kuntz | .05 |
| 74 Mike Krukow | .05 |
| 75 Willie Upshaw | .10 |
| 76 Alan Bannister | .05 |
| 77 Joe Beckwith | .05 |
| 78 Scott Fletcher | .05 |
| 79 Rick Mahler | .05 |
| 80 Keith Hernandez | .20 |
| 81 Lenn Sakata | .05 |
| 82 Joe Price | .05 |
| 83 Charlie Moore | .05 |
| 84 Spike Owen | .05 |
| 85 Mike Marshall | .12 |
| 86 Don Aase | .05 |
| 87 David Green | .05 |
| 88 Bryn Smith | .05 |
| 89 Jackie Gutierrez (R) | .12 |
| 90 Rich Gossage | .15 |
| 91 Jeff Burroughs | .05 |
| 92 Paul Owens (Mgr.) | .05 |
| 93 Don Schulze (R) | .12 |
| 94 Toby Harrah | .05 |
| 95 Jose Cruz | .08 |
| 96 Johnny Ray | .12 |
| 97 Pete Filson | .05 |
| 98 Steve Lake | .05 |
| 99 Milt Wilcox | .05 |
| 100 George Brett | .05 |
| 101 Jim Acker | .60 |
| 102 Tommy Dunbar | .05 |
| 103 Randy Lerch | .08 |
| 104 Mike Fitzgerald | .05 |
| 105 Ron Kittle | .15 |
| 106 Pascual Perez | .05 |
| 107 Tom Foley | .05 |
| 108 Darnell Coles | .15 |
| 109 Gary Roenicke | .05 |
| 110 Alejandro Pena | .05 |
| 111 Doug DeCinces | .10 |
| 112 Tom Tellmann | .05 |
| 113 Tom Herr | .15 |
| 114 Bob James | .05 |
| 115 Rickey Henderson | 2.50 |
| 116 Dennis Boyd | .20 |
| 117 Greg Gross | .05 |
| 118 Eric Show | .08 |
| 119 Pat Corrales (Mgr.) | .05 |
| 120 Steve Kemp | .05 |
| 121 Checklist No. 1 | .08 |
| 122 Tom Brunansky | .15 |

| NO. PLAYER | MINT |
|---|---|
| 123 Dave Smith | .05 |
| 124 Rich Hebner | .05 |
| 125 Ken Tekulve | .05 |
| 126 Ruppert Jones | .05 |
| 127 Mark Gubicza (R) | .50 |
| 128 Ernie Whitt | .05 |
| 129 Gene Garber | .05 |
| 130 Al Oliver | .10 |
| 131 Father & Son: | .07 |
| Gus and Buddy Bell | |
| 132 Father & Son: | .07 |
| Yogi and Dale Berra | |
| 133 Father & Son: | .07 |
| Ray and Bob Boone | |
| 134 Father & Son: | .07 |
| Tito and Terry Francona | |
| 135 Father & Son: | .07 |
| Bob and Terry Kennedy | |
| 136 Father & Son: | .07 |
| Jim and Jeff Kunkel | |
| 137 Father & Son: | .07 |
| Vern and Vance Law | |
| 138 Father & Son: | .07 |
| Dick and Dick Schofield | |
| 139 Father & Son: | .07 |
| Bob and Joel Skinner | |
| 140 Father & Son: | .07 |
| Roy and Roy Smalley | |
| 141 Father & Son: | .07 |
| Dave and Mike Stenhouse | |
| 142 Father & Son: | .07 |
| Dizzy and Steve Trout | |
| 143 Father & Son: | .07 |
| Ossie and Ozzie Virgil | |
| 144 Ron Gardenhire | .05 |
| 145 Alvin Davis (R) | 1.00 |
| 146 Gary Redus | .08 |
| 147 Bill Swaggerty (R) | .12 |
| 148 Steve Yeager | .05 |
| 149 Dickie Noles | .05 |
| 150 Jim Rice | .20 |
| 151 Moose Haas | .05 |
| 152 Steve Braun | .05 |
| 153 Frank LaCorte | .05 |
| 154 Argenis Salazar | .08 |
| 155 Yogi Berra (Mgr.) | .12 |
| 156 Craig Reynolds | .05 |
| 157 Tug McGraw | .08 |
| 158 Pat Tabler | .05 |
| 159 Carlos Diaz | .05 |
| 160 Lance Parrish | .20 |
| 161 Ken Schrom | .05 |
| 162 Benny Distefano (R) | .12 |
| 163 Dennis Eckersley | .20 |
| 164 Jorge Orta | .05 |
| 165 Dusty Baker | .08 |
| 166 Keith Atherton | .05 |
| 167 Rufino Linares | .05 |
| 168 Garth Iorg | .05 |
| 169 Dan Spillner | .05 |
| 170 George Foster | .15 |
| 171 Bill Stein | .05 |
| 172 Jack Perconte | .05 |
| 173 Mike Young | .10 |
| 174 Rick Honeycutt | .05 |
| 175 Dave Parker | .25 |

| NO. PLAYER | MINT |
|---|---|
| 176 Bill Schroeder | .05 |
| 177 Dave Von Ohlen | .05 |
| 178 Miguel Dilone | .05 |
| 179 Tommy John | .15 |
| 180 Dave Winfield | .40 |
| 181 Roger Clemens (R) | 18.00 |
| 182 Tim Flannery | .05 |
| 183 Larry McWilliams | .05 |
| 184 Carmen Castillo | .05 |
| 185 Al Holland | .05 |
| 186 Bob Lillis (Mgr.) | .05 |
| 187 Mike Walters | .05 |
| 188 Greg Pryor | .05 |
| 189 Warren Brusstar | .05 |
| 190 Rusty Staub | .12 |
| 191 Steve Nicosia | .05 |
| 192 Howard Johnson | 4.00 |
| 193 Jimmy Key (R) | 1.00 |
| 194 Dave Stegman | .05 |
| 195 Glenn Hubbard | .05 |
| 196 Pete O'Brien | .10 |
| 197 Mike Warren | .05 |
| 198 Eddie Milner | .05 |
| 199 Denny Martinez | .05 |
| 200 Reggie Jackson | .40 |
| 201 Burt Hooton | .05 |
| 202 Gorman Thomas | .08 |
| 203 Bob McClure | .05 |
| 204 Art Howe | .05 |
| 205 Steve Rogers | .05 |
| 206 Phil Garner | .05 |
| 207 Mark Clear | .05 |
| 208 Champ Summers | .05 |
| 209 Bill Campbell | .05 |
| 210 Gary Matthews | .08 |
| 211 Clay Christiansen (R) | .12 |
| 212 George Vukovich | .05 |
| 213 Billy Gardner (Mgr.) | .05 |
| 214 John Tudor | .15 |
| 215 Bob Brenly | .08 |
| 216 Jerry Don Gleaton | .05 |
| 217 Leon Roberts | .05 |
| 218 Doyle Alexander | .05 |
| 219 Gerald Perry | .05 |
| 220 Fred Lynn | .15 |
| 221 Ron Reed | .05 |
| 222 Hubie Brooks | .08 |
| 223 Tom Hume | .05 |
| 224 Al Cowens | .05 |
| 225 Mike Boddicker | .10 |
| 226 Juan Beniquez | .05 |
| 227 Danny Darwin | .05 |
| 228 Dion James | .20 |
| 229 Dave LaPoint | .05 |
| 230 Gary Carter | .30 |
| 231 Dwayne Murphy | .08 |
| 232 Dave Beard | .05 |
| 233 Ed Jurak | .05 |
| 234 Jerry Narron | .05 |
| 235 Garry Maddox | .05 |
| 236 Mark Thurmond | .08 |
| 237 Julio Franco | .50 |
| 238 Jose Rijo (R) | 1.00 |
| 239 Tim Teufel | .15 |
| 240 Dave Stieb | .15 |
| 241 Jim Frey (Mgr.) | .05 |

# 1985 Topps (Continued)

| NO. PLAYER | MINT |
|---|---|
| 242 Greg Harris | .05 |
| 243 Barbaro Garbey (R) | .12 |
| 244 Mike Jones | .05 |
| 245 Chili Davis | .15 |
| 246 Mike Norris | .05 |
| 247 Wayne Tolleston | .05 |
| 248 Terry Forster | .05 |
| 249 Harold Baines | .20 |
| 250 Jesse Orosco | .05 |
| 251 Brad Gulden | .05 |
| 252 Dan Ford | .05 |
| 253 Sid Bream (R) | .35 |
| 254 Pete Vuckovich | .08 |
| 255 Lonnie Smith | .08 |
| 256 Mike Stanton | .05 |
| 257 Bryan Little | .05 |
| 258 Mike Brown | .05 |
| 259 Gary Allenson | .05 |
| 260 Dave Righetti | .12 |
| 261 Checklist No. 2 | .08 |
| 262 Greg Booker (R) | .12 |
| 263 Mel Hall | .10 |
| 264 Joe Sambito | .05 |
| 265 Juan Samuel | .50 |
| 266 Frank Viola | .30 |
| 267 Henry Cotto | .12 |
| 268 Chuck Tanner (Mgr.) | .05 |
| 269 Doug Baker (R) | .12 |
| 270 Dan Quisenberry | .15 |

**No. 271 to 282 (# 1 Draft Picks)**

| NO. PLAYER | MINT |
|---|---|
| 271 Tim Foli (1968) | .12 |
| 272 Jeff Burroughs (1969) | .12 |
| 273 Bill Almon (1974) | .12 |
| 274 Floyd Bannister (1976) | .12 |
| 275 Harold Baines (1977) | .18 |
| 276 Bob Horner (1978) | .18 |
| 277 Al Chambers (1979) | .12 |
| 278 D. Strawberry (1980) | 1.50 |
| 279 Mike Moore (1981) | .12 |
| 280 S. Dunston (R) (1982) | 2.50 |
| 281 Tim Belcher (R) (1983) | 1.00 |
| 282 S. Abner (R) (1984) | .20 |
| 283 Fran Mullins | .05 |
| 284 Marty Bystrom | .05 |
| 285 Dan Driessen | .05 |
| 286 Rudy Law | .05 |
| 287 Walt Terrell | .05 |
| 288 Jeff Kunkel (R) | .12 |
| 289 Tom Underwood | .05 |
| 290 Cecil Cooper | .15 |
| 291 Bob Welch | .12 |
| 292 Brad Komminsk | .10 |
| 293 Curt Young (R) | .15 |
| 294 Tom Nieto (R) | .12 |
| 295 Joe Niekro | .12 |
| 296 Ricky Nelson | .05 |
| 297 Gary Lucas | .05 |
| 298 Marty Barrett | .12 |
| 299 Andy Hawkins | .08 |
| 300 Rod Carew | .40 |
| 301 John Montefusco | .05 |
| 302 Tim Corcoran | .05 |
| 303 Mike Jeffcoat | .08 |
| 304 Gary Gaetti | .15 |
| 305 Dale Berra | .05 |
| 306 Rick Reuschel | .10 |
| 307 Sparky Anderson (Mgr.) | .05 |
| 308 John Wathan | .05 |
| 309 Mike Witt | .10 |
| 310 Manny Trillo | .05 |
| 311 Jim Gott | .05 |
| 312 Marc Hill | .05 |
| 313 Dave Schmidt | .05 |
| 314 Ron Oester | .05 |
| 315 Doug Sisk | .05 |
| 316 John Lowenstein | .05 |
| 317 Jack Lazorko (R) | .12 |
| 318 Ted Simmons | .10 |
| 319 Jeff Jones | .05 |
| 320 Dale Murphy | .50 |
| 321 Ricky Horton (R) | .15 |
| 322 Dave Stapleton | .05 |
| 323 Andy McGaffigan | .05 |
| 324 Bruce Bochy | .05 |
| 325 John Denny | .05 |

| NO. PLAYER | MINT |
|---|---|
| 326 Kevin Bass | .15 |
| 327 Brook Jacoby | .15 |
| 328 Bob Shirley | .05 |
| 329 Ron Washington | .05 |
| 330 Leon Durham | .15 |
| 331 Bill Laskey | .05 |
| 332 Brian Harper | .15 |
| 333 Willie Hernandez | .15 |
| 334 Dick Howser (Mgr.) | .05 |
| 335 Bruce Benedict | .05 |
| 336 Rance Mulliniks | .05 |
| 337 Billy Sample | .05 |
| 338 Britt Burns | .05 |
| 339 Danny Heep | .05 |
| 340 Robin Yount | .65 |
| 341 Floyd Rayford | .05 |
| 342 Ted Power | .05 |
| 343 Bill Russell | .05 |
| 344 Dave Henderson | .30 |
| 345 Charlie Lea | .05 |
| 346 Terry Pendleton (R) | 1.50 |
| 347 Rick Langford | .05 |
| 348 Bob Boone | .05 |
| 349 Domingo Ramos | .05 |
| 350 Wade Boggs | 2.50 |
| 351 Juan Agosto | .05 |
| 352 Joe Morgan | .25 |
| 353 Julio Solano (R) | .12 |
| 354 Andre Robertson | .05 |
| 355 Bert Blyleven | .10 |
| 356 Dave Meier (R) | .12 |
| 357 Rich Bordi | .05 |
| 358 Tony Pena | .12 |
| 359 Pat Sheridan | .05 |
| 360 Steve Carlton | .35 |
| 361 Alfredo Griffin | .05 |
| 362 Craig McMurtry | .05 |
| 363 Ron Hodges | .05 |
| 364 Richard Dotson | .05 |
| 365 Danny Ozark (Mgr.) | .05 |
| 366 Todd Cruz | .05 |
| 367 Keefe Cato (R) | .12 |
| 368 Dave Bergman | .05 |
| 369 R.J. Reynolds (R) | .15 |
| 370 Bruce Sutter | .15 |
| 371 Mickey Rivers | .05 |
| 372 Roy Howell | .05 |
| 373 Mike Moore | .07 |
| 374 Brian Downing | .05 |
| 375 Jeff Reardon | .25 |
| 376 Jeff Newman | .05 |
| 377 Checklist No.3 | .08 |
| 378 Alan Wiggins | .08 |
| 379 Charles Hudson | .05 |
| 380 Ken Griffey | .15 |
| 381 Roy Smith (R) | .12 |
| 382 Denny Walling | .05 |
| 383 Rick Lysander | .05 |
| 384 Jody Davis | .10 |
| 385 Jose DeLeon | .05 |
| 386 Dan Gladden (R) | .40 |
| 387 Buddy Biancalana | .12 |
| 388 Bert Roberge | .05 |

**No. 389 to 404 (U.S. Olympic Team)**

| NO. PLAYER | MINT |
|---|---|
| 389 Rod Dedeaux (Coach) | .10 |
| 390 Sid Akins | .10 |
| 391 Flavio Alfaro | .10 |
| 392 Don August | .15 |
| 393 Scott Bankhead | .30 |
| 394 Bob Caffrey | .10 |
| 395 Mike Dunne (R) | .25 |
| 396 Gary Green | .10 |
| 397 John Hoover | .10 |
| 398 Shane Mack (R) | .75 |
| 399 John Marzano (R) | .15 |
| 400 Oddibe McDowell (R) | .20 |
| 401 Mark McGwire (R) | 12.00 |
| 402 Pat Pacillo (R) | .15 |
| 403 Cory Snyder (R) | 1.00 |
| 404 Billy Swift | .20 |
| 405 Tom Veryzer | .05 |
| 406 Len Whitehouse | .05 |
| 407 Bobby Ramos | .05 |
| 408 Sid Monge | .05 |
| 409 Brad Wellman | .05 |

| NO. PLAYER | MINT |
|---|---|
| 410 Bob Horner | .20 |
| 411 Bobby Cox (Mgr.) | .05 |
| 412 Bud Black | .05 |
| 413 Vance Law | .05 |
| 414 Gary Ward | .05 |
| 415 Ron Darling | .30 |
| 416 Wayne Gross | .05 |
| 417 John Franco (R) | .75 |
| 418 Ken Landreaux | .05 |
| 419 Mike Caldwell | .05 |
| 420 Andre Dawson | .50 |
| 421 Dave Rucker | .05 |
| 422 Carney Lansford | .10 |
| 423 Barry Bonnell | .05 |
| 424 Al Nipper (R) | .15 |
| 425 Mike Hargrove | .05 |
| 426 Vern Ruhle | .05 |
| 427 Mario Ramirez | .05 |
| 428 Larry Andersen | .05 |
| 429 Rick Cerone | .05 |
| 430 Ron Davis | .05 |
| 431 U.L. Washington | .05 |
| 432 Thad Bosley | .05 |
| 433 Jim Morrison | .05 |
| 434 Gene Richards | .05 |
| 435 Dan Petry | .12 |
| 436 Willie Aikens | .05 |
| 437 Al Jones (R) | .12 |
| 438 Joe Torre (Mgr.) | .07 |
| 439 Junior Ortiz | .05 |
| 440 Fernando Valenzuela | .20 |
| 441 Duane Walker | .05 |
| 442 Ken Forsch | .05 |
| 443 George Wright | .05 |
| 444 Tony Phillips | .05 |
| 445 Tippy Martinez | .05 |
| 446 Jim Sundberg | .05 |
| 447 Jeff Lahti | .05 |
| 448 Derrel Thomas | .05 |
| 449 Phil Bradley (R) | .25 |
| 450 Steve Garvey | .40 |
| 451 Bruce Hurst | .05 |
| 452 John Castino | .05 |
| 453 Tom Waddell (R) | .12 |
| 454 Glenn Wilson | .10 |
| 455 Bob Knepper | .05 |
| 456 Tim Foli | .05 |
| 457 Cecilio Guante | .05 |
| 458 Randy Johnson | .05 |
| 459 Charlie Leibrandt | .05 |
| 460 Ryne Sandberg | 3.00 |
| 461 Marty Castillo | .05 |
| 462 Gary Lavelle | .05 |
| 463 Dave Collins | .05 |
| 464 Mike Mason (R) | .12 |
| 465 Bob Grich | .07 |
| 466 Tony LaRussa (Mgr.) | .05 |
| 467 Ed Lynch | .05 |
| 468 Wayne Krenchicki | .05 |
| 469 Sammy Stewart | .05 |
| 470 Steve Sax | .25 |
| 471 Pete Ladd | .05 |
| 472 Jim Essian | .05 |
| 473 Tim Wallach | .12 |
| 474 Kurt Kepshire (R) | .12 |
| 475 Andre Thornton | .08 |
| 476 Jeff Stone (R) | .12 |
| 477 Bob Ojeda | .05 |
| 478 Kurt Bevacqua | .05 |
| 479 Mike Madden | .05 |
| 480 Lou Whitaker | .20 |
| 481 Dale Murray | .05 |
| 482 Harry Spilman | .05 |
| 483 Mike Smithson | .05 |
| 484 Larry Bowa | .05 |
| 485 Matt Young | .06 |
| 486 Steve Balboni | .06 |
| 487 Frank Williams (R) | .12 |
| 488 Joel Skinner | .10 |
| 489 Bryan Clark | .05 |
| 490 Jason Thompson | .08 |
| 491 Rick Camp | .05 |
| 492 Dave Johnson (Mgr.) | .20 |
| 493 Orel Hershiser (R) | 2.50 |
| 494 Rich Dauer | .05 |

| NO. PLAYER | MINT |
|---|---|
| 495 Mario Soto | .08 |
| 496 Donnie Scott (R) | .12 |
| 497 Gary Pettis (wrong photo—It's his brother—Lynn) | .15 |
| 498 Ed Romero | .05 |
| 499 Danny Cox | .25 |
| 500 Mike Schmidt | 1.25 |
| 501 Dan Schatzeder | .05 |
| 502 Rick Miller | .05 |
| 503 Tim Conroy | .05 |
| 504 Jerry Willard | .08 |
| 505 Jim Beattie | .05 |
| 506 Franklin Stubbs (R) | .30 |
| 507 Ray Fontenot | .05 |
| 508 John Shelby | .05 |
| 509 Milt May | .05 |
| 510 Kent Hrbek | .25 |
| 511 Lee Smith | .20 |
| 512 Tom Brookens | .05 |
| 513 Lynn Jones | .05 |
| 514 Jeff Cornell (R) | .12 |
| 515 Dave Concepcion | .08 |
| 516 Roy Lee Jackson | .05 |
| 517 Jerry Martin | .05 |
| 518 Chris Chambliss | .05 |
| 519 Doug Rader (Mgr.) | .05 |
| 520 LaMarr Hoyt | .08 |
| 521 Rick Dempsey | .05 |
| 522 Paul Molitor | .20 |
| 523 Candy Maldonado | .15 |
| 524 Rob Wilfong | .05 |
| 525 Darrell Porter | .05 |
| 526 Dave Palmer | .05 |
| 527 Checklist No. 4 | .08 |
| 528 Bill Krueger | .05 |
| 529 Rich Gedman | .08 |
| 530 Dave Dravecky | .08 |
| 531 Joe Lefebvre | .25 |
| 532 Frank DiPino | .05 |
| 533 Tony Bernazard | .05 |
| 534 Brian Dayett | .08 |
| 535 Pat Putnam | .05 |
| 536 Kirby Puckett (R) | 15.00 |
| 537 Don Robinson | .05 |
| 538 Keith Moreland | .05 |
| 539 Aurelio Lopez | .05 |
| 540 Claudell Washington | .08 |
| 541 Mark Davis | .10 |
| 542 Don Slaught | .05 |
| 543 Mike Squires | .05 |
| 544 Bruce Kison | .05 |
| 545 Lloyd Moseby | .15 |
| 546 Brent Gaff | .08 |
| 547 Pete Rose (Mgr.) | .50 |
| 548 Larry Parrish | .07 |
| 549 Mike Scioscia | .05 |
| 550 Scott McGregor | .07 |
| 551 Andy Van Slyke | .40 |
| 552 Chris Codiroli | .05 |
| 553 Bob Clark | .05 |
| 554 Doug Flynn | .05 |
| 555 Bob Stanley | .05 |
| 556 Sixto Lezcano | .05 |
| 557 Len Barker | .05 |
| 558 Carmelo Martinez | .05 |
| 559 Jay Howell | .05 |
| 560 Bill Madlock | .15 |
| 561 Darryl Motley | .05 |
| 562 Houston Jimenez | .05 |
| 563 Dick Ruthven | .05 |
| 564 Alan Ashby | .05 |
| 565 Kirk Gibson | .25 |
| 566 Ed Vande Berg | .05 |
| 567 Joel Youngblood | .05 |
| 568 Cliff Johnson | .05 |
| 569 Ken Oberkfell | .05 |
| 570 Darryl Strawberry | 4.00 |
| 571 Charlie Hough | .05 |
| 572 Tom Paciorek | .05 |
| 573 Jay Tibbs (R) | .12 |
| 574 Joe Altobelli (Mgr.) | .05 |
| 575 Pedro Guerrero | .20 |
| 576 Jaime Cocanower (R) | .12 |
| 577 Chris Speier | .05 |

| NO. PLAYER | MINT | NO. PLAYER | MINT | NO. PLAYER | MINT | NO. PLAYER | MINT |
|---|---|---|---|---|---|---|---|
| 578 Terry Francona | .05 | 632 Bruce Bochte | .05 | 686 Mike Easler | .05 | 740 Jack Clark | .20 |
| 579 Ron Romanick (R) | .12 | 633 Glenn Hoffman | .05 | 687 Bill Gullickson | .05 | 741 John Butcher | .05 |
| 580 Dwight Evans | .12 | 634 Bill Dawley | .05 | 688 Len Matuszek | .05 | 742 Ron Hassey | .05 |
| 581 Mark Wagner | .05 | 635 Terry Kennedy | .08 | 689 Luis DeLeon | .05 | 743 Frank White | .05 |
| 582 Ken Phelps | .20 | 636 Shane Rawley | .05 | 690 Alan Trammell | .35 | 744 Doug Bair | .05 |
| 583 Bobby Brown | .05 | 637 Brett Butler | .20 | 691 Dennis Rasmussen | .15 | 745 Buddy Bell | .10 |
| 584 Kevin Gross | .05 | 638 Mike Pagliarulo (R) | .30 | 692 Randy Bush | .05 | 746 Jim Clancy | .05 |
| 585 Butch Wynegar | .05 | 639 Ed Hodge (R) | .12 | 693 Tim Stoddard | .05 | 747 Alex Trevino | .05 |
| 586 Bill Scherrer | .05 | 640 Steve Henderson | .05 | 694 Joe Carter | 3.00 | 748 Lee Mazzilli | .05 |
| 587 Doug Frobel | .05 | 641 Rod Scurry | .05 | 695 Rick Rhoden | .05 | 749 Julio Cruz | .05 |
| 588 Bobby Castillo | .05 | 642 Dave Owen (R) | .12 | 696 John Rabb | .05 | 750 Rollie Fingers | .15 |
| 589 Bob Dernier | .05 | 643 Johnny Grubb | .05 | 697 Onix Concepcion | .05 | 751 Kelvin Chapman (R) | .12 |
| 590 Ray Knight | .05 | 644 Mark Huismann | .10 | 698 Jorge Bell | .50 | 752 Bob Owchinko | .05 |
| 591 Larry Herndon | .05 | 645 Damaso Garcia | .08 | 699 Donnie Moore | .08 | 753 Greg Brock | .08 |
| 592 Jeff Robinson (R) | .15 | 646 Scot Thompson | .05 | 700 Eddie Murray | .50 | 754 Larry Milbourne | .05 |
| 593 Rick Leach | .05 | 647 Rafael Ramierz | .05 | 701 Eddie Murray (AS) | .25 | 755 Ken Singleton | .08 |
| 594 Curt Wilkerson | .08 | 648 Bob Jones | .05 | 702 Damaso Garcia (AS) | .10 | 756 Rob Picciolo | .05 |
| 595 Larry Gura | .05 | 649 Sid Fernandez | .35 | 703 George Brett (AS) | .30 | 757 Willie McGee | .35 |
| 596 Jerry Hairston | .05 | 650 Greg Luzinski | .08 | 704 Cal Ripken (AS) | .40 | 758 Ray Burris | .05 |
| 597 Brad Lesley | .05 | 651 Jeff Russell | .05 | 705 Dave Winfield (AS) | .20 | 759 Jim Fanning (Mgr.) | .05 |
| 598 Jose Oquendo | .05 | 652 Joe Nolan | .05 | 706 Rickey Henderson (AS) | .50 | 760 Nolan Ryan | 3.00 |
| 599 Storm Davis | .08 | 653 Mark Brouhard | .05 | 707 Tony Armas (AS) | .10 | 761 Jerry Remy | .05 |
| 600 Pete Rose | .75 | 654 Dave Anderson | .05 | 708 Lance Parrish (AS) | .15 | 762 Eddie Whitson | .05 |
| 601 Tom Lasorda (Mgr.) | .08 | 655 Joaquin Andujar | .08 | 709 Mike Boddicker (AS) | .10 | 763 Kiko Garcia | .05 |
| 602 Jeff Dedmon (R) | .12 | 656 Chuck Cottier (Mgr.) | .05 | 710 Frank Viola (AS) | .10 | 764 Jamie Easterly | .05 |
| 603 Rick Manning | .05 | 657 Jim Slaton | .05 | 711 Dan Quisenberry (AS) | .15 | 765 Willie Randolph | .05 |
| 604 Daryl Sconiers | .05 | 658 Mike Stenhouse | .08 | 712 Keith Hernandez (AS) | .20 | 766 Paul Mirabella | .05 |
| 605 Ozzie Smith | .40 | 659 Checklist No. 5 | .08 | 713 Ryne Sandberg (AS) | .50 | 767 Darrell Brown | .05 |
| 606 Rich Gale | .05 | 660 Tony Gwynn | 1.50 | 714 Mike Schmidt (AS) | .40 | 768 Ron Cey | .10 |
| 607 Bill Almon | .05 | 661 Steve Crawford | .05 | 715 Ozzie Smith (AS) | .15 | 769 Joe Cowley | .05 |
| 608 Craig Lefferts | .05 | 662 Mike Heath | .05 | 716 Dale Murphy (AS) | .25 | 770 Carlton Fisk | .50 |
| 609 Broderick Perkins | .05 | 663 Luis Aguayo | .05 | 717 Tony Gwynn (AS) | .35 | 771 Geoff Zahn | .05 |
| 610 Jack Morris | .30 | 664 Steve Farr | .20 | 718 Jeff Leonard (AS) | .10 | 772 Johnnie LeMaster | .05 |
| 611 Ozzie Virgil | .05 | 665 Don Mattingly | 4.00 | 719 Gary Carter (AS) | .20 | 773 Hal McRae | .05 |
| 612 Mike Armstrong | .05 | 666 Mike LaCoss | .05 | 720 Rick Sutcliffe (AS) | .15 | 774 Dennis Lamp | .05 |
| 613 Terry Puhl | .05 | 667 Dave Engle | .05 | 721 Bob Knepper (AS) | .10 | 775 Mookie Wilson | .08 |
| 614 Al Williams | .05 | 668 Steve Trout | .05 | 722 Bruce Sutter (AS) | .15 | 776 Jerry Royster | .05 |
| 615 Marvell Wynne | .05 | 669 Lee Lacy | .05 | 723 Dave Stewart | .35 | 777 Ned Yost | .05 |
| 616 Scott Sanderson | .05 | 670 Tom Seaver | .45 | 724 Oscar Gamble | .05 | 778 Mike Davis | .08 |
| 617 Willie Wilson | .15 | 671 Dane Iorg | .05 | 725 Floyd Bannister | .05 | 779 Nick Esasky | .15 |
| 618 Pete Falcone | .05 | 672 Juan Berenguer | .05 | 726 Al Bumbry | .05 | 780 Mike Flanagan | .05 |
| 619 Jeff Leonard | .05 | 673 Buck Martinez | .05 | 727 Frank Pastore | .05 | 781 Jim Gantner | .05 |
| 620 Dwight Gooden (R) | 9.00 | 674 Atlee Hammaker | .05 | 728 Bob Bailor | .05 | 782 Tom Niedenfuer | .05 |
| 621 Marvis Foley | .05 | 675 Tony Perez | .15 | 729 Don Sutton | .20 | 783 Mike Jorgensen | .05 |
| 622 Luis Leal | .05 | 676 Albert Hall (R) | .12 | 730 Dave Kingman | .10 | 784 Checklist No. 6 | .08 |
| 623 Greg Walker | .12 | 677 Wally Backman | .05 | 731 Neil Allen | .05 | 785 Tony Armas | .12 |
| 624 Benny Ayala | .05 | 678 Joey McLaughlin | .05 | 732 John McNamara (Mgr.) | .05 | 786 Enos Cabell | .05 |
| 625 Mark Langston (R) | 2.00 | 679 Bob Kearney | .05 | 733 Tony Scott | .05 | 787 Jim Wohlford | .05 |
| 626 German Rivera (R) | .15 | 680 Jerry Reuss | .05 | 734 John Henry Johnson | .05 | 788 Steve Comer | .05 |
| 627 Eric Davis (R) | 8.00 | 681 Ben Oglivie | .05 | 735 Garry Templeton | .10 | 789 Luis Salazar | .05 |
| 628 R. Lachemann (Mgr.) | .05 | 682 Doug Corbett | .05 | 736 Jerry Mumphrey | .05 | 790 Ron Guidry | .15 |
| 629 Dick Schofield | .12 | 683 Whitey Herzog (Mgr.) | .05 | 737 Bo Diaz | .05 | 791 Ivan DeJesus | .05 |
| 630 Tim Raines | .30 | 684 Bill Doran | .10 | 738 Omar Moreno | .05 | 792 Darrell Evans | .12 |
| 631 Bob Forsch | .05 | 685 Bill Caudill | .08 | 739 Ernie Camacho | .05 | | |

## 1985 Topps Traded . . . Complete Set of 132 Cards—Value $30.00

Updates the main 1985 card set with players who changed teams during the season and rookies who joined their teams early in the season. Features the first Topps card of Vince Coleman, Tom Browning and Teddy Higuera. The complete set was packaged in a printed box and only distributed through card hobby dealers. Topps also tested a small quantity of wax packs. A "Tiffany" version of the set was also issued.

| NO. PLAYER | MINT | NO. PLAYER | MINT | NO. PLAYER | MINT | NO. PLAYER | MINT |
|---|---|---|---|---|---|---|---|
| 1 T Don Aase | .08 | 5 T G. Bamberger (Mgr.) | .06 | 9 T Hubie Brooks | .12 | 13 T Ray Burris | .06 |
| 2 T Bill Almon | .06 | 6 T Dale Berra | .10 | 10 T Chris Brown (RR) | .15 | 14 T Jeff Burroughs | .06 |
| 3 T Benny Ayala | .06 | 7 T Rich Bordi | .06 | 11 T T. Browning (RR) | 1.50 | 15 T Bill Campbell | .06 |
| 4 T Dusty Baker | .12 | 8 T Daryl Boston (RR) | .25 | 12 T Al Bumbry | .06 | 16 T Don Carman | .25 |

# 1985 Topps Traded

| NO. PLAYER | MINT | NO. PLAYER | MINT | NO. PLAYER | MINT | NO. PLAYER | MINT |
|---|---|---|---|---|---|---|---|
| 17 T Gary Carter | .75 | 46 T Toby Harrah | .08 | 75 T Sixto Lezcano | .06 | 104 T Rick Schu | .15 |
| 18 T Bobby Castillo | .06 | 47 T Greg Harris | .06 | 76 T Tim Lollar | .06 | 105 T Donnie Scott | .06 |
| 19 T Bill Caudill | .10 | 48 T Ron Hassey | .06 | 77 T Fred Lynn | .20 | 106 T Larry Sheets | .35 |
| 20 T Rick Cerone | .08 | 49 T Rickey Henderson | 6.00 | 78 T Billy Martin (Mgr.) | .15 | 107 T Don Slaught | .06 |
| 21 T Bryan Clark | .06 | 50 T Steve Henderson | .06 | 79 T Ron Mathis | .15 | 108 T Roy Smalley | .08 |
| 22 T Jack Clark | .40 | 51 T George Hendrik | .12 | 80 T Len Matuszek | .06 | 109 T Lonnie Smith | .12 |
| 23 T Pat Clements | .15 | 52 T Joe Hesketh (RR) | .15 | 81 T Gene Mauch (Mgr.) | .06 | 110 T Nate Snell | .15 |
| 24 T V. Coleman (RR) | 11.00 | 53 T T. Higuera (RR) | .75 | 82 T Oddibe McDowell | .30 | 111 T Chris Speier | .06 |
| 25 T Dave Collins | .08 | 54 T Donnie Hill | .06 | 83 T R. McDowell (RR) | .60 | 112 T Mike Stenhouse | .06 |
| 26 T Dave Darwin | .06 | 55 T Al Holland | .08 | 84 T J. McNamara (Mgr.) | .06 | 113 T Tim Stoddard | .06 |
| 27 T J. Davenport (Mgr.) | .06 | 56 T Burt Hooton | .06 | 85 T Donnie Moore | .08 | 114 T Jim Sundberg | .08 |
| 28 T Jerry Davis | .12 | 57 T Jay Howell | .08 | 86 T Gene Nelson | .06 | 115 T Bruce Sutter | .25 |
| 29 T Brian Dayett | .06 | 58 T Ken Howell | .20 | 87 T Steve Nicosia | .06 | 116 T Don Sutton | .50 |
| 30 T Ivan DeJesus | .06 | 59 T LaMarr Hoyt | .12 | 88 T Al Oliver | .12 | 117 T Kent Tekulve | .08 |
| 31 T Ken Dixon | .15 | 60 T Tim Hulett | .12 | 89 T Joe Orsulak | .35 | 118 T Tom Tellmann | .06 |
| 32 T M. Duncan (RR) | .75 | 61 T Bob James | .06 | 90 T Rob Picciolo | .06 | 119 T Walt Terrell | .05 |
| 33 T John Felske (Mgr.) | .06 | 62 T Steve Jeltz (RR) | .20 | 91 T Chris Pittaro | .15 | 120 T Mickey Tettleton (RR) | 1.50 |
| 34 T Mike Fitzgerald | .06 | 63 T Cliff Johnson | .06 | 92 T Jim Presley (RR) | .30 | 121 T Derrel Thomas | .06 |
| 35 T Ray Fontenot | .06 | 64 T Howard Johnson | 2.00 | 93 T Rick Reuschel | .15 | 122 T Rich Thompson | .15 |
| 36 T Greg Gagne | .30 | 65 T Ruppert Jones | .08 | 94 T Bert Roberge | .06 | 123 T Alex Trevino | .06 |
| 37 T Oscar Gamble | .10 | 66 T Steve Kemp | .06 | 95 T Bob Rodgers (Mgr.) | .06 | 124 T John Tudor | .20 |
| 38 T Scott Garrelts (RR) | .30 | 67 T Bruce Kison | .06 | 96 T Jerry Royster | .06 | 125 T Jose Uribe | .30 |
| 39 T Bob Gibson | .06 | 68 T Alan Knicely | .06 | 97 T Dave Rozema | .06 | 126 T B. Valentine (Mgr.) | .10 |
| 40 T Jim Gott | .06 | 69 T Mike LaCoss | .06 | 98 T Dave Rucker | .06 | 127 T Dave Von Ohlen | .06 |
| 41 T David Green | .12 | 70 T Lee Lacy | .08 | 99 T Vern Ruhle | .06 | 128 T U.L. Washington | .06 |
| 42 T Alfredo Griffin | .12 | 71 T Dave LaPoint | .06 | 100 T Paul Runge | .15 | 129 T Earl Weaver (Mgr.) | .12 |
| 43 T Ozzie Guillen (RR) | 2.00 | 72 T Gary Lavelle | .06 | 101 T Mark Salas (R) | .15 | 130 T Eddie Whitson | .08 |
| 44 T Eddie Haas (Mgr.) | .06 | 73 T Vance Law | .06 | 102 T Luis Salazar | .06 | 131 T Herm Winningham | .15 |
| 45 T Terry Harper | .06 | 74 T Johnnie LeMaster | .06 | 103 T Joe Sambito | .08 | 132 T Traded Checklist | .10 |

# 1986 Topps.... Complete Set of 792 Cards—Value $50.00

Features the rookie cards of Vince Coleman and Teddy Higuera. There are no card numbers 51 or 171. They were given wrong numbers in error. A "Tiffany" version of the set was also issued.

VINCE COLEMAN

TEDDY HIGUERA

ROGER McDOWELL

LEN DYKSTRA

HAROLD REYNOLDS

| NO. PLAYER | MINT | NO. PLAYER | MINT | NO. PLAYER | MINT | NO. PLAYER | MINT |
|---|---|---|---|---|---|---|---|
| 1 Pete Rose | 1.00 | 28 Eric Davis | 1.00 | 53 Len Dykstra (R) | 1.50 | 80 Darryl Strawberry | 1.50 |
| 2 Rose (Years 1963-66) | .35 | 29 Tony Phillips | .04 | 54 John Franco | .08 | 81 Gene Mauch (Mgr.) | .08 |
| 3 Rose (Years 1967-70) | .35 | 30 Eddie Murray | .40 | 55 Fred Lynn | .20 | Angels Checklist | |
| 4 Rose (Years 1971-74) | .35 | 31 Jamie Easterly | .04 | 56 Tom Niedenfuer | .08 | 82 Tippy Martinez | .04 |
| 5 Rose (Years 1975-78) | .35 | 32 Steve Yeager | .06 | 57 Bill Doran | .08 | 83 Phil Garner | .04 |
| 6 Rose (Years 1979-82) | .35 | 33 Jeff Lahti | .04 | 58 Bill Krueger | .04 | 84 Curt Young | .04 |
| 7 Rose (Years 1983-85) | .35 | 34 Ken Phelps | .04 | 59 Andre Thornton | .08 | 85 Tony Perez | .15 |
| 8 Dwayne Murphy | .08 | 35 Jeff Reardon | .12 | 60 Dwight Evans | .12 | 86 Tom Waddell | .04 |
| 9 Roy Smith | .04 | 36 Tigers Leaders: | .15 | 61 Karl Best | .12 | 87 Candy Maldonado | .04 |
| 10 Tony Gwynn | .75 | Lance Parrish | | 62 Bob Boone | .04 | 88 Tom Nieto | .04 |
| 11 Bob Ojeda | .05 | 37 Mark Thurmond | .04 | 63 Ron Roenicke | .04 | 89 Randy St. Claire | .08 |
| 12 Jose Uribe (R) | .15 | 38 Glenn Hoffman | .04 | 64 Floyd Bannister | .04 | 90 Garry Templeton | .15 |
| 13 Bob Kearney | .04 | 39 Dave Rucker | .04 | 65 Dan Driessen | .04 | 91 Steve Crawford | .04 |
| 14 Julio Cruz | .04 | 40 Ken Griffey | .10 | 66 Cardinals Leaders: | .08 | 92 Al Cowens | .04 |
| 15 Eddie Whitson | .06 | 41 Brad Wellman | .04 | Bob Forsch | | 93 Scot Thompson | .04 |
| 16 Rick Schu | .10 | 42 Geoff Zahn | .04 | 67 Carmelo Martinez | .04 | 94 Rich Bordi | .04 |
| 17 Mike Stenhouse | .04 | 43 Dave Engle | .04 | 68 Ed Lynch | .04 | 95 Ozzie Virgil | .04 |
| 18 Brent Gaff | .04 | 44 Lance McCullers (R) | .15 | 69 Luis Aguayo | .04 | 96 Blue Jays Leaders: | .06 |
| 19 Rich Hebner | .04 | 45 Damaso Garcia | .12 | 70 Dave Winfield | .30 | Jim Clancy | |
| 20 Lou Whitaker | .15 | 46 Billy Hatcher | .15 | 71 Ken Schrom | .04 | 97 Gary Gaetti | .15 |
| 21 G. Bamberger (Mgr.) | .04 | 47 Juan Berenguer | .04 | 72 Shawon Dunston | .40 | 98 Dick Ruthven | .04 |
| Brewers Checklist | | 48 Bill Almon | .04 | 73 Randy O'Neal | .08 | 99 Buddy Biancalana | .04 |
| 22 Duane Walker | .08 | 49 Rick Manning | .04 | 74 Rance Mulliniks | .04 | 100 Nolan Ryan | 2.00 |
| 23 Manny Lee | .15 | 50 Dan Quisenberry | .15 | 75 Jose DeLeon | .04 | 101 Dave Bergman | .04 |
| 24 Len Barker | .06 | 51 Rob Wine (Mgr.) | .08 | 76 Dion James | .04 | 102 Joe Orsulak (R) | .20 |
| 25 Willie Wilson | .20 | Braves Checklist | | 77 Charlie Leibrandt | .06 | 103 Luis Salazar | .04 |
| 26 Frank DePino | .04 | Error-reads card no. 57 | | 78 Bruce Benedict | .04 | 104 Sid Fernandez | .15 |
| 27 Ray Knight | .06 | 52 Chris Welsh | .04 | 79 Dave Schmidt | .04 | 105 Gary Ward | .04 |

| NO. | PLAYER | MINT |
|---|---|---|
| 106 | Ray Burris | .04 |
| 107 | Rafael Ramirez | .04 |
| 108 | Ted Power | .04 |
| 109 | Len Matuszek | .04 |
| 110 | Scott McGregor | .06 |
| 111 | Roger Craig (Mgr.) | .08 |
| | Giants Checklist | |
| 112 | Bill Campbell | .04 |
| 113 | U.L. Washington | .04 |
| 114 | Mike Brown | .04 |
| 115 | Jay Howell | .04 |
| 116 | Brook Jacoby | .10 |
| 117 | Bruce Kison | .04 |
| 118 | Jerry Royster | .04 |
| 119 | Barry Bonnell | .04 |
| 120 | Steve Carlton | .30 |
| 121 | Nelson Simmons | .15 |
| 122 | Pete Filson | .04 |
| 123 | Greg Walker | .10 |
| 124 | Luis Sanchez | .04 |
| 125 | Dave Lopes | .06 |
| 126 | Mets Leaders: | .08 |
| | Mookie Wilson | |
| 127 | Jack Howell (R) | .15 |
| 128 | John Wathan | .04 |
| 129 | Jeff Dedmon | .04 |
| 130 | Alan Trammell | .20 |
| 131 | Checklist No. 1 | .08 |
| 132 | Razor Shines | .08 |
| 133 | Andy McGaffigan | .04 |
| 134 | Carney Lansford | .08 |
| 135 | Joe Niekro | .08 |
| 136 | Mike Hargrove | .04 |
| 137 | Charlie Moore | .04 |
| 138 | Mark Davis | .10 |
| 139 | Daryl Boston | .15 |
| 140 | John Candelaria | .08 |
| 141 | Chuck Cottier (Mgr.) | .08 |
| | Mariners Checklist see card 171 | |
| 142 | Bob Jones | .04 |
| 143 | Dave Van Gorder | .04 |
| 144 | Doug Sisk | .04 |
| 145 | Pedro Guerrero | .20 |
| 146 | Jack Perconte | .04 |
| 147 | Larry Sheets | .15 |
| 148 | Mike Heath | .04 |
| 149 | Brett Butler | .10 |
| 150 | Joaquin Andujar | .08 |
| 151 | Dave Stapleton | .04 |
| 152 | Mike Morgan | .04 |
| 153 | Ricky Adams | .04 |
| 154 | Bert Roberge | .04 |
| 155 | Bob Grich | .06 |
| 156 | White Sox Leaders: | .08 |
| | Richard Dotson | |
| 157 | Ron Hassey | .04 |
| 158 | Derrel Thomas | .04 |
| 159 | Orel Hershiser | .30 |
| 160 | Chet Lemon | .06 |
| 161 | Lee Tunnell | .04 |
| 162 | Greg Gagne | .12 |
| 163 | Pete Ladd | .04 |
| 164 | Steve Balboni | .08 |
| 165 | Mike Davis | .06 |
| 166 | Dickie Thon | .04 |
| 167 | Zane Smith | .30 |
| 168 | Jeff Burroughs | .04 |
| 169 | George Wright | .04 |
| 170 | Gary Carter | .30 |
| 171 | Bob Rodgers (Mgr.) | .08 |
| | Expo Checklist error—reads #141 | |
| 172 | Jerry Reed | .15 |
| 173 | Wayne Gross | .04 |
| 174 | Brian Snyder | .15 |
| 175 | Steve Sax | .15 |
| 176 | Jay Tibbs | .04 |
| 177 | Joel Youngblood | .04 |
| 178 | Ivan DeJesus | .04 |
| 179 | Stu Cliburn | .15 |
| 180 | Don Mattingly | 1.50 |
| 181 | Al Nipper | .04 |
| 182 | Bobby Brown | .04 |
| 183 | Larry Andersen | .04 |

| NO. | PLAYER | MINT |
|---|---|---|
| 184 | Tim Laudner | .04 |
| 185 | Rollie Fingers | .15 |
| 186 | Astros Leaders: | .08 |
| | Jose Cruz | |
| 187 | Scott Fletcher | .04 |
| 188 | Bob Dernier | .04 |
| 189 | Mike Mason | .04 |
| 190 | George Hendrick | .08 |
| 191 | Wally Backman | .04 |
| 192 | Milt Wilcox | .04 |
| 193 | Daryl Sconiers | .04 |
| 194 | Craig McMurtry | .04 |
| 195 | Dave Concepcion | .08 |
| 196 | Doyle Alexander | .04 |
| 197 | Enos Cabell | .04 |
| 198 | Ken Dixon | .08 |
| 199 | Dick Howser (Mgr.) | .08 |
| | (Royals Checklist) | |
| 200 | Mike Schmidt | 1.00 |
| 201 | Record—V. Coleman | .30 |
| | Most Stolen Bases— Season, Rookie | |
| 202 | Record—D. Gooden | .40 |
| | Youngest 20-Game Winner | |
| 203 | Rec.—K. Hernandez | .15 |
| | Most Game Winning RBI, Season | |
| 204 | Record—Phil Niekro | .15 |
| | Oldest Shutout Pitcher | |
| 205 | Record—Tony Perez | .12 |
| | Oldest to Hit Grand Slam | |
| 206 | Record—Pete Rose | .40 |
| | Most Hits, Career | |
| 207 | Record—F. Valenzuela | .15 |
| | Most Consecutive Innings, No Earned Runs | |
| 208 | Ramon Romero | .15 |
| 209 | Randy Ready | .10 |
| 210 | Calvin Schiraldi | .10 |
| 211 | Ed Wojna | .15 |
| 212 | Chris Speier | .04 |
| 213 | Bob Shirley | .04 |
| 214 | Randy Bush | .04 |
| 215 | Frank White | .04 |
| 216 | A's Leaders: | .08 |
| | Dwayne Murphy | |
| 217 | Bill Scherrer | .04 |
| 218 | Randy Hunt | .12 |
| 219 | Dennis Lamp | .04 |
| 220 | Bob Horner | .15 |
| 221 | Dave Henderson | .15 |
| 222 | Craig Gerber | .15 |
| 223 | Atlee Hammaker | .06 |
| 224 | Cesar Cedeno | .08 |
| 225 | Ron Darling | .10 |
| 226 | Lee Lacy | .04 |
| 227 | Al Jones | .04 |
| 228 | Tom Lawless | .04 |
| 229 | Bill Gullickson | .04 |
| 230 | Terry Kennedy | .06 |
| 231 | Jim Frey (Mgr.) | .08 |
| | Cubs Checklist | |
| 232 | Rick Rhoden | .04 |
| 233 | Steve Lyons | .10 |
| 234 | Doug Corbett | .04 |
| 235 | Butch Wynegar | .06 |
| 236 | Frank Eufemia | .15 |
| 237 | Ted Simmons | .15 |
| 238 | Larry Parrish | .06 |
| 239 | Joel Skinner | .04 |
| 240 | Tommy John | .15 |
| 241 | Tony Fernandez | .20 |
| 242 | Rich Thompson | .12 |
| 243 | Johnny Grubb | .04 |
| 244 | Craig Lefferts | .04 |
| 245 | Jim Sundberg | .04 |
| 246 | Phillies Leaders: | .15 |
| | Steve Carlton | |
| 247 | Terry Harper | .04 |
| 248 | Spike Owen | .04 |
| 249 | Rob Deer | .30 |
| 250 | Dwight Gooden | 1.00 |
| 251 | Rich Dauer | .04 |
| 252 | Bobby Castillo | .04 |
| 253 | Dann Bilardello | .04 |

| NO. | PLAYER | MINT |
|---|---|---|
| 254 | Ozzie Guillen (R) | .75 |
| 255 | Tony Armas | .10 |
| 256 | Kurt Kepshire | .04 |
| 257 | Doug DeCinces | .08 |
| 258 | Tim Burke (R) | .15 |
| 259 | Dan Pasqua | .15 |
| 260 | Tony Pena | .10 |
| 261 | Bobby Valentine (Mgr.) | .08 |
| | Rangers Checklist | |
| 262 | Mario Ramirez | .04 |
| 263 | Checklist No. 2 | .08 |
| 264 | Darren Daulton (R) | .25 |
| 265 | Ron Davis | .04 |
| 266 | Keith Moreland | .04 |
| 267 | Paul Molitor | .15 |
| 268 | Mike Scott | .15 |
| 269 | Dane Iorg | .04 |
| 270 | Jack Morris | .30 |
| 271 | Dave Collins | .04 |
| 272 | Tim Tolman | .15 |
| 273 | Jerry Willard | .04 |
| 274 | Ron Gardenhire | .04 |
| 275 | Charlie Hough | .04 |
| 276 | Yankees Leaders: | .10 |
| | Willie Randolph | |
| 277 | Jaime Cocanower | .04 |
| 278 | Sixto Lezcano | .04 |
| 279 | Al Pardo | .15 |
| 280 | Tim Raines | .25 |
| 281 | Steve Mura | .04 |
| 282 | Jerry Mumphrey | .04 |
| 283 | Mike Fischlin | .04 |
| 284 | Brian Dayett | .04 |
| 285 | Buddy Bell | .10 |
| 286 | Luis DeLeon | .04 |
| 287 | John Christensen | .15 |
| 288 | Don Aase | .04 |
| 289 | Johnnie LeMaster | .04 |
| 290 | Carlton Fisk | .35 |
| 291 | Tom Lasorda (Mgr.) | .12 |
| | Dodgers Checklist | |
| 292 | Chuck Porter | .04 |
| 293 | Chris Chambliss | .06 |
| 294 | Danny Cox | .10 |
| 295 | Kirk Gibson | .30 |
| 296 | Geno Petralli | .08 |
| 297 | Tim Lollar | .04 |
| 298 | Craig Reynolds | .04 |
| 299 | Bryn Smith | .04 |
| 300 | George Brett | .50 |
| 301 | Dennis Rasmussen | .04 |
| 302 | Greg Gross | .04 |
| 303 | Curt Wardle | .15 |
| 304 | Mike Gallego | .15 |
| 305 | Phil Bradley | .15 |
| 306 | Padres Leaders: | .08 |
| | Terry Kennedy | |
| 307 | Dave Sax | .08 |
| 308 | Ray Fontenot | .04 |
| 309 | John Shelby | .04 |
| 310 | Greg Minton | .04 |
| 311 | Dick Schofield | .04 |
| 312 | Tom Filer | .04 |
| 313 | Joe De Sa | .15 |
| 314 | Frank Pastore | .04 |
| 315 | Mookie Wilson | .06 |
| 316 | Sammy Khalifa | .15 |
| 317 | Ed Romero | .04 |
| 318 | Terry Whitfield | .04 |
| 319 | Rick Camp | .04 |
| 320 | Jim Rice | .25 |
| 321 | Earl Weaver (Mgr.) | .12 |
| | Orioles Checklist | |
| 322 | Bob Forsch | .04 |
| 323 | Jerry Davis | .08 |
| 324 | Dan Schatzeder | .04 |
| 325 | Juan Beniquez | .04 |
| 326 | Kent Tekulve | .04 |
| 327 | Mike Pagliarulo | .12 |
| 328 | Pete O'Brien | .12 |
| 329 | Kirby Puckett | 2.50 |
| 330 | Rick Sutcliffe | .12 |
| 331 | Alan Ashby | .04 |
| 332 | Darryl Motley | .04 |
| 333 | Tom Henke | .25 |

| NO. | PLAYER | MINT |
|---|---|---|
| 334 | Ken Oberkfell | .04 |
| 335 | Don Sutton | .20 |
| 336 | Indians Leaders: | .08 |
| | Andre Thornton | |
| 337 | Darnell Coles | .04 |
| 338 | Jorge Bell | .30 |
| 339 | Bruce Berenyi | .04 |
| 340 | Cal Ripken | 1.50 |
| 341 | Frank Williams | .04 |
| 342 | Gary Redus | .04 |
| 343 | Carlos Diaz | .04 |
| 344 | Jim Wohlford | .04 |
| 345 | Donnie Moore | .04 |
| 346 | Bryan Little | .04 |
| 347 | Teddy Higuera (R) | .30 |
| 348 | Cliff Johnson | .04 |
| 349 | Mark Clear | .04 |
| 350 | Jack Clark | .15 |
| 351 | Chuck Tanner (Mgr.) | .08 |
| | Pirates Checklist | |
| 352 | Harry Spilman | .04 |
| 353 | Keith Atherton | .04 |
| 354 | Tony Bernazard | .04 |
| 355 | Lee Smith | .20 |
| 356 | Mickey Hatcher | .04 |
| 357 | Ed VandeBerg | .04 |
| 358 | Rick Dempsey | .04 |
| 359 | Mike LaCoss | .04 |
| 360 | Lloyd Moseby | .15 |
| 361 | Shane Rawley | .04 |
| 362 | Tom Paciorek | .04 |
| 363 | Terry Forster | .06 |
| 364 | Reid Nichols | .04 |
| 365 | Mike Flanagan | .06 |
| 366 | Reds Leaders: | .10 |
| | Dave Concepcion | |
| 367 | Aurelio Lopez | .04 |
| 368 | Greg Brock | .06 |
| 369 | Al Holland | .04 |
| 370 | Vince Coleman (R) | 2.50 |
| 371 | Bill Stein | .04 |
| 372 | Ben Ogilvie | .06 |
| 373 | Urbano Lugo | .15 |
| 374 | Terry Francona | .06 |
| 375 | Rich Gedman | .06 |
| 376 | Bill Dawley | .04 |
| 377 | Joe Carter | .50 |
| 378 | Bruce Bochte | .04 |
| 379 | Bobby Meacham | .04 |
| 380 | LaMarr Hoyt | .10 |
| 381 | Ray Miller (Mgr.) | .08 |
| | Twins Checklist | |
| 382 | Ivan Calderon (R) | .75 |
| 383 | Chris Brown (R) | .20 |
| 384 | Steve Trout | .04 |
| 385 | Cecil Cooper | .15 |
| 386 | Cecil Fielder (R) | 7.00 |
| 387 | Steve Kemp | .06 |
| 388 | Dickie Noles | .04 |
| 389 | Glenn Davis | 1.00 |
| 390 | Tom Seaver | .40 |
| 391 | Julio Franco | .25 |
| 392 | John Russell | .08 |
| 393 | Chris Pittaro | .15 |
| 394 | Checklist No. 3 | .08 |
| 395 | Scott Garrelts | .15 |
| 396 | Red Sox Leaders: | .08 |
| | Dwight Evans | |
| 397 | Steve Buechele (R) | .30 |
| 398 | Earnie Riles (R) | .12 |
| 399 | Bill Swift | .04 |
| 400 | Rod Carew | .40 |
| 401 | Turn Back the Clock: | .15 |
| | F. Valenzuela (1981) | |
| 402 | Turn Back the Clock: | .15 |
| | Tom Seaver (1976) | |
| 403 | Turn Back the Clock: | .15 |
| | Willie Mays (1971) | |
| 404 | Turn Back the Clock: | .15 |
| | Frank Robinson (1966) | |
| 405 | Turn Back the Clock: | .15 |
| | Roger Maris (1961) | |
| 406 | Scott Sanderson | .04 |
| 407 | Sal Butera | .04 |
| 408 | Dave Smith | .04 |

# 1986 Topps (Continued)

| NO. PLAYER | MINT |
|---|---|
| 409 Paul Runge (R) | .15 |
| 410 Dave Kingman | .10 |
| 411 Sparky Anderson (Mgr.) | .10 |
| Tigers Checklist | |
| 412 Jim Clancy | .04 |
| 413 Tim Flannery | .04 |
| 414 Tom Gorman | .04 |
| 415 Hal McRae | .04 |
| 416 Denny Martinez | .04 |
| 417 R.J. Reynolds | .04 |
| 418 Alan Knicely | .04 |
| 419 Frank Wills | .15 |
| 420 Von Hayes | .15 |
| 421 Dave Palmer | .04 |
| 422 Mike Jorgensen | .04 |
| 423 Dan Spillner | .04 |
| 424 Rick Miller | .04 |
| 425 Larry McWilliams | .04 |
| 426 Brewers Leaders: | .04 |
| Charlie Moore | |
| 427 Joe Cowley | .04 |
| 428 Max Venable | .04 |
| 429 Greg Booker | .04 |
| 430 Kent Hrbek | .15 |
| 431 George Frazier | .04 |
| 432 Mark Bailey | .04 |
| 433 Chirs Codiroli | .04 |
| 434 Curt Wilkerson | .04 |
| 435 Bill Caudill | .04 |
| 436 Doug Flynn | .04 |
| 437 Rick Mahler | .04 |
| 438 Clint Hurdle | .04 |
| 439 Rick Honeycutt | .04 |
| 440 Alvin Davis | .15 |
| 441 Whitey Herzog (Mgr.) | .10 |
| Cardinals Checklist | |
| 442 Ron Robinson | .20 |
| 443 Bill Buckner | .08 |
| 444 Alex Trevino | .04 |
| 445 Bert Blyleven | .10 |
| 446 Lenn Sakata | .04 |
| 447 Jerry Don Gleaton | .04 |
| 448 Herm Winningham | .15 |
| 449 Rod Scurry | .04 |
| 450 Graig Nettles | .15 |
| 451 Mark Brown | .15 |
| 452 Bob Clark | .04 |
| 453 Steve Jeltz | .10 |
| 454 Burt Hooton | .04 |
| 455 Willie Randolph | .08 |
| 456 Braves Leaders: | .15 |
| Dale Murphy | |
| 457 Mickey Tettleton | .35 |
| 458 Kevin Bass | .04 |
| 459 Luis Leal | .04 |
| 460 Leon Durham | .15 |
| 461 Walt Terrell | .04 |
| 462 Domingo Ramos | .04 |
| 463 Jim Gott | .04 |
| 464 Ruppert Jones | .04 |
| 465 Jesse Orosco | .04 |
| 466 Tom Foley | .04 |
| 467 Bob James | .04 |
| 468 Mike Scioscia | .04 |
| 469 Storm Davis | .08 |
| 470 Bill Madlock | .15 |
| 471 Bobby Cox (Mgr.) | .08 |
| Blue Jays Checklist | |
| 472 Joe Hesketh | .10 |
| 473 Mark Brouhard | .04 |
| 474 John Tudor | .15 |
| 475 Juan Samuel | .15 |
| 476 Ron Mathis | .12 |
| 477 Mike Easler | .04 |
| 478 Andy Hawkins | .08 |
| 479 Bob Melvin | .12 |
| 480 Oddibe McDowell | .20 |
| 481 Scott Bradley | .10 |
| 482 Rick Lysander | .04 |
| 483 George Vukovich | .04 |
| 484 Donnie Hill | .04 |
| 485 Gary Matthews | .06 |
| 486 Angels Leaders: | .08 |
| Bob Grich | |
| 487 Bret Saberhagen | .60 |

| NO. PLAYER | MINT |
|---|---|
| 488 Lou Thornton | .12 |
| 489 Jim Winn | .04 |
| 490 Jeff Leonard | .04 |
| 491 Pascual Perez | .04 |
| 492 Kelvin Chapman | .04 |
| 493 Gene Nelson | .04 |
| 494 Garry Roenicke | .04 |
| 495 Mark Langston | .25 |
| 496 Jay Johnstone | .04 |
| 497 John Stuper | .04 |
| 498 Tito Landrum | .04 |
| 499 Bob Gibson | .04 |
| 500 Rickey Henderson | 1.00 |
| 501 Dave Johnson (Mgr.) | .12 |
| Mets Checklist | |
| 502 Glen Cook | .12 |
| 503 Mike Fitzgerald | .04 |
| 504 Denny Walling | .04 |
| 505 Jerry Koosman | .08 |
| 506 Bill Russell | .04 |
| 507 Steve Ontiveros (R) | .15 |
| 508 Alan Wiggins | .08 |
| 509 Ernie Camacho | .04 |
| 510 Wade Boggs | 1.00 |
| 511 Ed Nunez | .04 |
| 512 Thad Bosley | .04 |
| 513 Ron Washington | .04 |
| 514 Mike Jones | .04 |
| 515 Darrell Evans | .08 |
| 516 Giants Leaders: | .08 |
| Greg Minton | |
| 517 Milt Thompson (R) | .20 |
| 518 Buck Martinez | .04 |
| 519 Danny Darwin | .04 |
| 520 Keith Hernandez | .15 |
| 521 Nate Snell | .12 |
| 522 Bob Bailor | .04 |
| 523 Joe Price | .04 |
| 524 Darrell Miller | .08 |
| 525 Marvell Wynne | .04 |
| 526 Charlie Lea | .04 |
| 527 Checklist No. 4 | .08 |
| 528 Terry Pendleton | .30 |
| 529 Marc Sullivan | .12 |
| 530 Rich Gossage | .15 |
| 531 Tony LaRussa (Mgr.) | .08 |
| White Sox Checklist | |
| 532 Don Carman (R) | .15 |
| 533 Billy Sample | .04 |
| 534 Jeff Calhoun | .12 |
| 535 Toby Harrah | .04 |
| 536 Jose Rijo | .15 |
| 537 Mark Salas | .15 |
| 538 Dennis Eckersley | .20 |
| 539 Glenn Hubbard | .04 |
| 540 Dan Petry | .15 |
| 541 Jorge Orta | .04 |
| 542 Don Schulze | .04 |
| 543 Jerry Narron | .04 |
| 544 Eddie Milner | .04 |
| 545 Jimmy Key | .12 |
| 546 Mariners Leaders: | .06 |
| Dave Henderson | |
| 547 Roger McDowell (R) | .15 |
| 548 Mike Young | .20 |
| 549 Bob Welch | .10 |
| 550 Tom Herr | .10 |
| 551 Dave LaPoint | .04 |
| 552 Marc Hill | .04 |
| 553 Jim Morrison | .04 |
| 554 Paul Householder | .04 |
| 555 Hubie Brooks | .08 |
| 556 John Denny | .06 |
| 557 Gerald Perry | .15 |
| 558 Tim Stoddard | .04 |
| 559 Tommy Dunbar | .04 |
| 560 Dave Righetti | .10 |
| 561 Bob Lillis (Mgr.) | .06 |
| Astros Checklist | |
| 562 Joe Beckwith | .04 |
| 563 Alejandro Sanchez | .08 |
| 564 Warren Brusstar | .04 |
| 565 Tom Brunansky | .12 |
| 566 Alfredo Griffin | .04 |
| 567 Jeff Barkley | .12 |

| NO. PLAYER | MINT |
|---|---|
| 568 Donnie Scott | .04 |
| 569 Jim Acker | .04 |
| 570 Rusty Staub | .08 |
| 571 Mike Jeffcoat | .04 |
| 572 Paul Zuvella | .08 |
| 573 Tom Hume | .04 |
| 574 Ron Kittle | .10 |
| 575 Mike Boddicker | .10 |
| 576 Expos Leaders: | .12 |
| Andre Dawson | |
| 577 Jerry Reuss | .06 |
| 578 Lee Mazzilli | .04 |
| 579 Jim Slaton | .04 |
| 580 Willie McGee | .20 |
| 581 Bruce Hurst | .04 |
| 582 Jim Gantner | .04 |
| 583 Al Bumbry | .04 |
| 584 Brian Fisher (R) | .20 |
| 585 Garry Maddox | .04 |
| 586 Greg Harris | .04 |
| 587 Rafael Santana | .04 |
| 588 Steve Lake | .04 |
| 589 Sid Bream | .04 |
| 590 Bob Knepper | .04 |
| 591 Jackie Moore (Mgr.) | .08 |
| A's Checklist | |
| 592 Frank Tanana | .06 |
| 593 Jesse Barfield | .15 |
| 594 Chris Bando | .04 |
| 595 Dave Parker | .25 |
| 596 Onix Concepcion | .04 |
| 597 Sammy Stewart | .04 |
| 598 Jim Presley | .25 |
| 599 Rick Aguilera (R) | .35 |
| 600 Dale Murphy | .25 |
| 601 Gary Lucas | .04 |
| 602 Mariano Duncan (R) | .20 |
| 603 Bill Laskey | .04 |
| 604 Gary Pettis | .08 |
| 605 Dennis Boyd | .06 |
| 606 Royals Leaders: | .10 |
| Hal McRae | |
| 607 Ken Dayley | .04 |
| 608 Bruce Bochy | .04 |
| 609 Barbaro Garbey | .04 |
| 610 Ron Guidry | .15 |
| 611 Gary Woods | .04 |
| 612 Richard Dotson | .06 |
| 613 Roy Smalley | .04 |
| 614 Rick Waits | .04 |
| 615 Johnny Ray | .08 |
| 616 Glenn Brummer | .04 |
| 617 Lonnie Smith | .08 |
| 618 Jim Pankovits | .06 |
| 619 Danny Heep | .04 |
| 620 Bruce Sutter | .15 |
| 621 John Felske (Mgr.) | .08 |
| Phillies Checklist | |
| 622 Gary Lavelle | .04 |
| 623 Floyd Rayford | .04 |
| 624 Steve McCatty | .04 |
| 625 Bob Brenly | .04 |
| 626 Roy Thomas | .04 |
| 627 Ron Oester | .04 |
| 628 Kirk McCaskill (R) | .15 |
| 629 Mitch Webster (R) | .12 |
| 630 Fernando Valenzuela | .15 |
| 631 Steve Braun | .04 |
| 632 Dave Von Ohlen | .04 |
| 633 Jackie Gutierrez | .04 |
| 634 Roy Lee Jackson | .04 |
| 635 Jason Thompson | .06 |
| 636 Cubs Leaders: | .10 |
| Lee Smith | |
| 637 Rudy Law | .04 |
| 638 John Butcher | .04 |
| 639 Bo Diaz | .04 |
| 640 Jose Cruz | .08 |
| 641 Wayne Tolleson | .04 |
| 642 Ray Searage | .04 |
| 643 Tom Brookens | .04 |
| 644 Mark Gubicza | .12 |
| 645 Dusty Baker | .06 |
| 646 Mike Moore | .04 |
| 647 Mel Hall | .06 |

| NO. PLAYER | MINT |
|---|---|
| 648 Steve Bedrosian | .10 |
| 649 Ronn Reynolds | .10 |
| 650 Dave Stieb | .15 |
| 651 Billy Martin (Mgr.) | .10 |
| Yankees Checklist | |
| 652 Tom Browning | .25 |
| 653 Jim Dwyer | .04 |
| 654 Ken Howell | .10 |
| 655 Manny Trillo | .04 |
| 656 Brian Harper | .08 |
| 657 Juan Agosto | .04 |
| 658 Rob Wilfong | .04 |
| 659 Checklist No. 5 | .08 |
| 660 Steve Garvey | .30 |
| 661 Roger Clemens | 4.00 |
| 662 Bill Schroeder | .04 |
| 663 Neil Allen | .04 |
| 664 Tim Corcoran | .04 |
| 665 Alejandro Pena | .06 |
| 666 Rangers Leaders: | .06 |
| Charlie Hough | |
| 667 Tim Tuefel | .08 |
| 668 Cecilio Guante | .04 |
| 669 Ron Cey | .10 |
| 670 Willie Hernandez | .12 |
| 671 Lynn Jones | .04 |
| 672 Rob Picciolo | .04 |
| 673 Ernie Whitt | .04 |
| 674 Pat Tabler | .04 |
| 675 Claudell Washington | .06 |
| 676 Matt Young | .04 |
| 677 Nick Esasky | .06 |
| 678 Dan Gladden | .06 |
| 679 Britt Burns | .06 |
| 680 George Foster | .15 |
| 681 Dick Williams (Mgr.) | .08 |
| Padres Checklist | |
| 682 Junior Ortiz | .04 |
| 683 Andy Van Slyke | .15 |
| 684 Bob McClure | .04 |
| 685 Tim Wallach | .08 |
| 686 Jeff Stone | .06 |
| 687 Mike Trujillo | .12 |
| 688 Larry Herndon | .04 |
| 689 Dave Stewart | .25 |
| 690 Ryne Sandberg | 2.00 |
| 691 Mike Madden | .04 |
| 692 Dale Berra | .04 |
| 693 Tom Tellmann | .04 |
| 694 Garth Iorg | .04 |
| 695 Mike Smithson | .04 |
| 696 Dodgers Leaders: | .10 |
| Bill Russell | |
| 697 Bud Black | .04 |
| 698 Brad Komminsk | .06 |
| 699 Pat Corrales (Mgr.) | .08 |
| Indians Checklist | |
| 700 Reggie Jackson | .40 |
| 701 Keith Hernandez (AS) | .15 |
| 702 Tom Herr (AS) | .08 |
| 703 Tim Wallach (AS) | .08 |
| 704 Ozzie Smith (AS) | .15 |
| 705 Dale Murphy (AS) | .20 |
| 706 Pedro Guerrero (AS) | .15 |
| 707 Willie McGee (AS) | .15 |
| 708 Gary Carter (AS) | .15 |
| 709 Dwight Gooden (AS) | .35 |
| 710 John Tudor (AS) | .08 |
| 711 Jeff Reardon (AS) | .08 |
| 712 Don Mattingly (AS) | .35 |
| 713 Damaso Garcia (AS) | .08 |
| 714 George Brett (AS) | .25 |
| 715 Cal Ripken (AS) | .30 |
| 716 Rickey Henderson (AS) | .30 |
| 717 Dave Winfield (AS) | .25 |
| 718 Jorge Bell (AS) | .15 |
| 719 Carlton Fisk (AS) | .10 |
| 720 Bret Saberhagen (AS) | .20 |
| 721 Ron Guidry (AS) | .10 |
| 722 Dan Quisenberry (AS) | .10 |
| 723 Marty Bystrom | .04 |
| 724 Tim Hulett | .08 |
| 725 Mario Soto | .08 |
| 726 Orioles Leaders: | .08 |
| Rick Dempsey | |

| NO. | PLAYER | MINT |
|-----|--------|------|
| 727 | David Green | .04 |
| 728 | Mike Marshall | .15 |
| 729 | Jim Beattie | .04 |
| 730 | Ozzie Smith | .35 |
| 731 | Don Robinson | .04 |
| 732 | Floyd Youmans (R) | .25 |
| 733 | Ron Romanick | .06 |
| 734 | Marty Barrett | .15 |
| 735 | Dave Dravecky | .04 |
| 736 | Glenn Wilson | .08 |
| 737 | Pete Vuckovich | .04 |
| 738 | Andre Robertson | .04 |
| 739 | Dave Rozema | .04 |
| 740 | Lance Parrish | .15 |
| 741 | Pete Rose (Mgr.) | .40 |
|     | Reds Checklist | |
| 742 | Frank Viola | .15 |
| 743 | Pat Sheridan | .04 |
| 744 | Lary Sorensen | .04 |
| 745 | Willie Upshaw | .08 |
| 746 | Denny Gonzalez | .08 |
| 747 | Rick Cerone | .04 |

| NO. | PLAYER | MINT |
|-----|--------|------|
| 748 | Steve Henderson | .04 |
| 749 | Ed Jurak | .04 |
| 750 | Gorman Thomas | .08 |
| 751 | Howard Johnson | .30 |
| 752 | Mike Krukow | .04 |
| 753 | Dan Ford | .04 |
| 754 | Pat Clements (R) | .12 |
| 755 | Harold Baines | .20 |
| 756 | Pirates Leaders: | .06 |
|     | Rick Rhoden | |
| 757 | Darrell Porter | .04 |
| 758 | Dave Anderson | .04 |
| 759 | Moose Haas | .04 |
| 760 | Andre Dawson | .40 |
| 761 | Don Slaught | .04 |
| 762 | Eric Show | .04 |
| 763 | Terry Puhl | .04 |
| 764 | Kevin Gross | .04 |
| 765 | Don Baylor | .15 |
| 766 | Rick Langford | .04 |
| 767 | Jody Davis | .08 |
| 768 | Vern Ruhle | .04 |

| NO. | PLAYER | MINT |
|-----|--------|------|
| 769 | Harold Reynolds (R) | .50 |
| 770 | Vida Blue | .08 |
| 771 | John McNamara (Mgr.) | .08 |
|     | Red Sox Checklist | |
| 772 | Brian Downing | .04 |
| 773 | Greg Pryor | .04 |
| 774 | Terry Leach | .04 |
| 775 | Al Oliver | .10 |
| 776 | Gene Garber | .04 |
| 777 | Wayne Krenchicki | .04 |
| 778 | Jerry Hairston | .04 |
| 779 | Rick Reuschel | .04 |
| 780 | Robin Yount | .30 |
| 781 | Joe Nolan | .04 |
| 782 | Ken Landreaux | .04 |
| 783 | Ricky Horton | .04 |
| 784 | Alan Bannister | .04 |
| 785 | Bob Stanley | .04 |
| 786 | Twins Leaders: | .06 |
|     | Mickey Hatcher | |
| 787 | Vance Law | .04 |
| 788 | Marty Castillo | .04 |

| NO. | PLAYER | MINT |
|-----|--------|------|
| 789 | Kurt Bevacqua | .04 |
| 790 | Phil Niekro | .15 |
| 791 | Checklist No. 6 | .08 |
| 792 | Charles Hudson | .06 |

# 1986 Topps Traded . . . Complete Set of 132 Cards—Value $30.00

Updates the main 1986 card set with players who changed teams during the season, and rookies. Features the first Topps card of Jose Canseco, Will Clark, Kevin Mitchell and Bo Jackson. The set was packaged in a printed box and distributed exclusively through card hobby dealers. A "Tiffany" version of the set was also issued.

JOSE CANSECO

WILL CLARK

KEVIN MITCHELL

BO JACKSON

WALLY JOYNER

| NO. | PLAYER | MINT |
|-----|--------|------|
| 1T | Andy Allanson | .15 |
| 2T | Neil Allen | .06 |
| 3T | Joaquin Andujar | .06 |
| 4T | Paul Assenmacher | .15 |
| 5T | Scott Bailes | .15 |
| 6T | Don Baylor | .10 |
| 7T | Steve Bedrosian | .10 |
| 8T | Juan Beniquez | .06 |
| 9T | Juan Berenguer | .06 |
| 10T | Mike Bielecki | .15 |
| 11T | Barry Bonds (RR) | 4.00 |
| 12T | Bobby Bonilla (RR) | 4.00 |
| 13T | Juan Bonilla | .06 |
| 14T | Rich Bordi | .06 |
| 15T | Steve Boros | .06 |
| 16T | Rick Burleson | .06 |
| 17T | Bill Campbell | .06 |
| 18T | Tom Candiotti | .15 |
| 19T | John Cangelosi | .15 |
| 20T | Jose Canseco (RR) | 9.00 |
| 21T | Carmen Castillo | .10 |
| 22T | Rick Cerone | .06 |
| 23T | John Cerutti | .10 |
| 24T | Will Clark (RR) | 9.00 |
| 25T | Mark Clear | .06 |
| 26T | Darrell Coles | .08 |
| 27T | Dave Collins | .06 |
| 28T | Tim Conroy | .06 |
| 29T | Joe Cowley | .10 |
| 30T | Joel Davis | .10 |
| 31T | Rob Deer | .20 |
| 32T | John Denny | .06 |
| 33T | Mike Easler | .06 |

| NO. | PLAYER | MINT |
|-----|--------|------|
| 34T | Mark Eichhorn | .15 |
| 35T | Steve Farr | .06 |
| 36T | Scott Fletcher | .06 |
| 37T | Terry Forster | .06 |
| 38T | Terry Francona | .06 |
| 39T | Jim Fregosi | .06 |
| 40T | Andres Galarraga (RR) | .50 |
| 41T | Ken Griffey | .06 |
| 42T | Bill Gullickson | .06 |
| 43T | Jose Guzman | .25 |
| 44T | Moose Haas | .06 |
| 45T | Billy Hatcher | .20 |
| 46T | Mike Heath | .06 |
| 47T | Tom Hume | .06 |
| 48T | Pete Incaviglia (RR) | .35 |
| 49T | Dane Iorg | .06 |
| 50T | Bo Jackson (RR) | 7.00 |
| 51T | Wa. Joyner (RR) | 1.25 |
| 52T | Charlie Kerfeld | .15 |
| 53T | Eric King | .12 |
| 54T | Bob Kipper | .06 |
| 55T | Wayne Krenchicki | .06 |
| 56T | John Kruk. (RR) | .40 |
| 57T | Mike LaCoss | .06 |
| 58T | Pete Ladd | .06 |
| 59T | Mike Laga | .06 |
| 60T | Hal Lanier | .06 |
| 61T | Dave LaPoint | .06 |
| 62T | Rudy Law | .06 |
| 63T | Rick Leach | .06 |
| 64T | Tim Leary | .06 |
| 65T | Dennis Leonard | .06 |
| 66T | Jim Leyland | .06 |

| NO. | PLAYER | MINT |
|-----|--------|------|
| 67T | Steve Lyons | .06 |
| 68T | Mickey Mahler | .06 |
| 69T | Candy Maldonado | .15 |
| 70T | Roger Mason | .10 |
| 71T | Bob McClure | .06 |
| 72T | Andy McGaffigan | .06 |
| 73T | Gene Michael | .06 |
| 74T | Kevin Mitchell (RR) | 3.00 |
| 75T | Omar Moreno | .06 |
| 76T | Jerry Mumphrey | .06 |
| 77T | Phil Niekro | .30 |
| 78T | Randy Nieman | .06 |
| 79T | Juan Nieves | .20 |
| 80T | Otis Nixon | .25 |
| 81T | Bob Ojeda | .08 |
| 82T | Jose Oquendo | .10 |
| 83T | Tom Paciorek | .06 |
| 84T | Dave Palmer | .06 |
| 85T | Frank Pastore | .06 |
| 86T | Lou Piniella | .08 |
| 87T | Dan Plesac | .20 |
| 88T | Darrell Porter | .06 |
| 89T | Rey Quinones | .20 |
| 90T | Gary Redus | .06 |
| 91T | Bip Roberts | .25 |
| 92T | Billy Jo Robidoux | .15 |
| 93T | Jeff Robinson | .06 |
| 94T | Gary Roenicke | .06 |
| 95T | Ed Romero | .06 |
| 96T | Argenis Salazar | .06 |
| 97T | Joe Sambito | .06 |
| 98T | Billy Sample | .06 |
| 99T | Dave Schmidt | .06 |

| NO. | PLAYER | MINT |
|-----|--------|------|
| 100T | Ken Schrom | .06 |
| 101T | Tom Seaver | .60 |
| 102T | Ted Simmons | .06 |
| 103T | Sammy Stewart | .06 |
| 104T | Kurt Stillwell | .20 |
| 105T | Franklin Stubbs | .30 |
| 106T | Dale Sveum | .20 |
| 107T | Chuck Tanner | .06 |
| 108T | Danny Tartabull | .60 |
| 109T | Tim Teufel | .06 |
| 110T | Bob Tewksbury | .15 |
| 111T | Andres Thomas | .20 |
| 112T | Milt Thomson | .06 |
| 113T | Robby Thompson | .35 |
| 114T | Jay Tibbs | .06 |
| 115T | Wayne Tolleson | .06 |
| 116T | Alex Trevino | .06 |
| 117T | Manny Trillo | .06 |
| 118T | Ed VandeBerg | .06 |
| 119T | Ozzie Virgil | .06 |
| 120T | Bob Walk | .06 |
| 121T | Gene Walter | .10 |
| 122T | C. Washington | .06 |
| 123T | Bill Wegman | .15 |
| 124T | Dick Williams | .06 |
| 125T | Mitch Williams | .20 |
| 126T | Bobby Witt (RR) | .35 |
| 127T | Todd Worrell (RR) | .15 |
| 128T | George Wright | .06 |
| 129T | Ricky Wright | .12 |
| 130T | Steve Yeager | .06 |
| 131T | Paul Zuvella | .06 |
| 132T | Checklist | .06 |

# 1987 Topps.... Complete Set of 792 Cards—Value $45.00

Features the rookie cards of Will Clark, Bo Jackson, Ruben Sierra and Mike Greenwell. A "Tiffany" version of the set was also issued.

| NO. PLAYER | MINT | NO. PLAYER | MINT | NO. PLAYER | MINT | NO. PLAYER | MINT |
|---|---|---|---|---|---|---|---|
| 1 '86 Record: Clemens | .40 | 67 Bill Swift | .04 | 133 Jose Oquendo | .04 | 199 Mariano Duncan | .10 |
| 2 '86 Record: Deshaies | .08 | 68 Tony LaRussa (Mgr.) | .04 | 134 Rich Yett (R) | .15 | 200 Pete Rose | .40 |
| 3 '86 Record: Evans | .10 | 69 Lonnie Smith | .04 | 135 Mike Easler | .04 | 201 John Cangelosi (R) | .20 |
| 4 '86 Record: Lopes | .10 | 70 Charlie Hough | .04 | 136 Ron Romanick | .04 | 202 Ricky Wright | .04 |
| 5 '86 Record: Righetti | .08 | 71 Mike Aldrete (R) | .12 | 137 Jerry Willard | .04 | 203 Mike Kingery (R) | .20 |
| 6 '86 Record: Sierra | .25 | 72 Walt Terrell | .04 | 138 Roy Lee Jackson | .04 | 204 Sammy Stewart | .04 |
| 7 '86 Record: Worrell | .10 | 73 Dave Anderson | .04 | 139 Devon White (R) | .40 | 205 Graig Nettles | .08 |
| 8 Terry Pendleton | .12 | 74 Dan Pasqua | .12 | 140 Bret Saberhagen | .20 | 206 Twins Leaders | .06 |
| 9 Jay Tibbs | .04 | 75 Ron Darling | .10 | 141 Herm Winningham | .04 | 207 George Frazier | .04 |
| 10 Cecil Cooper | .08 | 76 Rafael Ramirez | .04 | 142 Rick Sutcliffe | .12 | 208 John Shelby | .04 |
| 11 Indians Leaders | .06 | 77 Bryan Oelkers | .04 | 143 Steve Boros (Mgr.) | .04 | 209 Rick Schu | .04 |
| 12 Jeff Sellers (R) | .15 | 78 Tom Foley | .04 | 144 Mike Scioscia | .04 | 210 Lloyd Moseby | .12 |
| 13 Nick Esasky | .04 | 79 Juan Nieves | .12 | 145 Charlie Kerfeld | .15 | 211 John Morris | .04 |
| 14 Dave Stewart | .20 | 80 Wally Joyner (R) | .75 | 146 Tracy Jones (R) | .12 | 212 Mike Fitzgerald | .04 |
| 15 Claudell Washington | .04 | 81 Padres Leaders | .06 | 147 Randy Niemann | .04 | 213 Randy Myers (R) | .20 |
| 16 Pat Clements | .04 | 82 Rob Murphy (R) | .12 | 148 Dave Collins | .04 | 214 Omar Moreno | .04 |
| 17 Pete O'Brien | .10 | 83 Mike Davis | .04 | 149 Ray Searage | .04 | 215 Mark Langston | .15 |
| 18 Dick Howser (Mgr.) | .04 | 84 Steve Lake | .04 | 150 Wade Boggs | .40 | 216 B.J. Surhoff (R) | .15 |
| 19 Matt Young | .04 | 85 Kevin Bass | .04 | 151 Mike LaCoss | .04 | 217 Chris Codiroli | .04 |
| 20 Gary Carter | .20 | 86 Nate Snell | .04 | 152 Toby Harrah | .04 | 218 S. Anderson (Mgr.) | .04 |
| 21 Mark Davis | .04 | 87 Mark Salas | .04 | 153 Duane Ward (R) | .20 | 219 Cecillo Guante | .04 |
| 22 Doug DeCinces | .06 | 88 Ed Wojna | .04 | 154 Tom O'Malley | .04 | 220 Joe Carter | .25 |
| 23 Lee Smith | .15 | 89 Ozzie Guillen | .15 | 155 Eddie Whitson | .04 | 221 Vern Ruhle | .04 |
| 24 Tony Walker (R) | .15 | 90 Dave Stieb | .10 | 156 Mariners Leaders | .06 | 222 Denny Walling | .04 |
| 25 Bert Blyleven | .08 | 91 Harold Reynolds | .08 | 157 Danny Darwin | .04 | 223 Charlie Leibrandt | .04 |
| 26 C. Brock | .04 | 92 U. Lugo | .05 | 158 Tim Teufel | .04 | 224 Wayne Tolleson | .04 |
| 27 Joe Cowley | .04 | 92 U. Lugo (no t.m.) | .30 | 159 Ed Olwine (R) | .15 | 225 Mike Smithson | .04 |
| 28 Rick Dempsey | .04 | 93 Jim Leyland (Mgr.) | .04 | 160 Julio Franco | .15 | 226 Max Venable | .04 |
| 29 Jimmy Key | .15 | 94 Calvin Schiraldi | .08 | 161 Steve Ontiveros | .04 | 227 Jamie Moyer (R) | .15 |
| 30 Tim Raines | .20 | 95 Oddibe McDowell | .10 | 162 Mike LaValliere (R) | .15 | 228 Curt Wilkerson | .04 |
| 31 Braves Leaders | .06 | 96 Frank Williams | .04 | 163 Kevin Gross | .04 | 229 Mike Birkbeck (R) | .15 |
| 32 Tim Leary | .04 | 97 Glenn Wilson | .08 | 164 Sammy Khalifa | .04 | 230 Don Baylor | .12 |
| 33 Andy Van Slyke | .12 | 98 Bill Scherrer | .04 | 165 Jeff Reardon | .12 | 231 Giants Leaders | .06 |
| 34 Jose Rijo | .10 | 99 Darryl Motley | .04 | 166 Bob Boone | .04 | 232 Reggie Williams (R) | .12 |
| 35 Sid Bream | .04 | 100 Steve Garvey | .25 | 167 Jim Deshaies (R) | .15 | 233 Russ Morman (R) | .12 |
| 36 Eric King (R) | .15 | 101 Carl Willis (R) | .15 | 168 Lou Piniella (Mgr.) | .06 | 234 Pat Sheridan | .04 |
| 37 Marvell Wynne | .04 | 102 Paul Zuvella | .04 | 169 Ron Washington | .04 | 235 Alvin Davis | .12 |
| 38 Dennis Leonard | .04 | 103 Rick Aguilera | .04 | 170 Bo Jackson (R) | 3.00 | 236 Tommy John | .12 |
| 39 Marty Barrett | .06 | 104 Billy Sample | .04 | 171 Chuck Cary (R) | .15 | 237 Jim Morrison | .04 |
| 40 Dave Righetti | .10 | 105 Floyd Youmans | .15 | 172 Ron Oester | .04 | 238 Bill Krueger | .04 |
| 41 Bo Diaz | .04 | 106 Blue Jays Leaders | .06 | 173 Alex Trevino | .04 | 239 Juan Espino | .04 |
| 42 Gary Redus | .04 | 107 John Butcher | .04 | 174 Henry Cotto | .04 | 240 Steve Balboni | .08 |
| 43 Gene Michael (Mgr.) | .04 | 108 Jim Gantner | .04 | 175 Bob Stanley | .04 | 241 Danny Heep | .04 |
| 44 Greg Harris | .04 | 109 R. J. Reynolds | .04 | 176 Steve Buechele | .04 | 242 Rick Mahler | .04 |
| 45 Jim Presley | .15 | 110 John Tudor | .12 | 177 Keith Moreland | .04 | 243 Whitey Herzog (Mgr.) | .04 |
| 46 Danny Gladden | .04 | 111 Alfredo Griffin | .04 | 178 Cecil Fielder | 1.00 | 244 Dickie Noles | .04 |
| 47 Dennis Powell | .12 | 112 Alan Ashby | .04 | 179 Bill Wegman | .04 | 245 Willie Upshaw | .04 |
| 48 Wally Backman | .04 | 113 Neil Allen | .04 | 180 Chris Brown | .10 | 246 Jim Dwyer | .04 |
| 49 Terry Harper | .04 | 114 Billy Beane | .08 | 181 Cardinals Leaders | .06 | 247 Jeff Reed | .04 |
| 50 Dave Smith | .04 | 115 Donnie Moore | .04 | 182 Lee Lacy | .04 | 248 Gene Walter | .10 |
| 51 M. Hall | .04 | 116 Bill Russell | .04 | 183 Andy Hawkins | .04 | 249 Jim Pankovits | .04 |
| 52 Keith Atherton | .04 | 117 Jim Beattie | .04 | 184 Bobby Bonilla (R) | 2.50 | 250 Teddy Higuera | .10 |
| 53 Ruppert Jones | .04 | 118 Bobby Valentine (Mgr.) | .04 | 185 Roger McDowell | .10 | 251 Rob Wilfong | .04 |
| 54 Bill Dawley | .04 | 119 Ron Robinson | .04 | 186 Bruce Benedict | .04 | 252 Denny Martinez | .04 |
| 55 Tim Wallach | .08 | 120 Eddie Murray | .30 | 187 Mark Huismann | .04 | 253 Eddie Milner | .04 |
| 56 Brewers Leaders | .06 | 121 Kevin Romine (R) | .15 | 188 Tony Phillips | .04 | 254 Bob Tewksbury (R) | .15 |
| 57 Scott Nielsen (R) | .15 | 122 Jim Clancy | .04 | 189 Joe Hesketh | .04 | 255 Juan Samuel | .15 |
| 58 Thad Bosley | .04 | 123 John Kruk (R) | .30 | 190 Jim Sundberg | .04 | 256 Royals Leaders | .06 |
| 59 Ken Dayley | .04 | 124 Ray Fontenot | .04 | 191 Charles Hudson | .04 | 257 Bob Forsch | .04 |
| 60 Tony Pena | .10 | 125 Bob Brenly | .04 | 192 Cory Snyder | .15 | 258 Steve Yeager | .04 |
| 61 Bobby Thigpen (R) | .50 | 126 Mike Loynd (R) | .15 | 193 Roger Craig (Mgr.) | .04 | 259 Mike Greenwell (R) | 1.50 |
| 62 Bobby Meacham | .04 | 127 Vance Law | .04 | 194 Kirk McCaskill | .10 | 260 Vida Blue | .12 |
| 63 Fred Tollver | .12 | 128 Checklist: 1-132 | .06 | 195 Mike Pagliarulo | .12 | 261 Ruben Sierra (R) | 2.50 |
| 64 Harry Spilman | .04 | 129 Rick Cerone | .04 | 196 Randy O'Neal | .04 | 262 Jim Winn | .04 |
| 65 Tom Browning | .10 | 130 Dwight Gooden | .35 | 197 Mark Bailey | .04 | 263 Stan Javier | .08 |
| 66 Marc Sullivan | .04 | 131 Pirates Leaders | .06 | 198 Lee Mazzilli | .08 | 264 Checklist: 133-264 | .06 |
| | | 132 P. Assenmacher (R) | .15 | | | | |

| NO. PLAYER | MINT | NO. PLAYER | MINT | NO. PLAYER | MINT | NO. PLAYER | MINT |
|---|---|---|---|---|---|---|---|
| 265 Darrell Evans | .10 | 350 Keith Hernandez | .15 | 434 Mike Fischlin | .04 | 519 Curt Young | .04 |
| 266 Jeff Hamilton (R) | .15 | 351 Gene Garber | .04 | 435 Bruce Sutter | .10 | 520 Jack Clark | .15 |
| 267 Howard Johnson | .20 | 352 Mike Felder | .12 | 436 Andy Allanson (R) | .15 | 521 Rick Reuschel | .04 |
| 268 Pat Corrales (Mgr.) | .04 | 353 Ernie Camacho | .04 | 437 Ted Power | .04 | 522 Checklist: 397-528 | .06 |
| 269 Cliff Speck (R) | .15 | 354 Jamie Quick | .04 | 438 Kelly Downs (R) | .15 | 523 Earnie Riles | .04 |
| 270 Jody Davis | .04 | 355 Don Carman | .04 | 439 Karl Best | .04 | 524 Bob Shirley | .04 |
| 271 Mike Brown | .04 | 356 White Sox Leaders | .06 | 440 Willie McGee | .15 | 525 Phil Bradley | .12 |
| 272 Andres Galarraga | .15 | 357 Steve Fireovid (R) | .15 | 441 Dave Leiper (R) | .15 | 526 Roger Mason | .08 |
| 273 Gene Nelson | .04 | 358 Sal Butera | .04 | 442 Mitch Webster | .04 | 527 Jim Wohlford | .04 |
| 274 Jeff Hearron (R) | .15 | 359 Doug Corbett | .04 | 443 John Felske (Mgr.) | .04 | 528 Ken Dixon | .04 |
| 275 LaMarr Hoyt | .04 | 360 Pedro Guerrero | .15 | 444 Jeff Russell | .04 | 529 Alvaro Espinoza (R) | .15 |
| 276 Jackie Gutierrez | .04 | 361 Mark Thurmond | .04 | 445 Dave Lopes | .08 | 530 Tony Gwynn | .45 |
| 277 Juan Agosto | .04 | 362 Luis Quinones (R) | .15 | 446 Chuck Finley (R) | .75 | 531 Astros Leaders | .06 |
| 278 Gary Pettis | .04 | 363 Jose Guzman | .12 | 447 Bill Almon | .04 | 532 Jeff Stone | .04 |
| 279 Dan Plesac (R) | .15 | 364 Randy Bush | .04 | 448 Chris Bosio (R) | .15 | 533 Argenis Salazar | .04 |
| 280 Jeffrey Leonard | .04 | 365 Rick Rhoden | .04 | 449 Pat Dodson (R) | .20 | 534 Scott Sanderson | .04 |
| 281 Reds Leaders | .12 | 366 Mark McGwire | 1.50 | 450 Kirby Puckett | .75 | 535 Tony Armas | .06 |
| 282 Jeff Calhoun | .04 | 367 Jeff Lahti | .04 | 451 Joe Sambito | .04 | 536 Terry Mulholland (R) | .20 |
| 283 Doug Drabek (R) | .50 | 368 J. McNamara (Mgr.) | .04 | 452 Dave Henderson | .08 | 537 Rance Mulliniks | .04 |
| 284 John Moses | .10 | 369 Brian Dayett | .04 | 453 Scott Terry (R) | .20 | 538 Tom Niedenfuer | .04 |
| 285 Dennis Boyd | .12 | 370 Fred Lynn | .15 | 454 Luis Salazar | .04 | 539 Reid Nichols | .04 |
| 286 Mike Woodard | .10 | 371 Mark Eichhorn (R) | .12 | 455 Mike Boddicker | .04 | 540 Terry Kennedy | .04 |
| 287 Dave Von Ohlen | .04 | 372 Jerry Mumphrey | .04 | 456 A's Leaders | .06 | 541 Rafael Belliard (R) | .12 |
| 288 Tito Landrum | .04 | 373 Jeff Dedmon | .04 | 457 Len Matuszek | .04 | 542 Ricky Horton | .04 |
| 289 Bob Kipper | .04 | 374 Glenn Hoffman | .04 | 458 Kelly Gruber | .75 | 543 Dave Johnson (Mgr.) | .04 |
| 290 Leon Durham | .10 | 375 Ron Guidry | .15 | 459 Dennis Eckersley | .06 | 544 Zane Smith | .06 |
| 291 Mitch Williams (R) | .20 | 376 Scott Bradley | .04 | 460 Darryl Strawberry | .60 | 545 Buddy Bell | .10 |
| 292 Franklin Stubbs | .12 | 377 John Henry Johnson | .04 | 461 Craig McMurtry | .04 | 546 Mike Morgan | .04 |
| 293 Bob Rodgers (Mgr.) | .04 | 378 Rafael Santana | .04 | 462 Scott Fletcher | .04 | 547 Rob Deer | .15 |
| 294 Steve Jeltz | .04 | 379 John Russell | .04 | 463 Tom Candiotti | .04 | 548 Bill Mooneyham (R) | .15 |
| 295 Len Dykstra | .20 | 380 Rich Gossage | .12 | 464 Butch Wynegar | .04 | 549 Bob Melvin | .04 |
| 296 Andres Thomas (R) | .12 | 381 Expos Leaders | .06 | 465 Todd Worrell | .15 | 550 Pete Incaviglia (R) | .20 |
| 297 Don Schulze | .04 | 382 Rudy Law | .04 | 466 Kal Daniels | .30 | 551 Frank Wills | .04 |
| 298 Larry Herndon | .04 | 383 Ron Davis | .04 | 467 Randy St. Claire | .04 | 552 Larry Sheets | .15 |
| 299 Joel Davis | .10 | 384 Johnny Grubb | .04 | 468 G. Bamberger (Mgr.) | .04 | 553 Mike Maddux (R) | .15 |
| 300 Reggie Jackson | .30 | 385 Orel Hershiser | .20 | 469 Mike Diaz (R) | .15 | 554 Buddy Biancalana | .04 |
| 301 Luis Aquino (R) | .15 | 386 Dickie Thon | .04 | 470 Dave Dravecky | .04 | 555 Dennis Rasmussen | .10 |
| 302 Bill Schroeder | .04 | 387 T. R. Bryden (R) | .20 | 471 Ronn Reynolds | .04 | 556 Angels Leaders | .06 |
| 303 Juan Berenguer | .04 | 388 Geno Petralli | .04 | 472 Bill Doran | .08 | 557 John Cerutti (R) | .15 |
| 304 Phil Garner | .04 | 389 Jeff Robinson | .04 | 473 Steve Farr | .04 | 558 Greg Gagne | .04 |
| 305 John Franco | .10 | 390 Gary Matthews | .04 | 474 Jerry Narron | .04 | 559 Lance McCullers | .04 |
| 306 Red Sox Leaders | .10 | 391 Jay Howell | .04 | 475 Scott Garrelts | .04 | 560 Glenn Davis | .20 |
| 307 Lee Guetterman (R) | .12 | 392 Checklist: 265-396 | .06 | 476 Danny Tartabull | .35 | 561 Rey Quinones (R) | .20 |
| 308 Don Slaught | .04 | 393 Pete Rose (Mgr.) | .30 | 477 Ken Howell | .04 | 562 B. Clutterbuck (R) | .15 |
| 309 Mike Young | .04 | 394 Mike Bielecki | .12 | 478 Tim Laudner | .04 | 563 John Stefero | .04 |
| 310 Frank Viola | .15 | 395 Damaso Garcia | .04 | 479 Bob Sebra (R) | .15 | 564 Larry McWilliams | .04 |
| 311 Turn Back—1982 | .15 | 396 Tim Lollar | .04 | 480 Jim Rice | .15 | 565 Dusty Baker | .04 |
| 312 Turn Back-1977 | .15 | 397 Greg Walker | .08 | 481 Phillies Leaders | .06 | 566 Tim Hulett | .04 |
| 313 Turn Back—1972 | .15 | 398 Brad Havens | .04 | 482 Daryl Boston | .04 | 567 Greg Mathews (R) | .15 |
| 314 Turn Back—1967 | .15 | 399 Curt Ford | .12 | 483 Dwight Lowry (R) | .15 | 568 Earl Weaver (Mgr.) | .04 |
| 315 Turn Back—1962 | .15 | 400 George Brett | .35 | 484 Jim Traber | .10 | 569 Wade Rowdon | .15 |
| 316 Brian Fisher | .04 | 401 Billy Jo Robidoux | .15 | 485 Tony Fernandez | .12 | 570 Sid Fernandez | .12 |
| 317 Clint Hurdle | .04 | 402 Mike Trujillo | .04 | 486 Otis Nixon | .15 | 571 Ozzie Virgil | .04 |
| 318 Jim Fregosi (Mgr.) | .04 | 403 Jerry Royster | .04 | 487 Dave Gumpert | .04 | 572 Pete Ladd | .04 |
| 319 Greg Swindell (R) | .30 | 404 Doug Sisk | .04 | 488 Ray Knight | .04 | 573 Hal McRae | .04 |
| 320 Barry Bonds (R) | 2.50 | 405 Brook Jacoby | .10 | 489 Bill Gullickson | .04 | 574 Manny Lee | .04 |
| 321 Mike Laga | .04 | 406 Yankees Leaders | .25 | 490 Dale Murphy | .25 | 575 Pat Tabler | .04 |
| 322 Chris Bando | .04 | 407 Jim Acker | .04 | 491 Ron Karkovice (R) | .15 | 576 Frank Pastore | .04 |
| 323 Al Newman (R) | .12 | 408 John Mizerock | .04 | 492 Mike Heath | .04 | 577 Dann Bilardello | .04 |
| 324 Dave Palmer | .04 | 409 Milt Thompson | .04 | 493 Tom Lasorda | .04 | 578 Billy Hatcher | .08 |
| 325 Garry Templeton | .04 | 410 Fernando Valenzuela | .15 | 494 Barry Jones (R) | .15 | 579 Rick Burleson | .04 |
| 326 Mark Gubicza | .04 | 411 Darnell Coles | .04 | 495 Gorman Thomas | .10 | 580 Mike Krukow | .04 |
| 327 Dale Sveum (R) | .15 | 412 Eric Davis | .30 | 496 Bruce Bochte | .04 | 581 Cubs Leaders | .08 |
| 328 Bob Welch | .10 | 413 Moose Haas | .04 | 497 Dale Mohorcic (R) | .15 | 582 Bruce Berenyi | .04 |
| 329 Ron Roenicke | .04 | 414 Joe Orsulak | .04 | 498 Bob Kearney | .04 | 583 Junior Ortiz | .04 |
| 330 Mike Scott | .10 | 415 Bobby Witt (R) | .35 | 499 Bruce Ruffin (R) | .15 | 584 Ron Kittle | .08 |
| 331 Mets Leaders | .20 | 416 Tom Nieto | .04 | 500 Don Mattingly | .60 | 585 Scott Bailes (R) | .15 |
| 332 Joe Price | .04 | 417 Pat Perry | .08 | 501 Craig Lefferts | .04 | 586 Ben Oglivie | .04 |
| 333 Ken Phelps | .04 | 418 Dick Williams (Mgr.) | .04 | 502 Dick Schofield | .04 | 587 Eric Plunk | .10 |
| 334 Ed Correa (R) | .15 | 419 Mark Portugal (R) | .15 | 503 Larry Andersen | .04 | 588 Wallace Johnson | .04 |
| 335 Candy Maldonado | .06 | 420 Will Clark (R) | 4.00 | 504 Mickey Hatcher | .04 | 589 Steve Crawford | .04 |
| 336 Allan Anderson (R) | .15 | 421 Jose DeLeon | .04 | 505 Bryn Smith | .04 | 590 Vince Coleman | .30 |
| 337 Darrell Miller | .04 | 422 Jack Howell | .04 | 506 Orioles Leaders | .08 | 591 Spike Owen | .04 |
| 338 Tim Conroy | .04 | 423 Jaime Cocanower | .04 | 507 Dave Stapleton | .04 | 592 Chris Welsh | .04 |
| 339 Donnie Hill | .04 | 424 Chris Speier | .04 | 508 Scott Bankhead | .10 | 593 Chuck Tanner (Mgr.) | .08 |
| 340 Roger Clemens | .75 | 425 Tom Seaver | .30 | 509 Enos Cabell | .04 | 594 Rick Anderson (R) | .15 |
| 341 Mike Brown | .04 | 426 Floyd Rayford | .04 | 510 Tom Henke | .10 | 595 Keith Hernandez (AS) | .15 |
| 342 Bob James | .04 | 427 Ed Nunez | .04 | 511 Steve Lyons | .04 | 596 Steve Sax (AS) | .10 |
| 343 Hal Lanier (Mgr.) | .04 | 428 Bruce Bochy | .04 | 512 Dave Magadan (R) | .40 | 597 Mike Schmidt (AS) | .25 |
| 344 Joe Niekro | .06 | 429 Tim Pyznarski (R) | .15 | 513 Carmen Castillo | .04 | 598 Ozzie Smith (AS) | .10 |
| 345 Andre Dawson | .25 | 430 Mike Schmidt | .50 | 514 Orlando Mercado | .04 | 599 Tony Gwynn (AS) | .25 |
| 346 Shawon Dunston | .15 | 431 Dodgers Leaders | .15 | 515 Willie Hernandez | .10 | 600 Dave Parker (AS) | .15 |
| 347 Mickey Brantley | .15 | 432 Jim Slaton | .04 | 516 Ted Simmons | .10 | 601 Darryl Strawberry (AS) | .25 |
| 348 Carmelo Martinez | .04 | 433 Ed Hearn (R) | .12 | 517 Mario Soto | .04 | 602 Gary Carter (AS) | .12 |
| 349 Storm Davis | .06 | | | 518 Gene Mauch (Mgr.) | .04 | 603 Dwight Gooden (AS) | .35 |
| | | | | | | 603 D. Gooden (no t.m.) | 1.00 |

| NO. PLAYER | MINT |
|---|---|
| 604 F. Valenzuela (AS) | .15 |
| 605 Todd Worrell (AS) | .15 |
| 606 Don Mattingly (AS) | .25 |
| 606 D. Matt (no t.m.) | 1.25 |
| 607 Tony Bernazard (AS) | .08 |
| 608 Wade Boggs (AS) | .20 |
| 609 Cal Ripken (AS) | .25 |
| 610 Jim Rice (AS) | .10 |
| 611 Kirby Puckett (AS) | .25 |
| 612 George Bell (AS) | .15 |
| 613 Lance Parrish (AS) | .10 |
| 614 Roger Clemens (AS) | .35 |
| 615 Teddy Higuera (AS) | .10 |
| 616 Dave Righetti (AS) | .10 |
| 617 Al Nipper | .04 |
| 618 Tom Kelly (Mgr.) | .04 |
| 619 Jerry Reed | .04 |
| 620 Jose Canseco | 3.00 |
| 621 Danny Cox | .08 |
| 622 Glenn Braggs (R) | .15 |
| 623 Kurt Stillwell (R) | .15 |
| 624 Tim Burke | .04 |
| 625 Mookie Wilson | .04 |
| 626 Joel Skinner | .04 |
| 627 Ken Oberkfell | .04 |
| 628 Bob Walk | .04 |
| 629 Larry Parrish | .04 |
| 630 John Candelaria | .04 |
| 631 Tigers Leaders | .15 |
| 632 Rob Woodward | .08 |
| 633 Jose Uribe | .04 |
| 634 Rafael Palmeiro (R) | 1.25 |
| 635 Ken Schrom | .04 |
| 636 Darren Daulton | .04 |
| 637 Bip Roberts (R) | .20 |
| 638 Rich Bordi | .04 |
| 639 Gerald Perry | .10 |
| 640 Mark Clear | .04 |
| 641 Domino Ramos | .04 |
| 642 Al Pulido | .04 |
| 643 Ron Shepherd | .12 |
| 644 John Denny | .04 |
| 645 Dwight Evans | .12 |
| 646 Mike Mason | .04 |
| 647 Tom Lawless | .04 |
| 648 Barry Larkin (R) | 1.50 |
| 649 Mickey Tettleton | .10 |
| 650 Hubie Brooks | .10 |
| 651 Benny Distefano | .04 |
| 652 Terry Forster | .04 |
| 653 Kevin Mitchell (R) | 1.50 |

| NO. PLAYER | MINT |
|---|---|
| 654 Checklist: 529-660 | .06 |
| 655 Jesse Barfield | .15 |
| 656 Rangers Leaders | .06 |
| 657 Tom Waddell | .04 |
| 658 Robby Thompson (R) | .15 |
| 659 Aurelio Lopez | .04 |
| 660 Bob Horner | .10 |
| 661 Lou Whitaker | .10 |
| 662 Frank DiPino | .04 |
| 663 Cliff Johnson | .04 |
| 664 Mike Marshall | .12 |
| 665 Rod Scurry | .04 |
| 666 Von Hayes | .10 |
| 667 Ron Hassey | .04 |
| 668 Juan Bonilla | .04 |
| 669 Bud Black | .04 |
| 670 Jose Cruz | .08 |
| 671 Ray Soff (R) | .12 |
| 672 Chili Davis | .10 |
| 673 Don Sutton | .15 |
| 674 Bill Campbell | .04 |
| 675 Ed Romero | .04 |
| 676 Charlie Moore | .04 |
| 677 Bob Grich | .04 |
| 678 Carney Lansford | .10 |
| 679 Kent Hrbek | .15 |
| 680 Ryne Sandberg | .60 |
| 681 George Bell | .15 |
| 682 Jerry Reuss | .04 |
| 683 Gary Roenicke | .04 |
| 684 Kent Tekulve | .04 |
| 685 Jerry Hairston | .04 |
| 686 Doyle Alexander | .04 |
| 687 Alan Trammell | .12 |
| 688 Juan Beniquez | .04 |
| 689 Darrell Porter | .04 |
| 690 Dane Iorg | .04 |
| 691 Dave Parker | .20 |
| 692 Frank White | .04 |
| 693 Terry Puhl | .04 |
| 694 Phil Niekro | .15 |
| 695 Chico Walker (R) | .15 |
| 696 Gary Lucas | .04 |
| 697 Ed Lynch | .04 |
| 698 Ernie Whitt | .04 |
| 699 Ken Landreaux | .04 |
| 700 Dave Bergman | .04 |
| 701 Willie Randolph | .08 |
| 702 Greg Gross | .04 |
| 703 Dave Schmidt | .04 |

| NO. PLAYER | MINT |
|---|---|
| 704 Jesse Orosco | .06 |
| 705 Bruce Hurst | .12 |
| 706 Rick Manning | .04 |
| 707 Bob McClure | .04 |
| 708 Scott McGregor | .04 |
| 709 Dave Kingman | .10 |
| 710 Gary Gaetti | .10 |
| 711 Ken Griffey | .08 |
| 712 Don Robinson | .04 |
| 713 Tom Brookens | .04 |
| 714 Don Quisenberry | .12 |
| 715 Bob Dernier | .04 |
| 716 Rick Leach | .04 |
| 717 Ed Vande Berg | .04 |
| 718 Steve Carlton | .25 |
| 719 Tom Hume | .04 |
| 720 Richard Dotson | .04 |
| 721 Tom Herr | .04 |
| 722 Bob Knepper | .08 |
| 723 Brett Butler | .12 |
| 724 Greg Minton | .04 |
| 725 George Hendrick | .04 |
| 726 Frank Tanana | .04 |
| 727 Mike Moore | .04 |
| 728 Tippy Martinez | .04 |
| 729 Tom Paciorek | .04 |
| 730 Eric Show | .06 |
| 731 Dave Concepcion | .08 |
| 732 Manny Trillo | .04 |
| 733 Bill Caudill | .04 |
| 734 Bill Madlock | .12 |
| 735 Rickey Henderson | .50 |
| 736 Steve Bedrosian | .10 |
| 737 Floyd Bannister | .04 |
| 738 Jorge Orta | .04 |
| 739 Chet Lemon | .06 |
| 740 Rich Gedman | .04 |
| 741 Paul Molitor | .15 |
| 742 Andy McGaffigan | .04 |
| 743 Dwayne Murphy | .04 |
| 744 Roy Smalley | .04 |
| 745 Glenn Hubbard | .04 |
| 746 Bob Ojeda | .12 |
| 747 Johnny Ray | .04 |
| 748 Mike Flanagan | .06 |
| 749 Ozzie Smith | .15 |
| 750 Steve Trout | .04 |
| 751 Garth Iorg | .04 |
| 752 Dan Petry | .04 |
| 753 Rick Honeycutt | .04 |

| NO. PLAYER | MINT |
|---|---|
| 754 Dave LaPoint | .04 |
| 755 Luis Aguayo | .04 |
| 756 Carlton Fisk | .25 |
| 757 Nolan Ryan | .75 |
| 758 Tony Bernazard | .04 |
| 759 Joel Youngblood | .04 |
| 760 Mike Witt | .10 |
| 761 Greg Pryor | .04 |
| 762 Gary Ward | .04 |
| 763 Tim Flannery | .04 |
| 764 Bill Buckner | .04 |
| 765 Kirk Gibson | .20 |
| 766 Don Aase | .04 |
| 767 Ron Cey | .04 |
| 768 Dennis Lamp | .04 |
| 769 Steve Sax | .15 |
| 770 Dave Winfield | .25 |
| 771 Shane Rawley | .04 |
| 772 Harold Baines | .15 |
| 773 Robin Yount | .30 |
| 774 Wayne Krenchicki | .04 |
| 775 Joaquin Andujar | .04 |
| 776 Tom Brunansky | .12 |
| 777 Chris Chambliss | .04 |
| 778 Jack Morris | .15 |
| 779 Craig Reynolds | .04 |
| 780 Andre Thornton | .04 |
| 781 Atlee Hammaker | .04 |
| 782 Brian Downing | .04 |
| 783 Willie Wilson | .10 |
| 784 Cal Ripken | .60 |
| 785 Terry Francona | .04 |
| 786 Jimy Williams (Mgr.) | .04 |
| 787 Alejandro Pena | .04 |
| 788 Tim Stoddard | .04 |
| 789 Dan Schatzeder | .04 |
| 790 Julio Cruz | .04 |
| 791 Lance Parrish | .15 |
| 792 Checklist: 661-792 | .06 |

## 1987 Topps Traded . . . Complete Set of 132 Cards—Value $13.00

Updates the main 1987 card set with players who changed teams during the season and rookies who joined their teams early in the season. Features the first Topps card of Ellis Burks, David Cone, Fred McGriff and Matt Williams. The complete set was packaged in a printed box and primarily distributed through card hobby dealers. A "Tiffany" version of the set was also issued.

| NO. PLAYER | MINT |
|---|---|
| 1T Bill Almon | .06 |
| 2T Scott Bankhead | .10 |
| 3T Eric Bell | .10 |
| 4T Juan Beniquez | .06 |
| 5T Juan Berenguer | .06 |
| 6T Greg Booker | .06 |
| 7T Thad Bosley | .06 |

| NO. PLAYER | MINT |
|---|---|
| 8T Larry Bowa | .08 |
| 9T Greg Brock | .10 |
| 10T Bob Brower | .15 |
| 11T Jerry Browne | .15 |
| 12T Ralph Bryant | .15 |
| 13T DeWayne Buice | .12 |
| 14T Ellis Burks (RR) | 2.00 |

| NO. PLAYER | MINT |
|---|---|
| 15T Ivan Calderon | .15 |
| 16T Jeff Calhoun | .06 |
| 17T Casey Candaele | .15 |
| 18T John Cangelosi | .10 |
| 19T Steve Carlton | .25 |
| 20T Juan Castillo | .10 |
| 21T Rick Cerone | .06 |

| NO. PLAYER | MINT |
|---|---|
| 22T Ron Cey | .12 |
| 23T John Christensen | .06 |
| 24T Dave Cone | 1.25 |
| 25T Chuck Grim | .15 |
| 26T Storm Daviss | .06 |
| 27T Andre Dawson | .30 |
| 28T Rick Dempsey | .10 |

| NO. PLAYER | MINT | NO. PLAYER | MINT | NO. PLAYER | MINT | NO. PLAYER | MINT |
|---|---|---|---|---|---|---|---|
| 29T Doug Drabek | .35 | 55T Stan Jefferson | .20 | 81T Kevin Mitchell | 1.00 | 107T Mark Salas | .06 |
| 30T Mike Dunne | .15 | 56T Joe Johnson | .10 | 82T Charlie Moore | .06 | 108T Luis Salazar | .06 |
| 31T Dennis Eckersley | .15 | 57T Terry Kennedy | .08 | 83T Jeff Musselman | .20 | 109T Benny Santiago (RR) | .60 |
| 32T Lee Ella | .06 | 58T Mike Kingery | .10 | 84T Gene Nelson | .06 | 110T Dave Schmidt | .06 |
| 33T Brian Fisher | .10 | 59T Ray Knight | .08 | 85T Graig Nettles | .15 | 111T Kevin Seitzer (RR) | .20 |
| 34T Terry Francona | .06 | 60T Gene Larkin | .25 | 86T Al Newman | .06 | 112T John Shelby | .06 |
| 35T Willie Fraser | .12 | 61T Mike LaValliere | .10 | 87T Reid Nichols | .06 | 113T Steve Shields | .20 |
| 36T Billy Gardner | .06 | 62T Jack Lazorko | .06 | 88T Tom Niedenfuer | .06 | 114T John Smiley | .75 |
| 37T Ken Gerhart | .15 | 63T Terry Leach | .15 | 89T Joe Niekro | .15 | 115T Chris Speier | .06 |
| 38T Danny Gladden | .10 | 64T Tim Leary | .06 | 90T Tom Nieto | .06 | 116T Mike Stanley | .25 |
| 39T Jim Gott | .12 | 65T Jim Lindeman | .15 | 91T Matt Nokes (RR) | .50 | 117T Terry Steinbach (RR) | .40 |
| 40T Cecilio Guante | .06 | 66T Steve Lombardozzi | .15 | 92T Dickie Noles | .06 | 118T Les Straker | .15 |
| 41T Albert Hall | .08 | 67T Bill Long | .20 | 93T Pat Pacillo | .15 | 119T Jim Sundberg | .06 |
| 42T Terry Harper | .06 | 68T Barry Lyons | .15 | 94T Lance Parrish | .15 | 120T Danny Tartabull | .30 |
| 43T Mickey Hatcher | .06 | 69T Shane Mack | .15 | 95T Tony Pena | .15 | 121T Tom Trebelhorn | .06 |
| 44T Brad Havens | .06 | 70T Greg Maddux | .75 | 96T Luis Polonia | .40 | 122T Dave Valle | .10 |
| 45T Neal Heaton | .10 | 71T Bill Madlock | .15 | 97T Randy Ready | .08 | 123T Ed VandeBerg | .06 |
| 46T Mike Henneman | .40 | 72T Joe Magrane (RR) | .25 | 98T Jeff Reardon | .12 | 124T Andy Van Slyke | .15 |
| 47T Donnie Hill | .06 | 73T Dave Martinez | .25 | 99T Gary Redus | .08 | 125T Gary Ward | .06 |
| 48T Guy Hoffman | .06 | 74T Fred McGriff (RR) | 2.00 | 100T Jeff Reed | .06 | 126T Alan Wiggins | .06 |
| 49T Brian Holton | .15 | 75T Mark McLemore | .12 | 101T Rick Rhoden | .10 | 127T Bill Wilkinson | .10 |
| 50T Charles Hudson | .06 | 76T Kevin McReynolds | .25 | 102T Cal Ripken, Sr. | .06 | 128T Frank Williams | .06 |
| 51T Dany Jackson | .20 | 77T Dave Meads | .12 | 103T Wally Ritchie | .15 | 129T Matt Williams (RR) | 3.00 |
| 52T Reggie Jackson | .50 | 78T Eddie Milner | .06 | 104T Jeff Robinson (RR) | .15 | 130T Jim Winn | .06 |
| 53T Chris James (RR) | .20 | 79T Greg Minton | .06 | 105T Gary Roenicke | .06 | 131T Matt Young | .06 |
| 54T Dion James | .12 | 80T John Mitchell | .15 | 106T Jerry Royster | .06 | 132T Checklist | .06 |

## 1988 Topps . . . Complete Set of 792 Cards—Value $20.00  (Factory-Sealed Set—Value $25.00)

Features the rookie cards of Ellis Burks, Matt Williams, Sam Horn, and Al Leiter. A new feature of this year's set was "This Way to the Clubhouse" which explained how a player joined his current team. A "Tiffany" version of the set was also issued.

| NO. PLAYER | MINT | NO. PLAYER | MINT | NO. PLAYER | MINT | NO. PLAYER | MINT |
|---|---|---|---|---|---|---|---|
| 1 '87 Record: Coleman | .12 | 29 Argenis Salazar | .04 | 57 Tim Crews (R) | .12 | 85 Howard Johnson | .15 |
| 2 '87 Record: Mattingly | .15 | 30 Sid Fernandez | .08 | 58 Dave Magadan | .08 | 86 Ron Karkovice | .04 |
| 3 '87 Record: McGwire | .12 | 31 Bruce Bochy | .04 | 59 Danny Cox | .04 | 87 Mike Mason | .04 |
| 3 McGwire (error) | .30 | 32 Mike Morgan | .04 | 60 Rickey Henderson | .30 | 88 Earnie Riles | .04 |
| 4 '87 Record: Murray | .12 | 33 Rob Deer | .08 | 61 Mark Knudson (R) | .12 | 89 Gary Thurman (R) | .12 |
| 4 Murray (error) | .50 | 34 Rickey Horton | .04 | 62 Jeff Hamilton | .04 | 90 Dale Murphy | .20 |
| 5 '87 Record: Niekro Bros. | .10 | 35 Harold Baines | .10 | 63 Jimmy Jones | .08 | 91 Joey Cora (R) | .12 |
| 6 '87 Record: Ryan | .30 | 36 Jamie Moyer | .04 | 64 Ken Caminiti (R) | .20 | 92 Len Matuszek | .04 |
| 7 '87 Record: Santiago | .10 | 37 Ed Romero | .04 | 65 Leon Durham | .06 | 93 Bob Sebra | .04 |
| 8 Kevin Elster | .08 | 38 Jeff Calhoun | .04 | 66 Shane Rawley | .04 | 94 Chuck Johnson (R) | .12 |
| 9 Andy Hawkins | .04 | 39 Gerald Perry | .08 | 67 Ken Oberkfell | .04 | 95 Lance Parrish | .08 |
| 10 Ryne Sandberg | .30 | 40 Orel Hershiser | .15 | 68 Dave Dravecky | .06 | 96 Todd Benzinger (R) | .20 |
| 11 Mike Young | .04 | 41 Bob Melvin | .04 | 69 Mike Hart (R) | .12 | 97 Scott Garrelts | .04 |
| 12 Bill Schroeder | .04 | 42 Bill Landrum (R) | .12 | 70 Roger Clemens | .40 | 98 Rene Gonzales (R) | .12 |
| 13 Andres Thomas | .04 | 43 Dick Schofield | .04 | 71 Gary Pettis | .04 | 99 Chuck Finley | .04 |
| 14 Sparky Anderson | .04 | 44 Lou Piniella | .06 | 72 Dennis Eckersley | .10 | 100 Jack Clark | .10 |
| 15 Chili Davis | .06 | 45 Kent Hrbek | .10 | 73 Randy Bush | .04 | 101 Allan Anderson | .04 |
| 16 Kirk McCaskill | .06 | 46 Darnell Coles | .04 | 74 Tom Lasorda (Mgr.) | .04 | 102 Barry Larkin | .25 |
| 17 Ron Oester | .04 | 47 Joaquin Andujar | .04 | 75 Joe Carter | .15 | 103 Curt Young | .04 |
| 18 Al Leiter (error-R) | .25 | 48 Alan Ashby | .04 | 76 Denny Martinez | .04 | 104 Dick Williams | .04 |
| 18 Al Leiter (correct-R) | .10 | 49 Dave Clark | .08 | 77 Tom O'Malley | .04 | 105 Jesse Orosco | .06 |
| 19 Mark Davidson (R) | .12 | 50 Hubie Brooks | .04 | 78 Dan Petry | .06 | 106 Jim Walewander (R) | .12 |
| 20 Kevin Gross | .04 | 51 Oriole Team | .10 | 79 Ernie Whitt | .04 | 107 Scott Bailes | .04 |
| 21 Red Sox Team | .08 | 52 Don Robinson | .04 | 80 Mark Langston | .10 | 108 Steve Lyons | .04 |
| 22 Greg Swindell | .08 | 53 Curt Wilkerson | .04 | 81 Reds Team | .06 | 109 Joel Skinner | .04 |
| 23 Ken Landreaux | .04 | 54 Jim Clancy | .04 | 82 Darrel Akerfelds (R) | .12 | 110 Teddy Higuera | .08 |
| 24 Jim Deshaies | .04 | 55 Phil Bradley | .08 | 83 Jose Oquendo | .06 | 111 Expos Team | .06 |
| 25 Andres Galarraga | .08 | 56 Ed Hearn | .04 | 84 Cecilio Guante | .04 | 112 Les Lancaster (R) | .12 |
| 26 Mitch William | .04 | | | | | | |
| 27 R.J. Reynolds | .04 | | | | | | |
| 28 Jose Nunez (R) | .12 | | | | | | |

| NO. | PLAYER | MINT | NO. | PLAYER | MINT | NO. | PLAYER | MINT | NO. | PLAYER | MINT |
|---|---|---|---|---|---|---|---|---|---|---|---|
| 113 | Kelly Gruber | .15 | 198 | Franklin Stubbs | .06 | 283 | Phil Lombardi | .08 | 368 | Gerald Young (R) | .12 |
| 114 | Jeff Russell | .04 | 199 | Dave Meads (R) | .12 | 284 | Larry Bowa | .04 | 369 | Greg Harris | .04 |
| 115 | Johnny Ray | .04 | 200 | Wade Boggs | .30 | 285 | Jim Presley | .08 | 370 | Jose Canseco | .60 |
| 116 | J.D. Gleaton | .04 | 201 | Rangers Team | .06 | 286 | Chuck Grim (R) | .12 | 371 | Joe Hesketh | .04 |
| 117 | James Steels (R) | .10 | 202 | Glenn Hoffman | .04 | 287 | Manny Trillo | .04 | 372 | Matt Williams (R) | 1.25 |
| 118 | Bob Welch | .04 | 203 | Fred Toliver | .04 | 288 | Pat Pacillo | .08 | 373 | Checklist: 265-396 | .06 |
| 119 | Robbie Wine (R) | .12 | 204 | Paul O'Neill | .15 | 289 | Dave Bergman | .04 | 374 | Doc Edwards | .04 |
| 120 | Kirby Puckett | .30 | 205 | Nelson Liriano (R) | .12 | 290 | Tony Fernandez | .08 | 375 | Tom Brunansky | .08 |
| 121 | Checklist: 1-132 | .06 | 206 | Domingo Ramos | .04 | 291 | Astros Team | .06 | 376 | Bill Wilkinson (R) | .12 |
| 122 | Tony Bernazard | .04 | 207 | John Mitchell (R) | .12 | 292 | Carney Lansford | .04 | 377 | Sam Horn (R) | .15 |
| 123 | Tom Candiotti | .06 | 208 | Steve Lake | .04 | 293 | Doug Jones (R) | .15 | 378 | Todd Frohwirth (R) | .12 |
| 124 | Ray Knight | .04 | 209 | Richard Dotson | .04 | 294 | Al Pedrique (R) | .12 | 379 | Rafael Ramirez | .04 |
| 125 | Bruce Hurst | .06 | 210 | Willie Randolph | .08 | 295 | Bert Blyleven | .06 | 380 | Joe Magrane (R) | .15 |
| 126 | Steve Jeltz | .04 | 211 | Frank Dipino | .04 | 296 | Floyd Rayford | .04 | 381 | Angels Team | .06 |
| 127 | Jim Gott | .04 | 212 | Greg Brock | .04 | 297 | Zane Smith | .04 | 382 | Keith Miller (R) | .12 |
| 128 | Johnny Grubb | .04 | 213 | Albert Hall | .04 | 298 | Milt Thompson | .04 | 383 | Eric Bell (R) | .12 |
| 129 | Greg Minton | .04 | 214 | Dave Schmidt | .04 | 299 | Steve Crawford | .04 | 384 | Neil Allen | .04 |
| 130 | Buddy Bell | .08 | 215 | Von Hayes | .08 | 300 | Don Mattingly | .30 | 385 | Carlton Fisk | .20 |
| 131 | Don Schulze | .04 | 216 | Jerry Ruess | .04 | 301 | Bud Black | .06 | 386 | Don Mattingly (AS) | .20 |
| 132 | Donnie Hill | .04 | 217 | Harry Spillman | .04 | 302 | Jose Uribe | .04 | 387 | Willie Randolph (AS) | .08 |
| 133 | Greg Mathews | .04 | 218 | Dan Schatzeder | .04 | 303 | Eric Show | .06 | 388 | Wade Boggs (AS) | .20 |
| 134 | Chuck Tanner (mgr.) | .04 | 219 | Mike Stanley | .08 | 304 | George Hendrick | .06 | 389 | Alan Trammell (AS) | .08 |
| 135 | Dennis Rasmussen | .06 | 220 | Tom Henke | .04 | 305 | Steve Sax | .10 | 390 | George Bell (AS) | .10 |
| 136 | Brian Dayett | .04 | 221 | Rafael Belliard | .04 | 306 | Billy Hatcher | .10 | 391 | Kirby Puckett (AS) | .20 |
| 137 | Chris Bosio | .04 | 222 | Steve Farr | .04 | 307 | Mike Trujillo | .04 | 392 | Dave Winfield (AS) | .10 |
| 138 | Mitch Webster | .06 | 223 | Stan Jefferson | .08 | 308 | Lee Mazzilli | .06 | 393 | Matt Nokes (AS) | .08 |
| 139 | Jerry Browne | .08 | 224 | Tom Trebelhorn (R) | .12 | 309 | Bill Long (R) | .12 | 394 | Roger Clemens (AS) | .20 |
| 140 | Jesse Barfield | .10 | 225 | Mike Scioscia | .04 | 310 | Tom Herr | .04 | 395 | Jimmy Key (AS) | .04 |
| 141 | Royals Team | .08 | 226 | Dave Lopes | .06 | 311 | Scott Sanderson | .04 | 396 | Tom Henke (AS) | .04 |
| 142 | Andy Van Slyke | .10 | 227 | Ed Correa | .04 | 312 | Joey Meyer | .08 | 397 | Jack Clark (AS) | .08 |
| 143 | Mickey Tettleton | .04 | 228 | Wallace Johnson | .04 | 313 | Bob McClure | .04 | 398 | Juan Samuel (AS) | .08 |
| 144 | Don Gordon (R) | .10 | 229 | Jeff Musselman | .08 | 314 | Jimy Williams | .04 | 399 | Tim Wallach (AS) | .06 |
| 145 | Bill Madlock | .08 | 230 | Pat Tabler | .04 | 315 | Dave Parker | .15 | 400 | Ozzie Smith (AS) | .08 |
| 146 | Donnell Nixon (R) | .12 | 231 | Pirates Team | .06 | 316 | Jose Rijo | .04 | 401 | Andre Dawson (AS) | .12 |
| 147 | Bill Buckner | .04 | 232 | Bob James | .04 | 317 | Tom Nieto | .04 | 402 | Tony Gwynn (AS) | .15 |
| 148 | Carmelo Martinez | .04 | 233 | Rafael Santana | .04 | 318 | Mel Hall | .04 | 403 | Tim Raines (AS) | .08 |
| 149 | Ken Howell | .04 | 234 | Ken Dayley | .04 | 319 | Mike Loynd | .04 | 404 | Benny Santiago (AS) | .08 |
| 150 | Eric Davis | .20 | 235 | Gary Ward | .04 | 320 | Alan Trammell | .15 | 405 | Dwight Gooden (AS) | .15 |
| 151 | Bob Knepper | .04 | 236 | Ted Power | .04 | 321 | White Sox Team | .06 | 406 | Shane Rawley (AS) | .06 |
| 152 | Jody Reed (R) | .30 | 237 | Mike Heath | .04 | 322 | Vincente Palacios (R) | .12 | 407 | Steve Bedrosian (AS) | .06 |
| 153 | John Habyan | .08 | 238 | Luis Polonia (R) | .20 | 323 | Rick Leach | .04 | 408 | Dion James | .04 |
| 154 | Jeff Stone | .04 | 239 | Roy Smalley | .04 | 324 | Danny Jackson | .10 | 409 | Joel McKeon | .04 |
| 155 | Bruce Sutter | .08 | 240 | Lee Smith | .08 | 325 | Glenn Hubbard | .04 | 410 | Tony Pena | .04 |
| 156 | Gary Mathews | .04 | 241 | Damaso Garcia | .06 | 326 | Al Nipper | .04 | 411 | Wayne Tolleson | .04 |
| 157 | Atlee Hammaker | .04 | 242 | Tom Niedenfuer | .04 | 327 | Larry Sheets | .08 | 412 | Randy Myers | .06 |
| 158 | Tim Hulett | .04 | 243 | Mark Ryal | .08 | 328 | Greg Cadaret (R) | .12 | 413 | John Christensen | .04 |
| 159 | Brad Arnsberg (R) | .12 | 244 | Jeff D. Robinson | .04 | 329 | Chris Speier | .04 | 414 | John McNamara | .04 |
| 160 | Willie McGee | .10 | 245 | Rich Gedman | .04 | 330 | Eddie Whitson | .04 | 415 | Don Carman | .04 |
| 161 | Bryn Smith | .04 | 246 | Mike Campbell (R) | .12 | 331 | Brian Downing | .04 | 416 | Keith Moreland | .04 |
| 162 | Mark McLemore | .08 | 247 | Thad Bosley | .04 | 332 | Jerry Reed | .04 | 417 | Mark Ciardi (R) | .12 |
| 163 | Dale Mahorcic | .04 | 248 | Storm Davis | .04 | 333 | Wally Backman | .04 | 418 | Joel Youngblood | .04 |
| 164 | Dave Johnson | .04 | 249 | Mike Marshall | .08 | 334 | Dave LaPoint | .04 | 419 | Scott McGregor | .04 |
| 165 | Robin Yount | .20 | 250 | Nolan Ryan | .50 | 335 | C. Washington | .04 | 420 | Wally Joyner | .15 |
| 166 | Rick Rodriguez (R) | .12 | 251 | Tom Foley | .04 | 336 | Ed Lynch | .04 | 421 | Ed VandeBerg | .04 |
| 167 | Rance Mulliniks | .04 | 252 | Bob Brower | .08 | 337 | Jim Gantner | .04 | 422 | Dave Concepcion | .04 |
| 168 | Barry Jones | .04 | 253 | Checklist: 133-264 | .06 | 338 | Brian Holton | .08 | 423 | John Smiley (R) | .40 |
| 169 | Ross Jones (R) | .15 | 254 | Lee Elia | .04 | 339 | Kurt Stillwell | .08 | 424 | Dwayne Murphy | .04 |
| 170 | Rich Gossage | .08 | 255 | Mookie Wilson | .06 | 340 | Jack Morris | .12 | 425 | Jeff Reardon | .10 |
| 171 | Cubs Team | .06 | 256 | Ken Schrom | .04 | 341 | Carmen Castillo | .04 | 426 | Randy Ready | .04 |
| 172 | Lloyd McClendon (R) | .12 | 257 | Jerry Royster | .04 | 342 | Larry Andersen | .04 | 427 | Paul Kigus (R) | .12 |
| 173 | Eric Plunk | .04 | 258 | Ed Nunez | .04 | 343 | Greg Gagne | .04 | 428 | John Shelby | .04 |
| 174 | Phil Garner | .04 | 259 | Ron Kittle | .06 | 344 | Tony LaRussa | .04 | 429 | Tigers Team | .08 |
| 175 | Kevin Bass | .08 | 260 | Vince Coleman | .15 | 345 | Scott Fletcher | .04 | 430 | Glenn Davis | .10 |
| 176 | Jeff Reed | .04 | 261 | Giants Team | .06 | 346 | Vance Law | .04 | 431 | Casey Candaele | .08 |
| 177 | Frank Tanana | .06 | 262 | Drew Hall | .10 | 347 | Joe Johnson | .06 | 432 | Mike Moore | .04 |
| 178 | Dwayne Henry | .06 | 263 | Glenn Braggs | .10 | 348 | Jim Eisenreich | .04 | 433 | Bill Pecota (R) | .12 |
| 179 | Charlie Puleo | .04 | 264 | Les Straker (R) | .12 | 349 | Bob Walk | .04 | 434 | Rick Aguilera | .04 |
| 180 | Terry Kennedy | .04 | 265 | Bo Diaz | .04 | 350 | Will Clark | .50 | 435 | Mike Pagliarulo | .06 |
| 181 | Dave Cone | .25 | 266 | Paul Assenmacher | .04 | 351 | Cardinals Team | .06 | 436 | Mike Bielecki | .04 |
| 182 | Ken Phelps | .04 | 267 | Billy Bean (R) | .12 | 352 | Billy Ripken (R) | .15 | 437 | Fred Manrique (R) | .12 |
| 183 | Tom Lawless | .04 | 268 | Bruce Ruffin | .04 | 353 | Ed Olwine | .04 | 438 | Rob Ducey (R) | .12 |
| 184 | Ivan Calderon | .15 | 269 | Ellis Burks (R) | .75 | 354 | Marc Sullivan | .04 | 439 | Dave Martinez | .08 |
| 185 | Rick Rhoden | .04 | 270 | Mike Witt | .06 | 355 | Roger McDowell | .04 | 440 | Steve Bedrosian | .08 |
| 186 | Rafael Palmeiro | .25 | 271 | Ken Gerhart | .08 | 356 | Luis Aguayo | .04 | 441 | Rick Manning | .04 |
| 187 | Steve Kiefer | .08 | 272 | Steve Ontiveros | .04 | 357 | Floyd Bannister | .04 | 442 | Tom Bolton (R) | .12 |
| 188 | John Russell | .04 | 273 | Garth Iorg | .04 | 358 | Rey Quinones | .04 | 443 | Ken Griffey | .04 |
| 189 | Wes Gardner (R) | .12 | 274 | Junior Ortiz | .04 | 359 | Tim Stoddard | .04 | 444 | Cal Ripken, Sr. | .04 |
| 190 | Candy Maldonado | .06 | 275 | Kevin Seitzer | .12 | 360 | Tony Gwynn | .30 | 445 | Mike Krukow | .04 |
| 191 | John Cerutti | .04 | 276 | Luis Salazar | .04 | 361 | Greg Maddux | .25 | 446 | Doug DeCinces | .04 |
| 192 | Devon White | .10 | 277 | Alejandro Pena | .04 | 362 | Juan Castillo | .10 | 447 | Jeff Montgomery (R) | .20 |
| 193 | Brian Fisher | .06 | 278 | Jose Cruz | .10 | 363 | Willie Fraser | .10 | 448 | Mike Davis | .04 |
| 194 | Tom Kelly | .04 | 279 | Randy St. Claire | .04 | 364 | Nick Esasky | .04 | 449 | Jeff M. Robinson (R) | .12 |
| 195 | Dan Quisenberry | .06 | 280 | Pete Incaviglia | .08 | 365 | Floyd Youmans | .04 | 450 | Barry Bonds | .35 |
| 196 | Dave Engle | .04 | 281 | Jerry Hairston | .04 | 366 | Chet Lemon | .04 | 451 | Keith Atherton | .04 |
| 197 | Lance McCullers | .04 | 282 | Pat Perry | .04 | 367 | Tim Leary | .04 | 452 | Willie Wilson | .08 |

| NO. | PLAYER | MINT |
|---|---|---|
| 453 | Dennis Powell | .04 |
| 454 | Marvell Wynne | .04 |
| 455 | Shawn Hillegas (R) | .12 |
| 456 | Dave Anderson | .04 |
| 457 | Terry Leach | .04 |
| 458 | Ron Hassey | .04 |
| 459 | Yankees Team | .08 |
| 460 | Ozzie Smith | .12 |
| 461 | Danny Darwin | .04 |
| 462 | Don Slaught | .04 |
| 463 | Fred McGriff | .75 |
| 464 | Jay Tibbs | .04 |
| 465 | Paul Molitor | .15 |
| 466 | Jerry Mumphrey | .04 |
| 467 | Don Aase | .04 |
| 468 | Darren Daulton | .04 |
| 469 | Jeff Dedmon | .04 |
| 470 | Dwight Evans | .08 |
| 471 | Donnie Moore | .04 |
| 472 | Robby Thompson | .04 |
| 473 | Joe Niekro | .06 |
| 474 | Tom Brookens | .04 |
| 475 | Pete Rose (mgr.) | .25 |
| 476 | Dave Stewart | .15 |
| 477 | Jamie Quirk | .04 |
| 478 | Sid Bream | .04 |
| 479 | Brett Butler | .08 |
| 480 | Dwight Gooden | .25 |
| 481 | Mariano Duncan | .06 |
| 482 | Mark Davis | .04 |
| 483 | Rod Booker (R) | .12 |
| 484 | Pat Clements | .04 |
| 485 | Harold Reynolds | .04 |
| 486 | Pat Keedy (R) | .12 |
| 487 | Jim Pankovits | .04 |
| 488 | Andy McGaffigan | .04 |
| 489 | Dodgers Team | .10 |
| 490 | Larry Parrish | .04 |
| 491 | B.J. Surhoff | .08 |
| 492 | Doyle Alexander | .04 |
| 493 | Mike Greenwell | .25 |
| 494 | Wally Ritchie (R) | .12 |
| 495 | Eddie Murray | .20 |
| 496 | Guy Hoffman | .04 |
| 497 | Kevin Mitchell | .25 |
| 498 | Bob Boone | .04 |
| 499 | Eric King | .04 |
| 500 | Andre Dawson | .20 |
| 501 | Tim Birtsas | .04 |
| 502 | Danny Gladden | .04 |
| 503 | Junior Noboa (R) | .12 |
| 504 | Bob Rodgers | .04 |
| 505 | Willie Upshaw | .06 |
| 506 | John Cangelosi | .04 |
| 507 | Mark Gubicza | .04 |
| 508 | Tim Teufel | .04 |
| 509 | Bill Dawley | .04 |
| 510 | Dave Winfield | .15 |
| 511 | Joel Davis | .04 |
| 512 | Alex Trevino | .04 |
| 513 | Tim Flannery | .04 |
| 514 | Pat Sheridan | .04 |
| 515 | Juan Nieves | .04 |
| 516 | Jim Sundberg | .04 |
| 517 | Ron Robinson | .04 |
| 518 | Greg Gross | .04 |
| 519 | Mariners Team | .04 |
| 520 | Dave Smith | .04 |
| 521 | Jim Dwyer | .04 |
| 522 | Bob Patterson (R) | .12 |
| 523 | Gary Roenicke | .04 |
| 524 | Gary Lucas | .04 |
| 525 | Marty Barrett | .06 |
| 526 | Juan Berenguer | .04 |
| 527 | Steve Henderson | .04 |
| 528 | CL: 397-528 (correct) | .10 |
| 528 | CL: 397-528 (error) | .50 |
| 529 | Tim Burke | .04 |
| 530 | Gary Carter | .10 |
| 531 | Rich Yett | .04 |
| 532 | Mike Kingery | .04 |
| 533 | John Farrell (R) | .12 |
| 534 | John Wathan | .04 |
| 535 | Ron Guidry | .10 |
| 536 | John Morris | .04 |
| 537 | Steve Buechele | .04 |
| 538 | Bill Wegman | .04 |
| 539 | Mike LaValliere | .04 |
| 540 | Bret Saberhagen | .12 |
| 541 | Juan Beniquez | .04 |
| 542 | Paul Noce (R) | .12 |
| 543 | Kent Tekulve | .04 |
| 544 | Jim Traber | .04 |
| 545 | Don Baylor | .08 |
| 546 | John Candelaria | .06 |
| 547 | Felix Fermin (R) | .10 |
| 548 | Shane Mack | .08 |
| 549 | Braves Team | .06 |
| 550 | Pedro Guerrero | .10 |
| 551 | Terry Steinbach | .08 |
| 552 | Mark Thurmond | .04 |
| 553 | Tracy Jones | .06 |
| 554 | Mike Smithson | .04 |
| 555 | Brook Jacoby | .06 |
| 556 | Stan Clarke (R) | .10 |
| 557 | Craig Reynolds | .04 |
| 558 | Bob Ojeda | .04 |
| 559 | Ken Williams (R) | .12 |
| 560 | Tim Wallach | .08 |
| 561 | Rick Cerone | .04 |
| 562 | Jim Lindeman | .08 |
| 563 | Jose Guzman | .04 |
| 564 | Frank Lucchesi | .04 |
| 565 | Lloyd Moseby | .10 |
| 566 | Charlie O'Brien (R) | .10 |
| 567 | Mike Diaz | .04 |
| 568 | Chris Brown | .08 |
| 569 | C. Liebrandt | .06 |
| 570 | Jeffrey Leonard | .04 |
| 571 | Mark Williamson (R) | .12 |
| 572 | Chris James | .10 |
| 573 | Bob Stanley | .04 |
| 574 | Graig Nettles | .08 |
| 575 | Don Sutton | .12 |
| 576 | Tommy Hinzo (R) | .12 |
| 577 | Tom Browning | .06 |
| 578 | Gary Gaetti | .08 |
| 579 | Mets Team | .10 |
| 580 | Mark McGwire | .25 |
| 581 | Tito Landrum | .04 |
| 582 | Mike Henneman (R) | .15 |
| 583 | Dave Valle | .08 |
| 584 | Steve Trout | .04 |
| 585 | Ozzie Guillen | .04 |
| 586 | Bob Forsch | .04 |
| 587 | Terry Puhl | .04 |
| 588 | Jeff Parrett (R) | .10 |
| 589 | Geno Petralli | .04 |
| 590 | George Bell | .15 |
| 591 | Doug Drabek | .15 |
| 592 | Dale Sveum | .06 |
| 593 | Bob Tewksbury | .04 |
| 594 | Bobby Valentine | .04 |
| 595 | Frank White | .04 |
| 596 | John Kruk | .08 |
| 597 | Gene Garber | .04 |
| 598 | Lee Lacy | .04 |
| 599 | Calvin Schiraldi | .04 |
| 600 | Mike Schmidt | .35 |
| 601 | Jack Lazorko | .04 |
| 602 | Mike Aldrete | .04 |
| 603 | Rob Murphy | .04 |
| 604 | Chris Bando | .04 |
| 605 | Kirk Gibson | .10 |
| 606 | Moose Haas | .04 |
| 607 | Mickey Hatcher | .04 |
| 608 | Charlie Kerfeld | .06 |
| 609 | Twins Team | .08 |
| 610 | Keith Hernandez | .10 |
| 611 | Tommy John | .08 |
| 612 | Curt Ford | .04 |
| 613 | Bobby Thigpen | .10 |
| 614 | Herm Winningham | .04 |
| 615 | Jody Davis | .04 |
| 616 | Jay Aldrich (R) | .12 |
| 617 | Oddibe McDowell | .08 |
| 618 | Cecil Fielder | .30 |
| 619 | Mike Dunne | .20 |
| 620 | Cory Snyder | .10 |
| 621 | Gene Nelson | .04 |
| 622 | Kal Daniels | .10 |
| 623 | Mike Flanagan | .04 |
| 624 | Jim Leyland | .04 |
| 625 | Frank Viola | .10 |
| 626 | Glenn Wilson | .04 |
| 627 | Joe Boever (R) | .12 |
| 628 | Dave Henderson | .08 |
| 629 | Kelly Downs | .04 |
| 630 | Darrell Evans | .08 |
| 631 | Jack Howell | .04 |
| 632 | Steve Shields | .06 |
| 633 | Barry Lyons (R) | .12 |
| 634 | Jose DeLeon | .06 |
| 635 | Terry Pendleton | .06 |
| 636 | Charles Hudson | .04 |
| 637 | Jay Bell (R) | .25 |
| 638 | Steve Balboni | .04 |
| 639 | Brewers Team | .06 |
| 640 | Garry Templeton | .06 |
| 641 | Rick Honeycutt | .06 |
| 642 | Bob Dernier | .04 |
| 643 | Rocky Childress (R) | .12 |
| 644 | Terry McGriff | .10 |
| 645 | Matt Nokes (R) | .25 |
| 646 | Checklist: 529-660 | .06 |
| 647 | Pascual Perez | .04 |
| 648 | Al Newman | .04 |
| 649 | DeWayne Buice (R) | .15 |
| 650 | Cal Ripken | .35 |
| 651 | Mike Jackson | .12 |
| 652 | Bruce Benedict | .04 |
| 653 | Jeff Sellers | .04 |
| 654 | Roger Craig | .04 |
| 655 | Len Dykstra | .10 |
| 656 | Lee Guetterman | .04 |
| 657 | Gary Redus | .04 |
| 658 | Tim Conroy | .04 |
| 659 | Bobby Meacham | .04 |
| 660 | Rick Reuschel | .04 |
| 661 | Turn Back—1983 | .08 |
| 662 | Turn Back—1978 | .08 |
| 663 | Turn Back—1973 | .08 |
| 664 | Turn Back—1968 | .08 |
| 665 | Turn Back—1963 | .10 |
| 666 | Mario Soto | .04 |
| 667 | Luis Quinones | .04 |
| 668 | Walt Terrell | .04 |
| 669 | Phillies Team | .06 |
| 670 | Dan Plesac | .04 |
| 671 | Tim Laudner | .04 |
| 672 | John Davis (R) | .12 |
| 673 | Tony Phillips | .04 |
| 674 | Mike Fitzgerald | .04 |
| 675 | Jim Rice | .10 |
| 676 | Ken Dixon | .04 |
| 677 | Eddie Milner | .04 |
| 678 | Jim Acker | .04 |
| 679 | Darrell Miller | .04 |
| 680 | Charlie Hough | .06 |
| 681 | Bobby Bonilla | .35 |
| 682 | Jimmy Key | .08 |
| 683 | Julio Franco | .12 |
| 684 | Hal Lanier | .04 |
| 685 | Ron Darling | .08 |
| 686 | Terry Francona | .04 |
| 687 | Mickey Brantley | .08 |
| 688 | Jim Winn | .04 |
| 689 | Tom Pagnozzi (R) | .15 |
| 690 | Jay Howell | .04 |
| 691 | Dan Pasqua | .06 |
| 692 | Mike Birkbeck | .04 |
| 693 | Benny Santiago | .15 |
| 694 | Eric Nolte (R) | .10 |
| 695 | Shawon Dunston | .12 |
| 696 | Duane Ward | .04 |
| 697 | S. Lombardozzi | .10 |
| 698 | Brad Havens | .04 |
| 699 | Padres Team | .10 |
| 700 | George Brett | .25 |
| 701 | Sammy Stewart | .04 |
| 702 | Mike Gallego | .04 |
| 703 | Bob Brenly | .04 |
| 704 | Dennis Boyd | .04 |
| 705 | Juan Samuel | .08 |
| 706 | Rick Mahler | .04 |
| 707 | Fred Lynn | .08 |
| 708 | Gus Polidor | .06 |
| 709 | George Frazier | .04 |
| 710 | D. Strawberry | .40 |
| 711 | Bill Gullickson | .04 |
| 712 | John Moses | .04 |
| 713 | Willie Hernandez | .08 |
| 714 | Jim Fregosi | .04 |
| 715 | Todd Worrell | .06 |
| 716 | Lenn Sakata | .04 |
| 717 | Jay Baller | .06 |
| 718 | Mike Felder | .04 |
| 719 | Denny Walling | .04 |
| 720 | Tim Raines | .15 |
| 721 | Pete O'Brien | .10 |
| 722 | Manny Lee | .04 |
| 723 | Bob Kipper | .04 |
| 724 | Danny Tartabull | .15 |
| 725 | Mike Boddicker | .04 |
| 726 | Alfredo Griffin | .04 |
| 727 | Greg Booker | .04 |
| 728 | Andy Allanson | .04 |
| 729 | Blue Jays Team | .06 |
| 730 | John Franco | .06 |
| 731 | Rick Schu | .04 |
| 732 | Dave Palmer | .04 |
| 733 | Spike Owen | .04 |
| 734 | Craig Lefferts | .04 |
| 735 | Kevin McReynolds | .10 |
| 736 | Matt Young | .04 |
| 737 | Butch Wynegar | .04 |
| 738 | Scott Bankhead | .04 |
| 739 | Daryl Boston | .04 |
| 740 | Rick Sutcliffe | .10 |
| 741 | Mike Easler | .04 |
| 742 | Mark Clear | .04 |
| 743 | Larry Herndon | .04 |
| 744 | Whitey Herzog (mgr.) | .04 |
| 745 | Bill Doran | .10 |
| 746 | Gene Larkin (R) | .12 |
| 747 | Bobby Witt | .10 |
| 748 | Reid Nichols | .04 |
| 749 | Mark Eichhorn | .04 |
| 750 | Bo Jackson | .75 |
| 751 | Jim Morrison | .04 |
| 752 | Mark Grant | .08 |
| 753 | Danny Heep | .04 |
| 754 | Mike LaCoss | .04 |
| 755 | Ozzie Virgil | .06 |
| 756 | Mike Maddux | .04 |
| 757 | John Marzano | .08 |
| 758 | Eddie Williams (R) | .10 |
| 759 | A's Team | .20 |
| 760 | Mike Scott | .08 |
| 761 | Tony Armas | .06 |
| 762 | Scott Bradley | .04 |
| 763 | Doug Sisk | .04 |
| 764 | Greg Walker | .06 |
| 765 | Neal Heaton | .06 |
| 766 | Henry Cotto | .04 |
| 767 | Jose Lind (R) | .20 |
| 768 | Dickie Noles | .04 |
| 769 | Cecil Cooper | .06 |
| 770 | Lou Whitaker | .08 |
| 771 | Ruben Sierra | .30 |
| 772 | Sal Butera | .04 |
| 773 | Frank Williams | .04 |
| 774 | Gene Mauch | .04 |
| 775 | Dave Stieb | .06 |
| 776 | Checklist: 661-792 | .06 |
| 777 | Lonnie Smith | .04 |
| 778 | K. Comstock (R)(error) | 3.00 |
| 778 | K. Comstock (R)(correct) | .12 |
| 779 | Tom Glavine (R) | 1.00 |
| 780 | F. Valenzuela | .10 |
| 781 | Keith Hughes (R) | .15 |
| 782 | Jeff Ballard (R) | .12 |
| 783 | Ron Roenicke | .04 |
| 784 | Joe Sambito | .04 |
| 785 | Alvin Davis | .08 |
| 786 | Joe Price | .04 |
| 787 | Bill Almon | .04 |
| 788 | Ray Searage | .04 |
| 789 | Indians Team | .08 |
| 790 | Dave Righetti | .08 |
| 791 | Ted Simmons | .08 |
| 792 | John Tudor | .08 |

## 1988 Topps Traded.... Complete Set of 132 Cards—Value $25.00

Updates the main 1988 card set with players who changed teams during the season and rookies. Features the first Topps card for Mark Grace, Jim Abbott, Andy Benes and the USA Olympic Team. The complete set was packaged in a printed box and distributed primarily through card hobby dealers. A "Tiffany" version of the set was also issued.

| NO. | PLAYER | MINT | NO. | PLAYER | MINT | NO. | PLAYER | MINT | NO. | PLAYER | MINT |
|---|---|---|---|---|---|---|---|---|---|---|---|
| 1 T | Jim Abbott (OLY) | 5.00 | 34 T | Jose DeLeon | .06 | 67 T | Billy Masse (OLY) | .20 | 100 T | Luis Salazar | .06 |
| 2 T | Juan Agosto | .06 | 35 T | Richard Dotson | .06 | 68 T | Jack McDowell | .75 | 101 T | Rafael Santana | .06 |
| 3 T | Luis Alicea | .10 | 36 T | Cecil Espy | .15 | 69 T | Jack McKeon | .06 | 102 T | Nelson Santovenia | .12 |
| 4 T | Roberto Alomar (RR) | 3.00 | 37 T | Tom Filer | .06 | 70 T | Larry McWilliams | .06 | 103 T | Mackey Sasser | .15 |
| 5 T | Brady Anderson | .15 | 38 T | Mike Fiore (OLY) | .15 | 71 T | M. Morandini (OLY) | .40 | 104 T | Calvin Schiraldi | .06 |
| 6 T | Jack Armstrong | .30 | 39 T | Ron Gant (RR) | 1.50 | 72 T | Keith Moreland | .06 | 105 T | Mike Schooler | .15 |
| 7 T | Don August | .06 | 40 T | Kirk Gibson | .20 | 73 T | Mike Morgan | .06 | 106 T | Scott Servais (OLY) | .15 |
| 8 T | Floyd Bannister | .06 | 41 T | Rich Gossage | .15 | 74 T | Charles Nagy (OLY) | .35 | 107 T | Dave Silvestri (OLY) | .15 |
| 9 T | Bret Barberie (OLY) | .50 | 42 T | Mark Grace (RR) | 2.50 | 75 T | Al Nipper | .06 | 108 T | Don Slaught | .06 |
| 10 T | Jose Bautista | .10 | 43 T | Alfredo Griffin | .06 | 76 T | Russ Nixon | .06 | 109 T | Joe Slusarski (OLY) | .30 |
| 11 T | Don Baylor | .06 | 44 T | Ty Griffin (OLY) | .25 | 77 T | Jesse Orosco | .06 | 110 T | Lee Smith | .10 |
| 12 T | Tim Belcher | .10 | 45 T | Bryan Harvey | .50 | 78 T | Joe Orsulak | .06 | 111 T | Pete Smith | .15 |
| 13 T | Buddy Bell | .06 | 46 T | Ron Hassey | .06 | 79 T | Dave Palmer | .06 | 112 T | Jim Snyder | .06 |
| 14 T | Andy Benes (OLY) | 3.00 | 47 T | Ray Hayward | .10 | 80 T | Mark Parent | .10 | 113 T | Ed Sprague (OLY) | .40 |
| 15 T | Damon Berryhill | .20 | 48 T | Dave Henderson | .12 | 81 T | Dave Parker | .15 | 114 T | Pete Stanicek | .10 |
| 16 T | Bud Black | .06 | 49 T | Tom Herr | .06 | 82 T | Dan Pasqua | .06 | 115 T | Kurt Stillwell | .10 |
| 17 T | Pat Borders | .25 | 50 T | Bob Horner | .06 | 83 T | Melido Perez | .25 | 116 T | Todd Stottlemyre | .75 |
| 18 T | Phil Bradley | .06 | 51 T | Rickey Horton | .06 | 84 T | Steve Peters | .10 | 117 T | Bill Swift | .06 |
| 19 T | Jeff Branson (OLY) | .20 | 52 T | Jay Howell | .06 | 85 T | Dan Petry | .06 | 118 T | Pat Tabler | .06 |
| 20 T | Tom Brunansky | .15 | 53 T | Glenn Hubbard | .06 | 86 T | Gary Pettis | .06 | 119 T | Scott Terry | .06 |
| 21 T | Jay Buhner | .50 | 54 T | Jeff Innis | .15 | 87 T | Jeff Pico | .15 | 120 T | Mickey Tettleton | .06 |
| 22 T | Brett Butler | .06 | 55 T | Danny Jackson | .20 | 88 T | Jim Poole (OLY) | .20 | 121 T | Dickie Thon | .06 |
| 23 T | Jim Campanis (OLY) | .20 | 56 T | Darrin Jackson | .15 | 89 T | Ted Power | .06 | 122 T | Jeff Treadway | .25 |
| 24 T | Sil Campusano | .20 | 57 T | Roberto Kelly (RR) | .75 | 90 T | Rafael Ramirez | .06 | 123 T | Willie Upshaw | .06 |
| 25 T | John Candelaria | .06 | 58 T | Ron Kittle | .06 | 91 T | Dennis Rasmussen | .06 | 124 T | Robin Ventura (OLY) | 7.50 |
| 26 T | Jose Cecana | .08 | 59 T | Ray Knight | .06 | 92 T | Jose Rijo | .06 | 125 T | Ron Washington | .06 |
| 27 T | Rick Cerone | .06 | 60 T | Vance Law | .06 | 93 T | Ernie Riles | .06 | 126 T | Walt Weiss (RR) | .30 |
| 28 T | Jack Clark | .15 | 61 T | Jeffrey Leonard | .06 | 94 T | Luis Rivera | .10 | 127 T | Bob Welch | .06 |
| 29 T | Kevin Coffman | .10 | 62 T | Mike Macfarlane | .15 | 95 T | Doug Robbins | .15 | 128 T | David Wells | .15 |
| 30 T | Pat Combs (OLY) | .30 | 63 T | Scott Madison | .10 | 96 T | Frank Robinson | .15 | 129 T | Glenn Wilson | .06 |
| 31 T | Henry Cotto | .06 | 64 T | Kirt Manwaring | .10 | 97 T | Cookie Rojas | .06 | 130 T | Ted Wood (OLY) | .30 |
| 32 T | Chill Davis | .06 | 65 T | Mark Marquess | .06 | 98 T | Chris Sabo (RR) | 2.00 | 131 T | Don Zimmer | .06 |
| 33 T | Mike Davis | .06 | 66 T | Tino Martinez (OLY) | 3.00 | 99 T | Mark Salas | .06 | 132 T | Checklist | .06 |

## 1989 Topps . . . Complete Set of 792 Cards—Value $22.00    (Factory-Sealed Set—Value $27.00)

Features the rookie cards of Sandy Alomar, Jr., Ricky Jordan, Robin Ventura and Gary Sheffield. New features this year are "#1 Draft Picks" and 1988 "Monthly Scoreboard." A "Tiffany" version of the set was also issued.

| NO. | PLAYER | MINT | NO. | PLAYER | MINT | NO. | PLAYER | MINT | NO. | PLAYER | MINT |
|---|---|---|---|---|---|---|---|---|---|---|---|
| 1 | '88 Record: G. Bell | .10 | 4 | '88 Record: Dawson | .10 | 7 | '88 Rec.: McReynolds | .10 | 10 | Andre Dawson | .15 |
| 2 | '88 Record: Boggs | .15 | 5 | '88 Rec.: Hershiser | .10 | 8 | Dave Eiland (R) | .15 | 11 | Bruce Sutter | .08 |
| 3 | '88 Record: G. Carter | .05 | 6 | '88 Record: D. Jones | .05 | 9 | Tim Teufel | .05 | 12 | Dale Sveum | .08 |

| NO. | PLAYER | MINT |
|---|---|---|
| 13 | Doug Sisk | .05 |
| 14 | Tom Kelly | .05 |
| 15 | Robby Thompson | .05 |
| 16 | Ron Robinson | .08 |
| 17 | Brian Downing | .08 |
| 18 | Rick Rhoden | .05 |
| 19 | Greg Gagne | .05 |
| 20 | Steve Bedrosian | .08 |
| 21 | Walker: Bonus | .05 |
| 22 | Tim Crews | .05 |
| 23 | Mike Fitzgerald | .05 |
| 24 | Larry Andersen | .05 |
| 25 | Frank White | .05 |
| 26 | Dale Mohorcac | .05 |
| 27 | Orestes Destrade (R) | .15 |
| 28 | Mike Moore | .05 |
| 29 | Kelly Gruber | .10 |
| 30 | Doc Gooden | .20 |
| 31 | Terry Francona | .08 |
| 32 | Dennis Rasmussen | .05 |
| 33 | B.J. Surhoff | .08 |
| 34 | Ken Williams | .05 |
| 35 | John Tudor | .05 |
| 36 | Mitch Webster | .05 |
| 37 | Bob Stanley | .05 |
| 38 | Paul Runge | .05 |
| 39 | Mike Maddux | .05 |
| 40 | Steve Sax | .12 |
| 41 | Terry Mulholland | .05 |
| 42 | Jim Eppard | .08 |
| 43 | Guillermo Hernandez | .05 |
| 44 | Jim Snyder (R) | .10 |
| 45 | Kal Daniels | .10 |
| 46 | Mark Portugal | .05 |
| 47 | Carney Lansford | .08 |
| 48 | Tim Burke | .05 |
| 49 | Craig Biggio (R) | .40 |
| 50 | George Bell | .10 |
| 51 | McLemore: Bonus | .05 |
| 52 | Bob Brenly | .05 |
| 53 | Ruben Sierra | .20 |
| 54 | Steve Trout | .05 |
| 55 | Julio Franco | .10 |
| 56 | Pat Tabler | .08 |
| 57 | Alejandro Pena | .08 |
| 58 | Lee Mazzilli | .05 |
| 59 | Mark Davis | .10 |
| 60 | Tom Brunansky | .08 |
| 61 | Neil Allen | .05 |
| 62 | Alfredo Griffin | .05 |
| 63 | Mark Clear | .05 |
| 64 | Alex Trevino | .05 |
| 65 | Rick Reuschel | .05 |
| 66 | Manny Trillo | .05 |
| 67 | Dave Palmer | .05 |
| 68 | Darrell Miller | .05 |
| 69 | Jeff Ballard | .05 |
| 70 | Mark McGwire | .20 |
| 71 | Mike Boddicker | .08 |
| 72 | John Moses | .05 |
| 73 | Pascual Perez | .05 |
| 74 | Nick Leyva (R) | .05 |
| 75 | Tom Henke | .05 |
| 76 | Terry Blocker (R) | .12 |
| 77 | Doyle Alexander | .05 |
| 78 | Jim Sundberg | .05 |
| 79 | Scott Bankhead | .05 |
| 80 | Cory Snyder | .15 |
| 81 | Raines: Bonus | .08 |
| 82 | Dave Leiper | .05 |
| 83 | Jeff Blauser | .10 |
| 84 | Bill Bene (R) | .20 |
| 85 | Kevin McReynolds | .10 |
| 86 | Al Nipper | .05 |
| 87 | Larry Owen | .05 |
| 88 | Darryl Hamilton (R) | .12 |
| 89 | Dave LaPoint | .05 |
| 90 | Vince Coleman | .15 |
| 91 | Floyd Youmans | .05 |
| 92 | Jeff Kunkel | .05 |
| 93 | Ken Howell | .05 |
| 94 | Chris Speier | .05 |
| 95 | Gerald Young | .08 |
| 96 | Rick Cerone | .05 |
| 97 | Greg Mathews | .05 |
| 98 | Larry Sheets | .05 |
| 99 | Sherman Corbett (R) | .12 |
| 100 | Mike Schmidt | .30 |
| 101 | Les Straker | .05 |
| 102 | Mike Gallego | .05 |
| 103 | Tim Birtsas | .05 |
| 104 | Dallas Green | .05 |
| 105 | Ron Darling | .10 |
| 106 | Willie Upshaw | .05 |
| 107 | Jose DeLeon | .05 |
| 108 | Fred Manrique | .05 |
| 109 | Hipolito Pena (R) | .12 |
| 110 | Paul Molitor | .12 |
| 111 | Davis: Bonus | .08 |
| 112 | Jim Presley | .06 |
| 113 | Lloyd Moseby | .08 |
| 114 | Bob Kipper | .05 |
| 115 | Jody Davis | .05 |
| 116 | Jeff Montgomery | .05 |
| 117 | Dave Anderson | .05 |
| 118 | Checklist: 1-132 | .08 |
| 119 | Terry Puhl | .05 |
| 120 | Frank Viola | .10 |
| 121 | Garry Templeton | .05 |
| 122 | Lance Johnson | .10 |
| 123 | Spike Owen | .05 |
| 124 | Jim Traber | .05 |
| 125 | Mike Krukow | .08 |
| 126 | Sid Bream | .05 |
| 127 | Walt Terrell | .05 |
| 128 | Milt Thompson | .05 |
| 129 | Terry Clark (R) | .12 |
| 130 | Gerald Perry | .10 |
| 131 | Dave Otto | .08 |
| 132 | Curt Ford | .05 |
| 133 | Bill Long | .05 |
| 134 | Don Zimmer | .05 |
| 135 | Jose Rijo | .08 |
| 136 | Joey Meyer | .05 |
| 137 | Geno Petralli | .05 |
| 138 | Wallace Johnson | .05 |
| 139 | Mike Flanagan | .05 |
| 140 | Shawon Dunston | .10 |
| 141 | Jacoby: Bonus | .05 |
| 142 | Mike Diaz | .05 |
| 143 | Mike Campbell | .05 |
| 144 | Jay Bell | .05 |
| 145 | Dave Stewart | .10 |
| 146 | Gary Pettis | .05 |
| 147 | DeWayne Buice | .05 |
| 148 | Bill Pecota | .05 |
| 149 | Doug Dascenzo (R) | .12 |
| 150 | Fernando Valenzuela | .10 |
| 151 | Terry McGriff | .05 |
| 152 | Mark Thurmond | .05 |
| 153 | Jim Pankovits | .05 |
| 154 | Don Carman | .05 |
| 155 | Marty Barrett | .05 |
| 156 | Dave Gallagher (R) | .12 |
| 157 | Tom Glavine | .25 |
| 158 | Mike Aldrete | .05 |
| 159 | Pat Clements | .05 |
| 160 | Jeffrey Leonard | .05 |
| 161 | Gregg Olson (R) | .50 |
| 162 | John Davis | .05 |
| 163 | Bob Forsch | .05 |
| 164 | Hal Lanier | .05 |
| 165 | Mike Dunne | .05 |
| 166 | Doug Jennings (R) | .10 |
| 167 | Steve Searcy (R) | .12 |
| 168 | Willie Wilson | .08 |
| 169 | Mike Jackson | .05 |
| 170 | Tony Fernandez | .08 |
| 171 | Thomas: Bonus | .05 |
| 172 | Frank Williams | .05 |
| 173 | Mel Hall | .05 |
| 174 | Todd Burns (R) | .10 |
| 175 | John Shelby | .05 |
| 176 | Jeff Parrett | .08 |
| 177 | Monty Fariss (R) | .30 |
| 178 | Mark Grant | .05 |
| 179 | Ozzie Virgil | .05 |
| 180 | Mike Scott | .08 |
| 181 | Craig Worthington (R) | .12 |
| 182 | Bob McClure | .05 |
| 183 | Oddibe McDowell | .08 |
| 184 | John Costello (R) | .12 |
| 185 | Claudell Washington | .05 |
| 186 | Pat Perry | .05 |
| 187 | Darren Daulton | .05 |
| 188 | Dennis Lamp | .05 |
| 189 | Kevin Mitchell | .20 |
| 190 | Mike Witt | .08 |
| 191 | Sil Campusano (R) | .12 |
| 192 | Paul Mirabella | .05 |
| 193 | Sparky Anderson | .05 |
| 194 | Greg Harris (R) | .20 |
| 195 | Ozzie Guillen | .08 |
| 196 | Denny Walling | .05 |
| 197 | Neal Heaton | .05 |
| 198 | Danny Heep | .05 |
| 199 | Mike Schooler (R) | .12 |
| 200 | George Brett | .20 |
| 201 | Gruber: Bonus | .05 |
| 202 | Brad Moore (R) | .10 |
| 203 | Rob Ducey | .05 |
| 204 | Brad Havens | .05 |
| 205 | Dwight Evans | .10 |
| 206 | Roberto Alomar | .40 |
| 207 | Terry Leach | .05 |
| 208 | Tom Pagnozzi | .05 |
| 209 | Jeff Bittiger (R) | .12 |
| 210 | Dale Murphy | .15 |
| 211 | Mike Pagliarulo | .08 |
| 212 | Scott Sanderson | .05 |
| 213 | Rene Gonzales | .05 |
| 214 | Charlie O'Brien | .05 |
| 215 | Kevin Gross | .05 |
| 216 | Jack Howell | .08 |
| 217 | Joe Price | .05 |
| 218 | Mike LaValliere | .05 |
| 219 | Jim Clancy | .05 |
| 220 | Gary Gaetti | .10 |
| 221 | Cecil Espy | .10 |
| 222 | Mark Lewis (R) | .50 |
| 223 | Jay Buhner | .15 |
| 224 | Tony LaRussa | .05 |
| 225 | Ramon Martinez (R) | 1.50 |
| 226 | Bill Doran | .08 |
| 227 | John Farrell | .10 |
| 228 | Nelson Santovenia (R) | .12 |
| 229 | Jimmy Key | .12 |
| 230 | Ozzie Smith | .12 |
| 231 | R. Alomar: Bonus | .08 |
| 232 | Ricky Horton | .05 |
| 233 | Gregg Jefferies | .30 |
| 234 | Tom Browning | .08 |
| 235 | John Kruk | .08 |
| 236 | Charles Hudson | .08 |
| 237 | Glenn Hubbard | .05 |
| 238 | Eric King | .05 |
| 239 | Tim Laudner | .05 |
| 240 | Greg Maddux | .08 |
| 241 | Brett Butler | .05 |
| 242 | Ed VandeBerg | .05 |
| 243 | Bob Boone | .05 |
| 244 | Jim Acker | .05 |
| 245 | Jim Rice | .10 |
| 246 | Rey Quinones | .05 |
| 247 | Shawn Hillegas | .05 |
| 248 | Tony Phillips | .05 |
| 249 | Tim Leary | .10 |
| 250 | Cal Ripken | .35 |
| 251 | John Dopson (R) | .10 |
| 252 | Billy Hatcher | .05 |
| 253 | Jose Alvarez (R) | .12 |
| 254 | Tom Lasorda | .05 |
| 255 | Ron Guidry | .08 |
| 256 | Benny Santiago | .08 |
| 257 | Rick Aguilera | .05 |
| 258 | Checklist: 133-264 | .08 |
| 259 | Larry McWilliams | .05 |
| 260 | Dave Winfield | .12 |
| 261 | Brunansky Bonus | .08 |
| 262 | Jeff Pico (R) | .10 |
| 263 | Mike Felder | .05 |
| 264 | Rob Dibble (R) | .30 |
| 265 | Kent Hrbek | .10 |
| 266 | Luis Aquino | .05 |
| 267 | Jeff Robinson | .05 |
| 268 | Keith Miller (R) | .10 |
| 269 | Tom Bolton | .05 |
| 270 | Wally Joyner | .12 |
| 271 | Jay Tibbs | .05 |
| 272 | Ron Hassey | .05 |
| 273 | Jose Lind | .05 |
| 274 | Mark Eichhorn | .05 |
| 275 | Danny Tartabull | .10 |
| 276 | Paul Kilgus | .05 |
| 277 | Mike Davis | .05 |
| 278 | Andy McGaffigan | .05 |
| 279 | Scott Bradley | .05 |
| 280 | Bob Knepper | .05 |
| 281 | Gary Redus | .05 |
| 282 | Cris Carpenter (R) | .12 |
| 283 | Andy Allanson | .05 |
| 284 | Jim Leyland | .05 |
| 285 | John Candelaria | .08 |
| 286 | Darrin Jackson | .08 |
| 287 | Juan Nieves | .05 |
| 288 | Pat Sheridan | .05 |
| 289 | Ernie Whitt | .05 |
| 290 | John Franco | .08 |
| 291 | Strawberry: Bonus | .12 |
| 292 | Jim Corsi (R) | .10 |
| 293 | Glenn Wilson | .05 |
| 294 | Juan Berenguer | .05 |
| 295 | Scott Fletcher | .05 |
| 296 | Ron Gant | .30 |
| 297 | Oswald Peraza (R) | .10 |
| 298 | Chris James | .08 |
| 299 | Steve Ellsworth (R) | .10 |
| 300 | Darryl Strawberry | .35 |
| 301 | Charlie Leibrandt | .08 |
| 302 | Gary Ward | .05 |
| 303 | Felix Fermin | .05 |
| 304 | Joel Youngblood | .05 |
| 305 | Dave Smith | .05 |
| 306 | Tracy Woodson | .10 |
| 307 | Lance McCullers | .08 |
| 308 | Ron Karkovice | .05 |
| 309 | Mario Diaz | .10 |
| 310 | Rafael Palmeiro | .15 |
| 311 | Chris Bosio | .05 |
| 312 | Tom Lawless | .05 |
| 313 | Denny Martinez | .05 |
| 314 | Bobby Valentine | .05 |
| 315 | Greg Swindell | .08 |
| 316 | Walt Weiss | .08 |
| 317 | Jack Armstrong (R) | .15 |
| 318 | Gene Larkin | .05 |
| 319 | Greg Booker | .05 |
| 320 | Lou Whitaker | .08 |
| 321 | Reed: Bonus | .08 |
| 322 | John Smiley | .08 |
| 323 | Gary Thurman | .05 |
| 324 | Bob Milacki (R) | .20 |
| 325 | Jesse Barfield | .12 |
| 326 | Dennis Boyd | .08 |
| 327 | Mark Lemke (R) | .15 |
| 328 | Rick Honeycutt | .05 |
| 329 | Bob Melvin | .05 |
| 330 | Eric Davis | .15 |
| 331 | Curt Wilkerson | .05 |
| 332 | Tony Armas | .05 |
| 333 | Bob Ojeda | .08 |
| 334 | Steve Lyons | .05 |
| 335 | Dave Righetti | .08 |
| 336 | Steve Balboni | .05 |
| 337 | Calvin Schiraldi | .05 |
| 338 | Jim Adduci | .08 |
| 339 | Scott Bailes | .05 |
| 340 | Kirk Gibson | .10 |
| 341 | Jim Deshaies | .05 |
| 342 | Tom Brookens | .05 |
| 343 | Gary Sheffield (R) | .35 |
| 344 | Tom Trebelhorn | .05 |
| 345 | Charlie Hough | .08 |
| 346 | Rex Hudler | .06 |
| 347 | John Cerutti | .05 |
| 348 | Ed Hearn | .05 |
| 349 | Ron Jones (R) | .10 |
| 350 | Andy Van Slyke | .10 |
| 351 | Melvin: Bonus | .05 |
| 352 | Rick Schu | .05 |

| NO. | PLAYER | MINT |
|---|---|---|
| 353 | Marvell Wynne | .05 |
| 354 | Larry Parrish | .05 |
| 355 | Mark Langston | .10 |
| 356 | Kevin Elster | .08 |
| 357 | Jerry Reuss | .05 |
| 358 | Ricky Jordan (R) | .25 |
| 359 | Tommy John | .10 |
| 360 | Ryne Sandberg | .30 |
| 361 | Kelly Downs | .06 |
| 362 | Jack Lazorko | .05 |
| 363 | Rich Yett | .05 |
| 364 | Rob Deer | .08 |
| 365 | Mike Henneman | .05 |
| 366 | Herm Winningham | .05 |
| 367 | Johnny Paredes (R) | .12 |
| 368 | Brian Holton | .05 |
| 369 | Ken Caminiti | .05 |
| 370 | Dennis Eckersley | .10 |
| 371 | Manny Lee | .05 |
| 372 | Craig Lefferts | .05 |
| 373 | Tracy Jones | .05 |
| 374 | John Wathan | .05 |
| 375 | Terry Pendleton | .08 |
| 376 | Steve Lombardozzi | .05 |
| 377 | Mike Smithson | .05 |
| 378 | Checklist: 265-396 | .08 |
| 379 | Tim Flannery | .05 |
| 380 | Rickey Henderson | .35 |
| 381 | Sheets: Bonus | .05 |
| 382 | John Smoltz (R) | .50 |
| 383 | Howard Johnson | .15 |
| 384 | Mark Salas | .05 |
| 385 | Von Hayes | .08 |
| 386 | Andres Galarraga (AS) | .10 |
| 387 | Ryne Sandberg (AS) | .15 |
| 388 | Bobby Bonilla (AS) | .10 |
| 389 | Ozzie Smith (AS) | .08 |
| 390 | Darryl Strawberry (AS) | .20 |
| 391 | Andre Dawson (AS) | .10 |
| 392 | Andy Van Slyke (AS) | .10 |
| 393 | Gary Carter (AS) | .10 |
| 394 | Orel Hershiser (AS) | .10 |
| 395 | Danny Jackson (AS) | .08 |
| 396 | Kirk Gibson (AS) | .10 |
| 397 | Don Mattingly (AS) | .20 |
| 398 | Julio Franco (AS) | .08 |
| 399 | Wade Boggs (AS) | .12 |
| 400 | Alan Trammell (AS) | .08 |
| 401 | Jose Canseco (AS) | .20 |
| 402 | Mike Greenwell (AS) | .10 |
| 403 | Kirby Puckett (AS) | .15 |
| 404 | Bob Boone (AS) | .05 |
| 405 | Roger Clemens (AS) | .15 |
| 406 | Frank Viola (AS) | .08 |
| 407 | Dave Winfield (AS) | .08 |
| 408 | Greg Walker | .05 |
| 409 | Ken Dayley | .05 |
| 410 | Jack Clark | .10 |
| 411 | Mitch Williams | .05 |
| 412 | Barry Lyons | .05 |
| 413 | Mike Kingery | .05 |
| 414 | Jim Fregosi | .05 |
| 415 | Rich Gossage | .08 |
| 416 | Fred Lynn | .08 |
| 417 | Mike LaCoss | .05 |
| 418 | Bob Dernier | .05 |
| 419 | Tom Filer | .05 |
| 420 | Joe Carter | .15 |
| 421 | Kirk McCaskill | .05 |
| 422 | Bo Diaz | .05 |
| 423 | Brian Fisher | .05 |
| 424 | Luis Polonia | .05 |
| 425 | Jay Howell | .08 |
| 426 | Danny Gladden | .05 |
| 427 | Eric Show | .05 |
| 428 | Craig Reynolds | .05 |
| 429 | Gagne: Bonus | .05 |
| 430 | Mark Gubicza | .08 |
| 431 | Luis Rivera | .08 |
| 432 | Chad Kreuter (R) | .12 |
| 433 | Albert Hall | .05 |
| 434 | Ken Patterson (R) | .10 |
| 435 | Len Dykstra | .08 |
| 436 | Bobby Meacham | .05 |
| 437 | Andy Benes (R) | .60 |
| 438 | Greg Gross | .05 |
| 439 | Frank Dipino | .05 |
| 440 | Bobby Bonilla | .25 |
| 441 | Jerry Reed | .05 |
| 442 | Jose Oquendo | .05 |
| 443 | Rod Nichols (R) | .10 |
| 444 | Moose Stubing (R) | .10 |
| 445 | Matt Nokes | .08 |
| 446 | Rob Murphy | .05 |
| 447 | Donell Nixon | .05 |
| 448 | Eric Plunk | .05 |
| 449 | Carmelo Martinez | .05 |
| 450 | Roger Clemens | .30 |
| 451 | Mark Davidson | .05 |
| 452 | Israel Sanchez (R) | .10 |
| 453 | Tom Prince | .08 |
| 454 | Paul Assenmacher | .05 |
| 455 | Johnny Ray | .08 |
| 456 | Tim Belcher | .08 |
| 457 | Mackey Sasser | .10 |
| 458 | Donn Pall (R) | .12 |
| 459 | Valle: Bonus | .05 |
| 460 | Dave Stieb | .08 |
| 461 | Buddy Bell | .08 |
| 462 | Jose Guzman | .05 |
| 463 | Steve Lake | .05 |
| 464 | Bryn Smith | .05 |
| 465 | Mark Grace | .35 |
| 466 | Chuck Crim | .05 |
| 467 | Jim Walewander | .05 |
| 468 | Henry Cotto | .05 |
| 469 | Jose Bautista (R) | .10 |
| 470 | Lance Parrish | .10 |
| 471 | Steve Curry (R) | .10 |
| 472 | Brian Harper | .05 |
| 473 | Don Robinson | .05 |
| 474 | Bob Rodgers | .05 |
| 475 | Dave Parker | .10 |
| 476 | Jon Perlman | .05 |
| 477 | Dick Schofield | .05 |
| 478 | Doug Drabek | .10 |
| 479 | Mike Macfarlane (R) | .10 |
| 480 | Keith Hernandez | .10 |
| 481 | Chris Brown | .08 |
| 482 | Steve Peters (R) | .10 |
| 483 | Mickey Hatcher | .05 |
| 484 | Steve Shields | .05 |
| 485 | Hubie Brooks | .05 |
| 486 | Jack McDowell | .15 |
| 487 | Scott Lusader | .08 |
| 488 | Kevin Coffman | .08 |
| 489 | Schmidt: Bonus | .15 |
| 490 | Chris Sabo (R) | .50 |
| 491 | Mike Birkbeck | .05 |
| 492 | Alan Ashby | .05 |
| 493 | Todd Benzinger | .10 |
| 494 | Shane Rawley | .05 |
| 495 | Candy Maldonado | .05 |
| 496 | Dwayne Henry | .05 |
| 497 | Pete Stanicek | .08 |
| 498 | Dave Valle | .05 |
| 499 | Don Heinkel (R) | .12 |
| 500 | Jose Canseco | .50 |
| 501 | Vance Law | .05 |
| 502 | Duane Ward | .05 |
| 503 | Al Newman | .05 |
| 504 | Bob Walk | .05 |
| 505 | Pete Rose | .20 |
| 506 | Kirt Manwaring | .15 |
| 507 | Steve Farr | .05 |
| 508 | Wally Backman | .05 |
| 509 | Bud Black | .05 |
| 510 | Bob Horner | .05 |
| 511 | Richard Dotson | .08 |
| 512 | Donnie Hill | .05 |
| 513 | Jesse Orosco | .05 |
| 514 | Chet Lemon | .05 |
| 515 | Barry Larkin | .15 |
| 516 | Eddie Whitson | .05 |
| 517 | Greg Brock | .05 |
| 518 | Bruce Ruffin | .05 |
| 519 | Randolph: Bonus | .08 |
| 520 | Rick Sutcliffe | .10 |
| 521 | Mickey Tettleton | .05 |
| 522 | Randy Kramer (R) | .10 |
| 523 | Andres Thomas | .05 |
| 524 | Checklist: 397-528 | .08 |
| 525 | Chili Davis | .08 |
| 526 | Wes Gardner | .05 |
| 527 | Dave Henderson | .10 |
| 528 | Luis Medina (R) | .12 |
| 529 | Tom Foley | .05 |
| 530 | Nolan Ryan | .50 |
| 531 | Dave Hengel | .10 |
| 532 | Jerry Browne | .05 |
| 533 | Andy Hawkins | .05 |
| 534 | Doc Edwards | .05 |
| 535 | Todd Worrell | .08 |
| 536 | Joel Skinner | .05 |
| 537 | Pete Smith | .10 |
| 538 | Juan Castillo | .05 |
| 539 | Barry Jones | .05 |
| 540 | Bo Jackson | .40 |
| 541 | Cecil Fielder | .30 |
| 542 | Todd Frohwirth | .05 |
| 543 | Damon Berryhill | .08 |
| 544 | Jeff Sellers | .05 |
| 545 | Mookie Wilson | .08 |
| 546 | Mark Williamson | .05 |
| 547 | Mark McLemore | .05 |
| 548 | Bobby Witt | .05 |
| 549 | Moyer: Bonus | .05 |
| 550 | Orel Hershiser | .12 |
| 551 | Randy Ready | .05 |
| 552 | Greg Cadaret | .05 |
| 553 | Luis Salazar | .05 |
| 554 | Nick Esasky | .08 |
| 555 | Bert Blyleven | .10 |
| 556 | Bruce Fields | .06 |
| 557 | Keith Miller | .05 |
| 558 | Dan Pasqua | .08 |
| 559 | Juan Agosto | .05 |
| 560 | Tim Raines | .15 |
| 561 | Luis Aguayo | .05 |
| 562 | Danny Cox | .05 |
| 563 | Bill Schroeder | .05 |
| 564 | Russ Nixon | .05 |
| 565 | Jeff Russell | .05 |
| 566 | Al Pedrique | .05 |
| 567 | David Wells | .10 |
| 568 | Mickey Brantley | .08 |
| 569 | German Jimenez (R) | .10 |
| 570 | Tony Gwynn | .20 |
| 571 | Billy Ripken | .05 |
| 572 | Atlee Hammaker | .05 |
| 573 | Jim Abbott (R) | 1.00 |
| 574 | Dave Clark | .05 |
| 575 | Juan Samuel | .08 |
| 576 | Greg Minton | .05 |
| 577 | Randy Bush | .05 |
| 578 | John Morris | .05 |
| 579 | G. Davis: Bonus | .08 |
| 580 | Harold Reynolds | .05 |
| 581 | Gene Nelson | .05 |
| 582 | Mike Marshall | .08 |
| 583 | Paul Gibson (R) | .10 |
| 584 | Randy Velarde | .08 |
| 585 | Harold Baines | .10 |
| 586 | Joe Boever | .05 |
| 587 | Mike Stanley | .05 |
| 588 | Luis Alicea (R) | .10 |
| 589 | Dave Meads | .05 |
| 590 | Andres Galarraga | .08 |
| 591 | Jeff Musselman | .05 |
| 592 | John Cangelosi | .05 |
| 593 | Drew Hall | .05 |
| 594 | Jimy Williams | .05 |
| 595 | Teddy Higuera | .08 |
| 596 | Kurt Stillwell | .05 |
| 597 | Terry Taylor (R) | .10 |
| 598 | Ken Gerhart | .05 |
| 599 | Tom Candiotti | .08 |
| 600 | Wade Boggs | .20 |
| 601 | Dave Dravecky | .05 |
| 602 | Devon White | .08 |
| 603 | Frank Tanana | .08 |
| 604 | Paul O'Neill | .10 |
| 605 | Bob Welch (correct) | .12 |
| 605 | Bob Welch (error) | 3.00 |
| 606 | Rick Dempsey | .05 |
| 607 | Willie Ansley (R) | .25 |
| 608 | Phil Bradley | .08 |
| 609 | Tanana: Bonus | .08 |
| 610 | Randy Myers | .08 |
| 611 | Don Slaught | .05 |
| 612 | Dan Quisenberry | .08 |
| 613 | Gary Varsho (R) | .10 |
| 614 | Joe Hesketh | .05 |
| 615 | Robin Yount | .15 |
| 616 | Steve Rosenberg (R) | .10 |
| 617 | Mark Parent (R) | .10 |
| 618 | Rance Mulliniks | .05 |
| 619 | Checklist: 529-660 | .08 |
| 620 | Barry Bonds | .25 |
| 621 | Rick Mahler | .05 |
| 622 | Stan Javier | .05 |
| 623 | Fred Toliver | .05 |
| 624 | Jack McKeon | .05 |
| 625 | Eddie Murray | .15 |
| 626 | Jeff Reed | .05 |
| 627 | Greg Harris | .10 |
| 628 | Matt Williams | .20 |
| 629 | Pete O'Brien | .08 |
| 630 | Mike Greenwell | .15 |
| 631 | Dave Bergman | .05 |
| 632 | Bryan Harvey (R) | .20 |
| 633 | Daryl Boston | .05 |
| 634 | Marvin Freeman | .08 |
| 635 | Willie Randolph | .08 |
| 636 | Bill Wilkinson | .05 |
| 637 | Carmen Castillo | .05 |
| 638 | Floyd Bannister | .05 |
| 639 | Weiss: Bonus | .08 |
| 640 | Willie McGee | .08 |
| 641 | Curt Young | .05 |
| 642 | Argenis Salazar | .05 |
| 643 | Louie Meadows (R) | .10 |
| 644 | Lloyd McClendon | .05 |
| 645 | Jack Morris | .10 |
| 646 | Kevin Bass | .08 |
| 647 | Randy Johnson (R) | .30 |
| 648 | Sandy Alomar (R) | .50 |
| 649 | Stewart Cliburn | .05 |
| 650 | Kirby Puckett | .25 |
| 651 | Tom Niedenfuer | .05 |
| 652 | Rich Gedman | .05 |
| 653 | Tommy Barrett (R) | .10 |
| 654 | Whitey Herzog | .05 |
| 655 | Dave Magadan | .08 |
| 656 | Ivan Calderon | .10 |
| 657 | Joe Magrane | .10 |
| 658 | R.J. Reynolds | .05 |
| 659 | Al Leiter | .10 |
| 660 | Will Clark | .35 |
| 661 | Turn Back—1984 | .10 |
| 662 | Turn Back—1979 | .10 |
| 663 | Turn Back—1974 | .10 |
| 664 | Turn Back—1969 | .10 |
| 665 | Turn Back—1964 | .10 |
| 666 | Randy St. Claire | .15 |
| 667 | Dwayne Murphy | .05 |
| 668 | Mike Bielecki | .05 |
| 669 | Hershiser: Bonus | .08 |
| 670 | Kevin Seitzer | .08 |
| 671 | Jim Gantner | .05 |
| 672 | Allan Anderson | .08 |
| 673 | Don Baylor | .08 |
| 674 | Otis Nixon | .05 |
| 675 | Bruce Hurst | .08 |
| 676 | Ernie Riles | .05 |
| 677 | Dave Schmidt | .05 |
| 678 | Dion James | .05 |
| 679 | Willie Fraser | .05 |
| 680 | Gary Carter | .10 |
| 681 | Jeff Robinson | .08 |
| 682 | Rick Leach | .05 |
| 683 | Jose Cecena (R) | .10 |
| 684 | Dave Johnson | .05 |
| 685 | Jeff Treadway | .08 |
| 686 | Scott Terry | .08 |
| 687 | Alvin Davis | .08 |
| 688 | Zane Smith | .05 |
| 689 | Stan Jefferson | .08 |
| 690 | Doug Jones | .05 |
| 691 | Roberto Kelly | .20 |
| 692 | Steve Ontiveros | .05 |

| NO. | PLAYER | MINT |
|---|---|---|
| 693 | Pat Borders (R) | .15 |
| 694 | Les Lancaster | .05 |
| 695 | Carlton Fisk | .15 |
| 696 | Don August | .10 |
| 697 | Franklin Stubbs | .05 |
| 698 | Keith Atherton | .05 |
| 699 | Pedrique: Bonus | .05 |
| 700 | Don Mattingly | .30 |
| 701 | Storm Davis | .05 |
| 702 | Jamie Quirk | .05 |
| 703 | Scott Garrelts | .05 |
| 704 | Carlos Quintana (R) | .25 |
| 705 | Terry Kennedy | .05 |
| 706 | Pete Incaviglia | .08 |
| 707 | Steve Jeltz | .05 |
| 708 | Chuck Finley | .12 |
| 709 | Tom Herr | .05 |
| 710 | Dave Cone | .10 |
| 711 | Candy Sierra (R) | .10 |
| 712 | Bill Swift | .05 |
| 713 | Ty Griffin (R) | .15 |
| 714 | Joe Morgan | .05 |
| 715 | Tony Pena | .08 |
| 716 | Wayne Tolleson | .05 |
| 717 | Jamie Moyer | .05 |

| NO. | PLAYER | MINT |
|---|---|---|
| 718 | Glenn Braggs | .05 |
| 719 | Danny Darwin | .05 |
| 720 | Tim Wallach | .08 |
| 721 | Ron Tingley (R) | .10 |
| 722 | Todd Stottlemyre | .12 |
| 723 | Rafael Belliard | .05 |
| 724 | Jerry Don Gleaton | .05 |
| 725 | Terry Steinbach | .08 |
| 726 | Dickie Thon | .05 |
| 727 | Joe Orsulak | .05 |
| 728 | Charlie Puleo | .05 |
| 729 | Buechele: Bonus | .05 |
| 730 | Danny Jackson | .10 |
| 731 | Mike Young | .05 |
| 732 | Steve Buechele | .05 |
| 733 | Randy Bockus (R) | .10 |
| 734 | Jody Reed | .10 |
| 735 | Roger McDowell | .05 |
| 736 | Jeff Hamilton | .05 |
| 737 | Norm Charlton (R) | .15 |
| 738 | Darnell Coles | .05 |
| 739 | Brook Jacoby | .05 |
| 740 | Dan Plesac | .05 |
| 741 | Ken Phelps | .05 |
| 742 | Mike Harkey (R) | .12 |

| NO. | PLAYER | MINT |
|---|---|---|
| 743 | Mike Heath | .05 |
| 744 | Roger Craig | .05 |
| 745 | Fred McGriff | .20 |
| 746 | German Gonzalez (R) | .15 |
| 747 | Wil Tejada | .10 |
| 748 | Jimmy Jones | .05 |
| 749 | Rafael Ramirez | .05 |
| 750 | Bret Saberhagen | .10 |
| 751 | Ken Oberkfell | .05 |
| 752 | Jim Gott | .05 |
| 753 | Jose Uribe | .05 |
| 754 | Bob Brower | .05 |
| 755 | Mike Scioscia | .05 |
| 756 | Scott Medvin (R) | .10 |
| 757 | Brady Anderson (R) | .12 |
| 758 | Gene Walter | .05 |
| 759 | Deer: Bonus | .05 |
| 760 | Lee Smith | .08 |
| 761 | Dante Bichette (R) | .15 |
| 762 | Bobby Thigpen | .05 |
| 763 | Dave Martinez | .05 |
| 764 | Robin Ventura (R) | 1.50 |
| 765 | Glenn Davis | .10 |
| 766 | Cecilio Guante | .05 |
| 767 | Mike Capel (R) | .10 |

| NO. | PLAYER | MINT |
|---|---|---|
| 768 | Bill Wegman | .05 |
| 769 | Junior Ortiz | .05 |
| 770 | Alan Trammell | .10 |
| 771 | Ron Kittle | .08 |
| 772 | Ron Oester | .05 |
| 773 | Keith Moreland | .05 |
| 774 | Frank Robinson | .08 |
| 775 | Jeff Reardon | .08 |
| 776 | Nelson Liriano | .05 |
| 777 | Ted Power | .05 |
| 778 | Bruce Benedict | .05 |
| 779 | Craig McMurtry | .05 |
| 780 | Pedro Guerrero | .10 |
| 781 | Greg Briley (R) | .15 |
| 782 | Checklist: 681-792 | .08 |
| 783 | Trevor Wilson (R) | .12 |
| 784 | Steve Avery (R) | 2.00 |
| 785 | Ellis Burks | .20 |
| 786 | Melido Perez | .08 |
| 787 | Dave West (R) | .15 |
| 788 | Mike Morgan | .05 |
| 789 | Jackson: Bonus | .08 |
| 790 | Sid Fernandez | .10 |
| 791 | Jim Lindeman | .05 |
| 792 | Rafael Santana | .05 |

## 1989 Topps Traded . . . Complete Set of 132 Cards—Value $12.00

Updates the main 1989 card set with players who changed teams during the season and rookies who joined their teams early in the season. Features the first Topps Card of Ken Griffey, Jr., Jerome Walton, Tom Gordon, Junior Felix and Dwight Smith. The complete set was packaged in a printed box and distributed primarily through card hobby dealers.

| NO. | PLAYER | MINT |
|---|---|---|
| 1 | Don Aase | .05 |
| 2 | Jim Abbott | .75 |
| 3 | Kent Anderson (R) | .15 |
| 4 | Keith Atherton | .05 |
| 5 | Wally Backman | .05 |
| 6 | Steve Balboni | .05 |
| 7 | Jesse Barfield | .05 |
| 8 | Steve Bedrosian | .05 |
| 9 | Todd Benzinger | .05 |
| 10 | Geronimo Berroa | .10 |
| 11 | Bert Blyleven | .05 |
| 12 | Bob Boone | .05 |
| 13 | Phil Bradley | .05 |
| 14 | Jeff Brantley | .20 |
| 15 | Kevin Brown | .10 |
| 16 | Jerry Browne | .05 |
| 17 | Chuck Cary | .10 |
| 18 | Carmen Castillo | .05 |
| 19 | Jim Clancy | .05 |
| 20 | Jack Clark | .10 |
| 21 | Bryan Clutterbuck | .05 |
| 22 | Jody Davis | .05 |
| 23 | Mike Devereaux | .12 |
| 24 | Frank DiPino | .05 |
| 25 | Benny DiStefano | .05 |
| 26 | John Dopson | .10 |
| 27 | Len Dykstra | .12 |
| 28 | Jim Eisenreich | .05 |
| 29 | Nick Esasky | .10 |
| 30 | Alvaro Espinoza | .10 |
| 31 | Darrell Evans | .05 |
| 32 | Junior Felix (R) | .20 |
| 33 | Felix Fermin | .05 |

| NO. | PLAYER | MINT |
|---|---|---|
| 34 | Julio Franco | .15 |
| 35 | Terry Francona | .05 |
| 36 | Cito Gaston | .05 |
| 37 | Bob Geren | .12 |
| 38 | Tom Gordon (R) | .25 |
| 39 | Tommy Gregg | .15 |
| 40 | Ken Griffey | .15 |
| 41 | Ken Griffey, Jr. (R) | 5.00 |
| 42 | Kevin Gross | .05 |
| 43 | Lee Guetterman | .05 |
| 44 | Mel Hall | .05 |
| 45 | Erik Hanson (R) | .50 |
| 46 | Gene Harris | .10 |
| 47 | Andy Hawkins | .05 |
| 48 | Rickey Henderson | .35 |
| 49 | Tom Herr | .05 |
| 50 | Ken Hill (R) | .20 |
| 51 | Brian Holman | .25 |
| 52 | Brian Holton | .05 |
| 53 | Art Howe | .05 |
| 54 | Ken Howell | .05 |
| 55 | Bruce Hurst | .05 |
| 56 | Chris James | .05 |
| 57 | Randy Johnson | .10 |
| 58 | Jimmy Jones | .05 |
| 59 | Terry Kennedy | .05 |
| 60 | Paul Kilgus | .05 |
| 61 | Eric King | .05 |
| 62 | Ron Kittle | .05 |
| 63 | John Kruk | .05 |
| 64 | Randy Kutcher | .10 |
| 65 | Steve Lake | .05 |
| 66 | Mark Langston | .15 |

| NO. | PLAYER | MINT |
|---|---|---|
| 67 | Dave LaPoint | .05 |
| 68 | Rick Leach | .05 |
| 69 | Terry Leach | .05 |
| 70 | Jim Levebvre | .05 |
| 71 | Al Leiter | .05 |
| 72 | Jeffrey Leonard | .05 |
| 73 | Derek Lilliquist | .15 |
| 74 | Rick Mahler | .05 |
| 75 | Tom McCarthy | .15 |
| 76 | Lloyd McClendon | .10 |
| 77 | Lance McCullers | .05 |
| 78 | Oddibe McDowell | .05 |
| 79 | Roger McDowell | .05 |
| 80 | Larry McWilliams | .05 |
| 81 | Randy Milligan | .15 |
| 82 | Mike Moore | .10 |
| 83 | Keith Moreland | .05 |
| 84 | Mike Morgan | .05 |
| 85 | Jamie Moyer | .05 |
| 86 | Rob Murphy | .05 |
| 87 | Eddie Murray | .20 |
| 88 | Pete O'Brien | .05 |
| 89 | Gregg Olson | .40 |
| 90 | Steve Ontiveros | .05 |
| 91 | Jesse Orosco | .05 |
| 92 | Spike Owen | .05 |
| 93 | Rafael Palmeiro | .15 |
| 94 | Clay Parker | .12 |
| 95 | Jeff Parrett | .05 |
| 96 | Lance Parrish | .05 |
| 97 | Dennis Powell | .05 |
| 98 | Rey Quinones | .05 |
| 99 | Doug Rader | .05 |

| NO. | PLAYER | MINT |
|---|---|---|
| 100 | Willie Randolph | .05 |
| 101 | Shane Rawley | .05 |
| 102 | Randy Ready | .05 |
| 103 | Bip Roberts | .05 |
| 104 | Kenny Rogers | .15 |
| 105 | Ed Romero | .05 |
| 106 | Nolan Ryan | 1.25 |
| 107 | Luis Salazar | .05 |
| 108 | Juan Samuel | .05 |
| 109 | Alex Sanchez | .12 |
| 110 | Deion Sanders (R) | .60 |
| 111 | Steve Sax | .10 |
| 112 | Rick Schu | .05 |
| 113 | Dwight Smith (R) | .15 |
| 114 | Lonnie Smith | .05 |
| 115 | Billy Spiers (R) | .20 |
| 116 | Kent Tekulve | .05 |
| 117 | Walt Terrell | .05 |
| 118 | Milt Thompson | .05 |
| 119 | Dickie Thon | .05 |
| 120 | Jeff Torborg | .05 |
| 121 | Jeff Treadway | .05 |
| 122 | Omar Vizquel | .15 |
| 123 | Jerome Walton (R) | .35 |
| 124 | Gary Ward | .05 |
| 125 | Claudell Washington | .05 |
| 126 | Curt Wilkerson | .05 |
| 127 | Eddie Williams | .05 |
| 128 | Frank Williams | .05 |
| 129 | Ken Williams | .05 |
| 130 | Mitch Williams | .15 |
| 131 | Steve Wilson | .15 |
| 132 | Checklist | .05 |

# 1990 Topps . . . Complete Set of 792 Cards—Value $22.00 (Factory-Sealed Set—Value $28.00)

The front of the cards feature six different color schemes. A card was issued to honor deceased Commissioner Giamatti. Four special cards were issued to honor Nolan Ryan—each card showed him with a different team. In a revised checklist format, the cards were listed by team.

JUAN GONZALEZ

FRANK THOMAS

TODD ZEILE

ERIC ANTHONY

BEN McDONALD

| NO. | PLAYER | MINT |
|---|---|---|
| 1 | Nolan Ryan | .50 |
| 2 | Nolan Ryan | .20 |
|  | Mets (1965 to 1971) |  |
| 3 | Nolan Ryan | .20 |
|  | Angels (1972 to 1979) |  |
| 4 | Nolan Ryan | .20 |
|  | Astros (1980 to 1988) |  |
| 5 | Nolan Ryan | .20 |
|  | Rangers (1989) |  |
| 6 | '89 Record: V. Coleman | .08 |
| 7 | '89 Record: R. Henderson | .10 |
| 8 | '89 Record: C. Ripken | .08 |
| 9 | Eric Plunk | .05 |
| 10 | Barry Larkin | .10 |
| 11 | Paul Gibson | .05 |
| 12 | Joe Girardi | .08 |
| 13 | Mark Williamson | .05 |
| 14 | Mike Fetters (R) | .10 |
| 15 | Teddy Higuera | .05 |
| 16 | Kent Anderson | .08 |
| 17 | Kelly Downs | .08 |
| 18 | Carlos Quintana | .12 |
| 19 | Al Newman | .05 |
| 20 | Mark Gubicza | .05 |
| 21 | Jeff Torborg | .05 |
| 22 | Bruce Ruffin | .05 |
| 23 | Randy Velarde | .05 |
| 24 | Joe Hesketh | .05 |
| 25 | Willie Randolph | .08 |
| 26 | Don Slaught | .05 |
| 27 | Rick Leach | .05 |
| 28 | Duane Ward | .05 |
| 29 | John Cangelosi | .05 |
| 30 | David Cone | .10 |
| 31 | Henry Cotto | .05 |
| 32 | John Farrell | .08 |
| 33 | Greg Walker | .05 |
| 34 | Tony Fossas (R) | .10 |
| 35 | Benny Santiago | .08 |
| 36 | John Costello | .05 |
| 37 | Domingo Ramos | .05 |
| 38 | Wes Gardner | .05 |
| 39 | Curt Ford | .05 |
| 40 | Jay Howell | .08 |
| 41 | Matt Williams | .12 |
| 42 | Jeff Robinson | .05 |
| 43 | Dante Bichette | .05 |
| 44 | R. Salkeld (#1 DP)(R) | .40 |
| 45 | Dave Parker | .10 |
| 46 | Rob Dibble | .10 |
| 47 | Brian Harper | .08 |
| 48 | Zane Smith | .05 |
| 49 | Tom Lawless | .05 |
| 50 | Glenn Davis | .10 |
| 51 | Doug Rader | .05 |
| 52 | Jack Daugherty (R) | .10 |
| 53 | Mike LaCoss | .05 |
| 54 | Joel Skinner | .05 |
| 55 | Darrell Evans | .05 |
| 56 | Franklin Stubbs | .05 |
| 57 | Greg Vaughn | .50 |
| 58 | Keith Miller | .05 |
| 59 | Ted Power | .05 |
| 60 | George Brett | .15 |
| 61 | Deion Sanders | .15 |
| 62 | Ramon Martinez | .25 |
| 63 | Mike Pagliarulo | .08 |

| NO. | PLAYER | MINT |
|---|---|---|
| 64 | Danny Darwin | .05 |
| 65 | Devon White | .08 |
| 66 | Greg Litton | .10 |
| 67 | Scott Sanderson | .05 |
| 68 | Dave Henderson | .05 |
| 69 | Todd Frohwirth | .05 |
| 70 | Mike Greenwell | .10 |
| 71 | Allan Anderson | .08 |
| 72 | Jeff Huson (R) | .10 |
| 73 | Bob Milacki | .08 |
| 74 | J. Jackson (#1 DP) (R) | .15 |
| 75 | Doug Jones | .05 |
| 76 | Dave Valle | .05 |
| 77 | Dave Bergman | .05 |
| 78 | Mike Flanagan | .05 |
| 79 | Ron Kittle | .05 |
| 80 | Jeff Russell | .05 |
| 81 | Bob Rodgers | .05 |
| 82 | Scott Terry | .05 |
| 83 | Hensley Meulens | .20 |
| 84 | Ray Searage | .05 |
| 85 | Jaun Samuel | .08 |
| 86 | Paul Kilgus | .05 |
| 87 | Rick Luecken (R) | .10 |
| 88 | Glenn Braggs | .05 |
| 89 | Clint Zavaras (R) | .10 |
| 90 | Jack Clark | .08 |
| 91 | Steve Frey (R) | .10 |
| 92 | Mike Stanley | .05 |
| 93 | Shawn Hillegas | .05 |
| 94 | Herm Winningham | .05 |
| 95 | Todd Worrell | .08 |
| 96 | Jody Reed | .05 |
| 97 | Curt Schilling | .10 |
| 98 | Jose Gonzalez | .05 |
| 99 | Rich Monteleone | .10 |
| 100 | Will Clark | .30 |
| 101 | Shane Rawley | .05 |
| 102 | Stan Javier | .05 |
| 103 | Marvin Freeman | .05 |
| 104 | Bob Knepper | .05 |
| 105 | Randy Myers | .05 |
| 106 | Charlie O'Brien | .05 |
| 107 | Fred Lynn | .08 |
| 108 | Rod Nichols | .05 |
| 109 | Roberto Kelly | .08 |
| 110 | Tommy Helms (Mgr.) | .05 |
| 111 | Ed Whited (R) | .10 |
| 112 | Glenn Wilson | .05 |
| 113 | Manny Lee | .05 |
| 114 | Mike Bielecki | .05 |
| 115 | Tony Pena | .08 |
| 116 | Floyd Bannister | .05 |
| 117 | Mike Sharperson | .05 |
| 118 | Eric Hanson | .12 |
| 119 | Billy Hatcher | .05 |
| 120 | John Franco | .08 |
| 121 | Robin Ventura | .35 |
| 122 | Shawn Abner | .05 |
| 123 | Rich Gedman | .05 |
| 124 | Dave Dravecky | .05 |
| 125 | Kent Hrbek | .08 |
| 126 | Randy Kramer | .05 |
| 127 | Mike Devereaux | .08 |
| 128 | Checklist No. 1 | .05 |
| 129 | Ron Jones | .05 |
| 130 | Bert Blyleven | .08 |

| NO. | PLAYER | MINT |
|---|---|---|
| 131 | Matt Nokes | .08 |
| 132 | Lance Blankenship | .08 |
| 133 | Ricky Horton | .05 |
| 134 | Earl Cunningham (R) | .15 |
|  | (#1 DP' |  |
| 135 | Dave Magadan | .08 |
| 136 | Kevin Brown | .08 |
| 137 | Marty Pevey (R) | .10 |
| 138 | Al Leiter | .05 |
| 139 | Greg Brock | .05 |
| 140 | Andre Dawson | .12 |
| 141 | John Hart (Mgr.) | .05 |
| 142 | Jeff Wetherby (R) | .10 |
| 143 | Rafael Belliard | .05 |
| 144 | Bud Black | .05 |
| 145 | Terry Steinbach | .08 |
| 146 | Rob Richie | .08 |
| 147 | Chuck Finley | .08 |
| 148 | Edgar Martinez | .10 |
| 149 | Steve Farr | .05 |
| 150 | Kirk Gibson | .08 |
| 151 | Rick Mahler | .05 |
| 152 | Lonnie Smith | .05 |
| 153 | Randy Milligan | .08 |
| 154 | Mike Maddux | .05 |
| 155 | Ellis Burks | .10 |
| 156 | Ken Patterson | .05 |
| 157 | Craig Biggio | .10 |
| 158 | Craig Lefferts | .05 |
| 159 | Mike Felder | .05 |
| 160 | Dave Righetti | .10 |
| 161 | Harold Reynolds | .05 |
| 162 | Todd Zeile | .30 |
| 163 | Phil Bradley | .05 |
| 164 | Jeff Juden (# 1 DP) (R) | .35 |
| 165 | Walt Weiss | .05 |
| 166 | Bobby Witt | .05 |
| 167 | Kevin Appier | .20 |
| 168 | Jose Lind | .05 |
| 169 | Richard Dotson | .05 |
| 170 | George Bell | .10 |
| 171 | Russ Nixon (Mgr.) | .05 |
| 172 | Tom Lampkin | .05 |
| 173 | Tim Belcher | .08 |
| 174 | Jeff Kunkel | .05 |
| 175 | Mike Moore | .08 |
| 176 | Luis Quinones | .05 |
| 177 | Mike Henneman | .05 |
| 178 | Chris James | .05 |
| 179 | Brian Holton | .05 |
| 180 | Rock Raines | .12 |
| 181 | Juan Agosto | .05 |
| 182 | Mookie Wilson | .08 |
| 183 | Steve Lake | .05 |
| 184 | Danny Cox | .05 |
| 185 | Ruben Sierra | .20 |
| 186 | Dave LaPoint | .05 |
| 187 | Rick Wrona | .05 |
| 188 | Mike Smithson | .05 |
| 189 | Dick Schofield | .05 |
| 190 | Rick Reuschel | .08 |
| 191 | Pat Borders | .05 |
| 192 | Don August | .08 |
| 193 | Andy Benes | .10 |
| 194 | Glenallen Hill | .10 |
| 195 | Tim Burke | .05 |
| 196 | Gerard Young | .05 |
| 197 | Doug Drabek | .05 |

| NO. | PLAYER | MINT |
|---|---|---|
| 198 | Mike Marshall | .08 |
| 199 | Sergio Valdez (R) | .10 |
| 200 | Don Mattingly | .30 |
| 201 | Cito Gaston (Mgr.) | .05 |
| 202 | Mike MacFarlane | .05 |
| 203 | Mike Roesler (R) | .10 |
| 204 | Bob Dernier | .05 |
| 205 | Mark Davis | .08 |
| 206 | Nick Esasky | .05 |
| 207 | Bob Ojeda | .05 |
| 208 | Brook Jacoby | .05 |
| 209 | Greg Mathews | .05 |
| 210 | Ryne Sandberg | .25 |
| 211 | John Cerutti | .05 |
| 212 | Joe Orsulak | .05 |
| 213 | Scott Bankhead | .05 |
| 214 | Terry Francona | .05 |
| 215 | Kirk McCaskill | .08 |
| 216 | Ricky Jordan | .10 |
| 217 | Don Robinson | .05 |
| 218 | Wally Backman | .05 |
| 219 | Donn Pall | .05 |
| 220 | Barry Bonds | .20 |
| 221 | Gary Mielke (R) | .10 |
| 222 | Kurt Stillwell | .05 |
| 223 | Tommy Gregg | .05 |
| 224 | Delino DeShields (R) | .50 |
| 225 | Jim Deshaies | .05 |
| 226 | Mickey Hatcher | .05 |
| 227 | Kevin Tapani (R) | .30 |
| 228 | Dave Martinez | .05 |
| 229 | David Wells | .05 |
| 230 | Keith Hernandez | .08 |
| 231 | Jack McKeon (Mgr.) | .05 |
| 232 | Darnell Coles | .05 |
| 233 | Ken Hill | .08 |
| 234 | Mariano Duncan | .05 |
| 235 | Jeff Reardon | .08 |
| 236 | Hal Morris | .50 |
| 237 | Kevin Ritz (R) | .10 |
| 238 | Felix Jose | .20 |
| 239 | Eric Show | .05 |
| 240 | Mark Grace | .15 |
| 241 | Mike Krukow | .08 |
| 242 | Fred Manrique | .05 |
| 243 | Barry Jones | .05 |
| 244 | Bill Schroeder | .05 |
| 245 | Roger Clemens | .25 |
| 246 | Jim Eisenreich | .05 |
| 247 | Jerry Reed | .05 |
| 248 | Dave Anderson | .05 |
| 249 | Mike Smith (R) | .10 |
| 250 | Jose Canseco | .50 |
| 251 | Jeff Blauser | .05 |
| 252 | Otis Nixon | .05 |
| 253 | Mark Portugal | .05 |
| 254 | Francisco Cabrera (R) | .10 |
| 255 | Bobby Thigpen | .05 |
| 256 | Marvell Wynne | .05 |
| 257 | Jose DeLeon | .05 |
| 258 | Barry Lyons | .05 |
| 259 | Lance McCullers | .05 |
| 260 | Eric Davis | .15 |
| 261 | Whitey Herzog (Mgr.) | .05 |
| 262 | Checklist No. 2 | .05 |
| 263 | Mel Stottlemyre, Jr. | .08 |
| 264 | Bryan Clutterbuck | .05 |

| NO. | PLAYER | MINT |
|---|---|---|
| 265 | Pete O'Brien | .08 |
| 266 | German Gonzalez | .05 |
| 267 | Mark Davidson | .05 |
| 268 | Rob Murphy | .05 |
| 269 | Dickie Thon | .05 |
| 270 | Dave Stewart | .10 |
| 271 | Chet Lemon | .05 |
| 272 | Bryan Harvey | .05 |
| 273 | Bobby Bonilla | .20 |
| 274 | Goose Gozzo (R) | .10 |
| 275 | Mickey Tettleton | .05 |
| 276 | Gary Thurman | .05 |
| 277 | Lenny Harris | .05 |
| 278 | Pascual Perez | .05 |
| 279 | Steve Buechele | .05 |
| 280 | Lou Whitaker | .08 |
| 281 | Kevin Bass | .05 |
| 282 | Derek Lilliquist | .08 |
| 283 | Joey Belle | .50 |
| 284 | Mark Gardner (R) | .20 |
| 285 | Willie McGee | .08 |
| 286 | Lee Guetterman | .05 |
| 287 | Vance Law | .05 |
| 288 | Greg Briley | .10 |
| 289 | Norm Charlton | .05 |
| 290 | Robin Yount | .15 |
| 291 | Dave Johnson (Mgr.) | .05 |
| 292 | Jim Gott | .05 |
| 293 | Mike Gallego | .05 |
| 294 | Craig McMurtry | .05 |
| 295 | Fred McGriff | .15 |
| 296 | Jeff Ballard | .08 |
| 297 | Tom Herr | .08 |
| 298 | Danny Gladden | .05 |
| 299 | Adam Petterson | .08 |
| 300 | Bo Jackson | .50 |
| 301 | Don Aase | .05 |
| 302 | Marcus Lawton (R) | .15 |
| 303 | Rick Cerone | .05 |
| 304 | Marty Clary | .05 |
| 305 | Eddie Murray | .10 |
| 306 | Tom Niedenfuer | .05 |
| 307 | Bip Roberts | .05 |
| 308 | Jose Guzman | .05 |
| 309 | Eric Yelding | .08 |
| 310 | Steve Bedrosian | .05 |
| 311 | Dwight Smith | .08 |
| 312 | Dan Quisenberry | .05 |
| 313 | Gus Polidor | .05 |
| 314 | D. Harris (# 1 DP) (R) | .15 |
| 315 | Bruce Hurst | .05 |
| 316 | Carney Lansford | .08 |
| 317 | Mark Guthrie (R) | .10 |
| 318 | Wallace Johnson | .05 |
| 319 | Dion James | .05 |
| 320 | Dave Stieb | .05 |
| 321 | Joe Morgan (Mgr.) | .05 |
| 322 | Junior Ortiz | .05 |
| 323 | Willie Wilson | .08 |
| 324 | Pete Harnisch | .15 |
| 325 | Robby Thompson | .08 |
| 326 | Tom McCarthy | .05 |
| 327 | Ken Williams | .05 |
| 328 | Curt Young | .05 |
| 329 | Oddible McDowell | .05 |
| 330 | Ron Darling | .08 |
| 331 | Juan Gonzalez (R) | 1.50 |
| 332 | Paul O'Neill | .08 |
| 333 | Bill Wegman | .05 |
| 334 | Johnny Ray | .08 |
| 335 | Andy Hawkins | .05 |
| 336 | Ken Griffey, Jr. | 1.50 |
| 337 | Lloyd McClendon | .05 |
| 338 | Dannis Lamp | .05 |
| 339 | Dave Clark | .05 |
| 340 | Fernando Valenzuela | .10 |
| 341 | Tom Foley | .05 |
| 342 | Alex Trevino | .05 |
| 343 | Frank Tanana | .05 |
| 344 | George Canale (R) | .15 |
| 345 | Harold Baines | .08 |
| 346 | Jim Presley | .05 |
| 347 | Junior Felix | .10 |
| 348 | Gary Wayne | .08 |
| 349 | Steve Finley | .10 |
| 350 | Bret Saberhagen | .10 |

| NO. | PLAYER | MINT |
|---|---|---|
| 351 | Craig Roger (Mgr.) | .05 |
| 352 | Bryn Smith | .05 |
| 353 | Sandy Alomar | .15 |
| 354 | Stan Belinda (R) | .15 |
| 355 | Marty Barrett | .05 |
| 356 | Randy Ready | .05 |
| 357 | Dave West | .10 |
| 358 | Andres Thomas | .05 |
| 359 | Jimmy Jones | .05 |
| 360 | Paul Molitor | .10 |
| 361 | Randy McCament (R) | .10 |
| 362 | Damon Berryhill | .08 |
| 363 | Dan Petry | .05 |
| 364 | Rolando Roomes | .08 |
| 365 | Ozzie Guillen | .08 |
| 366 | Mike Heath | .05 |
| 367 | Mike Morgan | .05 |
| 368 | Bill Doran | .05 |
| 369 | Todd Burns | .05 |
| 370 | Tim Wallach | .05 |
| 371 | Jimmy Key | .08 |
| 372 | Terry Kennedy | .05 |
| 373 | Alvin Davis | .08 |
| 374 | Steve Cummings (R) | .10 |
| 375 | Dwight Evans | .08 |
| 376 | Checklist No. 3 | .05 |
| 377 | Mickey Weston (R) | .10 |
| 378 | Luis Salazar | .05 |
| 379 | Steve Rosenburg | .05 |
| 380 | Dave Winfield | .12 |
| 381 | Frank Robinson (Mgr.) | .10 |
| 382 | Jeff Mussleman | .05 |
| 383 | John Morris | .05 |
| 384 | Pat Combs | .10 |
| 385 | Fred McGriff (AS) | .10 |
| 386 | Franco Julio (AS) | .08 |
| 387 | Wade Boggs (AS) | .15 |
| 388 | Cal Ripken (AS) | .12 |
| 389 | Robin Yount (AS) | .12 |
| 390 | Ruben Sierra (AS) | .10 |
| 391 | Kirby Puckett (AS) | .15 |
| 392 | Carlton Fisk (AS) | .10 |
| 393 | Bret Saberhagen (AS) | .05 |
| 394 | Jeff Ballard (AS) | .08 |
| 395 | Jeff Russell (AS) | .05 |
| 396 | A. Bartlett Giamatti Baseball Commissioner (deceased) | .15 |
| 397 | Will Clark (AS) | .15 |
| 398 | Ryne Sandberg (AS) | .15 |
| 399 | Howard Johnson (AS) | .10 |
| 400 | Ozzie Smith (AS) | .08 |
| 401 | Kevin Mitchell (AS) | .10 |
| 402 | Eric Davis (AS) | .10 |
| 403 | Tony Gwynn (AS) | .15 |
| 404 | Craig Biggio (AS) | .08 |
| 405 | Mike Scott (AS) | .08 |
| 406 | Joe Magrane (AS) | .08 |
| 407 | Mark Davis (AS) | .08 |
| 408 | Trevor Wilson | .05 |
| 409 | Tom Brunansky | .05 |
| 410 | Jose Boever | .05 |
| 411 | Ken Phelps | .05 |
| 412 | Jamie Moyer | .05 |
| 413 | Brian Dubois (R) | .10 |
| 414 | F. Thomas (#1 DP) (R) | 4.00 |
| 415 | Shawon Dunston | .08 |
| 416 | Dave Johnson (R) | .10 |
| 417 | Jim Gantner | .05 |
| 418 | Tom Browning | .05 |
| 419 | Beau Allred (R) | .10 |
| 420 | Carlton Fisk | .15 |
| 421 | Greg Minton | .05 |
| 422 | Pat Sheridan | .05 |
| 423 | Fred Toliver | .05 |
| 424 | Jerry Reuss | .05 |
| 425 | Bill Landrum | .05 |
| 426 | Jeff Hamilton | .05 |
| 427 | Carmen Castillo | .05 |
| 428 | Steve Davis (R) | .10 |
| 429 | Tom Kelly (Mgr.) | .05 |
| 430 | Pete Incaviglia | .10 |
| 431 | Randy Johnson | .08 |
| 432 | Damaso Garcia | .05 |
| 433 | Steve Olin (R) | .10 |
| 434 | Mark Carreon | .05 |

| NO. | PLAYER | MINT |
|---|---|---|
| 435 | Kevin Seitzer | .08 |
| 436 | Mel Hall | .05 |
| 437 | Les Lancaster | .05 |
| 438 | Greg Myers | .05 |
| 439 | Jeff Parrett | .05 |
| 440 | Alan Trammell | .08 |
| 441 | Bob Kipper | .05 |
| 442 | Jerry Browne | .08 |
| 443 | Cris Carpenter | .05 |
| 444 | Kyle Abbott (#1 DP) (R) | .20 |
| 445 | Danny Jackson | .08 |
| 446 | Dan Pasqua | .05 |
| 447 | Atlee Hammaker | .05 |
| 448 | Greg Gagne | .05 |
| 449 | Dennis Rasmussen | .05 |
| 450 | Rickey Henderson | .30 |
| 451 | Mark Lemke | .05 |
| 452 | Luis de los Santos | .08 |
| 453 | Jody Davis | .05 |
| 454 | Jeff King | .10 |
| 455 | Jeffrey Leonard | .05 |
| 456 | Chris Gwynn | .08 |
| 457 | Gregg Jefferies | .10 |
| 458 | Bob McClure | .05 |
| 459 | Jim Lefebvre (Mgr.) | .05 |
| 460 | Mike Scott | .08 |
| 461 | Carlos Martinez | .10 |
| 462 | Denny Walling | .05 |
| 463 | Drew Hall | .05 |
| 464 | Jerome Walton | .10 |
| 465 | Kevin Gross | .05 |
| 466 | Rance Mullniks | .05 |
| 467 | Juan Nieves | .05 |
| 468 | Billy Ripken | .08 |
| 469 | John Kruk | .05 |
| 470 | Frank Viola | .10 |
| 471 | Mike Brumley | .05 |
| 472 | Jose Uribe | .05 |
| 473 | Joe Price | .05 |
| 474 | Rich Thompson | .08 |
| 475 | Bob Welch | .05 |
| 476 | Brad Komminsk | .05 |
| 477 | Willie Fraser | .05 |
| 478 | Mike LaValliere | .05 |
| 479 | Frank White | .05 |
| 480 | Sid Fernandez | .08 |
| 481 | Garry Templeton | .05 |
| 482 | Steve Carter | .08 |
| 483 | Alejandro Pena | .05 |
| 484 | Mike Fitzgerald | .05 |
| 485 | John Candelaria | .05 |
| 486 | Jeff Treadway | .05 |
| 487 | Steve Searcy | .08 |
| 488 | Ken Oberfell | .05 |
| 489 | Nick Leyva (Mgr.) | .05 |
| 490 | Dan Plesac | .05 |
| 491 | Dave Cochrane (R) | .10 |
| 492 | Ron Oester | .05 |
| 493 | Jason Grimsley (R) | .10 |
| 494 | Terry Puhl | .05 |
| 495 | Lee Smith | .08 |
| 496 | Cecil Espy | .05 |
| 497 | Dave Schmidt | .08 |
| 498 | Rick Schu | .05 |
| 499 | Bill Long | .05 |
| 500 | Kevin Mitchell | .15 |
| 501 | Matt Young | .05 |
| 502 | Mitch Webster | .05 |
| 503 | Randy St. Claire | .05 |
| 504 | Tom O'Malley | .05 |
| 505 | Kelly Gruber | .12 |
| 506 | Tom Glavine | .20 |
| 507 | Gary Redus | .05 |
| 508 | Terry Leach | .08 |
| 509 | Tom Pagnozzi | .05 |
| 510 | Doc Gooden | .15 |
| 511 | Clay Parker | .05 |
| 512 | Gary Pettis | .05 |
| 513 | Mark Eichhorn | .05 |
| 514 | Andy Allanson | .05 |
| 515 | Lenny Dykstra | .10 |
| 516 | Tim Leary | .08 |
| 517 | Roberto Alomar | .15 |
| 518 | Bill Krueger | .05 |
| 519 | Bucky Dent (Mgr.) | .05 |
| 520 | Mitch Williams | .08 |

| NO. | PLAYER | MINT |
|---|---|---|
| 521 | Craig Worthington | .08 |
| 522 | Mike Dunne | .05 |
| 523 | Jay Bell | .05 |
| 524 | Daryl Boston | .05 |
| 525 | Wally Joyner | .10 |
| 526 | Checklist No. 4 | .05 |
| 527 | Ron Hassey | .05 |
| 528 | Kevin Wickander | .08 |
| 529 | Greg Harris | .05 |
| 530 | Mark Langston | .10 |
| 531 | Ken Caminiti | .08 |
| 532 | Cecilio Guante | .10 |
| 533 | Tim Jones | .05 |
| 534 | Louie Meadows | .05 |
| 535 | John Smoltz | .15 |
| 536 | Bob Geren | .08 |
| 537 | Mark Grant | .05 |
| 538 | Billy Spiers | .10 |
| 539 | Neal Heaton | .05 |
| 540 | Danny Tartabull | .10 |
| 541 | Pat Perry | .05 |
| 542 | Darren Daulton | .05 |
| 543 | Nelson Liriano | .05 |
| 544 | Dennis Boyd | .05 |
| 545 | Kevin McReynolds | .10 |
| 546 | Kevin Hickey | .08 |
| 547 | Jack Howell | .05 |
| 548 | Pat Clements | .05 |
| 549 | Don Zimmer (Mgr.) | .05 |
| 550 | Julio Franco | .10 |
| 551 | Tim Crews | .05 |
| 552 | Mike Smith (R) | .10 |
| 553 | Scott Scudder | .12 |
| 554 | Jay Buhner | .08 |
| 555 | Jack Morris | .10 |
| 556 | Gene Larkin | .05 |
| 557 | Jeff Innis (R) | .10 |
| 558 | Rafael Ramirez | .05 |
| 559 | Andy McGaffigan | .05 |
| 560 | Steve Sax | .08 |
| 561 | Ken Dayley | .05 |
| 562 | Chad Kreuter | .05 |
| 563 | Alex Sanchez | .10 |
| 564 | T. Houston (#1 DP) (R) | .25 |
| 565 | Scott Fletcher | .05 |
| 566 | Mark Knudson | .05 |
| 567 | Ron Gant | .20 |
| 568 | John Smiley | .08 |
| 569 | Ivan Calderon | .05 |
| 570 | Cal Ripken | .25 |
| 571 | Brett Butler | .05 |
| 572 | Greg Harris | .05 |
| 573 | Danny Heep | .05 |
| 574 | Bill Swift | .05 |
| 575 | Lance Parrish | .08 |
| 576 | Mike Dyer (R) | .10 |
| 577 | Charlie Hayes | .05 |
| 578 | Joe Magrane | .10 |
| 579 | Art Howe (Mgr.) | .05 |
| 580 | Joe Carter | .10 |
| 581 | Ken Griffey | .05 |
| 582 | Rick Honeycutt | .05 |
| 583 | Bruce Benedict | .05 |
| 584 | Phil Stephenson | .08 |
| 585 | Kal Daniels | .10 |
| 586 | Ed Nunez | .05 |
| 587 | Lance Johnson | .05 |
| 588 | Rick Rhoden | .05 |
| 589 | Mike Aldrette | .05 |
| 590 | Ozzie Smith | .10 |
| 591 | Todd Stottlemyre | .10 |
| 592 | R.J. Reynolds | .05 |
| 593 | Scott Bradley | .05 |
| 594 | Luis Sojo (R) | .15 |
| 595 | Greg Swindell | .10 |
| 596 | Jose DeJesus | .05 |
| 597 | Chris Bosio | .05 |
| 598 | Brady Anderson | .10 |
| 599 | Frank Williams | .05 |
| 600 | Darryl Strawberry | .25 |
| 601 | Luis Rivera | .05 |
| 602 | Scott Garrelts | .08 |
| 603 | Tony Armas | .05 |
| 604 | Ron Robinson | .05 |
| 605 | Mike Scioscia | .08 |
| 606 | Storm Davis | .05 |

| NO. PLAYER | MINT | NO. PLAYER | MINT | NO. PLAYER | MINT | NO. PLAYER | MINT |
|---|---|---|---|---|---|---|---|
| 607 Steve Jeltz | .05 | 655 Gregg Olson | .15 | 698 Omar Vizquel | .10 | 746 Dave Smith | .08 |
| 608 Eric Anthony (R) | .20 | 656 Mackey Sasser | .05 | 699 Jim Leyland (Mgr.) | .05 | 747 Randy Bush | .05 |
| 609 Sparky Anderson (Mgr.) | .05 | 657 Terry Mulholland | .05 | 700 Kirby Pucket | .20 | 748 Doyle Alexander | .08 |
| 610 Pedro Guerrero | .10 | 658 Donell Nixon | .05 | 701 Bernie Williams (R) | .50 | 749 Mark Parent | .05 |
| 611 Walt Terrell | .05 | 659 Greg Cadaret | .05 | 702 Tony Phillips | .05 | 750 Dale Murphy | .12 |
| 612 Dave Gallagher | .05 | 660 Vince Coleman | .12 | 703 Jeff Brantley | .10 | 751 Steve Lyons | .05 |
| 613 Jeff Pico | .05 | 661 Turn Back Clock—1985 Dick Howser | .08 | 704 Chip Hale (R) | .10 | 752 Tom Gordon | .08 |
| 614 Nelson Santovenia | .05 | | | 705 Claudell Washington | .05 | 753 Chris Speier | .05 |
| 615 Rob Deer | .05 | 662 Turn Back Clock—1980 Mike Schmidt | .12 | 706 Geno Petralli | .05 | 754 Bob Walk | .05 |
| 616 Brian Holman | .08 | | | 707 Luis Aquino | .05 | 755 Rafael Palmeiro | .12 |
| 617 Geronimo Berroa | .05 | 663 Turn Back Clock—1975 Fred Lynn | .08 | 708 Larry Sheets | .05 | 756 Ken Howell | .05 |
| 618 Eddie Whitson | .05 | | | 709 Juan Berenguer | .05 | 757 Larry Walker (R) | .25 |
| 619 Rob Ducey | .07 | 664 Turn Back Clock—1970 Johnny Bench | .08 | 710 Von Hayes | .08 | 758 Mark Thurmond | .05 |
| 620 Tony Castillo | .08 | | | 711 Rick Aguilera | .05 | 759 Tom Trebelhorn (Mgr.) | .05 |
| 621 Melido Perez | .05 | 665 Turn Back Clock—1965 Sandy Koufax | .08 | 712 Todd Benzinger | .05 | 760 Wade Boggs | .15 |
| 622 Sid Bream | .05 | | | 713 Tim Drummond (R) | .10 | 761 Mike Jackson | .05 |
| 623 Jim Corsi | .05 | 666 Brian Fisher | .05 | 714 Marquis Grissom (R) | .40 | 762 Doug Dascenzo | .05 |
| 624 Darrin Jackson | .05 | 667 Curt Wilkerson | .05 | 715 Greg Maddux | .12 | 763 Denny Martinez | .05 |
| 625 Roger McDowell | .05 | 668 Joe Oliver | .10 | 716 Steve Balboni | .05 | 764 Tim Teufel | .05 |
| 626 Bob Melvin | .05 | 669 Tom Lasorda (Mgr.) | .05 | 717 Ron Karkovice | .05 | 765 Chili Davis | .05 |
| 627 Jose Rojo | .05 | 670 Dennis Eckersley | .08 | 718 Gary Sheffield | .10 | 766 Brian Meyer | .10 |
| 628 Candy Maldonado | .05 | 671 Bob Boone | .05 | 719 Wally Whitehurst | .08 | 767 Tracy Jones | .05 |
| 629 Eric Hetzel | .05 | 672 Roy Smith | .05 | 720 Andres Galarraga | .08 | 768 Chuck Crim | .05 |
| 630 Gary Gaetti | .10 | 673 Joey Meyer | .05 | 721 Lee Mazzilli | .05 | 769 Greg Hibbard (R) | .15 |
| 631 John Wetteland | .10 | 674 Spike Owen | .05 | 722 Felix Fermin | .05 | 770 Cory Snyder | .10 |
| 632 Scott Lusader | .05 | 675 Jim Abbott | .20 | 723 Jeff Robinson | .08 | 771 Pete Smith | .05 |
| 633 Dennis Cook | .08 | 676 Randy Kutcher | .05 | 724 Juan Bell | .10 | 772 Jeff Reed | .05 |
| 634 Luis Polonia | .05 | 677 Jay Tibbs | .05 | 725 Terry Pendleton | .05 | 773 Dave Leiper | .05 |
| 635 Brian Downing | .05 | 678 Kirt Manwaring | .05 | 726 Gene Nelson | .05 | 774 Ben McDonald (R) | .60 |
| 636 Jesse Orosco | .05 | 679 Gary Ward | .05 | 727 Pat Tabler | .05 | 775 Andy Van Slyke | .10 |
| 637 Craig Reynolds | .05 | 680 Howard Johnson | .10 | 728 Jim Acker | .05 | 776 Charlie Leibrandt | .08 |
| 638 Jeff Montgomery | .08 | 681 Mike Schooler | .10 | 729 Bobby Valentine (Mgr.) | .05 | 777 Tim Laudner | .05 |
| 639 Tony LaRussa (Mgr.) | .05 | 682 Dann Bilardello | .05 | 730 Tony Gwynn | .15 | 778 Mike Jeffcoat | .05 |
| 640 Rick Sutcliffe | .05 | 683 Kenny Rogers | .10 | 731 Don Carman | .05 | 779 Lloyd Moseby | .08 |
| 641 Doug Strange (R) | .10 | 684 Julio Machado (R) | .12 | 732 Ernie Riles | .05 | 780 Orel Hershiser | .10 |
| 642 Jack Armstrong | .05 | 685 Tony Fernandez | .10 | 733 John Dobson | .08 | 781 Mario Diaz | .05 |
| 643 Alfredo Griffin | .08 | 686 Carmelo Martinez | .05 | 734 Kevin Elster | .08 | 782 Jose Alvarez | .05 |
| 644 Paul Assenmacher | .05 | 687 Tim Birtsas | .05 | 735 Charlie Hough | .05 | 783 Checklist No. 6 | .05 |
| 645 Jose Oquendo | .05 | 688 Milt Thompson | .05 | 736 Rick Dempsey | .05 | 784 Scott Bailes | .05 |
| 646 Checklist No. 5 | .05 | 689 Rich Yett | .05 | 737 Chris Sabo | .15 | 785 Jim Rice | .10 |
| 647 Rex Hudler | .05 | 690 Mark McGwire | .15 | 738 Gene Harris | .08 | 786 Eric King | .05 |
| 648 Jim Clancy | .05 | 691 Chuck Cary | .05 | 739 Dale Sveum | .05 | 787 Rene Gonzales | .05 |
| 649 Dan Murphy (R) | .10 | 692 Sammy Sosa (R) | .30 | 740 Jesse Barfield | .05 | 788 Frank DiPino | .05 |
| 650 Mike Witt | .08 | 693 Calvin Schiraldi | .05 | 741 Steve Wilson | .08 | 789 John Wathan (Mgr.) | .05 |
| 651 Rafael Santana | .05 | 694 Mike Stanton (R) | .15 | 742 Ernie Whitt | .05 | 790 Gary Carter | .08 |
| 652 Mike Boddicker | .08 | 695 Tom Henke | .05 | 743 Tom Candiotti | .05 | 791 Alvaro Espinoza | .05 |
| 653 John Moses | .05 | 696 B.J. Surhoff | .05 | 744 Kelly Mann (R) | .10 | 792 Gerald Perry | .05 |
| 654 P. Coleman (#1 DP)(R) | .15 | 697 Mike Davis | .05 | 745 Hubie Brooks | .05 | | |

## 1990 Topps Traded. . . . Complete Set of 132 Cards—Value $12.00

Updates the main 1990 card set with players who changed teams during the season and rookies who joined their teams early in the season. For the first time Topps traded cards were available in wax packs (gray backs). The complete set version was sold in a box (white backs). Features the first Topps card of Dave Justice, Kevin Maas and John Olerud.

KEVIN MAAS

TRAVIS FRYMAN

DAVE JUSTICE

CARLOS BAERGA

JOHN OLERUD

| NO. PLAYER | MINT | NO. PLAYER | MINT | NO. PLAYER | MINT | NO. PLAYER | MINT |
|---|---|---|---|---|---|---|---|
| 1T Darrel Akerfelds | .05 | 5T Wally Backman | .05 | 9T Mike Blowers (R) | .10 | 13T Glenn Braggs | .05 |
| 2T Sandy Alomar Jr. | .10 | 6T Carlos Baerga (R) | .40 | 10T Shawn Boskie (R) | .12 | 14T Hubie Brooks | .08 |
| 3T Brad Arnsberg | .05 | 7T Kevin Bass | .05 | 11T Daryl Boston | .05 | 15T Tom Brunansky | .05 |
| 4T Steve Avery | .75 | 8T Willie Blair | .10 | 12T Dennis Boyd | .05 | 16T John Burkett | .12 |

| NO. | PLAYER | MINT |
|---|---|---|
| 17T | Casey Candaele | .05 |
| 18T | John Candelaria | .05 |
| 19T | Gary Carter | .10 |
| 20T | Joe Carter | .10 |
| 21T | Rick Cerone | .05 |
| 22T | Scott Coolbaugh (R) | .15 |
| 23T | Bobby Cox | .05 |
| 24T | Mark Davis | .05 |
| 25T | Storm Davis | .05 |
| 26T | Edgar Diaz | .10 |
| 27T | Wayne Edwards (R) | .10 |
| 28T | Mark Eichhorn | .05 |
| 29T | Scott Erickson (R) | 3.00 |
| 30T | Mick Esasky | .05 |
| 31T | Cecil Fielder | .30 |
| 32T | John Franco | .05 |
| 33T | Travis Fryman (R) | .75 |
| 34T | Bill Guillickson | .05 |
| 35T | Darryl Hamilton | .08 |
| 36T | Mike Harkey | .10 |
| 37T | Bud Harrelson | .05 |
| 38T | Billy Hatcher | .05 |
| 39T | Keith Hernandez | .05 |
| 40T | Joie Hesketh | .05 |
| 41T | Dave Hollins (R) | .30 |
| 42T | Sam Horn | .05 |
| 43T | Steve Howard (R) | .15 |
| 44T | Todd Hundley (R) | .30 |
| 45T | Jeff Huson | .05 |

| NO. | PLAYER | MINT |
|---|---|---|
| 46T | Chris James | .05 |
| 47T | Stan Javier | .05 |
| 48T | Dave Justice (R) | 2.50 |
| 49T | Jeff Kaiser | .10 |
| 50T | Dana Kiecker (R) | .12 |
| 51T | Joe Klink (R) | .12 |
| 52T | Brent Knackert (R) | .12 |
| 53T | Brad Komminsk | .05 |
| 54T | Mark Langston | .10 |
| 55T | Tim Layana (R) | .15 |
| 56T | Rick Leach | .05 |
| 57T | Terry Leach | .05 |
| 58T | Tim Leary | .05 |
| 59T | Craig Lefferts | .05 |
| 60T | Charlie Leibrandt | .05 |
| 61T | Jim Leyritz (R) | .12 |
| 62T | Fred Lynn | .05 |
| 63T | Kevin Maas (R) | 1.00 |
| 64T | Shane Mack | .05 |
| 65T | Candy Maldonado | .05 |
| 66T | Fred Manrique | .05 |
| 67T | Mike Marshall | .05 |
| 68T | Carmelo Martinez | .05 |
| 69T | John Marzana | .08 |
| 70T | Ben McDonald | .75 |
| 71T | Jack McDowell | .05 |
| 72T | John McNamara | .05 |
| 73T | Orlando Mercado | .05 |
| 74T | Stump Merrill | .05 |

| NO. | PLAYER | MINT |
|---|---|---|
| 75T | Alan Mills (R) | .12 |
| 76T | Hal Morris | .30 |
| 77T | Lloyd Moseby | .30 |
| 78T | Randy Myers | .08 |
| 79T | Tim Naehring (R) | .25 |
| 80T | Junior Noboa | .05 |
| 81T | Matt Nokes | .05 |
| 82T | Pete O'Brien | .05 |
| 83T | John Olerud (R) | 1.00 |
| 84T | Greg Olson (R) | .20 |
| 85T | Junior Ortiz | .05 |
| 86T | Dave Parker | .10 |
| 87T | Rick Parker (R) | .12 |
| 88T | Bob Patterson | .05 |
| 89T | Alejandro Pena | .05 |
| 90T | Tony Pena | .05 |
| 91T | Pascual Perez | .05 |
| 92T | Gerald Perry | .08 |
| 93T | Dan Petry | .05 |
| 94T | Gary Pettis | .05 |
| 95T | Tony Phillips | .05 |
| 96T | Lou Piniella | .05 |
| 97T | Luis Polonia | .05 |
| 98T | Jim Presley | .05 |
| 99T | Scott Radinsky (R) | .15 |
| 100T | Willie Randolph | .05 |
| 101T | Jeff Reardon | .05 |
| 102T | Greg Riddoch | .05 |
| 103T | Jeff Robinson | .05 |

| NO. | PLAYER | MINT |
|---|---|---|
| 104T | Ron Robinson | .05 |
| 105T | Kevin Romine | .05 |
| 106T | Scott Ruskin (R) | .15 |
| 107T | John Russell | .05 |
| 108T | Bill Sampen (R) | .15 |
| 109T | Juan Samuel | .05 |
| 110T | Scott Sanderson | .05 |
| 111T | Jack Savage | .05 |
| 112T | Dave Schmidt | .05 |
| 113T | Red Schoendienst | .05 |
| 114T | Terry Shumpert (R) | .12 |
| 115T | Matt Sinatro | .05 |
| 116T | Don Slaught | .05 |
| 117T | Bryn Smith | .05 |
| 118T | Lee Smith | .08 |
| 119T | Paul Sorrento (R) | .12 |
| 120T | Franklin Stubbs | .05 |
| 121T | Russ Swan (R) | .15 |
| 122T | Bob Tewksbury | .05 |
| 123T | Wayne Tolleson | .05 |
| 124T | John Tudor | .05 |
| 125T | Randy Veres | .05 |
| 126T | Hector Villanueva (R) | .12 |
| 127T | Mitch Webster | .05 |
| 128T | Ernie Whitt | .05 |
| 129T | Frank Wills | .05 |
| 130T | Dave Winfield | .10 |
| 131T | Matt Young | .05 |
| 132T | Checklist Card | .05 |

## 1991 Topps . . . Complete Set of 792 Cards—Value $22.00

**(Factory-Sealed Set—Value $27.00)**

All players of the same team have cards with the same border colors. Subsets include Record Breakers, No. 1 Draft Picks, Future Stars and Rookie All-Star Team. For the first time since 1974 some cards feature horizontal photos. In a special promotion, over 300,000 original Topps cards issued from 1952 to 1990 or certificates were randomly inserted in packs.

| NO. | PLAYER | MINT |
|---|---|---|
| 1 | Nolan Ryan | .30 |
| 2 | '89 Record: G. Brett | .08 |
| 3 | '89 Record: C. Fisk | .08 |
| 4 | '89 Record: K. Maas | .10 |
| 5 | '89 Record: C. Ripken | .15 |
| 6 | '89 Record: N. Ryan | .20 |
| 7 | '89 Record: R. Sandberg | .15 |
| 8 | '89 Record: B. Thigpen | .06 |
| 9 | Darrin Fletcher | .10 |
| 10 | Gregg Olson | .06 |
| 11 | Roberto Kelly | .08 |
| 12 | Paul Assenmacher | .05 |
| 13 | Mariano Duncan | .05 |
| 14 | Dennis Lamp | .05 |
| 15 | Von Hayes | .05 |
| 16 | Mike Heath | .05 |
| 17 | Jeff Brantley | .05 |
| 18 | Nelson Liriano | .05 |
| 19 | Jeff Robinson | .05 |
| 20 | Pedro Guerrero | .10 |
| 21 | Joe Morgan | .08 |
| 22 | Storm Davis | .05 |
| 23 | Jim Gantner | .05 |
| 24 | Dave Martinez | .05 |
| 25 | Tim Belcher | .05 |
| 26 | Luis Sojo | .05 |
| 27 | Bobby Witt | .05 |
| 28 | Alvaro Espinoza | .05 |
| 29 | Bob Walk | .05 |

| NO. | PLAYER | MINT |
|---|---|---|
| 30 | Gregg Jefferies | .10 |
| 31 | Colby Ward (R) | .12 |
| 32 | Mike Simms (R) | .12 |
| 33 | Barry Jones | .05 |
| 34 | Atlee Hammaker | .05 |
| 35 | Greg Maddux | .05 |
| 36 | Donnie Hill | .05 |
| 37 | Tom Bolton | .05 |
| 38 | Scott Bradley | .05 |
| 39 | Jim Neidlinger (R) | .12 |
| 40 | Kevin Mitchell | .12 |
| 41 | Ken Dayley | .05 |
| 42 | Chris Hoiles | .12 |
| 43 | Roger McDowell | .05 |
| 44 | Mike Felder | .05 |
| 45 | Chris Sabo | .08 |
| 46 | Tim Drummond | .05 |
| 47 | Brook Jacoby | .05 |
| 48 | Dennis Boyd | .05 |
| 49 | Pat Borders (error) "10 Stolen Bases" | .15 |
| 49 | Pat Borders (correct) "40 Stolen Bases" | .20 |
| 50 | Bob Welch | .05 |
| 51 | Art Howe | .05 |
| 52 | Francisco Oliveras | .05 |
| 53 | Mike Sharperson | .05 |
| 54 | Gary Mielke | .05 |
| 55 | Jeffrey Leonard | .05 |

| NO. | PLAYER | MINT |
|---|---|---|
| 56 | Jeff Parrett | .05 |
| 57 | Jack Howell | .05 |
| 58 | Mel Stottlemyre | .05 |
| 59 | Eric Yelding | .05 |
| 60 | Frank Viola | .10 |
| 61 | Stan Javier | .05 |
| 62 | Lee Guetterman | .05 |
| 63 | Milt Thompson | .05 |
| 64 | Tom Herr | .05 |
| 65 | Bruce Hurst | .08 |
| 66 | Terry Kennedy | .05 |
| 67 | Rick Honeycutt | .05 |
| 68 | Gary Sheffield | .10 |
| 69 | Steve Wilson | .05 |
| 70 | Ellis Burks | .10 |
| 71 | Jim Acker | .05 |
| 72 | Junior Ortiz | .05 |
| 73 | Craig Worthington | .05 |
| 74 | Shane Andrews (R) | .20 |
| 75 | Jack Morris | .05 |
| 76 | Jerry Browne | .05 |
| 77 | Drew Hall | .05 |
| 78 | Geno Petralli | .05 |
| 79 | Frank Thomas | 1.00 |
| 80 | F. Valenzuela (error) | .30 |
| 80 | F. Valenzuela (correct) | .10 |
| 81 | Cito Gaston | .05 |
| 82 | Tom Glavine | .10 |
| 83 | Daryl Boston | .05 |

| NO. | PLAYER | MINT |
|---|---|---|
| 84 | Bob McClure | .05 |
| 85 | Jesse Barfield | .05 |
| 86 | Les Lancaster | .05 |
| 87 | Tracy Jones | .05 |
| 88 | Bob Tewksbury | .05 |
| 89 | Darren Daulton | .05 |
| 90 | Danny Tartabull | .05 |
| 91 | Greg Colbrunn (R) | .20 |
| 92 | Danny Jackson | .05 |
| 93 | Ivan Calderon | .05 |
| 94 | John Dopson | .05 |
| 95 | Paul Molitor | .10 |
| 96 | Trevor Wilson | .05 |
| 97 | Brady Anderson | .05 |
| 98 | Segio Valdez | .05 |
| 99 | Chris Gwynn | .05 |
| 100 | D. Mattingly (error) "10 hits in 1990" | 1.00 |
| 100 | D. Mattingly (correct) "101 hits in 1990" | .20 |
| 101 | Rob Ducey | .05 |
| 102 | Gene Larkin | .05 |
| 103 | Tim Costo (R) | .25 |
| 104 | Don Robinson | .05 |
| 105 | Kevin McReynolds | .08 |
| 106 | Ed Nunez | .05 |
| 107 | Luis Polonia | .05 |
| 108 | Matt Young | .05 |
| 109 | Greg Riddoch | .05 |

| NO. | PLAYER | MINT |
|---|---|---|
| 110 | Tom Henke | .05 |
| 111 | Andres Thomas | .05 |
| 112 | Frank Dipino | .05 |
| 113 | Carl Everett (R) | .25 |
| 114 | Lance Dickson (R) | .20 |
| 115 | Hubie Brooks | .05 |
| 116 | Mark Davis | .05 |
| 117 | Dion James | .05 |
| 118 | Tom Edens (R) | .10 |
| 119 | Carl Nichols | .05 |
| 120 | Joe Carter | .08 |
| 121 | Eric King | .05 |
| 122 | Paul O'Neill | .05 |
| 123 | Greg Harris | .05 |
| 124 | Randy Bush | .05 |
| 125 | Steve Bedrosian | .05 |
| 126 | Bernard Gilkey | .15 |
| 127 | Joe Price | .05 |
| 128 | Travis Fryman | .35 |
| 129 | Mark Eichhorn | .05 |
| 130 | Ozzie Smith | .10 |
| 131 | Checklist No. 1 | .05 |
| 132 | Jamie Quirk | .05 |
| 133 | Gregg Briley | .05 |
| 134 | Kevin Elster | .05 |
| 135 | Jerome Walton | .10 |
| 136 | Dave Schmidt | .05 |
| 137 | Randy Ready | .05 |
| 138 | Jamie Moyer | .05 |
| 139 | Jeff Treadway | .05 |
| 140 | Fred McGriff | .12 |
| 141 | Nick Leyva | .05 |
| 142 | Curt Wilkerson | .05 |
| 143 | John Smiley | .05 |
| 144 | Dave Henderson | .05 |
| 145 | Lou Whitaker | .05 |
| 146 | Dan Plesac | .05 |
| 147 | Carlos Baerga | .08 |
| 148 | Rey Palacios | .05 |
| 149 | Al Osuna (R) | .12 |
| 150 | Cal Ripken | .20 |
| 151 | Tom Browning | .05 |
| 152 | Mickey Hatcher | .05 |
| 153 | Bryan Harvey | .05 |
| 154 | Jay Buhner | .05 |
| 155 | Dwight Evans | .08 |
| 156 | Carlos Martinez | .05 |
| 157 | John Smoltz | .10 |
| 158 | Jose Uribe | .05 |
| 159 | Joe Boever | .05 |
| 160 | Vince Coleman | .10 |
| 161 | Tim Leary | .05 |
| 162 | Ozzie Canseco | .10 |
| 163 | Dave Johnson | .05 |
| 164 | Edgar Diaz | .05 |
| 165 | Sandy Alomar | .10 |
| 166 | Harold Baines | .05 |
| 167 | R. Tomlin (R) (err.) | .50 |
| 167 | R. Tomlin (R) (cor.) | .15 |
| 168 | John Olerud | .10 |
| 169 | Luis Aquino | .05 |
| 170 | Carlton Fisk | .10 |
| 171 | Tony LaRussa | .05 |
| 172 | Pete Incaviglia | .05 |
| 173 | Jason Grimsley | .05 |
| 174 | Ken Caminiti | .05 |
| 175 | Jack Armstrong | .05 |
| 176 | John Orton | .05 |
| 177 | Reggie Harris | .10 |
| 178 | Dave Valle | .05 |
| 179 | Pete Harnisch | .05 |
| 180 | Tony Gwynn | .15 |
| 181 | Duane Ward | .05 |
| 182 | Junior Noboa | .05 |
| 183 | Clay Parker | .05 |
| 184 | Gary Green | .05 |
| 185 | Joe Magrane | .05 |
| 186 | Rod Booker | .05 |
| 187 | Greg Cadaret | .05 |
| 188 | Damon Berryhill | .05 |
| 189 | Daryl Irvine (R) | .12 |
| 190 | Matt Williams | .12 |
| 191 | Willie Blair | .05 |
| 192 | Rob Deer | .05 |
| 193 | Felix Fermin | .05 |
| 194 | Xavier Hernandez | .07 |
| 195 | Wally Joyner | .10 |
| 196 | Jim Vatcher (R) | .10 |
| 197 | Chris Nabholz | .12 |
| 198 | R.J. Reynolds | .05 |
| 199 | Mike Hartley | .10 |
| 200 | Darryl Strawberry | .20 |
| 201 | Tom Kelly | .05 |
| 202 | Jim Leyritz | .10 |
| 203 | Gene Harris | .05 |
| 204 | Herm Winningham | .05 |
| 205 | Mike Perez (R) | .12 |
| 206 | Carlos Quintana | .05 |
| 207 | Gary Wayne | .05 |
| 208 | Willie Wilson | .05 |
| 209 | Ken Howell | .05 |
| 210 | Lance Parrish | .05 |
| 211 | Brian Barnes (R) | .12 |
| 212 | Steve Finley | .05 |
| 213 | Frank Wills | .05 |
| 214 | Joe Girardi | .05 |
| 215 | Dave Smith | .05 |
| 216 | Greg Gagne | .05 |
| 217 | Chris Bosio | .05 |
| 218 | Rick Parker | .05 |
| 219 | Jack McDowell | .05 |
| 220 | Tim Wallach | .05 |
| 221 | Don Slaught | .05 |
| 222 | Brian McRae (R) | .50 |
| 223 | Allan Anderson | .05 |
| 224 | Juan Gonzalez | .30 |
| 225 | Randy Johnson | .05 |
| 226 | Alfredo Griffin | .05 |
| 227 | Steve Avery | .25 |
| 228 | Rex Hudler | .05 |
| 229 | Rance Mulliniks | .05 |
| 230 | Sid Fernandez | .05 |
| 231 | Doug Rader | .05 |
| 232 | Jose DeJesus | .05 |
| 233 | Al Leiter | .05 |
| 234 | Scott Erickson | .50 |
| 235 | Dave Parker | .10 |
| 236 | Frank Tanana | .05 |
| 237 | Rick Cerone | .05 |
| 238 | Mike Dunne | .05 |
| 238 | Walt Terrell | .10 |
| 239 | Darren Lewis | .20 |
| 240 | Mike Scott | .08 |
| 241 | Dave Clark | .05 |
| 242 | Mike LaCoss | .05 |
| 243 | Lance Johnson | .05 |
| 244 | Mike Jeffcoat | .05 |
| 245 | Kal Daniels | .08 |
| 246 | Kevin Wickander | .05 |
| 247 | Jody Reed | .05 |
| 248 | Tom Gordon | .08 |
| 249 | Bob Melvin | .05 |
| 250 | Dennis Eckersley | .10 |
| 251 | Mark Lemke | .05 |
| 252 | Mel Rojas | .05 |
| 253 | Garry Templeton | .05 |
| 254 | Shawn Boskie | .05 |
| 255 | Brian Downing | .05 |
| 256 | Greg Hibbard | .05 |
| 257 | Tom O'Malley | .05 |
| 258 | Chris Hammond | .05 |
| 259 | Hensley Meulens | .08 |
| 260 | Harold Reynolds | .08 |
| 261 | Bud Harrelson | .05 |
| 262 | Tim Jones | .05 |
| 263 | Checklist No. 2 | .05 |
| 264 | Dave Hollins | .05 |
| 265 | Mark Gubicza | .08 |
| 266 | Carmelo Castillo | .05 |
| 267 | Mark Knudson | .05 |
| 268 | Tom Brookens | .05 |
| 269 | Joe Hesketh | .05 |
| 270 | Mark McGwire | .05 |
| 271 | Omar Olivares (R) | .15 |
| 272 | Jeff King | .05 |
| 273 | Johnny Ray | .05 |
| 274 | Ken Williams | .05 |
| 275 | Alan Trammell | .10 |
| 276 | Bill Swift | .05 |
| 277 | Scott Coolbaugh | .05 |
| 278 | Alex Fernandez | .20 |
| 279 | J. Gonzalez (err.) | .20 |
|  | wrong photo |  |
| 279 | J. Gonzalez (cor.) | .10 |
| 280 | Bret Saberhagen | .10 |
| 281 | Larry Sheets | .05 |
| 282 | Don Carman | .05 |
| 283 | Marquis Grissom | .10 |
| 284 | Billy Spiers | .05 |
| 285 | Jim Abbott | .10 |
| 286 | Ken Oberkfell | .05 |
| 287 | Mark Grant | .05 |
| 288 | Derrick May | .10 |
| 289 | Tim Birtsas | .05 |
| 290 | Steve Sax | .08 |
| 291 | John Wathan | .05 |
| 292 | Bud Black | .05 |
| 293 | Jay Bell | .05 |
| 294 | Mike Moore | .05 |
| 295 | Rafael Palmeiro | .08 |
| 296 | Mark Williamson | .05 |
| 297 | Manny Lee | .05 |
| 298 | Omar Vizquel | .05 |
| 299 | Scott Radinsky | .05 |
| 300 | Kirby Puckett | .15 |
| 301 | Steve Farr | .05 |
| 302 | Tim Teufel | .05 |
| 303 | Mike Boddicker | .08 |
| 304 | Kevin Reimer | .08 |
| 305 | Mike Scioscia | .05 |
| 306 | Lonnie Smith | .05 |
| 307 | Andy Benes | .10 |
| 308 | Tom Pagnozzi | .05 |
| 309 | Norm Charlton | .08 |
| 310 | Gary Carter | .10 |
| 311 | Jeff Pico | .05 |
| 312 | Charlie Hayes | .05 |
| 313 | Ron Robinson | .05 |
| 314 | Gary Pettis | .05 |
| 315 | Roberto Alomar | .10 |
| 316 | Gene Nelson | .05 |
| 317 | Mike Fitzgerald | .05 |
| 318 | Rick Aguilera | .05 |
| 319 | Jeff McKnight | .08 |
| 320 | Tony Fernandez | .05 |
| 321 | Bob Rodgers | .05 |
| 322 | Terry Shumpert | .05 |
| 323 | Cory Snyder | .08 |
| 324 | Ron Kittle | .05 |
| 325 | Brett Butler | .05 |
| 326 | Ken Patterson | .05 |
| 327 | Ron Hassey | .05 |
| 328 | Walt Terrell | .05 |
| 329 | Dave Justice | .50 |
| 330 | Doc Gooden | .15 |
| 331 | Eric Anthony | .10 |
| 332 | Kenny Rogers | .05 |
| 333 | Chipper Jones (R) | .25 |
| 334 | Todd Benzinger | .08 |
| 335 | Mitch Williams | .05 |
| 336 | Matt Nokes | .05 |
| 337 | Keith Comstock | .05 |
| 338 | Luis Rivera | .05 |
| 339 | Larry Walker | .08 |
| 340 | Ramon Martinez | .12 |
| 341 | John Moses | .05 |
| 342 | Mickey Morandini | .10 |
| 343 | Jose Oquendo | .05 |
| 344 | Jeff Russell | .05 |
| 345 | Len Dykstra | .10 |
| 346 | Jesse Orosco | .05 |
| 347 | Greg Vaughn | .10 |
| 348 | Todd Stottlemyre | .05 |
| 349 | Dave Gallagher | .05 |
| 350 | Glenn Davis | .08 |
| 351 | Joe Torre | .05 |
| 352 | Frank White | .05 |
| 353 | Tony Castillo | .05 |
| 354 | Sid Bream | .05 |
| 355 | Chili Davis | .05 |
| 356 | Mike Marshall | .05 |
| 357 | Jack Savage | .05 |
| 358 | Mark Parent | .05 |
| 359 | Chuck Cary | .05 |
| 360 | Tim Raines | .10 |
| 361 | Scott Garrelts | .05 |
| 362 | Hector Villanueva | .08 |
| 363 | Rick Mahler | .05 |
| 364 | Dan Pasqua | .05 |
| 365 | Mike Schooler | .05 |
| 366 | Checklist No. 3 | .05 |
| 367 | Dave Walsh (R) | .12 |
| 368 | Felix Jose | .05 |
| 369 | Steve Searcy | .05 |
| 370 | Kelly Gruber | .10 |
| 371 | Jeff Montgomery | .05 |
| 372 | Spike Owen | .05 |
| 373 | Darrin Jackson | .05 |
| 374 | Larry Casian (R) | .12 |
| 375 | Tony Pena | .05 |
| 376 | Mike Harkey | .05 |
| 377 | Rene Gonzales | .05 |
| 378 | W. Alvarez (err.) | .05 |
| 378 | W. Alvarez (cor.) | .50 |
| 379 | Randy Velarde | .05 |
| 380 | Willie McGee | .10 |
| 381 | Jim Leyland | .05 |
| 382 | Mackey Sasser | .05 |
| 383 | Pete Smith | .05 |
| 384 | Gerald Perry | .05 |
| 385 | Mickey Tettleton | .05 |
| 386 | Cecil Fielder (AS) | .15 |
| 387 | Julio Franco (AS) | .05 |
| 388 | Kelly Gruber (AS) | .10 |
| 389 | Alan Trammell (AS) | .10 |
| 390 | Jose Canseco (AS) | .20 |
| 391 | Rickey Henderson (AS) | .15 |
| 392 | Ken Griffey Jr. (AS) | .30 |
| 393 | Carlton Fisk (AS) | .05 |
| 394 | Bob Welch (AS) | .05 |
| 395 | Chuck Finley (AS) | .05 |
| 396 | Bobby Thigpen (AS) | .08 |
| 397 | Eddie Murray (AS) | .10 |
| 398 | Ryne Sandberg (AS) | .15 |
| 399 | Matt Williams (AS) | .12 |
| 400 | Barry Larkin (AS) | .08 |
| 401 | Barry Bonds (AS) | .12 |
| 402 | Darryl Strawberry (AS) | .20 |
| 403 | Bobby Bonilla (AS) | .10 |
| 404 | Mike Scioscia (AS) | .05 |
| 405 | Doug Drabek (AS) | .05 |
| 406 | Frank Viola (AS) | .08 |
| 407 | John Franco (AS) | .05 |
| 408 | Ernie Riles | .05 |
| 409 | Mike Stanley | .05 |
| 410 | Dave Righetti | .05 |
| 411 | Lance Blankenship | .05 |
| 412 | Dave Bergman | .05 |
| 413 | Terry Mulholland | .05 |
| 414 | Sammy Sosa | .08 |
| 415 | Rick Sutcliffe | .08 |
| 416 | Randy Mulligan | .05 |
| 417 | Bill Krueger | .05 |
| 418 | Nick Esasky | .05 |
| 419 | Jeff Reed | .05 |
| 420 | Bobby Thigpen | .05 |
| 421 | Alex Cole | .10 |
| 422 | Rick Reuschel | .05 |
| 423 | Rafael Ramirez | .05 |
| 424 | Calvin Schiraldi | .05 |
| 425 | Andy Van Slyke | .10 |
| 426 | Joe Grahe (R) | .10 |
| 427 | Rick Dempsey | .05 |
| 428 | John Barfield (R) | .08 |
| 429 | Stump Merrill | .05 |
| 430 | Gary Gaetti | .05 |
| 431 | Paul Gibson | .05 |
| 432 | Delino DeShields | .12 |
| 433 | Pat Tabler | .05 |
| 434 | Julio Machado | .05 |
| 435 | Kevin Maas | .20 |
| 436 | Scott Bankhead | .05 |
| 437 | Doug Dascenzo | .05 |
| 438 | Vincente Palacios | .05 |
| 439 | Dickie Thon | .05 |
| 440 | George Bell | .10 |
| 441 | Zane Smith | .05 |
| 442 | Charlie O'Brien | .05 |
| 443 | Jeff Innis | .05 |
| 444 | Glenn Braggs | .05 |
| 445 | Greg Swindell | .05 |
| 446 | Craig Grebeck | .05 |
| 447 | John Burkett | .05 |
| 448 | Craig Lefferts | .05 |
| 449 | Juan Berenguer | .05 |
| 450 | Wade Boggs | .15 |
| 451 | Neal Heaton | .05 |

| NO. | PLAYER | MINT |
|---|---|---|
| 452 | Bill Schroeder | .05 |
| 453 | Lenny Harris | .05 |
| 454 | Kevin Appier | .05 |
| 455 | Walt Weiss | .05 |
| 456 | Charlie Liebrandt | .05 |
| 457 | Todd Hundley | .10 |
| 458 | Brian Holman | .05 |
| 459 | Tom Trebelhorn | .05 |
| 460 | Dave Stieb | .05 |
| 461 | Robin Ventura | .15 |
| 462 | Steve Frey | .05 |
| 463 | Dwight Smith | .05 |
| 464 | Steve Buechele | .05 |
| 465 | Ken Griffey | .05 |
| 466 | Charles Nagy | .10 |
| 467 | Dennis Cook | .05 |
| 468 | Tim Hulett | .05 |
| 469 | Chet Lemon | .05 |
| 470 | Howard Johnson | .08 |
| 471 | Mike Lieberthal (R) | .12 |
| 472 | Kirt Manwaring | .05 |
| 473 | Curt Young | .05 |
| 474 | Phil Plantier (R) | 1.00 |
| 475 | Teddy Higuera | .05 |
| 476 | Glenn Wilson | .05 |
| 477 | Mike Fetters | .05 |
| 478 | Kurt Stillwell | .05 |
| 479 | Bob Patterson | .05 |
| 480 | Dave Magadan | .10 |
| 481 | Eddie Whitson | .05 |
| 482 | Tino Martinez | .20 |
| 483 | Mike Aldrete | .05 |
| 484 | Dave LaPoint | .05 |
| 485 | Terry Pendleton | .05 |
| 486 | Tommy Greene | .08 |
| 487 | Rafael Belliard | .05 |
| 488 | Jeff Manto | .05 |
| 489 | Bobby Valentine | .05 |
| 490 | Kirk Gibson | .10 |
| 491 | Kurt Miller (R) | .15 |
| 492 | Ernie Whitt | .05 |
| 493 | Jose Rijo | .05 |
| 494 | Chris James | .05 |
| 495 | Charlie Hough | .05 |
| 496 | Marty Barrett | .05 |
| 497 | Ben McDonald | .10 |
| 498 | Mark Salas | .05 |
| 499 | Melido Perez | .05 |
| 500 | Will Clark | .20 |
| 501 | Mike Bielecki | .05 |
| 502 | Carney Lansford | .05 |
| 503 | Roy Smith | .05 |
| 504 | Julio Valera | .10 |
| 505 | Chuck Finley | .10 |
| 506 | Darnell Coles | .05 |
| 507 | Steve Jeltz | .05 |
| 508 | Mike York (R) | .10 |
| 509 | Glenallen Hill | .05 |
| 510 | John Franco | .05 |
| 511 | Steve Balboni | .05 |
| 512 | Jose Mesa | .05 |
| 513 | Jerald Clark | .05 |
| 514 | Mike Stanton | .05 |
| 515 | Alvin Davis | .05 |
| 516 | Karl Rhodes | .05 |
| 517 | Joe Oliver | .05 |
| 518 | Cris Carpenter | .05 |
| 519 | Sparky Anderson | .05 |
| 520 | Mark Grace | .10 |
| 521 | Joe Orsulak | .05 |
| 522 | Stan Belinda | .05 |
| 523 | Rodney McCray (R) | .10 |
| 524 | Darrel Akerfelds | .05 |
| 525 | Willie Randolph | .05 |
| 526 | M. Alou (err.) | .35 |
| 526 | M. Alou (cor.) | .08 |
| 527 | Checklist No. 4 | .05 |
| 528 | Denny Martinez | .05 |
| 529 | Marc Newfield (R) | .75 |
| 530 | Roger Clemens | .20 |
| 531 | Dave Rohde | .05 |
| 532 | Kirk McCaskill | .05 |
| 533 | Oddibe McDowell | .05 |
| 534 | Mike Jackson | .05 |
| 535 | Ruben Sierra | .10 |
| 536 | Mike Witt | .12 |
| 537 | Jose Lind | .05 |
| 538 | Bip Roberts | .05 |
| 539 | Scott Terry | .05 |
| 540 | George Brett | .12 |
| 541 | Domingo Ramos | .05 |
| 542 | Rob Murphy | .05 |
| 543 | Junior Felix | .05 |
| 544 | Alejandro Pena | .05 |
| 545 | Dale Murphy | .15 |
| 546 | Jeff Ballard | .05 |
| 547 | Mike Pagliarulo | .05 |
| 548 | Jaime Navarro | .05 |
| 549 | John McNamara | .05 |
| 550 | Eric Davis | .15 |
| 551 | Bob Kipper | .05 |
| 552 | Jeff Hamilton | .05 |
| 553 | Joe Klink (R) | .10 |
| 554 | Brian Harper | .05 |
| 555 | Turner Ward (R) | .15 |
| 556 | Gary Ward | .05 |
| 557 | Wally Whitehurst | .05 |
| 558 | Otis Nixon | .05 |
| 559 | Adam Peterson | .05 |
| 560 | Greg Smith | .08 |
| 561 | Tim McIntosh | .08 |
| 562 | Jeff Kunkel | .05 |
| 563 | Brent Knackert | .05 |
| 564 | Dante Bichette | .05 |
| 565 | Craig Biggio | .08 |
| 566 | Craig Wilson (R) | .10 |
| 567 | Dwayne Henry | .05 |
| 568 | Ron Karkovice | .05 |
| 569 | Curt Schilling | .05 |
| 570 | Barry Bonds | .15 |
| 571 | Pat Combs | .05 |
| 572 | Dave Anderson | .05 |
| 573 | Rich Rodriquez (R) | .10 |
| 574 | John Marzano | .05 |
| 575 | Robin Yount | .12 |
| 576 | Jeff Kaiser | .05 |
| 577 | Bill Doran | .05 |
| 578 | Dave West | .05 |
| 579 | Roger Craig | .05 |
| 580 | Dave Stewart | .10 |
| 581 | Luis Quinones | .05 |
| 582 | Marty Clary | .05 |
| 583 | Tony Phillips | .05 |
| 584 | Kevin Brown | .05 |
| 585 | Pete O'Brien | .05 |
| 586 | Fred Lynn | .05 |
| 587 | Jose Offerman | .10 |
| 588 | Mark Whiten | .20 |
| 589 | Scott Ruskin | .05 |
| 590 | Eddie Murray | .10 |
| 591 | Ken Hill | .05 |
| 592 | B.J. Surhoff | .05 |
| 593 | M. Walker (err.) | .20 |
| 593 | M. Walker (cor.) | .06 |
| 594 | Rich Garces (R) | .12 |
| 595 | Bill Landrum | .05 |
| 596 | Ronnie Walden (R) | .15 |
| 597 | Jerry Don Gleaton | .05 |
| 598 | Sam Horn | .05 |
| 599 | Greg Myers | .05 |
| 600 | Bo Jackson | .25 |
| 601 | Bob Ojeda | .05 |
| 602 | Casey Candaele | .05 |
| 603 | W. Chamberlain (err.) wrong photo | 1.50 |
| 603 | W. Chamberlain (cor.) | .50 |
| 604 | Billy Hatcher | .05 |
| 605 | Jeff Reardon | .05 |
| 606 | Jim Gott | .05 |
| 607 | Edgar Martinez | .05 |
| 608 | Todd Burns | .05 |
| 609 | Jeff Torborg | .05 |
| 610 | Andres Galarraga | .08 |
| 611 | Dave Eiland | .05 |
| 612 | Steve Lyons | .05 |
| 613 | Eric Show | .05 |
| 614 | Luis Salazar | .05 |
| 615 | Bert Blyeven | .05 |
| 616 | Todd Zeile | .10 |
| 617 | Bill Wegman | .05 |
| 618 | Sil Campusano | .05 |
| 619 | David Wells | .05 |
| 620 | Ozzie Guillen | .05 |
| 621 | Ted Power | .05 |
| 622 | Jack Daugherty | .05 |
| 623 | Jeff Blauser | .05 |
| 624 | Tom Candiotti | .05 |
| 625 | Terry Steinbach | .05 |
| 626 | Gerald Young | .05 |
| 627 | Tim Layana | .05 |
| 628 | Greg Litton | .05 |
| 629 | Wes Gardner | .05 |
| 630 | Dave Winfield | .15 |
| 631 | Mike Morgan | .05 |
| 632 | Lloyd Moseby | .08 |
| 633 | Kevin Tapani | .05 |
| 634 | Henry Cotto | .05 |
| 635 | Andy Hawkins | .05 |
| 636 | Geronimo Pena | .10 |
| 637 | Bruce Ruffin | .05 |
| 638 | Mike Macfarlane | .05 |
| 639 | Frank Robinson | .05 |
| 640 | Andre Dawson | .12 |
| 641 | Mike Henneman | .05 |
| 642 | Hal Morris | .12 |
| 643 | Jim Presley | .05 |
| 644 | Chuck Crim | .05 |
| 645 | Juan Samuel | .05 |
| 646 | Andujar Cedeno | .35 |
| 647 | Mark Portugal | .05 |
| 648 | Lee Stevens | .10 |
| 649 | Bill Sampen | .05 |
| 650 | Jack Clark | .12 |
| 651 | Alan Mills | .05 |
| 652 | Kevin Romine | .05 |
| 653 | Anthony Telford (R) | .12 |
| 654 | Paul Sorrento | .05 |
| 655 | Erik Hanson | .05 |
| 656 | Checklist No. 5 | .05 |
| 657 | Mike Kingery | .05 |
| 658 | Scott Aldred | .10 |
| 659 | Oscar Azocar | .10 |
| 660 | Lee Smith | .05 |
| 661 | Steve Lake | .05 |
| 662 | Rob Dibble | .05 |
| 663 | Greg Brock | .05 |
| 664 | John Farrell | .05 |
| 665 | Mike LaValliere | .05 |
| 666 | Danny Darwin | .05 |
| 667 | Kent Anderson | .05 |
| 668 | Bill Long | .05 |
| 669 | Lou Piniella | .05 |
| 670 | Rickey Henderson | .25 |
| 671 | Andy McGaffigan | .05 |
| 672 | Shane Mack | .05 |
| 673 | Greg Olson | .12 |
| 674 | Kevin Gross | .05 |
| 675 | Tom Brunansky | .05 |
| 676 | Scott Chiamparino | .12 |
| 677 | Billy Ripken | .05 |
| 678 | Mark Davidson | .05 |
| 679 | Bill Bathe | .05 |
| 680 | David Cone | .10 |
| 681 | Jeff Schaefer | .08 |
| 682 | Ray Lankford | .35 |
| 683 | Derek Lilliquist | .05 |
| 684 | Milt Cuyler | .12 |
| 685 | Doug Drabek | .05 |
| 686 | Mike Gallego | .05 |
| 687 | John Cerutti | .05 |
| 688 | Rosario Rodriguez (R) | .12 |
| 689 | John Kruk | .05 |
| 690 | Orel Hershiser | .10 |
| 691 | Mike Blowers | .05 |
| 692 | E. Valdez (err.) | .25 |
| 692 | E. Valdez (cor.) | .08 |
| 693 | Francisco Cabrera | .05 |
| 694 | Randy Veres | .05 |
| 695 | Kevin Seitzer | .05 |
| 696 | Steve Olin | .05 |
| 697 | Shawn Abner | .05 |
| 698 | Mark Guthrie | .05 |
| 699 | Jim Lefebvre | .05 |
| 700 | Jose Canseco | .30 |
| 701 | Pascual Perez | .05 |
| 702 | Tim Naehring | .10 |
| 703 | Juan Agosto | .05 |
| 704 | Devon White | .05 |
| 705 | Robby Thompson | .05 |
| 706 | Brad Arnsberg | .05 |
| 707 | Jim Eisenreich | .05 |
| 708 | John Mitchell | .05 |
| 709 | Matt Sinatro | .05 |
| 710 | Kent Hrbek | .12 |
| 711 | Jose DeLeon | .05 |
| 712 | Ricky Jordan | .05 |
| 713 | Scott Scudder | .05 |
| 714 | Marvell Wynne | .05 |
| 715 | Tim Burke | .05 |
| 716 | Bob Geren | .05 |
| 717 | Phil Bradley | .05 |
| 718 | Steve Crawford | .05 |
| 719 | Keith Miller | .05 |
| 720 | Cecil Fielder | .15 |
| 721 | Mark Lee (R) | .12 |
| 722 | Wally Backman | .05 |
| 723 | Candy Maldonado | .05 |
| 724 | David Segui | .10 |
| 725 | Ron Gant | .10 |
| 726 | Phil Stephenson | .05 |
| 727 | Mookie Wilson | .05 |
| 728 | Scott Sanderson | .05 |
| 729 | Don Zimmer | .05 |
| 730 | Barry Larkin | .10 |
| 731 | Jeff Gray (R) | .12 |
| 732 | Franklin Stubbs | .05 |
| 733 | Kelly Downs | .05 |
| 734 | John Russell | .05 |
| 735 | Ron Darling | .05 |
| 736 | Dick Schofield | .05 |
| 737 | Tim Crews | .05 |
| 738 | Mel Hall | .05 |
| 739 | Russ Swan | .05 |
| 740 | Ryne Sandberg | .20 |
| 741 | Jimmy Key (R) | .12 |
| 742 | Tommy Gregg | .05 |
| 743 | Bryn Smith | .05 |
| 744 | Nelson Santovenia | .05 |
| 745 | Doug Jones | .05 |
| 746 | John Shelby | .05 |
| 747 | Tony Fossas | .05 |
| 748 | Al Newman | .05 |
| 749 | Greg Harris | .05 |
| 750 | Bobby Bonilla | .15 |
| 751 | Wayne Edwards | .05 |
| 752 | Kevin Bass | .05 |
| 753 | Paul Marak (R) | .12 |
| 754 | Bill Pecota | .05 |
| 755 | Mark Langston | .08 |
| 756 | Jeff Huson | .05 |
| 757 | Mark Gardner | .05 |
| 758 | Mike Devereaux | .05 |
| 759 | Bobby Cox | .05 |
| 760 | Benny Santiago | .08 |
| 761 | Larry Anderson | .05 |
| 762 | Mitch Webster | .05 |
| 763 | Dana Kiecker | .05 |
| 764 | Mark Carreon | .05 |
| 765 | Shawon Dunston | .10 |
| 766 | Jeff Robinson | .05 |
| 767 | Dan Wilson (R) | .30 |
| 768 | Donn Pall | .05 |
| 769 | Tim Sherrill (R) | .12 |
| 770 | Jay Howell | .05 |
| 771 | Gary Redus | .05 |
| 772 | Kent Mercker | .05 |
| 773 | Tom Foley | .05 |
| 774 | Dennis Rasmussen | .05 |
| 775 | Julio Franco | .05 |
| 776 | Brent Mayne | .05 |
| 777 | John Candelaria | .05 |
| 778 | Danny Gladden | .05 |
| 779 | Carmelo Martinez | .05 |
| 780 | Randy Myers | .05 |
| 781 | Darryl Hamilton | .05 |
| 782 | Jim Deshaies | .05 |
| 783 | Joel Skinner | .05 |
| 784 | Willie Fraser | .05 |
| 785 | Scott Fletcher | .05 |
| 786 | Eric Plunk | .05 |
| 787 | Checklist No. 6 | .05 |
| 788 | Bob Milacki | .05 |
| 789 | Tom Lasorda | .05 |
| 790 | Ken Griffey Jr. | .75 |
| 791 | Mike Benjamin | .05 |
| 792 | Mike Greenwell | .12 |

# 1991 Topps Traded . . . Complete Set of 132 Cards—Value $12.00

Updates the main 1991 card set with players who changed teams during the season and rookies who joined their teams early in the season. The complete set was sold in a box. Features the rookie cards of Jeff Bagwell and Ivan Rodriguez.

| NO. PLAYER | MINT | NO. PLAYER | MINT | NO. PLAYER | MINT | NO. PLAYER | MINT |
|---|---|---|---|---|---|---|---|
| 1T Juan Agosto | .05 | 34T Darren Dreifort (R) | .15 | 67T Pat Kelly (R) | .35 | 100T Jeff Robinson | .05 |
| 2T Roberto Alomar | .08 | 35T Kirk Dressendorfer (R) | .20 | 68T Darryl Kile | .08 | 101T Ivan Rodriguez (R) | 2.00 |
| 3T Wally Backman | .05 | 36T Jim Essian | .05 | 69T Chuck Knoblauch | .40 | 102T Steve Rodriguez (R) | .15 |
| 4T Jeff Bagwell (R) | 3.00 | 37T Dwight Evans | .05 | 70T Bill Krueger | .05 | 103T Tom Runnells | .05 |
| 5T Skeeter Barnes | .05 | 38T Steve Farr | .05 | 71T Scott Leius | .15 | 104T Scott Sanderson | .05 |
| 6T Steve Bedrosian | .05 | 39T Jeff Fassero (R) | .15 | 72T Donnie Leshnock (R) | .15 | 105T Bob Scanlan (R) | .15 |
| 7T Derek Bell | .35 | 40T Junior Felix | .05 | 73T Mark Lewis | .30 | 106T Pete Schourek (R) | .15 |
| 8T George Bell | .10 | 41T Tony Fernandez | .05 | 74T Candy Maldonado | .05 | 107T Gary Scott (R) | .25 |
| 9T Rafael Belliard | .05 | 42T Steve Finley | .05 | 75T Jason McDonald (R) | .15 | 108T Paul Shuey (R) | .15 |
| 10T Dante Bichette | .05 | 43T Jim Fregosi | .05 | 76T Willie McGee | .10 | 109T Doug Simons (R) | .15 |
| 11T Bud Black | .05 | 44T Gary Gaetti | .05 | 77T Fred McGriff | .10 | 110T Dave Smith | .05 |
| 12T Mike Boddicker | .05 | 45T Jason Giambi (R) | .15 | 78T Billy McMillon (R) | .15 | 111T Cory Snyder | .05 |
| 13T Sid Bream | .05 | 46T Kirk Gibson | .10 | 79T Hal McRae | .05 | 112T Luis Sojo | .05 |
| 14T Hubie Brooks | .05 | 47T Leo Gomez | .20 | 80T Dan Melendez (R) | .15 | 113T Kennie Steenstra (R) | .15 |
| 15T Brett Butler | .08 | 48T Luis Gonzalez (R) | .50 | 81T Orlando Merced (R) | .40 | 114T Darryl Strawberry | .35 |
| 16T Ivan Calderon | .05 | 49T Jeff Granger (R) | .30 | 82T Jack Morris | .10 | 115T Franklin Stubbs | .05 |
| 17T John Candelaria | .05 | 50T Todd Greene (R) | .15 | 83T Phil Nevin (R) | .15 | 116T Todd Taylor (R) | .15 |
| 18T Tom Candiotti | .08 | 51T Jeffrey Hammonds (R) | .25 | 84T Otis Nixon | .08 | 117T Wade Taylor (R) | .25 |
| 19T Gary Carter | .10 | 52T Mike Hargrove | .05 | 85T Johnny Oates | .05 | 118T Garry Templeton | .05 |
| 20T Joe Carter | .12 | 53T Pete Harnisch | .05 | 86T Bob Ojeda | .05 | 119T Mikey Tettleton | .05 |
| 21T Rick Cerone | .05 | 54T Rick Helling (R) | .25 | 87T Mike Pagliarulo | .05 | 120T Tim Teufel | .05 |
| 22T Jack Clark | .10 | 55T Glenallen Hill | .05 | 88T Dean Palmer | .25 | 121T Mike Timlin (R) | .15 |
| 23T Vince Coleman | .10 | 56T Charlie Hough | .05 | 89T Dave Parker | .10 | 122T David Tuttle (R) | .15 |
| 24T Scott Coolbaugh | .05 | 57T Pete Incaviglia | .05 | 90T Terry Pendleton | .10 | 123T Mo Vaughn | .75 |
| 25T Danny Cox | .05 | 58T Bo Jackson | .75 | 91T Tony Phillips | .10 | 124T Jeff Ware (R) | .15 |
| 26T Danny Darwin | .05 | 59T Danny Jackson | .05 | 92T Doug Piatt (R) | .15 | 125T Devon White | .05 |
| 27T Chili Davis | .05 | 60T Reggie Jefferson | .30 | 93T Ron Polk (R) | .15 | 126T Mark Whiten | .15 |
| 28T Glenn Davis | .08 | 61T Charles Johnson (R) | .20 | 94T Rock Raines | .05 | 127T Mitch Williams | .05 |
| 29T Steve Decker (R) | .25 | 62T Jeff Johnson (R) | .30 | 95T Willie Randolph | .05 | 128T Craig Wilson (R) | .15 |
| 30T Rob Deer | .05 | 63T Todd Johnson (R) | .15 | 96T Dave Righetti | .05 | 129T Willie Wilson | .05 |
| 31T Rich DeLucia (R) | .15 | 64T Barry Jones | .05 | 97T Ernie Riles | .05 | 130T Chris Wimmer (R) | .15 |
| 32T John Dettmer (R) | .15 | 65T Chris Jones (R) | .15 | 98T Chris Roberts (R) | .35 | 131T Ivan Zweig (R) | .15 |
| 33T Brian Downing | .05 | 66T Scott Kamieniecki (R) | .15 | 99T Jeff Robinson | .05 | 132T Checklist | .05 |

# 1991 Topps Stadium Club . . . Series One Set of 300 Cards (#1 to 300)—Value $175.00
# Series Two Set of 300 Cards—(#301 to 600) Value $115.00

Revolutionary new deluxe printing and super glossy finish technology. Borderless design. Full color back features a mini reprint of the player's rookie card. Extremely limited production. Features the rookie cards of Jeff Bagwell and Phil Plantier.

| NO. PLAYER | MINT | NO. PLAYER | MINT | NO. PLAYER | MINT | NO. PLAYER | MINT |
|---|---|---|---|---|---|---|---|
| **SERIES 1—No. 1 to 300** | | 8 Marquis Grissom | .75 | 16 Eric Yelding | .20 | 24 Tom Henke | .20 |
| 1 Dave Stewart | 1.25 | 9 Erik Hanson | .25 | 17 Bryn Smith | .20 | 25 Jerry Browne | .20 |
| 2 Wally Joyner | .30 | 10 Geno Petralli | .20 | 18 Bip Roberts | .20 | 26 Dave Justice | 10.00 |
| 3 Shawson Dunston | .25 | 11 Jose Rijo | .20 | 19 Mike Scioscia | .20 | 27 Mark Langston | .30 |
| 4 Darren Daulton | .20 | 12 Carlos Quintana | .20 | 20 Mark Williamson | .20 | 28 Damon Berryhill | .20 |
| 5 Will Clark | 3.00 | 13 Junior Ortiz | .20 | 21 Don Mattingly | 1.50 | 29 Kevin Bass | .20 |
| 6 Sammy Sosa | .40 | 14 Bob Walk | .20 | 22 John Franco | .20 | 30 Scott Fletcher | .20 |
| 7 Dan Plesac | .20 | 15 Mike Macfarlane | .20 | 23 Chet Lemon | .20 | 31 Moises Alou | .20 |

| NO. | PLAYER | MINT |
|---|---|---|
| 32 | Dave Valle | .20 |
| 33 | Jody Reed | .20 |
| 34 | Dave West | .20 |
| 35 | Kevin McReynolds | .25 |
| 36 | Pat Combs | .20 |
| 37 | Eric Davis | .60 |
| 38 | Bret Saberhagen | .30 |
| 39 | Stan Javier | .20 |
| 40 | Chuck Cary | .20 |
| 41 | Tony Phillips | .20 |
| 42 | Lee Smith | .20 |
| 43 | Tim Teufel | .20 |
| 44 | Lance Dickson (R) | .75 |
| 45 | Greg Litton | .20 |
| 46 | Teddy Higuera | .20 |
| 47 | Edgar Martinez | .35 |
| 48 | Steve Avery | 7.50 |
| 49 | Walt Weiss | .20 |
| 50 | David Sequi | .30 |
| 51 | Andy Benes | .35 |
| 52 | Karl Rhodes | .20 |
| 53 | Neal Heaton | .20 |
| 54 | Danny Gladden | .20 |
| 55 | Luis Rivera | .20 |
| 56 | Kevin Brown | .20 |
| 57 | Frank Thomas | 30.00 |
| 58 | Terry Mulholland | .20 |
| 59 | Dick Schofield | .20 |
| 60 | Ron Darling | .20 |
| 61 | Sandy Alomar | .40 |
| 62 | Dave Stieb | .20 |
| 63 | Alan Trammell | .50 |
| 64 | Matt Nokes | .20 |
| 65 | Lenny Harris | .20 |
| 66 | Milt Thompson | .20 |
| 67 | Storm Davis | .20 |
| 68 | Joe Oliver | .20 |
| 69 | Andres Galarraga | .20 |
| 70 | Ozzie Guillen | .20 |
| 71 | Ken Howell | .20 |
| 72 | Garry Templeton | .20 |
| 73 | Derrick May | .30 |
| 74 | Xavier Hernandez | .20 |
| 75 | Dave Parker | .30 |
| 76 | Rick Aguilera | .20 |
| 77 | Robby Thompson | .20 |
| 78 | Pete Incaviglia | .20 |
| 79 | Bob Welch | .20 |
| 80 | Randy Milligan | .20 |
| 81 | Chuck Finley | .25 |
| 82 | Alvin Davis | .20 |
| 83 | Tim Naehring | .25 |
| 84 | Jay Bell | .20 |
| 85 | Joe Magrane | .20 |
| 86 | Howard Johnson | .50 |
| 87 | Jack McDowell | .20 |
| 88 | Kevin Seitzer | .20 |
| 89 | Bruce Ruffin | .20 |
| 90 | F. Valenzuela | .25 |
| 91 | Terry Kennedy | .20 |
| 92 | Barry Larkin | .60 |
| 93 | Larry Walker | .35 |
| 94 | Luis Salazar | .20 |
| 95 | Gary Sheffield | .25 |
| 96 | Bobby Witt | .20 |
| 97 | Lonnie Smith | .20 |
| 98 | Bryan Harvey | .20 |
| 99 | Mookie Wilson | .20 |
| 100 | Doc Gooden | .75 |
| 101 | Lou Whitaker | .20 |
| 102 | Ron Karkovice | .20 |
| 103 | Jesse Barfield | .20 |
| 104 | Jose De Jesus | .20 |
| 105 | Benny Santiago | .30 |
| 106 | Brian Holman | .20 |
| 107 | Rafael Ramirez | .20 |
| 108 | Ellis Burks | .50 |
| 109 | Mike Bielecki | .20 |
| 110 | Kirby Puckett | 1.25 |
| 111 | Terry Shumpert | .20 |
| 112 | Chuck Crim | .20 |
| 113 | Todd Benzinger | .20 |
| 114 | Brian Barnes (R) | .40 |
| 115 | Carlos Baerga | .75 |
| 116 | Kal Daniels | .25 |
| 117 | Dave Johnson | .20 |
| 118 | Andy Van Slyke | .30 |
| 119 | John Burkett | .20 |
| 120 | Rickey Henderson | 2.50 |
| 121 | Tim Jones | .20 |
| 122 | Daryl Irvine (R) | .35 |
| 123 | Ruben Sierra | 1.25 |
| 124 | Jim Abbott | 1.00 |
| 125 | Daryl Boston | .20 |
| 126 | Greg Maddux | .20 |
| 127 | Von Hayes | .20 |
| 128 | Mike Fitzgerald | .20 |
| 129 | Wayne Edwards | .20 |
| 130 | Greg Briley | .20 |
| 131 | Rob Dibble | .20 |
| 132 | Gene Larkin | .30 |
| 133 | David Wells | .20 |
| 134 | Steve Balboni | .20 |
| 135 | Greg Vaughn | 1.25 |
| 136 | Mark Davis | .20 |
| 137 | Dave Rohde | .25 |
| 138 | Eric Show | .20 |
| 139 | Bobby Bonilla | 1.00 |
| 140 | Dana Kiecker | .20 |
| 141 | Gary Pettis | .20 |
| 142 | Dennis Boyd | .20 |
| 143 | Mike Benjamin | .20 |
| 144 | Luis Polonia | .20 |
| 145 | Doug Jones | .20 |
| 146 | Al Newman | .20 |
| 147 | Alex Fernandez | .75 |
| 148 | Bill Doran | .20 |
| 149 | Kevin Elster | .20 |
| 150 | Len Dykstra | .30 |
| 151 | Mike Gallego | .20 |
| 152 | Tim Belcher | .20 |
| 153 | Jay Buhner | .20 |
| 154 | Ozzie Smith | .75 |
| 155 | Jose Canseco | 3.50 |
| 156 | Gregg Olson | .25 |
| 157 | Charlie O'Brien | .20 |
| 158 | Frank Tanana | .20 |
| 159 | Geroge Brett | .75 |
| 160 | Jeff Huston | .20 |
| 161 | Kevin Tapani | .40 |
| 162 | Jerome Walton | .20 |
| 163 | Charlie Hayes | .20 |
| 164 | Chris Bosio | .20 |
| 165 | Chris Sabo | .40 |
| 166 | Lance Parrish | .20 |
| 167 | Don Robinson | .20 |
| 168 | Manny Lee | .20 |
| 169 | Dennis Rasmussen | .20 |
| 170 | Wade Boggs | 1.25 |
| 171 | Bob Geren | .20 |
| 172 | Mackey Sasser | .20 |
| 173 | Julio Franco | .50 |
| 174 | Otis Nixon | .30 |
| 175 | Bert Blyleven | .20 |
| 176 | Craig Biggio | .40 |
| 177 | Eddie Murray | .60 |
| 178 | Randy Tomlin (R) | 1.00 |
| 179 | Tino Martinez | 1.00 |
| 180 | Carlton Fisk | .75 |
| 181 | Dwight Smith | .20 |
| 182 | Scott Garretts | .20 |
| 183 | Jim Gantner | .20 |
| 184 | Dickie Thon | .20 |
| 185 | John Farrell | .20 |
| 186 | Cecil Fielder | 2.00 |
| 187 | Glenn Braggs | .20 |
| 188 | Allan Anderson | .20 |
| 189 | Kurt Stillwell | .20 |
| 190 | Jose Oquendo | .20 |
| 191 | Joe Orsulak | .20 |
| 192 | Ricky Jordan | .20 |
| 193 | Kelly Downs | .20 |
| 194 | Delino de Shields | .75 |
| 195 | Omar Vizquel | .20 |
| 196 | Mark Carreon | .20 |
| 197 | Mike Harkey | .20 |
| 198 | Jack Howell | .20 |
| 199 | Lance Johnson | .20 |
| 200 | Nolan Ryan | 16.00 |
| 201 | John Marzano | .20 |
| 202 | Doug Drabek | .20 |
| 203 | Mark Lemke | .20 |
| 204 | Steve Sax | .20 |
| 205 | Greg Harris | .20 |
| 206 | B.J. Surhoff | .20 |
| 207 | Todd Burns | .20 |
| 208 | Jose Gonzalez | .20 |
| 209 | Mike Scott | .20 |
| 210 | Dave Magadan | .20 |
| 211 | Dante Bichette | .20 |
| 212 | Trevor Wilson | .20 |
| 213 | Hector Villanueva | .20 |
| 214 | Dan Pasqua | .20 |
| 215 | Greg Colbrunn (R) | .40 |
| 216 | Mike Jeffcoat | .20 |
| 217 | Harold Reynolds | .20 |
| 218 | Paul O'Neill | .20 |
| 219 | Mark Guthrie | .20 |
| 220 | Barry Bonds | 1.25 |
| 221 | Jimmy Key | .20 |
| 222 | Billy Ripken | .20 |
| 223 | Tom Pagnozzi | .20 |
| 224 | Bo Jackson | 3.00 |
| 225 | Sid Fernandez | .20 |
| 226 | Mike Marshall | .20 |
| 227 | John Kruk | .20 |
| 228 | Mike Fetters | .20 |
| 229 | Eric Anthony | .30 |
| 230 | Ryne Sandberg | 3.00 |
| 231 | Carney Lansford | .20 |
| 232 | Melido Perez | .20 |
| 233 | Jose Lind | .20 |
| 234 | Darryl Hamilton | .20 |
| 235 | Tom Browning | .20 |
| 236 | Spike Owen | .20 |
| 237 | Juan Gonzalez | 10.00 |
| 238 | Felix Fermin | .20 |
| 239 | Keith Miller | .20 |
| 240 | Mark Gubicza | .20 |
| 241 | Kent Anderson | .20 |
| 242 | Alvaro Espinoza | .20 |
| 243 | Dale Murphy | .40 |
| 244 | Orel Hershiser | .40 |
| 245 | Paul Molitor | .35 |
| 246 | Eddie Whitson | .20 |
| 247 | Joe Girardi | .20 |
| 248 | Kent Hrbek | .25 |
| 249 | Bill Sampen | .30 |
| 250 | Kevin Mitchell | .60 |
| 251 | Mariano Duncan | .20 |
| 252 | Scott Bradley | .20 |
| 253 | Mike Greenwell | .60 |
| 254 | Tom Gordon | .20 |
| 255 | Todd Zeile | .75 |
| 256 | Bobby Thigpen | .20 |
| 257 | Gregg Jefferies | .40 |
| 258 | Kenny Rogers | 1.25 |
| 259 | Shane Mark | .20 |
| 260 | Zane Smith | .20 |
| 261 | Mitch Williams | .20 |
| 262 | Jim Deshaies | .20 |
| 263 | Dave Winfield | .60 |
| 264 | Ben McDonald | 1.00 |
| 265 | Randy Ready | .20 |
| 266 | Pat Borders | .20 |
| 267 | Jose Uribe | .20 |
| 268 | Derek Lilliquist | .20 |
| 269 | Greg Brock | .20 |
| 270 | Ken Griffey, Jr. | 15.00 |
| 271 | Jeff Gray | .30 |
| 272 | Danny Tartabull | .35 |
| 273 | Denny Martinez | .20 |
| 274 | Robin Ventura | 3.00 |
| 275 | Randy Myers | .20 |
| 276 | Jack Daugherty | .20 |
| 277 | Greg Gagne | .20 |
| 278 | Jay Howell | .20 |
| 279 | Mike LaValliere | .20 |
| 280 | Rex Hudler | .20 |
| 281 | Mike Simms | .50 |
| 282 | Kevin Maas | 2.50 |
| 283 | Jeff Ballard | .20 |
| 284 | Dave Henderson | .30 |
| 285 | Pete O'Brien | .20 |
| 286 | Brook Jacoby | .20 |
| 287 | Mike Henneman | .20 |
| 288 | Greg Olson | .20 |
| 289 | Greg Myers | .20 |
| 290 | Mark Grace | .50 |
| 291 | Shawn Abner | .20 |
| 292 | Frank Viola | .30 |
| 293 | Lee Stevens | .50 |
| 294 | Jason Grimsley | .20 |
| 295 | Matt Williams | .60 |
| 296 | Ron Robinson | .20 |
| 297 | Tom Brunansky | .20 |
| 298 | Checklist 1-100 | .20 |
| 299 | Chklst: 101-200 | .20 |
| 300 | Chklst: 201-300 | .20 |

**SERIES 2—No. 301 to 600**

| NO. | PLAYER | MINT |
|---|---|---|
| 301 | Darryl Strawberry | 2.00 |
| 302 | Bud Black | .20 |
| 303 | Harold Baines | .20 |
| 304 | Roberto Alomar | 1.00 |
| 305 | Norm Charlton | .20 |
| 306 | Gary Thurman | .20 |
| 307 | Mike Felder | .20 |
| 308 | Tony Gwynn | 1.25 |
| 309 | Roger Clemens | 2.00 |
| 310 | Andre Dawson | .60 |
| 311 | Scott Radinsky | .20 |
| 312 | Bob Melvin | .20 |
| 313 | Kirk McCaskill | .20 |
| 314 | Pedro Guerrero | .25 |
| 315 | Walt Terrell | .20 |
| 316 | Sam Horn | .20 |
| 317 | Wes Chamberlain (R) | 3.00 |
| 318 | Pedro Munoz (R) | 1.00 |
| 319 | Roberto Kelly | .30 |
| 320 | Mark Protugal | .20 |
| 321 | Tim McIntosh | .20 |
| 322 | Jesse Orosco | .20 |
| 323 | Gary Green | .20 |
| 324 | Greg Harris | .20 |
| 325 | Hubie Brooks | .20 |
| 326 | Chris Nabholz | .30 |
| 327 | Terry Pendleton | .40 |
| 328 | Eric King | .20 |
| 329 | Chili Davis | .20 |
| 330 | Anthony Telford | .35 |
| 331 | Kelly Gruber | .35 |
| 332 | Dennis Eckersley | .35 |
| 333 | Mel Hall | .20 |
| 334 | Bob Kipper | .20 |
| 335 | Willie McGee | .20 |
| 336 | Steve Olin | .20 |
| 337 | Steve Buechele | .20 |
| 338 | Scott Leius | .30 |
| 339 | Hal Morris | 1.00 |
| 340 | Jose Offerman | .30 |
| 341 | Kent Mercker | .20 |
| 342 | Ken Griffey | .20 |
| 343 | Pete Harnisch | .20 |
| 344 | Kirk Gibson | .25 |
| 345 | Dave Smith | .20 |
| 346 | Dave Martinez | .20 |
| 347 | Atlee Hammaker | .20 |
| 348 | Brian Downing | .20 |
| 349 | Todd Hundley | .50 |
| 350 | Candy Maldonado | .20 |
| 351 | Dwight Evans | .20 |
| 352 | Steve Searcy | .20 |
| 353 | Gary Gaetti | .20 |
| 354 | Jeff Reardon | .20 |
| 355 | Travis Fryman | 4.00 |
| 356 | Dave Righetti | .20 |
| 357 | Fred McGriff | .50 |
| 358 | Don Slaught | .20 |
| 359 | Gene Nelson | .20 |
| 360 | Billy Spiers | .20 |
| 361 | Lee Guetterman | .20 |
| 362 | Darren Lewis | 1.00 |
| 363 | Duane Ward | .20 |
| 364 | Lloyd Moseby | .20 |
| 365 | John Smoltz | .40 |

| NO. | PLAYER | MINT |
|---|---|---|
| 366 | Felix Jose | .75 |
| 367 | David Cone | .20 |
| 368 | Wally Backman | .20 |
| 369 | Jeff Montgomery | .20 |
| 370 | Rich Garces (R) | .35 |
| 371 | Billy Hatcher | .20 |
| 372 | Bill Swift | .20 |
| 373 | Jim Eisenreich | .20 |
| 374 | Rob Ducey | .20 |
| 375 | Tim Crews | .20 |
| 376 | Steve Finely | .20 |
| 377 | Jeff Blauser | .20 |
| 378 | Willie Wilson | .20 |
| 379 | Gerald Perry | .20 |
| 380 | Jose Mesa | .20 |
| 381 | Pat Kelly (R) | 1.50 |
| 382 | Matt Merullo | .20 |
| 383 | Ivan Calderon | .20 |
| 384 | Scott Chiamparino | .20 |
| 385 | Lloyd McClendon | .20 |
| 386 | Dave Bergman | .20 |
| 387 | Ed Sprague | .50 |
| 388 | Jeff Bagwell (R) | 10.00 |
| 389 | Brett Butler | .20 |
| 390 | Larry Anderson | .20 |
| 391 | Glenn Davis | .35 |
| 392 | Alex Cole | .30 |
| 393 | Mike Heath | .20 |
| 394 | Danny Darwin | .20 |
| 395 | Steve Lake | .20 |
| 396 | Tim Layana | .20 |
| 397 | Terry Leach | .20 |
| 398 | Bill Wegman | .20 |
| 399 | Mark McGwire | .50 |
| 400 | Mike Boddicker | .20 |
| 401 | Steve Howe | .20 |
| 402 | Bernard Gilkey | .50 |
| 403 | Thomas Howard | .20 |
| 404 | Rafael Belliard | .20 |
| 405 | Tom Candiotti | .20 |
| 406 | Rene Gonzales | .20 |
| 407 | Chuck McElroy | .20 |
| 408 | Paul Sorrento | .20 |
| 409 | Randy Johnson | .20 |
| 410 | Brady Anderson | .20 |
| 411 | Dennis Cook | .20 |
| 412 | Mickey Tettleton | .20 |
| 413 | Mike Stanton | .20 |
| 414 | Ken Oberkfell | .20 |
| 415 | Rick Honeycutt | .20 |
| 416 | Nelson Santovenia | .20 |
| 417 | Bob Tewksbury | .20 |
| 418 | Brent Mayne | .30 |
| 419 | Steve Farr | .20 |
| 420 | Phil Stephenson | .20 |
| 421 | Jeff Russell | .20 |
| 422 | Chris James | .20 |
| 423 | Tim Leary | .20 |
| 424 | Gary Carter | .30 |
| 425 | Glenallen Hill | .20 |
| 426 | Matt Young | .20 |
| 427 | Sid Bream | .20 |
| 428 | Greg Swindell | .20 |
| 429 | Scott Aldred | .30 |
| 430 | Cal Ripken | 3.00 |
| 431 | Bill Landrum | .20 |
| 432 | Ernie Riles | .20 |
| 433 | Danny Jackson | .20 |
| 434 | Casey Candaele | .20 |
| 435 | Ken Hill | .20 |
| 436 | Jaime Navarro | .20 |
| 437 | Lance Blankenship | .20 |
| 438 | Randy Velarde | .20 |
| 439 | Frank DiPino | .20 |
| 440 | Carl Nichols | .20 |
| 441 | Jeff Robinson | .20 |
| 442 | Deion Sanders | .50 |
| 443 | Vicente Palacios | .20 |
| 444 | Devon White | .20 |
| 445 | John Cerutti | .20 |
| 446 | Tracy Jones | .20 |
| 447 | Jack Morris | .40 |
| 448 | Mitch Webster | .20 |
| 449 | Bob Ojeda | .20 |
| 450 | Oscar Azocar | .20 |
| 451 | Luis Aquino | .20 |
| 452 | Mark Whiten | 1.00 |
| 453 | Stan Belinda | .20 |
| 454 | Ron Gant | 1.00 |
| 455 | Jose DeLeon | .20 |
| 456 | Mark Salas | .20 |
| 457 | Junior Felix | .20 |
| 458 | Wally Whitehurst | .20 |
| 459 | Phil Plantier (R) | 12.00 |
| 460 | Juan Berenguer | .20 |
| 461 | Franklin Stubbs | .20 |
| 462 | Joe Boever | .20 |
| 463 | Tim Walach | .20 |
| 464 | Mike Moore | .20 |
| 465 | Albert Belle | 1.25 |
| 466 | Mike Witt | .20 |
| 467 | Craig Worthington | .20 |
| 468 | Jerald Clark | .20 |
| 469 | Scott Terry | .20 |
| 470 | Milt Cuyler | 1.00 |
| 471 | John Smiley | .20 |
| 472 | Charles Nagy | .40 |
| 473 | Alan Mills | .20 |
| 474 | John Russell | .20 |
| 475 | Bruce Hurst | .20 |
| 476 | Andujar Cedeno | 2.50 |
| 477 | Dave Eiland | .20 |
| 478 | Brian McRae (R) | 3.00 |
| 479 | Mike LaCoss | .20 |
| 480 | Chris Gwynn | .20 |
| 481 | Jamie Moyer | .20 |
| 482 | John Olerud | 1.00 |
| 483 | Efrain Valdez (R) | .40 |
| 484 | Sil Campusano | .20 |
| 485 | Pascual Perez | .20 |
| 486 | Gary Redus | .20 |
| 487 | Andy Hawkins | .20 |
| 488 | Cory Snyder | .25 |
| 489 | Chris Hoiles | .50 |
| 490 | Ron Hassey | .20 |
| 491 | Gary Wayne | .20 |
| 492 | Mark Lewis | 1.00 |
| 493 | Scott Coolbaugh | .20 |
| 494 | Gerald Yound | .20 |
| 495 | Juan Samuel | .20 |
| 496 | Willie Fraser | .20 |
| 497 | Jeff Treadway | .20 |
| 498 | Vince Coleman | .40 |
| 499 | Cris Carpenter | .20 |
| 500 | Jack Clark | .25 |
| 501 | Kevin Appier | .25 |
| 502 | Rafael Palmeiro | .75 |
| 503 | Hensley Meulens | .35 |
| 504 | George Bell | .40 |
| 505 | Tony Pena | .20 |
| 506 | Roger McDowell | .20 |
| 507 | Luis Sojo | .20 |
| 508 | Mike Schooler | .20 |
| 509 | Robin Yount | .75 |
| 510 | Jack Armstrong | .20 |
| 511 | Rick Cerone | .20 |
| 512 | Curt Wilkerson | .20 |
| 513 | Joe Carter | .50 |
| 514 | Tim Burke | .20 |
| 515 | Tony Fenandez | .20 |
| 516 | Ramon Martinez | 1.00 |
| 517 | Tim Hulett | .20 |
| 518 | Terry Steinbach | .20 |
| 519 | Pete Smith | .20 |
| 520 | Ken Caminiti | .20 |
| 521 | Shawn Boskie | .20 |
| 522 | Mike Pagliarulo | .20 |
| 523 | Rock Raines | .40 |
| 524 | Alfredo Griffin | .20 |
| 525 | Henry Cotto | .20 |
| 526 | Mike Stanley | .20 |
| 527 | Charlie Leibrandt | .20 |
| 528 | Jeff King | .20 |
| 529 | Eric Plunk | .20 |
| 530 | Tom Lampkin | .20 |
| 531 | Steve Bedrosian | .20 |
| 532 | Tom Herr | .20 |
| 533 | Craig Lefferts | .20 |
| 534 | Jeff Reed | .20 |
| 535 | Mickey Morandini | .50 |
| 536 | Greg Cadaret | .20 |
| 537 | Ray Lankford | 2.00 |
| 538 | John Candelaria | .20 |
| 539 | Rob Deer | .20 |
| 540 | Brad Arnsberg | .20 |
| 541 | Mike Sharperson | .20 |
| 542 | Jeff Robinson | .20 |
| 543 | Mo Vaughn | 3.00 |
| 544 | Jeff Parrett | .20 |
| 545 | Willie Randolph | .20 |
| 546 | Herm Winningham | .20 |
| 547 | Jeff Innis | .20 |
| 548 | Chuck Knoblauch | 5.00 |
| 549 | Tommy Greene | .30 |
| 550 | Jeff Hamilton | .20 |
| 551 | Barry Jones | .20 |
| 552 | Ken Dayley | .20 |
| 553 | Rick Dempsey | .20 |
| 554 | Greg Smith | .20 |
| 555 | Mike Devereaux | .20 |
| 556 | Keith Comstock | .20 |
| 557 | Paul Faries (R) | .30 |
| 558 | Tom Glavine | .75 |
| 559 | Craig Grebeck | .20 |
| 560 | Scott Erickson | 7.00 |
| 561 | Joel Skinner | .20 |
| 562 | Mike Morgan | .20 |
| 563 | Dave Gallagher | .20 |
| 564 | Todd Stottlemyre | .30 |
| 565 | Rich Rodriguez (R) | .30 |
| 566 | Craig Wilson (R) | .30 |
| 567 | Jeff Brantley | .20 |
| 568 | Scott Kamieniecki (R) | .40 |
| 569 | Steve Decker (R) | .75 |
| 570 | Juan Agosto | .20 |
| 571 | Tommy Gregg | .20 |
| 572 | Kevin Wickander | .20 |
| 573 | Jamie Quirk | .20 |
| 574 | Jerry Don Gleaton | .20 |
| 575 | Chris Hammond | .50 |
| 576 | Luis Gonzalez (R) | 3.00 |
| 577 | Russ Swan | .20 |
| 578 | Jeff Conine (R) | .35 |
| 579 | Charlie Hough | .20 |
| 580 | Jeff Kunkel | .20 |
| 581 | Darrel Akerfelds | .20 |
| 582 | Jeff Manto | .20 |
| 583 | Alejandro Pena | .20 |
| 584 | Mark Davidson | .20 |
| 585 | Bob MacDonald (R) | .30 |
| 586 | Paul Assenmacher | .20 |
| 587 | Dan Wilson (R) | .60 |
| 588 | Tom Bolton | .20 |
| 589 | Brian Harper | .20 |
| 590 | John Habyan | .20 |
| 591 | John Orton | .20 |
| 592 | Mark Gardner | .20 |
| 593 | Turner Ward (R) | .50 |
| 594 | Bob Patterson | .20 |
| 595 | Ed Nunez | .20 |
| 596 | Gary Scott (R) | .75 |
| 597 | Scott Bankhead | .20 |
| 598 | Checklist 301-400 | .20 |
| 599 | Checklist 401-500 | .20 |
| 600 | Checklist 501-600 | .20 |

## 1992 Topps . . . Complete Set of 792 Cards—Value $30.00

A Topps tradition since 1951 came to an end as Topps dropped bubble gum from its wax packs and switched from wax to a poly wrapper. White card stock was used for the first time since 1970. The complete set was issued in a *gold foil* version which was randomly packaged in packs.

| NO. | PLAYER | MINT |
|---|---|---|
| 1 | Nolan Ryan | 40 |
| 2 | '91 Rec: Henderson | 15 |
| 3 | '91 Rec: M. Reardon | 05 |
| 4 | '91 Rec: N. Ryan | 20 |
| 5 | '91 Rec: D. Winfield | 08 |
| 6 | Brien Taylor (R) | 1.25 |
| 7 | Jim Orlander (R) | 25 |
| 8 | Bryan Hickerson (R) | 15 |
| 9 | Jon Farrell (R) | 20 |
| 10 | Wade Boggs | 15 |
| 11 | Jack McDowell | 08 |
| 12 | Luis Gonzalez (ASR) | 10 |
| 13 | Mike Scioscia | 05 |
| 14 | Wes Chamberlain | 15 |
| 15 | Denny Martinez | 05 |
| 16 | Jeff Montgomery | 05 |
| 17 | Randy Milligan | 05 |
| 18 | Greg Cadaret | 05 |
| 19 | Jamie Quirk | 05 |
| 20 | Bip Roberts | 05 |
| 21 | Buck Rogers (Mgr.) | 05 |
| 22 | Bill Wegman | 05 |
| 23 | C. Knoblauch (ASR) | 15 |
| 24 | Randy Myers | 05 |
| 25 | Ron Gant | 08 |
| 26 | Mike Bielecki | 05 |
| 27 | Juan Gonzalez | 25 |
| 28 | Mike Schooler | 05 |
| 29 | Mickey Tettleton | 05 |
| 30 | John Kruk | 05 |
| 31 | Bryn Smith | 05 |
| 32 | Chris Nabholz | 05 |
| 33 | Carlos Baerga | 10 |
| 34 | Jeff Juden | 10 |
| 35 | Dave Righetti (R) | 05 |
| 36 | Scott Ruffcorn (DP) | 15 |
| 37 | Luis Polonia | 05 |
| 38 | Tom Candiotti | 05 |
| 39 | Greg Olson | 05 |
| 40 | Cal Ripken | 20 |
| 41 | Craig Lefferts | 05 |
| 42 | Mike MacFarlane | 05 |
| 43 | Jose Lind | 05 |
| 44 | Rick Aguilera | 05 |
| 45 | Gary Carter | 08 |
| 46 | Steve Farr | 05 |
| 47 | Rex Hudler | 05 |
| 48 | Scott Scudder | 05 |
| 49 | Damon Berryhill | 05 |
| 50 | Ken Griffey, Jr. | 50 |
| 51 | Tom Runnels (Mgr.) | 05 |
| 52 | Juan Bell | 05 |
| 53 | Tommy Gregg | 05 |
| 54 | David Wells | 05 |
| 55 | Rafael Palmiero | 08 |
| 56 | Charlie O'Brien | 05 |
| 57 | Donn Pall | 05 |
| | Prospects Catchers: | |
| 58 | B. Ausmus, J. Campanis, D. Nilsson, D. Robbins | 50 |
| 59 | Mo Vaughn | 25 |
| 60 | Tony Fernandez | 05 |
| 61 | Paul O'Neill | 05 |
| 62 | Gene Nelson | 05 |
| 63 | Randy Ready | 05 |
| 64 | Bob Kipper | 05 |
| 65 | Willie McGee | 10 |
| 66 | S. Stahoviak (R) (DP) | 30 |
| 67 | Luis Salazar | 05 |
| 68 | Marvin Freeman | 05 |
| 69 | Kenny Lofton | 15 |
| 70 | Gary Gaetti | 05 |
| 71 | Erik Hanson | 05 |
| 72 | Eddie Zosky | 08 |
| 73 | Brian Barnes | 05 |
| 74 | Scott Leius | 05 |
| 75 | Bret Saberhagen | 08 |
| 76 | Mike Gallego | 05 |
| 77 | Jack Armstrong | 05 |
| 78 | Ivan Rodriguez (ASR) | 50 |
| 79 | Jesse Orosco | 05 |
| 80 | David Justice | 30 |
| 81 | Ced Landrum | 05 |
| 82 | Doug Simons | 08 |
| 83 | Tommy Greene | 08 |
| 84 | Leo Gomez (ASR) | 08 |
| 85 | Jose DeLeon | 05 |
| 86 | Steve Finley | 05 |
| 87 | Bob MacDonald | 08 |
| 88 | Darrin Jackson | 05 |
| 89 | Neal Heaton | 05 |
| 90 | Robin Yount | 10 |
| 91 | Jeff Reed | 05 |
| 92 | Lenny Harris | 05 |
| 93 | Reggie Jefferson | 10 |
| 94 | Sammy Sosa | 05 |
| 95 | Scott Bailes | 05 |
| 96 | T. McKinnon (R) (DP) | 15 |
| 97 | Luis Rivera | 05 |
| 98 | Mike Harkey | 05 |
| 99 | Jeff Treadway | 05 |
| 100 | Jose Canseco | 25 |
| 101 | Omar Vizquel | 05 |
| 102 | Scott Kamieniecki | 08 |
| 103 | Ricky Jordan | 05 |
| 104 | Jeff Ballard | 05 |
| 105 | Felix Jose | 08 |
| 106 | Mike Boddicker | 05 |
| 107 | Dan Pasqua | 05 |
| 108 | Mike Timlin | 05 |
| 109 | Roger Craig (Mgr.) | 05 |
| 110 | Ryne Sandberg | 20 |
| 111 | Mark Carreon | 05 |
| 112 | Oscar Azocar | 05 |
| 113 | Mike Greenwell | 12 |
| 114 | Mark Portugal | 05 |
| 115 | Terry Pendleton | 10 |
| 116 | Willie Randolph | 05 |
| 117 | Scott Terry | 05 |
| 118 | Chili Davis | 05 |
| 119 | Mark Gardner | 05 |
| 120 | Alan Trammell | 08 |
| 121 | Derek Bell | 15 |
| 122 | Gary Varsho | 05 |
| 123 | Bob Ojeda | 05 |
| 124 | S. Livsey (R) (DP) | 15 |
| 125 | Chris Hoiles | 05 |
| | Prospects—1st B: | |
| 126 | R. Brogna, J. Jaha, R. Klesko, D. Staton | 1.25 |
| 127 | Carlos Quintana | 05 |
| 128 | Kurt Stillwell | 05 |
| 129 | Melido Perez | 05 |
| 130 | Alvin Davis | 05 |
| 131 | Checklist 1-132 | 05 |
| 132 | Eric Show | 05 |
| 133 | Rance Mulliniks | 05 |
| 134 | Darryl Kile | 08 |
| 135 | Von Hayes | 05 |
| 136 | Bill Doran | 05 |
| 137 | Jeff Robinson | 05 |
| 138 | Monty Fariss | 05 |
| 139 | Jeff Innis | 05 |
| 140 | Mark Grace | 10 |
| 141 | Jim Leyland (Mgr.) | 05 |
| 142 | Todd Van Poppel | 40 |
| 143 | Paul Gibson | 05 |
| 144 | Bill Swift | 05 |
| 145 | Danny Tartabull | 10 |
| 146 | Al Newman | 05 |
| 147 | Cris Carpenter | 05 |
| 148 | Anthony Young | 10 |
| 149 | Brian Bohanon | 05 |
| 150 | Roger Clemens | 20 |
| 151 | Jeff Hamilton | 05 |
| 152 | Charlie Leibrandt | 05 |
| 153 | Ron Karkovice | 05 |
| 154 | Hensley Meulens | 08 |
| 155 | Scott Bankhead | 05 |
| 156 | M. Ramirez (R) (DP) | 35 |
| 157 | Keith Miller | 05 |
| 158 | Todd Frohwirth | 05 |
| 159 | Darrin Fletcher | 05 |
| 160 | Bobby Bonilla | 10 |
| 161 | Casey Candaele | 05 |
| 162 | Paul Faries | 05 |
| 163 | Dana Kiecker | 05 |
| 164 | Shane Mack | 05 |
| 165 | Mark Langston | 08 |
| 166 | Geronimo Pena | 05 |
| 167 | Andy Allanson | 05 |
| 168 | Dwight Smith | 05 |
| 169 | Chuck Crim | 05 |
| 170 | Alex Cole | 05 |
| 171 | Bill Plummer (Mgr.) | 05 |
| 172 | Juan Berenguer | 05 |
| 173 | Brian Downing | 05 |
| 174 | Steve Frey | 05 |
| 175 | Orel Hershiser | 10 |
| 176 | Ramon Garcia | 05 |
| 177 | Danny Gladden | 05 |
| 178 | Jim Acker | 05 |
| | Prospects—2nd B: | |
| 179 | C. Bernhardt, B. De Jardin, A. Moreno, A. Stankiewicz | 35 |
| 180 | Kevin Mitchell | 10 |
| 181 | Hector Villanueva | 05 |
| 182 | Jeff Reardon | 05 |
| 183 | Brent Mayne | 08 |
| 184 | Jimmy Jones | 05 |
| 185 | Benny Santiago | 08 |
| 186 | Cliff Floyd (R) (DP) | 30 |
| 187 | Ernie Riles | 05 |
| 188 | Jose Guzman | 05 |
| 189 | Junior Felix | 05 |
| 190 | Glenn Davis | 10 |
| 191 | Charlie Hough | 05 |
| 192 | Dave Fleming | 08 |
| 193 | Omar Olivares | 05 |
| 194 | Eric Karros | 15 |
| 195 | David Cone | 10 |
| 196 | Frank Castillo | 08 |
| 197 | Glenn Braggs | 05 |
| 198 | Scott Aldred | 05 |
| 199 | Jeff Blauser | 05 |
| 200 | Len Dykstra | 05 |
| 201 | B. Showalter (Mgr.) | 05 |
| 202 | Rick Honeycutt | 05 |
| 203 | Greg Myers | 05 |
| 204 | Trevor Wilson | 05 |
| 205 | Jay Howell | 05 |
| 206 | Luis Sojo | 05 |
| 207 | Jack Clark | 08 |
| 208 | Julio Machado | 05 |
| 209 | Lloyd McClendon | 05 |
| 210 | Ozzie Guillen | 05 |
| 211 | J. Hernandez (R) | 15 |
| 212 | Randy Velarde | 05 |
| 213 | Les Lancaster | 05 |
| 214 | Andy Mota | 10 |
| 215 | Rich Gossage | 05 |
| 216 | B. Gates (R) (DP) | 25 |
| 217 | Brian Harper | 05 |
| 218 | Mike Flanagan | 05 |
| 219 | Jerry Browne | 05 |
| 220 | Jose Rijo | 05 |
| 221 | Skeeter Barnes | 05 |
| 222 | Jaime Navarro | 05 |
| 223 | Mel Hall | 08 |
| 224 | Bret Barberie | 15 |
| 225 | Roberto Alomar | 12 |
| 226 | Pete Smith | 05 |
| 227 | Daryl Boston | 05 |
| 228 | Eddie Whitson | 05 |
| 229 | Shawn Boskie | 05 |
| 230 | Dick Schofield | 05 |
| 231 | Brian Drahman | 05 |
| 232 | John Smiley | 05 |
| 233 | Mitch Webster | 05 |
| 234 | Terry Steinbach | 05 |
| 235 | Jack Morris | 08 |
| 236 | Bill Pecota | 05 |
| 237 | Jose Hernandez (R) | 15 |
| 238 | Greg Litton | 05 |
| 239 | Brian Holman | 05 |
| 240 | Andres Galarraga | 05 |
| 241 | Gerald Young | 05 |
| 242 | Mike Mussina | 15 |
| 243 | Alvaro Espinoza | 05 |
| 244 | Darren Daulton | 05 |
| 245 | John Smoltz | 10 |
| 246 | J. Pruitt (R) (DP) | 15 |
| 247 | Chuck Finley | 08 |
| 248 | Jim Gantner | 05 |
| 249 | Tony Fossas | 05 |
| 250 | Ken Griffey | 05 |
| 251 | Kevin Elster | 05 |
| 252 | Dennis Rasmussen | 05 |
| 253 | Terry Kennedy | 05 |
| 254 | Ryan Bowen | 05 |
| 255 | Robin Ventura | 10 |
| 256 | Mike Aldrete | 05 |
| 257 | Jeff Russell | 05 |
| 258 | Jim Lindeman | 05 |
| 259 | Ron Darling | 05 |
| 260 | Devon White | 05 |
| 261 | Tom Lasorda (Mgr.) | 05 |
| 262 | Terry Lee | 08 |
| 263 | Bob Patterson | 05 |
| 264 | Checklist 133-264 | 05 |
| 265 | Teddy Higuera | 05 |
| 266 | Roberto Kelly | 10 |
| 267 | Steve Bedrosian | 05 |
| 268 | Brady Anderson | 05 |
| 269 | Ruben Amaro | 10 |
| 270 | Tony Gwynn | 15 |
| 271 | Tracy Jones | 05 |
| 272 | Jerry Don Gleaton | 05 |
| 273 | Craig Grebeck | 05 |
| 274 | Bob Scanlan | 08 |
| 275 | Todd Zeile | 08 |
| 276 | S. Green (R) (DP) | 25 |
| 277 | Scott Chiamparino | 05 |
| 278 | Darryl Hamilton | 05 |
| 279 | Jim Clancy | 05 |
| 280 | Carlos Martinez | 05 |
| 281 | Kevin Appier | 05 |
| 282 | John Wehner | 08 |
| 283 | Reggie Sanders | 12 |
| 284 | Gene Larkin | 05 |
| 285 | Bob Welch | 05 |
| 286 | Gilberto Reyes | 05 |
| 287 | Pete Schourek | 08 |
| 288 | A. Cedeno (ASR) | 12 |
| 289 | Mike Morgan | 05 |
| 290 | Bo Jackson | 20 |
| 291 | Phil Garner (Mgr.) | 05 |
| 292 | Ray Lankford (ASR) | 08 |
| 293 | Mike Henneman | 05 |
| 294 | Dave Valle | 05 |
| 295 | Alonzo Powell | 05 |
| 296 | Tom Brunansky | 05 |
| 297 | Kevin Brown | 05 |
| 298 | Kelly Gruber | 08 |
| 299 | Charles Nagy | 05 |
| 300 | Don Mattingly | 15 |
| 301 | Kirk McCaskill | 05 |
| 302 | Joey Cora | 05 |
| 303 | Dan Plesac | 05 |
| 304 | Joe Oliver | 05 |
| 305 | Tom Glavine | 10 |
| 306 | Al Shirley (R) (DP) | 35 |
| 307 | Bruce Ruffin | 05 |
| 308 | Craig Shipley (R) | 15 |
| 309 | Dave Martinez | 05 |
| 310 | Jose Mesa | 05 |
| 311 | Henry Cotto | 05 |
| 312 | Mike LaValliere | 05 |
| 313 | Kevin Tapani | 08 |
| 314 | Jeff Huson | 05 |
| 315 | Juan Samuel | 05 |
| 316 | Curt Schilling | 05 |
| 317 | Mike Bordick | 05 |
| 318 | Steve Howe | 05 |
| 319 | Tony Phillips | 05 |
| 320 | George Bell | 08 |
| 321 | Lou Piniella (Mgr.) | 05 |
| 322 | Tim Burke | 05 |
| 323 | Milt Thompson | 05 |
| 324 | Danny Darwin | 05 |
| 325 | Joe Orsulak | 05 |
| 326 | Eric King | 05 |
| 327 | Jay Buhner | 05 |
| 328 | Joel Johnston | 08 |
| 329 | Franklin Stubbs | 05 |

| NO. | PLAYER | MINT |
|---|---|---|
| 330 | Will Clark | 15 |
| 331 | Steve Lake | 05 |
| 332 | Chris Jones | 05 |
| 333 | Pat Tabler | 05 |
| 334 | Kevin Gross | 05 |
| 335 | Dave Henderson | 08 |
| 336 | G. Anthony (R) (DP) | 15 |
| 337 | Alejandro Pena | 05 |
| 338 | Shawn Abner | 05 |
| 339 | Tom Browning | 05 |
| 340 | Otis Nixon | 05 |
| 341 | Bob Geren | 05 |
| 342 | Tim Spehr | 05 |
| 343 | Jon Vander Wal (R) | 20 |
| 344 | Jack Daugherty | 05 |
| 345 | Zane Smith | 05 |
| 346 | Rheal Cormier | 10 |
| 347 | Kent Hrbeck | 05 |
| 348 | Rick Wilkins | 08 |
| 349 | Steve Lyons | 05 |
| 350 | Gregg Olson | 08 |
| 351 | Greg Riddoch (Mgr.) | 05 |
| 352 | Ed Nunez | 05 |
| 353 | Braulio Castillo (R) | 30 |
| 354 | Dave Bergman | 05 |
| 355 | Warren Newson | 08 |
| 356 | Luis Quinones | 05 |
| 357 | Mike Witt | 05 |
| 358 | Ted Wood (R) | 15 |
| 359 | Mike Moore | 05 |
| 360 | Lance Parrish | 05 |
| 361 | Barry Jones | 05 |
| 362 | Javier Ortiz | 05 |
| 363 | John Candelaria | 05 |
| 364 | Glenallen Hill | 05 |
| 365 | Duane Ward | 05 |
| 366 | Checklist 265-336 | 05 |
| 367 | Rafael Belliard | 05 |
| 368 | Bill Krueger | 05 |
| 369 | S. Whitaker (R) (DP) | 15 |
| 370 | Shawon Dunston | 05 |
| 371 | Dante Bichette | 05 |
| 372 | Kip Gross (R) | 25 |
| 373 | Don Robinson | 05 |
| 374 | Bernie Williams | 15 |
| 375 | Bert Blyleven | 05 |
| 376 | Chris Donnels | 08 |
| 377 | Bob Zupcic (R) | 25 |
| 378 | Joel Skinner | 05 |
| 379 | Steve Chitren | 05 |
| 380 | Barry Bonds | 10 |
| 381 | S. Anderson (Mgr.) | 05 |
| 382 | Sid Fernandez | 05 |
| 383 | Dave Hollins | 05 |
| 384 | Mark Lee | 08 |
| 385 | Tim Wallach | 05 |
| 386 | Will Clark (AS) | 15 |
| 387 | Ryne Sandberg (AS) | 15 |
| 388 | Howard Johnson (AS) | 10 |
| 389 | Barry Larkin (AS) | 08 |
| 390 | Barry Bonds (AS) | 10 |
| 391 | Ron Gant (AS) | 08 |
| 392 | Bobby Bonilla (AS) | 08 |
| 393 | Craig Biggio (AS) | 06 |
| 394 | Denny Martinez (AS) | 08 |
| 395 | Tom Glavine (AS) | 10 |
| 396 | Lee Smith (AS) | 10 |
| 397 | Cecil Fielder (AS) | 10 |
| 398 | Julio Flanco (AS) | 08 |
| 399 | Wade Boggs (AS) | 10 |
| 400 | Cal Ripken (AS) | 15 |
| 401 | Jose Canseco (AS) | 15 |
| 402 | Joe Carter (AS) | 08 |
| 403 | Ruben Sierra (AS) | 08 |
| 404 | Matt Nokes (AS) | 06 |
| 405 | Roger Clemens (AS) | 15 |
| 406 | Jim Abbott (AS) | 08 |
| 407 | Bryan Harvey (AS) | 05 |
| 408 | Bob Milacki | 05 |
| 409 | Geno Petralli | 05 |
| 410 | Dave Stewart | 10 |
| 411 | Mike Jackson | 05 |
| 412 | Luis Aquino | 05 |
| 413 | Tim Teufel | 05 |
| 414 | Jeff Ware | 05 |
| 415 | Jim Deshaies | 05 |
| 416 | Ellis Burks | 05 |
| 417 | Allan Anderson | 05 |
| 418 | Alfredo Griffin | 05 |
| 419 | Wally Whitehurst | 05 |
| 420 | Sandy Alomar | 08 |
| 421 | Juan Agosto | 05 |
| 422 | Sam Horn | 05 |
| 423 | Jeff Fassero | 05 |
| 424 | Paul McClellan | 08 |
| 425 | Cecil Fielder | 15 |
| 426 | Rock Raines | 10 |
| 427 | E. Taubensee (R) | 15 |
| 428 | Dennis Boyd | 05 |
| 429 | Tony LaRussa (Mgr.) | 05 |
| 430 | Steve Sax | 05 |
| 431 | Tom Gordon | 08 |
| 432 | Billy Hatcher | 05 |
| 433 | Call Eldred | 05 |
| 434 | Wally Backman | 05 |
| 435 | Mark Eichhorn | 05 |
| 436 | Mookie Wilson | 05 |
| 437 | Scott Servais | 05 |
| 438 | Mike Maddux | 05 |
| 439 | Chico Walker | 05 |
| 440 | Doug Drabeck | 05 |
| 441 | Rob Deer | 05 |
| 442 | Dave West | 05 |
| 443 | Spike Owen | 05 |
| 444 | T. Hill (R) (DP) | 25 |
| 445 | Matt Williams | 10 |
| 446 | Mark Lewis | 10 |
| 447 | David Segui | 05 |
| 448 | Tom Pagnozzi | 05 |
| 449 | Jeff Johnson | 08 |
| 450 | Mark McGwire | 12 |
| 451 | Tom Henke | 05 |
| 452 | Wilson Alvarez | 05 |
| 453 | Gary Redus | 05 |
| 454 | Darren Holmes | 08 |
| 455 | Pete O'Brien | 05 |
| 456 | Pat Combs | 05 |
| 457 | Hubie Brooks | 05 |
| 458 | Frank Tanana | 05 |
| 459 | Tom Kelly (Mgr.) | 05 |
| 460 | Andre Dawson | 10 |
| 461 | Doug Jones | 05 |
| 462 | Rich Rodriguez | 08 |
| 463 | Mike Simms | 08 |
| 464 | Mike Jeffcoat | 05 |
| 465 | Barry Larkin | 08 |
| 466 | Stan Belinda | 05 |
| 467 | Lonnie Smith | 05 |
| 468 | Greg Harris | 05 |
| 469 | Jim Eisenreich | 05 |
| 470 | Pedro Guerrero | 08 |
| 471 | Jose DeJesus | 05 |
| 472 | Rich Rowland (R) | 15 |
| | Prospects-3rd B: | |
| 473 | F. Bolick, C. Paquette, T. Redington, P. Russo | 30 |
| 474 | M. Rossiter (R) (DP) | 15 |
| 475 | Robby Thompson | 05 |
| 476 | Randy Bush | 05 |
| 477 | Greg Hibbard | 05 |
| 478 | Dale Sveum | 05 |
| 479 | Chito Martinez | 20 |
| 480 | Scott Sanderson | 05 |
| 481 | Tino Martinez | 15 |
| 482 | Jimmy Key | 05 |
| 483 | Terry Shumpert | 05 |
| 484 | Mike Hartley | 05 |
| 485 | Chris Sabo | 10 |
| 486 | Bob Walk | 05 |
| 487 | John Cerutti | 05 |
| 488 | Scott Cooper | 08 |
| 489 | Bobby Cox (Mgr.) | 05 |
| 490 | Julio Franco | 05 |
| 491 | Jeff Brantley | 05 |
| 492 | Mike Devereaux | 05 |
| 493 | Jose Offerman | 08 |
| 494 | Gary Thurman | 05 |
| 495 | Carney Lansford | 05 |
| 496 | Joe Grahe | 05 |
| 497 | Andy Ashby | 08 |
| 498 | Gerald Perry | 05 |
| 499 | Dave Otto | 05 |
| 500 | Vince Coleman | 10 |
| 501 | Rob Mallicoat | 05 |
| 502 | Greg Briley | 05 |
| 503 | Pascual Perez | 05 |
| 504 | A. Sele (R) (DP) | 15 |
| 505 | Bobby Thigpen | 05 |
| 506 | Todd Benzinger | 05 |
| 507 | Candy Maldonado | 05 |
| 508 | Bill Gullickson | 05 |
| 509 | Doug Dascenzo | 05 |
| 510 | Frank Viola | 05 |
| 511 | Kenny Rogers | 05 |
| 512 | Mike Heath | 05 |
| 513 | Kevin Bass | 05 |
| 514 | Kim Batiste | 05 |
| 515 | Delino DeShields | 08 |
| 516 | Ed Sprague | 05 |
| 517 | Jim Gott | 05 |
| 518 | Jose Melendez | 08 |
| 519 | Hal McRae (Mgr.) | 05 |
| 520 | Jeff Bagwell (ASR) | 75 |
| 521 | Joe Hesketh | 05 |
| 522 | Milt Cuyler (ASR) | 08 |
| 523 | Shawn Hillegas | 05 |
| 524 | Don Slaught | 05 |
| 525 | Randy Johnson | 05 |
| 526 | Doug Piatt | 05 |
| 527 | Checklist 397-528 | 05 |
| 528 | Steve Foster (OR) | 20 |
| 529 | Joe Girardi | 05 |
| 530 | Jim Abbott | 12 |
| 531 | Larry Walker | 05 |
| 532 | Mike Huff | 05 |
| 533 | Mackey Sasser | 05 |
| 534 | Benji Gil (R) | 25 |
| 535 | Dave Stieb | 05 |
| 536 | Willie Wilson | 05 |
| 537 | Mark Leiter (ASR) | 08 |
| 538 | Jose Uribe | 05 |
| 539 | Thomas Howard | 05 |
| 540 | Ben McDonald | 08 |
| 541 | Jose Tolentino (R)— | 25 |
| 542 | Keith Mitchell | 20 |
| 543 | Jerome Walton | 05 |
| 544 | Cliff Brantley (R) | 15 |
| 545 | Andy Van Slyke | 08 |
| 546 | Paul Sorrento | 05 |
| 547 | Herm Winningham | 05 |
| 548 | Mark Guthrie | 05 |
| 549 | Joe Torre (Mgr.) | 05 |
| 550 | Darryl Strawberry | 20 |
| | Prospects—SS: | |
| 551 | M. Alexander, A. Arias, W. Cordero, C. Jones | 50 |
| 552 | Dave Gallagher | 05 |
| 553 | Edgar Martinez | 08 |
| 554 | Donald Harris | 05 |
| 555 | Frank Thomas | 75 |
| 556 | Storm Davis | 05 |
| 557 | Dickie Thon | 05 |
| 558 | Scott Garrelts | 05 |
| 559 | Steve Olin | 05 |
| 560 | Rickey Henderson | 20 |
| 561 | Jose Vizcaino | 05 |
| 562 | Wade Taylor | 05 |
| 563 | Pat Borders | 05 |
| 564 | J. Gonzalez (R) (DP) | 15 |
| 565 | Lee Smith | 05 |
| 566 | Bill Sampen | 05 |
| 567 | Dean Palmer | 20 |
| 568 | Bryan Harvey | 05 |
| 569 | Tony Pena | 05 |
| 570 | Lou Whitaker | 05 |
| 571 | Randy Tomlin | 08 |
| 572 | Greg Vaughn | 10 |
| 573 | Kelly Downs | 05 |
| 574 | Steve Avery | 25 |
| 575 | Kirby Puckett | 05 |
| 576 | Heathcliff Slocumb | 05 |
| 577 | Kevin Seitzer | 05 |
| 578 | Lee Guetterman | 05 |
| 579 | Johnny Oates (Mgr.) | 05 |
| 580 | Greg Maddux | 05 |
| 581 | Stan Javier | 05 |
| 582 | Vicente Palacios | 05 |
| 583 | Mel Rojas | 05 |
| 584 | W. Rosenthal (R) | 15 |
| 585 | Lenny Webster | 05 |
| 586 | Rod Nichols | 05 |
| 587 | Mickey Morandini | 05 |
| 588 | Russ Swan | 05 |
| 589 | Mariano Duncan | 05 |
| 590 | Howard Johnson | 08 |
| | Prospects OF: | |
| 591 | J. Brumfield, J. Burnitz, A. Cockrell, D.J. Dozier | 50 |
| 592 | Denny Neagle | 10 |
| 593 | Steve Decker | 10 |
| 594 | B. Barber (R) (CP) | 15 |
| 595 | Bruce Hurst | 05 |
| 596 | Kent Mercker | 05 |
| 597 | Mike Magnante (R) | 15 |
| 598 | Jody Reed | 05 |
| 599 | Steve Searcy | 05 |
| 600 | Paul Molitor | 10 |
| 601 | Dave Smith | 05 |
| 602 | Mike Fetters | 05 |
| 603 | Luis Mercedes | 12 |
| 604 | Chris Gwynn | 05 |
| 605 | Scott Erickson | 15 |
| 606 | Brook Jacoby | 05 |
| 607 | Todd Stottlemyre | 05 |
| 608 | Scott Bradley | 05 |
| 609 | M. Hargrove (Mgr.) | 05 |
| 610 | Eric Davis | 12 |
| 611 | Brian Hunter | 35 |
| 612 | Pat Kelly | 12 |
| 613 | Pedro Munoz | 08 |
| 614 | Al Osuna | 08 |
| 615 | Matt Merullo | 05 |
| 616 | Larry Andersen | 05 |
| 617 | Junior Ortiz | 05 |
| | Prospects—OF: | |
| 618 | C. Hernandez, S. Hosey, D. Peltier, J. McNeely | 50 |
| 619 | Danny Jackson | 05 |
| 620 | George Brett | 10 |
| 621 | Dan Gakeler | 05 |
| 622 | Steve Buechele | 05 |
| 623 | Bob Tewksbury | 05 |
| 624 | Shawn Estes (R) | 15 |
| 625 | Kevin McReynolds | 08 |
| 626 | Chris Haney | 08 |
| 627 | Mike Sharperson | 05 |
| 628 | Mark Williamson | 05 |
| 629 | Wally Joyner | 08 |
| 630 | Carlton Fisk | 10 |
| 631 | A. Reynoso (R) | 10 |
| 632 | Felix Fermin | 05 |
| 633 | Mitch Williams | 05 |
| 634 | Manuel Lee | 05 |
| 635 | Harold Baines | 05 |
| 636 | Greg Harris | 05 |
| 637 | Orlando Merced | 10 |
| 638 | Chris Bosio | 05 |
| 639 | Wayne Housie (R) | 15 |
| 640 | Xavier Hernandez | 05 |
| 641 | David Howard | 08 |
| 642 | Tim Crews | 05 |
| 643 | Rick Cerone | 05 |
| 644 | Terry Leach | 05 |
| 645 | Deion Sanders | 08 |
| 646 | Craig Wilson | 05 |
| 647 | Marquis Grissom | 08 |
| 648 | Scott Fletcher | 05 |
| 649 | Norm Charlton | 05 |
| 650 | Jesse Barfield | 05 |
| 651 | Joe Slusarski | 05 |
| 652 | Bobby Rose | 05 |
| 653 | Dennis Lamp | 05 |
| 654 | A. Watson (R) (DP) | 20 |
| 655 | Brett Butler | 05 |
| | Prospects—OF: | |

| NO. | PLAYER | MINT |
|---|---|---|
| 656 | R. Pemberton, L. Tinsley, H. Rodriquez, G. Williams | .50 |
| 657 | Dave Johnson | .05 |
| 658 | Checklist 529-660 | .05 |
| 659 | Brian McRae | .15 |
| 660 | Fred McGriff | .08 |
| 661 | Bill Landrum | .05 |
| 662 | Juan Guzman | .15 |
| 663 | Greg Gagne | .05 |
| 664 | Ken Hill | .05 |
| 665 | Dave Haas | .05 |
| 666 | Tom Foley | .05 |
| 667 | Roberto Hernandez | .10 |
| 668 | Dwayne Henry | .05 |
| 669 | Jim Fregosi (Mgr.) | .05 |
| 670 | Harold Reynolds | .05 |
| 671 | Mark Whiten | .08 |
| 672 | Erick Plunk | .05 |
| 673 | Todd Hundley | .05 |
| 674 | Mo Sanford | .12 |
| 675 | Bobby Witt | .05 |
|  | Prospects—Pitchers: |  |
| 676 | P. Mahomes, S. Miltello, R. Salkeld, T. Wendell | .50 |
| 677 | John Marzano | .05 |
| 678 | Joe Klink | .05 |
| 679 | Pete Incaviglia | .05 |
| 680 | Dale Murphy | .12 |
| 681 | Rene Gonzales | .05 |
| 682 | Andy Benes | .08 |
| 683 | Jim Poole | .05 |
| 684 | R. Miller (R) (DP) | .15 |
| 685 | Scott Livingstone | .08 |
| 686 | Rich DeLucia | .05 |
| 687 | Harvey Pulliam | .08 |

| NO. | PLAYER | MINT |
|---|---|---|
| 688 | Tim Belcher | .05 |
| 689 | Mark Lemke | .05 |
| 690 | John Franco | .05 |
| 691 | Walt Weiss | .05 |
| 692 | Scott Ruskin | .05 |
| 693 | Jeff King | .05 |
| 694 | Mike Gardiner | .08 |
| 695 | Gary Sheffield | .05 |
| 696 | Joe Boever | .05 |
| 697 | Mike Felder | .05 |
| 698 | John Habyan | .05 |
| 699 | Cito Gaston (Mgr.) | .05 |
| 700 | Ruben Sierra | .10 |
| 701 | Scott Radinsky | .05 |
| 702 | Lee Stevens | .05 |
| 703 | Mark Wohlers | .15 |
| 704 | Curt Young | .05 |
| 705 | Dwight Evans | .05 |
| 706 | Rob Murphy | .05 |
| 707 | Gregg Jefferies | .08 |
| 708 | Tom Bolton | .05 |
| 709 | Chris James | .05 |
| 710 | Kevin Maas | .10 |
| 711 | Ricky Bones | .08 |
| 712 | Curt Wilkerson | .05 |
| 713 | Roger McDowell | .05 |
| 714 | Calvin Reese (R) | .30 |
| 715 | Craig Biggio | .08 |
| 716 | Kirk Dressendorfer | .08 |
| 717 | Ken Dayley | .05 |
| 718 | B.J. Surhoff | .05 |
| 719 | Terry Mulholland | .05 |
| 720 | Kirk Gibson | .08 |
| 721 | Mike Pagliarulo | .05 |
| 722 | Walt Terrell | .05 |

| NO. | PLAYER | MINT |
|---|---|---|
| 723 | Jose Oquendo | .05 |
| 724 | Kevin Morton | .05 |
| 725 | Doc Gooden | .12 |
| 726 | Kirt Manwaring | .05 |
| 727 | Chuck McElroy | .05 |
| 728 | Dave Burba | .08 |
| 729 | Art Howe (Mgr.) | .05 |
| 730 | Ramon Martinez | .10 |
| 731 | Donnie Hill | .05 |
| 732 | Nelson Santovenia | .05 |
| 733 | Bob Melvin | .05 |
| 734 | Scott Hatteberg (R) | .15 |
| 735 | Greg Swindell | .05 |
| 736 | Lance Johnson | .05 |
| 737 | Kevin Reimer | .05 |
| 738 | Dennis Eckersley | .10 |
| 739 | Rob Ducey | .05 |
| 740 | Ken Caminiti | .05 |
| 741 | Mark Gubicza | .05 |
| 742 | Billy Spiers | .05 |
| 743 | Darren Lewis | .05 |
| 744 | Chris Hammond | .05 |
| 745 | Dave Magadan | .05 |
| 746 | Bernard Gilkey | .08 |
| 747 | Willie Banks | .05 |
| 748 | Matt Nokes | .05 |
| 749 | Jerald Clark | .05 |
| 750 | Travis Fryman | .10 |
| 751 | Steve Wilson | .05 |
| 752 | Billy Ripken | .05 |
| 753 | Paul Assenmacher | .05 |
| 754 | Charlie Hayes | .05 |
| 755 | Alex Fernandez | .08 |
| 756 | Gary Pettis | .05 |
| 757 | Rob Dibble | .05 |

| NO. | PLAYER | MINT |
|---|---|---|
| 758 | Tim Naehring | .05 |
| 759 | Jeff Torborg (Mgr.) | .05 |
| 760 | Ozzie Smith | .10 |
| 761 | Mike Fitzgerald | .05 |
| 762 | John Burkett | .05 |
| 763 | Kyle Abbott | .08 |
| 764 | Tyler Green (R) | .60 |
| 765 | Pete Harnisch | .05 |
| 766 | Mark Davis | .05 |
| 767 | Kal Daniels | .08 |
| 768 | Jim Thome | .25 |
| 769 | Jack Howell | .05 |
| 770 | Sid Bream | .05 |
| 771 | Arthur Rhodes | .12 |
| 772 | Garry Templeton | .05 |
| 773 | Hal Morris | .08 |
| 774 | Bud Black | .05 |
| 775 | Ivan Calderon | .05 |
| 776 | Doug Henry (R) | .12 |
| 777 | John Olerud | .08 |
| 778 | Tim Leary | .05 |
| 779 | Jay Bell | .05 |
| 780 | Eddie Murray | .12 |
| 781 | Paul Abbott | .05 |
| 782 | Phil Plantier | .35 |
| 783 | Joe Magrane | .05 |
| 784 | Ken Patterson | .05 |
| 785 | Albert Belle | .12 |
| 786 | Royce Clayton | .10 |
| 787 | Checklist 661-792 | .05 |
| 788 | Mike Stanton | .05 |
| 789 | B. Valentine (Mgr.) | .05 |
| 790 | Joe Carter | .08 |
| 791 | Danny Cox | .05 |
| 792 | Dave Winfeld | .10 |

# 1989 Bowman . . . Complete Set of 484 Cards (2½" × 3¾")—Value $18.00 (Factory-Sealed Set—Value $22.00)

This was the first Bowman card set since 1955 when Topps bought the Bowman Gum Co. The set which was released in July includes hot rookie stars from Spring training '89, traded players in their new uniforms, and all of the top stars of the game. The cards are the same size as the classic '53 Bowmans, 2½" × 3¾". Features the rookie cards of Ken Griffey, Jr., Jerome Walton, Gary Sheffield and Ricky Jordan.

| NO. | PLAYER | MINT |
|---|---|---|
| 1 | Oswald Peraza (R) | .12 |
| 2 | Briand Holton | .05 |
| 3 | Jose Bautista (R) | .10 |
| 4 | Pete Harnisch (R) | .20 |
| 5 | Dave Schmidt | .05 |
| 6 | Gregg Olson (R) | .50 |
| 7 | Jeff Ballard | .10 |
| 8 | Bob Melvin | .05 |
| 9 | Cal Ripken | .30 |
| 10 | Randy Milligan | .08 |
| 11 | Juan Bell (R) | .12 |
| 12 | Billy Ripken | .08 |
| 13 | Jim Traber | .05 |
| 14 | Pete Stanicek | .10 |
| 15 | Steve Finley (R) | .25 |
| 16 | Larry Sheets | .05 |
| 17 | Phil Bradley | .08 |
| 18 | Brady Anderson (R) | .10 |
| 19 | Lee Smith | .08 |
| 20 | Tom Fischer (R) | .10 |
| 21 | Mike Boddicker | .05 |
| 22 | Rob Murphy | .05 |
| 23 | Wes Gardner | .05 |
| 24 | John Dopson (R) | .10 |
| 25 | Bob Stanley | .05 |
| 26 | Roger Clemens | .25 |
| 27 | Rich Gedman | .05 |
| 28 | Marty Barrett | .05 |
| 29 | Luis Rivera | .05 |
| 30 | Jody Reed | .08 |
| 31 | Nick Esasky | .08 |
| 32 | Wade Boggs | .20 |
| 33 | Jim Rice | .10 |
| 34 | Mike Greenwell | .15 |
| 35 | Dwight Evans | .10 |
| 36 | Ellis Burks | .15 |
| 37 | Chuck Finley | .10 |
| 38 | Kirk McCaskill | .05 |
| 39 | Jim Abbott (R) | .75 |
| 40 | Bryan Harvey (R) | .20 |
| 41 | Bert Blyleven | .08 |
| 42 | Mike Witt | .08 |
| 43 | Bob McClure | .05 |
| 44 | Bill Schroeder | .05 |
| 45 | Lance Parrish | .10 |
| 46 | Dick Schofield | .05 |
| 47 | Wally Joyner | .10 |
| 48 | Jack Howell | .05 |
| 49 | Johnny Ray | .10 |
| 50 | Chili Davis | .08 |
| 51 | Tony Armas | .05 |
| 52 | Claudell Washington | .05 |
| 53 | Brian Downing | .08 |
| 54 | Devon White | .10 |
| 55 | Bobby Thigpen | .05 |
| 56 | Bill Long | .05 |
| 57 | Jerry Reuss | .05 |
| 58 | Shawn Hillegas | .05 |
| 59 | Melido Perez | .10 |
| 60 | Jeff Bittiger (R) | .10 |
| 61 | Jack McDowell | .12 |
| 62 | Carlton Fisk | .10 |
| 63 | Steve Lyons | .05 |
| 64 | Ozzie Guillen | .08 |
| 65 | Robin Ventura (R) | 1.00 |
| 66 | Fred Manrique | .05 |

| NO. | PLAYER | MINT |
|---|---|---|
| 67 | Dan Pasqua | .08 |
| 68 | Ivan Calderon | .08 |
| 69 | Ron Kittle | .05 |
| 70 | Daryl Boston | .05 |
| 71 | Dave Gallagher (R) | .10 |
| 72 | Harold Baines | .08 |
| 73 | Charles Nagy (R) | .20 |
| 74 | John Farrell | .05 |
| 75 | Kevin Wickander (R) | .20 |
| 76 | Greg Swindell | .10 |
| 77 | Mike Walker (R) | .10 |
| 78 | Doug Jones | .05 |
| 79 | Rich Yett | .05 |
| 80 | Tom Candiotti | .05 |
| 81 | Jesse Orosco | .05 |
| 82 | Bud Black | .05 |
| 83 | Andy Allanson | .05 |
| 84 | Pete O'Brien | .10 |
| 85 | Jerry Browne | .05 |
| 86 | Brook Jacoby | .05 |
| 87 | Mark Lewis (R) | .35 |
| 88 | Luis Aguayo | .05 |
| 89 | Cory Snyder | .10 |
| 90 | Oddibe McDowell | .05 |
| 91 | Joe Carter | .10 |
| 92 | Frank Tanana | .05 |
| 93 | Jack Morris | .10 |
| 94 | Doyle Alexander | .05 |
| 95 | Steve Searcy (R) | .10 |
| 96 | Randy Bockus (R) | .10 |
| 97 | Jeff Robinson | .08 |
| 98 | Mike Henneman | .05 |
| 99 | Paul Gibson (R) | .10 |
| 100 | Frank Williams | .05 |
| 101 | Matt Nokes | .10 |
| 102 | Ricco Brogna (R) | .30 |
| 103 | Lou Whitaker | .08 |
| 104 | Al Pedrique | .05 |
| 105 | Alan Trammell | .12 |
| 106 | Chris Brown | .05 |
| 107 | Pat Sheridan | .05 |
| 108 | Chet Lemon | .05 |
| 109 | Keith Moreland | .05 |
| 110 | Mel Stottlemyre, Jr. (R) | .10 |
| 111 | Bret Saberhagen | .12 |
| 112 | Floyd Bannister | .05 |
| 113 | Jeff Montgomery | .08 |
| 114 | Steve Farr | .05 |
| 115 | Tom Gordon | .15 |
| 116 | Charlie Leibrandt | .08 |
| 117 | Mark Gubicza | .08 |
| 118 | Mike Macfarlane (R) | .12 |
| 119 | Bob Boone | .05 |
| 120 | Kurt Stillwell | .05 |
| 121 | George Brett | .15 |
| 122 | Frank White | .05 |
| 123 | Kevin Seitzer | .08 |
| 124 | Willie Wilson | .08 |
| 125 | Pat Tabler | .05 |
| 126 | Bo Jackson | .35 |
| 127 | Hugh Walker (R) | .12 |
| 128 | Danny Tartabull | .10 |
| 129 | Teddy Higuera | .08 |
| 130 | Don August | .08 |
| 131 | Juan Nieves | .05 |
| 132 | Mike Birkbeck | .05 |

| NO. | PLAYER | MINT |
|---|---|---|
| 133 | Dan Plesac | .05 |
| 134 | Chris Bosio | .05 |
| 135 | Bill Wegman | .05 |
| 136 | Chuck Crim | .05 |
| 137 | B.J. Surhoff | .08 |
| 138 | Joey Meyer | .05 |
| 139 | Dale Sveum | .05 |
| 140 | Paul Molitor | .12 |
| 141 | Jim Gantner | .05 |
| 142 | Gary Sheffield (R) | .30 |
| 143 | Greg Brock | .05 |
| 144 | Robin Yount | .15 |
| 145 | Glenn Braggs | .05 |
| 146 | Rob Deer | .08 |
| 147 | Fred Toliver | .05 |
| 148 | Jeff Reardon | .08 |
| 149 | Allan Anderson | .08 |
| 150 | Frank Viola | .12 |
| 151 | Shane Rawley | .05 |
| 152 | Juan Berenguer | .05 |
| 153 | Johnny Ard (R) | .20 |
| 154 | Tim Laudner | .05 |
| 155 | Brian Harper | .05 |
| 156 | Al Newman | .05 |
| 157 | Kent Hrbek | .12 |
| 158 | Gary Gaetti | .12 |
| 159 | Wally Backman | .05 |
| 160 | Gene Larkin | .05 |
| 161 | Greg Gagne | .05 |
| 162 | Kirby Puckett | .25 |
| 163 | Danny Gladden | .05 |
| 164 | Randy Bush | .05 |
| 165 | Dave LaPoint | .05 |
| 166 | Andy Hawkins | .05 |
| 167 | Dave Righetti | .08 |
| 168 | Lance McCullers | .08 |
| 169 | Jimmy Jones | .05 |
| 170 | Al Leiter | .08 |
| 171 | John Candelaria | .08 |
| 172 | Don Slaught | .05 |
| 173 | Jamie Quirk | .05 |
| 174 | Rafael Santana | .05 |
| 175 | Mike Pagliarulo | .05 |
| 176 | Don Mattingly | .25 |
| 177 | Ken Phelps | .08 |
| 178 | Steve Sax | .10 |
| 179 | Dave Winfield | .10 |
| 180 | Stan Jefferson | .05 |
| 181 | Rickey Henderson | .30 |
| 182 | Bob Brower | .05 |
| 183 | Roberto Kelly | .15 |
| 184 | Curt Young | .05 |
| 185 | Gene Nelson | .05 |
| 186 | Bob Welch | .08 |
| 187 | Rick Honeycutt | .05 |
| 188 | Dave Stewart | .10 |
| 189 | Mike Moore | .05 |
| 190 | Dennis Eckersley | .10 |
| 191 | Eric Plunk | .05 |
| 192 | Storm Davis | .05 |
| 193 | Terry Steinbach | .10 |
| 194 | Ron Hassey | .05 |
| 195 | Stan Royer (R) | .15 |
| 196 | Walt Weiss | .08 |
| 197 | Mark McGwire | .15 |
| 198 | Carney Lansford | .08 |

| NO. | PLAYER | MINT |
|---|---|---|
| 199 | Glenn Hubbard | .05 |
| 200 | Dave Henderson | .08 |
| 201 | Jose Canseco | .35 |
| 202 | Dave Parker | .12 |
| 203 | Scott Bankhead | .10 |
| 204 | Tom Niedenfuer | .05 |
| 205 | Mark Langston | .10 |
| 206 | Erik Hanson (R) | .35 |
| 207 | Mike Jackson | .05 |
| 208 | Dave Valle | .05 |
| 209 | Scott Bradley | .05 |
| 210 | Harold Reynolds | .08 |
| 211 | Tino Martinez (R) | .60 |
| 212 | Rich Renteria (R) | .10 |
| 213 | Rey Quinones | .05 |
| 214 | Jim Presley | .08 |
| 215 | Alvin Davis | .08 |
| 216 | Edgar Martinez | .15 |
| 217 | Darnell Coles | .05 |
| 218 | Jeffrey Leonard | .05 |
| 219 | Jay Buhner | .15 |
| 220 | Ken Griffey, Jr. (R) | 5.00 |
| 221 | Drew Hall | .05 |
| 222 | Bobby Witt | .08 |
| 223 | Jamie Moyer | .05 |
| 224 | Charlie Hough | .05 |
| 225 | Nolan Ryan | .40 |
| 226 | Jeff Russell | .05 |
| 227 | Jim Sundberg | .05 |
| 228 | Julio Franco | .08 |
| 229 | Buddy Bell | .05 |
| 230 | Scott Fletcher | .05 |
| 231 | Jeff Kunkel | .05 |
| 232 | Steve Buechele | .05 |
| 233 | Monty Fariss ((R) | .25 |
| 234 | Rick Leach | .05 |
| 235 | Ruben Sierra | .20 |
| 236 | Cecil Espy | .08 |
| 237 | Rafael Palmeiro | .15 |
| 238 | Pete Incaviglia | .08 |
| 239 | Dave Stieb | .08 |
| 240 | Jeff Musselman | .05 |
| 241 | Mike Flanagan | .05 |
| 242 | Todd Stottlemyre | .15 |
| 243 | Jimmy Key | .08 |
| 244 | Tony Castillo (R) | .10 |
| 245 | Alex Sanchez (R) | .10 |
| 246 | Tom Henke | .05 |
| 247 | John Cerutti | .05 |
| 248 | Ernie Whitt | .05 |
| 249 | Bob Brenly | .05 |
| 250 | Rance Mulliniks | .05 |
| 251 | Kelly Gruber | .10 |
| 252 | Ed Sprague (R) | .20 |
| 253 | Fred McGriff | .15 |
| 254 | Tony Fernandez | .08 |
| 255 | Tom Lawless | .05 |
| 256 | George Bell | .10 |
| 257 | Jesse Barfield | .08 |
| 258 | S. Alomar, Jr./Sr. | .20 |
| 259 | Griffey, Jr./Sr. | .75 |
| 260 | Cal Ripken, Sr. | .05 |
| 261 | Mel Stottlemyre | .05 |
| 262 | Zane Smith | .05 |
| 263 | Charlie Puleo | .05 |
| 264 | Derek Lilliquist (R) | .12 |

| NO. | PLAYER | MINT |
|-----|--------|------|
| 265 | Paul Assenmacher | .05 |
| 266 | John Smoltz (R) | .50 |
| 267 | Tom Glavine | .25 |
| 268 | Steve Avery (R) | 1.25 |
| 269 | Pete Smith | .08 |
| 270 | Jody Davis | .05 |
| 271 | Bruce Benedict | .05 |
| 272 | Andres Thomas | .05 |
| 273 | Gerald Perry | .08 |
| 274 | Ron Gant | .30 |
| 275 | Darrell Evans | .05 |
| 276 | Dale Murphy | .10 |
| 277 | Dion James | .05 |
| 278 | Lonnie Smith | .05 |
| 279 | Geronimo Berroa | .10 |
| 280 | Steve Wilson (R) | .12 |
| 281 | Rick Sutcliffe | .08 |
| 282 | Kevin Coffman | .08 |
| 283 | Mitch Williams | .08 |
| 284 | Greg Maddux | .08 |
| 285 | Paul Kilgus | .05 |
| 286 | Mike Harkey (R) | .12 |
| 287 | Lloyd McClendon | .10 |
| 288 | Damon Berryhill | .08 |
| 289 | Ty Griffin (R) | .10 |
| 290 | Ryne Sandberg | .25 |
| 291 | Mark Grace | .25 |
| 292 | Curt Wilkerson | .05 |
| 293 | Vance Law | .05 |
| 294 | Shawon Dunston | .08 |
| 295 | Jerome Walton (R) | .35 |
| 296 | Mitch Webster | .05 |
| 297 | Dwight Smith (R) | .10 |
| 298 | Andre Dawson | .15 |
| 299 | Jeff Sellers | .05 |
| 300 | Jose Rijo | .10 |
| 301 | John Franco | .08 |
| 302 | Rick Mahler | .05 |
| 303 | Ron Robinson | .05 |
| 304 | Danny Jackson | .08 |
| 305 | Rob Dibble (R) | .25 |
| 306 | Tom Browning | .05 |
| 307 | Bo Diaz | .05 |
| 308 | Manny Trillo | .05 |
| 309 | Chris Sabo (R) | .50 |
| 310 | Ron Oester | .05 |
| 311 | Barry Larkin | .15 |
| 312 | Todd Benzinger | .08 |
| 313 | Paul O'Neill | .08 |
| 314 | Kal Daniels | .08 |
| 315 | Joel Youngblood | .05 |
| 316 | Eric Davis | .15 |
| 317 | Dave Smith | .05 |
| 318 | Mark Portugal | .05 |
| 319 | Brian Meyer (R) | .10 |

| NO. | PLAYER | MINT |
|-----|--------|------|
| 320 | Jim Deshaies | .05 |
| 321 | Juan Agosto | .05 |
| 322 | Mike Scott | .08 |
| 323 | Rick Rhoden | .05 |
| 324 | Jim Clancy | .05 |
| 325 | Larry Andersen | .05 |
| 326 | Alex Trevino | .05 |
| 327 | Alan Ashby | .05 |
| 328 | Craig Reynolds | .05 |
| 329 | Bill Doran | .05 |
| 330 | Rafael Ramirez | .05 |
| 331 | Glenn Davis | .10 |
| 332 | Willie Ansley (R) | .20 |
| 333 | Gerald Young | .05 |
| 334 | Cameron Drew (R) | .10 |
| 335 | Jay Howell | .05 |
| 336 | Tim Belcher | .08 |
| 337 | Fernando Valenzuela | .08 |
| 338 | Ricky Horton | .05 |
| 339 | Tim Leary | .05 |
| 340 | Bill Bene (R) | .10 |
| 341 | Orel Hershiser | .08 |
| 342 | Mike Scioscia | .05 |
| 343 | Rick Dempsey | .05 |
| 344 | Willie Randolph | .08 |
| 345 | Alfredo Griffin | .05 |
| 346 | Eddie Murray | .12 |
| 347 | Mickey Hatcher | .05 |
| 348 | Mike Sharperson | .05 |
| 349 | John Shelby | .05 |
| 350 | Mike Marshall | .08 |
| 351 | Kirk Gibson | .08 |
| 352 | Mike Davis | .05 |
| 353 | Bryn Smith | .05 |
| 354 | Pascual Perez | .05 |
| 355 | Kevin Gross | .05 |
| 356 | Andy McGaffigan | .05 |
| 357 | Brian Holman (R) | .15 |
| 358 | Dave Wainhouse (R) | .12 |
| 359 | Denny Martinez | .05 |
| 360 | Tim Burke | .05 |
| 361 | Nelson Santovenia (R) | .10 |
| 362 | Tim Wallach | .08 |
| 363 | Spike Owen | .05 |
| 364 | Rex Hudler | .05 |
| 365 | Andres Galarraga | .10 |
| 366 | Otis Nixon | .05 |
| 367 | Hubie Brooks | .05 |
| 368 | Mike Aldrete | .05 |
| 369 | Tim Raines | .10 |
| 370 | Dave Martinez | .05 |
| 371 | Bob Ojeda | .05 |
| 372 | Ron Darling | .10 |
| 373 | Wally Whitehurst (R) | .10 |
| 374 | Randy Myers | .05 |

| NO. | PLAYER | MINT |
|-----|--------|------|
| 375 | David Cone | .10 |
| 376 | Doc Gooden | .15 |
| 377 | Sid Fernandez | .05 |
| 378 | Dave Proctor (R) | .15 |
| 379 | Gary Carter | .08 |
| 380 | Keith Miller | .05 |
| 381 | Gregg Jefferies | .25 |
| 382 | Tim Teufel | .05 |
| 383 | Kevin Elster | .05 |
| 384 | Dave Magadan | .10 |
| 385 | Keith Hernandez | .10 |
| 386 | Mookie Wilson | .05 |
| 387 | Darryl Strawberry | .35 |
| 388 | Kevin McReynolds | .10 |
| 389 | Mark Carreon | .10 |
| 390 | Jeff Parrett | .05 |
| 391 | Mike Maddux | .05 |
| 392 | Don Carman | .05 |
| 393 | Bruce Ruffin | .05 |
| 394 | Ken Howell | .05 |
| 395 | Steve Bedrosian | .10 |
| 396 | Floyd Youmans | .05 |
| 397 | Larry McWilliams | .05 |
| 398 | Pat Combs (R) | .10 |
| 399 | Steve Lake | .05 |
| 400 | Dickie Thon | .05 |
| 401 | Ricky Jordan (R) | .15 |
| 402 | Mike Schmidt | .30 |
| 403 | Tom Herr | .08 |
| 404 | Chris James | .08 |
| 405 | Juan Samuel | .05 |
| 406 | Von Hayes | .08 |
| 407 | Ron Jones (R) | .12 |
| 408 | Curt Ford | .05 |
| 409 | Bob Walk | .05 |
| 410 | Jeff Robinson | .05 |
| 411 | Jim Gott | .05 |
| 412 | Scott Medvin | .12 |
| 413 | John Smiley | .08 |
| 414 | Bob Kipper | .05 |
| 415 | Brian Fisher | .05 |
| 416 | Doug Drabek | .08 |
| 417 | Mike LaValliere | .05 |
| 418 | Ken Oberkfell | .05 |
| 419 | Sid Bream | .05 |
| 420 | Austin Manahan (R) | .12 |
| 421 | Jose Lino | .05 |
| 422 | Bobby Bonilla | .15 |
| 423 | Glenn Wilson | .05 |
| 424 | Andy Van Slyke | .10 |
| 425 | Gary Redus | .05 |
| 426 | Barry Bonds | .20 |
| 427 | Don Heinkel (R) | .12 |
| 428 | Ken Dayley | .05 |
| 429 | Todd Worrell | .05 |

| NO. | PLAYER | MINT |
|-----|--------|------|
| 430 | Brad DuVall (R) | .12 |
| 431 | Jose DeLeon | .05 |
| 432 | Joe Magrane | .08 |
| 433 | John Ericks (R) | .20 |
| 434 | Frank DiPino | .05 |
| 435 | Tony Pena | .08 |
| 436 | Ozzie Smith | .15 |
| 437 | Terry Pendleton | .08 |
| 438 | Jose Oquendo | .05 |
| 439 | Tim Jones (R) | .12 |
| 440 | Pedro Guerrero | .10 |
| 441 | Milt Thompson | .08 |
| 442 | Willie McGee | .08 |
| 443 | Vince Coleman | .12 |
| 444 | Tom Brunansky | .05 |
| 445 | Walt Terrell | .05 |
| 446 | Eric Show | .05 |
| 447 | Mark Davis | .08 |
| 448 | Andy Benes (R) | .40 |
| 449 | Eddie Whitson | .05 |
| 450 | Dennis Rasmussen | .05 |
| 451 | Bruce Hurst | .08 |
| 452 | Pat Clements | .05 |
| 453 | Benny Santiago | .10 |
| 454 | Sandy Alomar, Jr. (R) | .35 |
| 455 | Garry Templeton | .05 |
| 456 | Jack Clark | .10 |
| 457 | Tim Flannery | .05 |
| 458 | Roberto Alomar | .40 |
| 459 | Carmelo Martinez | .05 |
| 460 | John Kruk | .08 |
| 461 | Tony Gwynn | .20 |
| 462 | Jerald Clark (R) | .15 |
| 463 | Don Robinson | .05 |
| 464 | Craig Lefferts | .05 |
| 465 | Kelly Downs | .05 |
| 466 | Rick Reuschel | .05 |
| 467 | Scott Garrelts | .05 |
| 468 | Wil Tejada | .05 |
| 469 | Kirt Manwaring | .05 |
| 470 | Terry Kennedy | .05 |
| 471 | Jose Uribe | .05 |
| 472 | Royce Clayton (R) | .15 |
| 473 | Robby Thompson | .05 |
| 474 | Kevin Mitchell | .30 |
| 475 | Ernie Riles | .05 |
| 476 | Will Clark | .50 |
| 477 | Donell Nixon | .05 |
| 478 | Candy Maldonado | .08 |
| 479 | Tracy Jones | .05 |
| 480 | Brett Butler | .08 |
| 481 | Checklist | .08 |
| 482 | Checklist | .08 |
| 483 | Checklist | .08 |
| 484 | Checklist | .08 |

## 1990 Bowman . . . Complete Set of 528 Cards—Value $18.00  (Factory-Sealed Set—Value $22.00)

Card size was reduced to the standard 2½″ x 3½″. The set was increased to 528 cards and issued in July. Features the rookie cards of John Olerud, Kevin Maas, Frank Thomas and Ben McDonald.

| NO. | PLAYER | MINT |
|---|---|---|
| 1 | Tommy Greene (R) | .25 |
| 2 | Tom Glavine | .15 |
| 3 | Andy Nezelek | .05 |
| 4 | Mike Stanton (R) | .10 |
| 5 | Rick Luecken (R) | .10 |
| 6 | Kent Mercker (R) | .15 |
| 7 | Derek Lilliquist | .05 |
| 8 | Charlie Leibrandt | .05 |
| 9 | Steve Avery | .50 |
| 10 | John Smoltz | .15 |
| 11 | Mark Lemke | .05 |
| 12 | Lonnie Smith | .05 |
| 13 | Oddibe McDowell | .05 |
| 14 | Tyler Houston (R) | .15 |
| 15 | Jeff Blauser | .05 |
| 16 | Ernie Whitt | .05 |
| 17 | Alexis Infante | .05 |
| 18 | Jim Presley | .05 |
| 19 | Dale Murphy | .10 |
| 20 | Nick Esasky | .05 |
| 21 | Rick Sutcliffe | .08 |
| 22 | Mike Bielecki | .05 |
| 23 | Steve Wilson | .05 |
| 24 | Kevin Blankenship | .05 |
| 25 | Mitch Williams | .05 |
| 26 | Dean Wilkins (R) | .12 |
| 27 | Greg Maddux | .05 |
| 28 | Mike Harkey | .05 |
| 29 | Mark Grace | .10 |
| 30 | Ryne Sandberg | .20 |
| 31 | Greg Smith (R) | .10 |
| 32 | Dwight Smith | .10 |
| 33 | Damon Berryhill | .05 |
| 34 | Earl Cunningham (R) | .15 |
| 35 | Jerome Walton | .12 |
| 36 | Lloyd McClendon | .05 |
| 37 | Ty Griffin | .08 |
| 38 | Shawon Dunston | .10 |
| 39 | Andre Dawson | .10 |
| 40 | Luis Salazar | .05 |
| 41 | Tim Layana (R) | .12 |
| 42 | Rob Dibble | .08 |
| 43 | Tom Browning | .05 |
| 44 | Danny Jackson | .05 |
| 45 | Jose Rijo | .05 |
| 46 | Scott Scudder | .10 |
| 47 | Randy Myers | .05 |
| 48 | Brian Lane (R) | .12 |
| 49 | Paul O'Neill | .05 |
| 50 | Barry Larkin | .12 |
| 51 | Reggie Jefferson (R) | .35 |
| 52 | Jeff Branson (R) | .12 |
| 53 | Chris Sabo | .10 |
| 54 | Joe Oliver | .10 |
| 55 | Todd Benzinger | .08 |
| 56 | Rolando Roomes | .05 |
| 57 | Hal Morris | .35 |
| 58 | Eric Davis | .12 |
| 59 | Scott Bryant (R) | .15 |
| 60 | Ken Griffey | .08 |
| 61 | Darryl Kile | .15 |
| 62 | Dave Smith | .05 |
| 63 | Mark Portugal | .05 |
| 64 | Jeff Juden (R) | .25 |
| 65 | Bill Gullickson | .05 |
| 66 | Danny Darwin | .05 |
| 67 | Larry Andersen | .05 |
| 68 | Jose Cano | .08 |
| 69 | Dan Schatzeder | .05 |
| 70 | Jim Deshaies | .05 |
| 71 | Mike Scott | .08 |
| 72 | Gerald Young | .05 |
| 73 | Ken Caminiti | .05 |
| 74 | Ken Oberkfell | .05 |
| 75 | Dave Rohde (R) | .12 |
| 76 | Bill Doran | .05 |
| 77 | Andujar Cedeno (R) | .60 |
| 78 | Craig Biggio | .05 |
| 79 | Karl Rhodes (R) | .15 |
| 80 | Glenn Davis | .08 |
| 81 | Eric Anthony (R) | .20 |
| 82 | John Wetteland | .10 |
| 83 | Jay Howell | .05 |
| 84 | Orel Hershiser | .10 |
| 85 | Tim Belcher | .05 |

| NO. | PLAYER | MINT |
|---|---|---|
| 86 | Kiki Jones (R) | .15 |
| 87 | Mike Hartley | .10 |
| 88 | Ramon Martinez | .20 |
| 89 | Mike Scioscia | .05 |
| 90 | Willie Randolph | .05 |
| 91 | Juan Samuel | .05 |
| 92 | Jose Offerman (R) | .25 |
| 93 | Dave Hansen (R) | .20 |
| 94 | Jeff Hamilton | .05 |
| 95 | Alfredo Griffin | .05 |
| 96 | Tom Goodwin (R) | .25 |
| 97 | Kirk Gibson | .10 |
| 98 | Jose Vizcaino (R) | .12 |
| 99 | Kal Daniels | .10 |
| 100 | Hubie Brooks | .05 |
| 101 | Eddie Murray | .10 |
| 102 | Dennis Boyd | .05 |
| 103 | Tim Burke | .05 |
| 104 | Bill Sampen (R) | .15 |
| 105 | Brett Gideon | .05 |
| 106 | Mark Gardner (R) | .15 |
| 107 | Howard Farmer (R) | .12 |
| 108 | Mel Rojas (R) | .12 |
| 109 | Kevin Gross | .05 |
| 110 | Dave Schmidt | .05 |
| 111 | Denny Martinez | .05 |
| 112 | Jerry Goff | .10 |
| 113 | Andres Galarraga | .08 |
| 114 | Tim Welch | .05 |
| 115 | Marquis Grissom (R) | .30 |
| 116 | Spike Owen | .05 |
| 117 | Larry Walker (R) | .20 |
| 118 | Tim Raines | .08 |
| 119 | Delino DeShields (R) | .35 |
| 120 | Tom Foley | .05 |
| 121 | Dave Martinez | .05 |
| 122 | Frank Viola | .10 |
| 123 | Julio Valera (R) | .12 |
| 124 | Alejandro Pena | .05 |
| 125 | David Cone | .08 |
| 126 | Doc Gooden | .15 |
| 127 | Kevin Brown (R) | .12 |
| 128 | John Franco | .05 |
| 129 | Terry Bross (R) | .12 |
| 130 | Blaine Beatty (R) | .12 |
| 131 | Sid Fernandez | .05 |
| 132 | Mike Marshall | .05 |
| 133 | Howard Johnson | .08 |
| 134 | Jaime Roseboro (R) | .12 |
| 135 | Alan Zinter (R) | .12 |
| 136 | Keith Miller | .05 |
| 137 | Kevin Elster | .05 |
| 138 | Kevin McReynolds | .10 |
| 139 | Barry Lyons | .05 |
| 140 | Gregg Jefferies | .10 |
| 141 | Darryl Strawberry | .20 |
| 142 | Todd Hundley (R) | .25 |
| 143 | Scott Service | .05 |
| 144 | Chuck Malone (R) | .12 |
| 145 | Steve Ontiveros | .05 |
| 146 | Roger McDowell | .05 |
| 147 | Ken Howell | .05 |
| 148 | Pat Combs | .08 |
| 149 | Jeff Parrett | .05 |
| 150 | Chuck McElroy (R) | .15 |
| 151 | Jason Grimsley | .12 |
| 152 | Len Dykstra | .10 |
| 153 | Mickey Morandini (R) | .15 |
| 154 | John Kruk | .05 |
| 155 | Dickie Thon | .05 |
| 156 | Ricky Jordan | .12 |
| 157 | Jeff Jackson (R) | .12 |
| 158 | Darren Daulton | .05 |
| 159 | Tom Herr | .05 |
| 160 | Von Hayes | .08 |
| 161 | Dave Hollins (R) | .25 |
| 162 | Carmelo Martinez | .05 |
| 163 | Bob Walk | .05 |
| 164 | Doug Drabek | .05 |
| 165 | Walt Terrell | .05 |
| 166 | Bill Landrum | .05 |
| 167 | Scott Ruskin (R) | .15 |
| 168 | Bob Patterson | .05 |
| 169 | Bobby Bonilla | .15 |
| 170 | Jose Lind | .05 |

| NO. | PLAYER | MINT |
|---|---|---|
| 171 | Andy Van Slyke | .10 |
| 172 | Mike LaValliere | .05 |
| 173 | Willie Greene (R) | .15 |
| 174 | Jay Bell | .05 |
| 175 | Sid Bream | .05 |
| 176 | Tom Prince | .05 |
| 177 | Wally Backman | .05 |
| 178 | Moises Alou (R) | .12 |
| 179 | Steve Carter | .05 |
| 180 | Gary Redus | .05 |
| 181 | Barry Bonds | .15 |
| 182 | Don Slaught | .05 |
| 183 | Joe Magrane | .05 |
| 184 | Bryn Smith | .05 |
| 185 | Todd Worrell | .05 |
| 186 | Jose DeLeon | .05 |
| 187 | Frank DiPino | .05 |
| 188 | John Tudor | .05 |
| 189 | Howard Hilton (R) | .12 |
| 190 | John Ericks | .05 |
| 191 | Ken Dayley | .05 |
| 192 | Ray Lankford (R) | .75 |
| 193 | Todd Zelle | .25 |
| 194 | Willie McGee | .10 |
| 195 | Ozzie Smith | .10 |
| 196 | Milt Thompson | .05 |
| 197 | Terry Pendelton | .05 |
| 198 | Vince Coleman | .10 |
| 199 | Paul Coleman (R) | .20 |
| 200 | Jose Oquendo | .05 |
| 201 | Pedro Guerrero | .10 |
| 202 | Tom Brunansky | .05 |
| 203 | Roger Smithberg (R) | .12 |
| 204 | Eddie Whitson | .05 |
| 205 | Dennis Rassmussen | .05 |
| 206 | Craig Lefferts | .05 |
| 207 | Andy Benes | .15 |
| 208 | Bruce Hurst | .05 |
| 209 | Eric Show | .05 |
| 210 | Rafael Valdez (R) | .12 |
| 211 | Joey Cora | .05 |
| 212 | Thomas Howard | .15 |
| 213 | Rob Nelson | .05 |
| 214 | Jack Clark | .10 |
| 215 | Garry Templeton | .05 |
| 216 | Fred Lynn | .08 |
| 217 | Tony Gwynn | .12 |
| 218 | Benny Santiago | .10 |
| 219 | Mike Pagliarulo | .05 |
| 220 | Joe Carter | .08 |
| 221 | Roberto Alomar | .10 |
| 222 | Bip Roberts | .05 |
| 223 | Rick Reuschel | .05 |
| 224 | Russ Swan (R) | .15 |
| 225 | Eric Gunderson (R) | .15 |
| 226 | Steve Bedrosian | .05 |
| 227 | Mike Remlinger (R) | .12 |
| 228 | Scott Garrelts | .05 |
| 229 | Ernie Camacho | .05 |
| 230 | Andres Santana (R) | .20 |
| 231 | Will Clark | .20 |
| 232 | Kevin Mitchell | .10 |
| 233 | Robby Thompson | .05 |
| 234 | Bill Bathe | .05 |
| 235 | Tony Perezchica | .05 |
| 236 | Gary Carter | .10 |
| 237 | Brett Butler | .05 |
| 238 | Matt Williams | .15 |
| 239 | Ernie Riles | .05 |
| 240 | Kevin Bass | .05 |
| 241 | Terry Kennedy | .05 |
| 242 | Steve Hosey (R) | .15 |
| 243 | Ben McDonald (R) | .50 |
| 244 | Jeff Ballard | .05 |
| 245 | Joe Price | .05 |
| 246 | Curt Schilling | .05 |
| 247 | Pete Harnisch | .05 |
| 248 | Mark Williamson | .05 |
| 249 | Gregg Olson | .10 |
| 250 | Chris Myers (R) | .12 |
| 251 | David Segui (R) | .15 |
| 252 | Joe Orsulak | .05 |
| 253 | C. Worthington | .10 |
| 254 | Mickey Tettleton | .05 |
| 255 | Cal Ripken | .30 |

| NO. | PLAYER | MINT |
|---|---|---|
| 256 | Billy Ripken | .05 |
| 257 | Randy Milligan | .08 |
| 258 | Brady Anderson | .05 |
| 259 | Chris Holles (R) | .20 |
| 260 | Mike Devereaux | .05 |
| 261 | Phil Bradley | .05 |
| 262 | Leo Gomez | .40 |
| 263 | Lee Smith | .05 |
| 264 | Mike Rochford | .05 |
| 265 | Jeff Reardon | .05 |
| 266 | Wes Gardner | .05 |
| 267 | Mike Boddicker | .08 |
| 268 | Roger Clemens | .25 |
| 269 | Rob Murphy | .05 |
| 270 | Mickey Pina (R) | .15 |
| 271 | Tony Pena | .05 |
| 272 | Jody Reed | .05 |
| 273 | Kevin Romine | .05 |
| 274 | Mike Greenwell | .12 |
| 275 | Maurice Vaughn (R) | .75 |
| 276 | Danny Heep | .05 |
| 277 | Scott Cooper (R) | .30 |
| 278 | Greg Blosser (R) | .20 |
| 279 | Dwight Evans | .08 |
| 280 | Ellis Burks | .10 |
| 281 | Wade Boggs | .15 |
| 282 | Marty Barrett | .05 |
| 283 | Kirk McCaskill | .05 |
| 284 | Mark Langston | .10 |
| 285 | Bert Blyleven | .05 |
| 286 | Mike Fetters (R) | .10 |
| 287 | Kyle Abbott (R) | .15 |
| 288 | Jim Abbott | .15 |
| 289 | Chuck Finley | .05 |
| 290 | Gary DiSarcina (R) | .10 |
| 291 | Dick Schofield | .05 |
| 292 | Devon White | .05 |
| 293 | Bobby Rose (R) | .12 |
| 294 | Brian Downing | .05 |
| 295 | Lance Parrish | .05 |
| 296 | Jack Howell | .05 |
| 297 | C. Washington | .05 |
| 298 | John Orton | .08 |
| 299 | Wally Joyner | .12 |
| 300 | Lee Stevens | .12 |
| 301 | Chili Davis | .08 |
| 302 | Johnny Ray | .05 |
| 303 | Greg Hibbard (R) | .15 |
| 304 | Eric King | .05 |
| 305 | Jack McDowell | .10 |
| 306 | Bobby Thigpen | .10 |
| 307 | Adam Peterson | .05 |
| 308 | Scott Radinsky (R) | .15 |
| 309 | Wayne Edwards (R) | .12 |
| 310 | Melido Perez | .05 |
| 311 | Robin Ventura | .35 |
| 312 | Sammy Sosa (R) | .20 |
| 313 | Dan Pasqua | .05 |
| 314 | Carlton Fisk | .10 |
| 315 | Ozzie Guillen | .05 |
| 316 | Ivan Calderon | .05 |
| 317 | Daryl Boston | .05 |
| 318 | Craig Grebeck (R) | .10 |
| 319 | Scott Fletcher | .05 |
| 320 | Frank Thomas (R) | 3.00 |
| 321 | Steve Lyons | .05 |
| 322 | Carlos Martinez | .10 |
| 323 | Joe Skaiski | .10 |
| 324 | Tom Candiotti | .05 |
| 325 | Greg Swindell | .05 |
| 326 | Steve Olin (R) | .10 |
| 327 | Kevin Wickander | .05 |
| 328 | Doug Jones | .05 |
| 329 | Jeff Shaw (R) | .10 |
| 330 | Kevin Bearse (R) | .12 |
| 331 | Dion James | .05 |
| 332 | Jerry Browne | .05 |
| 333 | Joey Bell | .40 |
| 334 | Felix Fermin | .05 |
| 335 | Candy Maldonado | .05 |
| 336 | Cory Snyder | .08 |
| 337 | Sandy Alomar | .10 |
| 338 | Mark Lewis | .15 |
| 339 | Carlos Baerga (R) | .30 |
| 340 | Chris James | .05 |

| NO. | PLAYER | MINT |
|---|---|---|
| 341 | Brook Jacoby | .05 |
| 342 | Keith Hernandez | .05 |
| 343 | Frank Tanana | .05 |
| 344 | Scott Aldred (R) | .12 |
| 345 | Mike Henneman | .05 |
| 346 | Steve Wapnick (R) | .10 |
| 347 | Greg Gohr (R) | .12 |
| 348 | Eric Stone (R) | .12 |
| 349 | Brian DuBois (R) | .10 |
| 350 | Kevin Ritz (R) | .10 |
| 351 | Rico Brogna | .05 |
| 352 | Mike Heath | .05 |
| 353 | Alan Trammell | .08 |
| 354 | Chet Lemon | .05 |
| 355 | Dave Bergman | .05 |
| 356 | Lou Whitaker | .05 |
| 357 | Cecil Fielder | .30 |
| 358 | Milt Cuyler (R) | .25 |
| 359 | Tony Phillips | .05 |
| 360 | Travis Fryman (R) | 1.00 |
| 361 | Ed Romero | .05 |
| 362 | Lloyd Moseby | .05 |
| 363 | Mark Gubicza | .05 |
| 364 | Bret Saberhagen | .10 |
| 365 | Tom Gordon | .08 |
| 366 | Steve Farr | .05 |
| 367 | Kevin Appler | .15 |
| 368 | Storm Davis | .05 |
| 369 | Mark Davis | .05 |
| 370 | Jeff Montgomery | .05 |
| 371 | Frank White | .05 |
| 372 | Brent Mayne (R) | .15 |
| 373 | Bob Boone | .05 |
| 374 | Jim Eisenreich | .05 |
| 375 | Danny Tartabull | .05 |
| 376 | Kurt Stillwell | .05 |
| 377 | Bill Pecota | .05 |
| 378 | Bo Jackson | .30 |
| 379 | Bob Hamelin (R) | .15 |
| 380 | Kevin Seltzer | .05 |
| 381 | Rey Palacios | .05 |
| 382 | George Brett | .15 |
| 383 | Gerald Perry | .05 |
| 384 | Teddy Higuera | .05 |
| 385 | Tom Filer | .05 |
| 386 | Dan Plesac | .05 |
| 387 | Cal Eldred (R) | .15 |

| NO. | PLAYER | MINT |
|---|---|---|
| 388 | Jaime Navarro | .08 |
| 389 | Chris Bosio | .05 |
| 390 | Randy Veres | .08 |
| 391 | Gary Sheffield | .08 |
| 392 | George Canale (R) | .10 |
| 393 | B.J. Surhoff | .05 |
| 394 | Tim McIntosh (R) | .12 |
| 395 | Greg Brock | .05 |
| 396 | Greg Vaughn | .50 |
| 397 | Darryl Hamilton | .10 |
| 398 | Dave Parker | .10 |
| 399 | Paul Molitor | .10 |
| 400 | Jim Gantner | .05 |
| 401 | Rob Deer | .05 |
| 402 | Billy Spiers | .10 |
| 403 | Glenn Braggs | .05 |
| 404 | Robin Yount | .10 |
| 405 | Rick Aguilera | .05 |
| 406 | Johnny Ard | .05 |
| 407 | Kevin Tapani (R) | .20 |
| 408 | Park Pittman (R) | .12 |
| 409 | Allan Anderson | .05 |
| 410 | Juan Berenguer | .05 |
| 411 | Willie Banks (R) | .25 |
| 412 | Rich Yett | .05 |
| 413 | Dave West | .05 |
| 414 | Greg Gagne | .05 |
| 415 | Chuck Knoblauch (R) | .75 |
| 416 | Randy Bush | .05 |
| 417 | Gary Gaetti | .05 |
| 418 | Kent Hrbek | .10 |
| 419 | Al Newman | .05 |
| 420 | Danny Gladden | .05 |
| 421 | Paul Sorrento (R) | .12 |
| 422 | Derek Parks (R) | .10 |
| 423 | Scott Lelus (R) | .25 |
| 424 | Kirby Puckett | .15 |
| 425 | Willie Smith (R) | .12 |
| 426 | Dave Righetti | .05 |
| 427 | Jeff Robinson | .05 |
| 428 | Alan Mills (R) | .12 |
| 429 | Tim Leary | .05 |
| 430 | Pascual Perez | .05 |
| 431 | Alvaro Espinoza | .05 |
| 432 | Dave Winfield | .12 |
| 433 | Jesse Barfield | .05 |
| 434 | Randy Velarde | .05 |

| NO. | PLAYER | MINT |
|---|---|---|
| 435 | Rick Cerone | .05 |
| 436 | Steve Balboni | .05 |
| 437 | Mel Hall | .05 |
| 438 | Bob Geren | .05 |
| 439 | Bernie Williams (R) | .30 |
| 440 | Kevin Mass (R) | 1.25 |
| 441 | Mike Blowers (R) | .12 |
| 442 | Steve Sax | .05 |
| 443 | Don Mattingly | .25 |
| 444 | Roberto Kelly | .08 |
| 445 | Mike Moore | .05 |
| 446 | Reggie Harris (R) | .15 |
| 447 | Scott Sanderson | .05 |
| 448 | Dave Otto | .05 |
| 449 | Dave Stewart | .10 |
| 450 | Rick Honeycutt | .05 |
| 451 | Dennis Eckersley | .08 |
| 452 | Carney Lansford | .05 |
| 453 | Scott Hemond (R) | .12 |
| 454 | Mark McGwire | .15 |
| 455 | Felix Jose | .15 |
| 456 | Terry Steinbach | .05 |
| 457 | Rickey Henderson | .25 |
| 458 | Dave Henderson | .05 |
| 459 | Mike Gallego | .05 |
| 460 | Jose Canseco | .35 |
| 461 | Walt Weiss | .05 |
| 462 | Ken Phelps | .05 |
| 463 | Darren Lewis (R) | .35 |
| 464 | Ron Hassey | .05 |
| 465 | Roger Salkeld (R) | .50 |
| 466 | Scott Bankhead | .05 |
| 467 | Keith Comstock | .05 |
| 468 | Randy Johnson | .10 |
| 469 | Erik Hanson | .10 |
| 470 | Mike Schooler | .08 |
| 471 | Gary Eave (R) | .10 |
| 472 | Jeffrey Leonard | .05 |
| 473 | Dave Valle | .05 |
| 474 | Omar Vizquel | .05 |
| 475 | Pete O'Brien | .05 |
| 476 | Henry Cotto | .05 |
| 477 | Jay Buhner | .05 |
| 478 | Harold Reynolds | .05 |
| 479 | Alvin Davis | .05 |
| 480 | Darnell Coles | .05 |
| 481 | Ken Griffey, Jr. | 1.75 |

| NO. | PLAYER | MINT |
|---|---|---|
| 482 | Greg Briley | .10 |
| 483 | Scott Bradley | .05 |
| 484 | Tino Martinez | .30 |
| 485 | Jeff Russell | .05 |
| 486 | Nolan Ryan | .35 |
| 487 | Robb Nen (R) | .12 |
| 488 | Kevin Brown | .10 |
| 489 | Brian Bohanon (R) | .12 |
| 490 | Ruben Sierra | .15 |
| 491 | Pete Incaviglia | .08 |
| 492 | Juan Gonzalez (R) | 1.50 |
| 493 | Steve Buechele | .05 |
| 494 | Scott Coolbaugh (R) | .12 |
| 495 | Geno Petralli | .05 |
| 496 | Rafael Palmeiro | .10 |
| 497 | Julio Franco | .05 |
| 498 | Gary Pettis | .05 |
| 499 | Donald Harris (R) | .12 |
| 500 | Monty Fariss | .05 |
| 501 | Harold Baines | .05 |
| 502 | Cecil Espy | .05 |
| 503 | Jack Daugherty (R) | .12 |
| 504 | Willie Blair (R) | .10 |
| 505 | Dave Stieb | .05 |
| 506 | Tom Henke | .05 |
| 507 | John Cerutti | .05 |
| 508 | Paul Kilgus | .05 |
| 509 | Jimmy Key | .05 |
| 510 | John Olerud (R) | .60 |
| 511 | Ed Sprague | .05 |
| 512 | Manny Lee | .05 |
| 513 | Fred McGriff | .10 |
| 514 | Glenallen Hill | .05 |
| 515 | George Bell | .10 |
| 516 | Mookie Wilson | .05 |
| 517 | Luis Sojo (R) | .12 |
| 518 | Nelson Liriano | .05 |
| 519 | Kelly Gruber | .08 |
| 520 | Greg Myers | .05 |
| 521 | Pat Borders | .05 |
| 522 | Junior Felix | .10 |
| 523 | Eddie Zosky (R) | .25 |
| 524 | Tony Fernandez | .05 |
| 525 | Checklist No. 1 | .05 |
| 526 | Checklist No. 2 | .05 |
| 527 | Checklist No. 3 | .05 |
| 528 | Checklist No. 4 | .05 |

## 1991 Bowman . . . Complete Set of 704 Cards—Value $20.00

The set was increased to 704 cards. Included 44 *gold foil* embossed commemorative cards (at least one card was included in every wax pack). A new feature on the back was *Super Statistics* that compared a player's performance against every team.

| NO. | PLAYER | MINT |
|---|---|---|
| 1 | Rod Carew—I | .15 |
| 2 | Rod Carew—II | .15 |
| 3 | Rod Carew—III | .15 |
| 4 | Rod Carew—IV | .15 |
| 5 | Rod Carew—V | .15 |
| 6 | Willie Fraser | .05 |
| 7 | John Olerud | .10 |
| 8 | William Suero | .05 |

| NO. | PLAYER | MINT |
|---|---|---|
| 9 | Roberto Alomar | .05 |
| 10 | Todd Stottlemyre | .05 |
| 11 | Joe Carter | .12 |
| 12 | Steve Karsay (R) | .15 |
| 13 | Mark Whiten | .15 |
| 14 | Pat Borders | .05 |
| 15 | Mike Timlin (R) | .12 |
| 16 | Tom Henke | .05 |

| NO. | PLAYER | MINT |
|---|---|---|
| 17 | Eddie Zosky | .05 |
| 18 | Kelly Gruber | .08 |
| 19 | Jimmy Key | .05 |
| 20 | Jerry Schunk (R) | .12 |
| 21 | Manny Lee | .05 |
| 22 | Dave Stieb | .08 |
| 23 | Pat Hentgen (R) | .12 |
| 24 | Glenallen Hill | .05 |

| NO. | PLAYER | MINT |
|---|---|---|
| 25 | Rene Gonzales | .05 |
| 26 | Ed Sprague | .08 |
| 27 | Ken Dayley | .05 |
| 28 | Pat Tabler | .05 |
| 29 | Denis Boucher (R) | .12 |
| 30 | Devon White | .05 |
| 31 | Dante Bichette | .05 |
| 32 | Paul Molitor | .08 |

| NO. | PLAYER | MINT |
|---|---|---|
| 33 | Greg Vaughn | .08 |
| 34 | Dan Plesac | .05 |
| 35 | Chris George (R) | .12 |
| 36 | Tim McIntosh | .05 |
| 37 | Franklin Stubbs | .05 |
| 38 | Bo Dodson (R) | .15 |
| 39 | Ron Robinson | .05 |
| 40 | Ed Nunez | .05 |
| 41 | Greg Brock | .05 |
| 42 | Jaime Navarro | .05 |
| 43 | Chris Bosio | .05 |
| 44 | B.J. Surhoff | .05 |
| 45 | Chris Johnson (R) | .12 |
| 46 | Willie Randolph | .08 |
| 47 | Narciso Elvira (R) | .12 |
| 48 | Jim Gantner | .05 |
| 49 | Kevin Brown | .05 |
| 50 | Julio Machado | .05 |
| 51 | Chuck Crim | .05 |
| 52 | Gary Sheffield | .08 |
| 53 | Angel Miranda (R) | .12 |
| 54 | Teddy Higuera | .05 |
| 55 | Robin Yount | .10 |
| 56 | Cal Eldred | .05 |
| 57 | Sandy Alomar | .08 |
| 58 | Greg Swindell | .05 |
| 59 | Brook Jacoby | .05 |
| 60 | Efrain Valdez (R) | .12 |
| 61 | Ever Magallanes (R) | .12 |
| 62 | Tom Candiotti | .05 |
| 63 | Eric King | .05 |
| 64 | Alex Cole | .08 |
| 65 | Charles Nagy | .05 |
| 66 | Mitch Webster | .05 |
| 67 | Chris James | .05 |
| 68 | Jim Thome (R) | .40 |
| 69 | Carlos Baerga | .08 |
| 70 | Mark Lewis | .08 |
| 71 | Jerry Browne | .05 |
| 72 | Jesse Orosco | .05 |
| 73 | Mike Huff | .05 |
| 74 | Jose Escobar (R) | .12 |
| 75 | Jeff Manto | .05 |
| 76 | Turner Ward (R) | .12 |
| 77 | Doug Jones | .05 |
| 78 | Bruce Egloff (R) | .12 |
| 79 | Tim Costo (R) | .20 |
| 80 | Beau Allred | .05 |
| 81 | Albert Belle | .15 |
| 82 | John Farrell | .05 |
| 83 | Glenn Davis | .08 |
| 84 | Joe Orsulak | .05 |
| 85 | Mark Williamson | .05 |
| 86 | Ben McDonald | .08 |
| 87 | Billy Ripken | .05 |
| 88 | Leo Gomez | .08 |
| 89 | Bob Melvin | .05 |
| 90 | Jeff Robinson | .05 |
| 91 | Jose Mesa | .05 |
| 92 | Gregg Olson | .08 |
| 93 | Mike Devereaux | .05 |
| 94 | Luis Mercedes (R) | .20 |
| 95 | Arthur Rhodes (R) | .25 |
| 96 | Juan Bell | .05 |
| 97 | Mike Mussina (R) | .35 |
| 98 | Jeff Ballard | .05 |
| 99 | Chris Hoiles | .08 |
| 100 | Brady Anderson | .05 |
| 101 | Bob Milacki | .05 |
| 102 | David Segui | .10 |
| 103 | Dwight Evans | .08 |
| 104 | Cal Ripken | .15 |
| 105 | Mike Linskey (R) | .12 |
| 106 | Jeff Tackett (R) | .12 |
| 107 | Jeff Reardon | .05 |
| 108 | Dana Kiecker | .05 |
| 109 | Ellis Burks | .08 |
| 110 | Dave Owen (R) | .12 |
| 111 | Danny Darwin | .05 |
| 112 | Mo Vaughn | .25 |
| 113 | Jeff McNeely (R) | .40 |
| 114 | Tom Bolton | .05 |
| 115 | Greg Blosser | .10 |
| 116 | Mike Greenwell | .10 |
| 117 | Phil Plantier (R) | 1.00 |
| 118 | Roger Clemens | .15 |
| 119 | John Marzano | .05 |
| 120 | Jody Reed | .05 |
| 121 | Scott Taylor (R) | .12 |
| 122 | Jack Clark | .08 |
| 123 | Derek Livernois (R) | .12 |
| 124 | Tony Pena | .05 |
| 125 | Tom Brunansky | .05 |
| 126 | Carlos Quintana | .05 |
| 127 | Tim Naehring | .05 |
| 128 | Matt Young | .05 |
| 129 | Wade Boggs | .15 |
| 130 | Kevin Morton (R) | .12 |
| 131 | Pete Incaviglia | .05 |
| 132 | Rob Deer | .05 |
| 133 | Bill Gullickson | .05 |
| 134 | Rico Brogna | .08 |
| 135 | Lloyd Moseby | .05 |
| 136 | Cecil Fielder | .12 |
| 137 | Tony Phillips | .05 |
| 138 | Mark Leiter (R) | .12 |
| 139 | John Cerutti | .05 |
| 140 | Mickey Tettleton | .05 |
| 141 | Milt Cuyler | .05 |
| 142 | Greg Gohr | .05 |
| 143 | Tony Bernazard | .05 |
| 144 | Dan Gakeler (R) | .12 |
| 145 | Travis Fryman | .20 |
| 146 | Dan Petry | .05 |
| 147 | Scott Aldred | .05 |
| 148 | John DeSilva (R) | .12 |
| 149 | Rusty Meacham (R) | .12 |
| 150 | Lou Whitaker | .05 |
| 151 | Dave Haas (R) | .12 |
| 152 | Luis de los Santos | .05 |
| 153 | Ivan Cruz (R) | .12 |
| 154 | Alan Trammell | .08 |
| 155 | Pat Kelly (R) | .30 |
| 156 | Carl Everett (R) | .20 |
| 157 | Greg Cadaret | .05 |
| 158 | Kevin Maas | .15 |
| 159 | Jeff Johnson (R) | .20 |
| 160 | Willie Smith | .05 |
| 161 | Gerald Williams (R) | .25 |
| 162 | Mike Humphreys (R) | .12 |
| 163 | Alvaro Espinoza | .05 |
| 164 | Matt Nokes | .05 |
| 165 | Wade Taylor (R) | .15 |
| 166 | Roberto Kelly | .08 |
| 167 | John Habyan | .05 |
| 168 | Steve Farr | .05 |
| 169 | Jesse Barfield | .05 |
| 170 | Steve Sax | .08 |
| 171 | Jim Leyritz | .05 |
| 172 | Robert Eenhoorn (R) | .15 |
| 173 | Bernie Williams | .10 |
| 174 | Scott Lusader | .05 |
| 175 | Torey Lovullo | .05 |
| 176 | Chuck Cary | .05 |
| 177 | Scott Sanderson | .05 |
| 178 | Don Mattingly | .15 |
| 179 | Mel Hall | .08 |

**No. 180 to 185—Gold Foil**

| NO. | PLAYER | MINT |
|---|---|---|
| 180 | Juan Gonzalez | .30 |
| 181 | Hensley Meulens | .08 |
| 182 | Jose Offerman | .10 |
| 183 | Jeff Bagwell (R) | 1.50 |
| 184 | Jeff Conine (R) | .12 |
| 185 | Henry Rodriguez (R) | .20 |
| 186 | Jimmie Reese | .05 |

**75 years in baseball**

| NO. | PLAYER | MINT |
|---|---|---|
| 187 | Kyle Abbott | .05 |
| 188 | Lance Parrish | .05 |
| 189 | Rafael Montalvo (R) | .12 |
| 190 | Floyd Bannister | .05 |
| 191 | Dick Schofield | .05 |
| 192 | Scott Lewis (R) | .12 |
| 193 | Jeff Robinson | .05 |
| 194 | Kent Anderson | .05 |
| 195 | Wally Joyner | .10 |
| 196 | Chuck Finley | .08 |
| 197 | Luis Sojo | .05 |
| 198 | Jeff Richardson (R) | .12 |
| 199 | Dave Parker | .10 |
| 200 | Jim Abbott | .10 |
| 201 | Junior Felix | .05 |
| 202 | Mark Langston | .08 |
| 203 | Tim Salmon (R) | .30 |
| 204 | Cliff Young | .05 |
| 205 | Scott Bailes | .05 |
| 206 | Bobby Rose | .08 |
| 207 | Gary Gaetti | .05 |
| 208 | Ruben Amaro (R) | .12 |
| 209 | Luis Polonia | .05 |
| 210 | Dave Winfield | .10 |
| 211 | Bryan Harvey | .05 |
| 212 | Mike Moore | .05 |
| 213 | Rickey Henderson | .25 |
| 214 | Steve Chitren (R) | .12 |
| 215 | Bob Welch | .05 |
| 216 | Terry Steinbach | .05 |
| 217 | Ernie Riles | .05 |
| 218 | Todd Van Poppel (R) | 1.00 |
| 219 | Mike Gallego | .05 |
| 220 | Curt Young | .05 |
| 221 | Todd Burns | .05 |
| 222 | Vance Law | .05 |
| 223 | Eric Show | .05 |
| 224 | Don Peters (R) | .12 |
| 225 | Dave Stewart | .10 |
| 226 | Dave Henderson | .08 |
| 227 | Jose Canseco | .20 |
| 228 | Walt Weiss | .05 |
| 229 | Dann Howitt | .05 |
| 230 | Willie Wilson | .05 |
| 231 | Harold Baines | .05 |
| 232 | Scott Hemond | .05 |
| 233 | Joe Slusarski (R) | .12 |
| 234 | Mark McGwire | .15 |
| 235 | Kirk Dressendorfer (R) | .20 |
| 236 | Craig Paquette (R) | .15 |
| 237 | Dennis Eckersley | .10 |
| 238 | Dana Allison (R) | .12 |
| 239 | Scott Bradley | .05 |
| 240 | Brian Holman | .05 |
| 241 | Mike Schooler | .05 |
| 242 | Rich DeLucia (R) | .12 |
| 243 | Edgar Martinez | .08 |
| 244 | Henry Cotto | .05 |
| 245 | Omar Vizquel | .05 |
| 246 | Ken Griffey, Jr. | .75 |
| 247 | Jay Buhner | .08 |
| 248 | Bill Krueger | .20 |
| 249 | Dave Fleming (R) | .12 |
| 250 | Patrick Lennon (R) | .20 |
| 251 | Dave Valle | .05 |
| 252 | Harold Reynolds | .05 |
| 253 | Randy Johnson | .05 |
| 254 | Scott Bankhead | .05 |
| 255 | Ken Griffey | .08 |
| 256 | Greg Briley | .05 |
| 257 | Tino Martinez | .20 |
| 258 | Alvin Davis | .05 |
| 259 | Pete O'Brien | .05 |
| 260 | Erik Hanson | .08 |
| 261 | Bret Boone (R) | .15 |
| 262 | Roger Salkeld | .15 |
| 263 | Dave Burba (R) | .12 |
| 264 | Kerry Woodson (R) | .12 |
| 265 | Julio Franco | .08 |
| 266 | Dan Peltier (R) | .15 |
| 267 | Jeff Russell | .05 |
| 268 | Steve Buechele | .05 |
| 269 | Donald Harris | .05 |
| 270 | Robb Nen | .05 |
| 271 | Rich Gossage | .05 |
| 272 | Ivan Rodriguez (R) | 1.50 |
| 273 | Jeff Huson | .05 |
| 274 | Kevin Brown | .05 |
| 275 | Dan Smith (R) | .12 |
| 276 | Gary Pettis | .05 |
| 277 | Jack Daugherty | .05 |
| 278 | Mike Jeffcoat | .05 |
| 279 | Brad Arnsberg | .05 |
| 280 | Nolan Ryan | .25 |
| 281 | Eric McCray (R) | .12 |
| 282 | Scott Chiamparino | .10 |
| 283 | Ruben Sierra | .12 |
| 284 | Geno Petralli | .05 |
| 285 | Monty Fariss | .05 |
| 286 | Raffael Palmeiro | .08 |
| 287 | Bobby Witt | .05 |
| 288 | Dean Palmer | .40 |
| 289 | Tony Scruggs (R) | .12 |
| 290 | Kenny Rogers | .05 |
| 291 | Bret Saberhagen | .08 |
| 292 | Brian McRae (R) | .35 |
| 293 | Storm Davis | .05 |
| 294 | Danny Tartabull | .08 |
| 295 | David Howard (R) | .12 |
| 296 | Mike Boddicker | .05 |
| 297 | Joel Johnston (R) | .12 |
| 298 | Tim Sehr (R) | .12 |
| 299 | Hector Wagner (R) | .12 |
| 300 | George Brett | .10 |
| 301 | Mike Macfarlane | .05 |
| 302 | Kirk Gibson | .08 |
| 303 | Harvey Pulliam (R) | .15 |
| 304 | Jim Eisenreich | .05 |
| 305 | Kevin Seitzer | .05 |
| 306 | Mark Davis | .05 |
| 307 | Kurt Stillwell | .05 |
| 308 | Jeff Montgomery | .05 |
| 309 | Kevin Appier | .05 |
| 310 | Bob Hamelin | .05 |
| 311 | Tom Gordon | .08 |
| 312 | Kerwin Moore (R) | .15 |
| 313 | Hugh Walker | .05 |
| 314 | Terry Shumpert | .08 |
| 315 | Warren Cromartie | .05 |
| 316 | Gary Thurman | .05 |
| 317 | Steve Bedrosian | .05 |
| 318 | Danny Gladden | .05 |
| 319 | Jack Morris | .08 |
| 320 | Kirby Puckett | .15 |
| 321 | Kent Hrbek | .08 |
| 322 | Kevin Tapani | .05 |
| 323 | Denny Neagle (R) | .25 |
| 324 | Rich Garces (R) | .12 |
| 325 | Larry Caslan (R) | .12 |
| 326 | Shane Mack | .05 |
| 327 | Allan Anderson | .05 |
| 328 | Junior Ortiz | .05 |
| 329 | Paul Abbott (R) | .12 |
| 330 | Chuck Knoblauch | .20 |
| 331 | Chili Davis | .05 |
| 332 | Todd Ritchie (R) | .15 |
| 333 | Brian Harper | .05 |
| 334 | Rick Aguilera | .05 |
| 335 | Scott Erickson | .50 |
| 336 | Pedro Munoz (R) | .15 |
| 337 | Scott Leius | .05 |
| 338 | Greg Cagne | .05 |
| 339 | Mike Pagliarulo | .05 |
| 340 | Terry Leach | .05 |
| 341 | Willie Banks | .08 |
| 342 | Bobby Thigpen | .05 |
| 343 | Roberto Hernandez (R) | .20 |
| 344 | Melido Perez | .05 |
| 345 | Carlton Fisk | .10 |
| 346 | Norberto Martin (R) | .12 |
| 347 | Johnny Ruffin (R) | .12 |
| 348 | Jeff Carter (R) | .12 |
| 349 | Lance Johnson | .05 |
| 350 | Sammy Sosa | .05 |
| 351 | Alex Fernandez | .15 |
| 352 | Jack McDowell | .08 |
| 353 | Bob Wickman (R) | .12 |
| 354 | Wilson Alvarez | .20 |
| 355 | Charlie Hough | .05 |
| 356 | Ozzie Guillen | .05 |
| 357 | Cory Snyder | .08 |
| 358 | Robin Ventura | .20 |
| 359 | Scott Fletcher | .05 |
| 360 | Cesar Bernhardt (R) | .12 |
| 361 | Dan Pasqua | .05 |
| 362 | Rock Raines | .08 |
| 363 | Brian Drahman (R) | .12 |
| 364 | Wayne Edwards | .05 |
| 365 | Scott Radinsky | .05 |
| 366 | Frank Thomas | .75 |

**367 to 384—Gold Foil Sluggers**

| NO. | PLAYER | MINT |
|---|---|---|
| 367 | Cecil Fielder | .15 |
| 368 | Julio Franco | .10 |
| 369 | Kelly Gruber | .10 |

| NO. | PLAYER | MINT |
|-----|--------|------|
| 370 | Alan Trammell | 10 |
| 371 | Rickey Henderson | 15 |
| 372 | Jose Canseco | 20 |
| 373 | Ellis Burks | 08 |
| 374 | Lance Parrish | 08 |
| 375 | Dave Parker | 08 |
| 376 | Eddie Murray | 10 |
| 377 | Ryne Sandberg | 15 |
| 378 | Matt Williams | 08 |
| 379 | Barry Larkin | 08 |
| 380 | Barry Bonds | 08 |
| 381 | Bobby Bonilla | 10 |
| 382 | Darryl Strawberry | 12 |
| 383 | Benny Santiago | 08 |
| 384 | Don Robinson | 08 |
| 385 | Paul Coleman | 05 |
| 386 | Milt Thompson | 05 |
| 387 | Lee Smith | 05 |
| 388 | Ray Lankford | 12 |
| 389 | Tom Pagnozzi | 05 |
| 390 | Ken Hill | 05 |
| 391 | Jamie Moyer | 05 |
| 392 | Greg Carmona (R) | 12 |
| 393 | John Ericks | 05 |
| 394 | Bob Tewksbury | 05 |
| 395 | Jose Oquendo | 05 |
| 396 | Rheal Cormier (R) | 35 |
| 397 | Mike Milchin (R) | 12 |
| 398 | Ozzie Smith | 10 |
| 399 | Aaron Holbert (R) | 12 |
| 400 | Jose DeLeon | 05 |
| 401 | Felix Jose | 08 |
| 402 | Juan Agosto | 05 |
| 403 | Pedro Guerrero | 08 |
| 404 | Todd Zeile | 08 |
| 405 | Gerald Perry | 05 |
| 406 | Donovan Osborne (R) | 12 |
| 407 | Bryn Smith | 05 |
| 408 | Bernard Gilkey | 15 |
| 409 | Rex Hudler | 05 |
| 410 | Thomson/Branca | 10 |
|     | shot heard rd. the world. | |
| 411 | Lance Dickson (R) | 20 |
| 412 | Danny Jackson | 05 |
| 413 | Jerome Walton | 08 |
| 414 | Sean Cheetham (R) | 12 |
| 415 | Joe Girardi | 05 |
| 416 | Ryne Sandberg | 15 |
| 417 | Mike Harkey | 05 |
| 418 | George Bell | 08 |
| 419 | Rick Wilkins (R) | 20 |
| 420 | Earl Cunningham | 05 |
| 421 | Heathcliff Slocumb (R) | 12 |
| 422 | Mike Bielecki | 05 |
| 423 | Jessie Hollins (R) | 12 |
| 424 | Shawon Dunston | 08 |
| 425 | Dave Smith | 05 |
| 426 | Greg Maddux | 05 |
| 427 | Jose Vizcaino | 05 |
| 428 | Luis Salazar | 05 |
| 429 | Andre Dawson | 12 |
| 430 | Rick Sutcliffe | 08 |
| 431 | Paul Assenmacher | 05 |
| 432 | Erik Pappas (R) | 12 |
| 433 | Mark Grace | 08 |
| 434 | Denny Martinez | 05 |
| 435 | Marquis Grissom | 08 |
| 436 | Wilfredo Cordero (R) | 20 |
| 437 | Tim Wallach | 05 |
| 438 | Brian Barnes (R) | 10 |
| 439 | Barry Jones | 05 |
| 440 | Ivan Calderon | 05 |
| 441 | Stan Spencer (R) | 10 |
| 442 | Larry Walker | 12 |
| 443 | Chris Haney (R) | 12 |
| 444 | Hector Rivera (R) | 12 |
| 445 | Delino DeShields | 08 |
| 446 | Andres Galarraga | 05 |
| 447 | Gilberto Reyes | 05 |
| 448 | Willie Greene | 05 |
| 449 | Greg Colbrunn (R) | 12 |
| 450 | Rondell White (R) | 25 |
| 451 | Steve Frey | 05 |
| 452 | Shane Andrews (R) | 20 |
| 453 | Mike Fitzgerald | 05 |

| NO. | PLAYER | MINT |
|-----|--------|------|
| 454 | Spike Owen | 05 |
| 455 | Dave Martinez | 05 |
| 456 | Dennis Boyd | 05 |
| 457 | Eric Bullock | 05 |
| 458 | Reid Cornelius (R) | 15 |
| 459 | Chris Nabholz | 05 |
| 460 | David Cone | 08 |
| 461 | Hubie Brooks | 05 |
| 462 | Sid Fernandez | 05 |
| 463 | Doug Simons (R) | 12 |
| 464 | Howard Johnson | 08 |
| 465 | Chris Donnels | 05 |
| 466 | Anthony Young (R) | 15 |
| 467 | Todd Hundley | 08 |
| 468 | Rick Cerone | 05 |
| 469 | Kevin Elster | 05 |
| 470 | Wally Whitehurst | 05 |
| 471 | Vince Coleman | 10 |
| 472 | Doc Gooden | 15 |
| 473 | Charlie O'Brien | 05 |
| 474 | Jeromy Burnitz (R) | 60 |
| 475 | John Franco | 05 |
| 476 | Daryl Boston | 05 |
| 477 | Frank Viola | 08 |
| 478 | D.J. Dozier | 10 |
| 479 | Kevin McReynolds | 08 |
| 480 | Tom Herr | 05 |
| 481 | Gregg Jefferies | 08 |
| 482 | Pete Schourek (R) | 12 |
| 483 | Ron Darling | 05 |
| 484 | Dave Magadan | 05 |
| 485 | Andy Ashby (R) | 12 |
| 486 | Dale Murphy | 08 |
| 487 | Von Hayes | 05 |
| 488 | Kim Batiste (R) | 12 |
| 489 | Tony Longmire (R) | 25 |
| 490 | Wally Backman | 05 |
| 491 | Jeff Jackson | 05 |
| 492 | Mickey Morandini | 05 |
| 493 | Darrel Akerfelds | 05 |
| 494 | Ricky Jordan | 05 |
| 495 | Randy Ready | 05 |
| 496 | Darrin Fletcher | 05 |
| 497 | Chuck Malone | 05 |
| 498 | Pat Combs | 05 |
| 499 | Dickie Thon | 05 |
| 500 | Roger McDowell | 05 |
| 501 | Len Dykstra | 08 |
| 502 | Joe Boever | 05 |
| 503 | John Kruk | 08 |
| 504 | Terry Mulholland | 05 |
| 505 | Wes Chamberlain (R) | 40 |
| 506 | Mike Lieberthal (R) | 15 |
| 507 | Darren Daulton | 05 |
| 508 | Charlie Hayes | 05 |
| 509 | John Smiley | 05 |
| 510 | Gary Varsho | 05 |
| 511 | Curt Wilkerson | 05 |
| 512 | Orlando Mercedi (R) | 30 |
| 513 | Barry Bonds | 12 |
| 514 | Mike Lavalliere | 05 |
| 515 | Doug Drabek | 08 |
| 516 | Gary Redus | 05 |
| 517 | W. Pennyfeather (R) | 20 |
| 518 | Randy Tomlin (R) | 20 |
| 519 | Mike Zimmerman (R) | 12 |
| 520 | Jeff King | 05 |
| 521 | Kurt Miller (R) | 15 |
| 522 | Jay Bell | 05 |
| 523 | Bill Landrum | 05 |
| 524 | Zane Smith | 05 |
| 525 | Bobby Bonilla | 15 |
| 526 | Bob Walk | 05 |
| 527 | Austin Manahan | 05 |
| 528 | Joe Ausanio (R) | 12 |
| 529 | Andy Van Slyke | 08 |
| 530 | Jose Lind | 05 |
| 531 | Carlos Garcia (R) | 12 |
| 532 | Don Slaught | 05 |
| 533 | Colin Powell | 15 |
|     | opening day Yank. Stad. | |

**No. 534 to 538—Gold Foil**

| NO. | PLAYER | MINT |
|-----|--------|------|
| 534 | Frank Bolick (R) | 20 |
| 535 | Gary Scott (R) | 25 |
| 536 | Nikco Riesgo (R) | 35 |

| NO. | PLAYER | MINT |
|-----|--------|------|
| 537 | Reggie Sanders (R) | 50 |
| 538 | Tim Howard (R) | 25 |
| 539 | Ryan Bowen (R) | 12 |
| 540 | Eric Anthony | 08 |
| 541 | Jim Deshales | 05 |
| 542 | Tom Nevers (R) | 12 |
| 543 | Ken Caminiti | 05 |
| 544 | Karl Rhodes | 08 |
| 545 | Xavier Hernandez | 05 |
| 546 | Mike Scott | 05 |
| 547 | Jeff Juden | 05 |
| 548 | Darryl Kile | 05 |
| 549 | Willie Ansley | 05 |
| 550 | Luis Gonzalez (R) | 50 |
| 551 | Mike Simms | 12 |
| 552 | Mark Portugal | 05 |
| 553 | Jimmy Jones | 05 |
| 554 | Jim Clancy | 05 |
| 555 | Pete Harnisch | 05 |
| 556 | Craig Biggio | 08 |
| 557 | Eric Yelding | 05 |
| 558 | Dave Rohde | 05 |
| 559 | Casey Candaele | 05 |
| 560 | Curt Schilling | 05 |
| 561 | Steve Finely | 05 |
| 562 | Javier Ortiz | 05 |
| 563 | Andujar Cedeno | 15 |
| 564 | Rafael Ramirez | 05 |
| 565 | Kenny Lofton (R) | 25 |
| 566 | Steve Avery | 30 |
| 567 | Lonnie Smith | 05 |
| 568 | Kent Mercker | 05 |
| 569 | Chipper Jones (R) | 35 |
| 570 | Terry Pendleton | 08 |
| 571 | Otis Nixon | 08 |
| 572 | Juan Berenguer | 05 |
| 573 | Charlie Liebrandt | 08 |
| 574 | David Justice | 35 |
| 575 | Keith Mitchell (R) | 30 |
| 576 | Tom Glavine | 12 |
| 577 | Greg Olson | 05 |
| 578 | Rafael Belliard | 05 |
| 579 | Ben Rivera (R) | 12 |
| 580 | John Smoltz | 10 |
| 581 | Tyler Houston | 35 |
| 582 | Mark Wohlers (R) | 35 |
| 583 | Ron Gant | 15 |
| 584 | Ramon Caraballo (R) | 12 |
| 585 | Sid Bream | 05 |
| 586 | Jeff Treadway | 05 |
| 587 | Javier Lopez (R) | 12 |
| 588 | Deion Sanders | 08 |
| 589 | Mike Heath | 05 |
| 590 | Ryan Klesko (R) | 1.00 |
| 591 | Bob Ojeda | 05 |
| 592 | Alfredo Griffin | 05 |
| 593 | Raul Mondesi (R) | 20 |
| 594 | Greg Smith | 05 |
| 595 | Orel Hershiser | 08 |
| 596 | Juan Samuel | 05 |
| 597 | Brett Butler | 08 |
| 598 | Gary Carter | 08 |
| 599 | Stan Javier | 05 |
| 600 | Kal Daniels | 08 |
| 601 | Jamie McAndrew (R) | 12 |
| 602 | Mike Sharperson | 05 |
| 603 | Jay Howell | 05 |
| 604 | Eric Karros (R) | 35 |
| 605 | Tim Belcher | 05 |
| 606 | Dan Opperman (R) | 12 |
| 607 | Lenny Harris | 05 |
| 608 | Tom Goodwin | 05 |
| 609 | Darryl Strawberry | 15 |
| 610 | Ramon Martinez | 10 |
| 611 | Kevin Gross | 05 |
| 612 | Zakary Shinall (R) | 12 |
| 613 | Mike Scioscia | 05 |
| 614 | Eddie Murray | 12 |
| 615 | Ronnie Walden (R) | 12 |
| 616 | Will Clark | 15 |
| 617 | Adam Hyzdu (R) | 15 |
| 618 | Matt Williams | 08 |
| 619 | Don Robinson | 05 |
| 620 | Jeff Brantley | 05 |
| 621 | Greg Litton | 05 |

| NO. | PLAYER | MINT |
|-----|--------|------|
| 622 | Steve Decker (R) | 20 |
| 623 | Robby Thompson | 05 |
| 624 | Mark Leonard (R) | 15 |
| 625 | Kevin Bass | 05 |
| 626 | Scott Garrelts | 05 |
| 627 | Jose Uribe | 05 |
| 628 | Eric Gunderson | 05 |
| 629 | Steve Hosey | 05 |
| 630 | Trevor Wilson | 05 |
| 631 | Terry Kennedy | 05 |
| 632 | Dave Righetti | 05 |
| 633 | Kelly Downs | 05 |
| 634 | Johnny Ard | 05 |
| 635 | E. Christopherson (R) | 12 |
| 636 | Kevin Mitchell | 10 |
| 637 | John Burkett | 05 |
| 638 | Kevin Rogers (R) | 12 |
| 639 | Bud Black | 05 |
| 640 | Willie McGee | 05 |
| 641 | Royce Clayton | 12 |
| 642 | Tony Fernandez | 05 |
| 643 | Ricky Bones (R) | 12 |
| 644 | Thomas Howard | 05 |
| 645 | Dave Staton (R) | 15 |
| 646 | Jim Presley | 05 |
| 647 | Tony Gwynn | 12 |
| 648 | Marty Barrett | 05 |
| 649 | Scott Coolbaugh | 05 |
| 650 | Craig Lefferts | 05 |
| 651 | Eddie Whitson | 05 |
| 652 | Oscar Azocar | 05 |
| 653 | Wes Gardner | 05 |
| 654 | Bip Roberts | 05 |
| 655 | Robbie Beckett (R) | 12 |
| 656 | Benny Santiago | 08 |
| 657 | Greg W. Harris | 05 |
| 658 | Jerald Clark | 05 |
| 659 | Fred McGriff | 10 |
| 660 | Larry Anderson | 05 |
| 661 | Bruce Hurst | 05 |
| 662 | Steve Martin (R) | 12 |
| 663 | Rafael Valdez | 05 |
| 664 | Paul Faries (R) | 12 |
| 665 | Andy Benes | 05 |
| 666 | Randy Myers | 05 |
| 667 | Rob Dibble | 05 |
| 668 | Glenn Sutko (R) | 12 |
| 669 | Glenn Braggs | 05 |
| 670 | Billy Hatcher | 05 |
| 671 | Joe Oliver | 05 |
| 672 | Freddie Benavides (R) | 12 |
| 673 | Barry Larkin | 08 |
| 674 | Chris Sabo | 08 |
| 675 | Mariano Duncan | 05 |
| 676 | Chris Jones (R) | 20 |
| 677 | Gino Minutelli (R) | 12 |
| 678 | Reggie Jefferson | 10 |
| 679 | Jack Armstrong | 05 |
| 680 | Chris Hammond | 05 |
| 681 | Jose Rijo | 05 |
| 682 | Bill Doran | 05 |
| 683 | Terry Lee (R) | 12 |
| 684 | Tom Browning | 05 |
| 685 | Paul O'Neill | 05 |
| 686 | Eric Davis | 10 |
| 687 | Dan Wilson (R) | 12 |
| 688 | Ted Power | 05 |
| 689 | Tim Layana | 05 |
| 690 | Norm Charlton | 05 |
| 691 | Hal Morris | 05 |
| 692 | Rickey Henderson | 15 |
|     | 938th stolen base | |

**No. 693 to 698—Gold Foil**

| NO. | PLAYER | MINT |
|-----|--------|------|
| 693 | Sam Militello (R) | 20 |
| 694 | Matt Mieske (R) | 40 |
| 695 | Paul Russo (R) | 20 |
| 696 | Domingo Mota (R) | 25 |
| 697 | Todd Guggiana (R) | 20 |
| 698 | Marc Newfeld (R) | 75 |
| 699 | Checklist I | 05 |
| 700 | Checklist II | 05 |
| 701 | Checklist III | 05 |
| 702 | Checklist IV | 05 |
| 703 | Checklist V | 05 |
| 704 | Checklist VI | 05 |

# 1981 Donruss . . . Complete Set of 605 Cards—Value $65.00

This was Donruss' *first* baseball card set. Over 35 cards contained *errors*; they were corrected in the 2nd printing run. There is very little interest by collectors in the *variety* (error) cards; none are scarce or worth much more than ordinary cards. If a *variety* (error) is significant, it is listed and explained; if it is *minor*, it is noted by an *asterisk*. This set features the rookie cards of Tim Raines and Leon Durham. The 2½"x3½" cards were printed on thinner than usual paper stock. The checklist *cards* are *not* numbered.

MOOKIE WILSON SHORTSTOP

JEFF REARDON PITCHER

LEON DURHAM INFIELD-O-F

JOHN TUDOR PITCHER

TIM RAINES SECOND BASE

| NO. PLAYER | MINT | NO. PLAYER | MINT | NO. PLAYER | MINT | NO. PLAYER | MINT |
|---|---|---|---|---|---|---|---|
| 1 Ozzie Smith | 2.50 | 65 George Foster | .20 | 131 Pete Rose* | 1.50 | 197 Rick Camp | .05 |
| 2 Rollie Fingers | .75 | 66 Jeff Burroughs | .05 | 132 Willie Stargell | .50 | 198 Andre Thornton | .10 |
| 3 Rick Wise | .05 | 67 Keith Hernandez | .40 | 133 Ed Ott | .05 | 199 Tom Veryzer | .05 |
| 4 Gene Richards | .05 | 68 Tommy Herr | .15 | 134 Jim Bibby | .05 | 200 Gary Alexander | .05 |
| 5 Alan Trammell | .75 | 69 Bob Forsch | .05 | 135 Bert Blyleven | .30 | 201 Rick Waits | .05 |
| 6 Tom Brookens | .05 | 70 John Fulgham | .05 | 136 Dave Parker | .50 | 202 Rick Manning | .05 |
| 7 Duffy Dyer* | .05 | 71 Bobby Bonds* | .12 | 137 Bill Robinson | .05 | 203 Paul Molitor | .50 |
| 8 Mark Fidrych | .08 | 72 Rennie Stennett* | .10 | 138 Enos Cabell | .05 | 204 Jim Gantner | .05 |
| 9 Dave Rozema | .05 | 73 Joe Strain | .05 | 139 Dave Bergman | .05 | 205 Paul Mitchell | .05 |
| 10 Ricky Peters | .05 | 74 Ed Whitson | .10 | 140 J.R. Richard | .05 | 206 Reggie Cleveland | .05 |
| 11 Mike Schmidt | 2.50 | 75 Tom Griffin | .05 | 141 Ken Forsch | .05 | 207 Sixto Lezcano | .05 |
| 12 Willie Stargell | .50 | 76 Bill North | .05 | 142 Larry Bowa | .05 | 208 Bruce Benedict | .05 |
| 13 Tim Foli | .05 | 77 Gene Garber | .05 | 143 Frank LaCorte | .05 | 209 Rodney Scott | .05 |
| 14 Manny Sanguillen | .05 | 78 Mike Hargrove | .05 | 144 Dennis Walling | .05 | 210 John Tamargo | .05 |
| 15 Grant Jackson | .05 | 79 Dave Rosello | .05 | 145 Buddy Bell | .10 | 211 Bill Lee | .05 |
| 16 Eddie Solomon | .05 | 80 Ron Hassey | .05 | 146 Ferguson Jenkins | .40 | 212 Andre Dawson | 1.50 |
| 17 Omar Moreno | .05 | 81 Sid Monge | .05 | 147 Danny Darwin | .05 | 213 Rowland Office | .05 |
| 18 Joe Morgan | .75 | 82 Joe Charboneau* | .10 | 148 Johnny Grubb | .05 | 214 Carl Yastrzemski | 1.50 |
| 19 Rafael Landestoy | .05 | 83 Cecil Cooper | .20 | 149 Alfredo Griffin | .05 | 215 Jerry Remy | .05 |
| 20 Bruce Bochy | .05 | 84 Sal Bando | .05 | 150 Jerry Garvin | .05 | 216 Mike Torrez | .05 |
| 21 Joe Sambito | .05 | 85 Moose Haas | .05 | 151 Paul Mirabella | .05 | 217 Skip Lockwood | .05 |
| 22 Manny Trillo | .05 | 86 Mike Caldwell | .05 | 152 Rick Bosetti | .05 | 218 Fred Lynn | .25 |
| 23 Dave Smith* (R) | .35 | 87 Larry Hisle* | .10 | 153 Dick Ruthven | .05 | 219 Chris Chambliss | .08 |
| 24 Terry Puhl | .05 | 88 Luis Gomez | .05 | 154 Frank Taveras | .05 | 220 Willie Aikens | .05 |
| 25 Bump Wills | .05 | 89 Larry Parrish | .10 | 155 Craig Swan | .05 | 221 John Wathan | .05 |
| 26 John Ellis (error) | .50 | 90 Gary Carter | .50 | 156 Jeff Reardon (R) | 3.00 | 222 Dan Quisenberry | .20 |
| (photo of Danny Walten) | | 91 Bill Gullickson (R) | .40 | 157 Steve Henderson | .05 | 223 Willie Wilson | .15 |
| 26 John Ellis (correct) | .10 | 92 Fred Norman | .05 | 158 Jim Morrison | .05 | 224 Clint Hurdle | .05 |
| 27 Jim Kern | .05 | 93 Tom Hutton | .05 | 159 Glenn Borgmann | .05 | 225 Bob Watson | .05 |
| 28 Richie Zisk | .05 | 94 Carl Yastrzemski | 1.25 | 160 LaMarr Hoyt | .12 | 226 Jim Spencer | .05 |
| 29 John Mayberry | .05 | 95 Glenn Hoffman | .08 | 161 Rich Wortham | .05 | 227 Ron Guidry | .25 |
| 30 Bob Davis | .05 | 96 Dennis Eckersley | .50 | 162 Thad Bosley | .05 | 228 Reggie Jackson | 2.00 |
| 31 Jackson Todd | .05 | 97 Tom Burgmeier* | .10 | 163 Julio Cruz | .05 | 229 Oscar Gamble | .05 |
| 32 Al Woods | .05 | 98 Win Remmerswaal | .05 | 164 Del Unser* | .05 | 230 Jeff Cox | .05 |
| 33 Steve Carlton | 1.25 | 99 Bob Horner | .15 | 165 Jim Anderson | .05 | 231 Luis Tiant | .05 |
| 34 Lee Mazzilli | .05 | 100 George Brett | 2.00 | 166 Jim Beattie | .05 | 232 Rich Dauer | .05 |
| 35 John Stearns | .05 | 101 Dave Chalk | .05 | 167 Shane Rawley | .05 | 233 Dan Graham | .05 |
| 36 Roy Jackson | .08 | 102 Dennis Leonard | .05 | 168 Joe Simpson | .05 | 234 Mike Flanagan | .05 |
| 37 Mike Scott | .50 | 103 Renie Martin | .05 | 169 Rod Carew | 1.25 | 235 John Lowenstein | .05 |
| 38 Lamar Johnson | .05 | 104 Amos Otis | .05 | 170 Freddie Patek | .05 | 236 Benny Ayala | .05 |
| 39 Kevin Bell | .05 | 105 Graig Nettles | .15 | 171 Frank Tanana | .05 | 237 Wayne Gross | .05 |
| 40 Ed Farmer | .05 | 106 Eric Soderholm | .05 | 172 Alfredo Martinez | .05 | 238 Rick Langford | .05 |
| 41 Ross Baumgarten | .05 | 107 Tommy John | .20 | 173 Chris Knapp | .05 | 239 Tony Armas | .20 |
| 42 Leo Sutherland | .05 | 108 Tom Underwood | .05 | 174 Joe Rudi | .05 | 240 Bob Lacey* | .10 |
| 43 Danny Meyer | .05 | 109 Lou Piniella | .15 | 175 Greg Luzinski | .10 | 241 Gene Tenace | .05 |
| 44 Ron Reed | .05 | 110 Mickey Klutts | .05 | 176 Steve Garvey | .75 | 242 Bob Shirley | .05 |
| 45 Mario Mendoza | .05 | 111 Bobby Murcer | .10 | 177 Joe Ferguson | .05 | 243 Gary Lucas | .05 |
| 46 Rick Honeycutt | .05 | 112 Eddie Murray | 2.00 | 178 Bob Welch | .40 | 244 Jerry Turner | .05 |
| 47 Glenn Abbott | .05 | 113 Rick Dempsey | .05 | 179 Dusty Baker | .10 | 245 John Wockenfuss | .05 |
| 48 Leon Roberts | .05 | 114 Scott McGregor | .05 | 180 Rudy Law | .05 | 246 Stan Papi | .05 |
| 49 Rod Carew | 1.25 | 115 Ken Singleton | .05 | 181 Dave Concepcion | .15 | 247 Milt Wilcox | .05 |
| 50 Bert Campaneris | .05 | 116 Gary Roenicke | .05 | 182 Johnny Bench | 1.25 | 248 Dan Schatzeder | .05 |
| 51 Tom Donohue* | .10 | 117 Dave Revering | .05 | 183 Mike LaCoss | .05 | 249 Steve Kemp | .08 |
| 52 Dave Frost | .05 | 118 Mike Norris | .05 | 184 Ken Griffey | .25 | 250 Jim Lentine | .05 |
| 53 Ed Halicki | .05 | 119 Rickey Henderson | 20.00 | 185 Dave Collins | .05 | 251 Pete Rose | 1.50 |
| 54 Dan Ford | .05 | 120 Mike Heath | .05 | 186 Brian Asselstine | .05 | 252 Bill Madlock | .25 |
| 55 Garry Maddox | .05 | 121 Dave Cash | .05 | 187 Garry Templeton | .10 | 253 Dale Berra | .05 |
| 56 Steve Garvey* | .75 | 122 Randy Jones | .05 | 188 Mike Phillips | .05 | 254 Kent Tekulve | .05 |
| 57 Bill Russell | .05 | 123 Eric Rasmussen | .05 | 189 Pete Vuckovich | .08 | 255 Enrique Romo | .05 |
| 58 Don Sutton | .50 | 124 Jerry Mumphrey | .05 | 190 John Urrea | .05 | 256 Mike Easler | .05 |
| 59 Reggie Smith | .10 | 125 Richie Hebner | .05 | 191 Tony Scott | .05 | 257 Chuck Tanner (Mgr.) | .05 |
| 60 Rick Monday | .05 | 126 Mark Wagner | .05 | 192 Darrell Evans | .10 | 258 Art Howe | .05 |
| 61 Ray Knight | .05 | 127 Jack Morris | .75 | 193 Milt May | .05 | 259 Alan Ashby | .05 |
| 62 Johnny Bench | 1.25 | 128 Dan Petry | .25 | 194 Bob Knepper | .05 | 260 Nolan Ryan | 5.00 |
| 63 Mario Soto | .15 | 129 Bruce Robbins | .05 | 195 Randy Moffitt | .05 | 261 Vern Ruhle (error) | .50 |
| 64 Doug Bair | .05 | 130 Champ Summers | .05 | 196 Larry Herndon | .05 | (Photo of Ken Forsch) | |

| NO. | PLAYER | MINT |
|---|---|---|
| 261 | Vern Ruhle (correct) | .10 |
| 262 | Bob Boone | .08 |
| 263 | Cesar Cedeno | .08 |
| 264 | Jeff Leonard | .15 |
| 265 | Pat Putnam | .05 |
| 266 | John Matlack | .05 |
| 267 | Dave Rajsich | .05 |
| 268 | Billy Sample | .05 |
| 269 | Damaso Garcia (R) | .15 |
| 270 | Tom Buskey | .05 |
| 271 | Joey McLaughlin | .05 |
| 272 | Barry Bonnell | .05 |
| 273 | Tug McGraw | .08 |
| 274 | Mike Jorgensen | .05 |
| 275 | Pat Zachry | .05 |
| 276 | Neil Allen | .05 |
| 277 | Joel Youngblood | .05 |
| 278 | Greg Pryor | .05 |
| 279 | Britt Burns (R) | .15 |
| 280 | Rich Dotson (R) | .20 |
| 281 | Chet Lemon | .10 |
| 282 | Rusty Kuntz | .05 |
| 283 | Ted Cox | .05 |
| 284 | Sparky Lyle | .08 |
| 285 | Larry Cox | .05 |
| 286 | Floyd Bannister | .05 |
| 287 | Byron McLaughlin | .05 |
| 288 | Rodney Craig | .05 |
| 289 | Bob Grich | .08 |
| 290 | Dickie Thon | .10 |
| 291 | Mark Clear | .05 |
| 292 | Dave Lemanczyk | .05 |
| 293 | Jason Thompson | .05 |
| 294 | Rick Miller | .05 |
| 295 | Lonnie Smith | .30 |
| 296 | Ron Cey | .15 |
| 297 | Steve Yeager | .05 |
| 298 | Bobby Castillo | .05 |
| 299 | Manny Mota | .05 |
| 300 | Jay Johnstone | .05 |
| 301 | Dan Driessen | .05 |
| 302 | Joe Nolan | .05 |
| 303 | Paul Householder | .10 |
| 304 | Harry Spilman | .05 |
| 305 | Cesar Geronimo | .05 |
| 306 | Gary Matthews* | .10 |
| 307 | Ken Reitz | .05 |
| 308 | Ted Simmons | .20 |
| 309 | John Littlefield | .05 |
| 310 | George Frazier | .05 |
| 311 | Dane Iorg | .05 |
| 312 | Mike Ivie | .05 |
| 313 | Dennis Littlejohn | .05 |
| 314 | Gary LaVelle | .05 |
| 315 | Jack Clark | .30 |
| 316 | Jim Wohlford | .05 |
| 317 | Rick Matula | .05 |
| 318 | Toby Harrah | .05 |
| 319 | Duane Kuiper* | .10 |
| 320 | Len Barker | .05 |
| 321 | Victor Cruz | .05 |
| 322 | Dell Alston | .05 |
| 323 | Robin Yount | 2.50 |
| 324 | Charlie Moore | .05 |
| 325 | Lary Sorensen | .05 |
| 326 | Gorman Thomas* | .15 |
| 327 | Bob Rodgers | .05 |
| 328 | Phil Niekro | .50 |
| 329 | Chris Speier | .05 |
| 330 | Steve Rogers* | .10 |
| 331 | Woodie Fryman | .05 |
| 332 | Warren Cromartie | .05 |
| 333 | Jerry White | .05 |
| 334 | Tony Perez | .35 |
| 335 | Carlton Fisk | 1.25 |
| 336 | Dick Drago | .05 |
| 337 | Steve Renko | .05 |
| 338 | Jim Rice | .25 |
| 339 | Jerry Royster | .05 |
| 340 | Frank White | .05 |
| 341 | Jamie Quirk | .05 |
| 342 | Paul Splittorff* | .10 |
| 343 | Marty Pattin | .05 |
| 344 | Pete LaCock | .05 |
| 345 | Willie Randolph | .15 |
| 346 | Rick Cerone | .05 |
| 347 | Rich Gossage | .20 |
| 348 | Reggie Jackson | 2.00 |
| 349 | Ruppert Jones | .05 |
| 350 | Dave McKay | .05 |
| 351 | Yogi Berra | .25 |
| 352 | Doug DeCinces | .12 |
| 353 | Jim Palmer | 1.00 |
| 354 | Tippy Martinez | .05 |
| 355 | Al Bumbry | .05 |
| 356 | Earl Weaver (Mgr.) | .10 |
| 357 | Rob Picciolo* | .10 |
| 358 | Matt Keough | .05 |
| 359 | Dwayne Murphy | .05 |
| 360 | Brian Kingman | .05 |
| 361 | Bill Fahey | .05 |
| 362 | Steve Mura | .05 |
| 363 | Dennis Kinney | .05 |
| 364 | Dave Winfield | 1.00 |
| 365 | Lou Whitaker | .50 |
| 366 | Lance Parrish | .30 |
| 367 | Tim Corcoran | .05 |
| 368 | Pat Underwood | .05 |
| 369 | Al Cowens | .05 |
| 370 | Sparky Anderson (Mgr.) | .05 |
| 371 | Pete Rose | 1.50 |
| 372 | Phil Garner | .05 |
| 373 | Steve Nicosia | .05 |
| 374 | John Candelaria | .05 |
| 375 | Don Robinson | .05 |
| 376 | Lee Lacy | .05 |
| 377 | John Milner | .05 |
| 378 | Craig Reynolds | .05 |
| 379 | Luis Pujols* | .10 |
| 380 | Joe Niekro | .10 |
| 381 | Joaquin Andujar | .10 |
| 382 | Keith Moreland (R) | .15 |
| 383 | Jose Cruz | .15 |
| 384 | Bill Virdon (Mgr.) | .05 |
| 385 | Jim Sundberg | .05 |
| 386 | Doc Medich | .05 |
| 387 | Al Oliver | .15 |
| 388 | Jim Norris | .05 |
| 389 | Bob Bailor | .05 |
| 390 | Ernie Whitt | .05 |
| 391 | Otto Velez | .05 |
| 392 | Roy Howell | .05 |
| 393 | Bob Walk | .25 |
| 394 | Doug Flynn | .05 |
| 395 | Pete Falcone | .05 |
| 396 | Tom Hausman | .05 |
| 397 | Elliott Maddox | .05 |
| 398 | Mike Squires | .05 |
| 399 | Marvis Foley | .05 |
| 400 | Steve Trout | .05 |
| 401 | Wayne Nordhagen | .05 |
| 402 | Tony LaRussa (Mgr.) | .05 |
| 403 | Bruce Bochte | .05 |
| 404 | Bake McBride | .05 |
| 405 | Jerry Narron | .05 |
| 406 | Rob Dressler | .05 |
| 407 | Dave Heaverlo | .05 |
| 408 | Tom Paciorek | .05 |
| 409 | Carney Lansford | .20 |
| 410 | Brian Downing | .05 |
| 411 | Don Aase | .05 |
| 412 | Jim Barr | .05 |
| 413 | Don Baylor | .20 |
| 414 | Jim Fregosi (Mgr.) | .05 |
| 415 | Dallas Green (Mgr.) | .05 |
| 416 | Dave Lopes | .10 |
| 417 | Jerry Reuss | .05 |
| 418 | Rick Sutcliffe | .20 |
| 419 | Derrel Thomas | .05 |
| 420 | Tommy Lasorda (Mgr.) | .15 |
| 421 | Charlie Leibrandt (R) | .40 |
| 422 | Tom Seaver | 1.50 |
| 423 | Ron Oester | .05 |
| 424 | Junior Kennedy | .05 |
| 425 | Tom Seaver | 1.50 |
| 426 | Bobby Cox (Mgr.) | .05 |
| 427 | Leon Durham (R) | .30 |
| 428 | Terry Kennedy | .10 |
| 429 | Silvio Martinez | .05 |
| 430 | George Hendrick | .05 |
| 431 | R. Schoendienst (Mgr.) | .10 |
| 432 | John LeMaster | .05 |
| 433 | Vida Blue | .05 |
| 434 | John Montefusco | .05 |
| 435 | Terry Whitfield | .05 |
| 436 | Dave Bristol (Mgr.) | .05 |
| 437 | Dale Murphy | 1.00 |
| 438 | Jerry Dybzinski | .05 |
| 439 | Jorge Orta | .05 |
| 440 | Wayne Garland | .05 |
| 441 | Miguel Dilone | .05 |
| 442 | Dave Garcia (Mgr.) | .05 |
| 443 | Don Money | .05 |
| 444 | Buck Martinez* | .10 |
| 445 | Jerry Augustine | .05 |
| 446 | Ben Oglivie | .10 |
| 447 | Jim Slaton | .05 |
| 448 | Doyle Alexander | .05 |
| 449 | Tony Bernazard | .05 |
| 450 | Scott Sanderson | .05 |
| 451 | Dave Palmer | .05 |
| 452 | Stan Bahnsen | .05 |
| 453 | Dick Williams (Mgr.) | .05 |
| 454 | Rick Burleson | .05 |
| 455 | Gary Allenson | .05 |
| 456 | Bob Stanley | .05 |
| 457 | John Tudor (R) | .75 |
| 458 | Dwight Evans | .40 |
| 459 | Glenn Hubbard | .05 |
| 460 | U.L. Washington | .05 |
| 461 | Larry Gura | .05 |
| 462 | Rich Gale | .05 |
| 463 | Hal McRae | .05 |
| 464 | Jim Frey (Mgr.) | .05 |
| 465 | Bucky Dent | .05 |
| 466 | Dennis Werth | .05 |
| 467 | Ron Davis | .05 |
| 468 | Reggie Jackson | 2.00 |
| 469 | Bobby Brown | .05 |
| 470 | Mike Davis (R) | .15 |
| 471 | Gaylord Perry | .50 |
| 472 | Mark Belanger | .05 |
| 473 | Jim Palmer | 1.00 |
| 474 | Sammy Stewart | .05 |
| 475 | Tim Stoddard | .05 |
| 476 | Steve Stone | .05 |
| 477 | Jeff Newman | .05 |
| 478 | Steve McCatty | .05 |
| 479 | Billy Martin (Mgr.) | .15 |
| 480 | Mitchell Page | .05 |
| 481 | S. Carlton (Cy Young) | .50 |
| 482 | Bill Buckner | .15 |
| 483 | Ivan DeJesus* | .10 |
| 484 | Cliff Johnson | .05 |
| 485 | Lenny Randle | .05 |
| 486 | Larry Milbourne | .05 |
| 487 | Roy Smalley | .05 |
| 488 | John Castino | .05 |
| 489 | Ron Jackson | .05 |
| 490 | Dave Roberts* | .05 |
| 491 | George Brett (MVP) | 1.50 |
| 492 | Mike Cubbage | .05 |
| 493 | Rob Wilfong | .05 |
| 494 | Danny Goodwin | .05 |
| 495 | Jose Morales | .05 |
| 496 | Mickey Rivers | .05 |
| 497 | Mike Edwards | .05 |
| 498 | Mike Sadek | .05 |
| 499 | Lenn Sakata | .05 |
| 500 | Gene Michael (Mgr.) | .05 |
| 501 | Dave Roberts | .05 |
| 502 | Steve Dillard | .05 |
| 503 | Jim Essian | .05 |
| 504 | Rance Mulliniks | .05 |
| 505 | Darrell Porter | .10 |
| 506 | Joe Torre (Mgr.) | .05 |
| 507 | Terry Crowley | .05 |
| 508 | Bill Travers | .05 |
| 509 | Nelson Norman | .05 |
| 510 | Bob McClure | .05 |
| 511 | Steve Howe (R) | .15 |
| 512 | Dave Rader | .05 |
| 513 | Mick Kelleher | .05 |
| 514 | Kiko Garcia | .05 |
| 515 | Larry Biittner | .05 |
| 516 | Willie Norwood* | .05 |
| 517 | Bo Diaz | .10 |
| 518 | Juan Beniquez | .05 |
| 519 | Scot Thompson | .05 |
| 520 | Jim Tracy | .05 |
| 521 | Carlos Lezcano | .05 |
| 522 | Joe Amalfitano | .05 |
| 523 | Preston Hanna | .05 |
| 524 | Ray Burris* | .10 |
| 525 | Broderick Perkins | .05 |
| 526 | Mickey Hatcher | .05 |
| 527 | John Goryl (Mgr.) | .05 |
| 528 | Dick Davis | .05 |
| 529 | Butch Wynegar | .05 |
| 530 | Sal Butera | .05 |
| 531 | Jerry Koosman | .05 |
| 532 | Jeff Zahn* | .10 |
| 533 | Dennis Martinez | .25 |
| 534 | Gary Thomasson | .05 |
| 535 | Steve Macko | .05 |
| 536 | Jim Kaat | .20 |
| 537 | Best Hitters: George Brett, Rod Care | 2.00 |
| 538 | Tim Raines (R) | 6.00 |
| 539 | Keith Smith | .05 |
| 540 | Ken Macha | .05 |
| 541 | Burt Hooton | .05 |
| 542 | Butch Hobson | .05 |
| 543 | Bill Stein | .05 |
| 544 | Dave Stapleton (R) | .15 |
| 545 | Bob Pate | .05 |
| 546 | Doug Corbett | .12 |
| 547 | Darrell Jackson | .05 |
| 548 | Pete Redfern | .05 |
| 549 | Roger Erickson | .05 |
| 550 | Al Hrabosky | .05 |
| 551 | Dick Tidrow | .05 |
| 552 | Dave Ford | .05 |
| 553 | Dave Kingman | .15 |
| 554 | Mike Vail* | .10 |
| 555 | Jerry Martin* | .10 |
| 556 | Jesus Figueroa* | .10 |
| 557 | Don Stanhouse | .05 |
| 558 | Barry Foote | .05 |
| 559 | Tim Blackwell | .05 |
| 560 | Bruce Sutter | .25 |
| 561 | Rick Reuschel | .05 |
| 562 | Lynn McGlothen | .05 |
| 563 | Bob Owchinko* | .10 |
| 564 | John Verhoeven | .05 |
| 565 | Ken Landreaux | .05 |
| 566 | Glenn Adams* | .10 |
| 567 | Hosken Powell | .05 |
| 568 | Dick Noles | .05 |
| 569 | Danny Ainge (R) | 1.00 |
| 570 | Bobby Mattick (Mgr.) | .05 |
| 571 | Joe LeFebvre (R) | .15 |
| 572 | Bobby Clark | .05 |
| 573 | Dennis Lamp | .05 |
| 574 | Randy Lerch | .05 |
| 575 | Mookie Wilson (R) | .50 |
| 576 | Ron LeFlore | .05 |
| 577 | Jim Dwyer | .05 |
| 578 | Bill Castro | .05 |
| 579 | Greg Minton | .05 |
| 580 | Mark Littell | .05 |
| 581 | Andy Hassler | .05 |
| 582 | Dave Stieb | .50 |
| 583 | Ken Oberkfell | .05 |
| 584 | Larry Bradford | .05 |
| 585 | Fred Stanley | .05 |
| 586 | Bill Caudill | .10 |
| 587 | Doug Capilla | .05 |
| 588 | George Riley | .05 |
| 589 | Willie Hernandez | .20 |
| 590 | Mike Schmidt (MVP) | 1.50 |
| 591 | Steve Stone (Cy Young) | .10 |
| 592 | Rick Sofield | .05 |
| 593 | Bombo Rivera | .05 |
| 594 | Gary Ward | .05 |
| 595 | Dave Edwards* | .10 |
| 596 | Mike Proly | .05 |
| 597 | Tommy Boggs | .05 |
| 598 | Greg Gross | .05 |
| 599 | Elias Sosa | .05 |
| 600 | Pat Kelly | .05 |
| — | Checklist No. 1* | .10 |
| — | Checklist No. 2 | .10 |
| — | Checklist No. 3* | .10 |
| — | Checklist No. 4* | .10 |
| — | Checklist No. 5* | .10 |

# 1982 Donruss . . . Complete Set of 660 Cards—Value $75.00

Features the rookie cards of Cal Ripken, George Bell and Dave Stewart. Several errors were corrected; none are scarce or worth much more than ordinary cards. If a *variety* (error) is significant, it is listed and explained; if it is minor, it is noted by an *asterisk*. The *checklist* cards are *not* numbered.

| NO. PLAYER | MINT | NO. PLAYER | MINT | NO. PLAYER | MINT | NO. PLAYER | MINT |
|---|---|---|---|---|---|---|---|
| **No. 1 to 26—Diamond Kings** | | 66 Bruce Kison | .05 | 132 Gorman Thomas | .15 | 198 Duane Kuiper | .05 |
| 1 Pete Rose (DK) | 1.50 | 67 Wayne Nordhagen | .05 | 133 Dan Petry | .15 | 199 Rick Cerone | .05 |
| 2 Gary Carter (DK) | .35 | 68 Woodie Fryman | .05 | 134 Bob Stanley | .05 | 200 Jim Rice | .30 |
| 3 Steve Garvey (DK) | .40 | 69 Billy Sample | .05 | 135 Lou Piniella | .10 | 201 Steve Yeager | .05 |
| 4 Vida Blue (DK) | .10 | 70 Amos Otis | .10 | 136 Pedro Guerrero | .50 | 202 Tom Brookens | .05 |
| 5 A. Trammell (DK) | .35 | 71 Matt Keough | .05 | 137 Len Barker | .05 | 203 Jose Morales | .05 |
| (correct) | | 72 Toby Harrah | .05 | 138 Richard Gale | .05 | 204 Roy Howell | .05 |
| 5 A. Trammell (DK) | 1.25 | 73 Dave Righetti (R) | 1.00 | 139 Wayne Gross | .05 | 205 Tippy Martinez | .05 |
| (error) | | 74 Carl Yastrzemski | 1.00 | 140 Tim Wallach (R) | 1.25 | 206 Moose Haas | .05 |
| 6 Len Barker (DK) | .10 | 75 Bob Welch | .35 | 141 Gene Mauch | .05 | 207 Al Cowens | .05 |
| 7 Dwight Evans (DK) | .15 | 76 A. Trammell (cor.) | .50 | 142 Doc Medich | .05 | 208 Dave Stapleton | .05 |
| 8 Rod Carew (DK) | .60 | 76 A. Trammell (error) | 1.25 | 143 Tony Bernazard | .05 | 209 Bucky Dent | .05 |
| 9 George Hendrick (DK) | .10 | 77 Rick Dempsey | .05 | 144 Bill Virdon (Mgr.) | .05 | 210 Ron Cey | .15 |
| 10 Phil Niekro (DK) | .25 | 78 Paul Molitor | .50 | 145 John Littlefield | .05 | 211 Jorge Orta | .05 |
| 11 Richie Zisk (DK) | .10 | 79 Dennis Martinez | .20 | 146 Dave Bergman | .05 | 212 Jamie Quirk | .05 |
| 12 Dave Parker (DK) | .30 | 80 Jim Slaton | .05 | 147 Dick Davis | .05 | 213 Jeff Jones | .05 |
| 13 Nolan Ryan (DK) | 2.50 | 81 Champ Summers | .05 | 148 Tom Seaver | 1.25 | 214 Tim Raines | 1.50 |
| 14 Ivan DeJesus (DK) | .10 | 82 Carney Lansford | .20 | 149 Matt Sinatro | .07 | 215 Jon Matlack | .05 |
| 15 George Brett (DK) | 1.00 | 83 Barry Foote | .05 | 150 Chuck Tanner (Mgr.) | .05 | 216 Rod Carew | 1.00 |
| 16 Tom Seaver (DK) | .75 | 84 Steve Garvey | .50 | 151 Leon Durham | .15 | 217 Jim Kaat | .10 |
| 17 Dave Kingman (DK) | .10 | 85 Rick Manning | .05 | 152 Gene Tenace | .05 | 218 Joe Pittman | .05 |
| 18 Dave Winfield (DK) | .50 | 86 John Wathan | .05 | 153 Al Bumbry | .05 | 219 Larry Christenson | .05 |
| 19 Mike Norris (DK) | .10 | 87 Brian Kingman | .05 | 154 Mark Brouhard | .05 | 220 Juan Bonilla | .07 |
| 20 Carlton Fisk (DK) | .50 | 88 Andre Dawson | 1.00 | 155 Rick Peters | .05 | 221 Mike Easler | .05 |
| 21 Ozzie Smith (DK) | .75 | 89 Jim Kern | .05 | 156 Jerry Remy | .05 | 222 Vida Blue | .05 |
| 22 Roy Smalley (DK) | .10 | 90 Bobby Grich | .05 | 157 Rick Reuschel | .10 | 223 Rick Camp | .05 |
| 23 Buddy Bell (DK) | .10 | 91 Bob Forsch | .05 | 158 Steve Howe | .05 | 224 Mike Jorgensen | .05 |
| 24 Ken Singleton (DK) | .10 | 92 Art Howe | .05 | 159 Alan Bannister | .05 | 225 Jody Davis (R) | .12 |
| 25 John Mayberry (DK) | .10 | 93 Marty Bystrom | .05 | 160 U.L. Wasington | .05 | 226 Mike Parrott | .05 |
| 26 Garmon Thomas (DK) | .10 | 94 Ozzie Smith | 1.00 | 161 Rick Langford | .05 | 227 Jim Clancy | .05 |
| 27 Earl Weaver (Mgr.) | .10 | 95 Dave Parker | .40 | 162 Bill Gullickson | .12 | 228 Hosken Powell | .05 |
| 28 Rollie Fingers | .50 | 96 Doyle Alexander | .05 | 163 Mark Wagner | .05 | 229 Tom Hume | .05 |
| 29 Sparky Anderson (Mgr.) | .10 | 97 Al Hrabosky | .05 | 164 Geoff Zahn | .05 | 230 Britt Burns | .05 |
| 30 Dennis Eckersley | .50 | 98 Frank Taveras | .05 | 165 Ron LeFlore | .05 | 231 Jim Palmer | 1.00 |
| 31 Dave Winfield | .75 | 99 Tim Blackwell | .05 | 166 Dane Iorg | .05 | 232 Bob Rodgers (Mgr.) | .05 |
| 32 Burt Hooton | .05 | 100 Floyd Bannister | .05 | 167 Joe Niekro | .10 | 233 Milt Wilcox | .05 |
| 33 Rick Waits | .05 | 101 Alfredo Griffin | .05 | 168 Pete Rose | 1.25 | 234 Dave Revering | .05 |
| 34 George Brett | 1.50 | 102 Dave Engle | .05 | 169 Dave Collins | .05 | 235 Mike Torrez | .05 |
| 35 Steve McCatty | .05 | 103 Mario Soto | .15 | 170 Rick Wise | .05 | 236 Bobby Castillo | .05 |
| 36 Steve Rogers | .05 | 104 Ross Baumgarten | .05 | 171 Jim Bibby | .05 | 237 Von Hayes (R) | .50 |
| 37 Bill Stein | .05 | 105 Ken Singleton | .10 | 172 Larry Herndon | .05 | 238 Renie Martin | .05 |
| 38 Steve Renko | .05 | 106 Ted Simmons | .15 | 173 Bob Horner | .15 | 239 Dwayne Murphy | .05 |
| 39 Mike Squires | .05 | 107 Jack Morris | .50 | 174 Steve Dillard | .05 | 240 Rodney Scott | .05 |
| 40 George Hendrick | .08 | 108 Bob Watson | .05 | 175 Mookie Wilson | .10 | 241 Freddie Patek | .05 |
| 41 Bob Knepper | .12 | 109 Dwight Evans | .25 | 176 Danny Meyer | .05 | 242 Mickey Rivers | .05 |
| 42 Steve Carlton | 1.00 | 110 Tommy LaSorda (Mgr.) | .10 | 177 Fernando Arroyo | .05 | 243 Steve Trout | .05 |
| 43 Larry Biittner | .05 | 111 Bert Blyleven | .25 | 178 Jackson Todd | .05 | 244 Jose Cruz | .10 |
| 44 Chris Welsh | .07 | 112 Dan Quisenberry | .25 | 179 Darrell Jackson | .05 | 245 Manny Trillo | .05 |
| 45 Steve Nicosia | .05 | 113 Rickey Henderson | 5.00 | 180 Al Woods | .05 | 246 Lary Sorensen | .05 |
| 46 Jack Clark | .30 | 114 Gary Carter | .50 | 181 Jim Anderson | .05 | 247 Dave Edwards | .05 |
| 47 Chris Chambliss | .05 | 115 Brian Downing | .05 | 182 Dave Kingman | .15 | 248 Dan Driessen | .05 |
| 48 Ivan DeJesus | .05 | 116 Al Oliver | .15 | 183 Steve Henderson | .05 | 249 Tommy Boggs | .05 |
| 49 Lee Mazzilli | .05 | 117 LaMarr Hoyt | .15 | 184 Brian Asselstine | .05 | 250 Dale Berra | .05 |
| 50 Julio Cruz | .05 | 118 Cesar Cedeno | .10 | 185 Rod Scurry | .05 | 251 Ed Whitson | .05 |
| 51 Pete Redfern | .05 | 119 Keith Moreland | .05 | 186 Fred Breining | .08 | 252 Lee Smith (R) | 2.50 |
| 52 Dave Stieb | .50 | 120 Bob Shirley | .05 | 187 Danny Boone | .05 | 253 Tom Paciorek | .05 |
| 53 Doug Corbett | .05 | 121 Terry Kennedy | .10 | 188 Junior Kennedy | .05 | 254 Pat Zachry | .05 |
| 54 Jorge Bell (R) | 7.50 | 122 Frank Pastore | .05 | 189 Sparky Lyle | .05 | 255 Luis Leal | .05 |
| 55 Joe Simpson | .05 | 123 Gene Garber | .05 | 190 Whitey Herzog (Mgr.) | .05 | 256 John Castino | .05 |
| 56 Rusty Staub | .10 | 124 Tony Pena | .35 | 191 Dave Smith | .15 | 257 Rich Dauer | .05 |
| 57 Hector Cruz | .05 | 125 Allen Ripley | .05 | 192 Ed Ott | .05 | 258 Cecil Cooper | .20 |
| 58 Claudell Washington | .10 | 126 Randy Martz | .05 | 193 Greg Luzinski | .10 | 259 Dave Rozema | .05 |
| 59 Enrique Romo | .05 | 127 Richie Zisk | .05 | 194 Bill Lee | .05 | 260 John Tudor | .12 |
| 60 Gary Lavelle | .05 | 128 Mike Scott | .25 | 195 Don Zimmer (Mgr.) | .05 | 261 Jerry Mumphrey | .05 |
| 61 Tim Flannery | .05 | 129 Lloyd Moseby | .15 | 196 Hal McRae | .05 | 262 Jay Johnstone | .05 |
| 62 Joe Nolan | .05 | 130 Rob Wilfong | .05 | 197 Mike Norris | .05 | 263 Bo Diaz | .05 |
| 63 Larry Bowa | .05 | 131 Tim Stoddard | .05 | | | | |
| 64 Sixto Lezcano | .05 | | | | | | |
| 65 Joe Sambito | .05 | | | | | | |

| NO. | PLAYER | MINT |
|-----|--------|------|
| 264 | Dennis Leonard | .05 |
| 265 | Jim Spencer | .05 |
| 266 | John Milner | .05 |
| 267 | Don Aase | .05 |
| 268 | Jim Sundberg | .05 |
| 269 | Lamar Johnson | .05 |
| 270 | Frank LaCorte | .05 |
| 271 | Barry Evans | .05 |
| 272 | Enos Cabell | .05 |
| 273 | Del Unser | .05 |
| 274 | George Foster | .20 |
| 275 | Brett Butler (R) | 2.00 |
| 276 | Lee Lacy | .05 |
| 277 | Ken Reitz | .05 |
| 278 | Keith Hernandez | .35 |
| 279 | Doug DeCinces | .10 |
| 280 | Charlie Moore | .05 |
| 281 | Lance Parrish | .25 |
| 282 | Ralph Houk (Mgr.) | .05 |
| 283 | Rich Gossage | .20 |
| 284 | Jerry Reuss | .05 |
| 285 | Mike Stanton | .05 |
| 286 | Frank White | .05 |
| 287 | Bob Owchinko | .05 |
| 288 | Scott Sanderson | .05 |
| 289 | Bump Wills | .05 |
| 290 | Dave Frost | .05 |
| 291 | Chet Lemon | .05 |
| 292 | Tito Landrum | .05 |
| 293 | Vern Ruhle | .05 |
| 294 | Mike Schmidt | 2.00 |
| 295 | San Mejias | .05 |
| 296 | Gary Lucas | .05 |
| 297 | John Candelaria | .05 |
| 298 | Jerry Martin | .05 |
| 299 | Dale Murphy | .75 |
| 300 | Mike Lum | .05 |
| 301 | Tom Hausman | .05 |
| 302 | Glenn Abbott | .05 |
| 303 | Roger Erickson | .05 |
| 304 | Otto Velez | .05 |
| 305 | Danny Goodwin | .05 |
| 306 | John Mayberry | .05 |
| 307 | Lenny Randle | .05 |
| 308 | Bob Bailor | .05 |
| 309 | Jerry Morales | .05 |
| 310 | Rufino Linares | .05 |
| 311 | Kent Tekulve | .05 |
| 312 | Joe Morgan | .50 |
| 313 | John Urrea | .05 |
| 314 | Paul Householder | .05 |
| 315 | Garry Maddox | .05 |
| 316 | Mike Ramsey | .05 |
| 317 | Alan Ashby | .05 |
| 318 | Bob Clark | .05 |
| 319 | Tony LaRussa (Mgr.) | .05 |
| 320 | Charlie Lea | .05 |
| 321 | Danny Darwin | .05 |
| 322 | Cesar Geronimo | .05 |
| 323 | Tom Underwood | .05 |
| 324 | Andre Thornton | .10 |
| 325 | Rudy May | .05 |
| 326 | Frank Tanana | .05 |
| 327 | Davey Lopes | .05 |
| 328 | Richie Hebner | .05 |
| 329 | Mike Flanagan | .08 |
| 330 | Mike Caldwell | .05 |
| 331 | Scott McGregor | .05 |
| 332 | Jerry Augustine | .05 |
| 333 | Stan Papi | .05 |
| 334 | Rick Miller | .05 |
| 335 | Graig Nettles | .15 |
| 336 | Dusty Baker | .10 |
| 337 | Dave Garcia (Mgr.) | .05 |
| 338 | Larry Gura | .05 |
| 339 | Cliff Johnson | .05 |
| 340 | Warren Cromartie | .05 |
| 341 | Steve Comer | .05 |
| 342 | Rick Burleson | .05 |
| 343 | John Martin | .05 |
| 344 | Craig Reynolds | .05 |
| 345 | Mike Proly | .05 |
| 346 | Ruppert Jones | .05 |
| 347 | Omar Moreno | .05 |
| 348 | Greg Minton | .05 |

| NO. | PLAYER | MINT |
|-----|--------|------|
| 349 | Rick Mahler (R) | .20 |
| 350 | Alex Trevino | .05 |
| 351 | Mike Krukow | .05 |
| 352 | Shane Rawley | .75 |
| | (photo of Jim Anderson) | |
| 352 | Shane Rawley (correct) | .10 |
| 353 | Garth Iorg | .05 |
| 354 | Pete Mackanin | .05 |
| 355 | Paul Moskau | .05 |
| 356 | Rich Dotson | .05 |
| 357 | Steve Stone | .05 |
| 358 | Larry Hisle | .05 |
| 359 | Aurelio Lopez | .05 |
| 360 | Oscar Gamble | .05 |
| 361 | Tom Burgmeier | .05 |
| 362 | Terry Forster | .08 |
| 363 | Joe Charboneau | .05 |
| 364 | Ken Brett | .05 |
| 365 | Tony Armas | .15 |
| 366 | Chris Speier | .05 |
| 367 | Fred Lynn | .20 |
| 368 | Buddy Bell | .10 |
| 369 | Jim Essian | .05 |
| 370 | Terry Puhl | .05 |
| 371 | Greg Gross | .05 |
| 372 | Bruce Sutter | .20 |
| 373 | Joe LeFebvre | .05 |
| 374 | Ray Knight | .05 |
| 375 | Bruce Benedict | .05 |
| 376 | Tim Foli | .05 |
| 377 | Al Holland | .05 |
| 378 | Ken Kravec | .05 |
| 379 | Jeff Burroughs | .05 |
| 380 | Pete Falcone | .05 |
| 381 | Ernie Whitt | .05 |
| 382 | Brad Havens | .05 |
| 383 | Terry Crowley | .05 |
| 384 | Don Money | .05 |
| 385 | Dan Schatzeder | .05 |
| 386 | Gary Allenson | .05 |
| 387 | Yogi Berra | .25 |
| 388 | Ken Landreaux | .05 |
| 389 | Mike Hargrove | .05 |
| 390 | Darryl Motley | .20 |
| 391 | Dave McKay | .05 |
| 392 | Stan Bahnsen | .05 |
| 393 | Ken Forsch | .05 |
| 394 | Mario Mendoza | .05 |
| 395 | Jim Morrison | .05 |
| 396 | Mike Ivie | .05 |
| 397 | Broderick Perkins | .05 |
| 398 | Darrell Evans | .10 |
| 399 | Ron Reed | .05 |
| 400 | Johnny Bench | 1.00 |
| 401 | Steve Bedrosian (R) | .50 |
| 402 | Bill Robinson | .05 |
| 403 | Bill Buckner | .15 |
| 404 | Ken Oberkfell | .05 |
| 405 | Cal Ripken Jr. (R) | 40.00 |
| 406 | Jim Gantner | .05 |
| 407 | Kirk Gibson | 1.50 |
| 408 | Tony Perez | .25 |
| 409 | Tommy John | .15 |
| 410 | Dave Stewart (R) | 6.00 |
| 411 | Dan Spillner | .05 |
| 412 | Willie Aikens | .05 |
| 413 | Mike Heath | .05 |
| 414 | Ray Burris | .05 |
| 415 | Leon Roberts | .05 |
| 416 | Mike Witt (R) | .25 |
| 417 | Bobby Molinaro | .05 |
| 418 | Steve Braun | .05 |
| 419 | Nolan Ryan | 5.00 |
| 420 | Tug McGraw | .05 |
| 421 | Dave Concepcion | .10 |
| 422 | Juan Eichelberger | .75 |
| | (photo of Gary Lucas) | |
| 422 | J. Eichelberger (correct) | .05 |
| 423 | Rick Rhoden | .05 |
| 424 | Frank Robinson (Mgr.) | .15 |
| 425 | Eddie Miller | .05 |
| 426 | Bill Caudill | .05 |
| 427 | Doug Flynn | .05 |
| 428 | Larry Andersen | .05 |
| 429 | Al Williams | .05 |

| NO. | PLAYER | MINT |
|-----|--------|------|
| 430 | Jerry Garvin | .05 |
| 431 | Glenn Adams | .05 |
| 432 | Barry Bonnell | .05 |
| 433 | Jerry Narron | .05 |
| 434 | John Stearns | .05 |
| 435 | Mike Tyson | .05 |
| 436 | Glenn Hubbard | .05 |
| 437 | Eddie Solomon | .05 |
| 438 | Jeff Leonard | .15 |
| 439 | Randy Bass | .05 |
| 440 | Mike LaCoss | .05 |
| 441 | Gary Matthews | .10 |
| 442 | Mark Littell | .05 |
| 443 | Don Sutton | .40 |
| 444 | John Harris | .05 |
| 445 | Vada Pinson | .05 |
| 446 | Elias Sosa | .05 |
| 447 | Charlie Hough | .05 |
| 448 | Willie Wilson | .15 |
| 449 | Fred Stanley | .05 |
| 450 | Tommy Veryzer | .05 |
| 451 | Ron Davis | .05 |
| 452 | Mark Clear | .05 |
| 453 | Bill Russell | .05 |
| 454 | Lou Whitaker | .30 |
| 455 | Dan Graham | .05 |
| 456 | Reggie Cleveland | .05 |
| 457 | Sammy Stewart | .05 |
| 458 | Pete Vuckovich | .10 |
| 459 | John Wockenfuss | .05 |
| 460 | Glenn Hoffman | .05 |
| 461 | Willie Randolph | .10 |
| 462 | Fernando Valenzuela | .75 |
| 463 | Ron Hassey | .05 |
| 464 | Paul Splittorff | .05 |
| 465 | Rob Picciolo | .05 |
| 466 | Larry Parrish | .05 |
| 467 | John Grubb | .05 |
| 468 | Dan Ford | .05 |
| 469 | Silvio Martinez | .05 |
| 470 | Kiko Garcia | .05 |
| 471 | Bob Boone | .05 |
| 472 | Luis Salazar | .15 |
| 473 | Randy Niemann | .05 |
| 474 | Tom Griffin | .05 |
| 475 | Phil Niekro | .35 |
| 476 | Hubie Brooks | .75 |
| 477 | Dick Tidrow | .05 |
| 478 | Jim Beattie | .05 |
| 479 | Damaso Garcia | .10 |
| 480 | Mickey Hatcher | .05 |
| 481 | Joe Price | .05 |
| 482 | Ed Farmer | .05 |
| 483 | Eddie Murray | 1.25 |
| 484 | Ben Oglivie | .10 |
| 485 | Kevin Saucier | .05 |
| 486 | Bobby Murcer | .10 |
| 487 | Bill Campbell | .05 |
| 488 | Reggie Smith | .10 |
| 489 | Wayne Garland | .05 |
| 490 | Jim Wright | .05 |
| 491 | Billy Martin (Mgr.) | .20 |
| 492 | Jim Fanning (Mgr.) | .05 |
| 493 | Don Baylor | .15 |
| 494 | Rick Honeycutt | .05 |
| 495 | Carlton Fisk | 1.00 |
| 496 | Denny Walling | .05 |
| 497 | Bake McBride | .05 |
| 498 | Darrell Porter | .05 |
| 499 | Gene Richards | .05 |
| 500 | Ron Oester | .05 |
| 501 | Ken Dayley (R) | .15 |
| 502 | Jason Thompson | .10 |
| 503 | Milt May | .05 |
| 504 | Doug Bird | .05 |
| 505 | Bruce Bochte | .05 |
| 506 | Neil Allen | .05 |
| 507 | Joey McLaughlin | .05 |
| 508 | Butch Wynegar | .06 |
| 509 | Gary Roenicke | .05 |
| 510 | Robin Yount | 2.00 |
| 511 | Dave Tobik | .05 |
| 512 | Rich Gedman (R) | .15 |
| 513 | Gene Nelson | .08 |
| 514 | Rick Monday | .05 |

| NO. | PLAYER | MINT |
|-----|--------|------|
| 515 | Miguel Dilone | .05 |
| 516 | Clint Hurdle | .05 |
| 517 | Jeff Newman | .05 |
| 518 | Grant Jackson | .05 |
| 519 | Andy Hassler | .05 |
| 520 | Pat Putnam | .05 |
| 521 | Greg Pryor | .05 |
| 522 | Tony Scott | .05 |
| 523 | Steve Mura | .05 |
| 524 | John LeMaster | .05 |
| 525 | Dick Ruthven | .05 |
| 526 | John McNamara (Mgr.) | .05 |
| 527 | Larry McWilliams | .05 |
| 528 | Johnny Ray (R) | .25 |
| 529 | Pat Tabler (R) | .20 |
| 530 | Tom Herr | .10 |
| 531 | San Diego Chicken* | .75 |
| 532 | Sal Butera | .05 |
| 533 | Mike Griffin | .05 |
| 534 | Kelvin Moore | .05 |
| 535 | Reggie Jackson | 1.50 |
| 536 | Ed Romero | .05 |
| 537 | Derrel Thomas | .05 |
| 538 | Mike O'Berry | .05 |
| 539 | Jack O'Connor | .05 |
| 540 | Bob Ojeda (R) | .50 |
| 541 | Roy Lee Jackson | .05 |
| 542 | Lynn Jones | .05 |
| 543 | Gaylord Perry | .35 |
| 544 | Phil Garner* | .10 |
| 545 | Garry Templeton | .10 |
| 546 | Rafael Ramirez | .05 |
| 547 | Jeff Reardon | .50 |
| 548 | Ron Guidry | .20 |
| 549 | Tim Laudner | .15 |
| 550 | John Henry Johnson | .05 |
| 551 | Chris Bando | .05 |
| 552 | Bobby Brown | .05 |
| 553 | Larry Bradford | .05 |
| 554 | Scott Fletcher (R) | .25 |
| 555 | Jerry Royster | .05 |
| 556 | Shooty Babbitt | .05 |
| 557 | Kent Hrbek (R) | 3.50 |
| 558 | Yankee Winners: | .15 |
| | Ron Guidry, Tommy John | |
| 559 | Mark Bomback | .05 |
| 560 | Julio Valdez | .08 |
| 561 | Buck Martinez | .05 |
| 562 | Mike Marshall (R) | .50 |
| 563 | Rennie Stennett | .05 |
| 564 | Steve Crawford | .07 |
| 565 | Bob Babcock | .05 |
| 566 | Johnny Podres | .05 |
| 567 | Paul Serna | .07 |
| 568 | Harold Baines | 1.50 |
| 569 | Dave LaRoche | .05 |
| 570 | Lee May | .05 |
| 571 | Gary Ward | .05 |
| 572 | John Denny | .05 |
| 573 | Roy Smalley | .05 |
| 574 | Bob Brenly (R) | .20 |
| 575 | Bronx Bombers: | .60 |
| | R. Jackson, D. Winfield | |
| 576 | Luis Pujols | .05 |
| 577 | Butch Hobson | .05 |
| 578 | Harvey Kuenn (Mgr.) | .05 |
| 579 | Cal Ripken, Sr. | .20 |
| 580 | Juan Berenguer | .05 |
| 581 | Benny Ayala | .05 |
| 582 | Vance Law | .15 |
| 583 | Rick Leach | .08 |
| 584 | George Frazier | .05 |
| 585 | Phillies Finest: | 1.00 |
| | Pete Rose, Mike Schmidt | |
| 586 | Joe Rudi | .05 |
| 587 | Juan Beniquez | .05 |
| 588 | Luis DeLeon (R) | .15 |
| 589 | Craig Swan | .05 |
| 590 | Dave Chalk | .05 |
| 591 | Billy Gardner (Mgr.) | .05 |
| 592 | Sal Bando | .05 |
| 593 | Bert Campaneris | .05 |
| 594 | Steve Kemp | .05 |
| 595 | Randy Lerch' (Braves) | .75 |
| 595 | Randy Lerch (Brewers) | .08 |

| NO. PLAYER | MINT | NO. PLAYER | MINT | NO. PLAYER | MINT | NO. PLAYER | MINT |
|---|---|---|---|---|---|---|---|
| 596 Bryan Clark | .08 | 613 Joel Youngblood | .05 | 629 Paul Mirabella | .05 | 646 Jesse Orosco | .10 |
| 597 Dave Ford | .05 | 614 Larry Milbourne | .05 | 630 Rance Mulliniks | .05 | 647 Jerry Dybzinski | .05 |
| 598 Mike Scioscia | .30 | 615 Phil Roof | .07 | 631 Kevin Hickey | .05 | 648 Tommy Davis | .05 |
| 599 John Lowenstein | .05 | 616 Keith Drumright | .05 | 632 Reid Nichols | .05 | 649 Ron Gardenhire | .10 |
| 600 Rene Lachmann (Mgr.) | .05 | 617 Dave Rosello | .05 | 633 Dave Geisel | .05 | 650 Felipe Alou | .05 |
| 601 Mick Kelleher | .05 | 618 Rickey Keeton | .05 | 634 Ken Griffey | .30 | 651 Harvey Haddix | .05 |
| 602 Ron Jackson | .05 | 619 Dennis Lamp | .05 | 635 Bob Lemon (Mgr.) | .10 | 652 Willie Upshaw | .10 |
| 603 Jerry Koosman | .15 | 620 Sid Monge | .05 | 636 Orlando Sanchez | .08 | 653 Bill Madlock | .15 |
| 604 Dave Goltz | .05 | 621 Jerry White | .05 | 637 Bill Almon | .05 | — DK Checklist* | .10 |
| 605 Ellis Valentine | .05 | 622 Luis Aguayo | .05 | 638 Danny Ainge | .30 | — Checklist No. 1 | .08 |
| 606 Lonnie Smith | .25 | 623 Jamie Easterly | .05 | 639 Willie Stargell | .50 | — Checklist No. 2 | .08 |
| 607 Joaquin Andujar | .15 | 624 Steve Sax (R) | 3.00 | 640 Bob Sykes | .05 | — Checklist No. 3 | .08 |
| 608 Garry Hancock | .05 | 625 Dave Roberts | .05 | 641 Ed Lynch (R) | .10 | — Checklist No. 4 | .08 |
| 609 Jerry Turner | .05 | 626 Rick Bosetti | .05 | 642 John Ellis | .05 | — Checklist No. 5 | .08 |
| 610 Bob Bonner | .05 | 627 Terry Francona (R) | .15 | 643 Fergie Jenkins | .30 | — Checklist No. 6 | .08 |
| 611 Jim Dwyer | .05 | 628 Pride of Reds: | .75 | 644 Lenn Sakata | .05 | | |
| 612 Terry Bulling | .05 | Tom Seaver, Johnny Bench | | 645 Julio Gonzalez | .05 | | |

# 1983 Donruss . . . Complete Set of 660 Cards—Value $125.00
**(Factory-Sealed set—Value $150.00)**

Features the rookie cards of Wade Boggs, Howard Johnson, Ryne Sandberg and Tony Gwynn. The *checklist* cards are *not* numbered.

| NO. PLAYER | MINT | NO. PLAYER | MINT | NO. PLAYER | MINT | NO. PLAYER | MINT |
|---|---|---|---|---|---|---|---|
| **No. 1 to 26—Diamond Kings** | | 41 Jose Cruz | .10 | 82 Rick Miller | .05 | 123 Chris Chambliss | .05 |
| 1 F. Valenzuela (DK) | .30 | 42 Pete Rose | 1.25 | 83 Graig Nettles | .10 | 124 Chuck Tanner (Mgr.) | .05 |
| 2 Rollie Fingers (DK) | .20 | 43 Cesar Cedeno | .10 | 84 Ron Cey | .15 | 125 Johnnie LeMaster | .05 |
| 3 Reggie Jackson (DK) | .60 | 44 Floyd Chiffer | .07 | 85 Miguel Dilone | .05 | 126 Mel Hall (R) | 1.50 |
| 4 Jim Palmer (DK) | .40 | 45 Larry McWilliams | .05 | 86 John Wathan | .05 | 127 Bruce Bochte | .05 |
| 5 Jack Morris (DK) | .35 | 46 Alan Fowlkes | .07 | 87 Kelvin Moore | .05 | 128 Charlie Puleo | .07 |
| 6 George Foster (DK) | .15 | 47 Dale Murphy | .75 | 88 Bryn Smith | .35 | 129 Luis Leal | .05 |
| 7 Jim Sundberg (DK) | .15 | 48 Doug Bird | .05 | 89 Dave Hostetler | .08 | 130 John Pacella | .05 |
| 8 Willie Stargell (DK) | .35 | 49 Hubie Brooks | .30 | 90 Rod Carew | .75 | 131 Glenn Gulliver | .07 |
| 9 Dave Stieb (DK) | .15 | 50 Floyd Bannister | .05 | 91 Lonnie Smith | .15 | 132 Don Money | .05 |
| 10 Joe Niekro (DK) | .10 | 51 Joe O'Connor | .05 | 92 Bob Knepper | .05 | 133 Dave Rozema | .05 |
| 11 Rickey Henderson (DK) | 2.00 | 52 Steve Senteney | .07 | 93 Marty Bystrom | .05 | 134 Bruce Hurst | .35 |
| 12 Dale Murphy (DK) | .40 | 53 Gary Gaetti (R) | 1.00 | 94 Chris Welsh | .05 | 135 Rudy May | .05 |
| 13 Toby Harrah (DK) | .10 | 54 Damaso Garcia | .10 | 95 Jason Thompson | .07 | 136 Tom LaSorda (Mgr.) | .10 |
| 14 Bill Buckner (DK) | .15 | 55 Gene Nelson | .05 | 96 Tom O'Malley | .08 | 137 Dan Spillner | .10 |
| 15 Willie Wilson (DK) | .15 | 56 Mookie Wilson | .08 | 97 Phil Niekro | .30 | (photo of Ed Whitson) | |
| 16 Steve Carlton (DK) | .40 | 57 Allen Ripley | .05 | 98 Neil Allen | .05 | 138 Jerry Martin | .05 |
| 17 Ron Guidry (DK) | .15 | 58 Bob Horner | .15 | 99 Bill Buckner | .10 | 139 Mike Norris | .05 |
| 18 Steve Rogers (DK) | .10 | 59 Tony Pena | .15 | 100 Ed VandeBerg | .10 | 140 Al Oliver | .10 |
| 19 Kent Hrbek (DK) | .25 | 60 Gary Lavelle | .05 | 101 Jim Clancy | .05 | 141 Daryl Sconiers | .05 |
| 20 Keith Hernandez (DK) | .15 | 61 Tim Lollar | .05 | 102 Robert Castillo | .05 | 142 Lamar Johnson | .05 |
| 21 Floyd Bannister (DK) | .10 | 62 Frank Pastore | .05 | 103 Bruce Berenyi | .05 | 143 Harold Baines | .40 |
| 22 Johnny Bench (DK) | .60 | 63 Garry Maddox | .05 | 104 Carlton Fisk | .75 | 144 Alan Ashby | .05 |
| 23 Britt Burns (DK) | .10 | 64 Bob Forsch | .05 | 105 Mike Flanagan | .10 | 145 Garry Templeton | .10 |
| 24 Joe Morgan (DK) | .35 | 65 Harry Spilman | .05 | 106 Cecil Cooper | .15 | 146 Al Holland | .05 |
| 25 Carl Yastrzemski (DK) | .50 | 66 Geoff Zahn | .05 | 107 Jack Morris | .50 | 147 Bo Diaz | .05 |
| 26 Jerry Kennedy (DK) | .10 | 67 Salome Barojas | .07 | 108 Mike Morgan | .05 | 148 Dave Concepcion | .10 |
| 27 Gary Roenicke | .05 | 68 David Palmer | .05 | 109 Luis Aponte | .05 | 149 Rick Camp | .05 |
| 28 Dwight Bernard | .05 | 69 Charlie Hough | .05 | 110 Pedro Guerrero | .30 | 150 Jim Morrison | .05 |
| 29 Pat Underwood | .05 | 70 Dan Quisenberry | .20 | 111 Len Barker | .05 | 151 Randy Martz | .05 |
| 30 Gary Allenson | .05 | 71 Tony Armas | .15 | 112 Willie Wilson | .20 | 152 Keith Hernandez | .30 |
| 31 Ron Guidry | .20 | 72 Rick Sutcliffe | .20 | 113 Dave Beard | .05 | 153 John Lowenstein | .05 |
| 32 Burt Hooton | .05 | 73 Steve Balboni | .10 | 114 Mike Gates | .07 | 154 Mike Caldwell | .05 |
| 33 Chris Bando | .05 | 74 Jerry Remy | .05 | 115 Reggie Jackson | 1.00 | 155 Milt Wilcox | .05 |
| 34 Vida Blue | .10 | 75 Mike Scioscia | .05 | 116 George Wright | .15 | 156 Rich Gedman | .05 |
| 35 Rickey Henderson | 4.00 | 76 John Wockenfuss | .05 | 117 Vance Law | .05 | 157 Rich Gossage | .20 |
| 36 Ray Burris | .05 | 77 Jim Palmer | .75 | 118 Nolan Ryan | 4.00 | 158 Jerry Reuss | .05 |
| 37 John Butcher | .05 | 78 Rollie Fingers | .30 | 119 Mike Krukow | .05 | 159 Ron Hassey | .05 |
| 38 Don Aase | .05 | 79 Joe Nolan | .05 | 120 Ozzie Smith | 1.00 | 160 Larry Gura | .05 |
| 39 Jerry Koosman | .05 | 80 Pete Vuckovich | .05 | 121 Broderick Perkins | .05 | 161 Dwayne Murphy | .05 |
| 40 Bruce Sutter | .20 | 81 Rick Leach | .05 | 122 Tom Seaver | .75 | 162 Woodie Fryman | .05 |

| NO. | PLAYER | MINT | NO. | PLAYER | MINT | NO. | PLAYER | MINT | NO. | PLAYER | MINT |
|---|---|---|---|---|---|---|---|---|---|---|---|
| 163 | Steve Comer | .05 | 247 | Joe Pittman | .10 | 330 | Jim Slaton | .20 | 414 | Charlie Lea | .05 |
| 164 | Ken Forsch | .05 | | (photo of Juan Eichelberger) | | 331 | Benny Ayala | .05 | 415 | Rick Honeycutt | .05 |
| 165 | Dennis Lamp | .05 | 248 | Mario Soto | .10 | 332 | Ted Simmons | .30 | 416 | Mike Witt | .15 |
| 166 | David Green (R) | .15 | 249 | Claudell Washington | .10 | 333 | Lou Whitaker | .30 | 417 | Steve Trout | .05 |
| 167 | Terry Puhl | .05 | 250 | Rick Rhoden | .05 | 334 | Chuck Rainey | .05 | 418 | Glenn Brummer | .05 |
| 168 | Mike Schmidt | 2.00 | 251 | Darrell Evans | .10 | 335 | Lou Piniella | .10 | 419 | Denny Walling | .05 |
| 169 | Eddie Milner (R) | .15 | 252 | Steve Henderson | .05 | 336 | Steve Sax | .50 | 420 | Gary Matthews | .10 |
| 170 | John Curtis | .05 | 253 | Manny Castillo | .05 | 337 | Toby Harrah | .05 | 421 | Charlie Leibrandt | .05 |
| 171 | Don Robinson | .05 | 254 | Craig Swan | .05 | 338 | George Brett | 1.25 | 422 | Juan Eichelberger | .05 |
| 172 | Richard Gale | .05 | 255 | Joey McLaughlin | .05 | 339 | Davey Lopes | .05 | 423 | Matt Guante | .07 |
| 173 | Steve Bedrosian | .15 | 256 | Pete Redfern | .05 | 340 | Gary Carter | .40 | 424 | Bill Laskey (R) | .15 |
| 174 | Willie Hernandez | .20 | 257 | Ken Singleton | .08 | 341 | John Grubb | .05 | 425 | Jerry Royster | .05 |
| 175 | Ron Gardenhire | .05 | 258 | Robin Yount | 1.25 | 342 | Tim Foli | .05 | 426 | Dickie Noles | .05 |
| 176 | Jim Beattie | .05 | 259 | Elias Sosa | .05 | 343 | Jim Kaat | .15 | 427 | George Foster | .20 |
| 177 | Tim Laudner | .05 | 260 | Bob Ojeda | .08 | 344 | Mike LaCoss | .05 | 428 | Mike Moore (R) | .75 |
| 178 | Buck Martinez | .05 | 261 | Bobby Murcer | .10 | 345 | Larry Christenson | .05 | 429 | Gary Ward | .05 |
| 179 | Kent Hrbek | .50 | 262 | Candy Maldonado (R) | .50 | 346 | Juan Bonilla | .05 | 430 | Barry Bonnell | .05 |
| 180 | Alfredo Griffin | .05 | 263 | Rick Waits | .05 | 347 | Omar Moreno | .05 | 431 | Ron Washington | .08 |
| 181 | Larry Andersen | .05 | 264 | Greg Pryor | .05 | 348 | Chili Davis | .50 | 432 | Rance Mulliniks | .05 |
| 182 | Pete Falcone | .05 | 265 | Bob Owchinko | .05 | 349 | Tommy Boggs | .05 | 433 | Mike Stanton | .05 |
| 183 | Jody Davis | .10 | 266 | Chris Speier | .05 | 350 | Rusty Staub | .10 | 434 | Jesse Orosco | .10 |
| 184 | Glenn Hubbard | .05 | 267 | Bruce Kison | .05 | 351 | Bump Wills | .05 | 435 | Larry Bowa | .08 |
| 185 | Dale Berra | .05 | 268 | Mark Wagner | .05 | 352 | Rick Sweet | .05 | 436 | Biff Pocoroba | .05 |
| 186 | Greg Minton | .05 | 269 | Steve Kemp | .05 | 353 | Jim Gott | .25 | 437 | Johnny Ray | .12 |
| 187 | Gary Lucas | .05 | 270 | Phil Garner | .05 | 354 | Terry Felton | .05 | 438 | Joe Morgan | .50 |
| 188 | Dave Van Gorder | .08 | 271 | Gene Richards | .05 | 355 | Jim Kern | .05 | 439 | Eric Show (R) | .25 |
| 189 | Bob Dernier | .05 | 272 | Renie Martin | .05 | 356 | Bill Almon | .05 | 440 | Larry Biittner | .05 |
| 190 | Willie McGee (R) | 3.00 | 273 | Dave Roberts | .05 | 357 | Tippy Martinez | .05 | 441 | Greg Gross | .05 |
| 191 | Dickie Thon | .07 | 274 | Dan Driessen | .05 | 358 | Roy Howell | .05 | 442 | Gene Tenace | .05 |
| 192 | Bob Boone | .05 | 275 | Rufino Linares | .05 | 359 | Dan Petry | .15 | 443 | Danny Heep | .05 |
| 193 | Britt Burns | .05 | 276 | Lee Lacy | .05 | 360 | Jerry Mumphrey | .05 | 444 | Bobby Clark | .05 |
| 194 | Jeff Reardon | .50 | 277 | Ryne Sandberg (R) | 30.00 | 361 | Mark Clear | .05 | 445 | Kevin Hickey | .05 |
| 195 | Jon Matlack | .05 | 278 | Darrell Porter | .05 | 362 | Mike Marshall | .12 | 446 | Scott Sanderson | .05 |
| 196 | Don Slaught (R) | .30 | 279 | Cal Ripken | 11.00 | 363 | Lary Sorensen | .05 | 447 | Frank Tanana | .10 |
| 197 | Fred Stanley | .05 | 280 | Jamie Easterly | .05 | 364 | Amos Otis | .08 | 448 | Cesar Geronimo | .05 |
| 198 | Rick Manning | .05 | 281 | Bill Fahey | .05 | 365 | Rick Langford | .05 | 449 | Jimmy Sexton | .05 |
| 199 | Dave Righetti | .25 | 282 | Glenn Hoffman | .05 | 366 | Brad Mills | .05 | 450 | Mike Hargrove | .05 |
| 200 | Dave Stapleton | .05 | 283 | Willie Randolph | .10 | 367 | Brian Downing | .05 | 451 | Doyle Alexander | .05 |
| 201 | Steve Yeager | .05 | 284 | Fernando Valenzuela | .25 | 368 | Mike Richardt | .07 | 452 | Dwight Evans | .20 |
| 202 | Enos Cabell | .05 | 285 | Alan Bannister | .05 | 369 | Aurelio Rodriguez | .05 | 453 | Terry Forster | .05 |
| 203 | Sammy Stewart | .05 | 286 | Paul Splittorff | .05 | 370 | Dave Smith | .05 | 454 | Tom Brookens | .05 |
| 204 | Moose Haas | .05 | 287 | Joe Rudi | .05 | 371 | Tug McGraw | .08 | 455 | Rich Dauer | .05 |
| 205 | Lenn Sakata | .05 | 288 | Bill Gullickson | .05 | 372 | Doug Bair | .10 | 456 | Rob Picciolo | .05 |
| 206 | Charlie Moore | .05 | 289 | Danny Darwin | .05 | 373 | Ruppert Jones | .05 | 457 | Terry Crowley | .05 |
| 207 | Alan Trammell | .50 | 290 | Andy Hassler | .05 | 374 | Alex Trevino | .05 | 458 | Ned Yost | .05 |
| 208 | Jim Rice | .30 | 291 | Ernesto Escarrega | .07 | 375 | Ken Dayley | .05 | 459 | Kirk Gibson | .40 |
| 209 | Roy Smalley | .05 | 292 | Steve Mura | .05 | 376 | Rod Scurry | .05 | 460 | Reid Nichols | .05 |
| 210 | Bill Russell | .05 | 293 | Tony Scott | .05 | 377 | Bob Brenly | .05 | 461 | Oscar Gamble | .05 |
| 211 | Andre Thornton | .07 | 294 | Manny Trillo | .05 | 378 | Scot Thompson | .05 | 462 | Dusty Baker | .10 |
| 212 | Willie Aikens | .05 | 295 | Greg Harris | .05 | 379 | Julio Cruz | .05 | 463 | Jack Perconte | .05 |
| 213 | Dave McKay | .05 | 296 | Luis DeLeon | .05 | 380 | John Stearns | .05 | 464 | Frank White | .05 |
| 214 | Tim Blackwell | .05 | 297 | Kent Tekulve | .05 | 381 | Dale Murray | .05 | 465 | Mickey Klutts | .05 |
| 215 | Buddy Bell | .10 | 298 | Atlee Hammaker | .05 | 382 | Frank Viola (R) | 4.00 | 466 | Warren Cromartie | .05 |
| 216 | Doug DeCinces | .15 | 299 | Bruce Benedict | .05 | 383 | Al Bumbry | .05 | 467 | Larry Parrish | .05 |
| 217 | Tom Herr | .10 | 300 | Fergie Jenkins | .25 | 384 | Ben Oglivie | .10 | 468 | Bobby Grich | .08 |
| 218 | Frank LaCorte | .05 | 301 | Dave Kingman | .10 | 385 | Dave Tobik | .05 | 469 | Dane Iorg | .05 |
| 219 | Steve Carlton | .75 | 302 | Bill Caudill | .05 | 386 | Bob Stanley | .05 | 470 | Joe Niekro | .10 |
| 220 | Terry Kennedy | .10 | 303 | John Castino | .05 | 387 | Andre Robertson | .05 | 471 | Ed Farmer | .05 |
| 221 | Mike Easler | .05 | 304 | Ernie Whitt | .05 | 388 | Jorge Orta | .05 | 472 | Tim Flannery | .05 |
| 222 | Jack Clark | .25 | 305 | Randy Johnson | .05 | 389 | Ed Whitson | .05 | 473 | Dave Parker | .40 |
| 223 | Gene Garber | .05 | 306 | Garth Iorg | .05 | 390 | Don Hood | .05 | 474 | Jeff Leonard | .05 |
| 224 | Scott Holman | .07 | 307 | Gaylord Perry | .25 | 391 | Tom Underwood | .05 | 475 | Al Hrabosky | .05 |
| 225 | Mike Proly | .05 | 308 | Ed Lynch | .05 | 392 | Tim Wallach | .20 | 476 | Ron Hodges | .05 |
| 226 | Terry Bulling | .05 | 309 | Keith Moreland | .10 | 393 | Steve Renko | .05 | 477 | Leon Durham | .20 |
| 227 | Jerry Garvin | .05 | 310 | Rafael Ramirez | .05 | 394 | Mickey Rivers | .05 | 478 | Jim Essian | .05 |
| 228 | Ron Davis | .05 | 311 | Bill Madlock | .15 | 395 | Greg Luzinski | .10 | 479 | Roy Lee Jackson | .05 |
| 229 | Tom Hume | .05 | 312 | Milt May | .05 | 396 | Art Howe | .05 | 480 | Brad Havens | .05 |
| 230 | Marc Hill | .05 | 313 | John Montefusco | .05 | 397 | Alan Wiggins | .15 | 481 | Joe Price | .05 |
| 231 | Dennis Martinez | .05 | 314 | Wayne Krenchicki | .05 | 398 | Jim Barr | .05 | 482 | Tony Bernazard | .05 |
| 232 | Jim Gantner | .05 | 315 | George Vukovich | .05 | 399 | Ivan DeJesus | .05 | 483 | Scott McGregor | .08 |
| 233 | Larry Pashnick | .07 | 316 | Joaquin Andujar | .10 | 400 | Tom Lawless | .08 | 484 | Paul Molitor | .30 |
| 234 | Dave Collins | .05 | 317 | Craig Reynolds | .05 | 401 | Bob Walk | .05 | 485 | Mike Ivie | .05 |
| 235 | Tom Burgmeier | .05 | 318 | Rick Burleson | .05 | 402 | Jimmy Smith | .07 | 486 | Ken Griffey | .25 |
| 236 | Ken Landreaux | .05 | 319 | Richard Dotson | .05 | 403 | Lee Smith | .50 | 487 | Dennis Eckersley | .35 |
| 237 | John Denny | .10 | 320 | Steve Rogers | .05 | 404 | George Hendrick | .10 | 488 | Steve Garvey | .40 |
| 238 | Hal McRae | .05 | 321 | Dave Schmidt | .10 | 405 | Eddie Murray | 1.00 | 489 | Mike Fischlin | .05 |
| 239 | Matt Keough | .05 | 322 | Bud Black (R) | .30 | 406 | Marshall Edwards | .05 | 490 | U.L. Washington | .05 |
| 240 | Doug Flynn | .05 | 323 | Jeff Burroughs | .05 | 407 | Lance Parrish | .20 | 491 | Steve McCatty | .05 |
| 241 | Fred Lynn | .20 | 324 | Von Hayes | .20 | 408 | Carney Lansford | .15 | 492 | Roy Johnson | .07 |
| 242 | Billy Sample | .05 | 325 | Butch Wynegar | .05 | 409 | Dave Winfield | .75 | 493 | Don Baylor | .10 |
| 243 | Tom Paciorek | .05 | 326 | Carl Yastrzemski | 1.00 | 410 | Bob Welch | .30 | 494 | Bobby Johnson | .05 |
| 244 | Joe Sambito | .05 | 327 | Ron Roenicke | .05 | 411 | Larry Milbourne | .05 | 495 | Mike Squires | .05 |
| 245 | Sid Monge | .05 | 328 | Howard Johnson (R) | 10.00 | 412 | Dennis Leonard | .05 | 496 | Bert Roberge | .05 |
| 246 | Ken Oberkfell | .05 | 329 | Rick Dempsey | .05 | 413 | Dan Meyer | .05 | 497 | Dick Ruthven | .05 |

| NO. PLAYER | MINT | NO. PLAYER | MINT | NO. PLAYER | MINT | NO. PLAYER | MINT |
|---|---|---|---|---|---|---|---|
| 498 Tito Landrum | .05 | 540 Tim Raines | .50 | 582 Bob McClure | .05 | 623 Gene Petralli | .07 |
| 499 Sixto Lezcano | .05 | 541 Paul Mirabella | .05 | 583 Jim Dwyer | .05 | 624 Duane Walker (R) | .15 |
| 500 Johnny Bench | .75 | 542 Luis Tiant | .10 | 584 Ed Romero | .05 | 625 Dick Williams (Mgr.) | .05 |
| 501 Larry Whisenton | .05 | 543 Ron LeFlore | .05 | 585 Larry Herndon | .05 | 626 Pat Corrales (Mgr.) | .05 |
| 502 Manny Sarmiento | .05 | 544 Dave LaPoint (R) | .12 | 586 Wade Boggs (R) | 22.00 | 627 Vern Ruhle | .05 |
| 503 Fred Breining | .05 | 545 Randy Moffitt | .05 | 587 Jay Howell | .05 | 628 Joe Torre (Mgr.) | .05 |
| 504 Bill Campbell | .05 | 546 Luis Aguayo | .05 | 588 Dave Stewart | 1.00 | 629 Anthony Johnson | .08 |
| 505 Todd Cruz | .05 | 547 Brad Lesley | .10 | 589 Bert Blyleven | .25 | 630 Steve Howe | .05 |
| 506 Bob Bailor | .05 | 548 Luis Salazar | .05 | 590 Dick Howser (Mgr.) | .08 | 631 Gary Woods | .05 |
| 507 Dave Stieb | .25 | 549 John Candelaria | .05 | 591 Wayne Gross | .05 | 632 LaMarr Hoyt | .15 |
| 508 Al Williams | .05 | 550 Dave Bergman | .05 | 592 Terry Francona | .08 | 633 Steve Swisher | .05 |
| 509 Dan Ford | .05 | 551 Bob Watson | .05 | 593 Don Werner | .05 | 634 Terry Leach | .15 |
| 510 Gorman Thomas | .10 | 552 Pat Tabler | .05 | 594 Bill Stein | .05 | 635 Jeff Newman | .05 |
| 511 Chet Lemon | .10 | 553 Brent Gaff | .08 | 595 Jesse Barfield | .50 | 636 Brett Butler | .40 |
| 512 Mike Torrez | .05 | 554 Al Cowens | .05 | 596 Bobby Molinaro | .05 | 637 Gary Gray | .05 |
| 513 Shane Rawley | .05 | 555 Tom Brunansky | .50 | 597 Mike Vail | .05 | 638 Lee Mazzilli | .05 |
| 514 Mark Belanger | .05 | 556 Lloyd Moseby | .15 | 598 Tony Gwynn (R) | 20.00 | 639 R. Jackson | .15 |
| 515 Rodney Craig | .05 | 557 Pascual Perez | .15 | 599 Gary Rajsich | .08 | 639 R. Jackson (error) | 10.00 |
| 516 Onix Concepcion (R) | .10 | 558 Willie Upshaw | .10 | 600 Jerry Ujdur | .05 | 640 Juan Beniquez | .05 |
| 517 Mike Heath | .05 | 559 Richie Zisk | .05 | 601 Cliff Johnson | .05 | 641 Dave Rucker | .05 |
| 518 Andre Dawson | 1.00 | 560 Pat Zachry | .05 | 602 Jerry White | .05 | 642 Luis Pujols | .05 |
| 519 Luis Sanchez | .05 | 561 Jay Johnstone | .05 | 603 Bryan Clark | .05 | 643 Rick Monday | .05 |
| 520 Terry Bogener | .07 | 562 Carlos Diaz | .08 | 604 Joe Ferguson | .05 | 644 Hosken Powell | .05 |
| 521 Rudy Law | .05 | 563 John Tudor | .12 | 605 Guy Sularz | .07 | 645 The Chicken | .20 |
| 522 Ray Knight | .05 | 564 Frank Robinson (Mgr.) | .15 | 606 Ozzie Virgil | .10 | 646 Dave Engle | .05 |
| 523 Joe LeFebvre | .05 | 565 Dave Edwards | .05 | 607 Terry Harper | .05 | 647 Dick Davis | .05 |
| 524 Jim Wohlford | .05 | 566 Paul Householder | .05 | 608 Harvey Kuenn (Mgr.) | .05 | 648 MVP's: Frank Robinson, | .15 |
| 525 Julio Franco (R) | 9.00 | 567 Ron Reed | .05 | 609 Jim Sundberg | .05 | Vida Blue, Joe Morgan | |
| 526 Ron Oester | .05 | 568 Mike Ramsey | .05 | 610 Willie Stargell | .50 | 649 Al Chambers | .15 |
| 527 Rick Mahler | .05 | 569 Kiko Garcia | .05 | 611 Reggie Smith | .10 | 650 Jesus Vega | .07 |
| 528 Steve Nicosia | .05 | 570 Tommy John | .20 | 612 Rob Wilfong | .05 | 651 Jeff Jones | .05 |
| 529 Junior Kennedy | .05 | 571 Tony LaRussa (Mgr.) | .05 | 613 Niekro Brothers | .15 | 652 Marvis Foley | .05 |
| 530 Whitey Herzog (Mgr.) | .05 | 572 Joel Youngblood | .05 | Joe and Phil | | 653 Ty Cobb Puzzle | .20 |
| 531 Don Sutton | .35 | 573 Wayne Tolleson | .15 | 614 Lee Elia (Mgr.) | .05 | — Checklist (DK) | .08 |
| 532 Mark Brouhard | .05 | 574 Keith Creel | .07 | 615 Mickey Hatcher | .05 | — Checklist No. 1 | .08 |
| 533 Sparky Anderson (Mgr.) | .05 | 575 Billy Martin (Mgr.) | .15 | 616 Jerry Hairston | .05 | — Checklist No. 2 | .08 |
| 534 Roger LaFrancois | .05 | 576 Jerry Dybzinski | .05 | 617 John Martin | .05 | — Checklist No. 3 | .08 |
| 535 George Frazier | .05 | 577 Rick Cerone | .05 | 618 Wally Backman | .15 | — Checklist No. 4 | .08 |
| 536 Tom Niedenfuer | .07 | 578 Tony Perez | .25 | 619 Storm Davis (R) | .20 | — Checklist No. 5 | .08 |
| 537 Ed Glynn | .05 | 579 Greg Brock (R) | .20 | 620 Alan Knicely | .05 | — Checklist No. 6 | .08 |
| 538 Lee May | .05 | 580 Glen Wilson (R) | .15 | 621 John Stuper | .10 | | |
| 539 Bob Kearney | .10 | 581 Tim Stoddard | .05 | 622 Matt Sinatro | .05 | | |

## 1984 Donruss . . . Complete Set of 658 Cards—Value $350.00

**(Factory-Sealed set which includes corrected cards no. 29 and 30—Value $400.00)**

Features the rookie cards of Don Mattingly, Darryl Strawberry, Ron Darling, Kevin McReynolds and Joe Carter. For the first time Donruss limited production of its main card set causing the price to rise substantially. *Living Legends* cards "A" and "B" were only issued in wax packs and were not part of the factory sealed set. The *checklist* cards are *not* numbered. Cards 29 and 30 exist with the card numbers deleted. Values for card no's. 1 to 26 are for the error cards (Perez "Steel") on the back. The corrected cards (Perez "Steele") are worth double the value.

| NO. PLAYER | MINT | NO. PLAYER | MINT | NO. PLAYER | MINT | NO. PLAYER | MINT |
|---|---|---|---|---|---|---|---|
| **No. 1 to 26—Diamond Kings** | | 18 Ron Kittle (DK) | .25 | 31 Dion James (R) | .30 | 49 Lance Parrish | .60 |
| 1 Robin Yount (DK) | 2.00 | 19 Jim Clancy (DK) | .15 | 32 Tony Fernandez (R) | 6.00 | 50 Jim Rice | .50 |
| 2 Dave Concepcion (DK) | .20 | 20 Bill Madlock (DK) | .20 | 33 Angel Salazar (R) | .15 | 51 Dav Winfeld | 2.00 |
| 3 Dwayne Murphy (DK) | .15 | 21 Larry Parrish (DK) | .20 | 34 Kevin McReynolds (R) | 7.50 | 52 Fernando Valenzuela | .50 |
| 4 John Castino (DK) | .15 | 22 Eddie Murray (DK) | 1.00 | 35 Dick Schofield (R) | .35 | 53 George Brett | 4.00 |
| 5 Leon Durham (DK) | .30 | 23 Mike Schmidt (DK) | 2.00 | 36 Brad Komminsk (R) | .25 | 54 Rickey Henderson | 15.00 |
| 6 Rusty Staub (DK) | .15 | 24 Pedro Guerrero (DK) | .30 | 37 Tim Teufel (R) | .45 | 55 Gary Carter | 1.00 |
| 7 Jack Clark (DK) | .30 | 25 Andre Thornton (DK) | .15 | 38 Doug Frobel (R) | .15 | 56 Buddy Bell | .15 |
| 8 Dave Dravecky (DK) | .15 | 26 Wade Bogg (DK) | 3.50 | 39 Greg Gagne (R) | .50 | 57 Reggie Jackson | 3.00 |
| 9 Al Oliver (DK) | .20 | **No. 27 to 46—(Rated Rookies)** | | 40 Mike Fuentes (R) | .15 | 58 Harold Baines | .75 |
| 10 Dave Righetti (DK) | .25 | 27 Joel Skinner (R) | .25 | 41 Joe Carter (R) | 25.00 | 59 Ozzie Smith | 2.50 |
| 11 Hal McRae (DK) | .15 | 28 Tommy Dunbar (R) | .15 | 42 Mike Brown (R) | .25 | 60 Nolan Ryan | 15.00 |
| 12 Ray Knight (DK) | .15 | 29 Mike Stenhouse (R) | .25 | 43 Mike Jeffcoat (R) | .15 | 61 Pete Rose | 3.00 |
| 13 Bruce Sutter (DK) | .25 | (no number on back) | | 44 Sid Fernandez (R) | 4.00 | 62 Ron Oester | .10 |
| 14 Bob Horner (DK) | .25 | 29 Mike Stenhouse (R) | 2.50 | 45 Brian Dayett (R) | .20 | 63 Steve Garvey | 1.00 |
| 15 Lance Parrish (DK) | .30 | 30 Ron Darling (R) | 3.00 | 46 Chris Smith (R) | .15 | 64 Jason Thompson | .15 |
| 16 Matt Young (DK) | .15 | (no number on back) | | 47 Eddie Murray | 3.00 | 65 Jack Clark | .35 |
| 17 Fred Lynn (DK) | .25 | 30 Ron Darling (R) | 15.00 | 48 Robin Yount | 3.50 | 66 Dale Murphy | 2.00 |

| NO. | PLAYER | MINT | NO. | PLAYER | MINT | NO. | PLAYER | MINT | NO. | PLAYER | MINT |
|---|---|---|---|---|---|---|---|---|---|---|---|
| 67 | Leon Durham | .25 | 152 | Don Baylor | .20 | 237 | Mike Caldwell | .10 | 322 | Jim Morrison | .10 |
| 68 | Darryl Strawberry (R) | 60.00 | 153 | Bob Welch | .50 | 238 | Keith Hernandez | .50 | 323 | Max Venable | .10 |
| 69 | Richie Zisk | .10 | 154 | Alan Bannister | .10 | 239 | Larry Bowa | .10 | 324 | Tony Gwynn | 11.00 |
| 70 | Kent Hrbek | .75 | 155 | Willie Aikens | .10 | 240 | Tony Bernazard | .10 | 325 | Duane Walker | .10 |
| 71 | Dave Stieb | .60 | 156 | Jeff Burroughs | .10 | 241 | Damaso Garcia | .15 | 326 | Ozzie Virgil | .10 |
| 72 | Ken Schrom | .10 | 157 | Bryan Little | .15 | 242 | Tom Brunansky | .40 | 327 | Jeff Lahti | .10 |
| 73 | George Bell | 2.50 | 158 | Bob Boone | .10 | 243 | Dan Driessen | .15 | 328 | Bill Dawley | .20 |
| 74 | Jon Moses | .15 | 159 | Dave Hostetler | .10 | 244 | Ron Kittle | .35 | 329 | Rob Wilfong | .10 |
| 75 | Ed Lynch | .10 | 160 | Jerry Dybzinski | .10 | 245 | Tim Stoddard | .10 | 330 | Marc Hill | .10 |
| 76 | Chuck Rainey | .10 | 161 | Mike Madden | .15 | 246 | Bob Gibson | .10 | 331 | Ray Burris | .10 |
| 77 | Biff Pocoroba | .10 | 162 | Luis DeLeon | .10 | 247 | Marty Castillo | .10 | 332 | Allan Ramirez | .12 |
| 78 | Cecilio Guante | .10 | 163 | Willie Hernandez | .25 | 248 | Don Mattingly (R) | 60.00 | 333 | Chuck Porter | .10 |
| 79 | Jim Barr | .10 | 164 | Frank Pastore | .10 | 249 | Jeff Newman | .10 | 334 | Wayne Krenchicki | .10 |
| 80 | Kurt Bevacqua | .10 | 165 | Rick Camp | .10 | 250 | Alejandro Pena | .75 | 335 | Gary Allenson | .10 |
| 81 | Tom Foley | .15 | 166 | Lee Mazzilli | .12 | 251 | Toby Harrah | .12 | 336 | Bob Meacham | .15 |
| 82 | Joe LeFebvre | .10 | 167 | Scot Thompson | .10 | 252 | Cesar Geronimo | .10 | 337 | Joe Beckwith | .10 |
| 83 | Andy Van Slyke (R) | 6.00 | 168 | Bob Forsch | .12 | 253 | Tom Underwood | .10 | 338 | Rick Sutcliffe | .25 |
| 84 | Bob Lillis (Mgr.) | .10 | 169 | Mike Flanagan | .10 | 254 | Doug Flynn | .10 | 339 | Mark Huismann | .15 |
| 85 | Rick Adams | .15 | 170 | Rick Manning | .10 | 255 | Andy Hassler | .10 | 340 | Tim Conroy | .15 |
| 86 | Jerry Hairston | .10 | 171 | Chet Lemon | .15 | 256 | Odell Jones | .10 | 341 | Scott Sanderson | .10 |
| 87 | Bob James | .15 | 172 | Jerry Remy | .10 | 257 | Rudy Law | .10 | 342 | Larry Biittner | .10 |
| 88 | Joe Altobelli (Mgr.) | .10 | 173 | Ron Guidry | .30 | 258 | Harry Spilman | .10 | 343 | Dave Stewart | 2.00 |
| 89 | Ed Romero | .10 | 174 | Pedro Guerrero | .50 | 259 | Marty Bystrom | .10 | 344 | Darryl Motley | .10 |
| 90 | John Grubb | .10 | 175 | Willie Wilson | .25 | 260 | Dave Rucker | .10 | 345 | Chris Codiroli | .12 |
| 91 | John H. Johnson | .10 | 176 | Carney Lansford | .15 | 261 | Ruppert Jones | .10 | 346 | Rich Behenna | .12 |
| 92 | Juan Espino | .12 | 177 | Al Oliver | .15 | 262 | Jeff Jones | .15 | 347 | Andre Robertson | .10 |
| 93 | Candy Maldonado | .30 | 178 | Jim Sundberg | .10 | 263 | Gerald Perry | .60 | 348 | Mike Marshall | .20 |
| 94 | Andre Thornton | .15 | 179 | Bobby Grich | .10 | 264 | Gene Tenace | .10 | 349 | Larry Herndon | .10 |
| 95 | Onix Concepcion | .10 | 180 | Richard Dotson | .10 | 265 | Brad Wellman | .12 | 350 | Rich Dauer | .10 |
| 96 | Don Hill | .10 | 181 | Joaquin Andujar | .15 | 266 | Dickie Noles | .12 | 351 | Cecil Cooper | .15 |
| 97 | Andre Dawson | 3.00 | 182 | Jose Cruz | .10 | 267 | Jamie Allen | .12 | 352 | Rod Carew | 3.00 |
| 98 | Frank Tanana | .15 | 183 | Mike Schmidt | 12.50 | 268 | Jim Gott | .12 | 353 | Willie McGee | 1.00 |
| 99 | Curt Wilkerson | .15 | 184 | Gary Redus (R) | .50 | 269 | Ron Davis | .10 | 354 | Phil Garner | .10 |
| 100 | Larry Gura | .10 | 185 | Garry Templeton | .15 | 270 | Benny Ayala | .10 | 355 | Joe Morgan | 1.50 |
| 101 | Dwayne Murphy | .15 | 186 | Tony Pena | .25 | 271 | Ned Yost | .10 | 356 | Luis Salazar | .10 |
| 102 | Tom Brennan | .10 | 187 | Greg Minton | .10 | 272 | Dave Rozema | .10 | 357 | John Candelaria | .15 |
| 103 | Dave Righetti | .30 | 188 | Phil Niekro | .75 | 273 | Dave Stapleton | .10 | 358 | Bill Laskey | .10 |
| 104 | Steve Sax | .75 | 189 | Ferguson Jenkins | .60 | 274 | Lou Piniella | .10 | 359 | Bob McClure | .10 |
| 105 | Dan Petry | .20 | 190 | Mookie Wilson | .15 | 275 | Jose Morales | .10 | 360 | Dave Kingman | .20 |
| 106 | Cal Ripken | 20.00 | 191 | Jim Beattie | .10 | 276 | Brod Perkins | .10 | 361 | Ron Cey | .15 |
| 107 | Paul Molitor | .75 | 192 | Gary Ward | .10 | 277 | Butch Davis | .15 | 362 | Matt Young (R) | .20 |
| 108 | Fred Lynn | .30 | 193 | Jesse Barfield | .40 | 278 | Tony Phillips | 1.00 | 363 | Lloyd Moseby | .20 |
| 109 | Neil Allen | .15 | 194 | Pete Filson | .15 | 279 | Jeff Reardon | .75 | 364 | Frank Viola | 2.00 |
| 110 | Joe Niekro | .15 | 195 | Roy Lee Jackson | .10 | 280 | Ken Forsch | .10 | 365 | Eddie Milner | .10 |
| 111 | Steve Carlton | 3.00 | 196 | Rick Sweet | .10 | 281 | Pete O'Brien (R) | .75 | 366 | Floyd Bannister | .12 |
| 112 | Terry Kennedy | .15 | 197 | Jesse Orosco | .15 | 282 | Tom Paciorek | .10 | 367 | Dan Ford | .12 |
| 113 | Bill Madlock | .20 | 198 | Steve Lake | .12 | 283 | Frank LaCorte | .10 | 368 | Moose Haas | .10 |
| 114 | Chili Davis | .15 | 199 | Ken Dayley | .10 | 284 | Tim Lollar | .10 | 369 | Doug Bair | .10 |
| 115 | Jim Gantner | .10 | 200 | Manny Sarmiento | .10 | 285 | Greg Gross | .10 | 370 | Ray Fontenot (R) | .15 |
| 116 | Tom Seaver | 5.00 | 201 | Mark Davis | .25 | 286 | Alex Trevino | .10 | 371 | Luis Aponte | .10 |
| 117 | Bill Buckner | .15 | 202 | Tim Flannery | .10 | 287 | Gene Garber | .10 | 372 | Jack Fimple | .10 |
| 118 | Bill Caudill | .10 | 203 | Bill Scherrer | .12 | 288 | Dave Parker | 1.00 | 373 | Neal Heaton | .40 |
| 119 | Jim Clancy | .10 | 204 | Al Holland | .10 | 289 | Lee Smith | .75 | 374 | Greg Pryor | .10 |
| 120 | John Castino | .10 | 205 | Dave Von Ohlen | .15 | 290 | Dave LaPoint | .10 | 375 | Wayne Gross | .10 |
| 121 | Dave Concepcion | .15 | 206 | Mike LaCoss | .10 | 291 | John Shelby | .35 | 376 | Charlie Lea | .10 |
| 122 | Greg Luzinski | .15 | 207 | Juan Beniquez | .10 | 292 | Charlie Moore | .10 | 377 | Steve Lubratich | .12 |
| 123 | Mike Boddicker | .15 | 208 | Juan Agosto | .15 | 293 | Alan Trammell | 2.00 | 378 | Jon Matlack | .12 |
| 124 | Pete Ladd | .10 | 209 | Bobby Ramos | .10 | 294 | Tony Armas | .15 | 379 | Julio Cruz | .10 |
| 125 | Juan Berenguer | .10 | 210 | Al Bumbry | .10 | 295 | Shane Rawley | .12 | 380 | John Mizerock | .12 |
| 126 | John Montefusco | .10 | 211 | Mark Brouhard | .10 | 296 | Greg Brock | .15 | 381 | Kevin Gross (R) | .60 |
| 127 | Ed Jurak | .12 | 212 | Howard Bailey | .10 | 297 | Hal McRae | .12 | 382 | Mike Ramsey | .10 |
| 128 | Tom Niedenfuer | .10 | 213 | Bruce Hurst | .15 | 298 | Mike Davis | .10 | 383 | Doug Gwosdz | .10 |
| 129 | Bert Blyleven | .40 | 214 | Bob Shirley | .10 | 299 | Tim Raines | 1.25 | 384 | Kelly Paris | .15 |
| 130 | Bud Black | .10 | 215 | Pat Zachry | .10 | 300 | Bucky Dent | .12 | 385 | Pete Falcone | .10 |
| 131 | Gorman Heimueller | .15 | 216 | Julio Franco | 4.00 | 301 | Tommy John | .30 | 386 | Milt May | .10 |
| 132 | Dan Schatzeder | .10 | 217 | Mike Armstrong | .10 | 302 | Carlton Fisk | 3.00 | 387 | Fred Breining | .10 |
| 133 | Ron Jackson | .10 | 218 | Dave Beard | .10 | 303 | Darrell Porter | .10 | 388 | Craig Lefferts (R) | .50 |
| 134 | Tom Henke (R) | 1.00 | 219 | Steve Rogers | .10 | 304 | Dickie Thon | .10 | 389 | Steve Henderson | .10 |
| 135 | Kevin Hickey | .10 | 220 | John Butcher | .10 | 305 | Garry Maddox | .10 | 390 | Randy Moffitt | .10 |
| 136 | Mike Scott | .50 | 221 | Mike Smithson | .15 | 306 | Cesar Cedeno | .15 | 391 | Ron Washington | .10 |
| 137 | Bo Diaz | .10 | 222 | Frank White | .12 | 307 | Gary Lucas | .10 | 392 | Gary Roenicke | .10 |
| 138 | Glenn Brummer | .10 | 223 | Mike Heath | .10 | 308 | Johnny Ray | .20 | 393 | Tom Candiotti (R) | 1.00 |
| 139 | Sid Monge | .10 | 224 | Chris Bando | .10 | 309 | Andy McGaffigan | .10 | 394 | Larry Pashnick | .10 |
| 140 | Rich Gale | .10 | 225 | Roy Smalley | .10 | 310 | Claudell Washington | .15 | 395 | Dwight Evans | .60 |
| 141 | Brett Butler | .60 | 226 | Dusty Baker | .10 | 311 | Ryne Sandberg | 20.00 | 396 | Goose Gossage | .30 |
| 142 | Brian Harper (R) | 1.25 | 227 | Lou Whitaker | .75 | 312 | George Foster | .30 | 397 | Derrel Thomas | .10 |
| 143 | John Rabb | .12 | 228 | John Lowenstein | .10 | 313 | Spike Owen (R) | .40 | 398 | Juan Eichelberger | .10 |
| 144 | Gary Woods | .10 | 229 | Ben Ogilvie | .10 | 314 | Gary Gaetti | .50 | 399 | Leon Roberts | .10 |
| 145 | Pat Putnam | .10 | 230 | Doug DeCinces | .15 | 315 | Willie Upshaw | .15 | 400 | Davey Lopes | .15 |
| 146 | Jim Acker | .15 | 231 | Lonnie Smith | .25 | 316 | Al Williams | .10 | 401 | Bill Gullickson | .12 |
| 147 | Mickey Hatcher | .10 | 232 | Ray Knight | .15 | 317 | Jorge Orta | .10 | 402 | Geoff Zahn | .10 |
| 148 | Todd Cruz | .10 | 233 | Gary Matthews | .15 | 318 | Orlando Mercado | .12 | 403 | Billy Sample | .10 |
| 149 | Tom Tellmann | .10 | 234 | Juan Bonilla | .10 | 319 | Junior Ortiz | .12 | 404 | Mike Squires | .10 |
| 150 | John Wockenfuss | .10 | 235 | Rod Scurry | .10 | 320 | Mike Proly | .10 | 405 | Craig Reynolds | .10 |
| 151 | Wade Boggs | 12.50 | 236 | Atlee Hammaker | .10 | 321 | Randy Johnson | .10 | 406 | Eric Show | .10 |

| NO. | PLAYER | MINT |
|---|---|---|
| 407 | John Denny | .15 |
| 408 | Dann Bilardello | .12 |
| 409 | Bruce Benedict | .10 |
| 410 | Kent Tekulve | .12 |
| 411 | Mel Hall | .50 |
| 412 | John Stuper | .10 |
| 413 | Rick Dempsey | .12 |
| 414 | Don Sutton | .75 |
| 415 | Jack Morris | 1.25 |
| 416 | John Tudor | .20 |
| 417 | Willie Randolph | .15 |
| 418 | Jerry Reuss | .12 |
| 419 | Don Slaught | .12 |
| 420 | Steve McCatty | .10 |
| 421 | Tim Wallach | .30 |
| 422 | Larry Parrish | .15 |
| 423 | Brian Downing | .15 |
| 424 | Britt Burns | .15 |
| 425 | David Green | .15 |
| 426 | Jerry Mumphrey | .10 |
| 427 | Ivn DeJesus | .10 |
| 428 | Mario Soto | .12 |
| 429 | Gene Richards | .10 |
| 430 | Dale Berra | .10 |
| 431 | Darrell Evans | .15 |
| 432 | Glenn Hubbard | .10 |
| 433 | Jody Davis | .12 |
| 434 | Danny Heep | .10 |
| 435 | Ed Nunez | .20 |
| 436 | Bobby Castillo | .10 |
| 437 | Ernie Whitt | .10 |
| 438 | Scott Ullger | .15 |
| 439 | Doyle Alexander | .15 |
| 440 | Domingo Ramos | .12 |
| 441 | Craig Swan | .10 |
| 442 | Warren Brusstar | .10 |
| 443 | Len Barker | .10 |
| 444 | Mike Easler | .10 |
| 445 | Renie Martin | .10 |
| 446 | Dennis Rasmussen (R) | .50 |
| 447 | Ted Power | .15 |
| 448 | Charlie Hudson (R) | .20 |
| 449 | Danny Cox (R) | .25 |
| 450 | Kevin Bass | .25 |
| 451 | Daryl Sconiers | .10 |
| 452 | Scott Fletcher | .12 |
| 453 | Bryn Smith | .12 |
| 454 | Jim Dwyer | .10 |
| 455 | Rob Picciolo | .10 |
| 456 | Enos Cabell | .10 |
| 457 | "Oil Can" Boyd (R) | .50 |
| 458 | Butch Wynegar | .10 |
| 459 | Burt Hooton | .10 |
| 460 | Ron Hassey | .10 |
| 461 | Danny Jackson (R) | 1.00 |
| 462 | Bob Kearney | .10 |
| 463 | Terry Francona | .10 |
| 464 | Wayne Tolleson | .10 |
| 465 | Mickey Rivers | .15 |
| 466 | John Wathan | .10 |
| 467 | Bill Almon | .10 |
| 468 | George Vukovich | .10 |
| 469 | Steve Kemp | .12 |
| 470 | Ken Landreaux | .10 |
| 471 | Milt Wilcox | .10 |

| NO. | PLAYER | MINT |
|---|---|---|
| 472 | Tippy Martinez | .10 |
| 473 | Ted Simmons | .15 |
| 474 | Tim Foli | .10 |
| 475 | George Hendrick | .10 |
| 476 | Terry Puhl | .15 |
| 477 | Von Hayes | .30 |
| 478 | Bobby Brown | .10 |
| 479 | Lee Lacy | .10 |
| 480 | Joel Youngblood | .10 |
| 481 | Jim Slaton | .10 |
| 482 | Mike Fitzgerald | .10 |
| 483 | Keith Moreland | .10 |
| 484 | Ron Roenicke | .10 |
| 485 | Luis Leal | .10 |
| 486 | Bryan Oelkers | .12 |
| 487 | Bruce Berenyi | .10 |
| 488 | LaMarr Hoyt | .15 |
| 489 | Joe Nolan | .10 |
| 490 | Marshall Edwards | .10 |
| 491 | Mike Laga | .12 |
| 492 | Rick Cerone | .10 |
| 493 | Rick Miller | .10 |
| 494 | Rick Honeycutt | .12 |
| 495 | Mike Hargrove | .12 |
| 496 | Joe Simpson | .10 |
| 497 | Keith Atherton | .10 |
| 498 | Chris Welsh | .10 |
| 499 | Bruce Kison | .10 |
| 500 | Bobby Johnson | .10 |
| 501 | Jerry Koosman | .20 |
| 502 | Frank DiPino | .10 |
| 503 | Tony Perez | .50 |
| 504 | Ken Oberkfell | .10 |
| 505 | Mark Thurmond (R) | .20 |
| 506 | Joe Price | .10 |
| 507 | Pascual Perez | .25 |
| 508 | Marvell Wynne | .20 |
| 509 | Mike Krukow | .15 |
| 510 | Dick Ruthven | .10 |
| 511 | Al Cowens | .10 |
| 512 | Cliff Johnson | .10 |
| 513 | Randy Bush | .25 |
| 514 | Sammy Stewart | .10 |
| 515 | Bill Schroeder (R) | .20 |
| 516 | Aurelio Lopez | .10 |
| 517 | Mike Brown | .15 |
| 518 | Graig Nettles | .20 |
| 519 | Dave Sax | .12 |
| 520 | Gerry Willard | .15 |
| 521 | Paul Splittorff | .12 |
| 522 | Tom Burgmeier | .10 |
| 523 | Chris Speier | .10 |
| 524 | Bobby Clark | .10 |
| 525 | George Wright | .10 |
| 526 | Dennis Lamp | .10 |
| 527 | Tony Scott | .10 |
| 528 | Ed Whitson | .12 |
| 529 | Ron Reed | .10 |
| 530 | Charlie Puleo | .10 |
| 531 | Jerry Royster | .10 |
| 532 | Don Robinson | .10 |
| 533 | Steve Trout | .10 |
| 534 | Bruce Sutter | .30 |
| 535 | Bob Horner | .20 |
| 536 | Pat Tabler | .15 |

| NO. | PLAYER | MINT |
|---|---|---|
| 537 | Chris Chambliss | .15 |
| 538 | Bob Ojeda | .20 |
| 539 | Alan Ashby | .10 |
| 540 | Jay Johnstone | .12 |
| 541 | Bob Dernier | .10 |
| 542 | Brook Jacoby (R) | 1.00 |
| 543 | U.L. Washington | .10 |
| 544 | Danny Darwin | .10 |
| 545 | Kiko Garcia | .10 |
| 546 | Vance Law | .10 |
| 547 | Tug McGraw | .15 |
| 548 | Dave Smith | .10 |
| 549 | Len Matuszek | .10 |
| 550 | Tom Hume | .10 |
| 551 | Dave Dravecky | .40 |
| 552 | Rick Rhoden | .15 |
| 553 | Duane Kuiper | .10 |
| 554 | Rusty Staub | .15 |
| 555 | Bill Campbell | .10 |
| 556 | Mike Torrez | .10 |
| 557 | Dave Henderson | 1.50 |
| 558 | Len Whitehouse | .12 |
| 559 | Barry Bonnell | .10 |
| 560 | Rick Lysander | .12 |
| 561 | Garth Iorg | .10 |
| 562 | Bryan Clark | .10 |
| 563 | Brian Giles | .10 |
| 564 | Vern Ruhle | .10 |
| 565 | Steve Bedrosian | .20 |
| 566 | Larry McWilliams | .10 |
| 567 | Jeff Leonard | .15 |
| 568 | Alan Wiggins | .12 |
| 569 | Jeff Russell | .75 |
| 570 | Salome Barojas | .10 |
| 571 | Dane Iorg | .10 |
| 572 | Bob Knepper | .15 |
| 573 | Gary Lavelle | .10 |
| 574 | Gorman Thomas | .15 |
| 575 | Manny Trillo | .10 |
| 576 | Jim Palmer | 2.50 |
| 577 | Dale Murray | .10 |
| 578 | Tom Brookens | .10 |
| 579 | Rich Gedman | .12 |
| 580 | Bill Doran (R) | 1.00 |
| 581 | Steve Yeager | .10 |
| 582 | Dan Spillner | .10 |
| 583 | Dan Quisenberry | .20 |
| 584 | Rance Mulliniks | .10 |
| 585 | Storm Davis | .15 |
| 586 | Dave Schmidt | .10 |
| 587 | Bill Russell | .10 |
| 588 | Pat Sheridan | .20 |
| 589 | Rafael Ramirez | .12 |
| 590 | Bud Anderson | .10 |
| 591 | George Frazier | .10 |
| 592 | Lee Tunnell | .15 |
| 593 | Kirk Gibson | 1.00 |
| 594 | Scott McGregor | .10 |
| 595 | Bob Bailor | .10 |
| 596 | Tom Herr | .15 |
| 597 | Luis Sanchez | .10 |
| 598 | Dave Engle | .10 |
| 599 | Craig McMurtry (R) | .15 |
| 600 | Carlos Diaz | .10 |
| 601 | Tom O'Malley | .10 |

| NO. | PLAYER | MINT |
|---|---|---|
| 602 | Nick Esasky (R) | .50 |
| 603 | Ron Hodges | .10 |
| 604 | Ed Vande Berg | .10 |
| 605 | Alfredo Griffin | .15 |
| 606 | Glenn Hoffman | .10 |
| 607 | Hubie Brooks | .40 |
| 608 | Richard Barnes | .12 |
| 609 | Greg Walker (R) | .15 |
| 610 | Ken Singleton | .15 |
| 611 | Mark Clear | .10 |
| 612 | Buck Martinez | .10 |
| 613 | Ken Griffey | .35 |
| 614 | Reid Nichols | .10 |
| 615 | Doug Sisk (R) | .15 |
| 616 | Bob Brenly | .10 |
| 617 | Joey McLaughlin | .10 |
| 618 | Glenn Wilson | .15 |
| 619 | Bob Stoddard | .10 |
| 620 | Len Sakata | .08 |
| 621 | Mike Young (R) | .20 |
| 622 | John Stefero | .12 |
| 623 | Carmelo Martinez (R) | .30 |
| 624 | Dave Bergman | .10 |
| 625 | Runnin' Redbirds: | .50 |
| | David Green, Willie McGee, | |
| | Lonnie Smith, Ozzie Smith | |
| 626 | Rudy May | .10 |
| 627 | Matt Keough | .10 |
| 628 | Jose DeLeon (R) | .50 |
| 629 | Jim Essian | .10 |
| 630 | Darnell Coles (R) | .20 |
| 631 | Mike Warren | .15 |
| 632 | Del Crandall (Mgr.) | .10 |
| 633 | Dennis Martinez | .12 |
| 634 | Mike Moore | .35 |
| 635 | Lary Sorensen | .10 |
| 636 | Ricky Nelson | .15 |
| 637 | Omar Moreno | .10 |
| 638 | Charlie Hough | .10 |
| 639 | Dennis Eckersley | 1.00 |
| 640 | Walt Terrell (R) | .35 |
| 641 | Denny Walling | .10 |
| 642 | Dave Anderson | .25 |
| 643 | Jose Oquendo (R) | .50 |
| 644 | Bob Stanley | .10 |
| 645 | Dave Geisel | .10 |
| 646 | Scott Garrelts (R) | .50 |
| 647 | Gary Pettis (R) | .40 |
| 648 | Duke Snider Puzzle | .15 |
| 649 | Johnnie LeMaster | .10 |
| 650 | Dave Collins | .12 |
| 651 | The Chicken | .30 |
| — | Checklist (DK) | .18 |
| — | Checklist No. 1 | .15 |
| — | Checklist No. 2 | .15 |
| — | Checklist No. 3 | .15 |
| — | Checklist No. 4 | .15 |
| — | Checklist No. 5 | .15 |
| — | Checklist No. 6 | .15 |

**Cards From Wax Packs**

| | | MINT |
|---|---|---|
| A | Living Legends: | 5.00 |
| | G. Perry, R. Fingers | |
| B | Living Legends: | 7.50 |
| | C. Yastrzemski, J. Bench | |

## 1985 Donruss.... Complete Set of 660 Cards—Value $175.00

(Factory-Sealed set which includes corrected cards no. 424 and 534—Value $200.00)

Features the rookie cards of Dwight Gooden, Roger Clemens, Eric Davis, Orel Hershiser, Bret Saberhagen and Kirby Puckett. As in 1984, Donruss limited the quantity of cards printed. The *checklist* cards are *not* numbered.

| NO. PLAYER | MINT | NO. PLAYER | MINT | NO. PLAYER | MINT | NO. PLAYER | MINT |
|---|---|---|---|---|---|---|---|
| **No. 1 to 26 (Diamond Kings)** | | 84 Bill Doran | .15 | 169 Cal Ripken, Jr. | 6.00 | 254 Pete Rose | 1.25 |
| 1 Ryne Sandberg (DK) | 2.50 | 85 Rod Carew | 1.00 | 170 Cecil Cooper | .15 | 255 Don Aase | .10 |
| 2 Doug DeCinces (DK) | .12 | 86 LaMarr Hoyt | .10 | 171 Alan Trammell | .50 | 256 George Wright | .08 |
| 3 Rich Dotson (DK) | .12 | 87 Tim Wallach | .12 | 172 Wade Boggs | 5.00 | 257 Britt Burns | .08 |
| 4 Bert Blyleven (DK) | .12 | 88 Mike Flanagan | .08 | 173 Don Baylor | .15 | 258 Mike Scott | .25 |
| 5 Lou Whitaker (DK) | .20 | 89 Jim Sundberg | .08 | 174 Pedro Guerrero | .20 | 259 Len Matuszek | .08 |
| 6 Dan Quisenberry (DK) | .20 | 90 Chet Lemon | .08 | 175 Frank White | .08 | 260 Dave Rucker | .08 |
| 7 Don Mattingly (DK) | 4.00 | 91 Bob Stanley | .08 | 176 Rickey Henderson | 5.00 | 261 Craig Lefferts | .08 |
| 8 Carney Lansford (DK) | .12 | 92 Willie Randolph | .08 | 177 Charlie Lea | .08 | 262 Jay Tibbs | .20 |
| 9 Frank Tanana (DK) | .12 | 93 Bill Russell | .08 | 178 Pete O'Brien | .12 | 263 Bruce Benedict | .08 |
| 10 Willie Upshaw (DK) | .12 | 94 Julio Franco | 1.00 | 179 Doug DeCinces | .12 | 264 Don Robinson | .08 |
| 11 C. Washington (DK) | .12 | 95 Dan Quisenberry | .20 | 180 Ron Kittle | .15 | 265 Gary Lavelle | .08 |
| 12 Mike Marshall (DK) | .15 | 96 Bill Caudill | .08 | 181 George Hendrick | .08 | 266 Scott Sanderson | .08 |
| 13 Joaquin Andujar (DK) | .12 | 97 Bill Gullickson | .08 | 182 Joe Niekro | .12 | 267 Matt Young | .08 |
| 14 Cal Ripken (DK) | 3.00 | 98 Danny Darwin | .08 | 183 Juan Samuel | 1.00 | 268 Ernie Whitt | .08 |
| 15 Jim Rice (DK) | .15 | 99 Curt Wilkerson | .08 | 184 Mario Soto | .12 | 269 Houston Jimenez | .08 |
| 16 Don Sutton (DK) | .15 | 100 Bud Black | .08 | 185 Goose Gossage | .15 | 270 Ken Dixon | .20 |
| 17 Frank Viola (DK) | .20 | 101 Tony Phillips | .08 | 186 Johnny Ray | .12 | 271 Peter Ladd | .08 |
| 18 Alvin Davis (DK) | .25 | 102 Tony Bernazard | .08 | 187 Bob Brenly | .08 | 272 Juan Berenguer | .08 |
| 19 Mario Soto (DK) | .10 | 103 Jay Howell | .08 | 188 Craig McMurtey | .08 | 273 Roger Clemens (R) | 35.00 |
| 20 Jose Cruz (DK) | .10 | 104 Burt Hooton | .08 | 189 Leon Durham | .15 | 274 Rick Cerone | .08 |
| 21 Charlie Lea (DK) | .10 | 105 Milt Wilcox | .08 | 190 Dwight Gooden (R) | 12.00 | 275 Dave Anderson | .08 |
| 22 Jesse Orosco (DK) | .10 | 106 Rich Dauer | .08 | 191 Barry Bonnell | .08 | 276 George Vukovich | .08 |
| 23 Juan Samuel (DK) | .25 | 107 Don Sutton | .30 | 192 Tim Teufel | .08 | 277 Greg Pryor | .08 |
| 24 Tony Pena (DK) | .10 | 108 Mike Witt | .12 | 193 Dave Stieb | .20 | 278 Mike Warren | .08 |
| 25 Tony Gwynn (DK) | 1.00 | 109 Bruce Sutter | .15 | 194 Mickey Hatcher | .08 | 279 Bob James | .08 |
| 26 Bob Brenly (DK) | .10 | 110 Enos Cabell | .08 | 195 Jesse Barfield | .20 | 280 Bobby Grich | .10 |
| **No. 27 to 46 (Rated Rookies)** | | 111 John Denny | .12 | 196 Al Cowens | .08 | 281 Mike Mason | .15 |
| 27 Danny Tartabull (R) | 6.00 | 112 Dave Dravecky | .15 | 197 Hubie Brooks | .15 | 282 Ron Reed | .08 |
| 28 Mike Bielecki (R) | .35 | 113 Marvell Wynne | .08 | 198 Steve Trout | .08 | 283 Alan Ashby | .08 |
| 29 Steve Lyons (R) | .30 | 114 John LeMaster | .08 | 199 Glenn Hubbard | .08 | 284 Mark Thurmond | .08 |
| 30 Jeff Reed (R) | .15 | 115 Chuck Porter | .08 | 200 Bill Madlock | .12 | 285 Joe Lefebvre | .08 |
| 31 Tony Brewer (R) | .15 | 116 John Gibbons | .15 | 201 Jeff Robinson (R) | .15 | 286 Ted Power | .08 |
| 32 John Morris (R) | .15 | 117 Keith Moreland | .08 | 202 Eric Show | .15 | 287 Chris Chambliss | .08 |
| 33 Daryl Boston (R) | .40 | 118 Darnell Coles | .08 | 203 Dave Concepcion | .12 | 288 Lee Tunnell | .08 |
| 34 Alfonso Pulido (R) | .15 | 119 Dennis Lamp | .08 | 204 Ivan DeJesus | .08 | 289 Rich Bordi | .08 |
| 35 Steve Kiefer (R) | .15 | 120 Ron Davis | .08 | 205 Neil Allen | .10 | 290 Glenn Brummer | .08 |
| 36 Larry Sheets (R) | .20 | 121 Nick Esasky | .20 | 206 Jerry Mumphrey | .08 | 291 Mike Boddicker | .10 |
| 37 Scott Bradley (R) | .20 | 122 Vance Law | .08 | 207 Mike Brown | .08 | 292 Rollie Fingers | .30 |
| 38 Calvin Schiraldi (R) | .20 | 123 Gary Roenicke | .08 | 208 Carlton Fisk | 1.00 | 293 Lou Whitaker | .35 |
| 39 Shawon Dunston (R) | 5.00 | 124 Bill Schroeder | .08 | 209 Bryn Smith | .08 | 294 Dwight Evans | .20 |
| 40 Charlie Mitchell (R) | .15 | 125 Dave Rozema | .08 | 210 Tippy Martinez | .08 | 295 Don Mattingly | 10.00 |
| 41 Billy Hatcher (R) | 1.00 | 126 Bobby Meacham | .08 | 211 Dion James | .08 | 296 Mike Marshall | .15 |
| 42 Russ Stephans (R) | .15 | 127 Marty Barrett | .15 | 212 Willie Hernandez | .15 | 297 Willie Wilson | .12 |
| 43 Alejandro Sanchez (R) | .15 | 128 R.J. Reynolds (R) | .20 | 213 Mike Easler | .08 | 298 Mike Heath | .08 |
| 44 Steve Jeltz (R) | .20 | 129 Ernie Camacho | .08 | 214 Ron Guidry | .20 | 299 Tim Raines | .40 |
| 45 Jim Traber (R) | .20 | 130 Jorge Orta | .08 | 215 Rick Honeycutt | .08 | 300 Larry Parrish | .08 |
| 46 Doug Loman (R) | .20 | 131 Lary Sorensen | .08 | 216 Brett Butler | .25 | 301 Geoff Zahn | .08 |
| 47 Eddie Murray | 1.00 | 132 Terry Francona | .08 | 217 Larry Gura | .08 | 302 Rich Dotson | .08 |
| 48 Robin Yount | 1.25 | 133 Fred Lynn | .20 | 218 Ray Burris | .08 | 303 David Green | .08 |
| 49 Lance Parrish | .20 | 134 Bobby Jones | .08 | 219 Steve Rogers | .08 | 304 Jose Cruz | .10 |
| 50 Jim Rice | .25 | 135 Jerry Hairston | .08 | 220 Frank Tanana | .08 | 305 Steve Carlton | .75 |
| 51 Dave Winfield | .75 | 136 Kevin Bass | .15 | 221 Ned Yost | .08 | 306 Gary Redus | .08 |
| 52 Fernando Valenzuela | .20 | 137 Garry Maddox | .08 | 222 Bret Saberhagen (R) | 8.00 | 307 Steve Garvey | .40 |
| 53 George Brett | 1.25 | 138 Dave LaPoint | .08 | 223 Mike Davis | .08 | 308 Jose DeLeon | .08 |
| 54 Dave Kingman | .10 | 139 Kevin McReynolds | .75 | 224 Bert Blyleven | .25 | 309 Randy Lerch | .08 |
| 55 Gary Carter | .30 | 140 Wayne Krenchicki | .08 | 225 Steve Kemp | .08 | 310 Claudell Washington | .10 |
| 56 Buddy Bell | .10 | 141 Rafael Ramirez | .08 | 226 Jerry Reuss | .08 | 311 Lee Smith | .35 |
| 57 Reggie Jackson | 1.00 | 142 Rod Scurry | .08 | 227 Darrell Evans | .15 | 312 Darryl Strawberry | 12.00 |
| 58 Harold Baines | .35 | 143 Greg Minton | .08 | 228 Wayne Gross | .08 | 313 Jim Beattie | .08 |
| 59 Ozzie Smith | 1.00 | 144 Tim Stoddard | .08 | 229 Jim Gantner | .08 | 314 John Butcher | .08 |
| 60 Nolan Ryan | 6.00 | 145 Steve Henderson | .08 | 230 Bob Boone | .08 | 315 Damaso Garcia | .10 |
| 61 Mike Schmidt | 3.00 | 146 George Bell | .75 | 231 Lonnie Smith | .08 | 316 Mike Smithson | .08 |
| 62 Dave Parker | .35 | 147 Dave Meier | .15 | 232 Frank DiPino | .08 | 317 Luis Leal | .08 |
| 63 Tony Gwynn | 4.00 | 148 Sammy Stewart | .08 | 233 Jerry Koosman | .08 | 318 Ken Phelps | .15 |
| 64 Tony Pena | .25 | 149 Mark Brouhard | .08 | 234 Graig Nettles | .15 | 319 Wally Backman | .08 |
| 65 Jack Clark | .25 | 150 Larry Herndon | .08 | 235 John Tudor | .15 | 320 Ron Cey | .12 |
| 66 Dale Murphy | .75 | 151 Oil Can Boyd | .15 | 236 John Rabb | .08 | 321 Brad Komminsk | .12 |
| 67 Ryne Sandberg | 6.00 | 152 Brian Dayett | .08 | 237 Rick Manning | .08 | 322 Jason Thompson | .10 |
| 68 Keith Hernandez | .30 | 153 Tom Niedenfuer | .08 | 238 Mike Fitzgerald | .08 | 323 Frank Williams | .12 |
| 69 Alvin Davis (R) | 2.00 | 154 Brook Jacoby | .15 | 239 Gary Matthews | .08 | 324 Tim Lollar | .08 |
| 70 Kent Hrbek | .40 | 155 Onix Concepcion | .08 | 240 Jim Presley (R) | .25 | 325 Eric Davis (R) | 12.50 |
| 71 Willie Upshaw | .10 | 156 Tim Conroy | .08 | 241 Dave Collins | .08 | 326 Von Hayes | .15 |
| 72 Dave Engle | .08 | 157 Joe Hesketh (R) | .20 | 242 Gary Gaetti | .20 | 327 Andy Van Slyke | .75 |
| 73 Alfredo Griffin | .08 | 158 Brian Downing | .15 | 243 Dann Bilardello | .08 | 328 Craig Reynolds | .08 |
| 74 Jack Perconte | .08 | 159 Tom Dunbar | .08 | 244 Rudy Law | .08 | 329 Dick Schofield | .10 |
| 75 Jesse Orosco | .10 | 160 Marc Hill | .08 | 245 John Lowenstein | .08 | 330 Scott Fletcher | .10 |
| 76 Jody Davis | .10 | 161 Phil Garner | .08 | 246 Tom Tellman | .08 | 331 Jeff Reardon | .35 |
| 77 Bob Horner | .15 | 162 Jerry Davis | .12 | 247 Howard Johnson | 2.00 | 332 Rick Dempsey | .10 |
| 78 Larry McWilliams | .08 | 163 Bill Campbell | .08 | 248 Ray Fontenot | .08 | 333 Ben Oglivie | .15 |
| 79 Joel Youngblood | .08 | 164 John Franco (R) | 1.50 | 249 Tony Armas | .12 | 334 Dan Petry | .15 |
| 80 Alan Wiggins | .10 | 165 Len Barker | .08 | 250 Candy Maldonado | .15 | 335 Jackie Gutierrez | .15 |
| 81 Ron Oester | .08 | 166 Benny Distefano | .12 | 251 Mike Jeffcoat | .08 | 336 Dave Righetti | .15 |
| 82 Ozzie Virgil | .08 | 167 George Frazier | .08 | 252 Dane Iorg | .08 | 337 Alejandro Pena | .08 |
| 83 Ricky Horton (R) | .20 | 168 Tito Landrum | .08 | 253 Bruce Bochte | .08 | 338 Mel Hall | .25 |

| NO. | PLAYER | MINT |
|---|---|---|
| 339 | Pat Sheridan | .08 |
| 340 | Keith Atherton | .08 |
| 341 | David Palmer | .08 |
| 342 | Gary Ward | .08 |
| 343 | Dave Stewart | .50 |
| 344 | Mark Gubicza (R) | .75 |
| 345 | Carney Lansford | .12 |
| 346 | Jerry Willard | .08 |
| 347 | Ken Griffey | .15 |
| 348 | Franklin Stubbs (R) | .40 |
| 349 | Aurelio Lopez | .08 |
| 350 | Al Bumbry | .08 |
| 351 | Charlie Moore | .08 |
| 352 | Luis Sanchez | .08 |
| 353 | Darrell Porter | .08 |
| 354 | Bill Dawley | .08 |
| 355 | Charlie Hudson | .08 |
| 356 | Garry Templeton | .12 |
| 357 | Cecilio Guante | .08 |
| 358 | Jeff Leonard | .12 |
| 359 | Paul Molitor | .50 |
| 360 | Ron Gardenhire | .08 |
| 361 | Larry Bowa | .08 |
| 362 | Bob Kearney | .08 |
| 363 | Garth Iorg | .08 |
| 364 | Tom Brunansky | .15 |
| 365 | Brad Gulden | .08 |
| 366 | Greg Walker | .12 |
| 367 | Mike Young | .12 |
| 368 | Rick Waits | .08 |
| 369 | Doug Bair | .08 |
| 370 | Bob Shirley | .08 |
| 371 | Bob Ojeda | .08 |
| 372 | Bob Welch | .25 |
| 373 | Neal Heaton | .08 |
| 374 | Dan Jackson | .15 |
| 375 | Donnie Hill | .08 |
| 376 | Mike Stenhouse | .08 |
| 377 | Bruce Kison | .08 |
| 378 | Wayne Tolleson | .08 |
| 379 | Floyd Bannister | .08 |
| 380 | Vern Ruhle | .08 |
| 381 | Tim Corcoran | .08 |
| 382 | Kurt Kepshire (R) | .15 |
| 383 | Bobby Brown | .08 |
| 384 | Dave Van Gorder | .08 |
| 385 | Rick Mahler | .08 |
| 386 | Lee Mazzilli | .08 |
| 387 | Bill Laskey | .08 |
| 388 | Thad Bosley | .08 |
| 389 | Al Chambers | .08 |
| 390 | Tony Fernandez | .75 |
| 391 | Ron Washington | .08 |
| 392 | Bill Swaggerty (R) | .15 |
| 393 | Bob L. Gibson | .08 |
| 394 | Marty Castillo | .08 |
| 395 | Steve Crawford | .08 |
| 396 | Clay Christiansen (R) | .15 |
| 397 | Bob Bailor | .08 |
| 398 | Mike Hargrove | .08 |
| 399 | Charlie Leibrandt | .08 |
| 400 | Tom Burgmeier | .08 |
| 401 | Razor Shines (R) | .15 |
| 402 | Rob Wilfong | .08 |
| 403 | Tom Henke | .15 |
| 404 | Al Jones (R) | .15 |
| 405 | Mike LaCoss | .08 |
| 406 | Luis DeLeon | .08 |
| 407 | Greg Gross | .08 |
| 408 | Tom Hume | .08 |
| 409 | Rick Camp | .08 |
| 410 | Milt May | .08 |
| 411 | Henry Cotto (R) | .20 |
| 412 | David Von Ohlen | .08 |
| 413 | Scott McGregor | .10 |
| 414 | Ted Simmons | .10 |
| 415 | Jack Morris | .50 |
| 416 | Bill Buckner | .10 |
| 417 | Butch Wynegar | .08 |
| 418 | Steve Sax | .35 |
| 419 | Steve Balboni | .08 |
| 420 | Dwayne Murphy | .08 |
| 421 | Andre Dawson | 1.00 |
| 422 | Charlie Hough | .08 |
| 423 | Tommy John | .15 |
| 424 | Tom Seaver | 1.25 |
|  | (photo of Floyd Bannister) |  |
| 424 | Tom Seaver | 20.00 |
| 425 | Tom Herr | .10 |
| 426 | Terry Puhl | .08 |
| 427 | Al Holland | .08 |
| 428 | Eddie Milner | .08 |
| 429 | Terry Kennedy | .08 |
| 430 | John Candelaria | .08 |
| 431 | Manny Trillo | .08 |
| 432 | Ken Oberkfell | .08 |
| 433 | Rick Sutcliffe | .15 |
| 434 | Ron Darling | .30 |
| 435 | Spike Owen | .08 |
| 436 | Frank Viola | .50 |
| 437 | Lloyd Moseby | .20 |
| 438 | Kirby Puckett (R) | 25.00 |
| 439 | Jim Clancy | .08 |
| 440 | Mike Moore | .08 |
| 441 | Doug Sisk | .08 |
| 442 | Dennis Eckersley | .40 |
| 443 | Gerald Perry | .25 |
| 444 | Dale Berra | .08 |
| 445 | Dusty Baker | .08 |
| 446 | Ed Whitson | .08 |
| 447 | Cesar Cedeno | .10 |
| 448 | Rick Schu (R) | .20 |
| 449 | Joaquin Andujar | .10 |
| 450 | Mark Bailey (R) | .15 |
| 451 | Ron Romanick (R) | .20 |
| 452 | Julio Cruz | .08 |
| 453 | Miguel Dilone | .08 |
| 454 | Storm Davis | .08 |
| 455 | Jaime Cocanower (R) | .15 |
| 456 | Barbaro Garbey (R) | .15 |
| 457 | Rich Gedman | .08 |
| 458 | Phil Niekro | .25 |
| 459 | Mike Scioscia | .08 |
| 460 | Pat Tabler | .12 |
| 461 | Darryl Motley | .08 |
| 462 | Chris Codorili | .08 |
| 463 | Doug Flynn | .08 |
| 464 | Billy Sample | .08 |
| 465 | Mickey Rivers | .08 |
| 466 | John Wathan | .08 |
| 467 | Bill Krueger | .08 |
| 468 | Andre Thornton | .12 |
| 469 | Rex Hudler (R) | .25 |
| 470 | Sid Bream (R) | .75 |
| 471 | Kirk Gibson | .35 |
| 472 | John Shelby | .08 |
| 473 | Moose Haas | .08 |
| 474 | Doug Corbett | .08 |
| 475 | Willie McGee | .50 |
| 476 | Bob Knepper | .12 |
| 477 | Kevin Gross | .08 |
| 478 | Carmelo Martinez | .12 |
| 479 | Kent Tekulve | .08 |
| 480 | Chili Davis | .15 |
| 481 | Bobby Clark | .08 |
| 482 | Mookie Wilson | .08 |
| 483 | Dave Owen (R) | .15 |
| 484 | Ed Nunez | .08 |
| 485 | Rance Mulliniks | .08 |
| 486 | Ken Schrom | .08 |
| 487 | Jeff Russell | .08 |
| 488 | Tom Paciorek | .08 |
| 489 | Dan Ford | .08 |
| 490 | Mike Caldwell | .08 |
| 491 | Scottie Earl | .15 |
| 492 | Jose Rijo (R) | 2.00 |
| 493 | Bruce Hurst | .08 |
| 494 | Ken Landreaux | .08 |
| 495 | Mike Fischlin | .08 |
| 496 | Don Slaught | .08 |
| 497 | Steve McCatty | .08 |
| 498 | Gary Lucas | .08 |
| 499 | Gary Pettis | .10 |
| 500 | Marvis Foley | .08 |
| 501 | Mike Squires | .08 |
| 502 | Jim Pankovitz | .12 |
| 503 | Luis Aguayo | .08 |
| 504 | Ralph Citarella | .12 |
| 505 | Bruce Bochy | .08 |
| 506 | Bob Owchinko | .08 |
| 507 | Pascual Perez | .08 |
| 508 | Lee Lacy | .08 |
| 509 | Atlee Hammaker | .08 |
| 510 | Bob Dernier | .08 |
| 511 | Ed Vande Berg | .08 |
| 512 | Cliff Johnson | .08 |
| 513 | Len Whitehouse | .08 |
| 514 | Dennis Martinez | .10 |
| 515 | Ed Romero | .08 |
| 516 | Rusty Kuntz | .08 |
| 517 | Rick Miller | .08 |
| 518 | Dennis Rasmussen | .10 |
| 519 | Steve Yeager | .08 |
| 520 | Chris Bando | .08 |
| 521 | U.L. Washington | .08 |
| 522 | Curt Young (R) | .20 |
| 523 | Angel Salazar | .08 |
| 524 | Curt Kaufman (R) | .15 |
| 525 | Odell Jones | .08 |
| 526 | Juan Agosto | .08 |
| 527 | Denny Walling | .08 |
| 528 | Andy Hawkins | .15 |
| 529 | Sixto Lezcano | .08 |
| 530 | Skeeter Barnes | .20 |
| 531 | Randy Johnson | .08 |
| 532 | Jim Morrison | .08 |
| 533 | Warren Brusstar | .08 |
| 534 | Jeff Pendleton | 4.00 |
|  | (incorrect first name) |  |
| 534 | Terry Pendleton | 8.00 |
| 535 | Vic Rodriguez (R) | .15 |
| 536 | Bob McClure | .08 |
| 537 | Dave Bergman | .08 |
| 538 | Mark Clear | .08 |
| 539 | Mike Pagliarulo (R) | .75 |
| 540 | Terry Whitfield | .08 |
| 541 | Joe Beckwith | .08 |
| 542 | Jeff Burroughs | .08 |
| 543 | Dan Schatzeder | .08 |
| 544 | Donnie Scott | .12 |
| 545 | Jim Slaton | .08 |
| 546 | Greg Luzinski | .10 |
| 547 | Mark Salas (R) | .15 |
| 548 | Dave Smith | .08 |
| 549 | John Wockenfuss | .08 |
| 550 | Frank Pastore | .08 |
| 551 | Tim Flannery | .08 |
| 552 | Rick Rhoden | .12 |
| 553 | Mark Davis | .20 |
| 554 | Jeff Dedmon (R) | .12 |
| 555 | Gary Woods | .08 |
| 556 | Danny Heep | .08 |
| 557 | Mark Langston (R) | 5.00 |
| 558 | Darrell Brown | .08 |
| 559 | Jimmy Key (R) | 2.00 |
| 560 | Rick Lysander | .08 |
| 561 | Doyle Alexander | .08 |
| 562 | Mike Stanton | .08 |
| 563 | Sid Fernandez | .50 |
| 564 | Richie Hebner | .08 |
| 565 | Alex Trevino | .08 |
| 566 | Brian Harper | .20 |
| 567 | Dan Gladden (R) | .50 |
| 568 | Luis Salazar | .08 |
| 569 | Tom Foley | .08 |
| 570 | Larry Andersen | .08 |
| 571 | Danny Cox | .12 |
| 572 | Joe Sambito | .08 |
| 573 | Juan Beniquez | .08 |
| 574 | Joel Skinner | .08 |
| 575 | Randy St. Claire | .12 |
| 576 | Floyd Rayford | .08 |
| 577 | Roy Howell | .08 |
| 578 | John Grubb | .08 |
| 579 | Ed Jurak | .08 |
| 580 | John Montefusco | .08 |
| 581 | Orel Hershiser (R) | 5.00 |
| 582 | Tom Waddell (R) | .15 |
| 583 | Mark Huismann | .08 |
| 584 | Joe Morgan | .40 |
| 585 | Jim Wohlford | .08 |
| 586 | Dave Schmidt | .08 |
| 587 | Jeff Kunkel | .15 |
| 588 | Hal McRae | .08 |
| 589 | Bill Almon | .08 |
| 590 | Carmen Castillo | .08 |
| 591 | Omar Moreno | .08 |
| 592 | Ken Howell (R) | .20 |
| 593 | Tom Brookens | .08 |
| 594 | Joe Nolan | .08 |
| 595 | Willie Lozado | .12 |
| 596 | Tom Nieto | .15 |
| 597 | Walt Terrell | .08 |
| 598 | Al Oliver | .10 |
| 599 | Shane Rawley | .08 |
| 600 | Denny Gonzalez | .12 |
| 601 | Mark Grant | .15 |
| 602 | Mike Armstrong | .08 |
| 603 | George Foster | .15 |
| 604 | Davey Lopes | .12 |
| 605 | Salome Barojas | .08 |
| 606 | Roy Lee Jackson | .08 |
| 607 | Pete Filson | .08 |
| 608 | Duane Walker | .08 |
| 609 | Glenn Wilson | .10 |
| 610 | Rafael Santana (R) | .20 |
| 611 | Roy Smith | .15 |
| 612 | Ruppert Jones | .08 |
| 613 | Joe Cowley | .08 |
| 614 | Al Nipper (R) | .20 |
| 615 | Gene Nelson | .08 |
| 616 | Joe Carter | 5.00 |
| 617 | Ray Knight | .10 |
| 618 | Chuck Rainey | .08 |
| 619 | Dan Driessen | .08 |
| 620 | Daryl Sconiers | .08 |
| 621 | Bill Stein | .08 |
| 622 | Roy Smalley | .08 |
| 623 | Ed Lynch | .08 |
| 624 | Jeff Stone (R) | .20 |
| 625 | Bruce Berenyi | .08 |
| 626 | Kelvin Chapman (R) | .15 |
| 627 | Joe Price | .08 |
| 628 | Steve Bedrosian | .12 |
| 629 | Vic Mata | .15 |
| 630 | Mike Krukow | .10 |
| 631 | Phil Bradley (R) | .30 |
| 632 | Jim Gott | .08 |
| 633 | Randy Bush | .08 |
| 634 | Tom Browning (R) | 1.50 |
| 635 | Lou Gehrig Puzzle | .15 |
| 636 | Reid Nichols | .08 |
| 637 | Dan Pasqua (R) | .75 |
| 638 | German Rivera | .12 |
| 639 | Don Schulze | .10 |
| 640 | Mike Jones | .10 |
| 641 | Pete Rose (Mgr.) | 1.00 |
| 642 | Wade Rowdon | .10 |
| 643 | Jerry Narron | .08 |
| 644 | Darrell Miller | .15 |
| 645 | Tim Hulett (R) | .15 |
| 646 | Andy McGaffigan | .08 |
| 647 | Kurt Bevacqua | .05 |
| 648 | John Russell (R) | .15 |
| 649 | Ron Robinson | .25 |
| 650 | Donnie Moore | .08 |
| 651 | Two for the Title: | 4.00 |
|  | D. Winfield, D. Mattingly |  |
| 652 | Tim Laudner | .08 |
| 653 | Steve Farr | .35 |
| — | Checklist (DK) | .10 |
| — | Checklist No. 1 | .08 |
| — | Checklist No. 2 | .08 |
| — | Checklist No. 3 | .08 |
| — | Checklist No. 4 | .08 |
| — | Checklist No. 5 | .08 |
| — | Checklist No. 6 | .08 |

Features the rookie cards of Jose Canseco and Fred McGriff. Donruss limited production. The *checklist* cards are *not* numbered.

| NO. PLAYER | MINT |
|---|---|
| **No. 1 to 26—Diamond Kings** | |
| 1 Kirk Gibson (DK) | .35 |
| 2 Goose Gossage (DK) | .15 |
| 3 Willie McGee (DK) | .20 |
| 4 George Bell (DK) | .20 |
| 5 Tony Armas (DK) | .10 |
| 6 Chili Davis (DK) | .10 |
| 7 Cecil Cooper (DK) | .15 |
| 8 Mike Boddicker (DK) | .10 |
| 9 Davey Lopes (DK) | .10 |
| 10 Bill Doran (DK) | .10 |
| 11 Bret Saberhagen (DK) | .40 |
| 12 Brett Butler (DK) | .15 |
| 13 Harold Baines (DK) | .20 |
| 14 Mike Davis (DK) | .10 |
| 15 Tony Perez (DK) | .15 |
| 16 Willie Randolph (DK) | .10 |
| 17 Bob Boone (DK) | .10 |
| 18 Orel Hershiser (DK) | .35 |
| 19 Johnny Ray (DK) | .10 |
| 20 Gary Ward (DK) | .10 |
| 21 Rick Mahler (DK) | .10 |
| 22 Phil Bradley (DK) | .15 |
| 23 Jerry Koosman (DK) | .10 |
| 24 Tom Brunansky (DK) | .10 |
| 25 Andre Dawson (DK) | .40 |
| 26 Dwight Gooden (DK) | .75 |
| **No. 27 to 46 (Rated Rookies)** | |
| 27 Kal Daniels (R) | 3.00 |
| 28 Fred McGriff (R) | 20.00 |
| 29 Cory Snyder (R) | .50 |
| 30 Jose Guzman (R) | .30 |
| 31 Ty Gainey (R) | .15 |
| 32 Johnny Abrego (R) | .15 |
| 33 Andres Galarraga (R) | 1.00 |
| 34 Dave Shipanoff (R) | .15 |
| 35 Mark McLemore (R) | .20 |
| 36 Marty Clary (R) | .15 |
| 37 Paul O'Neill (R) | 3.00 |
| 38 Danny Tartabull | 1.00 |
| 39 Jose Canseco (R) | 75.00 |
| 40 Juan Nieves (R) | .20 |
| 41 Lance McCullers (R) | .20 |
| 42 Rick Surhoff (R) | .15 |
| 43 Todd Worrell (R) | .20 |
| 44 Bob Kipper (R) | .20 |
| 45 John Habyan (R) | .15 |
| 46 Mike Woodard (R) | .15 |
| 47 Mike Boddicker | .10 |
| 48 Robin Yount | .75 |
| 49 Lou Whitaker | .25 |
| 50 Oil Can Boyd | .05 |
| 51 Ricky Henderson | 2.00 |
| 52 Mike Marshall | .10 |
| 53 George Brett | .75 |
| 54 Dave Kingman | .10 |
| 55 Hubie Brooks | .10 |
| 56 Oddibe McDowell | .15 |
| 57 Doug DeCinces | .10 |
| 58 Britt Burns | .05 |
| 59 Ozzie Smith | .75 |
| 60 Jose Cruz | .10 |
| 61 Mike Schmidt | 2.50 |
| 62 Pete Rose | .75 |
| 63 Steve Garvey | .35 |
| 64 Tony Pena | .10 |

| NO. PLAYER | MINT |
|---|---|
| 65 Chili Davis | .15 |
| 66 Dale Murphy | .50 |
| 67 Ryne Sandberg | 3.00 |
| 68 Gary Carter | .30 |
| 69 Alvin Davis | .15 |
| 70 Kent Hrbek | .20 |
| 71 George Bell | .40 |
| 72 Kirby Puckett | 6.00 |
| 73 Lloyd Moseby | .10 |
| 74 Bob Kearney | .07 |
| 75 Dwight Gooden | 2.00 |
| 76 Gary Matthews | .07 |
| 77 Rick Mahler | .07 |
| 78 Benny Distefano | .07 |
| 79 Jeff Leonard | .07 |
| 80 Kevin McReynolds | .30 |
| 81 Ron Oester | .07 |
| 82 John Russell | .07 |
| 83 Tommy Herr | .10 |
| 84 Jerry Mumphrey | .07 |
| 85 Ron Romanick | .07 |
| 86 Daryl Boston | .07 |
| 87 Andre Dawson | .60 |
| 88 Eddie Murray | .75 |
| 89 Dion James | .07 |
| 90 Chet Lemon | .07 |
| 91 Bob Stanley | .07 |
| 92 Willie Randolph | .07 |
| 93 Mike Scioscia | .07 |
| 94 Tom Waddell | .07 |
| 95 Danny Jackson | .20 |
| 96 Mike Davis | .07 |
| 97 Mike Fitzgerald | .07 |
| 98 Gary Ward | .07 |
| 99 Pete O'Brien | .07 |
| 100 Bret Saberhagen | 1.00 |
| 101 Alfredo Griffin | .07 |
| 102 Brett Butler | .20 |
| 103 Ron Guidry | .15 |
| 104 Jerry Reuss | .07 |
| 105 Jack Morris | .35 |
| 106 Rick Dempsey | .07 |
| 107 Ray Burris | .07 |
| 108 Brian Downing | .07 |
| 109 Willie McGee | .25 |
| 110 Bill Doran | .07 |
| 111 Kent Tekulve | .07 |
| 112 Tony Gwynn | 2.00 |
| 113 Marvell Wynne | .07 |
| 114 David Green | .07 |
| 115 Jim Gantner | .07 |
| 116 George Foster | .15 |
| 117 Steve Trout | .07 |
| 118 Mark Langston | .60 |
| 119 Tony Fernandez | .25 |
| 120 John Butcher | .07 |
| 121 Ron Robinson | .07 |
| 122 Dan Spillner | .07 |
| 123 Mike Young | .12 |
| 124 Paul Molitor | .25 |
| 125 Kirk Gibson | .30 |
| 126 Ken Griffey | .07 |
| 127 Tony Armas | .10 |
| 128 Mariano Duncan (R) | .35 |
| 129 Pat Tabler | .07 |
| 130 Frank White | .07 |

| NO. PLAYER | MINT |
|---|---|
| 131 Carney Lansford | .10 |
| 132 Vance Law | .07 |
| 133 Dick Schofield | .07 |
| 134 Wayne Tolleson | .07 |
| 135 Greg Walker | .10 |
| 136 Denny Walling | .07 |
| 137 Ozzie Virgil | .07 |
| 138 Ricky Horton | .07 |
| 139 LaMarr Hoyt | .10 |
| 140 Wayne Krenchicki | .07 |
| 141 Glenn Hubbard | .07 |
| 142 Cecilio Guante | .07 |
| 143 Mike Krukow | .07 |
| 144 Lee Smith | .30 |
| 145 Ed Nunez | .07 |
| 146 Dave Stieb | .15 |
| 147 Mike Smithson | .07 |
| 148 Ken Dixon | .07 |
| 149 Danny Darwin | .07 |
| 150 Chris Pittaro | .15 |
| 151 Bill Buckner | .10 |
| 152 Mike Pagliarulo | .15 |
| 153 Bill Russell | .07 |
| 154 Brook Jacoby | .10 |
| 155 Pat Sheridan | .07 |
| 156 Mike Gallego | .12 |
| 157 Jim Wohlford | .07 |
| 158 Gary Pettis | .10 |
| 159 Toby Harrah | .07 |
| 160 Rich Dotson | .07 |
| 161 Bob Knepper | .07 |
| 162 Dave Dravecky | .07 |
| 163 Greg Gross | .07 |
| 164 Eric Davis | 2.00 |
| 165 Gerald Perry | .20 |
| 166 Rick Rhoden | .07 |
| 167 Keith Moreland | .07 |
| 168 Jack Clark | .20 |
| 169 Storm Davis | .07 |
| 170 Cecil Cooper | .15 |
| 171 Alan Trammell | .50 |
| 172 Roger Clemens | 7.50 |
| 173 Don Mattingly | 4.00 |
| 174 Pedro Guerrero | .20 |
| 175 Willie Wilson | .15 |
| 176 Dwayne Murphy | .07 |
| 177 Tim Raines | .30 |
| 178 Larry Parrish | .07 |
| 179 Mike Witt | .10 |
| 180 Harold Baines | .20 |
| 181 Vince Coleman (R) | 6.00 |
| 182 Jeff Heathcock (R) | .15 |
| 183 Steve Carlton | .50 |
| 184 Mario Soto | .10 |
| 185 Goose Gossage | .15 |
| 186 Johnny Ray | .10 |
| 187 Dan Gladden | .07 |
| 188 Bob Horner | .15 |
| 189 Rick Sutcliffe | .15 |
| 190 Keith Hernandez | .20 |
| 191 Phil Bradley | .15 |
| 192 Tom Brunansky | .15 |
| 193 Jesse Barfield | .15 |
| 194 Frank Viola | .30 |
| 195 Willie Upshaw | .10 |
| 196 Jim Beattie | .07 |

| NO. PLAYER | MINT |
|---|---|
| 197 Darryl Strawberry | 5.00 |
| 198 Ron Cey | .10 |
| 199 Steve Bedrosian | .15 |
| 200 Steve Kemp | .07 |
| 201 Manny Trillo | .07 |
| 202 Garry Templeton | .07 |
| 203 Dave Parker | .25 |
| 204 John Denny | .07 |
| 205 Terry Pendleton | .50 |
| 206 Terry Puhl | .07 |
| 207 Bobby Grich | .07 |
| 208 Ozzie Guillen (R) | 1.25 |
| 209 Jeff Reardon | .35 |
| 210 Cal Ripken, Jr. | 2.50 |
| 211 Bill Schroeder | .07 |
| 212 Dan Petry | .15 |
| 213 Jim Rice | .20 |
| 214 Dave Righetti | .10 |
| 215 Fernando Valenzuela | .15 |
| 216 Julio Franco | .75 |
| 217 Darryl Motley | .07 |
| 218 Dave Collins | .07 |
| 219 Tim Wallach | .10 |
| 220 George Wright | .07 |
| 221 Tommy Dunbar | .07 |
| 222 Steve Balboni | .07 |
| 223 Jay Howell | .07 |
| 224 Joe Carter | 1.00 |
| 225 Ed Whitson | .07 |
| 226 Orel Hershiser | .75 |
| 227 Willie Hernandez | .15 |
| 228 Lee Lacy | .07 |
| 229 Rollie Fingers | .25 |
| 230 Bob Boone | .07 |
| 231 Joaquin Andujar | .10 |
| 232 Craig Reynolds | .07 |
| 233 Shane Rawley | .07 |
| 234 Eric Show | .07 |
| 235 Jose DeLeon | .07 |
| 236 Jose Uribe (R) | .20 |
| 237 Moose Haas | .07 |
| 238 Wally Backman | .07 |
| 239 Dennis Eckersley | .30 |
| 240 Mike Moore | .07 |
| 241 Damaso Garcia | .07 |
| 242 Tim Teufel | .07 |
| 243 Dave Concepcion | .07 |
| 244 Floyd Bannister | .07 |
| 245 Fred Lynn | .15 |
| 246 Charlie Moore | .07 |
| 247 Walt Terrell | .07 |
| 248 Dave Winfield | .60 |
| 249 Dwight Evans | .15 |
| 250 Dennis Powell | .12 |
| 251 Andre Thornton | .07 |
| 252 Onix Concepcion | .07 |
| 253 Mike Heath | .07 |
| 254 David Palmer | .07 |
| 255 Donnie Moore | .07 |
| 256 Curtis Wilkerson | .07 |
| 257 Julio Cruz | .07 |
| 258 Nolan Ryan | 4.00 |
| 259 Jeff Stone | .07 |
| 260 John Tudor | .15 |
| 261 Mark Thurmond | .07 |
| 262 Jay Tibbs | .07 |

| NO. | PLAYER | MINT | NO. | PLAYER | MINT | NO. | PLAYER | MINT | NO. | PLAYER | MINT |
|---|---|---|---|---|---|---|---|---|---|---|---|
| 263 | Rafael Ramirez | .07 | 348 | Carlos Diaz | .07 | 433 | Billy Hatcher | .15 | 518 | Rich Bordi | .07 |
| 264 | Larry McWilliams | .07 | 349 | Barbaro Garbey | .07 | 434 | Clint Hurdle | .07 | 519 | Steve Yeager | .07 |
| 265 | Mark Davis | .07 | 350 | Larry Sheets | .12 | 435 | Ivan Calderon (R) | 1.50 | 520 | Tony Bernazard | .07 |
| 266 | Bob Dernier | .07 | 351 | Teddy Higuera (R) | .50 | 436 | Pete Filson | .07 | 521 | Hal McRae | .07 |
| 267 | Matt Young | .07 | 352 | Juan Beniquez | .07 | 437 | Tom Henke | .10 | 522 | Jose Rijo | .30 |
| 268 | Jim Clancy | .07 | 353 | Bob Forsch | .07 | 438 | Dave Engle | .07 | 523 | Mitch Webster (R) | .20 |
| 269 | Mickey Hatcher | .07 | 354 | Mark Bailey | .07 | 439 | Tom Filer | .07 | 524 | Jack Howell (R) | .20 |
| 270 | Sammy Stewart | .07 | 355 | Larry Andersen | .07 | 440 | Gorman Thomas | .10 | 525 | Alan Bannister | .07 |
| 271 | Bob Gibson | .07 | 356 | Terry Kennedy | .07 | 441 | Rick Aguilera (R) | .75 | 526 | Ron Kittle | .10 |
| 272 | Nelson Simmons (R) | .15 | 357 | Don Robinson | .07 | 442 | Scott Sanderson | .07 | 527 | Phil Garner | .07 |
| 273 | Rich Gedman | .07 | 358 | Jim Gott | .07 | 443 | Jeff Dedmon | .07 | 528 | Kurt Bevacqua | .07 |
| 274 | Butch Wynegar | .07 | 359 | Earnest Riles (R) | .15 | 444 | Joe Orsulak (R) | .30 | 529 | Kevin Gross | .07 |
| 275 | Ken Howell | .07 | 360 | John Christensen | .15 | 445 | Atlee Hammaker | .07 | 530 | Bo Diaz | .07 |
| 276 | Mel Hall | .07 | 361 | Ray Fontenot | .07 | 446 | Jerry Royster | .07 | 531 | Ken Oberkfell | .07 |
| 277 | Jim Sundberg | .07 | 362 | Spike Owen | .07 | 447 | Buddy Bell | .10 | 532 | Rick Reuschel | .07 |
| 278 | Chris Codiroli | .07 | 363 | Jim Acker | .07 | 448 | Dave Rucker | .07 | 533 | Ron Meridith (R) | .15 |
| 279 | H. Winningham (R) | .15 | 364 | Ron Davis | .07 | 449 | Ivan DeJesus | .07 | 534 | Steve Braun | .07 |
| 280 | Rod Carew | .75 | 365 | Tom Hume | .07 | 450 | Jim Pankovits | .07 | 535 | Wayne Gross | .07 |
| 281 | Don Slaught | .07 | 366 | Carlton Fisk | .60 | 451 | Jerry Narron | .07 | 536 | Ray Searage | .07 |
| 282 | Scott Fletcher | .07 | 367 | Nate Snell (R) | .15 | 452 | Bryan Little | .07 | 537 | Tom Brookens | .07 |
| 283 | Bill Dawley | .07 | 368 | Rick Manning | .07 | 453 | Gary Lucas | .07 | 538 | Al Nipper | .07 |
| 284 | Andy Hawkins | .07 | 369 | Darrell Evans | .10 | 454 | Dennis Martinez | .07 | 539 | Billy Sample | .07 |
| 285 | Glenn Wilson | .10 | 370 | Ron Hassey | .07 | 455 | Ed Romero | .07 | 540 | Steve Sax | .20 |
| 286 | Nick Esasky | .07 | 371 | Wade Boggs | 2.50 | 456 | Bob Melvin (R) | .12 | 541 | Dan Quisenberry | .15 |
| 287 | Claudell Washington | .07 | 372 | Rick Honeycutt | .07 | 457 | Glenn Hoffman | .07 | 542 | Tony Phillips | .07 |
| 288 | Lee Mazzilli | .07 | 373 | Chris Bando | .07 | 458 | Bob Shirley | .07 | 543 | Floyd Youmans (R) | .20 |
| 289 | Jody Davis | .07 | 374 | Bud Black | .07 | 459 | Bob Welch | .15 | 544 | Steve Buechele (R) | .50 |
| 290 | Darrell Porter | .07 | 375 | Steve Henderson | .07 | 460 | Carmen Castillo | .07 | 545 | Craig Gerber (R) | .10 |
| 291 | Scott McGregor | .07 | 376 | Charlie Lea | .07 | 461 | Dave Leeper (R) | .12 | 546 | Joe DeSa (R) | .15 |
| 292 | Ted Simmons | .10 | 377 | Reggie Jackson | .75 | 462 | Tim Birtsas (R) | .15 | 547 | Brian Harper | .15 |
| 293 | Aurelio Lopez | .07 | 378 | Dave Schmidt | .07 | 463 | Randy St. Claire | .07 | 548 | Kevin Bass | .07 |
| 294 | Marty Barrett | .07 | 379 | Bob James | .07 | 464 | Chris Welsh | .07 | 549 | Tom Foley | .07 |
| 295 | Dale Berra | .07 | 380 | Glenn Davis | 2.50 | 465 | Greg Harris | .07 | 550 | Dave Van Gorder | .07 |
| 296 | Greg Brock | .07 | 381 | Tim Corcoran | .07 | 466 | Lynn Jones | .07 | 551 | Bruce Bochy | .07 |
| 297 | Charlie Leibrandt | .07 | 382 | Danny Cox | .10 | 467 | Dusty Baker | .07 | 552 | R.J. Reynolds | .07 |
| 298 | Bill Krueger | .07 | 383 | Tim Flannery | .07 | 468 | Roy Smith | .07 | 553 | Chris Brown (R) | .20 |
| 299 | Bryn Smith | .07 | 384 | Tom Browning | .20 | 469 | Andre Robertson | .07 | 554 | Bruce Benedict | .07 |
| 300 | Burt Hooton | .07 | 385 | Rick Camp | .07 | 470 | Ken Landreaux | .07 | 555 | Warren Brusstar | .07 |
| 301 | Stu Cliburn (R) | .15 | 386 | Jim Morrison | .07 | 471 | Dave Bergman | .07 | 556 | Danny Heep | .07 |
| 302 | Luis Salazar | .07 | 387 | Dave LaPoint | .07 | 472 | Gary Roenicke | .07 | 557 | Darnell Coles | .07 |
| 303 | Ken Dayley | .07 | 388 | Davey Lopes | .07 | 473 | Pete Vuckovich | .07 | 558 | Greg Gagne | .07 |
| 304 | Frank DiPino | .07 | 389 | Al Cowens | .07 | 474 | Kirk McCaskill (R) | .25 | 559 | Ernie Whitt | .07 |
| 305 | Von Hayes | .15 | 390 | Doyle Alexander | .07 | 475 | Jeff Lahti | .07 | 560 | Ron Washington | .07 |
| 306 | Gary Redus | .07 | 391 | Tim Laudner | .07 | 476 | Mike Scott | .20 | 561 | Jimmy Key | .25 |
| 307 | Craig Lefferts | .07 | 392 | Don Aase | .07 | 477 | Darren Daulton (R) | .30 | 562 | Billy Swift | .07 |
| 308 | Sam Khalifa | .15 | 393 | Jaime Cocanower | .07 | 478 | Graig Nettles | .10 | 563 | Ron Darling | .15 |
| 309 | Scott Garrelts | .07 | 394 | Randy O'Neal | .07 | 479 | Bill Almon | .07 | 564 | Dick Ruthven | .07 |
| 310 | Rick Cerone | .07 | 395 | Mike Easler | .07 | 480 | Greg Minton | .07 | 565 | Zane Smith | .40 |
| 311 | Shawon Dunston | .75 | 396 | Scott Bradley | .07 | 481 | Randy Ready | .07 | 566 | Sid Bream | .07 |
| 312 | Howard Johnson | .60 | 397 | Tom Niedenfuer | .07 | 482 | Len Dykstra (R) | 2.50 | 567 | Joel Youngblood | .07 |
| 313 | Jim Presley | .15 | 398 | Jerry Willard | .07 | 483 | Thad Bosley | .07 | 568 | Mario Ramirez | .07 |
| 314 | Gary Gaetti | .15 | 399 | Lonnie Smith | .10 | 484 | Harold Reynolds (R) | .75 | 569 | Tom Runnells (R) | .10 |
| 315 | Luis Leal | .07 | 400 | Bruce Bochte | .07 | 485 | Al Oliver | .10 | 570 | Rick Schu | .07 |
| 316 | Mark Salas | .07 | 401 | Terry Francona | .07 | 486 | Roy Smalley | .07 | 571 | Bill Campbell | .07 |
| 317 | Bill Caudill | .07 | 402 | Jim Slaton | .07 | 487 | John Franco | .15 | 572 | Dickie Thon | .07 |
| 318 | Dave Henderson | .30 | 403 | Bill Stein | .07 | 488 | Juan Agosto | .07 | 573 | Al Holland | .07 |
| 319 | Rafael Santana | .07 | 404 | Timmy Hulett | .07 | 489 | Al Pardo | .15 | 574 | Reid Nichols | .07 |
| 320 | Leon Durham | .15 | 405 | Alan Ashby | .07 | 490 | Bill Wegman (R) | .15 | 575 | Bert Roberge | .07 |
| 321 | Bruce Sutter | .15 | 406 | Tim Stoddard | .07 | 491 | Frank Tanana | .07 | 576 | Mike Flanagan | .07 |
| 322 | Jason Thompson | .07 | 407 | Garry Maddox | .07 | 492 | Brian Fisher (R) | .15 | 577 | Tim Leary | .15 |
| 323 | Bob Brenly | .07 | 408 | Ted Power | .07 | 493 | Mark Clear | .07 | 578 | Mike Laga | .07 |
| 324 | Carmelo Martinez | .07 | 409 | Len Barker | .07 | 494 | Len Matuszek | .07 | 579 | Steve Lyons | .07 |
| 325 | Eddie Milner | .07 | 410 | Denny Gonzalez | .07 | 495 | Ramon Romero (R) | .10 | 580 | Phil Niekro | .20 |
| 326 | Juan Samuel | .20 | 411 | George Frazier | .07 | 496 | John Wathan | .07 | 581 | Gilberto Reyes (R) | .15 |
| 327 | Tom Nieto | .07 | 412 | Andy Van Slyke | .30 | 497 | Rob Picciolo | .07 | 582 | Jamie Easterly | .07 |
| 328 | Dave Smith | .07 | 413 | Jim Dwyer | .07 | 498 | U.L. Washington | .07 | 583 | Mark Gubicza | .15 |
| 329 | Urbano Lugo (R) | .15 | 414 | Paul Householder | .07 | 499 | John Candelaria | .07 | 584 | Stan Javier (R) | .25 |
| 330 | Joel Skinner | .07 | 415 | Alejandro Sanchez | .07 | 500 | Duane Walker | .07 | 585 | Bill Laskey | .07 |
| 331 | Bill Gullickson | .07 | 416 | Steve Crawford | .07 | 501 | Gene Nelson | .07 | 586 | Jeff Russell | .07 |
| 332 | Floyd Rayford | .07 | 417 | Dan Pasqua | .15 | 502 | John Mizerock | .07 | 587 | Dickie Noles | .07 |
| 333 | Ben Oglivie | .07 | 418 | Enos Cabell | .07 | 503 | Luis Aguayo | .07 | 588 | Steve Farr | .07 |
| 334 | Lance Parrish | .20 | 419 | Mike Jones | .07 | 504 | Kurt Kepshire | .07 | 589 | Steve Ontiveros (R) | .15 |
| 335 | Jackie Gutierrez | .07 | 420 | Steve Kiefer | .07 | 505 | Ed Wojna (R) | .15 | 590 | Mike Hargrove | .07 |
| 336 | Dennis Rasmussen | .07 | 421 | Tim Burke (R) | .30 | 506 | Joe Price | .07 | 591 | Marty Bystrom | .07 |
| 337 | Terry Whitfield | .07 | 422 | Mike Mason | .07 | 507 | Milt Thompson (R) | .30 | 592 | Franklin Stubbs | .10 |
| 338 | Neal Heaton | .07 | 423 | Ruppert Jones | .07 | 508 | Junior Ortiz | .07 | 593 | Larry Herndon | .07 |
| 339 | Jorge Orta | .07 | 424 | Jerry Hairston | .07 | 509 | Vida Blue | .07 | 594 | Bill Swaggerty | .07 |
| 340 | Donnie Hill | .07 | 425 | Tito Landrum | .07 | 510 | Steve Engel (R) | .10 | 595 | Carlos Ponce (R) | .10 |
| 341 | Joe Hesketh | .10 | 426 | Jeff Calhoun (R) | .12 | 511 | Karl Best (R) | .10 | 596 | Pat Perry (R) | .10 |
| 342 | Charlie Hough | .07 | 427 | Don Carman (R) | .15 | 512 | Cecil Fielder (R) | 15.00 | 597 | Ray Knight | .07 |
| 343 | Dave Rozema | .07 | 428 | Tony Perez | .25 | 513 | Frank Eufemia (R) | .15 | 598 | Steve Lombardozzi (R) | .15 |
| 344 | Greg Pryor | .07 | 429 | Jerry Davis | .07 | 514 | Tippy Martinez | .07 | 599 | Brad Havens | .07 |
| 345 | Mickey Tettleton (R) | 1.00 | 430 | Bob Walk | .07 | 515 | Billy Robidoux (R) | .20 | 600 | Pat Clements (R) | .20 |
| 346 | George Vukovich | .07 | 431 | Brad Wellman | .07 | 516 | Bill Scherrer | .07 | 601 | Joe Niekro | .10 |
| 347 | Don Baylor | .10 | 432 | Terry Forster | .07 | 517 | Bruce Hurst | .10 | 602 | Hank Aaron Puzzle | .15 |

# 1986 Donruss (Continued)

| NO. PLAYER | MINT |
|---|---|
| 603 Dwayne Henry (R) | .15 |
| 604 Mookie Wilson | .07 |
| 605 Buddy Biancalana | .07 |
| 606 Rance Mulliniks | .07 |
| 607 Alan Wiggins | .07 |
| 608 Joe Cowley | .07 |
| 609 Tom Seaver | .75 |
| 610 Neil Allen | .07 |
| 611 Don Sutton | .75 |
| 612 Fred Toliver (R) | .07 |
| 613 Jay Baller (R) | .25 |
| 614 Marc Sullivan (R) | .15 |
| 615 John Grubb | .15 |
| 616 Bruce Kison | .10 |
| 617 Bill Madlock | .07 |
| 618 Chris Chambliss | .07 |
| 619 Dave Stewart | .10 |
| 620 Tim Lollar | .07 |
| 621 Gary Lavelle | .30 |

| NO. PLAYER | MINT |
|---|---|
| 622 Charles Hudson | .07 |
| 623 Joel Davis (R) | .15 |
| 624 Joe Johnson (R) | .15 |
| 625 Sid Fernandez | .15 |
| 626 Dennis Lamp | .07 |
| 627 Terry Harper | .07 |
| 628 Jack Lazorko | .07 |
| 629 Roger McDowell (R) | .35 |
| 630 Mark Funderburk (R) | .20 |
| 631 Ed Lynch | .07 |
| 632 Rudy Law | .07 |
| 633 Roger Mason (R) | .15 |
| 634 Mike Felder (R) | .20 |
| 635 Ken Schrom | .07 |
| 636 Bob Ojeda | .07 |
| 637 Ed Vande Berg | .07 |
| 638 Bobby Meacham | .07 |
| 639 Cliff Johnson | .07 |

| NO. PLAYER | MINT |
|---|---|
| 640 Garth Iorg | .07 |
| 641 Dan Driessen | .07 |
| 642 Mike Brown | .07 |
| 643 John Shelby | .07 |
| 644 Pete Rose Ty-Breaking Hit #4192: | .30 |
| 645 Knuckle Brothers: Phil and Joe Niekro | .10 |
| 646 Jesse Orosco | .07 |
| 647 Billy Beane (R) | .15 |
| 648 Cesar Cedeno | .07 |
| 649 Bert Blyleven | .10 |
| 650 Max Venable | .07 |
| 651 Fleet Feet: W. McGee, V. Coleman | .50 |
| 652 Calvin Schiraldi | .07 |
| 653 King of Kings: Pete Rose | .75 |

| NO. PLAYER | MINT |
|---|---|
| — Checklist (DK) | .08 |
| — Checklist No. 1 | .08 |
| — Checklist No. 2 | .08 |
| — Checklist No. 3 | .08 |
| — Checklist No. 4 | .08 |
| — Checklist No. 5 | .08 |
| — Checklist No. 6 | .08 |

## 1986 Donruss Rookies. . . . Complete Set of 56 Cards—Value $50.00

Features the outstanding rookies of the 1986 season. The cards are coated with a glossy finish. The entire set was packaged in a printed box, and distributed exclusively through card hobby dealers.

| NO. PLAYER | MINT |
|---|---|
| 1 Wally Joyner (RR) | 2.50 |
| 2 Tracy Jones | .20 |
| 3 Allan Anderson | .30 |
| 4 Ed Correa | .15 |
| 5 Reggie Williams | .15 |
| 6 Charlie Kerfeld | .15 |
| 7 Andres Galarraga | .50 |
| 8 Bob Tewksbury | .20 |
| 9 Al Newman | .15 |
| 10 Andres Thomas | .15 |
| 11 Barry Bonds (RR) | 7.00 |
| 12 Juan Nieves | .10 |
| 13 Mark Eichhorn | .15 |
| 14 Dan Plesac | .20 |

| NO. PLAYER | MINT |
|---|---|
| 15 Cory Snyder | .35 |
| 16 Kelly Gruber | 2.50 |
| 17 Kevin Mitchell (RR) | 6.00 |
| 18 Steve Lombardozzi | .15 |
| 19 Mitch Williams | .35 |
| 20 John Cerutti | .15 |
| 21 Todd Worrell | .15 |
| 22 Jose Canseco | 12.00 |
| 23 Pete Incaviglia (RR) | .75 |
| 24 Jose Guzman | .15 |
| 25 Scott Bailes | .15 |
| 26 Greg Matthews | .15 |
| 27 Eric King | .25 |
| 28 Paul Assenmacher | .15 |

| NO. PLAYER | MINT |
|---|---|
| 29 Jeff Sellers | .20 |
| 30 Bobby Bonilla (RR) | 7.00 |
| 31 Doug Drabek | 2.00 |
| 32 Will Clark (RR) | 10.00 |
| 33 Leon "Bip" Roberts | .50 |
| 34 Jim Deshaies | .25 |
| 35 Mike Lavalliere | .30 |
| 36 Scott Bankhead | .20 |
| 37 Dale Sveum | .15 |
| 38 Bo Jackson (RR) | 10.00 |
| 39 Rob Thompson | .40 |
| 40 Eric Plunk | .15 |
| 41 Bill Bathe | .20 |
| 42 John Kruk | .50 |

| NO. PLAYER | MINT |
|---|---|
| 43 Andy Allanson | .15 |
| 44 Mark Portugal | .20 |
| 45 Danny Tartabull | .75 |
| 46 Bob Kpper | .15 |
| 47 Gene Walter | .15 |
| 48 Rey Quinonez | .15 |
| 49 Bobby Witt | .75 |
| 50 Bill Mooneyham | .15 |
| 51 John Cangelos | .15 |
| 52 Ruben Sierra (RR) | 9.00 |
| 53 Rob Woodward | .15 |
| 54 Ed Hearn | .15 |
| 55 Joel McKeon | .15 |
| 56 Checklist | .20 |

# 1987 Donruss.... Complete Set of 660 Cards—Value $75.00 (Factory-Sealed set—Value-$90.00)

Features the rookie cards of Bo Jackson, Wally Joyner, Kevin Mitchell, Will Clark, Ruben Sierra and Mike Greenwell. Donruss limited production.
Cards 14, 22 and 25 exist with the "yellow" strip missing on back—worth triple the value of the corrected cards.

| NO. PLAYER | MINT | NO. PLAYER | MINT | NO. PLAYER | MINT | NO. PLAYER | MINT |
|---|---|---|---|---|---|---|---|
| **No. 1 to 26—Diamond Kings** | | 65 R.J. Reynolds | .05 | 131 Julio Franco | .30 | 197 Tom Henke | .10 |
| 1 Wally Joyner (DK) | .30 | 66 Will Clark (R) | 10.00 | 132 Bret Saberhagen | .25 | 198 Karl Best | .05 |
| 2 Roger Clemens (DK) | .60 | 67 Ozzie Virgil | .05 | 133 Mike Davis | .05 | 199 Dwight Gooden | .50 |
| 3 Dale Murphy (DK) | .15 | 68 Rick Sutcliffe | .10 | 134 Joe Hesketh | .05 | 200 Checklist: 134-209 | .08 |
| 4 Darryl Strawberry (DK) | .45 | 69 Gary Carter | .20 | 135 Wally Joyner (R) | 1.50 | 201 Steve Trout | .05 |
| 5 Ozzie Smith (DK) | .15 | 70 Mike Moore | .05 | 136 Don Slaught | .05 | 202 Rafael Ramirez | .05 |
| 6 Jose Canseco (DK) | 1.25 | 71 Bert Blyleven | .10 | 137 Daryl Boston | .05 | 203 Bob Walk | .05 |
| 7 Charlie Hough (DK) | .10 | 72 Tony Fernandez | .15 | 138 Nolan Ryan | 2.00 | 204 Roger Mason | .05 |
| 8 Brook Jacoby (DK) | .10 | 73 Kent Hrbek | .15 | 139 Mike Schmidt | 1.00 | 205 Terry Kennedy | .05 |
| 9 Fred Lynn (DK) | .15 | 74 Lloyd Moseby | .10 | 140 Tommy Herr | .05 | 206 Ron Oester | .05 |
| 10 Rick Rhoden (DK) | .10 | 75 Alvin Davis | .10 | 141 Garry Templeton | .05 | 207 John Russell | .05 |
| 11 Chris Brown (DK) | .10 | 76 Keith Hernandez | .15 | 142 Kal Daniels | .20 | 208 Greg Mathews (R) | .15 |
| 12 Von Hayes (DK) | .10 | 77 Ryne Sandberg | 1.00 | 143 Billy Sample | .05 | 209 Charlie Kerfeld | .10 |
| 13 Jack Morris (DK) | .20 | 78 Dale Murphy | .25 | 144 Johnny Ray | .08 | 210 Reggie Jackson | .35 |
| 14 K. McReynolds (DK) | .12 | 79 Sid Bream | .05 | 145 Rob Thompson (R) | .25 | 211 Floyd Bannister | .05 |
| 14 McReynolds (error) | .50 | 80 Chris Brown | .10 | 146 Bob Dernier | .05 | 212 Vance Law | .05 |
| 15 George Brett (DK) | .35 | 81 Steve Garvey | .25 | 147 Danny Tartabull | .25 | 213 Rich Bordi | .05 |
| 16 Ted Higuera (DK) | .10 | 82 Mario Soto | .05 | 148 Ernie Whitt | .05 | 214 Dan Plesac (R) | .15 |
| 17 Hubie Brooks (DK) | .10 | 83 Shane Rawley | .05 | 149 Kirby Puckett | 1.50 | 215 Dave Collins | .05 |
| 18 Mike Scott (DK) | .10 | 84 Willie McGee | .10 | 150 Mike Young | .05 | 216 Bob Stanley | .05 |
| 19 Kirby Puckett (DK) | .45 | 85 Jose Cruz | .10 | 151 Ernest Riles | .10 | 217 Joe Niekro | .10 |
| 20 Dave Winfield (DK) | .25 | 86 Brian Downing | .05 | 152 Frank Tanana | .05 | 218 Tom Niedenfuer | .05 |
| 21 Lloyd Moseby (DK) | .10 | 87 Ozzie Guillen | .15 | 153 Rich Gedman | .05 | 219 Brett Butler | .15 |
| 22 Eric Davis (DK) | .30 | 88 Hubie Brooks | .12 | 154 Willie Randolph | .08 | 220 Charlie Leibrandt | .05 |
| 22 E. Davis (error) | 1.00 | 89 Cal Ripken | 1.00 | 155 Bill Madlock | .10 | 221 Steve Ontiveros | .05 |
| 23 Jim Presley (DK) | .15 | 90 Juan Nieves | .10 | 156 Joe Carter | .40 | 222 Tim Burke | .05 |
| 24 Keith Moreland (DK) | .10 | 91 Lance Parrish | .15 | 157 Danny Jackson | .10 | 223 Curtis Wilkerson | .05 |
| 25 Greg Walker (DK) | .15 | 92 Jim Rice | .15 | 158 Carney Lansford | .05 | 224 Pete Incaviglia (R) | .30 |
| 26 St. Sax (DK) | .10 | 93 Ron Guidry | .10 | 159 Bryn Smith | .05 | 225 Lonnie Smith | .05 |
| 27 Checklist (DK) | .10 | 94 Fernando Valenzuela | .15 | 160 Gary Pettis | .05 | 226 Chris Codiroli | .05 |
| **No. 28 to 47—Rated Rookies** | | 95 Andy Allanson (R) | .15 | 161 Oddibe McDowell | .10 | 227 Scott Bailes (R) | .12 |
| 28 B.J. Surhoff (R) | .25 | 96 Willie Wilson | .10 | 162 John Cangelosi (R) | .12 | 228 Rickey Henderson | .75 |
| 29 Randy Myers (R) | .30 | 97 Jose Canseco | 10.00 | 163 Mike Scott | .10 | 229 Ken Howell | .05 |
| 30 Ken Gerhart (R) | .10 | 98 Jeff Reardon | .05 | 164 Eric Show | .05 | 230 Darnell Coles | .08 |
| 31 Benito Santiago | 1.25 | 99 Bobby Witt (R) | .60 | 165 Juan Samuel | .12 | 231 Don Aase | .05 |
| 32 Greg Swindell (R) | .60 | 100 Checklist: 28 to 133 | .10 | 166 Nick Esasky | .05 | 232 Tim Leary | .05 |
| 33 Mike Birkbeck (R) | .10 | 101 Jose Guzman | .10 | 167 Zane Smith | .05 | 233 Bob Boone | .05 |
| 34 Terry Steinbach (R) | .50 | 102 Steve Balboni | .10 | 168 Mike Brown | .05 | 234 Ricky Horton | .05 |
| 35 Bo Jackson (R) | 7.00 | 103 Tony Phillips | .05 | 169 Keith Moreland | .05 | 235 Mark Bailey | .05 |
| 36 Greg Maddux (R) | 1.25 | 104 Brook Jacoby | .10 | 170 John Tudor | .10 | 236 Kevin Gross | .05 |
| 37 Jim Lindeman (R) | .10 | 105 Dave Winfield | .25 | 171 Ken Dixon | .05 | 237 Lance McCullers | .10 |
| 38 Devon White (R) | .75 | 106 Orel Hershiser | .25 | 172 Jim Gantner | .05 | 238 Cecilio Guante | .05 |
| 39 Eric Bell (R) | .10 | 107 Lou Whitaker | .15 | 173 Jack Morris | .25 | 239 Bob Melvin | .05 |
| 40 Will Fraser (R) | .12 | 108 Fred Lynn | .10 | 174 Bruce Hurst | .10 | 240 Billy Jo Robidoux | .12 |
| 41 Jerry Browne (R) | .25 | 109 Bill Wegman | .05 | 175 Dennis Rasmussen | .10 | 241 Roger McDowell | .10 |
| 42 Chris James (R) | .30 | 110 Donnie Moore | .05 | 176 Mike Marshall | .10 | 242 Leon Durham | .10 |
| 43 Rafael Palmeiro (R) | 5.00 | 111 Jack Clark | .15 | 177 Dan Quisenberry | .10 | 243 Ed Nunez | .05 |
| 44 Pat Dodson (R) | .15 | 112 Bob Knepper | .05 | 178 Eric Plunk | .10 | 244 Jimmy Key | .10 |
| 45 Duane Ward (R) | .30 | 113 Von Hayes | .10 | 179 Tim Wallach | .05 | 245 Mike Smithson | .05 |
| 46 Mark McGwire (R) | 5.00 | 114 "Bip" Roberts (R) | .30 | 180 Steve Buechele | .05 | 246 Bo Diaz | .05 |
| 47 Bruce Fields (R) | .15 | 115 Tony Pena | .10 | 181 Don Sutton | .15 | 247 Carlton Fisk | .35 |
| 48 Eddie Murray | .35 | 116 Scott Garrelts | .05 | 182 Dave Schmidt | .05 | 248 Larry Sheets | .10 |
| 49 Ted Higuera | .10 | 117 Paul Molitor | .15 | 183 Terry Pendleton | .15 | 249 Juan Castillo | .10 |
| 50 Jose Rijo | .20 | 118 Darryl Strawberry | 1.00 | 184 Jim Deshaies (R) | .20 | 250 Eric King (R) | .15 |
| 51 Oil Can Boid | .10 | 119 Shawon Dunston | .25 | 185 Steve Bedrosian | .15 | 251 Doug Drabek (R) | 1.25 |
| 52 Don Mattingly | 1.00 | 120 Jim Presley | .10 | 186 Pete Rose (Mgr.) | .50 | 252 Wade Boggs | .75 |
| 53 Pedro Guerrero | .15 | 121 Jesse Barfield | .10 | 187 Dave Dravecky | .05 | 253 Mariano Duncan | .10 |
| 54 George Brett | .50 | 122 Gary Gaetti | .10 | 188 Rick Reuschel | .05 | 254 Pat Tabler | .05 |
| 55 Jose Rijo | .10 | 123 Kurt Stillwell (R) | .25 | 189 Dan Gladden | .05 | 255 Frank White | .05 |
| 56 Tim Raines | .20 | 124 Joel Davis | .05 | 190 Rick Mahler | .05 | 256 Alfredo Griffin | .05 |
| 57 Ed Correa (R) | .15 | 125 Mike Boddicker | .10 | 191 Thad Bosley | .05 | 257 Floyd Youmans | .10 |
| 58 Mike Witt | .08 | 126 Robin Yount | .45 | 192 Ron Darling | .10 | 258 Rob Wilfong | .05 |
| 59 Greg Walker | .05 | 127 Alan Trammell | .20 | 193 Matt Young | .05 | 259 Pete O'Brien | .08 |
| 60 Ozzie Smith | .25 | 128 Dave Righetti | .15 | 194 Tom Brunansky | .10 | 260 Tim Hulett | .05 |
| 61 Glenn Davis | .25 | 129 Dwight Evans | .15 | 195 Dave Stieb | .15 | 261 Dickie Thon | .05 |
| 62 Glenn Wilson | .10 | 130 Mike Scioscia | .05 | 196 Frank Viola | .20 | 262 Darren Daulton | .05 |
| 63 Tom Browning | .05 | | | | | | |
| 64 Tony Gwynn | .50 | | | | | | |

| NO. | PLAYER | MINT |
|---|---|---|
| 263 | Vince Coleman | .40 |
| 264 | Andy Hawkins | .05 |
| 265 | Eric Davis | .50 |
| 266 | Andres Thomas (R) | .15 |
| 267 | Mike Diaz (R) | .15 |
| 268 | Chili Davis | .10 |
| 269 | Jody Davis | .05 |
| 270 | Phil Bradley | .10 |
| 271 | George Bell | .25 |
| 272 | Keith Atherton | .05 |
| 273 | Storm Davis | .08 |
| 274 | Rob Deer | .15 |
| 275 | Walt Terrell | .05 |
| 276 | Roger Clemens | 1.50 |
| 277 | Mike Easler | .05 |
| 278 | Steve Sax | .15 |
| 279 | Andre Thornton | .05 |
| 280 | Jim Sundberg | .05 |
| 281 | Bill Bathe (R) | .15 |
| 282 | Jay Tibbs | .05 |
| 283 | Dick Schofield | .05 |
| 284 | Mike Mason | .05 |
| 285 | Jerry Hairston | .05 |
| 286 | Bill Doran | .05 |
| 287 | Tim Flannery | .05 |
| 288 | Gary Redus | .05 |
| 289 | John Franco | .05 |
| 290 | P. Assenmacher (R) | .15 |
| 291 | Joe Orsulak | .05 |
| 292 | Lee Smith | .15 |
| 293 | Mike Laga | .05 |
| 294 | Rick Dempsey | .05 |
| 295 | Mike Felder | .05 |
| 296 | Tom Brookens | .05 |
| 297 | Al Nipper | .05 |
| 298 | Mike Pagliarulo | .10 |
| 299 | Franklin Stubbs | .10 |
| 300 | Checklist: 240-345 | .08 |
| 301 | Steve Farr | .05 |
| 302 | Bill Mooneyham (R) | .15 |
| 303 | Andres Galarraga | .12 |
| 304 | Scott Fletcher | .05 |
| 305 | Jack Howell | .05 |
| 306 | Russ Morman (R) | .12 |
| 307 | Todd Worrell | .10 |
| 308 | Dave Smith | .05 |
| 309 | Jeff Stone | .05 |
| 310 | Ron Robinson | .05 |
| 311 | Bruce Bochy | .05 |
| 312 | Jim Winn | .08 |
| 313 | Mark Davis | .05 |
| 314 | Jeff Dedmon | .05 |
| 315 | Jamie Moyer (R) | .12 |
| 316 | Wally Backman | .05 |
| 317 | Ken Phelps | .05 |
| 318 | Steve Lombardozzi | .08 |
| 319 | Rance Mulliniks | .05 |
| 320 | Tim Laudner | .05 |
| 321 | Mark Eichhorn (R) | .15 |
| 322 | Lee Guetterman (R) | .15 |
| 323 | Sid Fernandez | .15 |
| 324 | Jerry Mumphrey | .05 |
| 325 | David Palmer | .05 |
| 326 | Bill Almon | .05 |
| 327 | Candy Maldonado | .10 |
| 328 | John Kruk (R) | .40 |
| 329 | John Denny | .05 |
| 330 | Milt Thompson | .05 |
| 331 | Mike LaValliere (R) | .25 |
| 332 | Alan Ashby | .05 |
| 333 | Doug Corbett | .05 |
| 334 | Ron Karkovice (R) | .15 |
| 335 | Mitch Webster | .05 |
| 336 | Lee Lacy | .05 |
| 337 | Glenn Braggs (R) | .25 |
| 338 | Dwight Lowry (R) | .15 |
| 339 | Don Baylor | .15 |
| 340 | Brian Fisher | .05 |
| 341 | Reggie Williams (R) | .15 |
| 342 | Tom Candiotti | .05 |
| 343 | Rudy Law | .05 |
| 344 | Curt Young | .05 |
| 345 | Mike Fitzgerald | .05 |
| 346 | Ruben Sierra (R) | 7.50 |
| 347 | Mitch Williams (R) | .30 |
| 348 | Jorge Orta | .05 |
| 349 | Mickey Tettleton | .15 |
| 350 | Ernie Camacho | .05 |
| 351 | Ron Kittle | .10 |
| 352 | Ken Landreaux | .05 |
| 353 | Chet Lemon | .08 |
| 354 | John Shelby | .05 |
| 355 | Mark Clear | .05 |
| 356 | Doug DeCinces | .08 |
| 357 | Ken Kayley | .05 |
| 358 | Phil Garner | .05 |
| 359 | Steve Jeltz | .05 |
| 360 | Ed Whitson | .05 |
| 361 | Barry Bonds (R) | 6.00 |
| 362 | Vida Blue | .08 |
| 363 | Cecil Cooper | .10 |
| 364 | Bob Ojeda | .15 |
| 365 | Dennis Eckersley | .08 |
| 366 | Mike Morgan | .05 |
| 367 | Willie Upshaw | .05 |
| 368 | Allan Anderson (R) | .20 |
| 369 | Bill Gullickson | .05 |
| 370 | Bobby Thigpen (R) | 1.00 |
| 371 | Juan Beniquez | .05 |
| 372 | Charlie Moore | .05 |
| 373 | Dan Petry | .08 |
| 374 | Rod Scurry | .05 |
| 375 | Tom Seaver | .40 |
| 376 | Ed Vande Berg | .05 |
| 377 | Tony Bernazard | .05 |
| 378 | Greg Pryor | .05 |
| 379 | Dwayne Murphy | .05 |
| 380 | Andy McGaffigan | .05 |
| 381 | Kirk McCaskill | .10 |
| 382 | Greg Harris | .05 |
| 383 | Rich Dotson | .05 |
| 384 | Craig Reynolds | .05 |
| 385 | Greg Gross | .05 |
| 386 | Tito Landrum | .05 |
| 387 | Craig Lefferts | .05 |
| 388 | Dave Parker | .20 |
| 389 | Bob Horner | .15 |
| 390 | Pat Clements | .05 |
| 391 | Jeff Leonard | .10 |
| 392 | Chris Speier | .05 |
| 393 | John Moses | .15 |
| 394 | Garth Iorg | .05 |
| 395 | Greg Gagne | .05 |
| 396 | Nate Snell | .05 |
| 397 | Bryan Clutterbuck (R) | .15 |
| 398 | Darrell Evans | .12 |
| 399 | Steve Crawford | .05 |
| 400 | Checklist: 346-451 | .08 |
| 401 | Phil Lombardi (R) | .15 |
| 402 | Rick Honeycutt | .05 |
| 403 | Ken Schrom | .05 |
| 404 | Bud Black | .05 |
| 405 | Donnie Hill | .05 |
| 406 | Wayne Krenchicki | .05 |
| 407 | Chuck Finley (R) | 1.50 |
| 408 | Toby Harrah | .05 |
| 409 | Steve Lyons | .05 |
| 410 | Kevin Bass | .10 |
| 411 | Marvell Wynne | .05 |
| 412 | Ron Roenicke | .05 |
| 413 | Tracy Jones (R) | .15 |
| 414 | Gene Garber | .05 |
| 415 | Mike Bielecki | .05 |
| 416 | Frank DiPino | .05 |
| 417 | Andy Van Slyke | .15 |
| 418 | Jim Dwyer | .05 |
| 419 | Ben Oglivie | .05 |
| 420 | Dave Bergman | .05 |
| 421 | Joe Sambito | .05 |
| 422 | Bob Tewksbury (R) | .15 |
| 423 | Len Matuszek | .05 |
| 424 | Mike Kingery (R) | .15 |
| 425 | Dave Kingman | .10 |
| 426 | Al Newman (R) | .15 |
| 427 | Gary Ward | .05 |
| 428 | Ruppert Jones | .05 |
| 429 | Harold Baines | .12 |
| 430 | Pat Perry | .05 |
| 431 | Terry Puhl | .05 |
| 432 | Don Carman | .05 |
| 433 | Eddie Milner | .05 |
| 434 | LaMarr Hoyt | .05 |
| 435 | Rick Rhoden | .05 |
| 436 | Jose Uribe | .05 |
| 437 | Ken Oberkfell | .05 |
| 438 | Ron Davis | .05 |
| 439 | Jesse Orosco | .08 |
| 440 | Scott Bradley | .05 |
| 441 | Randy Bush | .05 |
| 442 | John Cerutti (R) | .15 |
| 443 | Roy Smalley | .05 |
| 444 | Kelly Gruber | 1.50 |
| 445 | Bob Kearney | .05 |
| 446 | Ed Hearn (R) | .15 |
| 447 | Scott Sanderson | .05 |
| 448 | Bruce Benedict | .05 |
| 449 | Junior Ortiz | .05 |
| 450 | Mike Aldrete (R) | .20 |
| 451 | Kevin McReynolds | .15 |
| 452 | Rob Murphy | .15 |
| 453 | Kent Tekulve | .05 |
| 454 | Curt Ford | .12 |
| 455 | Davey Lopes | .08 |
| 456 | Bobby Grich | .05 |
| 457 | Jose DeLeon | .05 |
| 458 | Andre Dawson | .35 |
| 459 | Mike Flanagan | .05 |
| 460 | Joey Meyer (R) | .15 |
| 461 | Chuck Cary (R) | .12 |
| 462 | Bill Buckner | .08 |
| 463 | Bob Shirley | .05 |
| 464 | Jeff Hamilton (R) | .12 |
| 465 | Phil Niekro | .20 |
| 466 | Mark Gubicza | .05 |
| 467 | Jerry Willard | .05 |
| 468 | Bob Sebra (R) | .12 |
| 469 | Larry Parrish | .05 |
| 470 | Charlie Hough | .05 |
| 471 | Hal McRae | .05 |
| 472 | Dave Leiper | .08 |
| 473 | Mel Hall | .05 |
| 474 | Dan Pasqua | .08 |
| 475 | Bob Welch | .10 |
| 476 | Johnny Grubb | .05 |
| 477 | Jim Traber | .08 |
| 478 | Chris Bosio (R) | .25 |
| 479 | Mark McLemore | .08 |
| 480 | John Morris | .05 |
| 481 | Billy Hatcher | .05 |
| 482 | Dan Schatzeder | .05 |
| 483 | Rich Gossage | .12 |
| 484 | Jim Morrison | .05 |
| 485 | Bob Brenly | .05 |
| 486 | Bill Schroeder | .05 |
| 487 | Mookie Wilson | .05 |
| 488 | Dave Martinez (R) | .35 |
| 489 | Harold Reynolds | .08 |
| 490 | Jeff Hearron | .12 |
| 491 | Mickey Hatcher | .05 |
| 492 | Barry Larkin (R) | 3.00 |
| 493 | Bob James | .05 |
| 494 | John Habyan | .05 |
| 495 | Jim Adduci (R) | .12 |
| 496 | Mike Heath | .05 |
| 497 | Tim Stoddard | .05 |
| 498 | Tony Armas | .08 |
| 499 | Dennis Powell | .05 |
| 500 | Checklist: 452-557 | .08 |
| 501 | Chris Bando | .05 |
| 502 | David Cone (R) | 2.00 |
| 503 | Jay Howell | .05 |
| 504 | Tom Foley | .05 |
| 505 | Ray Chadwick (R) | .12 |
| 506 | Mike Loynd (R) | .12 |
| 507 | Neil Allen | .05 |
| 508 | Danny Darwin | .05 |
| 509 | Rick Schu | .05 |
| 510 | Jose Oquendo | .05 |
| 511 | Gene Walter | .10 |
| 512 | Terry McGriff (R) | .15 |
| 513 | Ken Griffey | .08 |
| 514 | Benny Distefano | .05 |
| 515 | Terry Mulholland (R) | .35 |
| 516 | Ed Lynch | .05 |
| 517 | Bill Swift | .05 |
| 518 | Manny Lee | .05 |
| 519 | Andre David | .05 |
| 520 | Scott McGregor | .05 |
| 521 | Rick Manning | .05 |
| 522 | Willie Hernandez | .05 |
| 523 | Marty Barrett | .10 |
| 524 | Wayne Tolleson | .05 |
| 525 | Jose Gonzalez (R) | .15 |
| 526 | Cory Snyder | .15 |
| 527 | Buddy Biancalana | .05 |
| 528 | Moose Haas | .05 |
| 529 | Wilfredo Tejada (R) | .15 |
| 530 | Stu Cliburn | .05 |
| 531 | Dale Mohorcic (R) | .15 |
| 532 | Ron Hassey | .05 |
| 533 | Ty Gainey | .05 |
| 534 | Jerry Royster | .05 |
| 535 | Mike Maddux (R) | .12 |
| 536 | Ted Power | .05 |
| 537 | Ted Simmons | .08 |
| 538 | Rafael Belliard (R) | .15 |
| 539 | Chico Walker | .15 |
| 540 | Bob Forsch | .05 |
| 541 | John Stefero | .05 |
| 542 | Dale Sveum (R) | .15 |
| 543 | Mark Thurmond | .05 |
| 544 | Jeff Sellers (R) | .20 |
| 545 | Joel Skinner | .05 |
| 546 | Alex Trevino | .05 |
| 547 | Randy Kutcher (R) | .15 |
| 548 | Joaquin Andujar | .05 |
| 549 | Casey Candaele (R) | .15 |
| 550 | Jeff Russell | .05 |
| 551 | John Candelaria | .08 |
| 552 | Joe Cowley | .05 |
| 553 | Danny Cox | .05 |
| 554 | Denny Walling | .05 |
| 555 | Bruce Ruffin (R) | .25 |
| 556 | Buddy Bell | .10 |
| 557 | Jimmy Jones (R) | .20 |
| 558 | Bobby Bonilla (R) | 5.00 |
| 559 | Jeff Robinson | .05 |
| 560 | Ed Olwine (R) | .15 |
| 561 | Glenallen Hill (R) | .30 |
| 562 | Lee Mazzilli | .08 |
| 563 | Mike Brown | .05 |
| 564 | George Frazier | .05 |
| 565 | Mike Sharperson (R) | .15 |
| 566 | Mark Portugal (R) | .20 |
| 567 | Rick Leach | .05 |
| 568 | Mark Langston | .20 |
| 569 | Rafael Santana | .05 |
| 570 | Manny Trillo | .05 |
| 571 | Cliff Speck (R) | .15 |
| 572 | Bob Kipper | .05 |
| 573 | Kelly Downs (R) | .20 |
| 574 | Randy Asadoor (R) | .15 |
| 575 | Dave Magadan (R) | 1.00 |
| 576 | Marvin Freeman (R) | .15 |
| 577 | Jeff Lahti | .05 |
| 578 | Jeff Calhoun | .05 |
| 579 | Gus Polidor | .08 |
| 580 | Gene Nelson | .05 |
| 581 | Tim Teufel | .05 |
| 582 | Odell Jones | .05 |
| 583 | Mark Ryal (R) | .15 |
| 584 | Randy O'Neal | .05 |
| 585 | Mike Greenwell | 6.00 |
| 586 | Ray Knight | .10 |
| 587 | Ralph Bryant | .20 |
| 588 | Carmen Castillo | .05 |
| 589 | Ed Wojna | .05 |
| 590 | Stan Javier | .05 |
| 591 | Jeff Musselman (R) | .15 |
| 592 | Mike Stanley (R) | .15 |
| 593 | Darrell Porter | .05 |
| 594 | Drew Hall (R) | .15 |
| 595 | Rob Nelson (R) | .05 |
| 596 | Bryan Oelkers | .05 |
| 597 | Scott Nielsen (R) | .15 |
| 598 | Brian Holton (R) | .15 |

# 1987 Donruss (Continued)

| NO. | PLAYER | MINT |
|---|---|---|
| 599 | Kevin Mitchell (R) | 5.00 |
| 600 | Checklist: 558-660 | .08 |
| 601 | Jackie Gutierrez | .05 |
| 602 | Barry Jones (R) | .15 |
| 603 | Jerry Narron | .05 |
| 604 | Steve Lake | .05 |
| 605 | Jim Pankovits | .05 |
| 606 | Ed Romero | .05 |
| 607 | Dave LaPoint | .05 |
| 608 | Don Robinson | .05 |
| 609 | Mike Krukow | .05 |
| 610 | Dave Valle | .12 |
| 611 | Len Dykstra | .30 |
| 612 | "Puzzle"—Clemente | .08 |
| 613 | Mike Trujillo | .08 |
| 614 | Damaso Garcia | .05 |
| 615 | Neal Heaton | .05 |
| 616 | Juan Berenguer | .05 |

| NO. | PLAYER | MINT |
|---|---|---|
| 617 | Steve Carlton | .30 |
| 618 | Gary Lucas | .05 |
| 619 | Geno Petralli | .05 |
| 620 | Rick Aguilera | .15 |
| 621 | Fred McGriff | 3.50 |
| 622 | Dave Henderson | .10 |
| 623 | Dave Clark (R) | .15 |
| 624 | Angel Salazar | .05 |
| 625 | Randy Hunt | .05 |
| 626 | John Gibbons | .05 |
| 627 | Kevin Brown (R) | .50 |
| 628 | Bill Dawley | .05 |
| 629 | Aurelio Lopez | .05 |
| 630 | Charlie Hudson | .05 |
| 631 | Ray Soff (R) | .15 |
| 632 | Ray Hayward (R) | .15 |
| 633 | Spike Owen | .05 |
| 634 | Glenn Hubbard | .05 |

| NO. | PLAYER | MINT |
|---|---|---|
| 635 | Kevin Elster (R) | .20 |
| 636 | Mike LaCoss | .05 |
| 637 | Dwayne Henry | .05 |
| 638 | Rey Quinones (R) | .15 |
| 639 | Jim Clancy | .05 |
| 640 | Larry Anderson | .05 |
| 641 | Calvin Schiraldi | .08 |
| 642 | Stan Jefferson (R) | .15 |
| 643 | Marc Sullivan | .05 |
| 644 | Mark Grant (R) | .15 |
| 645 | Cliff Johnson | .05 |
| 646 | Howard Johnson | .30 |
| 647 | Dave Sax | .05 |
| 648 | Dave Stewart | .20 |
| 649 | Danny Heep | .05 |
| 650 | Joe Johnson | .05 |
| 651 | Bob Brower (R) | .20 |
| 652 | Rob Woodward | .08 |

| NO. | PLAYER | MINT |
|---|---|---|
| 653 | John Mizerock | .05 |
| 654 | Tim Pyznarski (R) | .15 |
| 655 | Luis Aquino | .10 |
| 656 | Mickey Brantley | .12 |
| 657 | Doyle Alexander | .05 |
| 658 | Sammy Stewart | .05 |
| 659 | Jim Acker | .05 |
| 660 | Pete Ladd | .05 |

## 1987 Donruss Rookies.... Complete Set of 56 Cards—Value $20.00

Features the outstanding rookies of the 1987 season. The cards are coated with a glossy finish. The entire set was packaged in a printed box and distributed exclusively through card hobby dealers. Features Donruss' first card of Ellis Burks, Matt Williams and Matt Nokes.

| NO. | PLAYER | MINT |
|---|---|---|
| 1 | Mark McGwire | 2.25 |
| 2 | Eric Bell | .08 |
| 3 | Mark Williamson | .20 |
| 4 | Mike Greenwell | 2.50 |
| 5 | Ellis Burks (RR) | 3.00 |
| 6 | DeWayne Buice | .12 |
| 7 | Mark McLemore | .08 |
| 8 | Devon White | .30 |
| 9 | Willie Fraser | .08 |
| 10 | Les Lancaster | .20 |
| 11 | Ken Williams | .12 |
| 12 | Matt Nokes | .50 |
| 13 | Jeff Robinson | .20 |
| 14 | Bo Jackson | 4.00 |

| NO. | PLAYER | MINT |
|---|---|---|
| 15 | Kevin Seitzer (RR) | .30 |
| 16 | Billy Ripken | .25 |
| 17 | B.J. Surhoff | .20 |
| 18 | Chuck Crim | .12 |
| 19 | Mike Birkbeck | .08 |
| 20 | Chris Bosio | .08 |
| 21 | Les Straker | .12 |
| 22 | Mark Davidson | .15 |
| 23 | Gene Larkin | .25 |
| 24 | Ken Gerhart | .12 |
| 25 | Luis Polonia | .40 |
| 26 | Jerry Steinbach | .25 |
| 27 | Mickey Brantley | .15 |
| 28 | Mike Stanley | .15 |

| NO. | PLAYER | MINT |
|---|---|---|
| 29 | Jerry Browne | .08 |
| 30 | Todd Benzinger (RR) | .50 |
| 31 | Fred McGriff | 2.50 |
| 32 | Mike Henneman | .35 |
| 33 | Casey Candaele | .08 |
| 34 | Dave Magadan | .40 |
| 35 | David Cone | .75 |
| 36 | Mike Jackson | .25 |
| 37 | John Mitchell | .15 |
| 38 | Mike Dunne | .15 |
| 39 | John Smiley | 1.00 |
| 40 | Joe Magrane (RR) | .25 |
| 41 | Jim Lindeman | .15 |
| 42 | Shane Mack | .25 |

| NO. | PLAYER | MINT |
|---|---|---|
| 43 | Stanley Jefferson | .15 |
| 44 | Benito Santiago | .50 |
| 45 | Matt Williams (RR) | 5.00 |
| 46 | Dave Meads | .15 |
| 47 | Rafael Palmeiro | 2.00 |
| 48 | Bill Long | .15 |
| 49 | Bob Brower | .08 |
| 50 | James Steels | .15 |
| 51 | Paul Noci | .15 |
| 52 | Greg Maddux | .60 |
| 53 | Jeff Musselman | .08 |
| 54 | Brian Holton | .08 |
| 55 | Chuck Jackson | .15 |
| 56 | Checklist | .15 |

## 1988 Donruss ... Complete Set of 660 Cards—Value $20.00 (Factory-Sealed Set—Value $22.00)

Features the rookie cards of Mark Grace, Matt Williams, Ellis Burks and Gregg Jefferies. Donruss limited production. 26 cards were issued in much smaller quantities than other cards in the set (see asterisk) and are worth a premium. Six checklist cards were issued two ways to indicate the inclusion of the Bonus MVP cards.

**No. 1 to 26—Diamond Kings**

| NO. | PLAYER | MINT |
|---|---|---|
| 1 | Mark McGwire (DK) | .20 |
| 2 | Tim Raines (DK) | .10 |
| 3 | Benito Santiago (DK) | .10 |
| 4 | Alan Trammell (DK) | .10 |
| 5 | Danny Tartabull (DK) | .10 |
| 6 | Ron Darling (DK) | .08 |
| 7 | Paul Molitor (DK) | .08 |
| 8 | Devon White (DK) | .08 |
| 9 | Andre Dawson (DK) | .10 |
| 10 | Julio Franco (DK) | .08 |
| 11 | Scott Fletcher (DK) | .08 |
| 12 | Tony Fernandez (DK) | .10 |
| 13 | Shane Rawley (DK) | .08 |
| 14 | Kal Daniels (DK) | .08 |
| 15 | Jack Clark (DK) | .08 |
| 16 | Dwight Evans (DK) | .08 |
| 17 | Tommy John (DK) | .08 |
| 18 | Andy Van Slyke (DK) | .08 |
| 19 | Gary Gaetti (DK) | .08 |
| 20 | Mark Langston (DK) | .08 |
| 21 | Will Clark (DK) | .25 |
| 22 | Glenn Hubbard (DK) | .08 |
| 23 | Billy Hatcher (DK) | .08 |
| 24 | Bob Welch (DK) | .08 |
| 25 | Ivan Calderon (DK) | .08 |
| 26 | Cal Ripkin, Jr., (DK) | .25 |
| 27 | Checklist | .08 |

**No. 28 to 47—Rated Rookies**

| NO. | PLAYER | MINT |
|---|---|---|
| 28 | Mackey Sasser (R) | .15 |
| 29 | Jeff Treadway (R) | .20 |
| 30 | Mike Campbell (R) | .10 |
| 31 | Lance Johnson (R) | .15 |
| 32 | Nelson Liriano (R) | .10 |
| 33 | Shawn Abner | .10 |
| 34 | Roberto Alomar (R) | 2.50 |
| 35 | Shawn Hillegas (R) | .10 |
| 36 | Joey Meyer | .10 |
| 37 | Kevin Elster | .08 |
| 38 | Jose Lind (R) | .20 |
| 39 | Kirt Manwaring (R) | .15 |
| 40 | Mark Grace (R) | 2.00 |
| 41 | Jody Reed (R) | .25 |
| 42 | John Farrell (R) | .10 |
| 43 | Al Leiter (R) | .10 |
| 44 | Gary Thurman (R) | .12 |
| 45 | Vincente Palacios (R) | .12 |
| 46 | Eddie Williams (R) | .10 |
| 47 | Jack McDowell (R) | .40 |
| 48 | Ken Dixon | .05 |
| 49 | Mike Birkbeck | .05 |
| 50 | Eric King | .05 |
| 51 | Roger Clemen | .35 |
| 52 | Pat Clements | .05 |
| 53 | Fernando Valenzuela | .10 |
| 54 | Mark Gubicza | .05 |
| 55 | Jay Howell | .05 |
| 56 | Floyd Youmans | .08 |
| 57 | Ed Correa | .08 |
| 58 | DeWayne Buice (R) | .12 |
| 59 | Jose DeLeon | .05 |
| 60 | Danny Cox | .08 |
| 61 | Nolan Ryan | .50 |
| 62 | Steve Bedrosian | .08 |
| 63 | Tom Browning | .08 |
| 64 | Mark Davis | .05 |
| 65 | R.J. Reynolds | .08 |
| 66 | Kevin Mitchell | .30 |
| 67 | Ken Oberkfell | .05 |
| 68 | Rick Sutcliffe | .08 |
| 69 | Dwight Gooden | .20 |
| 70 | Scott Bankhead | .08 |
| 71 | Bert Blyleven | .08 |
| 72 | Jimmy Key | .08 |
| 73 | Les Straker (R) | .10 |
| 74 | Jim Clancy | .08 |
| 75 | Mike Moore | .08 |
| 76 | Ron Darling | .10 |
| 77 | Ed Lynch | .08 |
| 78 | Dale Murphy | .15 |
| 79 | Doug Drabek | .15 |
| 80 | Scott Garrelts | .05 |
| 81 | Ed Whitson | .05 |
| 82 | Rob Murphy | .05 |
| 83 | Shane Rawley | .05 |
| 84 | Greg Mathews | .08 |
| 85 | Jim Deshaies | .08 |
| 86 | Mike Witt | .08 |
| 87 | Donnie Hill | .08 |
| 88 | Jeff Reed | .08 |
| 89 | Mike Boddicker | .10 |
| 90 | Ted Higuera | .08 |
| 91 | Walt Terrell | .08 |
| 92 | Bob Stanley | .05 |
| 93 | Dave Righetti | .10 |
| 94 | Orel Hershiser | .12 |
| 95 | Chris Bando | .05 |
| 96 | Bret Saberhagen | .15 |
| 97 | Curt Young | .05 |
| 98 | Tim Burke | .05 |
| 99 | Charlie Hough | .05 |
| 100 | Checklist | .05 |
| 101 | Bobby Witt | .10 |
| 102 | George Brett | .20 |
| 103 | Mickey Tettleton | .05 |
| 104 | Scott Bailes | .05 |
| 105 | Mike Pagliarulo | .08 |
| 106 | Mike Scioscia | .05 |
| 107 | Tom Brookens | .05 |
| 108 | Ray Knight | .05 |
| 109 | Dan Plesac | .08 |
| 110 | Wally Joyner | .15 |
| 111 | Bob Forsch | .08 |
| 112 | Mike Scott | .10 |
| 113 | Kevin Gross | .08 |
| 114 | Benito Santiago | .15 |
| 115 | Bob Kipper | .05 |
| 116 | Mike Krukow | .05 |
| 117 | Chris Bosio | .05 |
| 118 | Sid Fernandez | .10 |
| 119 | Jody Davis | .05 |
| 120 | Mike Morgan | .05 |
| 121 | Mark Eichhorn | .05 |
| 122 | Jeff Reardon | .12 |
| 123 | John Franco | .08 |
| 124 | Richard Dotson | .05 |
| 125 | Eric Bell | .05 |
| 126 | Juan Nieves | .10 |
| 127 | Jack Morris | .15 |
| 128 | Rick Rhoden | .08 |
| 129 | Rich Gedman | .05 |
| 130 | Ken Howell | .05 |
| 131 | Brook Jacoby | .08 |
| 132 | Danny Jackson | .10 |
| 133 | Gene Nelson | .05 |
| 134 | Neal Heaton | .05 |
| 135 | Willie Fraser | .05 |
| 136 | Jose Guzman | .05 |
| 137 | Ozzie Guillen | .10 |
| 138 | Bob Knepper | .08 |
| 139 | Mike Jackson (R) | .12 |
| 140 | Joe Magrane (R) | .15 |
| 141 | Jimmy Jones | .05 |
| 142 | Ted Power | .05 |
| 143 | Ozzie Virgil | .05 |
| 144 | Felix Fermin (R) | .10 |
| 145 | Kelly Downs | .08 |
| 146 | Shawon Dunston | .10 |
| 147 | Scott Bradley | .05 |
| 148 | Dave Stieb | .08 |
| 149 | Frank Viola | .10 |
| 150 | Terry Kennedy | .05 |
| 151 | Bill Wegman | .05 |
| 152 | Matt Nokes (R) | .25 |
| 153 | Wade Boggs | .25 |
| 154 | Wayne Tolleson | .05 |
| 155 | Mariano Duncan | .05 |
| 156 | Julio Franco | .12 |
| 157 | Charlie Leibrandt | .08 |
| 158 | Terry Steinbach | .10 |
| 159 | Mike Fitzgerald | .05 |
| 160 | Jack Lazorko | .05 |
| 161 | Mitch Williams | .05 |
| 162 | Greg Walker | .05 |
| 163 | Alan Ashby | .05 |
| 164 | Tony Gwynn | .25 |
| 165 | Bruce Ruffin | .08 |
| 166 | Ron Robinson | .05 |
| 167 | Zane Smith | .08 |
| 168 | Junior Ortiz | .05 |
| 169 | Jamie Moyer | .05 |
| 170 | Tony Pena | .05 |
| 171 | Cal Ripken | .40 |
| 172 | B.J. Surhoff | .08 |
| 173 | Lou Whitaker | .10 |
| 174 | Ellis Burks (R) | .50 |
| 175 | Ron Guidry | .10 |
| 176 | Steve Sax | .10 |
| 177 | Danny Tartabull | .12 |
| 178 | Carney Lansford | .05 |
| 179 | Casey Candaele | .05 |
| 180 | Scott Fletcher | .05 |
| 181 | Mark McLemore | .05 |
| 182 | Ivan Calderon | .10 |
| 183 | Jack Clark | .08 |
| 184 | Glenn Davis | .10 |
| 185 | Luis Aguayo | .05 |
| 186 | Bo Diaz | .05 |
| 187 | Stan Jefferson | .08 |
| 188 | Sid Bream | .05 |
| 189 | Bob Brenly | .05 |
| 190 | Dion James | .05 |
| 191 | Leon Durham | .08 |
| 192 | Jesse Orosco | .05 |
| 193 | Alvin Davis | .08 |
| 194 | Gary Gaetti | .08 |
| 195 | Fred McGriff | .30 |
| 196 | Steve Lombardozzi | .08 |
| 197 | Rance Mulliniks | .05 |
| 198 | Rey Quinones | .05 |
| 199 | Gary Carter | .10 |
| 200 | Checklist | .08 |
| 201 | Keith Moreland | .05 |
| 202 | Ken Griffey | .05 |
| 203 | Tommy Gregg (R) | .10 |
| 204 | Will Clark | .75 |
| 205 | John Kruk | .08 |
| 206 | Buddy Bell | .08 |
| 207 | Von Hayes | .08 |
| 208 | Tommy Herr | .05 |
| 209 | Craig Reynolds | .05 |
| 210 | Gary Pettis | .05 |
| 211 | Harold Baines | .10 |
| 212 | Vance Law | .05 |
| 213 | Ken Gerhart | .05 |
| 214 | Jim Gantner | .05 |
| 215 | Chet Lemon | .08 |
| 216 | Dwight Evans | .10 |
| 217 | Don Mattingly | .25 |
| 218 | Franklin Stubbs | .08 |
| 219 | Pat Tabler | .05 |
| 220 | Bo Jackson | .50 |
| 221 | Tony Phillips | .05 |
| 222 | Tim Wallach | .08 |
| 223 | Ruben Sierra | .30 |
| 224 | Steve Buechele | .05 |
| 225 | Frank White | .05 |
| 226 | Alfredo Griffin | .05 |
| 227 | Greg Swindell | .08 |
| 228 | Willie Randolph | .10 |
| 229 | Mike Marshall | .08 |
| 230 | Alan Trammell | .15 |
| 231 | Eddie Murray | .15 |
| 232 | Dale Sveum | .08 |
| 233 | Dick Schofield | .05 |
| 234 | Jose Oquendo | .05 |
| 235 | Bill Doran | .05 |
| 236 | Milt Thompson | .05 |
| 237 | Marvell Wynne | .05 |
| 238 | Bobby Bonilla | .35 |
| 239 | Chris Speier | .05 |
| 240 | Glenn Braggs | .10 |
| 241 | Wally Backman | .05 |
| 242 | Ryne Sandberg | .30 |
| 243 | Phil Bradley | .08 |
| 244 | Kelly Gruber | .15 |
| 245 | Tom Brunansky | .08 |
| 246 | Ron Oester | .05 |
| 247 | Bobby Thigpen | .10 |
| 248 | Fred Lynn | .10 |
| 249 | Paul Molitor | .10 |
| 250 | Darrell Evans | .10 |
| 251 | Gary Ward | .08 |
| 252 | Bruce Hurst | .08 |
| 253 | Bob Welch | .05 |
| 254 | Joe Carter | .15 |
| 255 | Willie Wilson | .08 |
| 256 | Mark McGwire | .25 |
| 257 | Mitch Webster | .05 |
| 258 | Brian Downing | .05 |
| 259 | Mike Stanley | .05 |
| 260 | Carlton Fisk | .20 |
| 261 | Billy Hatcher | .08 |
| 262 | Glenn Wilson | .05 |
| 263 | Ozzie Smith | .15 |
| 264 | Randy Ready | .05 |
| 265 | Kurt Stillwell | .10 |
| 266 | David Palmer | .05 |
| 267 | Mike Diaz | .05 |
| 268 | Rob Thompson | .08 |
| 269 | Andre Dawson | .20 |
| 270 | Lee Guetterman | .05 |
| 271 | Willie Upshaw | .05 |
| 272 | Randy Bush | .05 |
| 273 | Larry Sheets | .08 |
| 274 | Rob Deer | .05 |
| 275 | Kirk Gibson | .10 |
| 276 | Marty Barrett | .05 |
| 277 | Rickey Henderson | .25 |
| 278 | Pedro Guerrero | .08 |
| 279 | Brett Butler | .10 |
| 280 | Kevin Seitzer | .10 |
| 281 | Mike Davis | .05 |
| 282 | Andres Galarraga | .08 |
| 283 | Devon White | .10 |
| 284 | Pete O'Brien | .05 |
| 285 | Jerry Hairston | .05 |
| 286 | Kevin Bass | .08 |
| 287 | Carmelo Martinez | .05 |
| 288 | Juan Samuel | .10 |
| 289 | Kal Daniels | .10 |
| 290 | Albert Hall | .05 |
| 291 | Andy Van Slyke | .10 |
| 292 | Lee Smith | .10 |
| 293 | Vince Coleman | .15 |
| 294 | Tom Niedenfuer | .05 |
| 295 | Robin Yount | .20 |
| 296 | Jeff Robinson (R) | .10 |
| 297 | Todd Benzinger (R) | .20 |
| 298 | Dave Winfield | .15 |
| 299 | Mickey Hatcher | .05 |
| 300 | Checklist | .08 |
| 301 | Bud Black | .05 |
| 302 | Jose Canseco | .75 |
| 303 | Tom Foley | .05 |
| 304 | Pete Incaviglia | .10 |
| 305 | Bob Boone | .05 |
| 306 | Bill Long (R) | .10 |
| 307 | Willie McGee | .10 |
| 308 | Ken Caminiti (R) | .15 |
| 309 | Darren Daulton | .05 |
| 310 | Tracy Jones | .10 |
| 311 | Greg Booker | .05 |
| 312 | Mike LaValliere | .05 |
| 313 | Chili Davis | .10 |
| 314 | Glenn Hubbard | .05 |
| 315 | Paul Noce (R) | .10 |
| 316 | Keith Hernandez | .10 |
| 317 | Mark Langston | .10 |
| 318 | Keith Atherton | .05 |
| 319 | Tony Fernandez | .10 |
| 320 | Kent Hrbek | .10 |
| 321 | John Cerutti | .05 |
| 322 | Mike Kingery | .05 |
| 323 | Dave Magadan | .08 |
| 324 | Rafael Palmeiro | .30 |
| 325 | Jeff Dedmon | .05 |
| 326 | Barry Bonds | .30 |
| 327 | Jeffrey Leonard | .05 |
| 328 | Tim Flannery | .05 |
| 329 | Dave Concepcion | .05 |
| 330 | Mike Schmidt | .30 |
| 331 | Bill Dawley | .05 |
| 332 | Larry Anderson | .05 |
| 333 | Jack Howell | .05 |
| 334 | Ken Williams (R) | .10 |
| 335 | Bryn Smith | .05 |
| 336 | Billy Ripken (R) | .15 |
| 337 | Greg Brock | .05 |
| 338 | Mike Heath | .05 |
| 339 | Mike Greenwell | .20 |
| 340 | Claudell Washington | .05 |
| 341 | Jose Gonzalez | .05 |
| 342 | Mel Hall | .05 |

| NO. | PLAYER | MINT |
|---|---|---|
| 343 | Jim Eisenreich | .08 |
| 344 | Tony Bernazard | .05 |
| 345 | Tim Raines | .15 |
| 346 | Bob Brower | .05 |
| 347 | Larry Parrish | .05 |
| 348 | Thad Bosley | .05 |
| 349 | Dennis Eckersley | .15 |
| 350 | Cory Snyder | .10 |
| 351 | Rick Cerone | .05 |
| 352 | John Shelby | .05 |
| 353 | Larry Herndon | .05 |
| 354 | John Habyan | .05 |
| 355 | Chuck Crim (R) | .10 |
| 356 | Gus Polidor | .05 |
| 357 | Ken Dayley | .05 |
| 358 | Danny Darwin | .05 |
| 359 | Lance Parrish | .15 |
| 360 | James Steels (R) | .10 |
| 361 | Al Pedrique (R) | .10 |
| 362 | Mike Aldrete | .05 |
| 363 | Juan Castillo | .05 |
| 364 | Len Dykstra | .12 |
| 365 | Luis Quinones | .05 |
| 366 | Jim Presley | .10 |
| 367 | Lloyd Moseby | .10 |
| 368 | Kirby Puckett | .30 |
| 369 | Eric Davis | .20 |
| 370 | Gary Redus | .05 |
| 371 | Dave Schmidt | .05 |
| 372 | Mark Clear | .05 |
| 373 | Dave Bergman | .05 |
| 374 | Charles Hudson | .05 |
| 375 | Calvin Schiraldi | .05 |
| 376 | Alex Trevino | .05 |
| 377 | Tom Candiotti | .05 |
| 378 | Steve Farr | .05 |
| 379 | Mike Gallego | .05 |
| 380 | Andy McGaffigan | .05 |
| 381 | Kirk McCaskill | .05 |
| 382 | Oddibe McDowell | .08 |
| 383 | Floyd Bannister | .08 |
| 384 | Denny Walling | .05 |
| 385 | Don Carman | .05 |
| 386 | Todd Worrell | .08 |
| 387 | Eric Show | .05 |
| 388 | Dave Parker | .15 |
| 389 | Rick Mahler | .05 |
| 390 | Mike Dunne | .10 |
| 391 | Candy Maldonado | .08 |
| 392 | Bob Dernier | .05 |
| 393 | Dave Valle | .05 |
| 394 | Ernie Whitt | .08 |
| 395 | Juan Berenguer | .05 |
| 396 | Mike Young | .08 |
| 397 | Mike Felder | .05 |
| 398 | Willie Hernandez | .08 |
| 399 | Jim Rice | .10 |
| 400 | Checklist | .08 |
| 401 | Tommy John | .10 |
| 402 | Brian Holton | .05 |
| 403 | Carmen Castillo | .05 |
| 404 | Jamie Quirk | .05 |
| 405 | Dwayne Murphy | .05 |
| 406 | Jeff Parrett (R) | .10 |
| 407 | Don Sutton | .15 |
| 408 | Jerry Browne | .05 |
| 409 | Jim Winn | .05 |
| 410 | Dave Smith | .05 |
| 411 | Shane Mack | .08 |
| 412 | Greg Gross | .05 |
| 413 | Nick Esasky | .05 |
| 414 | Damaso Garcia | .05 |
| 415 | Brian Fisher | .05 |
| 416 | Brian Dayett | .05 |
| 417 | Curt Ford | .05 |
| 418 | Mark Williamson (R) | .10 |
| 419 | Bill Schroeder | .05 |
| 420 | Mike Henneman (R) | .15 |
| 421 | John Marzano | .20 |
| 422 | Ron Kittle | .08 |
| 423 | Matt Young | .05 |
| 424 | Steve Balboni | .05 |
| 425 | Luis Polonia (R) | .20 |
| 426 | Randy St. Claire | .05 |
| 427 | Greg Harris | .05 |
| 428 | Johnny Ray | .05 |
| 429 | Ray Searage | .05 |
| 430 | Ricky Horton | .05 |
| 431 | Gerald Young (R) | .10 |
| 432 | Rick Schu | .05 |
| 433 | Paul O'Neill | .10 |
| 434 | Rich Gossage | .15 |
| 435 | John Cangelosi | .05 |
| 436 | Mike LaCoss | .05 |
| 437 | Gerald Perry | .10 |
| 438 | Dave Martinez | .05 |
| 439 | Darryl Strawberry | .40 |
| 440 | John Moses | .05 |
| 441 | Greg Gagne | .05 |
| 442 | Jesse Barfield | .10 |
| 443 | George Frazier | .05 |
| 444 | Garth Iorg | .05 |
| 445 | Ed Nunez | .05 |
| 446 | Rick Aguilera | .05 |
| 447 | Jerry Mumphrey | .05 |
| 448 | Rafael Ramirez | .05 |
| 449 | John Smiley (R) | .40 |
| 450 | Atlee Hammaker | .05 |
| 451 | Lance McCullers | .08 |
| 452 | Guy Hoffman | .05 |
| 453 | Chris James | .10 |
| 454 | Terry Pendleton | .10 |
| 455 | Dave Meads (R) | .15 |
| 456 | Bill Buckner | .05 |
| 457 | John Pawlowski (R) | .10 |
| 458 | Bob Sebra | .05 |
| 459 | Jim Dwyer | .05 |
| 460 | Jay Aldrich (R) | .10 |
| 461 | Frank Tanana | .05 |
| 462 | Oil Can Boyd | .05 |
| 463 | Dan Pasqua | .08 |
| 464 | Tim Crews (R) | .10 |
| 465 | Andy Allanson | .05 |
| 466 | Bill Pecota (R) | .10 |
| 467 | Steve Ontiveros | .05 |
| 468 | Hubie Brooks | .05 |
| 469 | Paul Kilgus (R) | .10 |
| 470 | Dale Mohorcic | .05 |
| 471 | Dan Quisenberry | .10 |
| 472 | Dave Stewart | .10 |
| 473 | Dave Clark | .05 |
| 474 | Joel Skinner | .05 |
| 475 | Dave Anderson | .05 |
| 476 | Dan Petry | .05 |
| 477 | Carl Nichols (R) | .10 |
| 478 | Ernest Riles | .05 |
| 479 | George Hendrick | .05 |
| 480 | John Morris | .05 |
| 481 | Manny Hernandez (R) | .10 |
| 482 | Jeff Stone | .05 |
| 483 | Chris Brown | .10 |
| 484 | Mike Bielecki | .05 |
| 485 | Dave Dravecky | .05 |
| 486 | Rick Manning | .05 |
| 487 | Bill Almon | .05 |
| 488 | Jim Sundberg | .05 |
| 489 | Ken Phelps | .05 |
| 490 | Tom Henke | .05 |
| 491 | Dan Gladden | .05 |
| 492 | Barry Larkin | .25 |
| 493 | Fred Manrique (R) | .10 |
| 494 | Mike Griffin | .05 |
| 495 | Mark Knudson (R) | .10 |
| 496 | Bill Madlock | .10 |
| 497 | Tim Stoddard | .05 |
| 498 | Sam Horn (R) | .15 |
| 499 | Tracy Woodson (R) | .12 |
| 500 | Checklist | .08 |
| 501 | Ken Schrom | .05 |
| 502 | Angel Salazar | .05 |
| 503 | Eric Plunk | .05 |
| 504 | Joe Hesketh | .05 |
| 505 | Greg Minton | .05 |
| 506 | Geno Petralli | .05 |
| 507 | Bob James | .05 |
| 508 | Robbie Wine (R) | .10 |
| 509 | Jeff Calhoun | .05 |
| 510 | Steve Lake | .05 |
| 511 | Mark Grant | .05 |
| 512 | Frank Williams | .05 |
| 513 | Jeff Blauser (R) | .20 |
| 514 | Bob Walk | .05 |
| 515 | Craig Lefferts | .05 |
| 516 | Manny Trillo | .05 |
| 517 | Jerry Reed | .05 |
| 518 | Rick Leach | .05 |
| 519 | Mark Davidson (R) | .10 |
| 520 | Jeff Ballard (R) | .10 |
| 521 | Dave Stapleton | .08 |
| 522 | Pat Sheridan | .05 |
| 523 | Al Nipper | .05 |
| 524 | Steve Trout | .05 |
| 525 | Jeff Hamilton | .05 |
| 526 | Tommy Hinzo (R) | .10 |
| 527 | Lonnie Smith | .08 |
| 528 | Greg Cadaret (R) | .10 |
| 529 | Rob McClure | .05 |
| 530 | Chuck Finley | .15 |
| 531 | Jeff Russell | .05 |
| 532 | Steve Lyons | .05 |
| 533 | Terry Puhl | .05 |
| 534 | Eric Nolte (R) | .10 |
| 535 | Kent Tekulve | .05 |
| 536 | Pat Pacillo | .08 |
| 537 | Charlie Puleo | .05 |
| 538 | Tom Prince | .10 |
| 539 | Greg Maddux | .15 |
| 540 | Jim Lindeman | .08 |
| 541 | Pete Stanicek (R) | .10 |
| 542 | Steve Kiefer | .05 |
| 543 | Jim Morrison | .05 |
| 544 | Spike Owen | .05 |
| 545 | Jay Buhner (R) | .35 |
| 546 | Mike Devereaux (R) | .15 |
| 547 | Jerry Don Gleaton | .05 |
| 548 | Jose Rijo | .05 |
| 549 | Dennis Martinez | .05 |
| 550 | Mike Loynd | .05 |
| 551 | Darrell Miller | .05 |
| 552 | Dave LaPoint | .05 |
| 553 | John Tudor | .08 |
| 554 | Rocky Childress (R) | .10 |
| 555 | Wally Ritchie (R) | .10 |
| 556 | Terry McGriff | .05 |
| 557 | Dave Leiper | .05 |
| 558 | Jeff Robinson | .05 |
| 559 | Jose Uribe | .05 |
| 560 | Ted Simmons | .05 |
| 561 | Lester Lancaster (R) | .10 |
| 562 | Keith Miller (R) | .12 |
| 563 | Harold Reynolds | .05 |
| 564 | Gene Larkin (R) | .12 |
| 565 | Cecil Fielder | .35 |
| 566 | Roy Smalley | .05 |
| 567 | Duane Ward | .05 |
| 568 | Bill Wilkinson (R) | .10 |
| 569 | Howard Johnson | .15 |
| 570 | Frank DiPino | .05 |
| 571 | Pete Smith (R) | .10 |
| 572 | Darnell Coles | .05 |
| 573 | Don Robinson | .05 |
| 574 | Rob Nelson | .05 |
| 575 | Dennis Rasmussen | .05 |
| 576 | Steve Jeltz | .05 |
| 577 | Tom Pagnozzi (R) | .12 |
| 578 | Ty Gainey | .05 |
| 579 | Gary Lucas | .05 |
| 580 | Ron Hassey | .05 |
| 581 | Herm Winningham | .05 |
| 582 | Rene Gonzales (R) | .10 |
| 583 | Brad Komminsk | .05 |
| 584 | Doyle Alexander | .05 |
| 585 | Jeff Sellers | .05 |
| 586 | Bill Gullickson | .05 |
| 587 | Tim Belcher | .15 |
| 588 | Doug Jones (R) | .15 |
| 589 | Melido Perez (R) | .15 |
| 590 | Rick Honeycutt | .05 |
| 591 | Pascual Perez | .05 |
| 592 | Curt Wilkerson | .05 |
| 593 | Steve Howe | .05 |
| 594 | John Davis (R) | .10 |
| 595 | Storm Davis | .05 |
| 596 | Sammy Stewart | .05 |
| 597 | Neil Allen | .05 |
| 598 | Alejandro Pena | .05 |
| 599 | Mark Thurmond | .05 |
| 600 | Checklist | .08 |
| 601 | Jose Mesa (R) | .10 |
| 602 | Don August | .10 |
| *603 | Terry Leach | .10 |
| 604 | Tom Newell (R) | .10 |
| *605 | Randall Byers (R) | .10 |
| 606 | Jim Gott | .05 |
| 607 | Harry Spilman | .05 |
| 608 | John Candelaria | .05 |
| 609 | Mike Brumley (R) | .10 |
| 610 | Mickey Brantley | .10 |
| *611 | Jose Nunez (R) | .10 |
| 612 | Tom Nieto | .05 |
| 613 | Rick Reuschel | .05 |
| *614 | Lee Mazzilli | .08 |
| 615 | Scott Lusader (R) | .10 |
| 616 | Bobby Meacham | .05 |
| *617 | Kevin McReynolds | .10 |
| 618 | Gene Garber | .05 |
| *619 | Barry Lyons | .10 |
| 620 | Randy Myers | .10 |
| 621 | Donnie Moore | .05 |
| 622 | Domingo Ramos | .05 |
| 623 | Ed Romero | .05 |
| 624 | Greg Myers (R) | .10 |
| 625 | Ripken Family | .15 |
| 626 | Pat Perry | .08 |
| *627 | Andres Thomas | .10 |
| *628 | Matt Williams (R) | 2.00 |
| 629 | Dave Hengel (R) | .10 |
| *630 | Jeff Musselman | .10 |
| 631 | Tim Laudner | .05 |
| 632 | Bob Ojeda | .08 |
| 633 | Rafael Santana | .05 |
| 634 | Wes Gardner (R) | .10 |
| *635 | Roberto Kelly (R) | .75 |
| *636 | Mike Flanagan | .10 |
| 637 | Jay Bell (R) | .25 |
| 638 | Bob Melvin | .05 |
| 639 | Damon Berryhill (R) | .12 |
| *640 | David Wells (R) | .20 |
| 641 | Puzzle Card | .05 |
| 642 | Doug Sisk | .05 |
| 643 | Keith Hughes (R) | .10 |
| 644 | Tom Glavine (R) | .75 |
| 645 | Al Newman | .08 |
| 646 | Scott Sanderson | .05 |
| 647 | Scott Terry | .08 |
| *648 | Tim Teufel | .08 |
| *649 | Garry Templeton | .08 |
| *650 | Manny Lee | .08 |
| *651 | Roger McDowell | .08 |
| *652 | Mookie Wilson | .08 |
| *653 | David Cone | .25 |
| *654 | Ron Gant (R) | 3.00 |
| *655 | Joe Price | .08 |
| *656 | George Bell | .20 |
| *657 | Gregg Jefferies (R) | 1.50 |
| *658 | Todd Stottlemyre (R) | .40 |
| *659 | Geronimo Berroa (R) | .15 |
| *660 | Jerry Royster | .08 |

## 1988 Donruss Rookies . . . Complete Set of 56 Cards—Value $12.00

Features the outstanding rookies of the 1988 season. The cards are coated with a glossy finish. The entire set was packaged in a printed box and distributed primarily through card hobby dealers. Features Donruss' first card of Chris Sabo and Walt Weiss.

| NO. | PLAYER | MINT |
|---|---|---|
| 1 | Mark Grace | 2.50 |
| 2 | Mike Campbell | .08 |
| 3 | Todd Frohwirth | .08 |
| 4 | Dave Stapleton | .08 |
| 5 | Shawn Abner | .08 |
| 6 | Jose Cecenazi | .08 |
| 7 | Dave Gallagher | .12 |
| 8 | Mark Parent | .10 |
| 9 | Cecil Espy | .12 |
| 10 | Pete Smith | .08 |
| 11 | Jay Buhner | .35 |
| 12 | Pat Borders | .30 |
| 13 | Doug Jennings | .08 |
| 14 | Brady Anderson | .15 |

| NO. | PLAYER | MINT |
|---|---|---|
| 15 | Pete Stanicek | .10 |
| 16 | Roberto Kelly | .40 |
| 17 | Jeff Treadway | .15 |
| 18 | Walt Weiss (RR) | .30 |
| 19 | Paul Gibson | .10 |
| 20 | Tim Crews | .10 |
| 21 | Melido Perez | .15 |
| 22 | Steve Peters | .10 |
| 23 | Craig Worthington | .15 |
| 24 | John Trautwein | .10 |
| 25 | DeWayne Vaughn | .10 |
| 26 | David Well | .10 |
| 27 | Al Leiter | .15 |
| 28 | Tim Belcher | .12 |

| NO. | PLAYER | MINT |
|---|---|---|
| 29 | Johnny Paredes | .10 |
| 30 | Chris Sabo (RR) | 2.00 |
| 31 | Dannon Berryhill | .10 |
| 32 | Randy Miligan | .35 |
| 33 | Gary Thurman | .08 |
| 34 | Kevin Elster | .08 |
| 35 | Roberto Alomar | 3.00 |
| 36 | Edgar Martinez | .75 |
| 37 | Todd Stottlemyre | .30 |
| 38 | Joey Meyer | .10 |
| 39 | Carl Nichols | .08 |
| 40 | Jack McDowell | .08 |
| 41 | Jose Bautista | .10 |
| 42 | Sil Campusano | .15 |

| NO. | PLAYER | MINT |
|---|---|---|
| 43 | John Dopson | .10 |
| 44 | Jody Reed | .25 |
| 45 | Darrin Jackson | .20 |
| 46 | Mike Capel | .10 |
| 47 | Ron Gant | 2.00 |
| 48 | John Davis | .10 |
| 49 | Kevin Coffman | .15 |
| 50 | Cris Carpenter | .25 |
| 51 | Mick Sasser | .15 |
| 52 | Luis Alicea | .10 |
| 53 | Bryan Harvey | .50 |
| 54 | Steve Ellsworth | .15 |
| 55 | Mike Macfarlane | .10 |
| 56 | Checklist | .08 |

## 1989 Donruss . . . Complete Set of 660 Cards—Value $20.00   (Factory-Sealed Set—Value $22.00)

Features the rookie cards of Sandy Alomar, Jr., Ken Griffey, Jr., Tom Gordon, Gary Sheffield and Rickey Jordan.

| NO. | PLAYER | MINT |
|---|---|---|
| | **No. 1 to 26—Diamond Kings** | |
| 1 | Mike Greenwell (DK) | .10 |
| 2 | Bobby Bonilla (DK) | .15 |
| 3 | Pete Incaviglia (DK) | .08 |
| 4 | Chris Sabo (DK) | .10 |
| 5 | Robin Yount (DK) | .08 |
| 6 | Tony Gwynn (DK) | .10 |

| NO. | PLAYER | MINT |
|---|---|---|
| 7 | Carlton Fisk (DK) | .10 |
| 8 | Cory Snyder (DK) | .08 |
| 9 | David Cone (DK) | .08 |
| 10 | Kevin Seitzer (DK) | .08 |
| 11 | Rick Rueschel (DK) | .08 |
| 12 | Johnny Ray (DK) | .08 |
| 13 | Dave Schmidt (DK) | .08 |

| NO. | PLAYER | MINT |
|---|---|---|
| 14 | Andres Galarraga (DK) | .08 |
| 15 | Kirk Gibson (DK) | .10 |
| 16 | Fred McGriff (DK) | .10 |
| 17 | Mark Grace (DK) | .15 |
| 18 | Jeff Robinson (DK) | .08 |
| 19 | Vince Coleman (DK) | .08 |
| 20 | Dave Henderson (DK) | .08 |

| NO. | PLAYER | MINT |
|---|---|---|
| 21 | Harold Reynolds (DK) | .08 |
| 22 | Gerald Perry (DK) | .08 |
| 23 | Frank Viola (DK) | .08 |
| 24 | Steve Bedrosian (DK) | .08 |
| 25 | Glenn Davis (DK) | .08 |
| 26 | Don Mattingly (DK) | .15 |
| 27 | Diamond King Checklist | .08 |

| NO. PLAYER | MINT | NO. PLAYER | MINT | NO. PLAYER | MINT | NO. PLAYER | MINT |
|---|---|---|---|---|---|---|---|
| **No. 28 to 47—Rated Rookies** | | 111 Keith Moreland | .08 | 195 John Tudor | .05 | 279 Denny Walling | .05 |
| 28 Sandy Alomar, Jr. (R) | .50 | 112 Tom Brunansky | .08 | 196 Neil Allen | .05 | 280 Roger Clemens | .25 |
| 29 Steve Searcy (R) | .12 | 113 Kelly Gruber | .10 | 197 Orel Hershiser | .10 | 281 Greg Mathews | .05 |
| 30 Cameron Drew (R) | .10 | 114 Brook Jacoby | .05 | 198 Kal Daniels | .08 | 282 Tom Niedenfuer | .05 |
| 31 Gary Sheffield (R) | .35 | 115 Keith Brown (R) | .10 | 199 Kent Hrbek | .10 | 283 Paul Kilgus | .05 |
| 32 Erik Hanson (R) | .50 | 116 Matt Nokes | .08 | 200 Checklist | .08 | 284 Jose Guzman | .05 |
| 33 Ken Griffey, Jr. (R) | 6.00 | 117 Keith Hernandez | .10 | 201 Joe Magrane | .08 | 285 Calvin Schiraldi | .05 |
| 34 Greg Harris (R) | .20 | 118 Bob Forsch | .05 | 202 Scott Bailes | .05 | 286 Charlie Puleo | .05 |
| 35 Gregg Jefferies | .30 | 119 Bert Blyleven | .08 | 203 Tim Belcher | .08 | 287 Joe Orsulak | .05 |
| 36 Luis Medina (R) | .10 | 120 Willie Wilson | .08 | 204 George Brett | .15 | 288 Jack Howell | .08 |
| 37 Carlos Quintana (R) | .30 | 121 Tommy Gregg | .05 | 205 Benito Santiago | .10 | 289 Kevin Elster | .08 |
| 38 Felix Jose (R) | 1.00 | 122 Jim Rice | .08 | 206 Tony Fernandez | .08 | 290 Jose Lind | .05 |
| 39 Cris Carpenter (R) | .12 | 123 Bob Knepper | .05 | 207 Gerald Young | .08 | 291 Paul Molitor | .08 |
| 40 Ron Jones (R) | .08 | 124 Danny Jackson | .08 | 208 Bo Jackson | .50 | 292 Cecil Espy | .10 |
| 41 Dave West (R) | .15 | 125 Eric Plunk | .05 | 209 Chet Lemon | .05 | 293 Bill Wegman | .05 |
| 42 Randy Johnson (R) | .35 | 126 Brian Fisher | .05 | 210 Storm Davis | .05 | 294 Dan Pasqua | .08 |
| 43 Mike Harkey (R) | .15 | 127 Mike Pagliarulo | .08 | 211 Doug Drabek | .08 | 295 Scott Garrelts | .05 |
| 44 Pete Harnisch (R) | .15 | 128 Tony Gwynn | .20 | 212 Mickey Brantley | .08 | 296 Walt Terrell | .05 |
| 45 Tom Gordon (R) | .20 | 129 Lance McCullers | .08 | 213 Devon White | .08 | 297 Ed Hearn | .05 |
| 46 Gregg Olson (R) | .50 | 130 Andres Galarraga | .10 | 214 Dave Stewart | .10 | 298 Lou Whitaker | .08 |
| 47 Alex Sanchez (R) | .10 | 131 Jose Uribe | .05 | 215 Dave Schmidt | .05 | 299 Ken Dayley | .05 |
| 48 Ruben Sierra | .20 | 132 Kirk Gibson | .10 | 216 Bryn Smith | .05 | 300 Checklist | .08 |
| 49 Rafael Palmeiro | .15 | 133 David Palmer | .05 | 217 Brett Butler | .05 | 301 Tommy Herr | .05 |
| 50 Ron Gant | .40 | 134 R. J. Reynolds | .05 | 218 Bob Ojeda | .08 | 302 Mike Brumley | .05 |
| 51 Cal Ripken, Jr. | .40 | 135 Greg Walker | .05 | 219 Steve Rosenberg (R) | .10 | 303 Ellis Burks | .20 |
| 52 Wally Joyner | .15 | 136 Kirk McCaskill | .05 | 220 Hubie Brooks | .05 | 304 Curt Young | .05 |
| 53 Gary Carter | .10 | 137 Shawon Dunston | .10 | 221 B.J. Surhoff | .08 | 305 Jody Reed | .10 |
| 54 Andy Van Slyke | .10 | 138 Andy Allanson | .05 | 222 Rick Mahler | .05 | 306 Bill Doran | .05 |
| 55 Robin Yount | .20 | 139 Rob Murphy | .05 | 223 Rick Sutcliffe | .10 | 307 David Wells | .05 |
| 56 Pete Incaviglia | .08 | 140 Mike Aldrete | .05 | 224 Neal Heaton | .05 | 308 Ron Robinson | .08 |
| 57 Greg Brock | .05 | 141 Terry Kennedy | .05 | 225 Mitch Williams | .05 | 309 Rafael Santana | .05 |
| 58 Melido Perez | .08 | 142 Scott Fletcher | .05 | 226 Chuck Finley | .12 | 310 Julio Franco | .08 |
| 59 Craig Lefferts | .05 | 143 Steve Balboni | .05 | 227 Mark Langston | .10 | 311 Jack Clark | .10 |
| 60 Gary Pettis | .05 | 144 Bret Saberhagen | .10 | 228 Jesse Orosco | .05 | 312 Chris James | .08 |
| 61 Danny Tartabull | .10 | 145 Ozzie Virgil | .05 | 229 Ed Whitson | .05 | 313 Milt Thompson | .05 |
| 62 Guillermo Hernandez | .05 | 146 Dale Sveum | .08 | 230 Terry Pendleton | .08 | 314 John Shelby | .05 |
| 63 Ozzie Smith | .15 | 147 Darryl Strawberry | .30 | 231 Lloyd Moseby | .08 | 315 Al Leiter | .10 |
| 64 Gary Gaetti | .08 | 148 Harold Baines | .08 | 232 Greg Swindell | .10 | 316 Mike Davis | .05 |
| 65 Mark Davis | .08 | 149 George Bell | .12 | 233 John Franco | .08 | 317 Chris Sabo (R) | .60 |
| 66 Lee Smith | .08 | 150 Dave Parker | .10 | 234 Jack Morris | .10 | 318 Greg Gagne | .05 |
| 67 Dennis Eckersley | .10 | 151 Bobby Bonilla | .20 | 235 Howard Johnson | .15 | 319 Jose Oquendo | .05 |
| 68 Wade Boggs | .20 | 152 Mookie Wilson | .08 | 236 Glenn Davis | .10 | 320 John Farrell | .10 |
| 69 Mike Scott | .08 | 153 Tod Power | .05 | 237 Frank Viola | .08 | 321 Franklin Stubbs | .05 |
| 70 Fred McGriff | .20 | 154 Nolan Ryan | .50 | 238 Kevin Seitzer | .08 | 322 Kurt Stillwell | .05 |
| 71 Tom Browning | .08 | 155 Jeff Reardon | .08 | 239 Gerald Perry | .08 | 323 Shawn Abner | .05 |
| 72 Claudell Washington | .05 | 156 Tim Wallach | .08 | 240 Dwight Evans | .10 | 324 Mike Flanagan | .05 |
| 73 Mel Hall | .05 | 157 Jamie Moyer | .05 | 241 Jim Deshaies | .05 | 325 Kevin Bass | .08 |
| 74 Don Mattingly | .25 | 158 Rich Gossage | .08 | 242 Bo Diaz | .05 | 326 Pat Tabler | .08 |
| 75 Steve Bedrosian | .08 | 159 Dave Winfield | .15 | 243 Carney Lansford | .08 | 327 Mike Henneman | .05 |
| 76 Juan Samuel | .08 | 160 Von Hayes | .08 | 244 Mike Lavalliere | .05 | 328 Rick Honeycutt | .05 |
| 77 Mike Scioscia | .05 | 161 Willie McGee | .08 | 245 Rickey Henderson | .30 | 329 John Smiley | .08 |
| 78 Dave Righetti | .08 | 162 Rich Gedman | .05 | 246 Roberto Alomar | .35 | 330 Rey Quinones | .05 |
| 79 Alfredo Griffin | .05 | 163 Tony Pena | .08 | 247 Jimmy Jones | .05 | 331 Johnny Ray | .05 |
| 80 Eric Davis | .15 | 164 Mike Morgan | .05 | 248 Pascual Perez | .05 | 332 Bob Welch | .08 |
| 81 Juan Berenquer | .05 | 165 Charlie Hough | .08 | 249 Will Clark | .40 | 333 Larry Sheets | .05 |
| 82 Todd Worrell | .05 | 166 Mike Stanley | .05 | 250 Fernando Valenzuela | .10 | 334 Jeff Parrett | .08 |
| 83 Joe Carter | .15 | 167 Andre Dawson | .15 | 251 Shane Rawley | .05 | 335 Rick Rueschel | .05 |
| 84 Steve Sax | .12 | 168 Joe Boever | .05 | 252 Sid Bream | .05 | 336 Randy Myers | .08 |
| 85 Frank White | .05 | 169 Pete Stanicek | .05 | 253 Steve Lyons | .05 | 337 Ken Williams | .05 |
| 86 John Kruk | .08 | 170 Bob Boone | .05 | 254 Brian Downing | .08 | 338 Andy McGaffigan | .05 |
| 87 Rance Mulliniks | .05 | 171 Ron Darling | .10 | 255 Mark Grace | .25 | 339 Joey Meyer | .05 |
| 88 Alan Ashby | .05 | 172 Bob Walk | .05 | 256 Tom Candiotti | .08 | 340 Dion James | .05 |
| 89 Charlie Leibrandt | .08 | 173 Rob Deer | .08 | 257 Barry Larkin | .15 | 341 Les Lancaster | .05 |
| 90 Frank Tanana | .08 | 174 Steve Buechele | .05 | 258 Mike Krukow | .08 | 342 Tom Foley | .05 |
| 91 Jose Canseco | .50 | 175 Ted Higuera | .10 | 259 Billy Ripken | .05 | 343 Geno Petralli | .05 |
| 92 Barry Bonds | .25 | 176 Ozzie Guillen | .08 | 260 Cecilio Guante | .05 | 344 Dan Petry | .05 |
| 93 Harold Reynolds | .08 | 177 Candy Maldonado | .10 | 261 Scott Bradley | .05 | 345 Alvin Davis | .08 |
| 94 Mark McLemore | .05 | 178 Doyle Alexander | .05 | 262 Floyd Bannister | .05 | 346 Mickey Hatcher | .05 |
| 95 Mark McGwire | .15 | 179 Mark Gubicza | .10 | 263 Pete Smith | .08 | 347 Marvelle Wynn | .05 |
| 96 Eddie Murray | .12 | 180 Alan Trammell | .10 | 264 Jim Gantner | .05 | 348 Danny Cox | .05 |
| 97 Tim Raines | .10 | 181 Vince Coleman | .15 | 265 Roger McDowell | .05 | 349 Dave Stieb | .08 |
| 98 Rob Thompsomn | .05 | 182 Kirby Puckett | .25 | 266 Bobby Thigpen | .05 | 350 Jay Bell | .05 |
| 99 Kevin McReynolds | .08 | 183 Chris Brown | .08 | 267 Jim Clancy | .05 | 351 Jeff Treadway | .05 |
| 100 Checklist | .08 | 184 Marty Barrett | .05 | 268 Terry Steinbach | .10 | 352 Luis Salazar | .05 |
| 101 Carlton Fisk | .15 | 185 Stan Javier | .05 | 269 Mike Dunne | .05 | 353 Lenny Dykstra | .10 |
| 102 Dave Martinez | .05 | 186 Mike Greenwell | .15 | 270 Dwight Gooden | .15 | 354 Juan Agosto | .05 |
| 103 Glenn Braggs | .05 | 187 Billy Hatcher | .05 | 271 Mike Heath | .05 | 355 Gene Larkin | .05 |
| 104 Dale Murphy | .12 | 188 Jimmy Key | .08 | 272 Dave Smith | .05 | 356 Steve Farr | .05 |
| 105 Ryne Sandberg | .30 | 189 Nick Esasky | .08 | 273 Keith Atherton | .05 | 357 Paul Assenmacher | .05 |
| 106 Dennis Martinez | .05 | 190 Don Slaught | .05 | 274 Tim Burke | .05 | 358 Todd Benzinger | .08 |
| 107 Pete O'Brien | .08 | 191 Cory Snyder | .10 | 275 Damon Beryhill | .08 | 359 Larry Andersen | .05 |
| 108 Dick Schofield | .05 | 192 John Candelaria | .08 | 276 Vance Law | .05 | 360 Paul O'Neill | .08 |
| 109 Henry Cotto | .05 | 193 Mike Schmidt | .30 | 277 Rich Dotson | .08 | 361 Ron Hassey | .05 |
| 110 Mike Marshall | .08 | 194 Kevin Gross | .05 | 278 Lance Parrish | .08 | 362 Jim Gott | .05 |

| NO. | PLAYER | MINT | NO. | PLAYER | MINT | NO. | PLAYER | MINT | NO. | PLAYER | MINT |
|---|---|---|---|---|---|---|---|---|---|---|---|
| 363 | Ken Phelps | .05 | 444 | Jerry Don Gleaton | .05 | 525 | Bryan Harvey (R) | .20 | 606 | Lance Johnson | .05 |
| 364 | Tim Flannery | .05 | 445 | Paul Gibson (R) | .08 | 526 | Rick Aguilera | .05 | 607 | Terry Clark (R) | .10 |
| 365 | Randy Ready | .05 | 446 | Walt Weiss | .10 | 527 | Tom Prince | .05 | 608 | Manny Trillo | .05 |
| 366 | Nelson Santovenia (R) | .10 | 447 | Glenn Wilson | .05 | 528 | Mark Clear | .05 | 609 | Scott Jordan (R) | .10 |
| 367 | Kelly Downs | .05 | 448 | Mike Moore | .05 | 529 | Jerry Browne | .05 | 610 | Jay Howell | .08 |
| 368 | Danny Heep | .05 | 449 | Chili Davis | .08 | 530 | Juan Castillo | .05 | 611 | Francisco Melendez (R) | .10 |
| 369 | Phil Bradley | .08 | 450 | Dave Henderson | .08 | 531 | Jack McDowell | .10 | 612 | Mike Boddicker | .08 |
| 370 | Jeff Robinson | .05 | 451 | Jose Bautista (R) | .10 | 532 | Chris Speier | .05 | 613 | Kevin Brown | .10 |
| 371 | Ivan Calderon | .08 | 452 | Rex Hudler | .10 | 533 | Darrell Evans | .05 | 614 | Dave Valle | .05 |
| 372 | Mike Witt | .08 | 453 | Bob Brenly | .05 | 534 | Luis Aquino | .05 | 615 | Tim Laudner | .05 |
| 373 | Greg Maddux | .08 | 454 | Mackey Sasser | .08 | 535 | Eric King | .05 | 616 | Andy Nezelek (R) | .10 |
| 374 | Carmen Castillo | .05 | 455 | Daryl Boston | .05 | 536 | Ken Hill (R) | .15 | 617 | Chuck Crim | .05 |
| 375 | Jose Rijo | .08 | 456 | Mike Fitzgerald | .05 | 537 | Randy Bush | .05 | 618 | Jack Savage | .08 |
| 376 | Joe Price | .05 | 457 | Jefferey Leonard | .05 | 538 | Shane Mack | .05 | 619 | Adam Peterson | .08 |
| 377 | R.C. Gonzalez | .05 | 458 | Bruce Sutter | .08 | 539 | Tom Bolton | .10 | 620 | Todd Stottlemyre | .12 |
| 378 | Oddibe McDowell | .08 | 459 | Mitch Webster | .05 | 540 | Gene Nelson | .05 | 621 | Lance Blankenship (R) | .10 |
| 379 | Jim Presley | .05 | 460 | Joe Hesketh | .05 | 541 | Wes Gardner | .05 | 622 | Miquel Garcia (R) | .10 |
| 380 | Brad Wellman | .05 | 461 | Bobby Witt | .05 | 542 | Ken Caminiti | .05 | 623 | Keith Miller | .05 |
| 381 | Tom Glavine | .30 | 462 | Stew Cliburn | .05 | 543 | Duane Ward | .05 | 624 | Ricky Jordan (R) | .15 |
| 382 | Dan Plesac | .05 | 463 | Scott Bankhead | .05 | 544 | Norm Charlton (R) | .15 | 625 | Ernest Riles | .05 |
| 383 | Wally Backman | .05 | 464 | Ramon Martinez (R) | 1.00 | 545 | Hal Morris (R) | .75 | 626 | John Moses | .05 |
| 384 | Dave Gallagher (R) | .10 | 465 | Dave Leiper | .05 | 546 | Rich Yett | .05 | 627 | Nelson Liriano | .05 |
| 385 | Tom Henke | .05 | 466 | Luis Alicea (R) | .10 | 547 | Hensley Meulens (R) | .25 | 628 | Mike Smithson | .05 |
| 386 | Luis Polonia | .05 | 467 | John Cerutti | .05 | 548 | Greg Harris | .15 | 629 | Scott Sanderson | .05 |
| 387 | Junior Ortiz | .05 | 468 | Ron Washington | .05 | 549 | Darren Daulton | .05 | 630 | Dale Mohorcic | .05 |
| 388 | David Cone | .08 | 469 | Jeff Reed | .05 | 550 | Jeff Hamilton | .05 | 631 | Marvin Freeman | .05 |
| 389 | Dave Bergman | .05 | 470 | Jeff Robinson | .08 | 551 | Luis Aguayo | .05 | 632 | Mike Young | .05 |
| 390 | Danny Darwin | .05 | 471 | Sid Fernandez | .08 | 552 | Tim Leary | .08 | 633 | Dennis Lamp | .05 |
| 391 | Dan Gladden | .05 | 472 | Terry Puhl | .05 | 553 | Ron Oester | .05 | 634 | Dante Bichette (R) | .15 |
| 392 | John Dopson (R) | .10 | 473 | Charlie Lea | .05 | 554 | Steve Lombardozzi | .05 | 635 | Curt Schilling (R) | .10 |
| 393 | Frank DiPino | .05 | 474 | Israel Sanchez (R) | .10 | 555 | Tim Jones (R) | .10 | 636 | Scott May (R) | .10 |
| 394 | Al Nipper | .05 | 475 | Bruce Benedict | .05 | 556 | Bud Black | .05 | 637 | Mike Schooler (R) | .10 |
| 395 | Willie Randolph | .08 | 476 | Oil Can Boyd | .08 | 557 | Alejandro Pena | .08 | 638 | Rick Leach | .05 |
| 396 | Don Carman | .05 | 477 | Craig Reynolds | .05 | 558 | Jose DeJesus (R) | .12 | 639 | Tom Lampkin (R) | .10 |
| 397 | Scott Terry | .05 | 478 | Frank Williams | .05 | 559 | Dennis Rasmussen | .05 | 640 | Brian Meyer (R) | .10 |
| 398 | Rick Cerone | .05 | 479 | Greg Cadaret | .05 | 560 | Pat Borders | .12 | 641 | Brian Harper | .05 |
| 399 | Tom Pagnozzi | .05 | 480 | Randy Kramer (R) | .10 | 561 | Craig Biggio (R) | .30 | 642 | John Smoltz (R) | .60 |
| 400 | Checklist | .08 | 481 | Dave Eiland (R) | .10 | 562 | Luis de los Santos (R) | .10 | 643 | Jose—40/40 Club | .20 |
| 401 | Mickey Tettleton | .05 | 482 | Eric Show | .05 | 563 | Fred Lynn | .08 | 644 | Bill Schroeder | .05 |
| 402 | Curtis Wilkerson | .05 | 483 | Garry Templeton | .05 | 564 | Todd Burns (R) | .10 | 645 | Edgar Martinez | .20 |
| 403 | Jeff Russel | .05 | 484 | Wallace Johnson | .05 | 565 | Felix Fermin | .05 | 646 | Dennis Cook (R) | .10 |
| 404 | Pat Perry | .05 | 485 | Kevin Mitchell | .20 | 566 | Darnell Coles | .05 | 647 | Barry Jones | .05 |
| 405 | Jose Alvarez (R) | .08 | 486 | Tim Crews | .05 | 567 | Willie Fraser | .05 | 648 | Orel—59 and Counting | .10 |
| 406 | Rick Schu | .05 | 487 | Mike Maddux | .05 | 568 | Glenn Hubbard | .05 | 649 | Rod Nichols (R) | .10 |
| 407 | Sherman Corbett (R) | .10 | 488 | Dave LaPoint | .05 | 569 | Craig Worthington (R) | .10 | 650 | Jody Davis | .05 |
| 408 | Dave Magadan | .10 | 489 | Fred Manrique | .05 | 570 | Johnny Paredes (R) | .10 | 651 | Bob Milacki (R) | .20 |
| 409 | Bob Kipper | .05 | 490 | Greg Minton | .05 | 571 | Don Robinson | .05 | 652 | Mike Jackson | .05 |
| 410 | Don August | .08 | 491 | Doug Dascenzo (R) | .10 | 572 | Barry Lyons | .05 | 653 | Derek Lilliquist (R) | .10 |
| 411 | Bob Brower | .05 | 492 | Willie Upshaw | .05 | 573 | Bill Long | .05 | 654 | Paul Mirabella | .05 |
| 412 | Chris Bosio | .05 | 493 | Jack Armstrong (R) | .10 | 574 | Tracy Jones | .05 | 655 | Mike Diaz | .05 |
| 413 | Jerry Reuss | .05 | 494 | Kirt Manwaring | .05 | 575 | Juan Nieves | .05 | 656 | Jeff Musselman | .05 |
| 414 | Atlee Hammaker | .05 | 495 | Jeff Ballard | .05 | 576 | Andres Thomas | .05 | 657 | Jerry Reed | .05 |
| 415 | Jim Walewander | .08 | 496 | Jeff Kunkel | .05 | 577 | Rolando Roomes (R) | .10 | 658 | Kevin Blankenship (R) | .10 |
| 416 | Mike Macfarlane (R) | .10 | 497 | Mike Campbell | .05 | 578 | Luis Rivera | .08 | 659 | Wayne Tolleson | .05 |
| 417 | Pat Sheridan | .05 | 498 | Gary Thurman | .05 | 579 | Chad Kreuter (R) | .10 | 660 | Eric Hetzel (R) | .10 |
| 418 | Pedro Guerrero | .08 | 499 | Zane Smith | .05 | 580 | Tony Armas | .05 | | | |
| 419 | Allan Anderson | .08 | 500 | Checklist | .08 | 581 | Jay Buhner | .12 | | | |
| 420 | Mark Parent (R) | .10 | 501 | Mike Birkbeck | .05 | 582 | Ricky Horton | .05 | | | |
| 421 | Bob Stanley | .05 | 502 | Terry Leach | .05 | 583 | Andy Hawkins | .05 | | | |
| 422 | Mike Gallego | .05 | 503 | Shawn Hillegas | .05 | 584 | Sil Campusano (R) | .15 | | | |
| 423 | Bruce Hurst | .08 | 504 | Manny Lee | .05 | 585 | Dave Cark | .05 | | | |
| 424 | Dave Meads | .05 | 505 | Doug Jennings (R) | .10 | 586 | Van Snider (R) | .10 | | | |
| 425 | Jesse Barfield | .08 | 506 | Ken Oberkfell | .05 | 587 | Todd Frohwirth | .05 | | | |
| 426 | Rob Dibble (R) | .30 | 507 | Tim Tuefel | .05 | 588 | Puzzle Card | .08 | | | |
| 427 | Joel Skinner | .05 | 508 | Tom Brookens | .05 | 589 | William Brennan (R) | .10 | | | |
| 428 | Ron Kittle | .08 | 509 | Rafael Ramirez | .05 | 590 | German Gonzalez (R) | .10 | | | |
| 429 | Rick Rhoden | .05 | 510 | Fred Toliver | .05 | 591 | Ernie Whitt | .05 | | | |
| 430 | Bob Dernier | .05 | 511 | Brian Holman (R) | .15 | 592 | Jeff Blauser | .05 | | | |
| 431 | Steve Jeltz | .05 | 512 | Mike Bielecki | .05 | 593 | Spike Owen | .05 | | | |
| 432 | Rick Dempsey | .05 | 513 | Jeff Pico (R) | .10 | 594 | Matt Williams | .20 | | | |
| 433 | Roberto Kelly | .15 | 514 | Charles Hudson | .08 | 595 | Lloyd McClendon | .10 | | | |
| 434 | Dave Anderson | .05 | 515 | Bruce Ruffin | .05 | 596 | Steve Ontiveros | .05 | | | |
| 435 | Herm Winningham | .05 | 516 | Larry McWilliams | .05 | 597 | Scott Medvin (R) | .10 | | | |
| 436 | Al Newman | .05 | 517 | Jeff Sellers | .05 | 598 | Hipolito Pena (R) | .10 | | | |
| 437 | Jose Deleon | .05 | 518 | John Costello (R) | .10 | 599 | Jerald Clark (R) | .20 | | | |
| 438 | Doug Jones | .05 | 519 | Brady Anderson (R) | .10 | 600 | Checklist | .08 | | | |
| 439 | Brian Holton | .05 | 520 | Craig McMurtry | .05 | 601 | Carmelo Martinez | .05 | | | |
| 440 | Jeff Montgomery | .10 | 521 | Ray Hayward | .05 | 602 | Mike LaCoss | .05 | | | |
| 441 | Dickie Thon | .05 | 522 | Drew Hall | .10 | 603 | Mike Devereaux | .05 | | | |
| 442 | Cecil Fielder | .30 | 523 | Mark Lemke (R) | .15 | 604 | Alex Madrid (R) | .10 | | | |
| 443 | John Fishel (R) | .10 | 524 | Oswald Peraza (R) | .10 | 605 | Gary Redus | .05 | | | |

# 1989 Donruss Rookies . . . Complete Set of 56 Cards—Value $15.00

Features the outstanding rookies of the 1989 Season. The cards are coated with a glossy finish. The entire set was packaged in a printed box and distributed primarily through card hobby dealers. Features Donruss' first card of Jim Abbott, Jerome Walton and Dwight Smith.

| NO. | PLAYER | MINT |
|---|---|---|
| 1 | Gary Sheffield | .35 |
| 2 | Gregg Jefferies | .30 |
| 3 | Ken Griffey, Jr. | 7.00 |
| 4 | Tom Gordon | .25 |
| 5 | Billy Spiers | .15 |
| 6 | Deion Sanders (R) | .60 |
| 7 | Donn Pall | .10 |
| 8 | Steve Carter | .10 |
| 9 | Francisco Oliveras | .10 |
| 10 | Steve Wilson | .10 |
| 11 | Bob Geren | .10 |
| 12 | Tony Castillo | .10 |
| 13 | Kenny Rogers | .10 |
| 14 | Carlos Martinez (R) | .20 |
| 15 | Edgar Martinez | .20 |
| 16 | Jim Abbott (R) | 1.00 |
| 17 | Torey Lovullo | .12 |
| 18 | Mark Carreon | .12 |
| 19 | Geronimo Berroa | .10 |
| 20 | Luis Medina | .15 |
| 21 | Sandy Alomar, Jr. | .50 |
| 22 | Bob Milacki | .12 |
| 23 | Joe Girardi | .12 |
| 24 | German Gonzalez | .10 |
| 25 | Craig Worthington | .10 |
| 26 | Jerome Walton (R) | .50 |
| 27 | Gary Wayne | .10 |
| 28 | Tim Jones | .10 |
| 29 | Dante Bichette | .10 |
| 30 | Alexis Infante | .12 |
| 31 | Ken Hill | .10 |
| 32 | Dwight Smith | .15 |
| 33 | Luis de los Santos | .15 |
| 34 | Eric Yelding | .12 |
| 35 | Gregg Olson | .60 |
| 36 | Phil Stephenson | .12 |
| 37 | Ken Patterson | .10 |
| 38 | Rick Wrona | .10 |
| 39 | Mike Brumley | .10 |
| 40 | Cris Carpenter | .10 |
| 41 | Jeff Brantley (R) | .20 |
| 42 | Ron Jones | .10 |
| 43 | Randy Johnson | .10 |
| 44 | Kevin Brown | .10 |
| 45 | Ramon Martinez | 1.25 |
| 46 | Greg Harris | .15 |
| 47 | Steve Finley (R) | .30 |
| 48 | Randy Kramer | .10 |
| 49 | Erik Hanson | .50 |
| 50 | Matt Merullo | .12 |
| 51 | Mike Devereaux | .10 |
| 52 | Clay Parker | .10 |
| 53 | Omar Vizquel | .10 |
| 54 | Derek Lilliquist | .15 |
| 55 | Junior Felix (R) | .20 |
| 56 | Checklist | .10 |

# 1990 Donruss . . . Complete Set of 716 Cards—Value $20.00 (Factory-Sealed Set—Value $22.00)

The set was increased from 660 to 716 cards. Special cards honor Mike Schmidt's retirement and Nolan Ryan's strikeout record. Features the rookie cards of Todd Zeile, Eric Anthony, Andy Benes and Ben McDonald. Special Packaging is being introduced this year to help reduce tampering.

| NO. | PLAYER | MINT |
|---|---|---|
| **No. 1 to 26—Diamond Kings** | | |
| 1 | Bo Jackson (DK) | .25 |
| 2 | Steve Sax (DK) | .10 |
| 3 | R. Sierra (DK) (correct) | .12 |
| 3 | R. Sierra (DK) (error) | 1.00 |
| 4 | Ken Griffey Jr. (DK) | .60 |
| 5 | Mickey Tettleton (DK) | .08 |
| 6 | Dave Stewart (DK) | .08 |
| 7 | Jim DeShaies (DK) | .08 |
| 8 | John Smoltz (DK) | .12 |
| 9 | Mike Bielecki (DK) | .08 |
| 10 | Brian Downing (DK) | .10 |
| 11 | Kevin Mitchell (DK) | .10 |
| 12 | Kelly Gruber (DK) | .08 |
| 13 | Joe Magrane (DK) | .08 |
| 14 | John Franco (DK) | .08 |
| 15 | Ozzie Guillen (DK) | .08 |
| 16 | Lou Whitaker (DK) | .08 |
| 17 | John Smiley (DK) | .08 |
| 18 | Howard Johnson (DK) | .08 |
| 19 | Willie Randolph (DK) | .08 |
| 20 | Chris Bosio (DK) | .08 |
| 21 | Tommy Herr (DK) | .08 |
| 22 | Dan Gladden (DK) | .08 |
| 23 | Ellis Burks (DK) | .08 |
| 24 | Pete O'Brien (DK) | .08 |
| 25 | Bryn Smith (DK) | .08 |
| 26 | Ed Whitson (DK) | .08 |
| 27 | DK Checklist | .05 |
| **No. 28 to 47—Rated Rookies** | | |
| 28 | Robin Ventura | .50 |
| 29 | Todd Zeile | .30 |
| 30 | Sandy Alomar Jr. | .12 |
| 31 | Kent Mercker (R) | .15 |
| 32 | Ben McDonald (R) | .75 |
| 33 | J. Gonzalez (R) (correct) | 2.00 |
| 33 | J. Gonzalez (R) (error) | 4.00 |
| 34 | Eric Anthony (R) | .20 |
| 35 | Mike Fetters (R) | .10 |
| 36 | Marquis Grissom (R) | .35 |
| 37 | Greg Vaughn | .50 |
| 38 | Brian Dubois (R) | .10 |
| 39 | Steve Avery | .75 |
| 40 | Mark Gardner (R) | .20 |
| 41 | Andy Benes | .20 |
| 42 | Delino Deshields (R) | .40 |
| 43 | Scott Coolbaugh (R) | .15 |
| 44 | Pat Combs | .10 |
| 45 | Alex Sanchez | .08 |
| 46 | Kelly Mann (R) | .08 |

| NO. | PLAYER | MINT | NO. | PLAYER | MINT | NO. | PLAYER | MINT | NO. | PLAYER | MINT |
|---|---|---|---|---|---|---|---|---|---|---|---|
| 47 | Julio Machado (R) | .10 | 131 | Ernest Riles | .05 | 215 | Steve Finley | .10 | 299 | Terry Pendleton | .08 |
| 48 | Pete Incaviglia | .08 | 132 | Mike Morgan | .05 | 216 | Tim Raines | .10 | 300 | Checklist No. 2 | .05 |
| 49 | Shawon Dunston | .08 | 133 | Steve Jeltz | .05 | 217 | Scott Garrelts | .08 | 301 | Juan Berenguer | .05 |
| 50 | Jeff Treadway | .05 | 134 | Jeff Robinson | .08 | 218 | Kevin McReynolds | .10 | 302 | Mark Davis | .10 |
| 51 | Jeff Ballard | .08 | 135 | Ozzie Guillen | .08 | 219 | Dave Gallagher | .05 | 303 | Nick Esasky | .05 |
| 52 | Claudell Washington | .08 | 136 | Chili Davis | .05 | 220 | Tim Wallach | .05 | 304 | Rickey Henderson | .25 |
| 53 | Juan Samuel | .08 | 137 | Mitch Webster | .05 | 221 | Chuck Crim | .05 | 305 | Rick Cerone | .05 |
| 54 | John Smiley | .10 | 138 | Jerry Browne | .08 | 222 | Lonnie Smith | .05 | 306 | Craig Biggio | .08 |
| 55 | Rob Deer | .05 | 139 | Bo Diaz | .05 | 223 | Andre Dawson | .10 | 307 | Duane Ward | .05 |
| 56 | Geno Petralli | .05 | 140 | Robby Thompson | .08 | 224 | Nelson Santovenia | .05 | 308 | Tom Browning | .05 |
| 57 | Chris Bosio | .05 | 141 | Craig Worthington | .05 | 225 | Rafael Palmeiro | .10 | 309 | Walt Terrell | .05 |
| 58 | Carlton Fisk | .12 | 142 | Julio Franco | .08 | 226 | Devon White | .08 | 310 | Greg Swindell | .08 |
| 59 | Kirt Manwaring | .05 | 143 | Brian Holman | .05 | 227 | Harold Reynolds | .05 | 311 | Dave Righetti | .08 |
| 60 | Chet Lemon | .05 | 144 | George Brett | .15 | 228 | Ellis Burks | .10 | 312 | Mike Maddux | .05 |
| 61 | Bo Jackson | .40 | 145 | Tom Glavine | .15 | 229 | Mark Parent | .05 | 313 | Lenny Dykstra | .08 |
| 62 | Doyle Alexander | .08 | 146 | Robin Yount | .15 | 230 | Will Clark | .30 | 314 | Jose Gonzalez | .05 |
| 63 | Pedro Guerrero | .08 | 147 | Gary Carter | .10 | 231 | Jimmy Key | .08 | 315 | Steve Balboni | .05 |
| 64 | Allan Anderson | .08 | 148 | Ron Kittle | .05 | 232 | John Ferrell | .08 | 316 | Mike Scioscia | .08 |
| 65 | Greg Harris | .05 | 149 | Tony Fernandez | .08 | 233 | Eric Davis | .15 | 317 | Ron Oester | .05 |
| 66 | Mike Greenwell | .15 | 150 | Dave Stewart | .08 | 234 | Johnny Ray | .08 | 318 | Gary Wayne (R) | .10 |
| 67 | Walt Weiss | .05 | 151 | Gary Gaetti | .10 | 235 | Darryl Strawberry | .25 | 319 | Todd Worrell | .08 |
| 68 | Wade Boggs | .15 | 152 | Kevin Elster | .08 | 236 | Bill Doran | .05 | 320 | Doug Jones | .05 |
| 69 | Jim Clancy | .05 | 153 | Gerald Perry | .05 | 237 | Greg Gagne | .05 | 321 | Jeff Hamilton | .05 |
| 70 | Junior Felix | .10 | 154 | Jesse Orosco | .05 | 238 | Jim Eisenreich | .05 | 322 | Danny Tartabull | .08 |
| 71 | Barry Larkin | .12 | 155 | Wally Backman | .05 | 239 | Tommy Gregg | .05 | 323 | Chris James | .05 |
| 72 | Dave LaPoint | .05 | 156 | Dennis Martinez | .05 | 240 | Marty Barrett | .05 | 324 | Mike Flanagan | .05 |
| 73 | Joel Skinner | .05 | 157 | Rick Sutcliffe | .05 | 241 | Rafael Ramirez | .05 | 325 | Gerald Young | .05 |
| 74 | Jesse Barfield | .05 | 158 | Greg Maddux | .08 | 242 | Chris Sabo | .10 | 326 | Bob Boone | .05 |
| 75 | Tommy Herr | .05 | 159 | Andy Hawkins | .05 | 243 | Dave Henderson | .08 | 327 | Frank Williams | .05 |
| 76 | Ricky Jordan | .10 | 160 | John Kruk | .08 | 244 | Andy Van Slyke | .10 | 328 | Dave Parker | .08 |
| 77 | Eddie Murray | .12 | 161 | Jose Oquendo | .05 | 245 | Alvaro Espinoza | .05 | 329 | Sid Bream | .05 |
| 78 | Steve Sax | .08 | 162 | John Dopson | .08 | 246 | Garry Templeton | .05 | 330 | Mike Schooler | .08 |
| 79 | Tim Belcher | .08 | 163 | Joe Magrane | .10 | 247 | Gene Harris | .10 | 331 | Bert Blyleven | .08 |
| 80 | Danny Jackson | .08 | 164 | Billy Ripken | .08 | 248 | Kevin Gross | .05 | 332 | Bob Welch | .05 |
| 81 | Kent Hrbek | .10 | 165 | Fred Manrique | .05 | 249 | Brett Butler | .05 | 333 | Bob Milacki | .08 |
| 82 | Milt Thompson | .05 | 166 | Nolan Ryan | .50 | 250 | Willie Randolph | .10 | 334 | Tim Burke | .05 |
| 83 | Brook Jacoby | .05 | 167 | Damon Berryhill | .08 | 251 | Roger McDowell | .05 | 335 | Jose Uribe | .05 |
| 84 | Mike Marshall | .08 | 168 | Dale Murphy | .12 | 252 | Rafael Belliard | .05 | 336 | Randy Myers | .08 |
| 85 | Kevin Seitzer | .08 | 169 | Mickey Tettleton | .05 | 253 | Steve Rosenberg | .05 | 337 | Eric King | .05 |
| 86 | Tony Gwynn | .15 | 170 | Kirk McCaskill | .08 | 254 | Jack Howell | .05 | 338 | Mark Langston | .10 |
| 87 | Dave Stieb | .05 | 171 | Dwight Gooden | .15 | 255 | Marvell Wynne | .05 | 339 | Ted Higuera | .05 |
| 88 | Dave Smith | .08 | 172 | Jose Lind | .05 | 256 | Tom Candiotti | .05 | 340 | Oddibe McDowell | .05 |
| 89 | Bret Saberhagen | .10 | 173 | B.J. Surhoff | .05 | 257 | Todd Benzinger | .08 | 341 | Lloyd McClendon | .05 |
| 90 | Alan Trammell | .10 | 174 | Ruben Sierra | .20 | 258 | Don Robinson | .05 | 342 | Pascual Perez | .05 |
| 91 | Tony Phillips | .05 | 175 | Dan Plesac | .05 | 259 | Phil Bradley | .08 | 343 | Kevin Brown | .05 |
| 92 | Doug Drabek | .10 | 176 | Dan Pasqua | .05 | 260 | Cecil Espy | .05 | 344 | Chuck Finley | .08 |
| 93 | Jeffrey Leonard | .05 | 177 | Kelly Downs | .08 | 261 | Scott Bankhead | .05 | 345 | Erik Hanson | .08 |
| 94 | Wally Joyner | .10 | 178 | Matt Nokes | .08 | 262 | Frank White | .05 | 346 | Rich Gedman | .05 |
| 95 | Carney Lansford | .08 | 179 | Luis Aquino | .05 | 263 | Andres Thomas | .05 | 347 | Bip Roberts | .05 |
| 96 | Cal Ripken | .35 | 180 | Frank Tanana | .05 | 264 | Glenn Braggs | .05 | 348 | Matt Williams | .15 |
| 97 | Andres Galarraga | .10 | 181 | Tony Pena | .08 | 265 | David Cone | .10 | 349 | Tom Henke | .05 |
| 98 | Kevin Mitchell | .15 | 182 | Dan Gladden | .05 | 266 | Bobby Thigpen | .05 | 350 | Brad Komminsk | .05 |
| 99 | Howard Johnson | .10 | 183 | Bruce Hurst | .05 | 267 | Nelson Liriano | .05 | 351 | Jeff Reed | .05 |
| 100 | Checklist | .05 | 184 | Roger Clemens | .25 | 268 | Terry Steinbach | .10 | 352 | Brian Downing | .05 |
| 101 | Melido Perez | .05 | 185 | Mark McGwire | .15 | 269 | Kirby Puckett | .20 | 353 | Frank Viola | .08 |
| 102 | Spike Owen | .05 | 186 | Rob Murphy | .05 | 270 | Gregg Jefferies | .10 | 354 | Terry Puhl | .05 |
| 103 | Paul Molitor | .10 | 187 | Jim Deshaies | .05 | 271 | Jeff Blauser | .05 | 355 | Brian Harper | .05 |
| 104 | Geronimo Berroa | .05 | 188 | Fred McGriff | .15 | 272 | Cory Snyder | .10 | 356 | Steve Farr | .05 |
| 105 | Ryne Sandberg | .25 | 189 | Rob Dibble | .08 | 273 | Roy Smith | .05 | 357 | Joe Boever | .05 |
| 106 | Bryn Smith | .05 | 190 | Don Mattingly | .20 | 274 | Tom Foley | .05 | 358 | Danny Heep | .05 |
| 107 | Steve Buechele | .05 | 191 | Felix Fermin | .05 | 275 | Mitch Williams | .08 | 359 | Larry Anderson | .05 |
| 108 | Jim Abbott | .20 | 192 | Roberto Kelly | .10 | 276 | Paul Kilgus | .05 | 360 | Rolando Roomes | .08 |
| 109 | Alvin Davis | .08 | 193 | Dennis Cook | .05 | 277 | Don Slaught | .05 | 361 | Mike Gallego | .05 |
| 110 | Leo Smith | .10 | 194 | Darren Daulton | .05 | 278 | Von Hayes | .05 | 362 | Bob Kipper | .05 |
| 111 | Roberto Alomar | .15 | 195 | Alfredo Griffen | .08 | 279 | Vince Coleman | .10 | 363 | Clay Parker | .08 |
| 112 | Rick Reuschel | .08 | 196 | Eric Plunk | .05 | 280 | Mike Boddicker | .08 | 364 | Mike Pagliarulo | .08 |
| 113 | Kelly Gruber | .10 | 197 | Orel Hershiser | .10 | 281 | Ken Dayley | .05 | 365 | Ken Griffey Jr. | 1.50 |
| 114 | Joe Carter | .12 | 198 | Paul O'Brien | .08 | 282 | Mike Devereaux | .08 | 366 | Rex Hudler | .05 |
| 115 | Jose Rijo | .05 | 199 | Randy Bush | .05 | 283 | Kenny Rogers | .08 | 367 | Pat Sheridan | .05 |
| 116 | Greg Minton | .05 | 200 | Checklist | .05 | 284 | Jeff Russell | .05 | 368 | Kirk Gibson | .10 |
| 117 | Bob Ojeda | .05 | 201 | Ozzie Smith | .12 | 285 | Jerome Walton | .10 | 369 | Jeff Parrett | .05 |
| 118 | Glenn Davis | .08 | 202 | Pete O'Brien | .08 | 286 | Derek Lilliquist | .08 | 370 | Bob Walk | .05 |
| 119 | Jeff Reardon | .08 | 203 | Jay Howell | .05 | 287 | Joe Orsulak | .05 | 371 | Ken Patterson | .08 |
| 120 | Kurt Stillwell | .05 | 204 | Mark Gubicza | .05 | 288 | Dick Schofield | .05 | 372 | Bryan Harvey | .05 |
| 121 | John Smoltz | .15 | 205 | Ed Whitson | .05 | 289 | Ron Darling | .10 | 373 | Mike Bielecki | .05 |
| 122 | Dwight Evans | .08 | 206 | George Bell | .10 | 290 | Bobby Bonilla | .15 | 374 | Tom Magrann (R) | .10 |
| 123 | Eric Yelding | .08 | 207 | Mike Scott | .08 | 291 | Jim Gantner | .05 | 375 | Rick Mahler | .05 |
| 124 | John Franco | .10 | 208 | Charlie Leibrandt | .05 | 292 | Bobby Witt | .05 | 376 | Craig Lefferts | .05 |
| 125 | Jose Canseco | .40 | 209 | Mike Heath | .05 | 293 | Greg Brock | .05 | 377 | Gregg Olson | .10 |
| 126 | Barry Bonds | .20 | 210 | Dennis Eckersley | .10 | 294 | Ivan Calderon | .05 | 378 | Jamie Moyer | .05 |
| 127 | Lee Guetterman | .05 | 211 | Mike LaValliere | .05 | 295 | Steve Bedrosian | .05 | 379 | Randy Johnson | .08 |
| 128 | Jack Clark | .08 | 212 | Darnell Coles | .05 | 296 | Mike Henneman | .05 | 380 | Jeff Montgomery | .08 |
| 129 | Dave Valle | .05 | 213 | Lance Parrish | .08 | 297 | Tim Gordon | .10 | 381 | Marty Clary | .05 |
| 130 | Hubie Brooks | .05 | 214 | Mike Moore | .08 | 298 | Lou Whitaker | .08 | 382 | Bill Spiers | .08 |

| NO. | PLAYER | MINT |
|---|---|---|
| 383 | Dave Magadan | .08 |
| 384 | Greg Hibbard (R) | .20 |
| 385 | Ernie Whitt | .05 |
| 386 | Rick Honeycutt | .05 |
| 387 | Dave West | .08 |
| 388 | Keith Hernandez | .08 |
| 389 | Jose Alvarez | .05 |
| 390 | Joey Belle | .50 |
| 391 | Rick Aguilera | .05 |
| 392 | Mike Fitzgerald | .05 |
| 393 | Dwight Smith | .15 |
| 394 | Steve Wilson | .10 |
| 395 | Bob Geren | .15 |
| 396 | Randy Ready | .05 |
| 397 | Ken Hill | .08 |
| 398 | Jody Reed | .05 |
| 399 | Tom Brunansky | .05 |
| 400 | Checklist No. 3 | .05 |
| 401 | Rene Gonzales | .05 |
| 402 | Harold Baines | .05 |
| 403 | Cecilio Guante | .05 |
| 404 | Joe Girardi | .08 |
| 405 | Sergio Valdez (R) | .10 |
| 406 | Mark Williamson | .05 |
| 407 | Glenn Hoffman | .05 |
| 408 | Jeff Innis | .10 |
| 409 | Randy Kramer | .05 |
| 410 | Charlie O'Brien | .05 |
| 411 | Charlie Hough | .05 |
| 412 | Gus Polidor | .05 |
| 413 | Ron Karkovice | .05 |
| 414 | Trevor Wilson | .10 |
| 415 | Kevin Ritz (R) | .10 |
| 416 | Gary Thurman | .05 |
| 417 | Jeff Robinson | .08 |
| 418 | Scott Terry | .05 |
| 419 | Tim Laudner | .05 |
| 420 | Dennis Rasmussen | .05 |
| 421 | Luis Rivera | .05 |
| 422 | Jim Corsi | .05 |
| 423 | Dennis Lampl | .05 |
| 424 | Ken Caminiti | .05 |
| 425 | David Wells | .05 |
| 426 | Norm Charlton | .05 |
| 427 | Deion Sanders | .15 |
| 428 | Dion James | .05 |
| 429 | Chuck Cary | .05 |
| 430 | Ken Howell | .05 |
| 431 | Steve Lake | .05 |
| 432 | Kal Daniels | .10 |
| 433 | Lance McCullers | .05 |
| 434 | Lenny Harris | .05 |
| 435 | Scott Scudder | .10 |
| 436 | Gene Larkin | .05 |
| 437 | Dan Quisenberry | .05 |
| 438 | Steve Olin (R) | .10 |
| 439 | Mickey Hatcher | .05 |
| 440 | Willie Wilson | .08 |
| 441 | Mark Grant | .05 |
| 442 | Mookie Wilson | .08 |
| 443 | Alex Trevino | .05 |
| 444 | Pat Tabler | .05 |
| 445 | Dave Bergman | .05 |
| 446 | Todd Burns | .05 |
| 447 | R.J. Reynolds | .05 |
| 448 | Jay Buhner | .08 |
| 449 | Les Stevens | .20 |
| 450 | Ron Hassey | .05 |
| 451 | Bob Melvin | .05 |
| 452 | Dave Martinez | .05 |
| 453 | Greg Litton | .08 |
| 454 | Mark Carreon | .05 |
| 455 | Scott Fletcher | .05 |
| 456 | Otis Nixon | .05 |
| 457 | Tony Fossas (R) | .10 |
| 458 | John Russel | .05 |
| 459 | Paul Assenmacher | .05 |
| 460 | Zane Smith | .05 |
| 461 | Jack Daugherty (R) | .10 |
| 462 | Rich Monteleone | .08 |
| 463 | Greg Briley | .08 |
| 464 | Mike Smithson | .05 |
| 465 | Benito Santiago | .08 |
| 466 | Jeff Brantley | .08 |
| 467 | Jose Nunez | .05 |
| 468 | Scott Bailes | .05 |
| 469 | Ken Griffey | .05 |
| 470 | Bob McClure | .05 |
| 471 | Mackey Sasser | .05 |
| 472 | Glenn Wilson | .05 |
| 473 | Kevin Tapani (R) | .35 |
| 474 | Bill Buckner | .05 |
| 475 | Ron Gant | .20 |
| 476 | Kevin Romine | .05 |
| 477 | Juan Agosto | .05 |
| 478 | Herm Winningham | .05 |
| 479 | Storm Davis | .05 |
| 480 | Jeff King | .10 |
| 481 | Kevin Mmahat (R) | .10 |
| 482 | Carmelo Martinez | .05 |
| 483 | Omar Vizquel | .15 |
| 484 | Jim Dwyer | .05 |
| 485 | Bob Knepper | .05 |
| 486 | Dave Anderson | .05 |
| 487 | Ron Jones | .05 |
| 488 | Jay Bell | .05 |
| 489 | Sammy Sosa (R) | .25 |
| 490 | Kent Anderson | .10 |
| 491 | Domingo Ramos | .05 |
| 492 | Dave Clark | .05 |
| 493 | Tim Birtsas | .05 |
| 494 | Ken Oberkfell | .05 |
| 495 | Larry Sheets | .05 |
| 496 | Jeff Kunkel | .05 |
| 497 | Jim Presley | .05 |
| 498 | Mike Macfarlane | .05 |
| 499 | Pete Smith | .05 |
| 500 | Checklist | .05 |
| 501 | Gary Sheffield | .10 |
| 502 | Terry Bross (R) | .12 |
| 503 | Jerry Kutzler (R) | .10 |
| 504 | Lloyd Moseby | .05 |
| 505 | Curt Young | .05 |
| 506 | Al Newman | .05 |
| 507 | Keith Miller | .05 |
| 508 | Mike Stanton (R) | .12 |
| 509 | Rich Yett | .05 |
| 510 | Tim Drummond (R) | .10 |
| 511 | Joe Hesketh | .05 |
| 512 | Rick Wrona | .08 |
| 513 | Luis Salazar | .05 |
| 514 | Hal Morns | .30 |
| 515 | Terry Mulholland | .05 |
| 516 | John Morris | .05 |
| 517 | Carlos Quintana | .10 |
| 518 | Frank DiPino | .08 |
| 519 | Randy Milligan | .10 |
| 520 | Chad Kreuter | .05 |
| 521 | Mike Jeffcoat | .05 |
| 522 | Mike Harkey | .08 |
| 523 | Andy Nezelek | .05 |
| 524 | Dave Schmidt | .08 |
| 525 | Tony Armas | .05 |
| 526 | Barry Lyons | .05 |
| 527 | Rick Reed (R) | .10 |
| 528 | Jerry Reuss | .05 |
| 529 | Dean Palmer (R) | .75 |
| 530 | Jeff Peterek | .15 |
| 531 | Carlos Martinez | .10 |
| 532 | Atlee Hammaker | .05 |
| 533 | Mike Brumley | .05 |
| 534 | Terry Leach | .05 |
| 535 | Doug Strange (R) | .10 |
| 536 | Jose DeLeon | .05 |
| 537 | Shane Rawley | .05 |
| 538 | Joey Cora | .05 |
| 539 | Eric Hetzel | .05 |
| 540 | Gene Nelson | .05 |
| 541 | Wes Gardner | .05 |
| 542 | Mark Portugal | .05 |
| 543 | Al Leiter | .05 |
| 544 | Jack Armstrong | .05 |
| 545 | Greg Cadaret | .05 |
| 546 | Rod Nichols | .05 |
| 547 | Luis Polonia | .05 |
| 548 | Charles Hayes | .05 |
| 549 | Dickie Thon | .05 |
| 550 | Tim Crews | .05 |
| 551 | Dave Winfield | .12 |
| 552 | Mike Davis | .05 |
| 553 | Ron Robinson | .05 |
| 554 | Carmen Castillo | .05 |
| 555 | John Costello | .05 |
| 556 | Bud Black | .05 |
| 557 | Rick Dempsey | .05 |
| 558 | Jim Acker | .05 |
| 559 | Eric Show | .05 |
| 560 | Pat Borders | .05 |
| 561 | Danny Darwin | .05 |
| 562 | Rick Luecken (R) | .10 |
| 563 | Edwin Nunez | .05 |
| 564 | Felix Jose | .20 |
| 565 | John Cangelosi | .05 |
| 566 | Billy Swift | .05 |
| 567 | Bill Schroeder | .05 |
| 568 | Stan Javier | .05 |
| 569 | Jim Traber | .05 |
| 570 | Wallace Johnson | .05 |
| 571 | Donnell Nixon | .05 |
| 572 | Sid Fernandez | .08 |
| 573 | Lance Johnson | .05 |
| 574 | Andy McGaffigan | .05 |
| 575 | Mark Knudson | .05 |
| 576 | Tommy Greene (R) | .25 |
| 577 | Mark Grace | .15 |
| 578 | Larry Walker (R) | .25 |
| 579 | Mike Stanley | .05 |
| 580 | Mike Witt | .08 |
| 581 | Scott Bradley | .05 |
| 582 | Greg Harris | .05 |
| 583 | Kevin Hickey | .08 |
| 584 | Lee Mazzilli | .05 |
| 585 | Jeff Pico | .05 |
| 586 | Joe Oliver | .12 |
| 587 | Willie Fraser | .05 |
| 588 | Puzzle Card | .05 |
| 589 | Kevin Bass | .05 |
| 590 | John Moses | .05 |
| 591 | Tom Pagnozzi | .05 |
| 592 | Tony Castillo | .10 |
| 593 | Jerald Clark | .05 |
| 594 | Dan Schatzeder | .05 |
| 595 | Luis Quinones | .05 |
| 596 | Pete Harnisch | .08 |
| 597 | Gary Redus | .05 |
| 598 | Mel Hall | .08 |
| 599 | Rick Schu | .05 |
| 600 | Checklist | .05 |
| 601 | Mike Kingery | .05 |
| 602 | Terry Kennedy | .05 |
| 603 | Mike Sharperson | .05 |
| 604 | Don Carman | .05 |
| 605 | Jim Gott | .05 |
| 606 | Donn Pall | .05 |
| 607 | Rance Mulliniks | .05 |
| 608 | Curt Wilkerson | .05 |
| 609 | Mike Felder | .05 |
| 610 | Guillermo Hermandez | .05 |
| 611 | Candy Maldonado | .05 |
| 612 | Mark Thurmond | .05 |
| 613 | Rick Leach | .05 |
| 614 | Jerry Reed | .05 |
| 615 | Franklin Stubbs | .05 |
| 616 | Billy Hatcher | .05 |
| 617 | Don August | .08 |
| 618 | Tim Teufel | .05 |
| 619 | Shawn Hillegas | .05 |
| 620 | Manny Lee | .05 |
| 621 | Gary Ward | .05 |
| 622 | Mark Guthrie (R) | .10 |
| 623 | Jeff Musselman | .05 |
| 624 | Mark Lemke | .05 |
| 625 | Fernando Valenzuela | .10 |
| 626 | Paul Sorrento (R) | .12 |
| 627 | Glenallen Hill | .10 |
| 628 | Les Lancaster | .05 |
| 629 | Vance Law | .05 |
| 630 | Randy Velarde | .05 |
| 631 | Todd Frohwirth | .05 |
| 632 | Willie McGee | .08 |
| 633 | Oil Can Boyd | .05 |
| 634 | Cris Carpenter | .05 |
| 635 | Brian Holton | .05 |
| 636 | Tracy Jones | .05 |
| 637 | Terry Steinbach (AS) | .08 |
| 638 | Brady Anderson | .05 |
| 639 | Jack Morris | .15 |
| 640 | Jaime Navarro | .10 |
| 641 | Darrin Jackson | .08 |
| 642 | Mike Dyer (R) | .12 |
| 643 | Mike Schmidt | .25 |
| 644 | Henry Cotto | .05 |
| 645 | John Cerutti | .05 |
| 646 | Francisco Cabera | .10 |
| 647 | Scott Sanderson | .05 |
| 648 | Brian Meyer | .08 |
| 649 | Ray Searage | .05 |
| 650 | Bo Jackson (AS) | .35 |
| 651 | Steve Lyons | .05 |
| 652 | Mike LaCoss | .05 |
| 653 | Ted Power | .05 |
| 654 | Howard Johnson (AS) | .10 |
| 655 | Mauro Gozzo (R) | .12 |
| 656 | Mike Blowers (R) | .10 |
| 657 | Paul Gibson | .05 |
| 658 | Neal Heaton | .05 |
| 659 | N. Ryan 5000 K (cor.) | .75 |
| 659 | N. Ryan 5000 K (error) | 7.00 |
| 660 | Harold Baines (AS) | .10 |
| 661 | Steve Lyons | .05 |
| 662 | Clint Zavaras (R) | .12 |
| 663 | Rick Reuschel (AS) | .08 |
| 664 | Alejandro Pena | .05 |
| 665 | Nolan Ryan (correct) | .75 |
| 665 | Nolan Ryan (error) | 7.00 |
| 666 | Ricky Horton | .05 |
| 667 | Curt Schilling | .05 |
| 668 | Bill Landrum | .05 |
| 669 | Todd Stottlemyre | .10 |
| 670 | Tim Leary | .08 |
| 671 | John Wetteland | .08 |
| 672 | Calvin Schiraldi | .05 |
| 673 | Ruben Sierra (AS) | .20 |
| 674 | Pedro Guerrero (AS) | .12 |
| 675 | Ken Phelps | .05 |
| 676 | Cal Ripken (AS) | .15 |
| 677 | Denny Walling | .05 |
| 678 | Goose Gossage | .05 |
| 679 | Gary Mielke (R) | .10 |
| 680 | Bill Bathe | .05 |
| 681 | Tom Lawless | .05 |
| 682 | Xavier Hernandez (R) | .10 |
| 683 | Kirby Puckett (AS) | .25 |
| 684 | Mariano Duncan | .05 |
| 685 | Ramon Martinez | .25 |
| 686 | Tim Jones | .05 |
| 687 | Tom Filer | .05 |
| 688 | Steve Lombardozzi | .05 |
| 689 | Bernie Williams (R) | .50 |
| 690 | Chip Hale (R) | .10 |
| 691 | Beau Allred (R) | .15 |
| 692 | Ryne Sandberg (AS) | .20 |
| 693 | Jeff Huson (R) | .10 |
| 694 | Curt Ford | .05 |
| 695 | Eric Davis (AS) | .15 |
| 696 | Scott Lusader | .05 |
| 697 | Mark McGwire (AS) | .20 |
| 698 | Steve Cummings (R) | .10 |
| 699 | George Canale (R) | .15 |
| 700 | Checklist | .05 |
| 701 | Julio Franco (AS) | .10 |
| 702 | Dave Johnson | .05 |
| 703 | Dave Stewart (AS) | .10 |
| 704 | Dave Justice (R) | 2.50 |
| 705 | Tony Gwynn (AS) | .20 |
| 706 | Greg Myers | .05 |
| 707 | Will Clark (AS) | .35 |
| 708 | Benito Santiago (AS) | .08 |
| 709 | Larry McWilliams | .05 |
| 710 | Ozzie Smith (AS) | .10 |
| 711 | John Olerud (R) | 1.00 |
| 712 | Wade Boggs (AS) | .20 |
| 713 | Gary Eave (R) | .15 |
| 714 | Bob Tewksbury | .05 |
| 715 | Kevin Mitchell (AS) | .20 |
| 716 | A. Bartlett Giamatti | .15 |
| | BB Commissioner | |

# 1990 Donruss Rookies. . . . Complete Set of 56 Cards—Value $12.00

Features the outstanding rookies of the 1989 season. The cards are coated with a glossy finish. The entire set was packaged in a printed box, and distributed through card hobby dealers.

| NO. PLAYER | MINT | NO. PLAYER | MINT | NO. PLAYER | MINT | NO. PLAYER | MINT |
|---|---|---|---|---|---|---|---|
| 1 Sandy Alomar | .10 | 15 Robin Ventura | .75 | 29 Willie Blair (R) | .12 | 43 Mark Lemke | .05 |
| 2 John Olerud | 1.00 | 16 Greg Vaughn | .50 | 30 Ben McDonald | .75 | 44 Alan Mills (R) | .15 |
| 3 Pat Combs | .08 | 17 Wayne Edwards (R) | .12 | 31 Todd Zeile | .40 | 45 Marquis Grissom | .35 |
| 4 Brian DuBois | .05 | 18 Shawn Boskie (R) | .12 | 32 Scott Coolbaugh | .15 | 46 Greg Olson (R) | .20 |
| 5 Felix Jose | .08 | 19 Carlos Baerga (R) | .40 | 33 Xavier Hernandez | .05 | 47 Dave Hollins (R) | .30 |
| 6 Delino DeShields | .35 | 20 Mark Gardner | .15 | 34 Mike Hartley (R) | .15 | 48 Jerald Clark | .10 |
| 7 Mike Stanton | .05 | 21 Kevin Appier | .20 | 35 Kevin Tapani | .25 | 49 Eric Anthony | .25 |
| 8 Mike Munoz (R) | .10 | 22 Mike Harkey | .10 | 36 Kevin Wickander | .10 | 50 Tim Drummond | .05 |
| 9 Craig Grebeck (R) | .10 | 23 Tim Layana (R) | .15 | 37 C. Hernandez (R) | .10 | 51 John Burkett | .15 |
| 10 Joe Kraemer (R) | .10 | 24 Glenallen Hill | .10 | 38 Brian Traxler (R) | .12 | 52 Brent Knacker (R) | .15 |
| 11 Jeff Huson | .05 | 25 Jerry Kutzler | .05 | 39 Marty Brown | .12 | 53 Jeff Shaw (R) | .12 |
| 12 Bill Sampen (R) | .15 | 26 Mike Blowers | .10 | 40 Scott Radinsky (R) | .15 | 54 John Orton (R) | .12 |
| 13 Brian Bohanon (R) | .15 | 27 Scott Ruskin (R) | .12 | 41 Julio Machado | .05 | 55 Terry Shumpert (R) | .12 |
| 14 Dave Justice | 2.50 | 28 Dana Kiecker (R) | .12 | 42 Steve Avery | .75 | 56 Checklist | .05 |

# 1991 Donruss . . . Series One Set of 396 Cards—Value $10.00; Series Two Set of 396 Cards—Value $10.00

(Cpl. Set with 4 Leaf Previews—$33.00; with 4 Studio Previews—$28.00. Factory Set-$22.00)

The set was increased from 716 to 792 cards. For the first time Donruss cards were issued in two series (396 cards each). Heavier card stock was used this year. Features 40 Rated Rookies cards—(twice as many as last year) and 22 Highlights cards.

| NO. PLAYER | MINT | NO. PLAYER | MINT | NO. PLAYER | MINT | NO. PLAYER | MINT |
|---|---|---|---|---|---|---|---|
| **SERIES NO. 1** | | 17 Dave Magadan (DK) | .05 | 34 Terry Bross | .08 | 52 Cal Ripken (AS) | .10 |
| **No. 1 to 26—Diamond Kings** | | 18 Matt Williams (DK) | .08 | 35 Leo Gomez | .25 | 53 Rickey Henderson (AS) | .15 |
| 1 Dave Stieb (DK) | .08 | 19 Rafael Palmeiro (DK) | .08 | 36 Derrick May | .08 | 54 Bob Welch (AS) | .05 |
| 2 Craig Biggio (DK) | .05 | 20 Bob Welch (DK) | .05 | 37 Kevin Morton (R) | .15 | 55 Wade Boggs (AS) | .12 |
| 3 Cecil Fielder (DK) | .10 | 21 Dave Righetti (DK) | .05 | 38 Moises Alou | .10 | 56 Mark McGwire (AS) | .10 |
| 4 Barry Bonds (DK) | .10 | 22 Brian Harper (DK) | .05 | 39 Julio Valera | .08 | 57 Jack McDowell | .05 |
| 5 Barry Larkin (DK) | .08 | 23 Gregg Olson (DK) | .05 | 40 Milt Cuyler | .15 | 58 Jose Lind | .05 |
| 6 Dave Parker (DK) | .08 | 24 Kurt Stillwell (DK) | .05 | 41 Phil Plantier (R) | 1.00 | 59 Alex Fernandez | .25 |
| 7 Len Dykstra (DK) | .05 | 25 Pedro Guerrero (DK) | .08 | 42 Scott Chiamparino | .08 | 60 Pat Combs | .05 |
| 8 Bobby Thigpen (DK) | .05 | 26 Chuck Finley (DK) | .05 | 43 Ray Lankford | .35 | 61 Mike Walker | .05 |
| 9 Roger Clemens (DK) | .12 | 27 Diamond King Checklist | .05 | 44 Mickey Morandini | .12 | 62 Juan Samuel | .05 |
| 10 Ron Gant (DK) | .08 | **No. 28 to 47—Rated Rookies** | | 45 Dave Hansen | .10 | 63 Mike Blowers | .05 |
| 11 Delino DeShields (DK) | .08 | 28 Tino Martinez | .15 | 46 Kevin Belcher (R) | .12 | 64 Mark Guthrie | .05 |
| 12 Roberto Alomar (DK) | .08 | 29 Mark Lewis | .20 | 47 Darrin Fletcher | .10 | 65 Mark Salas | .05 |
| 13 Sandy Alomar (DK) | .08 | 30 Bernard Gilkey | .15 | 48 Steve Sax (AS) | .08 | 66 Tim Jones | .05 |
| 14 Ryne Sandberg (DK) | .15 | 31 Hensley Meulens | .08 | 49 Ken Griffey, Jr. (AS) | .25 | 67 Tim Leary | .05 |
| 15 Ramon Martinez (DK) | .08 | 32 Derek Bell | .30 | 50 Jose Canseco (AS) | .20 | 68 Andres Galarraga | .08 |
| 16 Edgar Martinez (DK) | .05 | 33 Jose Offerman | .10 | 51 Sandy Alomar (AS) | .10 | 69 Bob Milacki | .05 |

| NO. | PLAYER | MINT |
|---|---|---|
| 70 | Tim Belcher | .05 |
| 71 | Todd Zeile | .10 |
| 72 | Jerome Walton | .10 |
| 73 | Kevin Seltzer | .05 |
| 74 | Jerald Clark | .05 |
| 75 | John Smoltz | .10 |
| 76 | Mike Henneman | .05 |
| 77 | Ken Griffey, Jr. | .75 |
| 78 | Jim Abbott | .10 |
| 79 | Gregg Jefferies | .10 |
| 80 | Kevin Reimer | .05 |
| 81 | Roger Clemens | .15 |
| 82 | Mike Fitzgerald | .05 |
| 83 | Bruce Hurst | .05 |
| 84 | Eric Davis | .12 |
| 85 | Paul Molitor | .10 |
| 86 | Will Clark | .20 |
| 87 | Mike Bielecki | .05 |
| 88 | Bret Saberhagen | .10 |
| 89 | Nolan Ryan | .30 |
| 90 | Bobby Thigpen | .08 |
| 91 | Dickie Thon | .05 |
| 92 | Duane Ward | .05 |
| 93 | Luis Polonia | .05 |
| 94 | Terry Kennedy | .05 |
| 95 | Kent Hrbek | .10 |
| 96 | Danny Jackson | .05 |
| 97 | Sid Fernandez | .05 |
| 98 | Jimmy Key | .05 |
| 99 | Franklin Stubbs | .05 |
| 100 | Checklist No. 1 | .05 |
| 101 | R. J. Reynolds | .05 |
| 102 | Dave Stewart | .10 |
| 103 | Dan Pasqua | .05 |
| 104 | Dan Plesac | .05 |
| 105 | Mark McGwire | .10 |
| 106 | John Farrell | .05 |
| 107 | Don Mattingly | .15 |
| 108 | Carlton Fisk | .10 |
| 109 | Ken Oberkfell | .05 |
| 110 | Darrel Akerfelds | .05 |
| 111 | Gregg Olson | .08 |
| 112 | Mike Scioscia | .05 |
| 113 | Bryn Smith | .05 |
| 114 | Bob Geren | .05 |
| 115 | Tom Candiotti | .05 |
| 116 | Kevin Tapani | .05 |
| 117 | Jeff Treadway | .05 |
| 118 | Alan Trammell | .08 |
| 119 | Pete O'Brien | .05 |
| 120 | Joel Skinner | .05 |
| 121 | Mike LaValliere | .05 |
| 122 | Dwight Evans | .05 |
| 123 | Jody Reed | .05 |
| 124 | Lee Guetterman | .05 |
| 125 | Tim Burke | .05 |
| 126 | Dave Johnson | .05 |
| 127 | Fernando Valenzuela | .10 |
| 128 | Jose DeLeon | .05 |
| 129 | Andre Dawson | .10 |
| 130 | Gerald Perry | .05 |
| 131 | Greg Harris | .05 |
| 132 | Tom Glavine | .05 |
| 133 | Lance McCullers | .05 |
| 134 | Randy Johnson | .05 |
| 135 | Lance Parrish | .05 |
| 136 | Mackey Sasser | .05 |
| 137 | Geno Petralli | .05 |
| 138 | Dennis Lamp | .05 |
| 139 | Dennis Martinez | .05 |
| 140 | Mike Pagliarulo | .05 |
| 141 | Hal Morris | .10 |
| 142 | Dave Parker | .10 |
| 143 | Brett Butler | .05 |
| 144 | Paul Assenmacher | .05 |
| 145 | Mark Gubicza | .05 |
| 146 | Charlie Hough | .05 |
| 147 | Sammy Sosa | .08 |
| 148 | Randy Ready | .05 |
| 149 | Kelly Gruber | .10 |
| 150 | Devon White | .05 |
| 151 | Gary Carter | .10 |
| 152 | Gene Larkin | .05 |
| 153 | Chris Sabo | .10 |
| 154 | David Cone | .08 |
| 155 | Todd Stottlemyre | .05 |
| 156 | Glenn Wilson | .05 |
| 157 | Bob Walk | .05 |
| 158 | Mike Gallego | .05 |
| 159 | Greg Hibbard | .05 |
| 160 | Chris Bosio | .05 |
| 161 | Mike Moore | .05 |
| 162 | Jerry Browne | .05 |
| 163 | Steve Sax | .05 |
| 164 | Melido Perez | .05 |
| 165 | Danny Darwin | .05 |
| 166 | Roger McDowell | .05 |
| 167 | Billy Ripken | .05 |
| 168 | Mike Sharperson | .05 |
| 169 | Lee Smith | .05 |
| 170 | Matt Nokes | .05 |
| 171 | Jesse Orosco | .05 |
| 172 | Rick Aguilera | .05 |
| 173 | Jim Presley | .05 |
| 174 | Lou Whitaker | .05 |
| 175 | Harold Reynolds | .05 |
| 176 | Brook Jacoby | .05 |
| 177 | Wally Backman | .05 |
| 178 | Wade Boggs | .15 |
| 179 | Chuck Cary | .05 |
| 180 | Tom Foley | .05 |
| 181 | Peter Harnisch | .05 |
| 182 | Mike Morgan | .05 |
| 183 | Bob Tewksbury | .05 |
| 184 | Joe Girardi | .05 |
| 185 | Storm Davis | .05 |
| 186 | Ed Whitson | .05 |
| 187 | Steve Avery | .30 |
| 188 | Lloyd Moseby | .05 |
| 189 | Scott Bankhead | .05 |
| 190 | Mark Langston | .08 |
| 191 | Kevin McReynolds | .10 |
| 192 | Julio Franco | .08 |
| 193 | John Dopson | .05 |
| 194 | Oil Can Boyd | .05 |
| 195 | Bip Roberts | .05 |
| 196 | Billy Hatcher | .05 |
| 197 | Edgar Diaz | .08 |
| 198 | Greg Litton | .05 |
| 199 | Mark Grace | .10 |
| 200 | Checklist No. 2 | .05 |
| 201 | George Brett | .12 |
| 202 | Jeff Russell | .05 |
| 203 | Ivan Calderon | .05 |
| 204 | Ken Howell | .05 |
| 205 | Tom Henke | .05 |
| 206 | Bryan Harvey | .05 |
| 207 | Steve Bedrosian | .05 |
| 208 | Al Newman | .05 |
| 209 | Randy Myers | .05 |
| 210 | Daryl Boston | .05 |
| 211 | Manny Lee | .05 |
| 212 | Dave Smith | .05 |
| 213 | Don Slaught | .05 |
| 214 | Walt Weiss | .05 |
| 215 | Donn Pall | .05 |
| 216 | Jamie Navarro | .05 |
| 217 | Willie Randolph | .05 |
| 218 | Rudy Seanez | .08 |
| 219 | Jim Leyritz | .08 |
| 220 | Ron Karkovice | .05 |
| 221 | Ken Caminiti | .05 |
| 222 | Von Hayes | .05 |
| 223 | Cal Ripken | .20 |
| 224 | Lenny Harris | .05 |
| 225 | Milt Thompson | .05 |
| 226 | Alvaro Espinoza | .05 |
| 227 | Chris James | .05 |
| 228 | Dan Gladden | .05 |
| 229 | Jeff Blauser | .05 |
| 230 | Mike Heath | .05 |
| 231 | Omar Vizquel | .05 |
| 232 | Doug Jones | .05 |
| 233 | Jeff King | .05 |
| 234 | Luis Rivera | .05 |
| 235 | Ellis Burks | .08 |
| 236 | Greg Cadaret | .05 |
| 237 | Dave Martinez | .05 |
| 238 | Mark Williamson | .05 |
| 239 | Stan Javier | .05 |
| 240 | Ozzie Smith | .10 |
| 241 | Shawn Boskie | .05 |
| 242 | Tom Gordon | .10 |
| 243 | Tony Gwynn | .15 |
| 244 | Tommy Gregg | .05 |
| 245 | Jeff Robinson | .05 |
| 246 | Keith Comstock | .05 |
| 247 | Jack Howell | .05 |
| 248 | Keith Miller | .05 |
| 249 | Bobby Witt | .05 |
| 250 | Rob Murphy | .05 |
| 251 | Spike Owen | .05 |
| 252 | Garry Templeton | .05 |
| 253 | Glenn Braggs | .05 |
| 254 | Ron Robinson | .05 |
| 255 | Kevin Mitchell | .10 |
| 256 | Les Lancaster | .05 |
| 257 | Mel Stottlemyre | .05 |
| 258 | Kenny Rogers | .05 |
| 259 | Lance Johnson | .05 |
| 260 | John Kruk | .05 |
| 261 | Fred McGriff | .10 |
| 262 | Dick Schofield | .05 |
| 263 | Trevor Wilson | .05 |
| 264 | David West | .05 |
| 265 | Scott Scudder | .05 |
| 266 | Dwight Gooden | .15 |
| 267 | Willie Blair | .05 |
| 268 | Mark Portugal | .05 |
| 269 | Doug Drabek | .05 |
| 270 | Dennis Eckersley | .10 |
| 271 | Eric King | .05 |
| 272 | Robin Yount | .15 |
| 273 | Carney Lansford | .05 |
| 274 | Carlos Baerga | .10 |
| 275 | Dave Righetti | .05 |
| 276 | Scott Fletcher | .05 |
| 277 | Eric Yelding | .05 |
| 278 | Charles Hayes | .05 |
| 279 | Jeff Ballard | .05 |
| 280 | Orel Hershiser | .10 |
| 281 | Jose Oquendo | .05 |
| 282 | Mike Witt | .05 |
| 283 | Mitch Webster | .05 |
| 284 | Greg Gagne | .05 |
| 285 | Greg Olson | .10 |
| 286 | Tony Phillips | .05 |
| 287 | Scott Bradley | .05 |
| 288 | Cory Snyder | .08 |
| 289 | Jay Bell | .05 |
| 290 | Kevin Romine | .05 |
| 291 | Jeff Robinson | .05 |
| 292 | Steve Frey | .05 |
| 293 | Craig Worthington | .05 |
| 294 | Tim Crews | .05 |
| 295 | Joe Magrane | .05 |
| 296 | Hector Villanueva | .05 |
| 297 | Terry Shumpert | .05 |
| 298 | Joe Carter | .05 |
| 299 | Kent Mercker | .08 |
| 300 | Checklist No. 3 | .05 |
| 301 | Chet Lemon | .05 |
| 302 | Mike Schooler | .05 |
| 303 | Dante Bichette | .05 |
| 304 | Kevin Elster | .05 |
| 305 | Jeff Huson | .05 |
| 306 | Greg Harris | .05 |
| 307 | Marquis Grissom | .10 |
| 308 | Calvin Schiraldi | .05 |
| 309 | Mariano Duncan | .05 |
| 310 | Bill Spiers | .05 |
| 311 | Scott Garrelts | .05 |
| 312 | Mitch Williams | .05 |
| 313 | Mike Macfarlane | .05 |
| 314 | Kevin Brown | .05 |
| 315 | Robin Ventura | .15 |
| 316 | Darren Daulton | .05 |
| 317 | Pat Borders | .05 |
| 318 | Mark Eichhorn | .05 |
| 319 | Jeff Brantley | .05 |
| 320 | Shane Mack | .05 |
| 321 | Rob Dibble | .05 |
| 322 | John Franco | .05 |
| 323 | Junior Felix | .10 |
| 324 | Casey Candaele | .05 |
| 325 | Bobby Bonilla | .15 |
| 326 | Dave Henderson | .08 |
| 327 | Wayne Edwards | .05 |
| 328 | Mark Knudson | .05 |
| 329 | Terry Steinbach | .05 |
| 330 | Colby Ward (R) | .12 |
| 331 | Oscar Azocar | .08 |
| 332 | Scott Radinsky | .05 |
| 333 | Eric Anthony | .08 |
| 334 | Steve Lake | .05 |
| 335 | Bob Melvin | .05 |
| 336 | Kal Daniels | .08 |
| 337 | Tom Pagnozzi | .05 |
| 338 | Alan Mills | .05 |
| 339 | Steve Olin | .05 |
| 340 | Juan Berenguer | .05 |
| 341 | Francisco Cabrera | .05 |
| 342 | Dave Bergman | .05 |
| 343 | Henry Cotto | .05 |
| 344 | Sergio Valdez | .05 |
| 345 | Bob Patterson | .05 |
| 346 | John Marzano | .05 |
| 347 | Dana Kiecker | .05 |
| 348 | Dion James | .05 |
| 349 | Hubie Brooks | .05 |
| 350 | Bill Landrum | .05 |
| 351 | Bill Sampen | .05 |
| 352 | Greg Briley | .05 |
| 353 | Paul Gibson | .05 |
| 354 | Dave Eiland | .05 |
| 355 | Steve Finley | .05 |
| 356 | Bob Boone | .05 |
| 357 | Steve Buechele | .05 |
| 358 | Chris Hoiles | .10 |
| 359 | Larry Walker | .08 |
| 360 | Frank DiPino | .05 |
| 361 | Mark Grant | .05 |
| 362 | Dave Magadan | .08 |
| 363 | Robby Thompson | .05 |
| 364 | Lonnie Smith | .05 |
| 365 | Steve Farr | .05 |
| 366 | Dave Valle | .05 |
| 367 | Tim Naehring | .10 |
| 368 | Jim Acker | .05 |
| 369 | Jeff Reardon | .05 |
| 370 | Tim Teufel | .05 |
| 371 | Juan Gonzalez | .25 |
| 372 | Luis Salazar | .05 |
| 373 | Rick Honeycutt | .05 |
| 374 | Greg Maddux | .05 |
| 375 | Jose Uribe | .05 |
| 376 | Donnie Hill | .05 |
| 377 | Don Carman | .05 |
| 378 | Craig Grebeck | .05 |
| 379 | Willie Fraser | .05 |
| 380 | Glenallen Hill | .05 |
| 381 | Joe Oliver | .05 |
| 382 | Randy Bush | .05 |
| 383 | Alex Cole | .08 |
| 384 | Norm Charlton | .05 |
| 385 | Gene Nelson | .05 |
| 386 | Checklist No. 4 | .05 |

**SERIES NO. 2**
**NO. 387 TO 412—MVP's**

| NO. | PLAYER | MINT |
|---|---|---|
| 387 | R. Henderson-MVP | .15 |
| 388 | Lance Parris-MVP | .05 |
| 389 | Fred McGriff-MVP | .10 |
| 390 | Dave Parker-MVP | .08 |
| 391 | C. Maldonado-MVP | .05 |
| 392 | Ken Griffey Jr.-MVP | .30 |
| 393 | Gregg Olson-MVP | .08 |
| 394 | Rafael Palmeiro-MVP | .08 |
| 395 | Roger Clemens-MVP | .12 |
| 396 | George Brett-MVP | .10 |
| 397 | Cecil Fielder-MVP | .10 |
| 398 | Brian Harper-MVP | .15 |
| 399 | Bobby Thigpen-MVP | .08 |
| 400 | Roberto Kelly-MVP | .08 |
| 401 | Danny Darwin-MVP | .08 |
| 402 | Dave Justice-MVP | .25 |
| 403 | Lee Smith-MVP | .05 |
| 404 | Ryne Sandberg-MVP | .15 |
| 405 | Eddie Murray-MVP | .10 |
| 406 | Tim Wallach-MVP | .05 |
| 407 | Kevin Mitchell-MVP | .08 |
| 408 | Darryl Strawberry-MVP | .15 |

# 1991 Donruss (Continued)

| NO. | PLAYER | MINT |
|---|---|---|
| 409 | Joe Carter-MVP | .05 |
| 410 | Len Dykstra-MVP | .05 |
| 411 | Doug Drabek-MVP | .05 |
| 412 | Chris Sabo-MVP | .08 |
| **No. 413 to 432—Rated Rookies** | | |
| 413 | Paul Marak (R) | .12 |
| 414 | Tim McIntosh | .10 |
| 415 | Brian Barnes (R) | .12 |
| 416 | Eric Gunderson | .08 |
| 417 | Mike Gardiner (R) | .12 |
| 418 | Steve Carter | .05 |
| 419 | Gerald Alexander (R) | .12 |
| 420 | Rich Garces (R) | .12 |
| 421 | Chuck Knoblauch | .30 |
| 422 | Scott Alfred | .10 |
| 423 | Wes Chamberlain (R) | .40 |
| 424 | Lance Dickson (R) | .15 |
| 425 | Greg Colbrunn (R) | .15 |
| 426 | Rich Delucia (R) | .15 |
| 427 | Jeff Conine (R) | .15 |
| 428 | Steve Decker (R) | .20 |
| 429 | Turner Ward (R) | .15 |
| 430 | Mo Vaughn | .50 |
| 431 | Steve Chitren (R) | .10 |
| 432 | Mike Benjamin | .10 |
| 433 | Ryne Sandberg (AS) | .15 |
| 434 | Len Dykstra (AS) | .08 |
| 435 | Andre Dawson (AS) | .08 |
| 436 | Mike Scioscia (AS) | .08 |
| 437 | Ozzie Smith (AS) | .08 |
| 438 | Kevin Mitchell (AS) | .08 |
| 439 | Jack Armstrong (AS) | .05 |
| 440 | Chris Sabo (AS) | .08 |
| 441 | Will Clark (AS) | .12 |
| 442 | Mel Hall | .05 |
| 443 | Mark Gardner | .05 |
| 444 | Mike Devereaux | .05 |
| 445 | Kirk Gibson | .10 |
| 446 | Terry Pendleton | .05 |
| 447 | Mike Harkey | .05 |
| 448 | Jim Eisenreich | .05 |
| 449 | Benito Satiago | .08 |
| 450 | Oddibe McDowell | .05 |
| 451 | Cecil Fielder | .15 |
| 452 | Ken Griffey, Sr. | .05 |
| 453 | Bert Blyleven | .05 |
| 454 | Howard Johnson | .10 |
| 455 | Monty Farris | .10 |
| 456 | Tony Pena | .05 |
| 457 | Tim Raines | .10 |
| 458 | Dennis Rasmussen | .05 |
| 459 | Luis Quinones | .05 |
| 460 | B. J. Surhoff | .05 |
| 461 | Ernest Riles | .05 |
| 462 | Rick Sutcliffe | .05 |
| 463 | Danny Tartabull | .05 |
| 464 | Peter Incaviglia | .05 |
| 465 | Carlos Martinez | .05 |
| 466 | Ricky Jordan | .08 |
| 467 | John Cerutti | .05 |
| 468 | Dave Winfield | .12 |
| 469 | Francisco Oliveras | .05 |
| 470 | Roy Smith | .05 |
| 471 | Barry Larkin | .10 |
| 472 | Ron Darling | .05 |
| 473 | David Wells | .05 |
| 474 | Glenn Davis | .08 |
| 475 | Neal Heaton | .05 |
| 476 | Ron Hassey | .05 |
| 477 | Frank Thomas | 1.00 |
| 478 | Greg Vaughn | .12 |
| 479 | Todd Burns | .05 |
| 480 | Candy Maldonado | .05 |
| 481 | Dave Lapoint | .05 |
| 482 | Alvin Davis | .05 |
| 483 | Mike Scott | .08 |
| 484 | Dale Murphy | .12 |
| 485 | Ben McDonald | .10 |
| 486 | Jay Howell | .05 |
| 487 | Vince Coleman | .10 |
| 488 | Alfredo Griffin | .05 |
| 489 | Sandy Alomar | .08 |
| 490 | Kirby Puckett | .15 |
| 491 | Andres Thomas | .05 |
| 492 | Jack Morris | .08 |
| 493 | Matt Young | .05 |
| 494 | Greg Myers | .05 |
| 495 | Barry Bonds | .15 |
| 496 | Scott Cooper | .15 |
| 497 | Dan Schatzeder | .05 |
| 498 | Jesee Barfield | .05 |
| 499 | Jerry Goff | .08 |
| 500 | Checklist | .05 |
| 501 | Anthony Telford (R) | .10 |
| 502 | Eddie Murray | .12 |
| 503 | Omar Oliveras (R) | .12 |
| 504 | Ryne Sandberg | .20 |
| 505 | Jeff Montgomery | .05 |
| 506 | Mark Parent | .05 |
| 507 | Ron Gant | .15 |
| 508 | Frank Tanana | .05 |
| 509 | Jay Buhner | .05 |
| 510 | Max Venable | .05 |
| 511 | Wally Whithurst | .05 |
| 512 | Gary Pettis | .05 |
| 513 | Tom Brunansky | .08 |
| 514 | Tim Wallach | .05 |
| 515 | Craig Lefferts | .05 |
| 516 | Tim Layana | .05 |
| 517 | Darryl Hamilton | .05 |
| 518 | Rick Rueschel | .05 |
| 519 | Steve Wilson | .05 |
| 520 | Kurt Stillwell | .05 |
| 521 | Rafael Palmeiro | .10 |
| 522 | Ken Patterson | .05 |
| 523 | Len Dykstra | .10 |
| 524 | Tony Fernandez | .05 |
| 525 | Kent Anderson | .05 |
| 526 | Mark Leonard (R) | .15 |
| 527 | Allan Anderson | .05 |
| 528 | Tom Browning | .05 |
| 529 | Frank Viola | .10 |
| 530 | John Olerud | .10 |
| 531 | Juan Agosto | .05 |
| 532 | Zane Smith | .05 |
| 533 | Scott Sanderson | .05 |
| 534 | Barry Jones | .05 |
| 535 | Mike Felder | .05 |
| 536 | Jose Canseco | .30 |
| 537 | Felix Fermin | .05 |
| 538 | Roberto Kelly | .08 |
| 539 | Brian Holman | .05 |
| 540 | Mark Davidson | .05 |
| 541 | Terry Mulholland | .05 |
| 542 | Randy Milligan | .05 |
| 543 | Jose Gonzalez | .05 |
| 544 | Craig Wilson (R) | .12 |
| 545 | Mike Hartley | .05 |
| 546 | Greg Swindell | .05 |
| 547 | Gary Gaetti | .05 |
| 548 | Dave Justice | .50 |
| 549 | Steve Searcy | .05 |
| 550 | Erik Hanson | .05 |
| 551 | Dave Stieb | .08 |
| 552 | Andy Van Slyke | .08 |
| 553 | Mike Greenwell | .10 |
| 554 | Kevin Maas | .20 |
| 555 | Delino DeShields | .10 |
| 556 | Curt Shilling | .05 |
| 557 | Ramon Martinez | .12 |
| 558 | Pedro Guerrero | .08 |
| 559 | Dwight Smith | .05 |
| 560 | Mark Davis | .05 |
| 561 | Shawn Abner | .05 |
| 562 | Charlie Liebrandt | .05 |
| 563 | John Shelby | .05 |
| 564 | Bill Swift | .05 |
| 565 | Mike Fetters | .05 |
| 566 | Alejandro Pena | .05 |
| 567 | Ruben Sierra | .12 |
| 568 | Carlos Quintana | .10 |
| 569 | Kevin Gross | .05 |
| 570 | Derek Lilliquist | .05 |
| 571 | Jack Armstrong | .05 |
| 572 | Greg Brock | .05 |
| 573 | Mike Kingery | .05 |
| 574 | Greg Smith | .05 |
| 575 | Brian McRae (R) | .40 |
| 576 | Jack Daugherty | .05 |
| 577 | Ozzie Guillen | .05 |
| 578 | Joe Boever | .05 |
| 579 | Luis Sojo | .05 |
| 580 | Chili Davis | .05 |
| 581 | Don Robinson | .05 |
| 582 | Brain Harper | .05 |
| 583 | Paul O'Neill | .05 |
| 584 | Bob Ojeda | .05 |
| 585 | Mookie Wilson | .05 |
| 586 | Rafael Ramirez | .05 |
| 587 | Gary Redus | .05 |
| 588 | Jamie Quirk | .05 |
| 589 | Shawn Hillegas | .05 |
| 590 | Tom Edens (R) | .10 |
| 591 | Joe Klink | .08 |
| 592 | Charles Nagy | .12 |
| 593 | Eric Plunk | .05 |
| 594 | Tracy Jones | .05 |
| 595 | Craig Biggio | .05 |
| 596 | Jose DeJesus | .05 |
| 597 | Mickey Tettleton | .05 |
| 598 | Chris Gwynn | .05 |
| 599 | Rex Hudler | .05 |
| 600 | Checklist | .05 |
| 601 | Jim Gott | .05 |
| 602 | Jeff Manto | .12 |
| 603 | Nelson Liriano | .05 |
| 604 | Mark Lemke | .05 |
| 605 | Clay Parker | .05 |
| 606 | Edgar Martinez | .05 |
| 607 | Mark Whiten | .15 |
| 608 | Ted Power | .05 |
| 609 | Tom Bolton | .05 |
| 610 | Tom Herr | .05 |
| 611 | Andy Hawkins | .05 |
| 612 | Scott Ruskin | .05 |
| 613 | Ron Kittle | .05 |
| 614 | John Wetteland | .05 |
| 615 | Mike Perez (R) | .12 |
| 616 | Dave Clark | .05 |
| 617 | Brent Mayne | .08 |
| 618 | Jack Clark | .10 |
| 619 | Marvin Freeman | .05 |
| 620 | Edwin Nunez | .05 |
| 621 | Russ Swan | .08 |
| 622 | Johnny Ray | .05 |
| 623 | Charlie O'Brien | .05 |
| 624 | Joe Bitker (R) | .12 |
| 625 | Mike Marshall | .05 |
| 626 | Otis Nixon | .05 |
| 627 | Andy Benes | .10 |
| 628 | Ron Oester | .05 |
| 629 | Ted Higuera | .05 |
| 630 | Kevin Bass | .05 |
| 631 | Damon Berryhill | .05 |
| 632 | Bo Jackson | .25 |
| 633 | Brad Arnsberg | .05 |
| 634 | Jerry Willard | .05 |
| 635 | Tommy Greene | .05 |
| 636 | Bob MacDonald (R) | .12 |
| 637 | Kirk McCaskill | .05 |
| 638 | John Burkett | .05 |
| 639 | Paul Abbott (R) | .12 |
| 640 | Todd Benzinger | .05 |
| 641 | Todd Hundley | .12 |
| 642 | George Bell | .08 |
| 643 | Javier Oritz | .08 |
| 644 | Sid Bream | .05 |
| 645 | Bob Welch | .10 |
| 646 | Phil Bradley | .05 |
| 647 | Bill Krueger | .05 |
| 648 | Rickey Henderson | .20 |
| 649 | Kevin Wickander | .05 |
| 650 | Steve Balboni | .05 |
| 651 | Gene Harris | .05 |
| 652 | Jim Deshales | .05 |
| 653 | Jason Grimsley | .10 |
| 654 | Joe Orsulak | .05 |
| 655 | Jimmy Poole (R) | .12 |
| 656 | Felix Jose | .10 |
| 657 | Dennis Cook | .05 |
| 658 | Tom Brookens | .05 |
| 659 | Junior Ortiz | .05 |
| 660 | Jeff Parrett | .05 |
| 661 | Jerry Don Gleaton | .05 |
| 662 | Brent Knackert | .05 |
| 663 | Rance Mulliniks | .05 |
| 664 | John Smiley | .05 |
| 665 | Larry Andersen | .05 |
| 666 | Willie McGee | .08 |
| 667 | Chris Nabholz | .08 |
| 668 | Brady Anderson | .05 |
| 669 | Darren Holmes | .10 |
| 670 | Ken Hill | .05 |
| 671 | Gary Varsho | .05 |
| 672 | Bill Pecoa | .05 |
| 673 | Fred Lynn | .05 |
| 674 | Kevin Brown | .10 |
| 675 | Dan Petry | .05 |
| 676 | Mike Jackson | .05 |
| 677 | Wally Joyner | .08 |
| 678 | Danny Jackson | .05 |
| 679 | Bill Haselman (R) | .10 |
| 680 | Mike Boddicker | .05 |
| 681 | Mel Rojas | .05 |
| 682 | Roberto Alomar | .10 |
| 683 | Dave Justice (ROY) | .30 |
| 684 | Chuck Crim | .05 |
| 685 | Matt William | .12 |
| 686 | Shawon Dunston | .08 |
| 687 | Jeff Schulz (R) | .12 |
| 688 | John Barfield (R) | .10 |
| 689 | Gerald Young | .05 |
| 690 | Luis Gonzalez (R) | .40 |
| 691 | Frank Wills | .05 |
| 692 | Chuck Finley | .08 |
| 693 | Sandy Alomar (ROY) | .10 |
| 694 | Tim Drummond | .05 |
| 695 | Herm Winningham | .05 |
| 696 | Darryl Strawberry | .20 |
| 697 | Al Leiter | .05 |
| 698 | Karl Rhodes | .10 |
| 699 | Stan Belinda | .10 |
| 700 | Checklist | .05 |
| 701 | Lance Blankenship | .05 |
| 702 | Puzzle—Stargell | .05 |
| 703 | Jim Gantner | .05 |
| 704 | Reggie Harris | .08 |
| 705 | Rob Ducey | .05 |
| 706 | Tim Hulett | .05 |
| 707 | Atlee Hammaker | .05 |
| 708 | Xavier Hernandez | .05 |
| 709 | Chuck McElroy | .08 |
| 710 | John Mitchell | .05 |
| 711 | Carlos Hernandez | .05 |
| 712 | Geronimo Pena | .08 |
| 713 | Jim Neidlinger (R) | .12 |
| 714 | John Orton | .05 |
| 715 | Terry Leach | .05 |
| 716 | Mike Stanton | .05 |
| 717 | Walt Terrell | .05 |
| 718 | Luis Aquino | .05 |
| 719 | Bud Black | .05 |
| 720 | Bob Kipper | .05 |
| 721 | Jeff Gray (R) | .12 |
| 722 | Jose Rijo | .08 |
| 723 | Curt Young | .05 |
| 724 | Jose Vizcaino | .08 |
| 725 | Randy Tomlin (R) | .15 |
| 726 | Junior Noboa | .05 |
| 727 | Bob Welch (CY) | .08 |
| 728 | Gary Ward | .05 |
| 729 | Rob Deer | .05 |
| 730 | David Segui | .10 |
| 731 | Mark Carreon | .05 |
| 732 | Vincente Palacios | .05 |
| 733 | Sam Horn | .05 |
| 734 | Howard Farmer | .10 |
| 735 | Ken Dayley | .05 |
| 736 | Kelly Mann | .10 |
| 737 | Joe Grahe (R) | .10 |
| 738 | Kelly Downs | .05 |
| 739 | Jimmy Kremers | .08 |
| 740 | Kevin Appier | .05 |
| 741 | Jeff Reed | .05 |
| 742 | Jose Rijo (WS) | .08 |
| 743 | Dave Rohde | .08 |
| 744 | Dr. Dirt/Mr. Clean | .10 |
| 745 | Paul Sorrento | .05 |
| 746 | Thomas Howard | .10 |
| 747 | Matt Stark (R) | .12 |

# 1991 Donruss (Continued)

| NO. | PLAYER | MINT | NO. | PLAYER | MINT | NO. | PLAYER | MINT | NO. | PLAYER | MINT |
|-----|--------|------|-----|--------|------|-----|--------|------|-----|--------|------|
| 748 | Harold Baines | .05 | 754 | Lee Stevens | .08 | 760 | Checklist | .05 | 766 | Willie Randolph (WS) | .05 |
| 749 | Doug Dascenzo | .05 | 755 | Randy Veres | .08 | 761 | Rickey Henderson (MVP) | .15 | 767 | Scott Erickson | .60 |
| 750 | Doug Drabek (CY) | .05 | 756 | Bill Doran | .05 | 762 | Barry Bonds (MVP) | .12 | 768 | Travis Fryman | .60 |
| 751 | Gary Sheffield | .10 | 757 | Gary Wayne | .05 | 763 | Billy Hatcher (WS) | .05 | 769 | Rich Rodriquez (R) | .12 |
| 752 | Terry Lee (R) | .12 | 758 | Pedro Munoz (R) | .15 | 764 | Julio Machado | .05 | 770 | Checklist | |
| 753 | Jim Vatcher (R) | .12 | 759 | Chris Hammond | .08 | 765 | Jose Mesa | .05 | | | |

## 1991 Donruss Studio . . . Complete Set of 264 Cards—Value $50.00

Features black & white close-up photos of better known players. Features the rookie cards of Phil Plantier and Jeff Bagwell.

| NO. | PLAYER | MINT | NO. | PLAYER | MINT | NO. | PLAYER | MINT | NO. | PLAYER | MINT |
|-----|--------|------|-----|--------|------|-----|--------|------|-----|--------|------|
| 1 | Glenn Davis | .12 | 47 | Eric King | .08 | 93 | Steve Howe | .08 | 139 | Devon White | .08 |
| 2 | Dwight Evans | .08 | 48 | Mark Lewis | .50 | 94 | Roberto Kelly | .15 | 140 | Mookie Wilson | .08 |
| 3 | Leo Gomez | .75 | 49 | Greg Swindell | .08 | 95 | Tim Leary | .08 | 141 | Steve Avery | 3.00 |
| 4 | Chris Hoiles | .20 | 50 | Mark Whiten | .35 | 96 | Kevin Maas | .50 | 142 | Sid Bream | .08 |
| 5 | Sam Horn | .08 | 51 | Milt Cuyler | .45 | 97 | Don Mattingly | .50 | 143 | Nick Esasky | .08 |
| 6 | Ben McDonald | .30 | 52 | Rob Deer | .08 | 98 | Hensley Meulens | .12 | 144 | Ron Gant | .35 |
| 7 | Randy Milligan | .08 | 53 | Cecil Fielder | .75 | 99 | Scott Sanderson | .08 | 145 | Tom Glavine | .25 |
| 8 | Gregg Olson | .08 | 54 | Travis Fryman | 2.00 | 100 | Steve Sax | .08 | 146 | David Justice | 4.00 |
| 9 | Cal Ripken, Jr. | 1.00 | 55 | Bill Gullickson | .08 | 101 | Jose Canseco | 1.25 | 147 | Kelly Mann | .08 |
| 10 | David Segui | .15 | 56 | Lloyd Moseby | .08 | 102 | Dennis Eckersley | .15 | 148 | Terry Pendleton | .20 |
| 11 | Wade Boggs | .50 | 57 | Frank Tanana | .08 | 103 | Dave Henderson | .15 | 149 | John Smoltz | .20 |
| 12 | Ellis Burks | .20 | 58 | Mickey Tettleton | .08 | 104 | Rickey Henderson | .75 | 150 | Jeff Treadway | .08 |
| 13 | Jack Clark | .15 | 59 | Alan Trammell | .15 | 105 | Rick Honeycutt | .08 | 151 | George Bell | .20 |
| 14 | Roger Clemens | .75 | 60 | Lou Whitaker | .08 | 106 | Mark McGwire | .20 | 152 | Shawn Boskie | .08 |
| 15 | Mike Greenwell | .25 | 61 | Mike Boddicker | .08 | 107 | Dave Stewart | .15 | 153 | Andre Dawson | .30 |
| 16 | Tim Naehring | .15 | 62 | George Brett | .35 | 108 | Eric Show | .08 | 154 | Lance Dickson (R) | .40 |
| 17 | Tony Pena | .08 | 63 | Jeff Conine (R) | .20 | 109 | Todd Van Poppel (R) | 3.50 | 155 | Shawon Dunston | .15 |
| 18 | Phil Plantier (R) | 6.00 | 64 | Warren Cromartie | .08 | 110 | Bob Welch | .08 | 156 | Joe Girardi | .08 |
| 19 | Jeff Reardon | .08 | 65 | Storm Davis | .08 | 111 | Alvin Davis | .08 | 157 | Mark Grace | .20 |
| 20 | Mo Vaughn | .08 | 66 | Kirk Gibson | .15 | 112 | Ken Griffey, Jr. | 5.00 | 158 | Ryne Sandberg | 1.00 |
| 21 | Jimmy Reese | .08 | 67 | Mark Gubicza | .08 | 113 | Ken Griffey, Sr. | .08 | 159 | Gary Scott | .40 |
| 22 | Jim Abbott | .35 | 68 | Brian McRae (R) | 2.00 | 114 | Eric Hanson | .08 | 160 | Dave Smith | .08 |
| 23 | Bert Blyleven | .08 | 69 | Bret Saberhagen | .15 | 115 | Brian Holman | .08 | 161 | Tom Browning | .08 |
| 24 | Chuck Finley | .15 | 70 | Kurt Stillwell | .08 | 116 | Randy Johnson | .08 | 162 | Erick Davis | .30 |
| 25 | Gary Gaetti | .08 | 71 | Tim McIntosh | .08 | 117 | Edgar Martinez | .15 | 163 | Rob Dibble | .15 |
| 26 | Wally Joyner | .25 | 72 | Candy Maldonado | .08 | 118 | Tino Martinez | .35 | 164 | Mariano Duncan | .08 |
| 27 | Mark Langston | .15 | 73 | Paul Molitor | .15 | 119 | Harold Reynolds | .08 | 165 | Chris Hammond | .15 |
| 28 | Kirk McCaskill | .08 | 74 | Willie Randolph | .08 | 120 | David Valle | .08 | 166 | Billy Hatcher | .08 |
| 29 | Lance Parrish | .08 | 75 | Ron Robinson | .08 | 121 | Kevin Belcher (R) | .15 | 167 | Barry Larkin | .25 |
| 30 | Dave Winfield | .30 | 76 | Gary Sheffield | .15 | 122 | Scott Chiamparino | .15 | 168 | Hal Morris | .30 |
| 31 | Alex Fernandez | .50 | 77 | Franklin Stubbs | .08 | 123 | Julio Franco | .08 | 169 | Paul O'Neill | .08 |
| 32 | Carlton Fisk | .30 | 78 | B.J. Surhoff | .08 | 124 | Juan Gonzalez | 4.00 | 170 | Chris Sabo | .15 |
| 33 | Scott Fletcher | .08 | 79 | Greg Vaughn | .30 | 125 | Rich Gossage | .08 | 171 | Eric Anthony | .15 |
| 34 | Greg Hibbard | .08 | 80 | Robin Yount | .35 | 126 | Jeff Kunkel | .08 | 172 | Jeff Bagwell (R) | 6.00 |
| 35 | Charlie Hough | .08 | 81 | Rick Aguilera | .08 | 127 | Rafael Palmeiro | .25 | 173 | Craig Biggio | .20 |
| 36 | Jack McDowell | .15 | 82 | Steve Bedrosian | .08 | 128 | Nolan Ryan | 2.50 | 174 | Ken Caminiti | .08 |
| 37 | Tim Raines | .15 | 83 | Scott Erickson | 3.00 | 129 | Ruben Sierra | .50 | 175 | Jim Deshaies | .08 |
| 38 | Sammy Sosa | .15 | 84 | Greg Gagne | .08 | 130 | Bobby Witt | .08 | 176 | Steve Finley | .08 |
| 39 | Bobby Thigpen | .08 | 85 | Dan Gladden | .08 | 131 | Roberto Alomar | .35 | 177 | Pete Harnisch | .08 |
| 40 | Frank Thomas | 7.50 | 86 | Brian Harper | .08 | 132 | Tom Candiotti | .08 | 178 | Darryl Kile | .25 |
| 41 | Sandy Alomar | .12 | 87 | Kent Hrbek | .08 | 133 | Joe Carter | .25 | 179 | Curt Schilling | .08 |
| 42 | John Farrell | .08 | 88 | Shane Mack | .08 | 134 | Ken Dayley | .08 | 180 | Mike Scott | .08 |
| 43 | Glenallen Hill | .08 | 89 | Jack Morris | .08 | 135 | Kelly Gruber | .15 | 181 | Brett Butler | .08 |
| 44 | Brook Jacoby | .08 | 90 | Kirby Puckett | .60 | 136 | John Olerud | .35 | 182 | Gary Carter | .15 |
| 45 | Chris James | .08 | 91 | Jesse Barfield | .08 | 137 | Dave Stieb | .08 | 183 | Orel Hershiser | .15 |
| 46 | Doug Jones | .08 | 92 | Steve Farr | .08 | 138 | Turner Ward (R) | .25 | 184 | Ramon Martinez | .50 |

| NO. | PLAYER | MINT |
|---|---|---|
| 185 | Eddie Murray | .30 |
| 186 | Jose Offerman | .15 |
| 187 | Bob Ojeda | .08 |
| 188 | Juan Samuel | .08 |
| 189 | Mike Scioscia | .08 |
| 190 | Darryl Strawberry | .75 |
| 191 | Moises Alou | .08 |
| 192 | Brian Barnes (R) | .30 |
| 193 | Oil Can Boyd | .08 |
| 194 | Ivan Calderon | .08 |
| 195 | Delino DeShields | .25 |
| 196 | Mike Fitzgerald | .08 |
| 197 | Andres Galarraga | .08 |
| 198 | Marquis Grissom | .25 |
| 199 | Bill Sampen | .12 |
| 200 | Tim Wallach | .08 |
| 201 | Daryl Boston | .08 |
| 202 | Vince Coleman | .15 |
| 203 | John Franco | .08 |
| 204 | Dwight Gooden | .35 |

| NO. | PLAYER | MINT |
|---|---|---|
| 205 | Tom Herr | .08 |
| 206 | Gregg Jefferies | .15 |
| 207 | Howard Johnson | .25 |
| 208 | Dave Magadan | .08 |
| 209 | Kevin McReynolds | .15 |
| 210 | Frank Viola | .15 |
| 211 | Wes Chamberlain (R) | 1.50 |
| 212 | Darren Daulton | .08 |
| 213 | Lenny Dykstra | .08 |
| 214 | Charlie Hayes | .08 |
| 215 | Ricky Jordan | .08 |
| 216 | Steve Lake | .08 |
| 217 | Roger McDowell | .08 |
| 218 | Mickey Morandini | .15 |
| 219 | Terry Mulholland | .08 |
| 220 | Dale Murphy | .20 |
| 221 | Jay Bell | .08 |
| 222 | Barry Bonds | .50 |
| 223 | Bobby Bonilla | .50 |
| 224 | Doug Drabek | .08 |

| NO. | PLAYER | MINT |
|---|---|---|
| 225 | Bill Landrum | .08 |
| 226 | Mike LaValliere | .08 |
| 227 | Jose Lind | .08 |
| 228 | Don Slaught | .08 |
| 229 | John Smiley | .08 |
| 230 | Andy Van Slyke | .20 |
| 231 | Bernard Gilkey | .20 |
| 232 | Pedro Guerrero | .15 |
| 233 | Rex Hudler | .08 |
| 234 | Ray Lankford | .75 |
| 235 | Joe Magrane | .08 |
| 236 | Jose Oquendo | .08 |
| 237 | Lee Smith | .08 |
| 238 | Ozzie Smith | .40 |
| 239 | Milt Thompson | .08 |
| 240 | Todd Zeile | .30 |
| 241 | Larry Anderson | .08 |
| 242 | Andy Benes | .25 |
| 243 | Paul Faries | .15 |
| 244 | Tony Fernandez | .08 |

| NO. | PLAYER | MINT |
|---|---|---|
| 245 | Tony Gwynn | .40 |
| 246 | Atlee Hammaker | .08 |
| 247 | Fred McGriff | .30 |
| 248 | Bip Roberts | .08 |
| 249 | Benito Santiago | .15 |
| 250 | Ed Whitson | .08 |
| 251 | Dave Anderson | .08 |
| 252 | Mike Benjamin | .08 |
| 253 | John Burkett | .08 |
| 254 | Will Clark | .75 |
| 255 | Scott Garrelts | .08 |
| 256 | Willie McGee | .15 |
| 257 | Kevin Mitchell | .25 |
| 258 | Dave Righetti | .08 |
| 259 | Matt William | .30 |
| 260 | Black & Decker | .15 |
| 261 | Checklist—Title Card | .10 |
| 262 | Checklist—Title Card | .10 |
| 263 | Checklist—Title Card | .10 |

## 1991 Donruss Rookies . . . Complete Set of 56 Cards—Value $10.00

Features the outstanding rookies of the 1990 season. The cards were coated with a glossy finish. The entire set was packaged in a printed box, and distributed through card hobby dealers.

| NO. | PLAYER | MINT |
|---|---|---|
| 1 | Pat Kelly (R) | .50 |
| 2 | Rich DeLucia | .10 |
| 3 | Wes Chamberlain | .30 |
| 4 | Scott Leius | .15 |
| 5 | Darryl Kile | .12 |
| 6 | Milt Cuyler | .10 |
| 7 | Todd Van Poppel (R) | 1.25 |
| 8 | Ray Lankford | .25 |
| 9 | Brian Hunter (R) | .75 |
| 10 | Tony Perezchica | .08 |
| 11 | Ced Landrum (R) | .20 |
| 12 | Dave Burba (R) | .12 |
| 13 | Ramon Garcia (R) | .12 |
| 14 | Ed Sprague | .12 |

| NO. | PLAYER | MINT |
|---|---|---|
| 15 | Warren Newson (R) | .25 |
| 16 | Paul Faries (R) | .12 |
| 17 | Luis Gonzalez | .30 |
| 18 | Charles Nagy | .08 |
| 19 | Chris Hammond | .08 |
| 20 | Frank Castillo (R) | .15 |
| 21 | Pedro Munoz | .15 |
| 22 | Orlando Merced (R) | .35 |
| 23 | Jose Melendez (R) | .12 |
| 24 | Kirk Dressendorfer (R) | .25 |
| 25 | Heathcliff Slocumb (R) | .15 |
| 26 | Doug Simons (R) | .15 |
| 27 | Mike Timlin (R) | .15 |
| 28 | Jeff Fassero (R) | .15 |

| NO. | PLAYER | MINT |
|---|---|---|
| 29 | Mark Leiter (R) | .15 |
| 30 | Jeff Bagwell (R) | 3.00 |
| 31 | Brian McRae | .35 |
| 32 | Mark Whiten | .25 |
| 33 | Ivan Rodriguez (R) | 2.00 |
| 34 | Wade Taylor (R) | .25 |
| 35 | Darren Lewis | .20 |
| 36 | Mo Vaughn | .50 |
| 37 | Mike Remlinger | .08 |
| 38 | Rick Wilkins (R) | .15 |
| 39 | Chuck Knoblauch | .40 |
| 40 | Kevin Morton | .08 |
| 41 | Carlos Rodriguez (R) | .15 |
| 42 | Mark Lewis | .15 |

| NO. | PLAYER | MINT |
|---|---|---|
| 43 | Brent Mayne | .08 |
| 44 | Chris Haney (R) | .15 |
| 45 | Denis Boucher (R) | .15 |
| 46 | Mike Gardiner | .08 |
| 47 | Jeff Johnson (R) | .20 |
| 48 | Dean Palmer | .40 |
| 49 | Chuck McElroy | .08 |
| 50 | Chris Jones (R) | .15 |
| 51 | Scott Kamieniecki (R) | .25 |
| 52 | Al Osuna (R) | .15 |
| 53 | Rusty Meacham (R) | .15 |
| 54 | Chito Martinez (R) | .50 |
| 55 | Reggie Jefferson | .35 |
| 56 | Checklist | .08 |

## 1992 Donruss . . . Series One Set of 396 Cards (#1 to 396)—Value $30.00

New features included a thicker, glossy-coated card stock, color photos on front and back, an anti-counterfeiting feature and new foil packaging. Limited edition cards included in foil packs were the Signature Series (5,000 Cal Ripken cards), the Legends Series (7,500 Rickey Henderson cards) and the Elite Series, (10,000 each of 10 cards). 26 Diamond Kings cards stamped in gold foil (no longer part of the set) were randomly inserted in foil packs. Production for 1992 was reduced significantly and the factory cost of the cards was doubled.

# 1992 Donruss (Continued)

**Series 1—No. 1 to 396**
**No. 1 to 20—Rated Rookies**

| No. | Player | Mint |
|---|---|---|
| 1 | Mark Wohlers | .40 |
| 2 | Wil Cordero | .25 |
| 3 | Kyle Abbott | .15 |
| 4 | Dave Nilsson | .50 |
| 5 | Kenny Lofton | .40 |
| 6 | Luis Mercedes | .35 |
| 7 | Roger Salkeld | .30 |
| 8 | Eddie Zosky | .15 |
| 9 | Todd Van Poppel | .75 |
| 10 | Frank Seminara (R) | .15 |
| 11 | Andy Ashby | .12 |
| 12 | Reggie Jefferson | .25 |
| 13 | Ryan Klesko | 2.00 |
| 14 | Carlos Garcia | .08 |
| 15 | John Ramos | .15 |
| 16 | Eric Karros | .40 |
| 17 | Pat Lennon | .30 |
| 18 | E. Taubensee (R) | .25 |
| 19 | Roberto Hernandez | .15 |
| 20 | D.J. Dozier | .15 |
| 21 | Dave Henderson (AS) | .08 |
| 22 | Cal Ripken (AS) | .20 |
| 23 | Wade Boggs (AS) | .15 |
| 24 | Ken Griffey, Jr. (AS) | .35 |
| 25 | Jack Morris (AS) | .10 |
| 26 | Danny Tartabull (AS) | .08 |
| 27 | Cecil Fielder (AS) | .20 |
| 28 | Roberto Alomar (AS) | .10 |
| 29 | Sandy Alomar (AS) | .08 |
| 30 | Rickey Henderson (AS) | .20 |
| 31 | Ken Hill | .06 |
| 32 | John Habyan | .06 |
| 33 | Otis Nixon (HL) | .06 |
| 34 | Tim Wallach | .06 |
| 35 | Cal Ripken | .35 |
| 36 | Gary Carter | .12 |
| 37 | Juan Agosto | .06 |
| 38 | Doug Dascenzo | .06 |
| 39 | Kirk Gibson | .10 |
| 40 | Benito Santiago | .10 |
| 41 | Otis Nixon | .06 |
| 42 | Andy Allanson | .06 |
| 43 | Brian Holman | .06 |
| 44 | Dick Schofield | .06 |
| 45 | Dave Magadan | .06 |
| 46 | Rafael Palmeiro | .15 |
| 47 | Jody Reed | .06 |
| 48 | Ivan Calderon | .06 |
| 49 | Greg Harris | .06 |
| 50 | Chris Sabo | .10 |
| 51 | Paul Molitor | .12 |
| 52 | Robby Thompson | .06 |
| 53 | Dave Smith | .06 |
| 54 | Mark Davis | .06 |
| 55 | Kevin Brown | .06 |
| 56 | Donn Pall | .06 |
| 57 | Lenny Dykstra | .06 |
| 58 | Roberto Alomar | .15 |
| 59 | Jeff Robinson | .06 |
| 60 | Willie McGee | .12 |
| 61 | Jay Buhner | .06 |
| 62 | Mike Pagliarulo | .06 |
| 63 | Paul O'Neill | .06 |
| 64 | Hubie Brooks | .06 |
| 65 | Kelly Gruber | .10 |
| 66 | Ken Caminiti | .06 |
| 67 | Gary Redus | .06 |
| 68 | Harold Baines | .06 |
| 69 | Charlie Hough | .06 |
| 70 | B.J. Surhoff | .06 |
| 71 | Walt Weiss | .06 |
| 72 | Shawn Hillegas | .06 |
| 73 | Roberto Kelly | .12 |
| 74 | Jeff Ballard | .06 |
| 75 | Craig Biggio | .08 |
| 76 | Pat Combs | .06 |
| 77 | Jeff Robinson | .06 |
| 78 | Tim Belcher | .06 |
| 79 | Cris Carpenter | .06 |
| 80 | Checklist | .06 |
| 81 | Steve Avery | .35 |
| 82 | Chris James | .06 |
| 83 | Brian Harper | .06 |
| 84 | Charlie Leibrandt | .06 |
| 85 | Mickey Tettleton | .06 |
| 86 | Pete O'Brien | .06 |
| 87 | Danny Darwin | .06 |
| 88 | Bob Walk | .06 |
| 89 | Jeff Reardon | .06 |
| 90 | Bobby Rose | .06 |
| 91 | Danny Jackson | .06 |
| 92 | John Morris | .06 |
| 93 | Bud Black | .06 |
| 94 | Tommy Greene (HL) | .06 |
| 95 | Rick Aguilera | .06 |
| 96 | Gary Gaetti | .06 |
| 97 | David Cone | .10 |
| 98 | John Olerud | .12 |
| 99 | Joel Skinner | .06 |
| 100 | Jay Bell | .06 |
| 101 | Bob Milacki | .06 |
| 102 | Norm Charlton | .06 |
| 103 | Chuck Crim | .06 |
| 104 | Terry Steinbach | .06 |
| 105 | Juan Samuel | .06 |
| 106 | Steve Howe | .06 |
| 107 | Rafael Belliard | .06 |
| 108 | Joey Cora | .06 |
| 109 | Tommy Greene | .10 |
| 110 | Gregg Olson | .12 |
| 111 | Frank Tanana | .06 |
| 112 | Lee Smith | .06 |
| 113 | Greg Harris | .06 |
| 114 | Dwayne Henry | .06 |
| 115 | Chili Davis | .06 |
| 116 | Kent Mercker | .06 |
| 117 | Brian Barnes | .06 |
| 118 | Rich DeLucia | .06 |
| 119 | Andre Dawson | .12 |
| 120 | Carlos Baerga | .10 |
| 121 | Mike LaValliere | .06 |
| 122 | Jeff Gray | .06 |
| 123 | Bruce Hurst | .06 |
| 124 | Alvin Davis | .06 |
| 125 | John Candelaria | .06 |
| 126 | Matt Nokes | .06 |
| 127 | George Bell | .10 |
| 128 | Bret Saberhagen | .12 |
| 129 | Jeff Russell | .06 |
| 130 | Jim Abbott | .15 |
| 131 | Bill Gullickson | .06 |
| 132 | Todd Zeile | .10 |
| 133 | Dave Winfield | .12 |
| 134 | Wally Whitehurst | .06 |
| 135 | Matt Williams | .10 |
| 136 | Tom Browning | .06 |
| 137 | Marquis Grissom | .10 |
| 138 | Erik Hanson | .06 |
| 139 | Rob Dibble | .06 |
| 140 | Don August | .06 |
| 141 | Tom Henke | .06 |
| 142 | Dan Pasqua | .06 |
| 143 | George Brett | .15 |
| 144 | Jerald Clark | .06 |
| 145 | Robin Ventura | .15 |
| 146 | Dale Murphy | .15 |
| 147 | Dennis Eckersley | .12 |
| 148 | Eric Yelding | .06 |
| 149 | Mario Diaz | .06 |
| 150 | Casey Candaele | .06 |
| 151 | Steve Olin | .06 |
| 152 | Luis Salazar | .06 |
| 153 | Kevin Maas | .15 |
| 154 | Nolan Ryan (HL) | .50 |
| 155 | Barry Jones | .06 |
| 156 | Chris Hoiles | .06 |
| 157 | Bobby Ojeda | .06 |
| 158 | Pedro Guerrero | .10 |
| 159 | Paul Assenmacher | .06 |
| 160 | Checklist | .06 |
| 161 | Mike Macfarlane | .06 |
| 162 | Craig Lefferts | .06 |
| 163 | Brian Hunter | .60 |
| 164 | Alan Trammell | .10 |
| 165 | Ken Griffey, Jr. | .75 |
| 166 | Lance Parrish | .06 |
| 167 | Brian Downing | .06 |
| 168 | John Barfield | .06 |
| 169 | Jack Clark | .06 |
| 170 | Chris Nabholz | .06 |
| 171 | Tim Teufel | .06 |
| 172 | Chris Hammond | .06 |
| 173 | Robin Yount | .15 |
| 174 | Dave Righetti | .06 |
| 175 | Joe Girardi | .06 |
| 176 | Mike Boddicker | .06 |
| 177 | Dean Palmer | .20 |
| 178 | Greg Hibbard | .06 |
| 179 | Randy Ready | .06 |
| 180 | Devon White | .06 |
| 181 | Mark Eichhorn | .06 |
| 182 | Mike Felder | .06 |
| 183 | Joe Klink | .06 |
| 184 | Steve Bedrosian | .06 |
| 185 | Barry Larkin | .15 |
| 186 | John Franco | .06 |
| 187 | Ed Sprague | .10 |
| 188 | Mark Portugal | .06 |
| 189 | Jose Lind | .06 |
| 190 | Bob Welch | .06 |
| 191 | Alex Fernandez | .15 |
| 192 | Gary Sheffield | .08 |
| 193 | Rickey Henderson | .30 |
| 194 | Rod Nichols | .06 |
| 195 | Scott Kamieniecki | .10 |
| 196 | Mike Flanagan | .06 |
| 197 | Steve Finley | .06 |
| 198 | Darren Daulton | .06 |
| 199 | Leo Gomez | .10 |
| 200 | Mike Morgan | .06 |
| 201 | Bob Tewksbury | .06 |
| 202 | Sid Bream | .06 |
| 203 | Sandy Alomar | .08 |
| 204 | Greg Gagne | .06 |
| 205 | Juan Berenguer | .06 |
| 206 | Cecil Fielder | .20 |
| 207 | Randy Johnson | .06 |
| 208 | Tony Pena | .06 |
| 209 | Doug Drabek | .06 |
| 210 | Wade Boggs | .15 |
| 211 | Bryan Harvey | .06 |
| 212 | Jose Vizcaino | .06 |
| 213 | Alonzo Powell | .08 |
| 214 | Will Clark | .30 |
| 215 | R. Henderson (HL) | .15 |
| 216 | Jack Morris | .10 |
| 217 | Junior Felix | .06 |
| 218 | Vince Coleman | .10 |
| 219 | Jimmy Key | .06 |
| 220 | Alex Cole | .06 |
| 221 | Bill Landrum | .06 |
| 222 | Randy Miligan | .06 |
| 223 | Jose Rijo | .06 |
| 224 | Greg Vaughn | .10 |
| 225 | Dave Stewart | .10 |
| 226 | Lenny Harris | .06 |
| 227 | Scott Sanderson | .06 |
| 228 | Jeff Blauser | .06 |
| 229 | Ozzie Guillen | .06 |
| 230 | John Kruk | .06 |
| 231 | Bob Melvin | .06 |
| 232 | Milt Cuyler | .08 |
| 233 | Felix Jose | .15 |
| 234 | Ellis Burks | .10 |
| 235 | Pete Hamisch | .06 |
| 236 | Kevin Tapani | .08 |
| 237 | Terry Pendleton | .10 |
| 238 | Mark Gardner | .06 |
| 239 | Harold Reynolds | .06 |
| 240 | Checklist | .06 |
| 241 | Mike Harkey | .06 |
| 242 | Felix Fermin | .06 |
| 243 | Barry Bonds | .20 |
| 244 | Roger Clemens | .20 |
| 245 | Dennis Rasmussen | .06 |
| 246 | Jose DeLeon | .06 |
| 247 | Orel Hershiser | .10 |
| 248 | Mel Hall | .06 |
| 249 | Rick Wilkins | .06 |
| 250 | Torn Gordon | .08 |
| 251 | Kevin Reimer | .06 |
| 252 | Luis Polonia | .06 |
| 253 | Mike Henneman | .06 |
| 254 | Tom Pagnozzi | .06 |
| 255 | Chuck Finley | .08 |
| 256 | Mackey Sasser | .06 |
| 257 | John Burkett | .06 |
| 258 | Hal Morris | .10 |
| 259 | Larry Walker | .06 |
| 260 | Billy Swift | .06 |
| 261 | Joe Oliver | .06 |
| 262 | Julio Machado | .06 |
| 263 | Todd Stottlemyre | .06 |
| 264 | Matt Meruillo | .06 |
| 265 | Brent Mayne | .08 |
| 266 | Thomas Howard | .06 |
| 267 | Lance Johnson | .06 |
| 268 | Terry Mulholland | .06 |
| 269 | Rick Honeycutt | .06 |
| 270 | Luis Gonzalez | .20 |
| 271 | Jose Guzman | .06 |
| 272 | Jimmy Jones | .06 |
| 273 | Mark Lewis | .15 |
| 274 | Rene Gonzales | .06 |
| 275 | Jeff Johnson | .10 |
| 276 | Dennis Martinez (HL) | .08 |
| 277 | Delino DeShields | .10 |
| 278 | Sam Horn | .06 |
| 279 | Kevin Gross | .06 |
| 280 | Jose Oquendo | .06 |
| 281 | Mark Grace | .10 |
| 282 | Mark Gubicza | .06 |
| 283 | Fred McGriff | .10 |
| 284 | Ron Gant | .12 |
| 285 | Lou Whitaker | .06 |
| 286 | Edgar Martinez | .10 |
| 287 | Ron Tingley | .06 |
| 288 | Kevin McReynolds | .06 |
| 289 | Ivan Rodriguez | 1.00 |
| 290 | Mike Gardiner | .08 |
| 291 | Chris Haney | .10 |
| 292 | Darrin Jackson | .06 |
| 293 | Bill Doran | .06 |
| 294 | Ted Higuera | .06 |
| 295 | Jeff Brantley | .06 |
| 296 | Les Lancaster | .06 |
| 297 | Jim Eisenreich | .06 |
| 298 | Ruben Sierra | .15 |
| 299 | Scott Radinsky | .06 |
| 300 | Jose DeJesus | .06 |
| 301 | Mike Timlin | .10 |
| 302 | Luis Sojo | .06 |
| 303 | Kelly Downs | .06 |
| 304 | Scott Bankhead | .06 |
| 305 | Pedro Munoz | .15 |
| 306 | Scott Scudder | .06 |
| 307 | Kevin Elster | .06 |
| 308 | Duane Ward | .06 |
| 309 | Darryl Kile | .08 |
| 310 | Orlando Merced | .15 |
| 311 | Dave Henderson | .10 |
| 312 | Tim Raines | .12 |
| 313 | Mark Lee | .08 |
| 314 | Mike Gallego | .06 |
| 315 | Charles Nagy | .06 |
| 316 | Jesse Barfield | .06 |
| 317 | Todd Frohwirth | .06 |
| 318 | Al Osuna | .06 |
| 319 | Darrin Fletcher | .06 |
| 320 | Checklist | .06 |
| 321 | David Segui | .06 |
| 322 | Stan Javier | .06 |
| 323 | Bryn Smith | .06 |
| 324 | Jeff Treadway | .06 |
| 325 | Mark Whiten | .15 |
| 326 | Kent Hrbek | .06 |
| 327 | Dave Justice | .50 |
| 328 | Tony Phillips | .06 |
| 329 | Rob Murphy | .06 |
| 330 | Kevin Morton | .10 |
| 331 | John Smiley | .06 |
| 332 | Luis Rivera | .06 |
| 333 | Wally Joyner | .10 |
| 334 | Heathcliff Slobcumb | .06 |

| NO. | PLAYER | MINT |
|-----|--------|------|
| 335 | Rick Cerone | .06 |
| 336 | Mike Remlinger | .06 |
| 337 | Mike Moore | .06 |
| 338 | Lloyd McClendon | .06 |
| 339 | Al Newman | .06 |
| 340 | Kirk McCaskill | .06 |
| 341 | Howard Johnson | .10 |
| 342 | Greg Myers | .06 |
| 343 | Kal Daniels | .10 |
| 344 | Bernie Williams | .30 |
| 345 | Shane Mack | .06 |
| 346 | Gary Thurman | .06 |
| 347 | Dante Bichette | .06 |
| 348 | Mark McGwire | .15 |
| 349 | Travis Fryman | .20 |
| 350 | Ray Lankford | .15 |

| NO. | PLAYER | MINT |
|-----|--------|------|
| 351 | Mike Jeffcoat | .06 |
| 352 | Jack McDowell | .08 |
| 353 | Mitch Williams | .06 |
| 354 | Mike Devereaux | .06 |
| 355 | Andres Galarraga | .06 |
| 356 | Henry Cotto | .06 |
| 357 | Scott Bailes | .06 |
| 358 | Jeff Bagwell | 1.50 |
| 359 | Scott Leius | .06 |
| 360 | Zane Smith | .06 |
| 361 | Bill Pecota | .06 |
| 362 | Tony Fernandez | .06 |
| 363 | Glenn Braggs | .06 |
| 364 | Bill Spiers | .06 |
| 365 | Vicente Palacios | .08 |

| NO. | PLAYER | MINT |
|-----|--------|------|
| 366 | Tim Burke | .06 |
| 367 | Randy Tomlin | .10 |
| 368 | Kenny Rogers | .06 |
| 369 | Brett Butler | .06 |
| 370 | Pat Kelly | .20 |
| 371 | Bip Roberts | .06 |
| 372 | Gregg Jefferies | .10 |
| 373 | Kevin Bass | .06 |
| 374 | Ron Karkovice | .06 |
| 375 | Paul Gibson | .06 |
| 376 | Bernard Gilkey | .10 |
| 377 | Dave Gallagher | .06 |
| 378 | Bill Wegman | .06 |
| 379 | Pat Borders | .06 |
| 380 | Ed Whitson | .06 |

| NO. | PLAYER | MINT |
|-----|--------|------|
| 381 | Gilberto Reyes | .06 |
| 382 | Russ Swan | .06 |
| 383 | Andy Van Slyke | .08 |
| 384 | Wes Chamberlain | .20 |
| 385 | Steve Chitren | .06 |
| 386 | Greg Olson | .06 |
| 387 | Brian McRae | .15 |
| 388 | Rich Rodriguez | .06 |
| 389 | Steve Decker | .15 |
| 390 | Chuck Knoblauch | .35 |
| 391 | Bobby Witt | .06 |
| 392 | Eddie Murray | .15 |
| 393 | Juan Gonzalez | .40 |
| 394 | Scott Ruskin | .06 |
| 395 | Jay Howell | .06 |
| 396 | Checklist | .06 |

**SERIES NO. 2 NOT RELEASED
AT PRESS TIME**

# 1981 Fleer . . . Complete Set of 660 Cards—Value $65.00

This was Fleer's first baseball card set since 1963. Over 30 cards contained errors; they were corrected in the 2nd and 3rd printing runs. The "Craig" Nettles error was corrected during the first printing. There is very little interest by collectors in the *variety* (error) cards; none are scarce or worth much more than ordinary cards, except card 87, "Craig" Nettles. If a *variety* (error) is significant, it is listed and explained; if it is *minor*, it is noted by an *asterisk*. This set features the rookie cards of Fernando Valenzuela, Kirk Gibson and Harold Baines.

| NO. PLAYER | MINT |
|---|---|
| **PHILADELPHIA PHILLIES** | |
| 1 Pete Rose | 1.50 |
| 2 Larry Bowa | .12 |
| 3 Manny Trillo | .05 |
| 4 Bob Boone | .05 |
| 5 Mike Schmidt | .05 |
| (MVP) Third Base | 2.50 |
| See No. 640 | |
| 6 Steve Carlton | |
| (Pitcher of Year) | 1.00 |
| See No. 660 | |
| Error—"1066" | |
| Cardinals" on Back | |
| 6 Steve Carlton | 2.00 |
| Corrected "1966" Cardinals | |
| 7 Tug McGraw | .07 |
| See No. 657 | |
| 8 Larry Christenson | .05 |
| 9 Bake McBride | .05 |
| 10 Greg Luzinski | .10 |
| 11 Ron Reed | .05 |
| 12 Dickie Noles | .05 |
| 13 Keith Moreland (R) | .20 |
| 14 Bob Walk | .25 |
| 15 Lonnie Smith | .35 |
| 16 Dick Ruthven | .05 |
| 17 Sparky Lyle | .07 |
| 18 Greg Gross | .05 |
| 19 Garry Maddox | .05 |
| 20 Nino Espinosa | .05 |
| 21 George Vukovich | .05 |
| 22 John Vukovich | .05 |
| 23 Ramon Aviles | .05 |
| 24 Ken Saucier* | .08 |
| 25 Randy Lerch | .05 |
| 26 Del Uncer | .05 |
| 27 Tim McCarver | .08 |
| **KANSAS CITY ROYALS** | |
| 28 George Brett—MVP | 2.50 |
| See No. 655 | |
| 29 Willie Wilson | .20 |
| See No. 653 | |
| 30 Paul Splittorff | .05 |
| 31 Dan Quisenberry | .25 |
| 32 Amos Otis* | .10 |
| 33 Steve Busby | .05 |
| 34 U.L. Washington | .05 |
| 35 Dave Chalk | .05 |
| 36 Darrell Porter | .08 |
| 37 Marty Pattin | .05 |
| 38 Larry Gura | .05 |
| 39 Renie Martin | .05 |
| 40 Rich Gale | .05 |
| 41 Hal McRae* | .25 |
| 42 Dennis Leonard | .05 |
| 43 Willie Aikens | .05 |
| 44 Frank White | .08 |
| 45 Clint Hurdle | .05 |
| 46 John Wathan | .05 |
| 47 Pete LaCock | .05 |
| 48 Rance Mulliniks | .05 |

| NO. PLAYER | MINT |
|---|---|
| 49 Jeff Twitty | .05 |
| 50 Jamie Quirk | .05 |
| **HOUSTON ASTROS** | |
| 51 Art How | .05 |
| 52 Ken Forsch | .05 |
| 53 Vern Ruhle | .05 |
| 54 Joe Niekro | .08 |
| 55 Frank LaCorte | .05 |
| 56 J.R. Richard | .08 |
| 57 Nolan Ryan | 5.00 |
| 58 Enos Cabell | .05 |
| 59 Cesar Cedeno | .08 |
| 60 Jose Cruz | .15 |
| 61 Bill Virdon (Mgr.) | .05 |
| 62 Terry Puhl | .05 |
| 63 Joaquin Andujar | .10 |
| 64 Alan Ashby | .05 |
| 65 Joe Sambito | .05 |
| 66 Denny Walling | .05 |
| 67 Jeff Leonard | .15 |
| 68 Luis Pujols | .05 |
| 69 Bruce Bochy | .05 |
| 70 Rafael Landestoy | .05 |
| 71 Dave Smith (R) | .30 |
| 72 Danny Heep | .20 |
| 73 Julio Gonzalez | .05 |
| 74 Craig Reynolds | .05 |
| 75 Gary Woods | .05 |
| 76 Dave Bergman | .05 |
| 77 Randy Niemann | .05 |
| 78 Joe Morgan | .75 |
| **NEW YORK YANKEES** | |
| 79 Reggie Jackson | 2.00 |
| See No. 650 | |
| 80 Bucky Dent | .07 |
| 81 Tommy John | .20 |
| 82 Luis Tiant | .05 |
| 83 Rick Cerone | .05 |
| 84 Dick Howser (Mgr.) | .05 |
| 85 Lou Piniella | .10 |
| 86 Ron Davis | .05 |
| 87 Graig Nettles | 11.00 |
| Error—"Craig" on Back | |
| 87 Graig Nettles | .30 |
| Corrected—"Graig" | |
| 88 Ron Guidry | .25 |
| 89 Rich Gossage | .20 |
| 90 Rudy May | .05 |
| 91 Gaylord Perry | .40 |
| 92 Eric Soderholm | .05 |
| 93 Bob Watson | .05 |
| 94 Bobby Murcer | .08 |
| 95 Bobby Brown | .05 |
| 96 Jim Spencer | .05 |
| 97 Tom Underwood | .05 |
| 98 Oscar Gamble | .05 |
| 99 Johnny Oates | .05 |
| 100 Fred Stanley | .05 |
| 101 Ruppert Jones | .05 |
| 102 Dennis Werth | .05 |
| 103 Joe LeFebvre | .12 |

| NO. PLAYER | MINT |
|---|---|
| 104 Brian Doyle | .05 |
| 105 Aurelio Rodriguez | .05 |
| 106 Doug Bird | .05 |
| 107 Mike Griffin | .05 |
| 108 Tim Lollar (R) | .20 |
| 109 Willie Randolph | .12 |
| **LOS ANGELES DODGERS** | |
| 110 Steve Garvey | .50 |
| 111 Reggie Smith | .08 |
| 112 Don Sutton | .40 |
| 113 Burt Hooton | .05 |
| 114 Dave Lopes* | .08 |
| 115 Dusty Baker | .10 |
| 116 Tom Lasorda (Mgr.) | .08 |
| 117 Bill Russell | .05 |
| 118 Jerry Reuss | .08 |
| 119 Terry Forster | .05 |
| 120 Robert Welch* | .50 |
| 121 Don Stanhouse | .05 |
| 122 Rick Monday | .08 |
| 123 Derrel Thomas | .05 |
| 124 Joe Ferguson | .05 |
| 125 Rick Sutcliffe | .20 |
| 126 Ron Cey* | .15 |
| 127 Dave Goltz | .05 |
| 128 Jay Johnstone | .05 |
| 129 Steve Yeager | .05 |
| 130 Gary Weiss | .05 |
| 131 Mike Scioscia (R) | .75 |
| 132 Vic Davalillo | .05 |
| 133 Doug Rau | .05 |
| 134 Pepe Frias | .05 |
| 135 Mickey Hatcher | .05 |
| 136 Steve Howe (R) | .15 |
| 137 Robert Castillo | .05 |
| 138 Gary Thomasson | .05 |
| 139 Rudy Law | .05 |
| 140 F. Valenzuela (R) | 3.00 |
| 141 Manny Mota | .08 |
| **MONTREAL EXPOS** | |
| 142 Gary Carter | .75 |
| 143 Steve Rogers | .08 |
| 144 Warren Cromartie | .05 |
| 145 Andre Dawson | 1.50 |
| 146 Larry Parrish | .05 |
| 147 Rowland Office | .05 |
| 148 Ellis Valentine | .05 |
| 149 Dick Williams (Mgr.) | .05 |
| 150 Bill Gullickson (R) | .50 |
| 151 Elias Sosa | .05 |
| 152 John Tamargo | .05 |
| 153 Chris Speier | .05 |
| 154 Ron LeFlore | .05 |
| 155 Rodney Scott | .05 |
| 156 Stan Bahnsen | .05 |
| 157 Bill Lee | .05 |
| 158 Fred Norman | .05 |
| 159 Woodie Fryman | .05 |
| 160 Dave Palmer | .05 |
| 161 Jerry White | .05 |
| 162 Roberto Ramos | .05 |

| NO. PLAYER | MINT |
|---|---|
| 163 John D'Acquisto | .05 |
| 164 Tommy Hutton | .05 |
| 165 Charlie Lea (R) | .15 |
| 166 Scott Sanderson | .05 |
| 167 Ken Macha | .05 |
| 168 Tony Bernazard | .05 |
| **BALTIMORE ORIOLES** | |
| 169 Jim Palmer | .75 |
| 170 Steve Stone | .05 |
| 171 Mike Flanagan | .08 |
| 172 Al Bumbry | .05 |
| 173 Doug DeCinces | .12 |
| 174 Scott McGregor | .08 |
| 175 Mark Belanger | .05 |
| 176 Tim Stoddard | .05 |
| 177 Rick Dempsey* | .10 |
| 178 Earl Weaver (Mgr.) | .10 |
| 179 Tippy Martinez | .05 |
| 180 Dennis Martinez | .25 |
| 181 Sammy Stewart | .05 |
| 182 Rich Dauer | .05 |
| 183 Lee May | .05 |
| 184 Eddie Murray | 2.00 |
| 185 Benny Ayala | .05 |
| 186 John Lowenstein | .05 |
| 187 Gary Roenicke | .05 |
| 188 Ken Singleton | .08 |
| 189 Dan Graham | .05 |
| 190 Terry Crowley | .05 |
| 191 Kiko Garcia | .05 |
| 192 Dave Ford | .05 |
| 193 Mark Corey | .05 |
| 194 Lenn Sakata | .05 |
| 195 Doug DeCinces | .08 |
| **CINCINNATI REDS** | |
| 196 Johnny Bench | 1.50 |
| 197 Dave Concepcion | .15 |
| 198 Ray Knight | .08 |
| 199 Ken Griffey | .25 |
| 200 Tom Seaver | 1.25 |
| 201 Dave Collins | .07 |
| 202 George Foster | .20 |
| (Slugger) Error—No. 216 | |
| 202 George Foster | .20 |
| (Slugger) Correct No. 202 | |
| 203 Junior Kennedy | .05 |
| 204 Frank Pastore | .05 |
| 205 Dan Driessen | .05 |
| 206 Hector Cruz | .05 |
| 207 Paul Moskau | .05 |
| 208 Charlie Leibrandt (R) | .40 |
| 209 Harry Spilman | .05 |
| 210 Joe Price | .05 |
| 211 Tom Hume | .05 |
| 212 Joe Nolan | .05 |
| 213 Doug Bair | .05 |
| 214 Mario Soto | .08 |
| 215 Bill Bonham* | .08 |
| 216 George Foster | .15 |
| See No. 202 | |
| 217 Paul Householder | .10 |

| NO. | PLAYER | MINT |
|---|---|---|
| 218 | Ron Oester | .05 |
| 219 | Sam Mejias | .05 |
| 220 | Sheldon Burnside | .05 |

**BOSTON RED SOX**

| NO. | PLAYER | MINT |
|---|---|---|
| 221 | Carl Yastrzemski | 1.25 |
| 222 | Jim Rice | .30 |
| 223 | Fred Lynn | .25 |
| 224 | Carlton Fisk | 1.25 |
| 225 | Rick Burleson | .05 |
| 226 | Dennis Eckersley | .50 |
| 227 | Butch Hobson | .05 |
| 228 | Tom Burgmeier | .05 |
| 229 | Garry Hancock | .05 |
| 230 | Don Zimmer (Mgr.) | .05 |
| 231 | Steve Renko | .05 |
| 232 | Dwight Evans | .35 |
| 233 | Mike Torrez | .05 |
| 234 | Bob Stanley | .08 |
| 235 | Jim Dwyer | .05 |
| 236 | Dave Stapleton | .10 |
| 237 | Glenn Hoffman | .08 |
| 238 | Jerry Remy | .05 |
| 239 | Dick Drago | .05 |
| 240 | Bill Campbell | .05 |
| 241 | Tony Perez | .25 |

**ATLANTA BRAVES**

| NO. | PLAYER | MINT |
|---|---|---|
| 242 | Phil Niekro | .50 |
| 243 | Dale Murphy | 1.00 |
| 244 | Bob Horner | .20 |
| 245 | Jeff Burroughs | .05 |
| 246 | Rick Camp | .05 |
| 247 | Bob Cox (Mgr.) | .05 |
| 248 | Bruce Benedict | .05 |
| 249 | Gene Garber | .05 |
| 250 | Jerry Royster | .05 |
| 251 | Gary Matthews* | .10 |
| 252 | Chris Chambliss | .08 |
| 253 | Luis Gomez | .05 |
| 254 | Bill Nahorodny | .05 |
| 255 | Doyle Alexander | .10 |
| 256 | Brian Asselstine | .05 |
| 257 | Biff Pocoroba | .05 |
| 258 | Mike Lum | .05 |
| 259 | Charlie Spikes | .05 |
| 260 | Glenn Hubbard | .05 |
| 261 | Tommy Boggs | .05 |
| 262 | Al Hrabosky | .05 |
| 263 | Rick Matula | .05 |
| 264 | Preston Hanna | .05 |
| 265 | Larry Bradford | .05 |
| 266 | Rafael Ramirez | .20 |
| 267 | Larry McWilliams | .05 |

**CALIFORNIA ANGELS**

| NO. | PLAYER | MINT |
|---|---|---|
| 268 | Rod Carew | 1.50 |
| 269 | Bobby Grich | .08 |
| 270 | Carney Lansford | .20 |
| 271 | Don Baylor | .20 |
| 272 | Joe Rudi | .05 |
| 273 | Dan Ford | .05 |
| 274 | Jim Fregosi | .05 |
| 275 | Dave Frost | .05 |
| 276 | Frank Tanana | .10 |
| 277 | Dickie Thon | .07 |
| 278 | Jason Thompson | .08 |
| 279 | Rick Miller | .05 |
| 280 | Bert Campaneris | .10 |
| 281 | Tom Donohue | .05 |
| 282 | Brian Downing | .05 |
| 283 | Fred Patek | .05 |
| 284 | Bruce Kison | .05 |
| 285 | Dave LaRoche | .05 |
| 286 | Don Aase | .05 |
| 287 | Jim Barr | .05 |
| 288 | Alfredo Martinez | .05 |
| 289 | Larry Harlow | .05 |
| 290 | Andy Hassler | .05 |

**CHICAGO CUBS**

| NO. | PLAYER | MINT |
|---|---|---|
| 291 | Dave Kingman | .12 |
| 292 | Bill Buckner | .10 |
| 293 | Rick Reuschel | .10 |
| 294 | Bruce Sutter | .20 |
| 295 | Jerry Martin | .05 |
| 296 | Scot Thompson | .05 |
| 297 | Ivan DeJesus | .05 |
| 298 | Steve Dillard | .05 |

| NO. | PLAYER | MINT |
|---|---|---|
| 299 | Dick Tidrow | .05 |
| 300 | Randy Martz | .05 |
| 301 | Lenny Randle | .05 |
| 302 | Lynn McGlothen | .05 |
| 303 | Cliff Johnson | .05 |
| 304 | Tim Blackwell | .05 |
| 305 | Dennis Lamp | .05 |
| 306 | Bill Caudill | .08 |
| 307 | Carlos Lezcano | .05 |
| 308 | Jim Tracy | .05 |
| 309 | Doug Capilla | .05 |
| 310 | Willie Hernandez | .20 |
| 311 | Mike Vail | .05 |
| 312 | Mike Krukow | .05 |
| 313 | Barry Foote | .05 |
| 314 | Larry Biittner | .05 |
| 315 | Mike Tyson | .05 |

**NEW YORK METS**

| NO. | PLAYER | MINT |
|---|---|---|
| 316 | Lee Mazzilli | .05 |
| 317 | John Stearns | .05 |
| 318 | Alex Trevino | .05 |
| 319 | Craig Swan | .05 |
| 320 | Frank Taveras | .05 |
| 321 | Steve Henderson | .05 |
| 322 | Neil Allen | .05 |
| 323 | Mark Bomback | .05 |
| 324 | Mike Jorgensen | .05 |
| 325 | Joe Torre | .07 |
| 326 | Elliott Maddox | .05 |
| 327 | Pete Falcone | .05 |
| 328 | Ray Burris | .05 |
| 329 | Claudell Washington | .08 |
| 330 | Doug Flynn | .05 |
| 331 | Joel Youngblood | .05 |
| 332 | Bill Almon | .05 |
| 333 | Tom Hausman | .05 |
| 334 | Pat Zachry | .05 |
| 335 | Jeff Reardon (R) | 3.50 |
| 336 | Wally Backman (R) | .30 |
| 337 | Dan Norman | .05 |
| 338 | Jerry Morales | .05 |

**CHICAGO WHITE SOX (Except 351)**

| NO. | PLAYER | MINT |
|---|---|---|
| 339 | Ed Farmer | .05 |
| 340 | Bob Molinaro | .05 |
| 341 | Todd Cruz | .05 |
| 342 | Britt Burns* | .35 |
| 343 | Kevin Bell | .05 |
| 344 | Tony LaRussa (Mgr.) | .05 |
| 345 | Steve Trout | .05 |
| 346 | Harold Baines (R) | 3.00 |
| 347 | Richard Wortham | .05 |
| 348 | Wayne Nordhagen | .05 |
| 349 | Mike Squires | .05 |
| 350 | Lamar Johnson | .05 |
| 351 | Rickey Henderson | 10.00 |
| | Most Stolen Bases, AL | |
| 352 | Francisco Barrios | .05 |
| 353 | Thad Bosley | .05 |
| 354 | Chet Lemon | .08 |
| 355 | Bruce Kimm | .05 |
| 356 | Richard Dotson (R) | .20 |
| 357 | Jim Morrison | .05 |
| 358 | Mike Proly | .05 |
| 359 | Greg Pryor | .05 |

**PITTSBURGH PIRATES**

| NO. | PLAYER | MINT |
|---|---|---|
| 360 | Dave Parker | .50 |
| 361 | Omar Moreno | .05 |
| 362 | Kent Tekulve* | .10 |
| 363 | Willie Stargell | .50 |
| 364 | Phil Garner | .05 |
| 365 | Ed Ott | .05 |
| 366 | Don Robinson | .05 |
| 367 | Chuck Tanner (Mgr.) | .05 |
| 368 | Jim Bibby | .05 |
| 369 | Dale Berra | .05 |
| 370 | Jim Bibby | .05 |
| 371 | Steve Nicosia | .05 |
| 372 | Mike Easler | .10 |
| 373 | Bill Robinson | .05 |
| 374 | Lee Lacy | .05 |
| 375 | John Candelaria | .10 |
| 376 | Manny Sanguillen | .05 |
| 377 | Rick Rhoden | .12 |
| 378 | Grant Jackson | .05 |
| 379 | Tim Foli | .05 |

| NO. | PLAYER | MINT |
|---|---|---|
| 380 | Rod Scurry | .05 |
| 381 | Bill Madlock | .15 |
| 382 | Kurt Bevacqua* | .08 |
| 383 | Bert Blyleven | .20 |
| 384 | Eddie Solomon | .05 |
| 385 | Enrique Romo | .05 |
| 386 | John Milner | .05 |

**CLEVELAND INDIANS**

| NO. | PLAYER | MINT |
|---|---|---|
| 387 | Mike Hargrove | .05 |
| 388 | Jorge Orta | .05 |
| 389 | Toby Harrah | .05 |
| 390 | Tom Veryzer | .05 |
| 391 | Miguel Dilone | .05 |
| 392 | Dan Spillner | .05 |
| 393 | Jack Brohamer | .05 |
| 394 | Wayne Garland | .05 |
| 395 | Sid Monge | .05 |
| 396 | Rick Waits | .05 |
| 397 | Joe Charboneau | .12 |
| 398 | Gary Alexander | .05 |
| 399 | Jerry Dybzinski | .05 |
| 400 | Mike Stanton | .05 |
| 401 | Mike Paxton | .05 |
| 402 | Gary Gray | .05 |
| 403 | Rick Manning | .05 |
| 404 | Bo Diaz | .08 |
| 405 | Ron Hassey | .05 |
| 406 | Ross Grimsley | .05 |
| 407 | Victor Cruz | .05 |
| 408 | Len Barker | .08 |

**TORONTO BLUE JAYS**

| NO. | PLAYER | MINT |
|---|---|---|
| 409 | Bob Bailor | .05 |
| 410 | Otto Velez | .05 |
| 411 | Ernie Whitt | .05 |
| 412 | Jim Clancy | .05 |
| 413 | Barry Bonnell | .05 |
| 414 | Dave Stieb | .75 |
| 415 | Damaso Garcia (R) | .15 |
| 416 | John Mayberry | .05 |
| 417 | Roy Howell | .05 |
| 418 | Dan Ainge | 1.00 |
| 419 | Jesse Jefferson* | .08 |
| 420 | Joey McLaughlin | .05 |
| 421 | Lloyd Moseby (R) | .35 |
| 422 | Al Woods | .05 |
| 423 | Garth Iorg | .05 |
| 424 | Doug Ault | .05 |
| 425 | Ken Schrom | .15 |
| 426 | Mike Willis | .05 |
| 427 | Steve Braun | .05 |
| 428 | Bob Davis | .05 |
| 429 | Jerry Garvin | .05 |
| 430 | Alfredo Griffin | .08 |
| 431 | Bob Mattick (Mgr.) | .05 |

**SAN FRANCISCO GIANTS**

| NO. | PLAYER | MINT |
|---|---|---|
| 432 | Vida Blue | .08 |
| 433 | Jack Clark | .30 |
| 434 | Willie McCovey | .75 |
| 435 | Mike Ivie | .05 |
| 436 | Darrell Evans* | .15 |
| 437 | Terry Whitfield | .05 |
| 438 | Rennie Stennett | .05 |
| 439 | John Montefusco | .05 |
| 440 | Jim Wohlford | .05 |
| 441 | Bill North | .05 |
| 442 | Milt May | .05 |
| 443 | Max Venable | .05 |
| 444 | Ed Whitson | .05 |
| 445 | Al Holland | .15 |
| 446 | Randy Moffitt | .05 |
| 447 | Bob Knepper | .05 |
| 448 | Gary Lavelle | .05 |
| 449 | Greg Minton | .05 |
| 450 | Johnnie LeMaster | .05 |
| 451 | Larry Herndon | .05 |
| 452 | Rich Murray | .05 |
| 453 | Joe Pettini | .05 |
| 454 | Allen Ripley | .05 |
| 455 | Dennis Littlejohn | .05 |
| 456 | Tom Griffin | .05 |
| 457 | Alan Hargesheimer | .05 |
| 458 | Joe Strain | .05 |

**DETROIT TIGERS**

| NO. | PLAYER | MINT |
|---|---|---|
| 459 | Steve Kemp | .08 |
| 460 | Sparky Anderson (Mgr.) | .08 |

| NO. | PLAYER | MINT |
|---|---|---|
| 461 | Alan Trammell | .75 |
| 462 | Mark Fidrych | .08 |
| 463 | Lou Whitaker | .50 |
| 464 | Dave Rozema | .05 |
| 465 | Milt Wilcox | .05 |
| 466 | Champ Summers | .05 |
| 467 | Lance Parrish | .35 |
| 468 | Dan Petry | .15 |
| 469 | Pat Underwood | .05 |
| 470 | Rick Peters | .10 |
| 471 | Al Cowens | .05 |
| 472 | John Wockenfuss | .05 |
| 473 | Tom Brookens | .05 |
| 474 | Richie Hebner | .05 |
| 475 | Jack Morris | .75 |
| 476 | Jim Lentine | .05 |
| 477 | Bruce Robbins | .05 |
| 478 | Mark Wagner | .05 |
| 479 | Tim Corcoran | .05 |
| 480 | Stan Papi* | .08 |
| 481 | Kirk Gibson (R) | 3.00 |
| 482 | Dan Schatzeder | .05 |
| 483 | Amos Otis | .60 |
| | See card No. 32 | |

**SAN DIEGO PADRES**

| NO. | PLAYER | MINT |
|---|---|---|
| 484 | Dave Winfield | 1.00 |
| 485 | Rollie Fingers | .75 |
| 486 | Gene Richards | .05 |
| 487 | Randy Jones | .05 |
| 488 | Ozzie Smith | 2.00 |
| 489 | Gene Tenace | .05 |
| 490 | Bill Fahey | .05 |
| 491 | John Curtis | .05 |
| 492 | Dave Cash | .05 |
| 493 | Tim Flannery* | .12 |
| 494 | Jerry Mumphrey | .05 |
| 495 | Bob Shirley | .05 |
| 496 | Steve Mura | .05 |
| 497 | Eric Rasmussen | .05 |
| 498 | Broderick Perkins | .05 |
| 499 | Barry Evans | .05 |
| 500 | Chuck Baker | .05 |
| 501 | Luis Salazar | .15 |
| 502 | Gary Lucas | .10 |
| 503 | Mike Armstrong | .05 |
| 504 | Jerry Turner | .05 |
| 505 | Dennis Kinney | .05 |
| 506 | Willie Montanez | .05 |

**MILWAUKEE BREWERS**

| NO. | PLAYER | MINT |
|---|---|---|
| 507 | Gorman Thomas | .10 |
| 508 | Ben Oglivie | .08 |
| 509 | Larry Hisle | .05 |
| 510 | Sal Bando | .30 |
| 511 | Robin Yount | 2.00 |
| 512 | Mike Caldwell | .05 |
| 513 | Sixto Lezcano | .05 |
| 514 | Bill Travers | .15 |
| | Error—Jerry Augustine photo and back | |
| 514 | Bill Travers | .08 |
| 515 | Paul Molitor | .50 |
| 516 | Moose Haas | .05 |
| 517 | Bill Castro | .05 |
| 518 | Jim Slaton | .05 |
| 519 | Lary Sorensen | .05 |
| 520 | Bob McClure | .05 |
| 521 | Charlie Moore | .05 |
| 522 | Jim Gantner* | .05 |
| 523 | Reggie Cleveland | .05 |
| 524 | Don Money | .05 |
| 525 | Bill Travers | .05 |
| 526 | Buck Martinez | .05 |
| 527 | Dick Davis | .05 |

**ST. LOUIS CARDINALS**

| NO. | PLAYER | MINT |
|---|---|---|
| 528 | Ted Simmons | .15 |
| 529 | Garry Templeton | .12 |
| 530 | Ken Reitz | .05 |
| 531 | Tony Scott | .05 |
| 532 | Ken Oberkfell | .05 |
| 533 | Bob Sykes | .05 |
| 534 | Keith Smith | .05 |
| 535 | John Littlefield | .05 |
| 536 | Jim Kaat | .20 |
| 537 | Bob Forsch | .05 |
| 538 | Mike Phillips | .05 |

| NO. PLAYER | MINT |
|---|---|
| 539 Terry Landrum | .08 |
| 540 Leon Durham (R) | .30 |
| 541 Terry Kennedy | .08 |
| 542 George Hendrick | .08 |
| 543 Dane Iorg | .05 |
| 544 Mark Littell | .05 |
| 545 Keith Hernandez | .30 |
| 546 Silvio Martinez | .05 |
| 547 Don Hood | .25 |
| Error—Pete Vuckovich photo and back | |
| 547 Don Hood | .10 |
| 548 Bobby Bonds | .08 |
| 549 Mike Ramsey | .05 |
| 550 Tom Herr | .15 |
| **MINNESOTA TWINS** | |
| 551 Roy Smalley | .05 |
| 552 Jerry Koosman | .15 |
| 553 Ken Landreaux | .05 |
| 554 John Castino | .05 |
| 555 Doug Corbett | .12 |
| 556 Bombo Rivera | .05 |
| 557 Ron Jackson | .05 |
| 558 Butch Wynegar | .05 |
| 559 Hosken Powell | .05 |
| 560 Pete Redfern | .05 |
| 561 Roger Erickson | .05 |
| 562 Glenn Adams | .08 |
| 563 Rick Sofield | .05 |
| 564 Geoff Zahn | .05 |
| 565 Pete Mackanin | .05 |
| 566 Mike Cubbage | .05 |
| 567 Darrell Jackson | .05 |
| 568 Dave Edwards | .05 |
| 569 Rob Wilfong | .05 |
| 570 Sal Butera | .05 |
| 571 Jose Morales | .05 |
| **OAKLAND A'S** | |
| 572 Rick Langford | .05 |
| 573 Mike Norris | .05 |

| NO. PLAYER | MINT |
|---|---|
| 574 Rickey Henderson | 15.00 |
| 575 Tony Armas | .15 |
| 576 Dave Revering | .05 |
| 577 Jeff Newman | .05 |
| 578 Bob Lacey | .05 |
| 579 Brian Kingman | .05 |
| 580 Mitchell Page | .05 |
| 581 Billy Martin (Mgr.) | .15 |
| 582 Rob Picciolo | .05 |
| 583 Mike Heath | .05 |
| 584 Mickey Klutts | .05 |
| 585 Orlando Gonzalez | .05 |
| 586 Mike Davis (R) | .20 |
| 587 Wayne Gross | .05 |
| 588 Matt Keough | .05 |
| 589 Steve McCatty | .05 |
| 590 Dwayne Murphy | .08 |
| 591 Mario Guerrero | .05 |
| 592 Dave McKay | .05 |
| 593 Jim Essian | .05 |
| 594 Dave Heaverlo | .05 |
| **SEATTLE MARINERS (Except 606)** | |
| 595 Maury Wills (Mgr.) | .10 |
| 596 Juan Beniquez | .05 |
| 597 Rodney Craig | .05 |
| 598 Jim Anderson | .05 |
| 599 Floyd Bannister | .08 |
| 600 Bruce Bochte | .05 |
| 601 Julio Cruz | .05 |
| 602 Ted Cox | .05 |
| 603 Dan Meyer | .05 |
| 604 Larry Cox | .05 |
| 605 Bill Stein | .05 |
| 606 Steve Garvey | .50 |
| Most Hits, NL | |
| 607 Dave Roberts | .05 |
| 608 Leon Roberts | .05 |
| 609 Reggie Walton | .05 |
| 610 Dave Edler | .05 |

| NO. PLAYER | MINT |
|---|---|
| 611 Larry Milbourne | .05 |
| 612 Kim Allen | .05 |
| 613 Mario Mendoza | .05 |
| 614 Tom Paciorek | .05 |
| 615 Glenn Abbott | .05 |
| 616 Joe Simpson | .05 |
| **TEXAS RANGERS** | |
| 617 Mickey Rivers | .08 |
| 618 Jim Kern | .05 |
| 619 Jim Sundberg | .05 |
| 620 Richie Zisk | .05 |
| 621 Jon Matlack | .05 |
| 622 Ferguson Jenkins | .40 |
| 623 Pat Corrales (Mgr.) | .05 |
| 624 Ed Figueroa | .05 |
| 625 Buddy Bell | .15 |
| 626 Al Oliver | .15 |
| 627 Doc Medich | .05 |
| 628 Bump Wills | .05 |
| 629 Rusty Staub | .12 |
| 630 Pat Putnam | .05 |
| 631 John Grubb | .05 |
| 632 Danny Darwin | .05 |
| 633 Ken Clay | .05 |
| 634 Jim Norris | .05 |
| 635 John Butcher | .15 |
| 636 Dave Roberts | .05 |
| 637 Billy Sample | .05 |
| **SPECIAL CARDS** | |
| 638 Carl Yastrzemski | 1.25 |
| 400 Home Run Club | |
| 639 Cecil Cooper | .20 |
| 640 Mike Schmidt | 1.75 |
| (Third Base) Error—No. 5 | |
| 640 Mike Schmidt | 1.50 |
| (Home Run King) | |
| 641 Checklist (1 to 50)* | .08 |
| 642 Checklist (51 to 109) | .08 |
| 643 Checklist (110 to 168) | .08 |

| NO. PLAYER | MINT |
|---|---|
| 644 Checklist (169 to 220)* | .08 |
| 645 Triple Threat:* | 1.75 |
| Schmidt, Rose, Bowa | |
| 646 Checklist (221 to 267) | .08 |
| 647 Checklist (268 to 315) | .08 |
| 648 Checklist (316 to 359) | .08 |
| 649 Checklist (360 to 408) | .08 |
| 650 Reggie Jackson | 1.75 |
| Mr. Baseball Error—No. 79 | |
| 650 Reggie Jackson | 1.50 |
| Mr. Baseball | |
| 651 Checklist (409 to 458) | .08 |
| 652 Checklist (459 to 506)* | .08 |
| 653 Willie Wilson | .15 |
| Most Hits, Most Runs Error—No. 29 | |
| 653 Willie Wilson | .15 |
| Most Hits, Most Runs | |
| 654 Checklist (507 to 550)* | .08 |
| 655 G. Brett (.390 Avg.) | 1.25 |
| Error—No. 28* | |
| 656 Checklist (551 to 593) | .08 |
| 657 Tug McGraw | .08 |
| Game Saver, Error—No. 7 | |
| 657 Tug McGraw | .08 |
| Game Saver | |
| 658 Checklist (594 to 637) | .08 |
| 659 Checklist (Specials)* | .08 |
| 660 Steve Carlton | 1.00 |
| "Lefty"—The Golden Arm Errors—Card No.6 and "1066" Cardinals | |
| 660 Steve Carlton | .75 |
| "Lefty"—The Golden Arm Error—"1066" Cardinals | |
| 660 Steve Carlton | 2.00 |
| "Lefty"—The Golden Arm Corrected—"1966" Cardinals | |

## 1982 Fleer . . . Complete Set of 660 Cards—Value $75.00

Features the rookie cards of Cal Ripken, Dave Stewart and George Bell. Several errors were corrected; none are scarce or worth much more than ordinary cards, except cards 438 and 576. If a *variety* (error) is significant, it is listed and explained; if it is minor it is noted by an *asterisk*.

| NO. PLAYER | MINT |
|---|---|
| **LOS ANGELES DODGERS** | |
| 1 Dusty Baker | .10 |
| 2 Robert Castillo | .05 |
| 3 Roy Cey | .15 |
| 4 Terry Forster | .05 |
| 5 Steve Garvey | .40 |
| 6 Dave Goltz | .05 |
| 7 Pedro Guerrero | .50 |
| 8 Burt Hooton | .05 |
| 9 Steve Howe | .05 |
| 10 Jay Johnstone | .05 |
| 11 Ken Landreaux | .05 |
| 12 Davey Lopes | .05 |
| 13 Mike Marshall (R) | .35 |
| 14 Bobby Mitchell | .09 |
| 15 Rick Monday | .10 |
| 16 Tom Niedenfuer (R) | .15 |
| 17 Ted Power (R) | .20 |

| NO. PLAYER | MINT |
|---|---|
| 18 Jerry Reuss | .10 |
| 19 Ron Roenicke | .05 |
| 20 Bill Russell | .05 |
| 21 Steve Sax (R) | 3.00 |
| 22 Mike Scioscia | .30 |
| 23 Reggie Smith | .10 |
| 24 Dave Stewart (R) | 5.00 |
| 25 Rick Sutcliffe | .15 |
| 26 Darrell Thomas | .05 |
| 27 Fernando Valenzuela | .50 |
| 28 Bob Welch | .35 |
| 29 Steve Yeager | .05 |
| **NEW YORK YANKEES** | |
| 30 Bobby Brown | .05 |
| 31 Rick Cerone | .05 |
| 32 Ron Davis | .05 |
| 33 Bucky Dent | .08 |
| 34 Barry Foote | .05 |

| NO. PLAYER | MINT |
|---|---|
| 35 George Frazier | .05 |
| 36 Oscar Gamble | .05 |
| 37 Rich Gossage | .20 |
| 38 Ron Guidry | .20 |
| 39 Reggie Jackson | 1.50 |
| 40 Tommy John | .15 |
| 41 Rudy May | .05 |
| 42 Larry Milbourne | .05 |
| 43 Jerry Mumphrey | .05 |
| 44 Bobby Murcer | .10 |
| 45 Gene Nelson (R) | .15 |
| 46 Graig Nettles | .15 |
| 47 Johnny Oates | .05 |
| 48 Lou Piniella | .10 |
| 49 Willie Randolph | .12 |
| 50 Rick Reuschel | .12 |
| 51 Dave Reverink | .05 |
| 52 Dave Righetti (R) | 1.25 |

| NO. PLAYER | MINT |
|---|---|
| 53 Aurelio Rodriguez | .05 |
| 54 Bob Watson | .05 |
| 55 Dennis Werth | .05 |
| 56 Dave Winfield | 1.00 |
| **CINCINNATI REDS** | |
| 57 Johnny Bench | 1.25 |
| 58 Bruce Berenyi | .05 |
| 59 Larry Biittner | .05 |
| 60 Scott Brown | .09 |
| 61 Dave Collins | .05 |
| 62 Geoff Combe | .05 |
| 63 Dave Concepcion | .10 |
| 64 Dan Driessen | .05 |
| 65 Joe Edelen | .05 |
| 66 George Foster | .20 |
| 67 Ken Griffey | .25 |
| 68 Paul Householder | .05 |
| 69 Tom Hume | .05 |

| NO. | PLAYER | MINT |
|---|---|---|
| 70 | Junior Kennedy | .05 |
| 71 | Ray Knight | .10 |
| 72 | Mike LaCoss | .05 |
| 73 | Rafael Landestoy | .05 |
| 74 | Charlie Leibrandt | .05 |
| 75 | Sam Mejias | .05 |
| 76 | Paul Moskau | .05 |
| 77 | Joe Nolan | .05 |
| 78 | Mike O'Berry | .05 |
| 79 | Ron Oester | .05 |
| 80 | Frank Pastore | .05 |
| 81 | Joe Price | .05 |
| 82 | Tom Seaver | 1.00 |
| 83 | Mario Soto | .10 |
| 84 | Mike Vail | .05 |

**OAKLAND A'S**

| NO. | PLAYER | MINT |
|---|---|---|
| 85 | Tony Armas | .10 |
| 86 | Shooty Babitt | .05 |
| 87 | Dave Beard | .05 |
| 88 | Rick Bosetti | .05 |
| 89 | Keith Drumright | .05 |
| 90 | Wayne Gross | .05 |
| 91 | Mike Heath | .05 |
| 92 | Rickey Henderson | 5.00 |
| 93 | Cliff Johnson | .05 |
| 94 | Jeff Jones | .05 |
| 95 | Matt Keough | .05 |
| 96 | Brian Kingman | .05 |
| 97 | Mickey Klutts | .05 |
| 98 | Rick Langford | .05 |
| 99 | Steve McCatty | .05 |
| 100 | Dave McKay | .05 |
| 101 | Dwayne Murphy | .07 |
| 102 | Jeff Newman | .05 |
| 103 | Mike Norris | .05 |
| 104 | Bob Owchinko | .05 |
| 105 | Mitchell Page | .05 |
| 106 | Rob Picciolo | .05 |
| 107 | Jim Spencer | .05 |
| 108 | Fred Stanley | .05 |
| 109 | Tom Underwood | .05 |

**ST. LOUIS CARDINALS**

| NO. | PLAYER | MINT |
|---|---|---|
| 110 | Joaquin Andujar | .15 |
| 111 | Steve Braun | .05 |
| 112 | Bob Forsch | .05 |
| 113 | George Hendrick | .08 |
| 114 | Keith Hernandez | .30 |
| 115 | Tom Herr | .15 |
| 116 | Dane Iorg | .05 |
| 117 | Jim Kaat | .10 |
| 118 | Tito Landrum | .05 |
| 119 | Sixto Lezcano | .05 |
| 120 | Mark Littell | .05 |
| 121 | John Martin | .05 |
| 122 | Silvio Martinez | .05 |
| 123 | Ken Oberkfell | .05 |
| 124 | Darrell Porter | .05 |
| 125 | Mike Ramsey | .05 |
| 126 | Orlando Sanchez | .08 |
| 127 | Bob Shirley | .05 |
| 128 | Lary Sorensen | .05 |
| 129 | Bruce Sutter | .15 |
| 130 | Bob Sykes | .05 |
| 131 | Garry Templeton | .15 |
| 132 | Gene Tenace | .05 |

**MILWAUKEE BREWERS**

| NO. | PLAYER | MINT |
|---|---|---|
| 133 | Jerry Augustine | .05 |
| 134 | Sal Bando | .05 |
| 135 | Mark Brouhard | .08 |
| 136 | Mike Caldwell | .05 |
| 137 | Reggie Cleveland | .05 |
| 138 | Cecil Cooper | .20 |
| 139 | Jamie Easterly | .05 |
| 140 | Marshall Edwards | .05 |
| 141 | Rollie Fingers | .50 |
| 142 | Jim Gantner | .05 |
| 143 | Moose Haas | .05 |
| 144 | Larry Hisle | .05 |
| 145 | Roy Howell | .05 |
| 146 | Rickey Keeton | .05 |
| 147 | Randy Lerch | .05 |
| 148 | Paul Molitor | .50 |
| 149 | Don Money | .05 |
| 150 | Charlie Moore | .05 |
| 151 | Ben Oglivie | .10 |
| 152 | Ted Simmons | .10 |
| 153 | Jim Slaton | .05 |
| 154 | Gorman Thomas | .10 |
| 155 | Robin Yount | 2.00 |
| 156 | Pete Vuckovich | .10 |

**BALTIMORE ORIOLES**

| NO. | PLAYER | MINT |
|---|---|---|
| 157 | Benny Ayala | .05 |
| 158 | Mark Belanger | .05 |
| 159 | Al Bumbry | .05 |
| 160 | Terry Crowley | .05 |
| 161 | Rich Dauer | .05 |
| 162 | Doug DeCinces | .10 |
| 163 | Rick Dempsey | .05 |
| 164 | Jim Dwyer | .05 |
| 165 | Mike Flanagan | .10 |
| 166 | Dave Ford | .05 |
| 167 | Dan Graham | .05 |
| 168 | Wayne Krenchicki | .05 |
| 169 | John Lowenstein | .05 |
| 170 | Dennis Martinez | .15 |
| 171 | Tippy Martinez | .05 |
| 172 | Scott McGregor | .10 |
| 173 | Jose Morales | .05 |
| 174 | Eddie Murray | 1.25 |
| 175 | Jim Palmer | 1.00 |
| 176 | Cal Ripken, Jr. (R) | 40.00 |
| 177 | Gary Roenicke | .05 |
| 178 | Lenn Sakata | .05 |
| 179 | Ken Singleton | .10 |
| 180 | Sammy Stewart | .05 |
| 181 | Tim Stoddard | .05 |
| 182 | Steve Stone | .05 |

**MONTREAL EXPOS**

| NO. | PLAYER | MINT |
|---|---|---|
| 183 | Stan Bahnsen | .05 |
| 184 | Ray Burris | .05 |
| 185 | Gary Carter | .50 |
| 186 | Warren Cromartie | .05 |
| 187 | Andre Dawson | 1.00 |
| 188 | Terry Francona (R) | .20 |
| 189 | Woodie Fryman | .05 |
| 190 | Bill Gullickson | .10 |
| 191 | Grant Jackson | .05 |
| 192 | Wallace Johnson | .05 |
| 193 | Charlie Lea | .05 |
| 194 | Bill Lee | .05 |
| 195 | Jerry Manuel | .05 |
| 196 | Brad Mills | .07 |
| 197 | John Milner | .05 |
| 198 | Rowland Office | .05 |
| 199 | David Palmer | .05 |
| 200 | Larry Parrish | .05 |
| 201 | Mike Phillips | .05 |
| 202 | Tim Raines | 2.50 |
| 203 | Bobby Ramos | .05 |
| 204 | Jeff Reardon | .75 |
| 205 | Steve Rogers | .10 |
| 206 | Scott Sanderson | .05 |
| 207 | Rodney Scott | .15 |
| 208 | Elias Sosa | .05 |
| 209 | Chris Speier | .05 |
| 210 | Tim Wallach (R) | 1.00 |
| 211 | Jerry White | .05 |

**HOUSTON ASTROS**

| NO. | PLAYER | MINT |
|---|---|---|
| 212 | Alan Ashby | .05 |
| 213 | Cesar Cedeno | .10 |
| 214 | Jose Cruz | .15 |
| 215 | Kiko Garcia | .05 |
| 216 | Phil Garner | .05 |
| 217 | Danny Heep | .05 |
| 218 | Art Howe | .05 |
| 219 | Bob Knepper | .05 |
| 220 | Frank LaCorte | .05 |
| 221 | Joe Niekro | .10 |
| 222 | Joe Pittman | .05 |
| 223 | Terry Puhl | .05 |
| 224 | Luis Pujols | .05 |
| 225 | Craig Reynolds | .05 |
| 226 | J.R. Richard | .10 |
| 227 | Dave Roberts | .05 |
| 228 | Vern Ruhle | .05 |
| 229 | Nolan Ryan | 6.00 |
| 230 | Joe Sambito | .05 |
| 231 | Tony Scott | .05 |
| 232 | Dave Smith | .15 |
| 233 | Harry Spilman | .05 |

| NO. | PLAYER | MINT |
|---|---|---|
| 234 | Don Sutton | .35 |
| 235 | Dickie Thon | .10 |
| 236 | Denny Walling | .05 |
| 237 | Gary Woods | .05 |

**PHILADELPHIA PHILLIES**

| NO. | PLAYER | MINT |
|---|---|---|
| 238 | Luis Aguayo | .05 |
| 239 | Ramon Aviles | .05 |
| 240 | Bob Boone | .05 |
| 241 | Larry Bowa | .10 |
| 242 | Warren Brusstar | .05 |
| 243 | Steve Carlton | 1.00 |
| 244 | Larry Christenson | .05 |
| 245 | Dick Davis | .05 |
| 246 | Greg Gross | .05 |
| 247 | Sparky Lyle | .08 |
| 248 | Garry Maddox | .10 |
| 249 | Gary Matthews | .10 |
| 250 | Bake McBride | .05 |
| 251 | Tug McGraw | .10 |
| 252 | Keith Moreland | .08 |
| 253 | Dickie Noles | .05 |
| 254 | Mike Proly | .05 |
| 255 | Ron Reed | .05 |
| 256 | Pete Rose | 1.25 |
| 257 | Dick Ruthven | .05 |
| 258 | Mike Schmidt | 2.00 |
| 259 | Lonnie Smith | .30 |
| 260 | Manny Trillo | .05 |
| 261 | Del Unser | .05 |
| 262 | George Vukovich | .05 |

**DETROIT TIGERS**

| NO. | PLAYER | MINT |
|---|---|---|
| 263 | Tom Brookens | .05 |
| 264 | George Cappuzzello | .05 |
| 265 | Marty Castillo | .05 |
| 266 | Al Cowens | .05 |
| 267 | Kirk Gibson | .75 |
| 268 | Richie Hebner | .05 |
| 269 | Ron Jackson | .05 |
| 270 | Lynn Jones | .05 |
| 271 | Steve Kemp | .10 |
| 272 | Rick Leach | .08 |
| 273 | Aurelio Lopez | .05 |
| 274 | Jack Morris | .50 |
| 275 | Kevin Saucier | .05 |
| 276 | Lance Parrish | .25 |
| 277 | Rick Peters | .05 |
| 278 | Dan Petry | .15 |
| 279 | David Rozema | .05 |
| 280 | Stan Papi | .05 |
| 281 | Dan Schatzeder | .05 |
| 282 | Champ Summers | .05 |
| 283 | Alan Trammell | .50 |
| 284 | Lou Whitaker | .30 |
| 285 | Milt Wilcox | .05 |
| 286 | John Wockenfuss | .05 |

**BOSTON RED SOX**

| NO. | PLAYER | MINT |
|---|---|---|
| 287 | Gary Allenson | .05 |
| 288 | Tom Burgmeier | .05 |
| 289 | Bill Campbell | .05 |
| 290 | Mark Clear | .05 |
| 291 | Steve Crawford | .05 |
| 292 | Dennis Eckersley | .50 |
| 293 | Dwight Evans | .20 |
| 294 | Rich Gedman (R) | .20 |
| 295 | Garry Hancock | .05 |
| 296 | Glenn Hoffman | .05 |
| 297 | Bruce Hurst | .60 |
| 298 | Carney Lansford | .20 |
| 299 | Rick Miller | .05 |
| 300 | Reid Nichols | .05 |
| 301 | Bob Ojeda (R) | .50 |
| 302 | Tony Perez | .35 |
| 303 | Chuck Rainey | .05 |
| 304 | Jerry Remy | .05 |
| 305 | Jim Rice | .25 |
| 306 | Joe Rudi | .05 |
| 307 | Bob Stanley | .05 |
| 308 | Dave Stapleton | .05 |
| 309 | Frank Tanana | .15 |
| 310 | Mike Torrez | .05 |
| 311 | John Tudor | .20 |
| 312 | Carl Yastrzemski | 1.00 |

**TEXAS RANGERS**

| NO. | PLAYER | MINT |
|---|---|---|
| 313 | Buddy Bell | .15 |
| 314 | Steve Comer | .05 |
| 315 | Danny Darwin | .05 |
| 316 | John Ellis | .05 |
| 317 | John Grubb | .05 |
| 318 | Rick Honeycutt | .05 |
| 319 | Charlie Hough | .05 |
| 320 | Ferguson Jenkins | .40 |
| 321 | John Henry Johnson | .05 |
| 322 | Jim Kern | .05 |
| 323 | Jon Matlack | .05 |
| 324 | Doc Medich | .05 |
| 325 | Mario Mendoza | .05 |
| 326 | Al Oliver | .15 |
| 327 | Pat Putnam | .05 |
| 328 | Mickey Rivers | .05 |
| 329 | Leon Roberts | .05 |
| 330 | Billy Sample | .05 |
| 331 | Bill Stein | .05 |
| 332 | Jim Sundberg | .05 |
| 333 | Mark Wagner | .05 |
| 334 | Bump Wills | .05 |

**CHICAGO WHITE SOX**

| NO. | PLAYER | MINT |
|---|---|---|
| 335 | Bill Almon | .05 |
| 336 | Harold Baines | .75 |
| 337 | Ross Baumgarten | .05 |
| 338 | Tony Bernazard | .05 |
| 339 | Britt Burns | .10 |
| 340 | Richard Dotson | .10 |
| 341 | Jim Essian | .05 |
| 342 | Ed Farmer | .05 |
| 343 | Carlton Fisk | 1.00 |
| 344 | Kevin Hickey | .05 |
| 345 | LaMarr Hoyt | .10 |
| 346 | Lamar Johnson | .05 |
| 347 | Jerry Koosman | .05 |
| 348 | Rusty Kuntz | .05 |
| 349 | Dennis Lamp | .05 |
| 350 | Ron LeFlore | .05 |
| 351 | Chet Lemon | .08 |
| 352 | Greg Luzinski | .10 |
| 353 | Bob Molinaro | .05 |
| 354 | Jim Morrison | .05 |
| 355 | Wayne Nordhagen | .05 |
| 356 | Greg Pryor | .05 |
| 357 | Mike Squires | .05 |
| 358 | Steve Trout | .05 |

**CLEVELAND INDIANS**

| NO. | PLAYER | MINT |
|---|---|---|
| 359 | Alan Bannister | .05 |
| 360 | Len Barker | .05 |
| 361 | Bert Blyleven | .25 |
| 362 | Joe Charboneau | .05 |
| 363 | John Denny | .10 |
| 364 | Bo Diaz | .05 |
| 365 | Miguel Dilone | .05 |
| 366 | Jerry Dybzinski | .05 |
| 367 | Wayne Garland | .05 |
| 368 | Mike Hargrove | .05 |
| 369 | Toby Harrah | .05 |
| 370 | Ron Hassey | .05 |
| 371 | Von Hayes (R) | .50 |
| 372 | Pat Kelly | .05 |
| 373 | Duane Kuiper | .05 |
| 374 | Rick Manning | .05 |
| 375 | Sid Monge | .05 |
| 376 | Jorge Orta | .05 |
| 377 | Dave Rosello | .05 |
| 378 | Dan Spillner | .05 |
| 379 | Mike Stanton | .05 |
| 380 | Andre Thornton | .10 |
| 381 | Tom Veryzer | .05 |
| 382 | Rick Waits | .05 |

**SAN FRANCISCO GIANTS**

| NO. | PLAYER | MINT |
|---|---|---|
| 383 | Doyle Alexander | .05 |
| 384 | Vida Blue | .05 |
| 385 | Fred Breining | .07 |
| 386 | Enos Cabell | .05 |
| 387 | Jack Clark | .25 |
| 388 | Darrell Evans | .10 |
| 389 | Tom Griffin | .05 |
| 390 | Larry Herndon | .05 |
| 391 | Al Holland | .05 |
| 392 | Gary Lavelle | .05 |
| 393 | Johnnie LeMaster | .05 |
| 394 | Jerry Martin | .05 |
| 395 | Milt May | .05 |
| 396 | Greg Minton | .05 |

| NO. | PLAYER | MINT |
|---|---|---|
| 397 | Joe Morgan | .50 |
| 398 | Joe Pettini | .05 |
| 399 | Alan Ripley | .05 |
| 400 | Billy Smith | .05 |
| 401 | Rennie Stennett | .05 |
| 402 | Ed Whitson | .05 |
| 403 | Jim Wohlford | .05 |
| **KANSAS CITY ROYALS** | | |
| 404 | Willie Aikens | .05 |
| 405 | George Brett | 2.00 |
| 406 | Ken Brett | .05 |
| 407 | Dave Chalk | .05 |
| 408 | Rich Gale | .05 |
| 409 | Cesar Geronimo | .05 |
| 410 | Larry Gura | .05 |
| 411 | Clint Hurdle | .05 |
| 412 | Mike Jones | .05 |
| 413 | Dennis Leonard | .05 |
| 414 | Renie Martin | .05 |
| 415 | Lee May | .05 |
| 416 | Hal McRae | .05 |
| 417 | Darryl Motley (R) | .15 |
| 418 | Rance Mulliniks | .05 |
| 419 | Amos Otis | .05 |
| 420 | Ken Phelps (R) | .15 |
| 421 | Jamie Quirk | .05 |
| 422 | Dan Quisenberry | .20 |
| 423 | Paul Splittorff | .05 |
| 424 | U.L. Washington | .05 |
| 425 | John Wathan | .05 |
| 426 | Frank White | .05 |
| 427 | Willie Wilson | .15 |
| **ATLANTA BRAVES** | | |
| 428 | Brian Asselstine | .05 |
| 429 | Bruce Benedict | .05 |
| 430 | Tom Boggs | .05 |
| 431 | Larry Bradford | .05 |
| 432 | Rick Camp | .05 |
| 433 | Chris Chambliss | .05 |
| 434 | Gene Garber | .05 |
| 435 | Preston Hanna | .05 |
| 436 | Bob Horner | .20 |
| 437 | Glenn Hubbard | .05 |
| 438 | "All" Hrabosky (error) | 16.00 |
| | "Al" misspelled | |
| 438 | Al Hrabosky | 1.00 |
| | (height 5'1"—error) | |
| 438 | Al Hrabosky | .12 |
| | (height 5'10" correct) | |
| 439 | Rufino Linares | .05 |
| 440 | Rick Mahler (R) | .20 |
| 441 | Ed Miller | .05 |
| 442 | John Montefusco | .05 |
| 443 | Dale Murphy | 1.00 |
| 444 | Phil Niekro | .35 |
| 445 | Gaylord Perry | .40 |
| 446 | Biff Pocoroba | .05 |
| 447 | Rafael Ramirez | .05 |
| 448 | Jerry Royster | .05 |
| 449 | Claudell Washington | .08 |
| **CALIFORNIA ANGELS** | | |
| 450 | Don Aase | .05 |
| 451 | Don Baylor | .15 |
| 452 | Juan Beniquez | .05 |
| 453 | Rick Burleson | .05 |
| 454 | Bert Campaneris | .05 |
| 455 | Rod Carew | 1.00 |
| 456 | Bob Clark | .05 |
| 457 | Brian Downing | .05 |
| 458 | Dan Ford | .05 |
| 459 | Ken Forsch | .05 |
| 460 | Dave Frost* | .05 |
| 461 | Bobby Grich | .10 |
| 462 | Larry Harlow | .05 |
| 463 | John Harris | .05 |
| 464 | Andy Hassler | .05 |

| NO. | PLAYER | MINT |
|---|---|---|
| 465 | Butch Hobson | .05 |
| 466 | Jesse Jefferson | .05 |
| 467 | Bruce Kison | .05 |
| 468 | Fred Lynn | .25 |
| 469 | Angel Moreno | .05 |
| 470 | Ed Ott | .05 |
| 471 | Fred Patek | .05 |
| 472 | Steve Renko | .05 |
| 473 | Mike Witt (R) | .25 |
| 474 | Geoff Zahn | .05 |
| **PITTSBURGH PIRATES** | | |
| 475 | Gary Alexander | .05 |
| 476 | Dale Berra | .05 |
| 477 | Kurt Bevacqua | .05 |
| 478 | Jim Bibby | .05 |
| 479 | John Candelaria | .05 |
| 480 | Victor Cruz | .05 |
| 481 | Mike Easler | .05 |
| 482 | Tim Foli | .05 |
| 483 | Lee Lacy | .05 |
| 484 | Vance Law | .12 |
| 485 | Bill Madlock | .15 |
| 486 | Willie Montanez | .05 |
| 487 | Omar Moreno | .05 |
| 488 | Steve Nicosia | .05 |
| 489 | Dave Parker | .50 |
| 490 | Tony Pena | .35 |
| 491 | Pascual Perez | .20 |
| 492 | Johnny Ray (R) | .15 |
| 493 | Rick Rhoden | .05 |
| 494 | Bill Robinson | .05 |
| 495 | Don Robinson | .05 |
| 496 | Enrique Romo | .05 |
| 497 | Rod Scurry | .05 |
| 498 | Eddie Solomon | .05 |
| 499 | Willie Stargell | .40 |
| 500 | Kent Tekulve | .05 |
| 501 | Jason Thompson | .05 |
| **SEATTLE MARINERS** | | |
| 502 | Glenn Abbott | .05 |
| 503 | Jim Anderson | .05 |
| 504 | Floyd Bannister | .05 |
| 505 | Bruce Bochte | .05 |
| 506 | Jeff Burroughs | .05 |
| 507 | Bryan Clark | .07 |
| 508 | Ken Clay | .05 |
| 509 | Julio Cruz | .05 |
| 510 | Dick Drago | .05 |
| 511 | Gary Gray | .05 |
| 512 | Dan Meyer | .05 |
| 513 | Jerry Narron | .05 |
| 514 | Tom Paciorek | .05 |
| 515 | Casey Parsons | .05 |
| 516 | Lenny Randle | .05 |
| 517 | Shane Rawley | .05 |
| 518 | Joe Simpson | .05 |
| 519 | Richie Zisk | .05 |
| **NEW YORK METS** | | |
| 520 | Neil Allen | .05 |
| 521 | Bob Bailor | .05 |
| 522 | Hubie Brooks | .60 |
| 523 | Mike Cubbage | .05 |
| 524 | Pete Falcone | .05 |
| 525 | Doug Flynn | .05 |
| 526 | Tom Hausman | .05 |
| 527 | Ron Hodges | .05 |
| 528 | Randy Jones | .05 |
| 529 | Mike Jorgensen | .05 |
| 530 | Dave Kingman | .15 |
| 531 | Ed Lynch | .10 |
| 532 | Mike Marshall | .05 |
| 533 | Lee Mazzilli | .05 |
| 534 | Dyar Miller | .05 |
| 535 | Mike Scott | .35 |
| 536 | Rusty Staub | .10 |
| 537 | John Stearns | .05 |

| NO. | PLAYER | MINT |
|---|---|---|
| 538 | Craig Swan | .05 |
| 539 | Frank Taveras | .05 |
| 540 | Alex Trevino | .05 |
| 541 | Ellis Valentine | .05 |
| 542 | Mookie Wilson | .05 |
| 543 | Joel Youngblood | .05 |
| 544 | Pat Zachry | .05 |
| **MINNESOTA TWINS** | | |
| 545 | Glenn Adams | .05 |
| 546 | Fernando Arroyo | .05 |
| 547 | John Verhoeven | .05 |
| 548 | Sal Butera | .05 |
| 549 | John Castino | .05 |
| 550 | Don Cooper | .05 |
| 551 | Doug Corbett | .05 |
| 552 | Dave Engle | .05 |
| 553 | Roger Erickson | .05 |
| 554 | Danny Goodwin | .05 |
| 555 | Darrell Jackson | 1.00 |
| | (error—black hat) | |
| 555 | Darrell Jackson | .10 |
| | (correct—red hat) | |
| 556 | Pete Mackanin | .05 |
| 557 | Jack O'Connor | .05 |
| 558 | Hosken Powell | .05 |
| 559 | Pete Redfern | .05 |
| 560 | Roy Smalley | .05 |
| 561 | Chuck Baker | .05 |
| 562 | Gary Ward | .05 |
| 563 | Rob Wilfong | .05 |
| 564 | Al Williams | .05 |
| 565 | Butch Wynegar | .05 |
| **SAN DIEGO PADRES** | | |
| 566 | Randy Bass | .05 |
| 567 | Juan Bonilla | .07 |
| 568 | Danny Boone | .05 |
| 569 | John Curtis | .05 |
| 570 | Juan Eichelberger | .05 |
| 571 | Barry Evans | .05 |
| 572 | Tim Flannery | .05 |
| 573 | Ruppert Jones | .05 |
| 574 | Terry Kennedy | .10 |
| 575 | Joe LeFebvre | .05 |
| 576 | John Littlefield | 150.00 |
| | (left handed—error) | |
| 576 | John Littlefield | .10 |
| | (right handed—corrected) | |
| 577 | Gary Lucas | .05 |
| 578 | Steve Mura | .05 |
| 579 | Broderick Perkins | .05 |
| 580 | Gene Richards | .05 |
| 581 | Luis Salazar | .05 |
| 582 | Ozzie Smith | 1.25 |
| 583 | John Urrea | .05 |
| 584 | Chris Welsh | .07 |
| 585 | Rick Wise | .05 |
| **CHICAGO CUBS** | | |
| 586 | Doug Bird | .05 |
| 587 | Tim Blackwell | .05 |
| 588 | Bobby Bonds | .10 |
| 589 | Bill Buckner | .10 |
| 590 | Bill Caudill | .05 |
| 591 | Hector Cruz | .05 |
| 592 | Jody Davis (R) | .15 |
| 593 | Ivan DeJesus | .05 |
| 594 | Steve Dillard | .05 |
| 595 | Leon Durham | .15 |
| 596 | Rawly Eastwick | .05 |
| 597 | Steve Henderson | .05 |
| 598 | Mike Krukow | .05 |
| 599 | Mike Lum | .05 |
| 600 | Randy Martz | .05 |
| 601 | Jerry Morales | .05 |
| 602 | Ken Reitz | .05 |
| 603 | Lee Smith (R)* | 2.50 |
| 604 | Dick Tidrow | .05 |

| NO. | PLAYER | MINT |
|---|---|---|
| 605 | Jim Tracy | .05 |
| 606 | Mike Tyson | .05 |
| 607 | Ty Waller | .08 |
| **TORONTO BLUE JAYS** | | |
| 608 | Danny Ainge | .30 |
| 609 | Jorge Bell (R) | 8.00 |
| 610 | Mark Bomback | .05 |
| 611 | Barry Bonnell | .05 |
| 612 | Jim Clancy | .05 |
| 613 | Damaso Garcia | .10 |
| 614 | Jerry Garvin | .05 |
| 615 | Alfredo Griffin | .10 |
| 616 | Garth Iorg | .05 |
| 617 | Luis Leal | .05 |
| 618 | Ken Macha | .05 |
| 619 | John Mayberry | .05 |
| 620 | Joey McLaughlin | .05 |
| 621 | Lloyd Moseby | .15 |
| 622 | Dave Stieb | .35 |
| 623 | Jackson Todd | .05 |
| 624 | Willie Upshaw | .15 |
| 625 | Otto Velez | .05 |
| 626 | Ernie Whitt | .05 |
| 627 | Al Woods | .05 |
| **SPECIAL CARDS** | | |
| 628 | All-Star Game | .05 |
| 629 | All-Star Infielders: | .05 |
| | Frank White, Bucky Dent | |
| 630 | Big Red Machine: | .10 |
| | Driessen, Concepcion, | |
| | Foster | |
| 631 | Bruce Sutter | .10 |
| | "Top NL Relief Pitcher" | |
| 632 | "Steve and Carlton" | .50 |
| | Steve Carlton, Carlton Fisk | |
| 633 | Carl Yastrzemski | .50 |
| | "3000th Game" | |
| 634 | "Dynamic Duo" | .60 |
| | Johnny Bench, Tom Seaver | |
| 635 | "West Meets East" | .25 |
| | Valenzuela, Carter | |
| 636 | Fernando Valenzuela:* | .40 |
| | "NL Strikeout King" | |
| 637 | Mike Schmidt | .75 |
| | "Home Run King" | |
| 638 | "NL All Stars" | .30 |
| | Gary Carter, Dave Parker | |
| 639 | "Perfect Game" | .10 |
| | Len Barker, Bo Diaz | |
| 640 | "Pete & Re-Pete" | 2.00 |
| | Pete Rose and Son | |
| 641 | "Phillies' Finest" | .50 |
| | Carlton, Smith, Schmidt | |
| 642 | "Red Sox Reunion" | .10 |
| | Fred Lynn, Dwight Evans | |
| 643 | Rickey Henderson | 2.50 |
| | "Most Hits, Most Runs" | |
| 644 | Rollie Fingers | .20 |
| | "Most 'Saves AL" | |
| 645 | Tom Seaver | .60 |
| | "Most 1981 Wins" | |
| 646 | "Yankee Powerhouse"* | .75 |
| | R. Jackson, D. Winfield | |
| 647 | Checklist No. 1 | .08 |
| 648 | Checklist No. 2 | .08 |
| 649 | Checklist No. 3 | .08 |
| 650 | Checklist No. 4 | .08 |
| 651 | Checklist No. 5 | .08 |
| 652 | Checklist No. 6 | .08 |
| 653 | Checklist No. 7 | .08 |
| 654 | Checklist No. 8 | .08 |
| 655 | Checklist No. 9 | .08 |
| 656 | Checklist No. 10 | .08 |
| 657 | Checklist No. 11 | .08 |
| 658 | Checklist No. 12 | .08 |
| 659 | Checklist No. 13 | .08 |
| 660 | Checklist No. 14 | .08 |

# 1983 Fleer . . . Complete Set of 660 Cards—Value $125.00

Features the rookie cards of Wade Boggs, Tony Gwynn, Howard Johnson and Ryne Sandberg. The back of the card is printed in two shades of brown.

Willie McGee

Howard Johnson

Wade Boggs

Tony Gwynn

Ryne Sandberg

| NO. PLAYER | MINT |
|---|---|
| **ST. LOUIS CARDINALS** | |
| 1 Joaquin Andujar | .10 |
| 2 Doug Bair | .05 |
| 3 Steve Braun | .05 |
| 4 Glenn Brummer | .05 |
| 5 Bob Forsch | .05 |
| 6 David Green (R) | .15 |
| 7 George Hendrick | .10 |
| 8 Keith Hernandez | .30 |
| 9 Tom Herr | .10 |
| 10 Dane Iorg | .05 |
| 11 Jim Kaat | .15 |
| 12 Jeff Lahti | .10 |
| 13 Tito Landrum | .05 |
| 14 Dave LaPoint (R) | .15 |
| 15 Willie McGee (R) | 4.00 |
| 16 Steve Mura | .05 |
| 17 Ken Oberkfell | .05 |
| 18 Darrell Porter | .05 |
| 19 Mike Ramsey | .05 |
| 20 Gene Roof | .05 |
| 21 Lonnie Smith | .20 |
| 22 Ozzie Smith | 1.00 |
| 23 John Stuper | .12 |
| 24 Bruce Sutter | .15 |
| 25 Gene Tenace | .05 |
| **MILWAUKEE BREWERS** | |
| 26 Jerry Augustin | .05 |
| 27 Dwight Bernard | .05 |
| 28 Mark Brouhard | .05 |
| 29 Mike Caldwell | .05 |
| 30 Cecil Cooper | .15 |
| 31 Jamie Easterly | .05 |
| 32 Marshall Edwards | .05 |
| 33 Rollie Fingers | .35 |
| 34 Jim Gantner | .05 |
| 35 Moose Haas | .05 |
| 36 Roy Howell | .05 |
| 37 Peter Ladd | .05 |
| 38 Bob McClure | .05 |
| 39 Doc Medich | .05 |
| 40 Paul Molitor | .40 |
| 41 Don Money | .05 |
| 42 Charlie Moore | .05 |
| 43 Ben Oglivie | .07 |
| 44 Ed Romero | .05 |
| 45 Ted Simmons | .10 |
| 46 Jim Slaton | .05 |
| 47 Don Sutton | .35 |
| 48 Gorman Thomas | .10 |
| 49 Pete Vuckovich | .05 |
| 50 Ned Yost | .05 |
| 51 Robin Yount | 1.25 |
| **BALTIMORE ORIOLES** | |
| 52 Benny Ayala | .05 |
| 53 Bob Bonner | .05 |
| 54 Al Bumbry | .05 |
| 55 Terry Crowley | .05 |
| 56 Storm Davis (R) | .25 |
| 57 Rich Dauer | .05 |
| 58 Rick Dempsey | .05 |
| 59 Jim Dwyer | .05 |
| 60 Mike Flanagan | .10 |
| 61 Dan Ford | .05 |
| 62 Glenn Gulliver | .12 |
| 63 John Lowenstein | .05 |

| NO. PLAYER | MINT |
|---|---|
| 64 Dennis Martinez | .05 |
| 65 Tippy Martinez | .05 |
| 66 Scott McGregor | .10 |
| 67 Eddie Murray | 1.00 |
| 68 Joe Nolan | .05 |
| 69 Jim Palmer | .75 |
| 70 Cal Ripken Jr. | 15.00 |
| 71 Gary Roenicke | .05 |
| 72 Lenn Sakata | .05 |
| 73 Ken Singleton | .05 |
| 74 Sammy Stewart | .05 |
| 75 Tim Stoddard | .05 |
| **CALIFORNIA ANGELS** | |
| 76 Don Aase | .05 |
| 77 Don Baylor | .10 |
| 78 Juan Beniquez | .05 |
| 79 Bob Boone | .05 |
| 80 Rick Burleson | .05 |
| 81 Rod Carew | 1.00 |
| 82 Bobby Clark | .05 |
| 83 Doug Corbett | .05 |
| 84 John Curtis | .05 |
| 85 Doug DeCinces | .10 |
| 86 Brian Downing | .05 |
| 87 Joe Ferguson | .05 |
| 88 Tim Foli | .05 |
| 89 Ken Forsch | .05 |
| 90 Dave Goltz | .05 |
| 91 Bobby Grich | .05 |
| 92 Andy Hassler | .05 |
| 93 Reggie Jackson | .75 |
| 94 Ron Jackson | .05 |
| 95 Tommy John | .15 |
| 96 Bruce Kison | .05 |
| 97 Fred Lynn | .20 |
| 98 Ed Ott | .05 |
| 99 Steve Renko | .05 |
| 100 Luis Sanchez | .05 |
| 101 Rob Wilfong | .05 |
| 102 Mike Witt | .15 |
| 103 Geoff Zahn | .05 |
| **KANSAS CITY ROYALS** | |
| 104 Willie Aikens | .05 |
| 105 Mike Armstrong | .05 |
| 106 Vida Blue | .10 |
| 107 Bud Black (R) | .35 |
| 108 George Brett | 1.25 |
| 109 Bill Castro | .05 |
| 110 Onix Concepcion | .12 |
| 111 Dave Frost | .05 |
| 112 Cesar Geronimo | .05 |
| 113 Larry Gura | .05 |
| 114 Steve Hammond | .12 |
| 115 Don Hood | .05 |
| 116 Dennis Leonard | .05 |
| 117 Jerry Martin | .05 |
| 118 Lee May | .05 |
| 119 Hal McRae | .05 |
| 120 Amos Otis | .05 |
| 121 Greg Pryor | .05 |
| 122 Dan Quisenberry | .20 |
| 123 Don Slaught (R) | .25 |
| 124 Paul Splittorff | .05 |
| 125 U.L. Washington | .05 |
| 126 John Wathan | .05 |
| 127 Frank White | .07 |

| NO. PLAYER | MINT |
|---|---|
| 128 Willie Wilson | .20 |
| **ATLANTA BRAVES** | |
| 129 Steve Bedrosian | .20 |
| 130 Bruce Benedict | .05 |
| 131 Tommy Boggs | .05 |
| 132 Brett Butler | .75 |
| 133 Rick Camp | .05 |
| 134 Chris Chambliss | .05 |
| 135 Ken Dayley | .05 |
| 136 Gene Garber | .05 |
| 137 Terry Harper | .05 |
| 138 Bob Horner | .15 |
| 139 Glenn Hubbard | .05 |
| 140 Rufino Linares | .05 |
| 141 Rick Mahler | .05 |
| 142 Dale Murphy | .75 |
| 143 Phil Niekro | .30 |
| 144 Pascual Perez | .10 |
| 145 Biff Pocoroba | .05 |
| 146 Rafael Ramirez | .05 |
| 147 Jerry Royster | .05 |
| 148 Ken Smith | .12 |
| 149 Bob Walk | .05 |
| 150 Claudell Washington | .10 |
| 151 Bob Watson | .05 |
| 152 Larry Whisenton | .05 |
| **PHILADELPHIA PHILLIES** | |
| 153 Porfirio Altamirano | .12 |
| 154 Marty Bystrom | .05 |
| 155 Steve Carlton | .75 |
| 156 Larry Christenson | .05 |
| 157 Ivan DeJesus | .05 |
| 158 John Denny | .10 |
| 159 Bob Dernier | .05 |
| 160 Bo Diaz | .05 |
| 161 Ed Farmer | .05 |
| 162 Greg Gross | .05 |
| 163 Mike Krukow | .05 |
| 164 Garry Maddox | .05 |
| 165 Gary Matthews | .10 |
| 166 Tug McGraw | .08 |
| 167 Bob Molinaro | .05 |
| 168 Sid Monge | .05 |
| 169 Ron Reed | .05 |
| 170 Bill Robinson | .05 |
| 171 Pete Rose | 1.00 |
| 172 Dick Ruthven | .05 |
| 173 Mike Schmidt | 2.00 |
| 174 Manny Trillo | .05 |
| 175 Ozzie Virgil | .05 |
| 176 George Vuckovich | .05 |
| **BOSTON RED SOX** | |
| 177 Gary Allenson | .05 |
| 178 Luis Aponte | .12 |
| 179 Wade Boggs (R) | 20.00 |
| 180 Tom Burgmeier | .05 |
| 181 Mark Clear | .05 |
| 182 Dennis Eckersley | .35 |
| 183 Dwight Evans | .20 |
| 184 Rich Gedman | .05 |
| 185 Glenn Hoffman | .05 |
| 186 Bruce Hurst | .10 |
| 187 Carney Lansford | .15 |
| 188 Rick Miller | .05 |
| 189 Reid Nichols | .05 |
| 190 Bob Ojeda | .10 |

| NO. PLAYER | MINT |
|---|---|
| 191 Tony Perez | .30 |
| 192 Chuck Rainey | .05 |
| 193 Jerry Remy | .05 |
| 194 Jim Rice | .25 |
| 195 Bob Stanley | .05 |
| 196 Dave Stapleton | .05 |
| 197 Mike Torrez | .05 |
| 198 John Tudor | .15 |
| 199 Julio Valdez | .05 |
| 200 Carl Yastrzemski | 1.00 |
| **LOS ANGELES DODGERS** | |
| 201 Dusty Baker | .10 |
| 202 Joe Beckwith | .05 |
| 203 Greg Brock (R) | .15 |
| 204 Roy Cey | .15 |
| 205 Terry Forster | .05 |
| 206 Steve Garvey | .40 |
| 207 Pedro Guerrero | .30 |
| 208 Burt Hooton | .05 |
| 209 Steve Howe | .05 |
| 210 Ken Landreaux | .05 |
| 211 Mike Marshall | .25 |
| 212 Candy Maldonado (R) | .50 |
| 213 Rick Monday | .05 |
| 214 Tom Niedenfuer | .05 |
| 215 Jorge Orta | .05 |
| 216 Jerry Reuss | .05 |
| 217 Ron Roenicke | .05 |
| 218 Vicente Romo | .05 |
| 219 Bill Russell | .05 |
| 220 Steve Sax | .50 |
| 221 Mike Scioscia | .05 |
| 222 Dave Stewart | .75 |
| 223 Derrel Thomas | .05 |
| 224 Fernando Valenzuela | .30 |
| 225 Bob Welch | .25 |
| 226 Ricky Wright | .12 |
| 227 Steve Yeager | .05 |
| **CHICAGO WHITE SOX** | |
| 228 Bill Almon | .05 |
| 229 Harold Baines | .50 |
| 230 Salome Barojas | .12 |
| 231 Tony Bernazard | .05 |
| 232 Britt Burns | .05 |
| 233 Richard Dotson | .05 |
| 234 Ernesto Escarrega | .12 |
| 235 Carlton Fisk | .75 |
| 236 Jerry Hairston | .05 |
| 237 Kevin Hickey | .05 |
| 238 LaMarr Hoyt | .15 |
| 239 Steve Kemp | .05 |
| 240 Jim Kern | .05 |
| 241 Ron Kittle (R) | .50 |
| 242 Jerry Koosman | .15 |
| 243 Dennis Lamp | .05 |
| 244 Rudy Law | .05 |
| 245 Vance Law | .05 |
| 246 Ron LeFlore | .05 |
| 247 Greg Luzinski | .10 |
| 248 Tom Paciorek | .05 |
| 249 Aurelio Rodriguez | .05 |
| 250 Mike Squires | .05 |
| 251 Steve Trout | .05 |
| **SAN FRANCISCO GIANTS** | |
| 252 Jim Barr | .05 |
| 253 Dave Bergman | .05 |

| NO. | PLAYER | MINT |
|---|---|---|
| 254 | Fred Breining | .05 |
| 255 | Bob Brenly | .05 |
| 256 | Jack Clark | .25 |
| 257 | Chili Davis | .40 |
| 258 | Darrell Evans | .10 |
| 259 | Alan Fowlkes | .12 |
| 260 | Rich Gale | .05 |
| 261 | Atlee Hammaker | .05 |
| 262 | Al Holland | .05 |
| 263 | Duane Kuiper | .05 |
| 264 | Bill Laskey (R) | .15 |
| 265 | Gary Lavelle | .05 |
| 266 | Johnnie LeMaster | .05 |
| 267 | Renie Martin | .05 |
| 268 | Milt May | .05 |
| 269 | Greg Minton | .05 |
| 270 | Joe Morgan | .40 |
| 271 | Tom O'Malley | .12 |
| 272 | Reggie Smith | .10 |
| 273 | Guy Sularz | .12 |
| 274 | Champ Summers | .05 |
| 275 | Max Venable | .05 |
| 276 | Jim Wohlford | .05 |

**MONTREAL EXPOS**

| NO. | PLAYER | MINT |
|---|---|---|
| 277 | Ray Burris | .05 |
| 278 | Gary Carter | .35 |
| 279 | Warren Cromartie | .05 |
| 280 | Andre Dawson | 1.00 |
| 281 | Terry Francona | .05 |
| 282 | Doug Flynn | .05 |
| 283 | Woody Fryman | .05 |
| 284 | Bill Gullickson | .05 |
| 285 | Wallace Johnson | .05 |
| 286 | Charlie Lea | .05 |
| 287 | Randy Lerch | .05 |
| 288 | Brad Mills | .05 |
| 289 | Dan Norman | .05 |
| 290 | Al Oliver | .15 |
| 291 | David Palmer | .05 |
| 292 | Tim Raines | .40 |
| 293 | Jeff Reardon | .50 |
| 294 | Steve Rogers | .10 |
| 295 | Scott Sanderson | .05 |
| 296 | Dan Schatzeder | .05 |
| 297 | Bryn Smith | .15 |
| 298 | Chris Speier | .05 |
| 299 | Tim Wallach | .20 |
| 300 | Jerry White | .05 |
| 301 | Joel Youngblood | .05 |

**PITTSBURGH PIRATES**

| NO. | PLAYER | MINT |
|---|---|---|
| 302 | Ross Baumgarten | .05 |
| 303 | Dale Berra | .05 |
| 304 | John Candelaria | .05 |
| 305 | Dick Davis | .05 |
| 306 | Mike Easler | .05 |
| 307 | Richie Hebner | .05 |
| 308 | Lee Lacy | .05 |
| 309 | Bill Madlock | .15 |
| 310 | Larry McWilliams | .05 |
| 311 | John Milner | .05 |
| 312 | Omar Moreno | .05 |
| 313 | Jim Morrison | .05 |
| 314 | Steve Nicosia | .05 |
| 315 | Dave Parker | .40 |
| 316 | Tony Pena | .15 |
| 317 | Johnny Ray | .15 |
| 318 | Rick Rhoden | .05 |
| 319 | Don Robinson | .05 |
| 320 | Enrique Romo | .05 |
| 321 | Manny Sarmiento | .05 |
| 322 | Rod Scurry | .05 |
| 323 | Jim Smith | .12 |
| 324 | Willie Stargell | .50 |
| 325 | Jason Thompson | .10 |
| 326 | Kent Tekulve | .05 |

**DETROIT TIGERS**

| NO. | PLAYER | MINT |
|---|---|---|
| 327 | Tom Brookens | .05 |
| 328 | Enos Cabell | .05 |
| 329 | Kirk Gibson | .40 |
| 330 | Larry Herndon | .05 |
| 331 | Mike Ivie | .05 |
| 332 | Howard Johnson (R) | 10.00 |
| 333 | Lynn Jones | .05 |
| 334 | Rick Leach | .05 |
| 335 | Chet Lemon | .07 |

| NO. | PLAYER | MINT |
|---|---|---|
| 336 | Jack Morris | .50 |
| 337 | Lance Parrish | .25 |
| 338 | Larry Pashnick | .12 |
| 339 | Dan Petry | .15 |
| 340 | Dave Rozema | .05 |
| 341 | Dave Rucker | .05 |
| 342 | Elias Sosa | .05 |
| 343 | Dave Tobik | .05 |
| 344 | Alan Trammell | .50 |
| 345 | Jerry Turner | .05 |
| 346 | Jerry Ujdur | .05 |
| 347 | Pat Underwood | .05 |
| 348 | Lou Whitaker | .30 |
| 349 | Milt Wilcox | .05 |
| 350 | Glenn Wilson (R) | .15 |
| 351 | John Wockenfuss | .05 |

**SAN DIEGO PADRES**

| NO. | PLAYER | MINT |
|---|---|---|
| 352 | Kurt Bevacqua | .05 |
| 353 | Juan Bonilla | .05 |
| 354 | Floyd Chiffer | .12 |
| 355 | Luis DeLeon | .05 |
| 356 | Dave Dravecky (R) | .40 |
| 357 | Dave Edwards | .05 |
| 358 | Juan Eichelberger | .05 |
| 359 | Tim Flannery | .05 |
| 360 | Tony Gwynn (R) | 20.00 |
| 361 | Ruppert Jones | .05 |
| 362 | Terry Kennedy | .10 |
| 363 | Joe Lefebvre | .05 |
| 364 | Sixto Lezcano | .05 |
| 365 | Tim Lollar | .05 |
| 366 | Gary Lucas | .05 |
| 367 | John Montefusco | .05 |
| 368 | Broderick Perkins | .05 |
| 369 | Joe Pittman | .05 |
| 370 | Gene Richards | .05 |
| 371 | Luis Salazar | .05 |
| 372 | Eric Show (R) | .20 |
| 373 | Garry Templeton | .10 |
| 374 | Chris Welsh | .05 |
| 375 | Alan Wiggins (R) | .15 |

**NEW YORK YANKEES**

| NO. | PLAYER | MINT |
|---|---|---|
| 376 | Rick Cerone | .05 |
| 377 | Dave Collins | .05 |
| 378 | Roger Erickson | .05 |
| 379 | George Frazier | .05 |
| 380 | Oscar Gamble | .05 |
| 381 | Goose Gossage | .20 |
| 382 | Ken Griffey | .25 |
| 383 | Ron Guidry | .20 |
| 384 | Dave LaRoche | .05 |
| 385 | Rudy May | .05 |
| 386 | John Mayberry | .05 |
| 387 | Lee Mazzilli | .05 |
| 388 | Mike Morgan | .05 |
| 389 | Jerry Mumphrey | .05 |
| 390 | Bobby Murcer | .10 |
| 391 | Graig Nettles | .15 |
| 392 | Lou Piniella | .10 |
| 393 | Willie Randolph | .05 |
| 394 | Shane Rawley | .05 |
| 395 | Dave Righetti | .15 |
| 396 | Andre Robertson | .05 |
| 397 | Roy Smalley | .05 |
| 398 | Dave Winfield | .60 |
| 399 | Butch Wynegar | .05 |

**CLEVELAND INDIANS**

| NO. | PLAYER | MINT |
|---|---|---|
| 400 | Chris Bando | .05 |
| 401 | Alan Bannister | .05 |
| 402 | Len Barker | .05 |
| 403 | Tom Brennan | .05 |
| 404 | Carmelo Castillo (R) | .10 |
| 405 | Miguel Dilone | .05 |
| 406 | Jerry Dybzinski | .05 |
| 407 | Mike Fischlin | .05 |
| 408 | Ed Glynn | .05 |
| 409 | Mike Hargrove | .05 |
| 410 | Toby Harrah | .05 |
| 411 | Ron Hassey | .05 |
| 412 | Von Hayes | .15 |
| 413 | Rick Manning | .05 |
| 414 | Bake McBride | .05 |
| 415 | Larry Milbourne | .05 |
| 416 | Bill Nahorodny | .05 |
| 417 | Jack Perconte | .05 |

| NO. | PLAYER | MINT |
|---|---|---|
| 418 | Lary Sorensen | .05 |
| 419 | Dan Spillner | .05 |
| 420 | Rick Sutcliffe | .20 |
| 421 | Andre Thornton | .10 |
| 422 | Rick Waits | .05 |
| 423 | Eddie Whitson | .05 |

**TORONTO BLUE JAYS**

| NO. | PLAYER | MINT |
|---|---|---|
| 424 | Jesse Barfield | .50 |
| 425 | Barry Bonnell | .05 |
| 426 | Jim Clancy | .05 |
| 427 | Damaso Garcia | .10 |
| 428 | Jerry Garvin | .05 |
| 429 | Alfredo Griffin | .05 |
| 430 | Garth Iorg | .05 |
| 431 | Roy Lee Jackson | .05 |
| 432 | Luis Leal | .05 |
| 433 | Buck Martinez | .05 |
| 434 | Joey McLaughlin | .05 |
| 435 | Lloyd Moseby | .15 |
| 436 | Rance Mulliniks | .05 |
| 437 | Dale Murray | .05 |
| 438 | Wayne Nordhagen | .05 |
| 439 | Gene Petralli | .12 |
| 440 | Hosken Powell | .05 |
| 441 | Dave Stieb | .30 |
| 442 | Willie Upshaw | .10 |
| 443 | Ernie Whitt | .05 |
| 444 | Al Woods | .05 |

**HOUSTON ASTROS**

| NO. | PLAYER | MINT |
|---|---|---|
| 445 | Alan Ashby | .05 |
| 446 | Jose Cruz | .15 |
| 447 | Kiko Garcia | .05 |
| 448 | Phil Garner | .05 |
| 449 | Danny Heep | .05 |
| 450 | Art Howe | .05 |
| 451 | Bob Knepper | .05 |
| 452 | Alan Knicely | .05 |
| 453 | Ray Knight | .05 |
| 454 | Frank LaCorte | .05 |
| 455 | Mike LaCoss | .05 |
| 456 | Randy Moffitt | .05 |
| 457 | Joe Niekro | .05 |
| 458 | Terry Puhl | .05 |
| 459 | Luis Pujols | .05 |
| 460 | Craig Reynolds | .05 |
| 461 | Bert Roberge | .05 |
| 462 | Vern Ruhle | .05 |
| 463 | Nolan Ryan | 5.00 |
| 464 | Joe Sambito | .05 |
| 465 | Tony Scott | .05 |
| 466 | Dave Smith | .05 |
| 467 | Harry Spilman | .05 |
| 468 | Dickie Thon | .05 |
| 469 | Denny Walling | .05 |

**SEATTLE MARINERS**

| NO. | PLAYER | MINT |
|---|---|---|
| 470 | Larry Andersen | .05 |
| 471 | Floyd Bannister | .08 |
| 472 | Jim Beattie | .05 |
| 473 | Bruce Bochte | .05 |
| 474 | Manny Castillo | .05 |
| 475 | Bill Caudill | .05 |
| 476 | Bryan Clark | .05 |
| 477 | Al Cowens | .05 |
| 478 | Julio Cruz | .05 |
| 479 | Todd Cruz | .05 |
| 480 | Gary Gray | .05 |
| 481 | Dave Henderson | 1.25 |
| 482 | Mike Moore (R) | .75 |
| 483 | Gaylord Perry | .30 |
| 484 | Dave Revering | .05 |
| 485 | Joe Simpson | .05 |
| 486 | Mike Stanton | .05 |
| 487 | Rick Sweet | .05 |
| 488 | Ed VandeBerg (R) | .15 |
| 489 | Richie Zisk | .05 |

**CHICAGO CUBS**

| NO. | PLAYER | MINT |
|---|---|---|
| 490 | Doug Bird | .05 |
| 491 | Larry Bowa | .10 |
| 492 | Bill Buckner | .10 |
| 493 | Bill Campbell | .05 |
| 494 | Jody Davis | .10 |
| 495 | Leon Durham | .15 |
| 496 | Steve Henderson | .05 |
| 497 | Willie Hernandez | .20 |
| 498 | Ferguson Jenkins | .30 |

| NO. | PLAYER | MINT |
|---|---|---|
| 499 | Jay Johnstone | .05 |
| 500 | Junior Kennedy | .05 |
| 501 | Randy Martz | .05 |
| 502 | Jerry Morales | .05 |
| 503 | Keith Moreland | .05 |
| 504 | Dickie Noles | .05 |
| 505 | Mike Proly | .05 |
| 506 | Allen Ripley | .05 |
| 507 | Ryne Sandberg (R) | 30.00 |
| 508 | Lee Smith | .50 |
| 509 | Pat Tabler | .15 |
| 510 | Dick Tidrow | .05 |
| 511 | Bump Wills | .05 |
| 512 | Gary Woods | .05 |

**OAKLAND A'S**

| NO. | PLAYER | MINT |
|---|---|---|
| 513 | Tony Armas | .15 |
| 514 | Dave Beard | .05 |
| 515 | Jeff Burroughs | .05 |
| 516 | John D'Acquisto | .05 |
| 517 | Wayne Gross | .05 |
| 518 | Mike Heath | .05 |
| 519 | Rickey Henderson | 5.00 |
| 520 | Cliff Johnson | .05 |
| 521 | Matt Keough | .05 |
| 522 | Brian Kingman | .05 |
| 523 | Rick Langford | .05 |
| 524 | Davey Lopes | .05 |
| 525 | Steve McCatty | .05 |
| 526 | Dave McKay | .05 |
| 527 | Dan Meyer | .05 |
| 528 | Dwayne Murphy | .05 |
| 529 | Jeff Newman | .05 |
| 530 | Mike Norris | .05 |
| 531 | Bob Owchinko | .05 |
| 532 | Joe Rudi | .05 |
| 533 | Jimmy Sexton | .05 |
| 534 | Fred Stanley | .05 |
| 535 | Tom Underwood | .05 |

**NEW YORK METS**

| NO. | PLAYER | MINT |
|---|---|---|
| 536 | Neil Allen | .05 |
| 537 | Wally Backman | .05 |
| 538 | Bob Bailor | .05 |
| 539 | Hubie Brooks | .25 |
| 540 | Carlos Diaz (R) | .15 |
| 541 | Pete Falcone | .05 |
| 542 | George Foster | .15 |
| 543 | Ron Gardenhire | .05 |
| 544 | Brian Giles | .12 |
| 545 | Ron Hodges | .05 |
| 546 | Randy Jones | .05 |
| 547 | Mike Jorgensen | .05 |
| 548 | Dave Kingman | .15 |
| 549 | Ed Lynch | .05 |
| 550 | Jesse Orosco | .10 |
| 551 | Rick Ownbey | .12 |
| 552 | Charlie Puleo | .05 |
| 553 | Gary Rajsich | .12 |
| 554 | Mike Scott | .20 |
| 555 | Rusty Staub | .10 |
| 556 | John Stearns | .05 |
| 557 | Craig Swan | .05 |
| 558 | Ellis Valentine | .05 |
| 559 | Tom Veryzer | .05 |
| 560 | Mookie Wilson | .10 |
| 561 | Pat Zachry | .05 |

**TEXAS RANGERS**

| NO. | PLAYER | MINT |
|---|---|---|
| 562 | Buddy Bell | .15 |
| 563 | John Butcher | .05 |
| 564 | Steve Comer | .05 |
| 565 | Danny Darwin | .05 |
| 566 | Bucky Dent | .05 |
| 567 | John Grubb | .05 |
| 568 | Rick Honeycutt | .05 |
| 569 | Dave Hostetler | .12 |
| 570 | Charlie Hough | .05 |
| 571 | Lamar Johnson | .05 |
| 572 | Jon Matlack | .05 |
| 573 | Paul Mirabella | .05 |
| 574 | Larry Parrish | .05 |
| 575 | Mike Richardt | .12 |
| 576 | Mickey Rivers | .05 |
| 577 | Billy Sample | .05 |
| 578 | Dave Schmidt | .10 |
| 579 | Bill Stein | .05 |
| 580 | Jim Sundberg | .05 |

| NO. PLAYER | MINT | NO. PLAYER | MINT | NO. PLAYER | MINT | NO. PLAYER | MINT |
|---|---|---|---|---|---|---|---|
| 581 Frank Tanana | .10 | 606 Duane Walker (R) | .15 | 630 "300 Career Wins": Perry and Bulling | .15 | 642 Last Perfect Game: Hassey, Barker | .08 |
| 582 Mark Wagner | .05 | **MINNESOTA TWINS** | | 631 Pride of Venezuela: Concepcion, Trillo | .10 | 643 Black and Blue: Vida Blue | .08 |
| 583 George Wright (R) | .15 | 607 Tom Brunansky | .50 | 632 All-Star Infielders: Yount and Bell | .25 | 644 Black and Blue: Bud Black | .08 |
| **CINCINNATI REDS** | | 608 Bobby Castillo | .05 | 633 Mr. Vet & Mr. Rookie: Winfield, Hrbek | .25 | 645 Speed and Power: Reggie Jackson | .35 |
| 584 Johnny Bench | 1.00 | 609 John Castino | .05 | 634 Fountain of Youth: Stargell, Rose | .60 | 646 Speed and Power: Rickey Henderson | 1.00 |
| 585 Bruce Berenyi | .05 | 610 Ron Davis | .05 | 635 Big Chiefs: Harrah, Thornton | .10 | 647 Checklist No. 1 | .08 |
| 586 Larry Biittner | .05 | 611 Lenny Gaetti | .05 | 636 Smith Brothers: Ozzie and Lonnie | .35 | 648 Checklist No. 2 | .08 |
| 587 Cesar Cedeno | .10 | 612 Terry Felton | .12 | 637 Base Stealers' Threat: Diaz and Carter | .10 | 649 Checklist No. 3 | .08 |
| 588 Dave Concepcion | .10 | 613 Gary Gaetti (R) | 1.00 | 638 All-Star Catchers: Fisk, Carter | .15 | 650 Checklist No. 4 | .08 |
| 589 Dan Driessen | .05 | 614 Mickey Hatcher | .05 | 639 The Silver Shoe: Rickey Henderson | 2.00 | 651 Checklist No. 5 | .08 |
| 590 Greg Harris | .05 | 615 Brad Havens | .05 | 640 Home Run Threats: Oglivie, Jackson | .25 | 652 Checklist No. 6 | .08 |
| 591 Ben Hayes | .12 | 616 Kent Hrbek | 1.00 | 641 Two Teams on the Same Day: Joel Youngblood 8/4/82 | .08 | 653 Checklist No. 7 | .08 |
| 592 Paul Householder | .05 | 617 Randy Johnson | .05 | | | 654 Checklist No. 8 | .08 |
| 593 Tom Hume | .05 | 618 Tim Laudner | .05 | | | 655 Checklist No. 9 | .08 |
| 594 Wayne Krenchicki | .05 | 619 Jeff Little | .08 | | | 656 Checklist No. 10 | .08 |
| 595 Rafael Landestoy | .05 | 620 Bob Mitchell | .05 | | | 657 Checklist No. 11 | .08 |
| 596 Charlie Leibrandt | .05 | 621 Jack O'Connor | .05 | | | 658 Checklist No. 12 | .08 |
| 597 Eddie Milner | .10 | 622 John Pacella | .05 | | | 659 Checklist No. 13 | .08 |
| 598 Ron Oester | .05 | 623 Pete Redfern | .05 | | | 660 Checklist No. 14 | .08 |
| 599 Frank Pastore | .05 | 624 Jesus Vega | .12 | | | | |
| 600 Joe Price | .05 | 625 Frank Viola (R) | 4.00 | | | | |
| 601 Tom Seaver | .75 | 626 Ron Washington | .12 | | | | |
| 602 Bob Shirley | .05 | 627 Gary Ward | .05 | | | | |
| 603 Mario Soto | .10 | 628 Al Williams | .05 | | | | |
| 604 Alex Trevino | .05 | **SPECIAL CARDS** | | | | | |
| 605 Mike Vail | .05 | 629 Red Sox All-Stars: Eckersley, Yaz, Clear | .25 | | | | |

# 1984 Fleer . . . Complete Set of 660 Cards—Value $225.00

Features the rookie cards of Don Mattingly, Darryl Strawberry and Kevin McReynolds. For the first time a traded update set was issued.

| NO. PLAYER | MINT | NO. PLAYER | MINT | NO. PLAYER | MINT | NO. PLAYER | MINT |
|---|---|---|---|---|---|---|---|
| **BALTIMORE ORIOLES** | | 33 Von Hayes | .25 | 66 Dennis Lamp | .05 | 98 Greg Brock | .10 |
| 1 Mike Boddicker | .20 | 34 Willie Hernandez | .20 | 67 Rudy Law | .05 | 99 Jack Fimple | .12 |
| 2 Al Bumbry | .05 | 35 Al Holland | .05 | 68 Vance Law | .05 | 100 Pedro Guerrero | .35 |
| 3 Todd Cruz | .05 | 36 Charles Hudson (R) | .20 | 69 Greg Luzinski | .10 | 101 Rick Honeycutt | .05 |
| 4 Rich Dauer | .05 | 37 Joe Lefebvre | .05 | 70 Tom Paciorek | .05 | 102 Burt Hooton | .05 |
| 5 Storm Davis | .10 | 38 Sixto Lezcano | .05 | 71 Mike Squires | .05 | 103 Steve Howe | .05 |
| 6 Rick Dempsey | .05 | 39 Garry Maddox | .05 | 72 Dick Tidrow | .05 | 104 Ken Landreaux | .05 |
| 7 Jim Dwyer | .05 | 40 Gary Matthews | .10 | 73 Greg Walker (R) | .15 | 105 Mike Marshall | .15 |
| 8 Mike Flanagan | .10 | 41 Len Matuszek | .05 | **DETROIT TIGERS** | | 106 Rick Monday | .05 |
| 9 Dan Ford | .05 | 42 Tug McGraw | .10 | 74 Glenn Abbott | .05 | 107 Jose Morales | .05 |
| 10 John Lowenstein | .05 | 43 Joe Morgan | .75 | 75 Howard Bailey | .05 | 108 Tom Niedenfuer | .05 |
| 11 Dennis Martinez | .10 | 44 Tony Perez | .50 | 76 Doug Bair | .05 | 109 Alejandro Pena (R) | .50 |
| 12 Tippy Martinez | .05 | 45 Ron Reed | .05 | 77 Juan Berenguer | .05 | 110 Jerry Reuss | .05 |
| 13 Scott McGregor | .10 | 46 Pete Rose | 1.50 | 78 Tom Brookens | .05 | 111 Bill Russell | .05 |
| 14 Eddie Murray | 2.00 | 47 Juan Samuel (R) | 4.00 | 79 Enos Cabell | .05 | 112 Steve Sax | .40 |
| 15 Joe Nolan | .05 | 48 Mike Schmidt | 7.50 | 80 Kirk Gibson | .75 | 113 Mike Scioscia | .05 |
| 16 Jim Palmer | 1.50 | 49 Ozzie Virgil | .05 | 81 John Grubb | .05 | 114 Derrel Thomas | .05 |
| 17 Cal Ripken, Jr. | 12.00 | **CHICAGO WHITE SOX** | | 82 Larry Herndon | .05 | 115 Fernando Valenzuela | .35 |
| 18 Gary Roenicke | .05 | 50 Juan Agosto | .15 | 83 Wayne Krenchicki | .05 | 116 Bob Welch | .30 |
| 19 Lenn Sakata | .05 | 51 Howard Baines | .50 | 84 Rick Leach | .05 | 117 Steve Yeager | .05 |
| 20 John Shelby (R) | .25 | 52 Floyd Bannister | .10 | 85 Chet Lemon | .10 | 118 Pat Zachry | .05 |
| 21 Ken Singleton | .10 | 53 Salome Barojas | .05 | 86 Aurelio Lopez | .05 | **NEW YORK YANKEES** | |
| 22 Sammy Stewart | .05 | 54 Britt Burns | .05 | 87 Jack Morris | 1.00 | 119 Don Baylor | .10 |
| 23 Tim Stoddard | .05 | 55 Julio Cruz | .05 | 88 Lance Parrish | .35 | 120 Bert Campaneris | .05 |
| **PHILADELPHIA PHILLIES** | | 56 Richard Dotson | .10 | 89 Dan Petry | .15 | 121 Rick Cerone | .05 |
| 24 Marty Bystrom | .05 | 57 Jerry Dybzinski | .05 | 90 Dave Rozema | .05 | 122 Ray Fontenot (R) | .15 |
| 25 Steve Carlton | 1.50 | 58 Carlton Fisk | 2.00 | 91 Alan Trammell | 1.25 | 123 George Frazier | .05 |
| 26 Ivon DeJesus | .05 | 59 Scott Fletcher | .15 | 92 Lou Whitaker | .50 | 124 Oscar Gamble | .05 |
| 27 John Denny | .10 | 60 Jerry Hairston | .05 | 93 Milt Wilcox | .05 | 125 Goose Gossage | .25 |
| 28 Bob Dernier | .05 | 61 Kevin Hickey | .05 | 94 Glenn Wilson | .10 | 126 Ken Griffey | .20 |
| 29 Bo Diaz | .05 | 62 Marc Hill | .05 | 95 John Wockenfuss | .05 | 127 Ron Guidry | .25 |
| 30 Kiko Garcia | .05 | 63 LaMarr Hoyt | .10 | **LOS ANGELES DODGERS** | | 128 Jay Howell | .15 |
| 31 Greg Gross | .05 | 64 Ron Kittle | .15 | 96 Dusty Baker | .10 | 129 Steve Kemp | .05 |
| 32 Kevin Gross (R) | .30 | 65 Jerry Koosman | .15 | 97 Joe Beckwith | .05 | 130 Matt Keough | .05 |

| NO. PLAYER | MINT |
|---|---|
| 131 Don Mattingly (R) | 40.00 |
| 132 John Montefusco | .05 |
| 133 Omar Moreno | .05 |
| 134 Dale Murray | .05 |
| 135 Graig Nettles | .10 |
| 136 Lou Piniella | .10 |
| 137 Willie Randolph | .10 |
| 138 Shane Rawley | .05 |
| 139 Dave Righetti | .15 |
| 140 Andre Robertson | .05 |
| 141 Bob Shirley | .05 |
| 142 Roy Smalley | .05 |
| 143 Dave Winfield | 1.50 |
| 144 Butch Wynegar | .05 |
| **TORONTO BLUE JAYS** | |
| 145 Jim Acker (R) | .15 |
| 146 Doyle Alexander | .10 |
| 147 Jesse Barfield | .25 |
| 148 Jorge Bell | 2.00 |
| 149 Barry Bonnell | .05 |
| 150 Jim Clancy | .05 |
| 151 Dave Collins | .05 |
| 152 Tony Fernandez (R) | 4.00 |
| 153 Damaso Garcia | .10 |
| 154 Dave Geisel | .05 |
| 155 Jim Gott | .15 |
| 156 Alfredo Griffin | .05 |
| 157 Garth Iorg | .05 |
| 158 Roy Lee Jackson | .05 |
| 159 Cliff Johnson | .05 |
| 160 Luis Leal | .05 |
| 161 Buck Martinez | .05 |
| 162 Joey McLaughlin | .05 |
| 163 Randy Moffitt | .05 |
| 164 Lloyd Moseby | .15 |
| 165 Rance Mulliniks | .05 |
| 166 Jorge Orta | .05 |
| 167 Dave Stieb | .35 |
| 168 Willie Upshaw | .15 |
| 169 Ernie Whitt | .05 |
| **ATLANTA BRAVES** | |
| 170 Len Barker | .05 |
| 171 Steve Bedrosian | .15 |
| 172 Bruce Benedict | .05 |
| 173 Brett Butler | .40 |
| 174 Rick Camp | .05 |
| 175 Chris Chambliss | .05 |
| 176 Ken Dayley | .05 |
| 177 Pete Falcone | .05 |
| 178 Terry Forster | .05 |
| 179 Gene Garber | .05 |
| 180 Terry Harper | .05 |
| 181 Bob Horner | .15 |
| 182 Glenn Hubbard | .05 |
| 183 Randy Johnson | .05 |
| 184 Craig McMurtry | .10 |
| 185 Donnie Moore | .05 |
| 186 Dale Murphy | 1.25 |
| 187 Phil Niekro | .50 |
| 188 Pascual Perez | .05 |
| 189 Biff Pocoroba | .05 |
| 190 Rafael Ramirez | .05 |
| 191 Jerry Royster | .05 |
| 192 Claudell Washington | .10 |
| 193 Bob Watson | .05 |
| **MILWAUKEE BREWERS** | |
| 194 Jerry Augustine | .05 |
| 195 Mark Brouhard | .05 |
| 196 Mike Caldwell | .05 |
| 197 Tom Candiotti (R) | .50 |
| 198 Cecil Cooper | .15 |
| 199 Rollie Fingers | .50 |
| 200 Jim Gantner | .05 |
| 201 Bob Gibson | .12 |
| 202 Moose Haas | .05 |
| 203 Roy Howell | .05 |
| 204 Pete Ladd | .05 |
| 205 Rick Manning | .05 |
| 206 Bob McClure | .05 |
| 207 Paul Molitor | .40 |
| 208 Don Money | .05 |
| 209 Charlie Moore | .05 |
| 210 Ben Oglivie | .10 |
| 211 Chuck Porter | .05 |
| 212 Ed Romero | .05 |

| NO. PLAYER | MINT |
|---|---|
| 213 Ted Simmons | .10 |
| 214 Jim Slaton | .05 |
| 215 Don Sutton | .50 |
| 216 Tom Tellmann | .05 |
| 217 Pete Vuckovich | .05 |
| 218 Ned Yost | .05 |
| 219 Robin Yount | 2.50 |
| **HOUSTON ASTROS** | |
| 220 Alan Ashby | .05 |
| 221 Kevin Bass | .20 |
| 222 Jose Cruz | .10 |
| 223 Bill Dawley (R) | .20 |
| 224 Frank DiPino | .05 |
| 225 Bill Doran (R) | .50 |
| 226 Phil Garner | .05 |
| 227 Art Howe | .05 |
| 228 Bob Knepper | .10 |
| 229 Ray Knight | .10 |
| 230 Frank LaCorte | .05 |
| 231 Mike LaCoss | .05 |
| 232 Mike Madden (R) | .15 |
| 233 Jerry Mumphrey | .05 |
| 234 Joe Niekro | .10 |
| 235 Terry Puhl | .05 |
| 236 Luis Pujols | .05 |
| 237 Craig Reynolds | .05 |
| 238 Vern Ruhle | .05 |
| 239 Nolan Ryan | 10.00 |
| 240 Mike Scott | .25 |
| 241 Tony Scott | .05 |
| 242 Dave Smith | .05 |
| 243 Dickie Thon | .08 |
| 244 Denny Walling | .05 |
| **PITTSBURGH PIRATES** | |
| 245 Dale Berra | .05 |
| 246 Jim Bibby | .05 |
| 247 John Candelaria | .05 |
| 248 Jose DeLeon (R) | .35 |
| 249 Mike Easler | .08 |
| 250 Cecilio Guante | .05 |
| 251 Richie Hebner | .05 |
| 252 Lee Lacy | .05 |
| 253 Bill Madlock | .15 |
| 254 Milt May | .05 |
| 255 Lee Mazzilli | .05 |
| 256 Larry McWilliams | .05 |
| 257 Jim Morrison | .05 |
| 258 Dave Parker | .75 |
| 259 Tony Pena | .20 |
| 260 Johnny Ray | .15 |
| 261 Rick Rhoden | .05 |
| 262 Don Robinson | .05 |
| 263 Manny Sarmiento | .05 |
| 264 Rod Scurry | .05 |
| 265 Kent Tekulve | .05 |
| 266 Gene Tenace | .05 |
| 267 Jason Thompson | .10 |
| 268 Lee Tunnell (R) | .15 |
| 269 Marvell Wynne (R) | .15 |
| **MONTREAL EXPOS** | |
| 270 Ray Burris | .05 |
| 271 Gary Carter | .75 |
| 272 Warren Cromartie | .05 |
| 273 Andre Dawson | 2.00 |
| 274 Doug Flynn | .05 |
| 275 Terry Francona | .05 |
| 276 Bill Gullickson | .05 |
| 277 Bob James (R) | .20 |
| 278 Charlie Lea | .05 |
| 279 Bryan Little | .05 |
| 280 Al Oliver | .15 |
| 281 Tim Raines | .75 |
| 282 Bobby Ramos | .05 |
| 283 Jeff Reardon | .50 |
| 284 Steve Rogers | .05 |
| 285 Scott Sanderson | .05 |
| 286 Dan Schatzeder | .05 |
| 287 Bryn Smith | .05 |
| 288 Chris Speier | .05 |
| 289 Manny Trillo | .05 |
| 290 Mike Vail | .05 |
| 291 Tim Wallach | .25 |
| 292 Chris Welsh | .05 |
| 293 Jim Wohlford | .05 |

| NO. PLAYER | MINT |
|---|---|
| **SAN DIEGO PADRES** | |
| 294 Kurt Bevacqua | .05 |
| 295 Juan Bonilla | .05 |
| 296 Bobby Brown | .05 |
| 297 Luis DeLeon | .05 |
| 298 Dave Dravecky | .10 |
| 299 Tim Flannery | .05 |
| 300 Steve Garvey | .50 |
| 301 Tony Gwynn | 8.00 |
| 302 Andy Hawkins (R) | .35 |
| 303 Ruppert Jones | .05 |
| 304 Terry Kennedy | .10 |
| 305 Tim Lollar | .05 |
| 306 Gary Lucas | .05 |
| 307 Kevin McReynolds (R) | 5.00 |
| 308 Sid Monge | .05 |
| 309 Mario Ramirez | .05 |
| 310 Gene Richards | .12 |
| 311 Luis Salazar | .05 |
| 312 Eric Show | .05 |
| 313 Elias Sosa | .05 |
| 314 Garry Templeton | .10 |
| 315 Mark Thurmond (R) | .15 |
| 316 Ed Whitson | .05 |
| 317 Alan Wiggins | .10 |
| **ST. LOUIS CARDINALS** | |
| 318 Neil Allen | .05 |
| 319 Joaquin Andujar | .10 |
| 320 Steve Braun | .05 |
| 321 Glenn Brummer | .05 |
| 322 Bob Forsch | .10 |
| 323 David Green | .05 |
| 324 George Hendrick | .08 |
| 325 Tom Herr | .10 |
| 326 Dane Iorg | .05 |
| 327 Jeff Lahti | .05 |
| 328 Dave LaPoint | .05 |
| 329 Willie McGee | .75 |
| 330 Ken Oberkfell | .05 |
| 331 Darrell Porter | .05 |
| 332 Jamie Quirk | .05 |
| 333 Mike Ramsey | .05 |
| 334 Floyd Rayford | .05 |
| 335 Lonnie Smith | .25 |
| 336 Ozzie Smith | 1.50 |
| 337 John Stuper | .05 |
| 338 Bruce Sutter | .15 |
| 339 Andy Van Slyke (R) | 3.50 |
| 340 Dave Von Ohlen | .12 |
| **KANSAS CITY ROYALS** | |
| 341 Willie Aikens | .05 |
| 342 Mike Armstrong | .05 |
| 343 Bud Black | .15 |
| 344 George Brett | 2.50 |
| 345 Onix Concepcion | .05 |
| 346 Keith Creel | .05 |
| 347 Larry Gura | .05 |
| 348 Don Hood | .05 |
| 349 Dennis Leonard | .05 |
| 350 Hal McRae | .05 |
| 351 Amos Otis | .05 |
| 352 Gaylord Perry | .50 |
| 353 Greg Pryor | .05 |
| 354 Dan Quisenberry | .20 |
| 355 Steve Renko | .05 |
| 356 Leon Roberts | .05 |
| 357 Pat Sheridan (R) | .20 |
| 358 Joe Simpson | .05 |
| 359 Don Slaught | .05 |
| 360 Paul Splittorff | .05 |
| 361 U.L. Washington | .05 |
| 362 John Wathan | .05 |
| 363 Frank White | .05 |
| 364 Willie Wilson | .15 |
| **SAN FRANCISCO GIANTS** | |
| 365 Jim Barr | .05 |
| 366 Dave Bergman | .05 |
| 367 Fred Breining | .05 |
| 368 Bob Brenly | .05 |
| 369 Jack Clark | .30 |
| 370 Chili Davis | .30 |
| 371 Mark Davis | .20 |
| 372 Darrell Evans | .10 |
| 373 Atlee Hammaker | .05 |
| 374 Mike Krukow | .05 |

| NO. PLAYER | MINT |
|---|---|
| 375 Duane Kuiper | .05 |
| 376 Bill Laskey | .05 |
| 377 Gary Lavelle | .05 |
| 378 Johnnie LeMaster | .05 |
| 379 Jeff Leonard | .05 |
| 380 Randy Lerch | .05 |
| 381 Renie Martin | .05 |
| 382 Andy McGaffigan | .05 |
| 383 Greg Minton | .05 |
| 384 Tom O'Malley | .05 |
| 385 Max Venable | .05 |
| 386 Brad Wellman | .05 |
| 387 Joel Youngblood | .12 |
| **BOSTON RED SOX** | |
| 388 Gary Allenson | .05 |
| 389 Luis Aponte | .05 |
| 390 Tony Armas | .15 |
| 391 Doug Bird | .05 |
| 392 Wade Boggs | 9.00 |
| 393 Dennis Boyd (R) | .35 |
| 394 Mike Brown | .12 |
| 395 Mark Clear | .05 |
| 396 Dennis Eckersley | .75 |
| 397 Dwight Evans | .30 |
| 398 Rich Gedman | .10 |
| 399 Glenn Hoffman | .05 |
| 400 Bruce Hurst | .15 |
| 401 John Henry Johnson | .05 |
| 402 Ed Jurak | .12 |
| 403 Rick Miller | .05 |
| 404 Jeff Newman | .05 |
| 405 Reid Nichols | .05 |
| 406 Bob Ojeda | .10 |
| 407 Jerry Remy | .05 |
| 408 Jim Rice | .30 |
| 409 Bob Stanley | .05 |
| 410 Dave Stapleton | .05 |
| 411 John Tudor | .20 |
| 412 Carl Yastrzemski | 1.50 |
| **TEXAS RANGERS** | |
| 413 Buddy Bell | .15 |
| 414 Larry Biittner | .05 |
| 415 John Butcher | .05 |
| 416 Danny Darwin | .05 |
| 417 Bucky Dent | .05 |
| 418 Dave Hostetler | .05 |
| 419 Charlie Hough | .05 |
| 420 Bobby Johnson | .05 |
| 421 Odell Jones | .05 |
| 422 Jon Matlack | .05 |
| 423 Pete O'Brien (R) | .50 |
| 424 Larry Parrish | .05 |
| 425 Mickey Rivers | .10 |
| 426 Billy Sample | .05 |
| 427 Dave Schmidt | .05 |
| 428 Mike Smithson (R) | .15 |
| 429 Bill Stein | .05 |
| 430 Dave Stewart | 1.00 |
| 431 Jim Sundberg | .05 |
| 432 Frank Tanana | .10 |
| 433 Dave Tobik | .05 |
| 434 Wayne Tolleson | .15 |
| 435 George Wright | .05 |
| **OAKLAND A'S** | |
| 436 Bill Almon | .05 |
| 437 Keith Atherton | .12 |
| 438 Dave Beard | .05 |
| 439 Tom Burgmeier | .05 |
| 440 Jeff Burroughs | .05 |
| 441 Chris Codiroli | .10 |
| 442 Tim Conroy | .12 |
| 443 Mike Davis | .10 |
| 444 Wayne Gross | .05 |
| 445 Garry Hancock | .05 |
| 446 Mike Heath | .05 |
| 447 Rickey Henderson | 9.00 |
| 448 Don Hill | .12 |
| 449 Bob Kearney | .05 |
| 450 Bill Krueger | .12 |
| 451 Rick Langford | .05 |
| 452 Carney Lansford | .15 |
| 453 Davey Lopes | .10 |
| 454 Steve McCatty | .05 |
| 455 Dan Meyer | .05 |
| 456 Dwayne Murphy | .05 |

| NO. PLAYER | MINT |
|---|---|
| 457 Mike Norris | .05 |
| 458 Ricky Peters | .05 |
| 459 Tony Phillips | .75 |
| 460 Tom Underwood | .05 |
| 461 Mike Warren (R) | .15 |

**CINCINNATI REDS**

| NO. PLAYER | MINT |
|---|---|
| 462 Johnny Bench | 1.50 |
| 463 Bruce Berenyi | .05 |
| 464 Dann Bilardello | .05 |
| 465 Cesar Cedeno | .05 |
| 466 Dave Concepcion | .10 |
| 467 Dan Driessen | .05 |
| 468 Nick Esasky (R) | .30 |
| 469 Rich Gale | .05 |
| 470 Ben Hayes | .05 |
| 471 Paul Householder | .05 |
| 472 Tom Hume | .05 |
| 473 Alan Knicely | .05 |
| 474 Eddie Milner | .05 |
| 475 Ron Oester | .05 |
| 476 Kelly Paris | .10 |
| 477 Frank Pastore | .05 |
| 478 Ted Power | .05 |
| 479 Joe Price | .05 |
| 480 Charlie Puleo | .05 |
| 481 Gary Redus (R) | .35 |
| 482 Bill Scherrer | .12 |
| 483 Mario Soto | .10 |
| 484 Alex Trevino | .05 |
| 485 Duane Walker | .05 |

**CHICAGO CUBS**

| NO. PLAYER | MINT |
|---|---|
| 486 Larry Bowa | .05 |
| 487 Warren Brusstar | .05 |
| 488 Bill Buckner | .10 |
| 489 Bill Campbell | .05 |
| 490 Ron Cey | .15 |
| 491 Jody Davis | .05 |
| 492 Leon Durham | .50 |
| 493 Mel Hall | .25 |
| 494 Ferguson Jenkins | .60 |
| 495 Jay Johnstone | .05 |
| 496 Craig Lefferts (R) | .40 |
| 497 Carmelo Martinez (R) | .15 |
| 498 Jerry Morales | .05 |
| 499 Keith Moreland | .05 |
| 500 Dickie Noles | .05 |
| 501 Mike Proly | .05 |
| 502 Chuck Rainey | .05 |
| 503 Dick Ruthven | .05 |
| 504 Ryne Sandberg | 15.00 |
| 505 Lee Smith | .50 |
| 506 Steve Trout | .05 |
| 507 Gary Woods | .05 |

**CALIFORNIA ANGELS**

| NO. PLAYER | MINT |
|---|---|
| 508 Juan Beniquez | .05 |
| 509 Bob Boone | .05 |
| 510 Rick Burleson | .10 |
| 511 Rod Carew | 1.50 |
| 512 Bobby Clark | .05 |

| NO. PLAYER | MINT |
|---|---|
| 513 John Curtis | .05 |
| 514 Doug DeCinces | .10 |
| 515 Brian Downing | .05 |
| 516 Tim Foli | .05 |
| 517 Ken Forsch | .05 |
| 518 Bobby Grich | .05 |
| 519 Andy Hassler | .05 |
| 520 Reggie Jackson | 2.00 |
| 521 Ron Jackson | .05 |
| 522 Tommy John | .20 |
| 523 Bruce Kison | .05 |
| 524 Steve Lubratich | .12 |
| 525 Fred Lynn | .25 |
| 526 Gary Pettis (R) | .30 |
| 527 Luis Sanchez | .05 |
| 528 Daryl Sconiers | .10 |
| 529 Ellis Valentine | .05 |
| 530 Rob Wilfong | .05 |
| 531 Mike Witt | .10 |
| 532 Geoff Zahn | .05 |

**CLEVELAND INDIANS**

| NO. PLAYER | MINT |
|---|---|
| 533 Bud Anderson | .05 |
| 534 Chris Bando | .05 |
| 535 Alan Bannister | .05 |
| 536 Bert Blyleven | .30 |
| 537 Tom Brennan | .05 |
| 538 Jamie Easterly | .05 |
| 539 Juan Eichelberger | .05 |
| 540 Jim Essian | .05 |
| 541 Mike Fischlin | .05 |
| 542 Julio Franco | 3.00 |
| 543 Mike Hargrove | .05 |
| 544 Toby Harrah | .05 |
| 545 Ron Hassey | .05 |
| 546 Neal Heaton (R) | .25 |
| 547 Bake McBride | .05 |
| 548 Broderick Perkins | .12 |
| 549 Lary Sorensen | .05 |
| 550 Dan Spillner | .05 |
| 551 Rick Sutcliffe | .25 |
| 552 Pat Tabler | .10 |
| 553 Gorman Thomas | .10 |
| 554 Andre Thornton | .10 |
| 555 George Vukovich | .05 |

**MINNESOTA TWINS**

| NO. PLAYER | MINT |
|---|---|
| 556 Darrell Brown | .05 |
| 557 Tom Brunansky | .25 |
| 558 Randy Bush | .25 |
| 559 Bobby Castillo | .05 |
| 560 John Castino | .05 |
| 561 Ron Davis | .05 |
| 562 Dave Engle | .05 |
| 563 Lenny Faedo | .05 |
| 564 Pete Filson | .12 |
| 565 Gary Gaetti | .30 |
| 566 Mickey Hatcher | .05 |
| 567 Kent Hrbek | .50 |
| 568 Rusty Kuntz | .05 |

| NO. PLAYER | MINT |
|---|---|
| 569 Tim Laudner | .05 |
| 570 Rick Lysander | .12 |
| 571 Bobby Mitchell | .05 |
| 572 Ken Schrom | .05 |
| 573 Ray Smith | .12 |
| 574 Tim Teufel (R) | .30 |
| 575 Frank Viola | 1.25 |
| 576 Gary Ward | .05 |
| 577 Ron Washington | .05 |
| 578 Len Whitehouse | .05 |
| 579 Al Williams | .05 |

**NEW YORK METS**

| NO. PLAYER | MINT |
|---|---|
| 580 Bob Bailor | .05 |
| 581 Mark Bradley | .10 |
| 582 Hubie Brooks | .25 |
| 583 Carlos Diaz | .05 |
| 584 George Foster | .15 |
| 585 Brian Giles | .05 |
| 586 Danny Heep | .05 |
| 587 Keith Hernandez | .30 |
| 588 Ron Hodges | .05 |
| 589 Scott Holman | .05 |
| 590 Dave Kingman | .15 |
| 591 Ed Lynch | .05 |
| 592 Jose Oquendo | .50 |
| 593 Jesse Orosco | .10 |
| 594 Junior Ortiz | .12 |
| 595 Tom Seaver | 3.00 |
| 596 Doug Sisk | .15 |
| 597 Rusty Staub | .10 |
| 598 John Stearns | .05 |
| 599 Darryl Strawberry (R) | 35.00 |
| 600 Craig Swan | .05 |
| 601 Walt Terrell (R) | .30 |
| 602 Mike Torrez | .05 |
| 603 Mookie Wilson | .10 |

**SEATTLE MARINERS**

| NO. PLAYER | MINT |
|---|---|
| 604 Jamie Allen | .12 |
| 605 Jim Beattie | .05 |
| 606 Tony Bernazard | .05 |
| 607 Manny Castillo | .05 |
| 608 Bill Caudill | .05 |
| 609 Bryan Clark | .05 |
| 610 Al Cowens | .05 |
| 611 Dave Henderson | .75 |
| 612 Steve Henderson | .05 |
| 613 Orlando Mercado | .12 |
| 614 Mike Moore | .25 |
| 615 Ricky Nelson | .12 |
| 616 Spike Owen (R) | .30 |
| 617 Pat Putnam | .05 |
| 618 Ron Roenicke | .05 |
| 619 Mike Stanton | .05 |
| 620 Bob Stoddard | .05 |
| 621 Rick Sweet | .05 |
| 622 Roy Thomas | .05 |
| 623 Ed Vande Berg | .05 |
| 624 Matt Young (R) | .15 |

**SPECIAL CARDS**

| NO. PLAYER | MINT |
|---|---|
| 626 Fred Lynn: "All-Star Record Breaker" | .15 |
| 627 Manny Trillo: "All-Star Record Breaker" | .05 |
| 628 Steve Garvey: "NL Iron Man" | .25 |
| 629 Rod Carew: "AL Batting Runner-Up" | .50 |
| 630 Wade Boggs: "AL Batting Champion" | .75 |
| 631 Tim Raines: "Letting Go Of The Raines" | .40 |
| 632 Al Oliver: "Double Trouble" | .15 |
| 633 Steve Sax: "All-Star Second Base" | .10 |
| 634 Dickie Thon: "All-Star Shortstop" | .10 |
| 635 Quisenberry & Martinez: "Ace Fireman" | .10 |
| 636 Perez, Rose, & Morgan "Reds Reunited" | .50 |
| 637 Parrish & Boone: "Backstop Stars" | .10 |
| 638 Brett & Perry: "Pine Tar Incident" | .60 |
| 639 Forsch, Warren & Righetti "1983 No-Hitters" | .10 |
| 640 Bench and Yaz: "Retiring Superstars" | 2.00 |
| 641 Gaylord Perry: "Going Out In Style" | .25 |
| 642 Steve Carlton: 300 Club and Strikeout Record | .40 |
| 643 Altobelli and Owens: "World Series Managers" | .05 |
| 644 Rick Dempsey: "World Series MVP" | .05 |
| 645 Mike Boddicker: "Rookie Winner" | .10 |
| 646 Scott McGregor: "The Clincher" | .10 |
| 647 Checklist No. 1 | .08 |
| 648 Checklist No. 2 | .08 |
| 649 Checklist No. 3 | .08 |
| 650 Checklist No. 4 | .08 |
| 651 Checklist No. 5 | .08 |
| 652 Checklist No. 6 | .08 |
| 653 Checklist No. 7 | .08 |
| 654 Checklist No. 8 | .08 |
| 655 Checklist No. 9 | .08 |
| 656 Checklist No. 10 | .08 |
| 657 Checklist No. 11 | .08 |
| 658 Checklist No. 12 | .08 |
| 659 Checklist No 13 | .08 |
| 660 Checklist No. 14 | .08 |

# 1984 Fleer Traded Update . . . Complete Set of 132 Cards—Value $600.00

This was Fleer's first traded update set. It updates the main 1984 card set with players who had changed teams during the season and rookies. This set features Fleer's first card of Dwight Gooden, Roger Clemens, Bret Saberhagen and Kirby Puckett. Production was extremely limited. The complete set was packaged in its own printed box and distributed exclusively through card hobby dealers.

Card values shown here fluctuate considerably.

| NO. | PLAYER | MINT | NO. | PLAYER | MINT | NO. | PLAYER | MINT | NO. | PLAYER | MINT |
|---|---|---|---|---|---|---|---|---|---|---|---|
| U1 | Willie Aikens | .40 | U34 | Dennis Eckersley | 4.00 | U67 | Frank LaCorte | .35 | U100 | Jeff Robinson | .35 |
| U2 | Luis Aponte | .35 | U35 | Jim Essian | .35 | U68 | Dennis Lamp | .35 | U101 | R. Romanick | .40 |
| U3 | Mark Bailey | .40 | U36 | Darrell Evans | .60 | U69 | Tito Landrum | .20 | U102 | Pete Rose | 15.00 |
| U4 | Bob Bailor | .35 | U37 | Mike Fitzgerald | .40 | U70 | Mark Langston (RR) | 20.00 | U103 | B. Saberhagen (RR) | 35.00 |
| U5 | Dusty Baker | .40 | U38 | Tim Foli | .35 | U71 | Rick Leach | .35 | U104 | Scott Sanderson | .35 |
| U6 | Steve Balboni | .40 | U39 | John Franco (RR) | 8.00 | U72 | Craig Lefferts | .35 | U105 | Dick Schofield | .50 |
| U7 | Alan Bannister | .35 | U40 | George Frazier | .35 | U73 | Gary Lucas | .35 | U106 | Tom Seaver | 20.00 |
| U8 | Marty Barrett (RR) | .60 | U41 | Rich Gale | .35 | U74 | Jerry Martin | .35 | U107 | Jim Slaton | .35 |
| U9 | Dave Beard | .35 | U42 | Barbaro Garbey | .35 | U75 | Carmelo Martinez | .35 | U108 | Mike Smithson | .35 |
| U10 | Joe Beckwith | .35 | U43 | Dwight Gooden (RR) | 125.00 | U76 | Mike Mason | .35 | U109 | Lary Sorensen | .35 |
| U11 | Dave Bergman | .35 | U44 | Goose Gossage | 1.50 | U77 | Gary Matthews | .35 | U110 | Tim Stoddard | .35 |
| U12 | Tony Bernazard | .35 | U45 | Wayne Gross | .35 | U78 | Andy McGaffigan | .35 | U111 | Jeff Stone | .40 |
| U13 | Bruce Bochte | .35 | U46 | Mark Gubicza (RR) | 4.00 | U79 | Joey McLaughlin | .35 | U112 | Champ Summers | .35 |
| U14 | Barry Bonnell | .35 | U47 | Jackie Gutierrez | .50 | U80 | Joe Morgan | 5.00 | U113 | Jim Sundberg | .35 |
| U15 | Phil Bradley (RR) | 1.25 | U48 | Toby Harrah | .35 | U81 | Darryl Motley | .35 | U114 | Rick Sutcliffe | .75 |
| U16 | Fred Breining | .35 | U49 | Ron Hassey | .35 | U82 | Graig Nettles | .50 | U115 | Craig Swan | .35 |
| U17 | Mike Brown | .40 | U50 | Richie Hebner | .35 | U83 | Phil Niekro | 3.00 | U116 | Derrel Thomas | .35 |
| U18 | Bill Buckner | .45 | U51 | Willie Hernandes | .50 | U84 | Ken Oberkfell | .35 | U117 | Gorman Thomas | .40 |
| U19 | Ray Burris | .35 | U52 | Ed Hodge | .40 | U85 | Al Oliver | .40 | U118 | Alex Trevino | .35 |
| U20 | John Butcher | .35 | U53 | Ricky Horton | .40 | U86 | Jorge Orta | .35 | U119 | Manny Trillo | .35 |
| U21 | Brett Butler | 1.50 | U54 | Art Howe | .40 | U87 | Amos Otis | .45 | U120 | John Tudor | .50 |
| U22 | Enos Cabell | .35 | U55 | Dane Iorg | .35 | U88 | Bob Owchinko | .30 | U121 | Tom Underwood | .35 |
| U23 | Bill Campbell | .35 | U56 | Brook Jacoby (RR) | 2.00 | U89 | Dave Parker | 4.00 | U122 | Mike Vail | .35 |
| U24 | Bill Caudill | .35 | U57 | Dion James | .40 | U90 | Jack Perconte | .35 | U123 | Tom Waddell | .40 |
| U25 | Bobby Clark | .35 | U58 | Mike Jeffcoat | .50 | U91 | Tony Perez | 4.00 | U124 | Gary Ward | .35 |
| U26 | Brian Clark | .35 | U59 | Ruppert Jones | .35 | U92 | Gerald Perry | 1.00 | U125 | Terry Whitfield | .35 |
| U27 | R. Clemens (RR) | 250.00 | U60 | Bob Kearney | .35 | U93 | Kirby Puckett (RR) | 200.00 | U126 | Curtis Wilkerson | .40 |
| U28 | Jaime Cocanower | .50 | U61 | Jimmy Key (RR) | 9.00 | U94 | Shane Rawley | .45 | U127 | Frank Williams | .40 |
| U29 | Ron Darling (RR) | 4.00 | U62 | Dave Kingman | .50 | U95 | Floyd Rayford | .35 | U128 | Glenn Wilson | .40 |
| U30 | Alvin Davis (RR) | 9.00 | U63 | B. Komminsk | .50 | U96 | Ron Reed | .35 | U129 | John Wockenfuss | .35 |
| U31 | Bob Dernier | .40 | U64 | Jerry Koosman | .50 | U97 | R.J. Reynolds | 1.00 | U130 | Ned Yost | .35 |
| U32 | Carlos Diaz | .35 | U65 | Wayne Krenchicki | .35 | U98 | Gene Richards | .35 | U131 | Mike Young | .40 |
| U33 | Mike Easler | .35 | U66 | Rusty Kuntz | .35 | U99 | Jose Rijo (RR) | 10.00 | U132 | Checklist | .50 |

# 1985 Fleer . . . Complete Set of 660 Cards—Value $175.00

Features the rookie cards of Dwight Gooden, Roger Clemens, Bret Saberhagen, Eric Davis, Orel Hershiser and Kirby Puckett. The frames on the front of the cards are color coded to the player's team. The back is printed in two shades of black and red ink. A new feature was "Major League Prospect" cards—each featuring two rookies.

| NO. | PLAYER | MINT | NO. | PLAYER | MINT | NO. | PLAYER | MINT | NO. | PLAYER | MINT |
|---|---|---|---|---|---|---|---|---|---|---|---|
| **DETROIT TIGERS** | | | 7 | Barbaro Garbey (R) | .15 | 14 | Rusty Kuntz | .05 | 21 | Dave Rozema | .05 |
| 1 | Doug Bair | .10 | 8 | Kirk Gibson | .40 | 15 | Chet Lemon | .05 | 22 | Bill Scherrer | .05 |
| 2 | Juan Berenguer | .05 | 9 | John Grubb | .05 | 16 | Aurelio Lopez | .05 | 23 | Alan Trammell | .50 |
| 3 | Dave Bergman | .05 | 10 | Willie Hernandez | .15 | 17 | Sid Monge | .05 | 24 | Lou Whitaker | .30 |
| 4 | Tom Brookens | .05 | 11 | Larry Herndon | .05 | 18 | Jack Morris | .50 | 25 | Milt Wilcox | .05 |
| 5 | Marty Castillo | .05 | 12 | Howard Johnson | 2.00 | 19 | Lance Parrish | .20 | **SAN DIEGO PADRES** | | |
| 6 | Darrell Evans | .10 | 13 | Ruppert Jones | .05 | 20 | Dan Petry | .15 | 26 | Curt Bevacqua | .05 |

| NO. | PLAYER | MINT |
|---|---|---|
| 27 | Greg Booker (R) | .10 |
| 28 | Bobby Brown | .05 |
| 29 | Luis DeLeon | .05 |
| 30 | Dave Dravecky | .05 |
| 31 | Tim Flannery | .05 |
| 32 | Steve Garvey | .40 |
| 33 | Goose Gossage | .15 |
| 34 | Tony Gwynn | 4.00 |
| 35 | Greg Harris | .05 |
| 36 | Andy Hawkins | .05 |
| 37 | Terry Kennedy | .05 |
| 38 | Craig Lefferts | .05 |
| 39 | Tim Lollar | .05 |
| 40 | Carmelo Martinez | .05 |
| 41 | Kevin McReynolds | .75 |
| 42 | Graig Nettles | .10 |
| 43 | Luis Salazar | .05 |
| 44 | Eric Show | .05 |
| 45 | Garry Templeton | .12 |
| 46 | Mark Thurmond | .05 |
| 47 | Ed Whitson | .05 |
| 48 | Alan Wiggins | .10 |

**CHICAGO CUBS**

| NO. | PLAYER | MINT |
|---|---|---|
| 49 | Rich Bordi | .05 |
| 50 | Larry Bowa | .10 |
| 51 | Warren Brusster | .05 |
| 52 | Ron Cey | .15 |
| 53 | Henry Cotto (R) | .15 |
| 54 | Jody Davis | .10 |
| 55 | Bob Dernier | .05 |
| 56 | Leon Durham | .15 |
| 57 | Dennis Eckersley | .50 |
| 58 | George Frazier | .05 |
| 59 | Richie Hebner | .05 |
| 60 | Dave Lopes | .10 |
| 61 | Gary Matthews | .10 |
| 62 | Keith Moreland | .05 |
| 63 | Rick Reuschel | .10 |
| 64 | Dick Ruthven | .05 |
| 65 | Ryne Sandberg | 6.00 |
| 66 | Scott Sanderson | .05 |
| 67 | Lee Smith | .35 |
| 68 | Tim Stoddard | .05 |
| 69 | Rick Sutcliffe | .20 |
| 70 | Steve Trout | .05 |
| 71 | Gary Woods | .05 |

**NEW YORK METS**

| NO. | PLAYER | MINT |
|---|---|---|
| 72 | Wally Backman | .05 |
| 73 | Bruce Berenyi | .05 |
| 74 | Hubie Brooks | .10 |
| 75 | Kelvin Chapman (R) | .15 |
| 76 | Ron Darling | .35 |
| 77 | Sid Fernandez | .50 |
| 78 | Mike Fitzgerald | .05 |
| 79 | George Foster | .15 |
| 80 | Brent Gaff | .05 |
| 81 | Ron Gardenhire | .05 |
| 82 | Dwight Gooden (R) | 12.00 |
| 83 | Tom Gorman | .05 |
| 84 | Danny Heep | .05 |
| 85 | Keith Hernandez | .30 |
| 86 | Ray Knight | .10 |
| 87 | Ed Lynch | .05 |
| 88 | Jose Oquendo | .12 |
| 89 | Jesse Orosco | .10 |
| 90 | Rafael Santana (R) | .20 |
| 91 | Doug Sisk | .05 |
| 92 | Rusty Staub | .10 |
| 93 | Darryl Strawberry | 10.00 |
| 94 | Walt Terrell | .05 |
| 95 | Mookie Wilson | .05 |

**TORONTO BLUE JAYS**

| NO. | PLAYER | MINT |
|---|---|---|
| 96 | Jim Acker | .05 |
| 97 | Willie Aikens | .05 |
| 98 | Doyle Alexander | .05 |
| 99 | Jesse Barfield | .25 |
| 100 | George Bell | .75 |
| 101 | Jim Clancy | .05 |
| 102 | Dave Collins | .05 |
| 103 | Tony Fernandez | .75 |
| 104 | Damaso Garcia | .10 |
| 105 | Jim Gott | .05 |
| 106 | Alfredo Griffin | .05 |
| 107 | Garth Iorg | .05 |
| 108 | Roy Lee Jackson | .05 |
| 109 | Cliff Johnson | .05 |

| NO. | PLAYER | MINT |
|---|---|---|
| 110 | Jimmy Key (R) | 1.50 |
| 111 | Dennis Lamp | .05 |
| 112 | Rick Leach | .05 |
| 113 | Luis Leal | .05 |
| 114 | Buck Martinez | .05 |
| 115 | Lloyd Moseby | .15 |
| 116 | Rance Mulliniks | .05 |
| 117 | Dave Stieb | .15 |
| 118 | Willie Upshaw | .10 |
| 119 | Ernie Whitt | .05 |

**NEW YORK YANKEES**

| NO. | PLAYER | MINT |
|---|---|---|
| 120 | Mike Armstrong | .05 |
| 121 | Don Baylor | .10 |
| 122 | Marty Bystrom | .05 |
| 123 | Rick Cerone | .05 |
| 124 | Joe Cowley | .05 |
| 125 | Brian Dayett | .05 |
| 126 | Tim Foli | .05 |
| 127 | Ray Fontenot | .05 |
| 128 | Ken Griffey | .20 |
| 129 | Ron Guidry | .20 |
| 130 | Toby Harrah | .05 |
| 131 | Jay Howell | .05 |
| 132 | Steve Kemp | .05 |
| 133 | Don Mattingly | 12.00 |
| 134 | Bobby Meacham | .05 |
| 135 | John Montefusco | .05 |
| 136 | Omar Moreno | .05 |
| 137 | Dale Murray | .05 |
| 138 | Phil Niekro | .30 |
| 139 | Mike Pagliarulo (R) | .50 |
| 140 | Willie Randolph | .05 |
| 141 | Dennis Rasmussen | .15 |
| 142 | Dave Righetti | .15 |
| 143 | Jose Rijo (R) | 2.00 |
| 144 | Andre Robertson | .05 |
| 145 | Bob Shirley | .05 |
| 146 | Dave Winfield | .75 |
| 147 | Butch Wynegar | .05 |

**BOSTON RED SOX**

| NO. | PLAYER | MINT |
|---|---|---|
| 148 | Gary Allenson | .05 |
| 149 | Tony Armas | .10 |
| 150 | Marty Barrett | .15 |
| 151 | Wade Boggs | 5.00 |
| 152 | Dennis Boyd | .10 |
| 153 | Bill Buckner | .10 |
| 154 | Mark Clear | .05 |
| 155 | Roger Clemens (R) | 35.00 |
| 156 | Steve Crawford | .05 |
| 157 | Mike Easler | .05 |
| 158 | Dwight Evans | .25 |
| 159 | Rich Gedman | .10 |
| 160 | Jackie Gutierrez (R) | .15 |
| 161 | Bruce Hurst | .15 |
| 162 | John H. Johnson | .05 |
| 163 | Rick Miller | .05 |
| 164 | Reid Nichols | .05 |
| 165 | Al Nipper (R) | .15 |
| 166 | Bob Ojeda | .10 |
| 167 | Jerry Remy | .05 |
| 168 | Jim Rice | .30 |
| 169 | Bob Stanley | .05 |

**BALTIMORE ORIOLES**

| NO. | PLAYER | MINT |
|---|---|---|
| 170 | Mike Boddicker | .10 |
| 171 | Al Bumbry | .05 |
| 172 | Todd Cruz | .05 |
| 173 | Rich Dauer | .05 |
| 174 | Storm Davis | .05 |
| 175 | Rick Dempsey | .05 |
| 176 | Jim Dwyer | .05 |
| 177 | Mike Flanagan | .05 |
| 178 | Dan Ford | .05 |
| 179 | Wayne Gross | .05 |
| 180 | John Lowenstein | .05 |
| 181 | Dennis Martinez | .10 |
| 182 | Tippy Martinez | .05 |
| 183 | Scott McGregor | .05 |
| 184 | Eddie Murray | 1.00 |
| 185 | Joe Nolan | .05 |
| 186 | Floyd Rayford | .05 |
| 187 | Cal Ripken, Jr. | 5.00 |
| 188 | Gary Roenicke | .05 |
| 189 | Lenn Sakata | .05 |
| 190 | John Shelby | .05 |
| 191 | Ken Singleton | .05 |

| NO. | PLAYER | MINT |
|---|---|---|
| 192 | Sammy Stewart | .05 |
| 193 | Bill Swaggerty (R) | .15 |
| 194 | Tom Underwood | .05 |
| 195 | Mike Young | .10 |

**KANSAS CITY ROYALS**

| NO. | PLAYER | MINT |
|---|---|---|
| 196 | Steve Balboni | .10 |
| 197 | Joe Beckwith | .05 |
| 198 | Bud Black | .05 |
| 199 | George Brett | 1.00 |
| 200 | Onix Concepcion | .05 |
| 201 | Mark Gubicza (R) | .75 |
| 202 | Larry Gura | .05 |
| 203 | Mark Huismann | .05 |
| 204 | Dane Iorg | .05 |
| 205 | Danny Jackson | .30 |
| 206 | Charlie Leibrandt | .05 |
| 207 | Hal McRae | .05 |
| 208 | Darryl Motley | .05 |
| 209 | Jorge Orta | .05 |
| 210 | Greg Pryor | .05 |
| 211 | Dan Quisenberry | .15 |
| 212 | Bret Saberhagen (R) | 6.00 |
| 213 | Pat Sheridan | .05 |
| 214 | Don Slaught | .05 |
| 215 | U.L. Washington | .05 |
| 216 | John Wathan | .05 |
| 217 | Frank White | .05 |
| 218 | Willie Wilson | .15 |

**ST. LOUIS CARDINALS**

| NO. | PLAYER | MINT |
|---|---|---|
| 219 | Neil Allen | .05 |
| 220 | Joaquin Andujar | .10 |
| 221 | Steve Braun | .05 |
| 222 | Danny Cox | .05 |
| 223 | Bob Forsch | .10 |
| 224 | David Green | .05 |
| 225 | George Hendrick | .08 |
| 226 | Tom Herr | .10 |
| 227 | Ricky Horton (R) | .15 |
| 228 | Art Howe | .05 |
| 229 | Mike Jorgensen | .05 |
| 230 | Kurt Kepshire (R) | .15 |
| 231 | Jeff Lahti | .05 |
| 232 | Tito Landrum | .05 |
| 233 | Dave LaPoint | .05 |
| 234 | Willie McGee | .50 |
| 235 | Tom Nieto (R) | .15 |
| 236 | Terry Pendleton (R) | 4.00 |
| 237 | Darrell Porter | .05 |
| 238 | Dave Rucker | .05 |
| 239 | Lonnie Smith | .12 |
| 240 | Ozzie Smith | 1.00 |
| 241 | Bruce Sutter | .15 |
| 242 | Andy Van Slyke | .75 |
| 243 | Dave Von Ohlen | .05 |

**PHILADELPHIA PHILLIES**

| NO. | PLAYER | MINT |
|---|---|---|
| 244 | Larry Andersen | .05 |
| 245 | Bill Campbell | .05 |
| 246 | Steve Carlton | .75 |
| 247 | Tim Corcoran | .05 |
| 248 | Ivan DeJesus | .05 |
| 249 | John Denny | .05 |
| 250 | Bo Diaz | .05 |
| 251 | Greg Gross | .05 |
| 252 | Kevin Gross | .05 |
| 253 | Von Hayes | .15 |
| 254 | Al Holland | .05 |
| 255 | Charles Hudson | .05 |
| 256 | Jerry Koosman | .10 |
| 257 | Joe Lefebvre | .05 |
| 258 | Sixto Lezcano | .05 |
| 259 | Garry Maddox | .05 |
| 260 | Len Matuszek | .05 |
| 261 | Tug McGraw | .10 |
| 262 | Al Oliver | .10 |
| 263 | Shane Rawley | .05 |
| 264 | Juan Samuel | .50 |
| 265 | Mike Schmidt | 3.00 |
| 266 | Jeff Stone (R) | .20 |
| 267 | Ozzie Virgil | .05 |
| 268 | Glenn Wilson | .10 |
| 269 | John Wockenfuss | .05 |

**MINNESOTA TWINS**

| NO. | PLAYER | MINT |
|---|---|---|
| 270 | Darrell Brown | .05 |
| 271 | Tom Brunansky | .20 |
| 272 | Randy Bush | .05 |

| NO. | PLAYER | MINT |
|---|---|---|
| 273 | John Butcher | .05 |
| 274 | Bobby Castillo | .05 |
| 275 | Ron Davis | .05 |
| 276 | Dave Engle | .05 |
| 277 | Pete Filson | .05 |
| 278 | Gary Gaetti | .20 |
| 279 | Mickey Hatcher | .05 |
| 280 | Ed Hodge (R) | .15 |
| 281 | Kent Hrbek | .35 |
| 282 | Houston Jimenez | .05 |
| 283 | Tim Laudner | .05 |
| 284 | Rick Lysander | .05 |
| 285 | Dave Meier (R) | .15 |
| 286 | Kirby Puckett (R) | 25.00 |
| 287 | Pat Putnam | .05 |
| 288 | Ken Schrom | .05 |
| 289 | Mike Smithson | .05 |
| 290 | Tim Teufel | .05 |
| 291 | Frank Viola | .50 |
| 292 | Ron Washington | .05 |

**CALIFORNIA ANGELS**

| NO. | PLAYER | MINT |
|---|---|---|
| 293 | Don Aase | .05 |
| 294 | Juan Beniquez | .05 |
| 295 | Bob Boone | .05 |
| 296 | Mike Brown | .05 |
| 297 | Rod Carew | .75 |
| 298 | Doug Corbett | .05 |
| 299 | Doug DeCinces | .05 |
| 300 | Brian Downing | .10 |
| 301 | Ken Forsch | .05 |
| 302 | Bobby Grich | .05 |
| 303 | Reggie Jackson | 1.00 |
| 304 | Tommy John | .15 |
| 305 | Curt Kaufman (R) | .15 |
| 306 | Bruce Kison | .05 |
| 307 | Fred Lynn | .15 |
| 308 | Gary Pettis | .10 |
| 309 | Ron Romanick (R) | .20 |
| 310 | Luis Sanchez | .05 |
| 311 | Dick Schofield | .15 |
| 312 | Daryl Sconiers | .05 |
| 313 | Jim Slaton | .05 |
| 314 | Derrel Thomas | .05 |
| 315 | Rob Wilfong | .05 |
| 316 | Mike Witt | .10 |
| 317 | Geoff Zahn | .05 |

**ATLANTA BRAVES**

| NO. | PLAYER | MINT |
|---|---|---|
| 318 | Len Barker | .05 |
| 319 | Steve Bedrosian | .10 |
| 320 | Bruce Benedict | .05 |
| 321 | Rick Camp | .05 |
| 322 | Chris Chambliss | .10 |
| 323 | Jeff Dedmon (R) | .10 |
| 324 | Terry Forster | .05 |
| 325 | Gene Garber | .05 |
| 326 | Albert Hall (R) | .15 |
| 327 | Terry Harper | .05 |
| 328 | Bob Horner | .15 |
| 329 | Glenn Hubbard | .05 |
| 330 | Randy Johnson | .05 |
| 331 | Brad Komminsk | .05 |
| 332 | Rick Mahler | .05 |
| 333 | Craig McMurtry | .05 |
| 334 | Donnie Moore | .05 |
| 335 | Dale Murphy | .60 |
| 336 | Ken Oberkfell | .05 |
| 337 | Pascual Perez | .05 |
| 338 | Gerald Perry | .15 |
| 339 | Rafael Ramirez | .05 |
| 340 | Jerry Royster | .05 |
| 341 | Alex Trevino | .05 |
| 342 | Claudell Washington | .08 |

**HOUSTON ASTROS**

| NO. | PLAYER | MINT |
|---|---|---|
| 343 | Alan Ashby | .05 |
| 344 | Mark Bailey | .10 |
| 345 | Kevin Bass | .10 |
| 346 | Enos Cabell | .05 |
| 347 | Jose Cruz | .10 |
| 348 | Bill Dawley | .05 |
| 349 | Frank DiPino | .05 |
| 350 | Bill Doran | .05 |
| 351 | Phil Garner | .05 |
| 352 | Bob Knepper | .10 |
| 353 | Mike LaCoss | .05 |
| 354 | Jerry Mumphrey | .05 |
| 355 | Joe Niekro | .10 |

| NO. | PLAYER | MINT |
|---|---|---|
| 356 | Terry Puhl | .05 |
| 357 | Craig Reynolds | .05 |
| 358 | Vern Ruhle | .05 |
| 359 | Nolan Ryan | 6.00 |
| 360 | Joe Sambito | .05 |
| 361 | Mike Scott | .25 |
| 362 | Dave Smith | .05 |
| 363 | Julio Solano (R) | .10 |
| 364 | Dickie Thon | .05 |
| 365 | Denny Walling | .05 |

**LOS ANGELES DODGERS**

| NO. | PLAYER | MINT |
|---|---|---|
| 366 | Dave Anderson | .05 |
| 367 | Bob Bailor | .05 |
| 368 | Greg Brock | .05 |
| 369 | Carlos Diaz | .05 |
| 370 | Pedro Guerrero | .25 |
| 371 | Orel Hershiser (R) | 5.00 |
| 372 | Rick Honeycutt | .05 |
| 373 | Burt Hooton | .05 |
| 374 | Ken Howell (R) | .20 |
| 375 | Ken Landreaux | .05 |
| 376 | Candy Maldonado | .20 |
| 377 | Mike Marshall | .10 |
| 378 | Tom Niedenfuer | .05 |
| 379 | Alejandro Pena | .05 |
| 380 | Jerry Reuss | .10 |
| 381 | R.J. Reynolds (R) | .20 |
| 382 | German Rivera (R) | .15 |
| 383 | Bill Russell | .05 |
| 384 | Steve Sax | .35 |
| 385 | Mike Scioscia | .05 |
| 386 | Franklin Stubbs (R) | .50 |
| 387 | Fernando Valenzuela | .25 |
| 388 | Bob Welch | .20 |
| 389 | Terry Whitfield | .05 |
| 390 | Steve Yeager | .05 |
| 391 | Pat Zachry | .05 |

**MONTREAL EXPOS**

| NO. | PLAYER | MINT |
|---|---|---|
| 392 | Fred Breining | .05 |
| 393 | Gary Carter | .35 |
| 394 | Andre Dawson | .75 |
| 395 | Miguel Dilone | .05 |
| 396 | Dan Driessen | .05 |
| 397 | Doug Flynn | .05 |
| 398 | Terry Francona | .05 |
| 399 | Bill Gullickson | .05 |
| 400 | Bob James | .05 |
| 401 | Chrlie Lea | .05 |
| 402 | Bryan Little | .05 |
| 403 | Gary Lucas | .05 |
| 404 | David Palmer | .05 |
| 405 | Tim Raines | .50 |
| 406 | Mike Ramsey | .05 |
| 407 | Jeff Reardon | .30 |
| 408 | Steve Rogers | .05 |
| 409 | Dan Schatzeder | .05 |
| 410 | Bryn Smith | .05 |
| 411 | Mike Stenhouse | .05 |
| 412 | Tim Wallach | .12 |
| 413 | Jim Wohlford | .05 |

**OAKLAND A'S**

| NO. | PLAYER | MINT |
|---|---|---|
| 414 | Bill Almon | .05 |
| 415 | Keith Atherton | .05 |
| 416 | Bruce Bochte | .05 |
| 417 | Tom Burgmeier | .05 |
| 418 | Ray Burris | .05 |
| 419 | Bill Caudill | .05 |
| 420 | Chris Codiroli | .05 |
| 421 | Tim Conroy | .05 |
| 422 | Mike Davis | .05 |
| 423 | Jim Essian | .05 |
| 424 | Mike Heath | .05 |
| 425 | Rickey Henderson | 4.00 |
| 426 | Donnie Hill | .05 |
| 427 | Dave Kingman | .10 |
| 428 | Bill Krueger | .05 |
| 429 | Carney Lansford | .10 |
| 430 | Steve McCatty | .05 |
| 431 | Joe Morgan | .35 |
| 432 | Dwayne Murphy | .05 |
| 433 | Tony Phillips | .05 |
| 434 | Lary Sorensen | .05 |
| 435 | Mike Warren | .05 |
| 436 | Curt Young (R) | .20 |

**CLEVELAND INDIANS**

| NO. | PLAYER | MINT |
|---|---|---|
| 437 | Luis Aponte | .05 |
| 438 | Chris Bando | .05 |
| 439 | Tony Bernazard | .05 |
| 440 | Bert Blyleven | .25 |
| 441 | Brett Butler | .30 |
| 442 | Ernie Camacho | .05 |
| 443 | Joe Carter | 6.00 |
| 444 | Carmelo Castillo | .05 |
| 445 | Jamie Easterly | .05 |
| 446 | Steve Farr (R) | .30 |
| 447 | Mike Fischlin | .05 |
| 448 | Julio Franco | 1.00 |
| 449 | Mel Hall | .25 |
| 450 | Mike Hargrove | .05 |
| 451 | Neal Heaton | .05 |
| 452 | Brook Jacoby | .20 |
| 453 | Mike Jeffcoat | .05 |
| 454 | Don Schulze (R) | .15 |
| 455 | Roy Smith (R) | .15 |
| 456 | Pat Tabler | .05 |
| 457 | Andre Thornton | .05 |
| 458 | George Vukovich | .05 |
| 459 | Tom Waddell (R) | .15 |
| 460 | Jerry Willard | .05 |

**PITTSBURGH PIRATES**

| NO. | PLAYER | MINT |
|---|---|---|
| 461 | Dale Berra | .05 |
| 462 | John Candelaria | .10 |
| 463 | Jose DeLeon | .05 |
| 464 | Doug Frobel | .05 |
| 465 | Cecilio Guante | .05 |
| 466 | Brian Harper | .30 |
| 467 | Lee Lacy | .05 |
| 468 | Bill Madlock | .10 |
| 469 | Lee Mazzilli | .05 |
| 470 | Larry McWilliams | .05 |
| 471 | Jim Morrison | .05 |
| 472 | Tony Pena | .10 |
| 473 | Johnny Ray | .10 |
| 474 | Rick Rhoden | .10 |
| 475 | Don Robinson | .05 |
| 476 | Rod Scurry | .05 |
| 477 | Kent Tekulve | .05 |
| 478 | Jason Thompson | .05 |
| 479 | John Tudor | .10 |
| 480 | Lee Tunnell | .05 |
| 481 | Marvell Wynne | .05 |

**SEATTLE MARINERS**

| NO. | PLAYER | MINT |
|---|---|---|
| 482 | Salome Barojas | .05 |
| 483 | Dave Beard | .05 |
| 484 | Jim Beattie | .05 |
| 485 | Barry Bonnell | .05 |
| 486 | Phil Bradley (R) | .35 |
| 487 | Al Cowens | .05 |
| 488 | Alvin Davis (R) | 2.00 |
| 489 | Dave Henderson | .40 |
| 490 | Steve Henderson | .05 |
| 491 | Bob Kearney | .05 |
| 492 | Mark Langston (R) | 4.00 |
| 493 | Larry Milbourne | .05 |
| 494 | Paul Mirabella | .05 |
| 495 | Mike Moore | .05 |
| 496 | Edwin Nunez | .05 |
| 497 | Spike Owen | .05 |
| 498 | Jack Perconte | .05 |
| 499 | Ken Phelps | .05 |
| 500 | Jim Presley (R) | .25 |
| 501 | Mike Stanton | .05 |
| 502 | Bob Stoddard | .05 |
| 503 | Gorman Thomas | .10 |
| 504 | Ed VandeBerg | .05 |
| 505 | Matt Young | .05 |

**CHICAGO WHITE SOX**

| NO. | PLAYER | MINT |
|---|---|---|
| 506 | Juan Agosto | .05 |
| 507 | Harold Baines | .30 |
| 508 | Floyd Bannister | .10 |
| 509 | Britt Burns | .05 |
| 510 | Julio Cruz | .05 |
| 511 | Richard Dotson | .05 |
| 512 | Jerry Dybzinski | .05 |
| 513 | Carlton Fisk | 1.00 |
| 514 | Scott Fletcher | .05 |
| 515 | Jerry Hairston | .05 |
| 516 | Marc Hill | .05 |
| 517 | LaMarr Hoyt | .10 |
| 518 | Ron Kittle | .15 |

| NO. | PLAYER | MINT |
|---|---|---|
| 519 | Rudy Law | .05 |
| 520 | Vance Law | .05 |
| 521 | Greg Luzinski | .10 |
| 522 | Gene Nelson | .05 |
| 523 | Tom Paciorek | .05 |
| 524 | Ron Reed | .05 |
| 525 | Bert Roberge | .05 |
| 526 | Tom Seaver | .75 |
| 527 | Roy Smalley | .05 |
| 528 | Dan Spillner | .05 |
| 529 | Mike Squires | .05 |
| 530 | Greg Walker | .10 |

**CINCINNATI REDS**

| NO. | PLAYER | MINT |
|---|---|---|
| 531 | Cesar Cedeno | .10 |
| 532 | Dave Concepcion | .10 |
| 533 | Eric Davis (R) | 12.00 |
| 534 | Nick Esasky | .15 |
| 535 | Tom Foley | .05 |
| 536 | John Franco (R) | 1.50 |
| 537 | Brad Guden | .05 |
| 538 | Tom Hume | .05 |
| 539 | Wayne Krenchicki | .05 |
| 540 | Andy McGaffigan | .05 |
| 541 | Eddie Milner | .05 |
| 542 | Ron Oester | .05 |
| 543 | Bob Owchinko | .05 |
| 544 | Dave Parker | .35 |
| 545 | Frank Pastore | .05 |
| 546 | Tony Perez | .25 |
| 547 | Ted Power | .05 |
| 548 | Joe Price | .05 |
| 549 | Gary Redus | .05 |
| 550 | Pete Rose | 1.00 |
| 551 | Jeff Russell | .20 |
| 552 | Mario Soto | .10 |
| 553 | Jay Tibbs (R) | .20 |
| 554 | Duane Walker | .05 |

**TEXAS RANGERS**

| NO. | PLAYER | MINT |
|---|---|---|
| 555 | Alan Bannister | .05 |
| 556 | Buddy Bell | .10 |
| 557 | Danny Darwin | .05 |
| 558 | Charlie Hough | .05 |
| 559 | Bobby Jones | .05 |
| 560 | Odell Jones | .05 |
| 561 | Jeff Kunkel (R) | .15 |
| 562 | Mike Mason (R) | .15 |
| 563 | Pete O'Brien | .10 |
| 564 | Larry Parrish | .05 |
| 565 | Mickey Rivers | .10 |
| 566 | Billy Sample | .05 |
| 567 | Dave Schmidt | .05 |
| 568 | Donnie Scott (R) | .15 |
| 569 | Dave Stewart | .40 |
| 570 | Frank Tanana | .10 |
| 571 | Wayne Tolleson | .05 |
| 572 | Gary Ward | .05 |
| 573 | Curtis Wilkerson | .05 |
| 574 | George Wright | .05 |
| 575 | Ned Yost | .05 |

**MILWAUKEE BREWERS**

| NO. | PLAYER | MINT |
|---|---|---|
| 576 | Mark Brouhard | .05 |
| 577 | Mike Caldwell | .05 |
| 578 | Bobby Clark | .05 |
| 579 | Jaime Cocanower (R) | .15 |
| 580 | Cecil Cooper | .10 |
| 581 | Rollie Fingers | .30 |
| 582 | Jim Gantner | .05 |
| 583 | Moose Haas | .05 |
| 584 | Dion James | .15 |
| 585 | Pete Ladd | .05 |
| 586 | Rick Manning | .05 |
| 587 | Bob McClure | .05 |
| 588 | Paul Molitor | .35 |
| 589 | Charlie Moore | .05 |
| 590 | Ben Oglivie | .05 |
| 591 | Chuck Porter | .05 |
| 592 | Randy Ready (R) | .15 |
| 593 | Ed Romero | .05 |
| 594 | Bill Schroeder | .05 |
| 595 | Ray Searage | .05 |
| 596 | Ted Simmons | .10 |
| 597 | Jim Sundberg | .05 |
| 598 | Don Sutton | .30 |
| 599 | Tom Tellmann | .05 |
| 600 | Rick Waits | .05 |

| NO. | PLAYER | MINT |
|---|---|---|
| 601 | Robin Yount | 1.00 |

**SAN FRANCISCO GIANTS**

| NO. | PLAYER | MINT |
|---|---|---|
| 602 | Dusty Baker | .05 |
| 603 | Bob Brenly | .05 |
| 604 | Jack Clark | .25 |
| 605 | Chili Davis | .15 |
| 606 | Mark Davis | .20 |
| 607 | Dan Gladden (R) | .50 |
| 608 | Atlee Hammaker | .05 |
| 609 | Mike Krukow | .05 |
| 610 | Duane Kuiper | .05 |
| 611 | Bob Lacey | .05 |
| 612 | Bill Laskey | .05 |
| 613 | Gary Lavelle | .05 |
| 614 | Johnnie LeMaster | .05 |
| 615 | Jeff Leonard | .15 |
| 616 | Randy Lerch | .05 |
| 617 | Greg Minton | .05 |
| 618 | Steve Nicosia | .05 |
| 619 | Gene Richards | .05 |
| 620 | Jeff Robinson (R) | .20 |
| 621 | Scot Thompson | .05 |
| 622 | Manny Trillo | .05 |
| 623 | Brad Wellman | .05 |
| 624 | Frank Williams (R) | .15 |
| 625 | Joel Youngblood | .05 |

**SPECIAL CARDS**

| NO. | PLAYER | MINT |
|---|---|---|
| 626 | Ripken-In-Action | 2.00 |
| 627 | Schmidt-In-Action | .75 |
| 628 | Giving The Signs: Sparky Anderson | .05 |
| 629 | AL Pitcher's Nightmare: Henderson & Winfield | .75 |
| 630 | NL Pitcher's Nightmare: Schmidt & Sandberg | 1.00 |
| 631 | NL All-Stars: Strawberry, Carter, Garvey, Smith | .75 |
| 632 | All-Star Game Winning Battery: Carter, Lea | .10 |
| 633 | NL Pennant Clinchers: Garvey, Gossage | .15 |
| 634 | NL Rookie Phenoms: Samuel, Gooden | 1.00 |
| 635 | Toronto's Big Guns: Willie Upshaw | .10 |
| 636 | Toronto's Big Guns: Lloyd Moseby | .25 |
| 637 | Al Holland | .10 |
| 638 | Lee Tunnell | .10 |
| 639 | 500th Homer: Reggie Jackson | .35 |
| 640 | 4,000th Hit: Pete Rose | .50 |
| 641 | Father and Son: Cal Ripken & Cal, Jr. | 1.25 |
| 642 | Cubs: Division Champs | .05 |
| 643 | Two Perfect Games and One No-Hitter: Witt, Palmer, Morris | .10 |
| 644 | Willie Lozado (R), Vic Mata (R) | .15 |
| 645 | Kelly Gruber (R), Randy O'Neal (R) | 9.00 |
| 646 | Jose Roman (R), Joel Skinner (R) | .20 |
| 647 | Steve Kiefer (R), Danny Tartabull (R) | 6.00 |
| 648 | Rob Deer (R), Alejandro Sanchez (R) | 1.50 |
| 649 | Bill Hatcher (R), Shawon Dunston (R) | 6.00 |
| 650 | Ron Robinson (R), Mike Bielecki (R) | .50 |
| 651 | Zane Smith (R), Paul Zuvella (R) | 1.00 |
| 652 | Joe Hesketh (R), Glenn Davis (R) | 10.00 |
| 653 | John Russell (R), Steve Jeltz (R) | .20 |
| 654 | Checklist No. 1 | .08 |
| 655 | Checklist No. 2 | .08 |
| 656 | Checklist No. 3 | .08 |
| 657 | Checklist No. 4 | .08 |
| 658 | Checklist No. 5 | .08 |
| 659 | Checklist No. 6 | .08 |
| 660 | Checklist No. 7 | .08 |

# 1985 Fleer Traded Update . . . Complete Set of 132 Cards—Value $35.00

This set updates the main 1985 card with players who had changed teams during the season, and rookies. This set features Fleer's first card of Vince Coleman, Tom Browning and Teddy Higuera. The set was packaged in a printed box and distributed exclusively through card hobby dealers.

| NO. | PLAYER | MINT |
|---|---|---|
| U1 | Don Aase | .15 |
| U2 | Bill Almon | .07 |
| U3 | Dusty Baker | .10 |
| U4 | Dale Berra | .07 |
| U5 | Karl Best | .15 |
| U6 | Tim Birtsas | .15 |
| U7 | Vida Blue | .07 |
| U8 | Rich Bordi | .07 |
| U9 | Daryl Boston | .30 |
| U10 | Hubie Brooks | .25 |
| U11 | Chris Brown | .15 |
| U12 | T. Browning | 1.00 |
| U13 | Al Bumbry | .07 |
| U14 | Tim Burke | .50 |
| U15 | Ray Burris | .07 |
| U16 | Jeff Burroughs | .07 |
| U17 | Ivan Calderon (RR) | 2.50 |
| U18 | Jeff Calhoun | .15 |
| U19 | Bill Campbell | .07 |
| U20 | Don Carman | .20 |
| U21 | Gary Carter | .60 |
| U22 | Bobby Castillo | .07 |
| U23 | Bill Caudill | .07 |
| U24 | Rick Cerone | .07 |
| U25 | Jack Clark | .40 |
| U26 | Pat Clement | .15 |
| U27 | Stewart Cliburn | .15 |
| U28 | V. Coleman (RR) | 10.00 |
| U29 | Dave Collins | .07 |
| U30 | Fritz Connally | .15 |
| U31 | Henry Cotto | .07 |
| U32 | Danny Darwin | .07 |
| U33 | Darren Daulton | .40 |

| NO. | PLAYER | MINT |
|---|---|---|
| U34 | Jerry Davis | .15 |
| U35 | Brian Dayett | .15 |
| U36 | Ken Dixon | .20 |
| U37 | Tommy Dunbar | .20 |
| U38 | M. Duncan | .75 |
| U39 | Bob Fallon | .15 |
| U40 | Brian Fisher | .15 |
| U41 | Mike Fitzgerald | .07 |
| U42 | Ray Fontenot | .07 |
| U43 | Greg Gagne | .35 |
| U44 | Oscar Gamble | .07 |
| U45 | Jim Gott | .07 |
| U46 | David Green | .07 |
| U47 | Alfredo Griffin | .07 |
| U48 | Ozzie Guillen (RR) | 2.00 |
| U49 | Toby Harrah | .07 |
| U50 | Ron Hassey | .07 |
| U51 | Rickey Hendersen | 4.00 |
| U52 | Steve Henderson | .07 |
| U53 | George Hendrick | .07 |
| U54 | Teddy Higuera (RR) | .75 |
| U55 | Al Holland | .07 |
| U56 | Burt Hooton | .07 |
| U57 | Jay Howell | .15 |
| U58 | LaMarr Hoyt | .12 |
| U59 | Tim Hulett | .15 |
| U60 | Bob James | .07 |
| U61 | Cliff Johnson | .05 |
| U62 | Howard Johnson | 2.00 |
| U63 | Ruppert Jones | .07 |
| U64 | Steve Kemp | .07 |
| U65 | Bruce Kison | .07 |
| U66 | Mike LaCoss | .07 |

| NO. | PLAYER | MINT |
|---|---|---|
| U67 | Lee Lacy | .07 |
| U68 | Dave LaPoint | .07 |
| U69 | Gary Lavelle | .07 |
| U70 | Vance Law | .07 |
| U71 | Manny Lee | .15 |
| U72 | Sixto Lezcano | .07 |
| U73 | Tim Lollar | .07 |
| U74 | Urbano Lugo | .12 |
| U75 | Fred Lynn | .20 |
| U76 | Steve Lyons | .25 |
| U77 | Mickey Mahler | .07 |
| U78 | Ron Mathis | .15 |
| U79 | Len Matuszek | .10 |
| U80 | O. McDowell (RR) | .25 |
| U81 | R. McDowell (RR) | .50 |
| U82 | Donnie Moore | .10 |
| U83 | Ron Musselman | .12 |
| U84 | Al Oliver | .15 |
| U85 | Joe Orsulak | .30 |
| U86 | Dan Pasqua | .45 |
| U87 | Chris Pittaro | .15 |
| U88 | Rick Reuschel | .12 |
| U89 | Earnie Riles | .20 |
| U90 | Jerry Royster | .07 |
| U91 | Dave Rozema | .07 |
| U92 | Dave Rucker | .07 |
| U93 | Vern Ruhle | .07 |
| U94 | Mark Salas | .15 |
| U95 | Luis Salazar | .07 |
| U96 | Joe Sambito | .07 |
| U97 | Billy Sample | .10 |
| U98 | Alex Sanchez | .07 |
| U99 | Calvin Schiraldi | .15 |

| NO. | PLAYER | MINT |
|---|---|---|
| U100 | Rick Schu | .15 |
| U101 | Larry Sheets | .15 |
| U102 | Ron Shephard | .15 |
| U103 | Nelson Simmons | .15 |
| U104 | Don Slaught | .10 |
| U105 | Roy Smalley | .10 |
| U106 | Lonnie Smith | .10 |
| U107 | Nate Snell | .10 |
| U108 | Lary Sorensen | .07 |
| U109 | Chris Speier | .07 |
| U110 | Mike Stenhouse | .07 |
| U111 | Tim Stoddard | .07 |
| U112 | John Stuper | .07 |
| U113 | Jim Sundberg | .07 |
| U114 | Bruce Sutter | .25 |
| U115 | Don Sutton | .50 |
| U116 | Bruce Tanner | .15 |
| U117 | Kent Tekulve | .10 |
| U118 | Walt Terrell | .10 |
| U119 | Mickey Tettleton | 1.00 |
| U120 | Rich Thompson | .10 |
| U121 | Louis Thornton | .10 |
| U122 | Alex Trevino | .07 |
| U123 | John Tudor | .15 |
| U124 | Jose Uribe | .25 |
| U125 | Dave Valle | .12 |
| U126 | Dave Von Ohlen | .07 |
| U127 | Curt Wardle | .12 |
| U128 | U.L. Washington | .07 |
| U129 | Ed Whitson | .07 |
| U130 | Herm Winningham | .15 |
| U131 | Rich Yett | .12 |
| U132 | Update Checklist | .20 |

# 1986 Fleer . . . Complete Set of 660 Cards—Value $135.00

(Factory-Sealed Set—Value $145.00)

Features the rookie cards of Vince Coleman, Jose Canseco, Andres Galarraga, Kal Daniels and Cory Snyder.

| NO. | PLAYER | MINT |
|---|---|---|
| **KANSAS CITY ROYALS** | | |
| 1 | Steve Balboni | .10 |
| 2 | Joe Beckwith | .05 |
| 3 | Buddy Biancalana | .05 |
| 4 | Bud Black | .05 |
| 5 | George Brett | .75 |
| 6 | Onix Concepcion | .05 |
| 7 | Steve Farr | .05 |

| NO. | PLAYER | MINT |
|---|---|---|
| 8 | Mark Gubicza | .15 |
| 9 | Dane Iorg | .05 |
| 10 | Danny Jackson | .25 |
| 11 | Lynn Jones | .05 |
| 12 | Mike Jones | .05 |
| 13 | Charlie Leibrandt | .05 |
| 14 | Hal McRae | .05 |
| 15 | Omar Moreno | .05 |

| NO. | PLAYER | MINT |
|---|---|---|
| 16 | Darryl Motley | .05 |
| 17 | Jorge Orta | .05 |
| 18 | Dan Quisenberry | .15 |
| 19 | Bret Saberhagen | 1.00 |
| 20 | Pat Sheridan | .05 |
| 21 | Lonnie Smith | .05 |
| 22 | Jim Sundberg | .05 |
| 23 | John Wathan | .05 |

| NO. | PLAYER | MINT |
|---|---|---|
| 24 | Frank White | .05 |
| 25 | Willie Wilson | .15 |
| **ST. LOUIS CARDINALS** | | |
| 26 | Joaquin Andejar | .10 |
| 27 | Steve Braun | .05 |
| 28 | Bill Campbell | .05 |
| 29 | Cesar Cedeno | .05 |
| 30 | Jack Clark | .25 |

| NO. | PLAYER | MINT |
|---|---|---|
| 31 | Vince Coleman (R) | 6.00 |
| 32 | Danny Cox | .10 |
| 33 | Ken Dayley | .05 |
| 34 | Ivan DeJesus | .05 |
| 35 | Bob Forsch | .05 |
| 36 | Brian Harper | .15 |
| 37 | Tom Herr | .10 |
| 38 | Ricky Horton | .05 |
| 39 | Kurt Kepshire | .05 |
| 40 | Jeff Lahti | .05 |
| 41 | Tito Landrum | .05 |
| 42 | Willie McGee | .20 |
| 43 | Tom Nieto | .05 |
| 44 | Terry Pendleton | .50 |
| 45 | Darrell Porter | .05 |
| 46 | Ozzie Smith | .75 |
| 47 | John Tudor | .15 |
| 48 | Andy Van Slyke | .30 |
| 49 | Todd Worrell (R) | .20 |

**TORONTO BLUE JAYS**

| NO. | PLAYER | MINT |
|---|---|---|
| 50 | Jim Acker | .05 |
| 51 | Doyl Alexander | .05 |
| 52 | Jesse Barfield | .15 |
| 53 | George Bell | .40 |
| 54 | Jeff Burroughs | .05 |
| 55 | Bill Caudill | .05 |
| 56 | Jim Clancy | .05 |
| 57 | Tony Fernandez | .20 |
| 58 | Tom Filer | .05 |
| 59 | Damaso Garcia | .10 |
| 60 | Tom Henke | .30 |
| 61 | Garth Iorg | .05 |
| 62 | Cliff Johnson | .05 |
| 63 | Jimmy Key | .20 |
| 64 | Dennis Lamp | .05 |
| 65 | Gary Lavelle | .05 |
| 66 | Buck Martinez | .05 |
| 67 | Lloyd Moseby | .10 |
| 68 | Rance Mulliniks | .05 |
| 69 | Al Oliver | .10 |
| 70 | Dave Stieb | .15 |
| 71 | Louis Thornton | .15 |
| 72 | Willie Upshaw | .10 |
| 73 | Ernie Whitt | .05 |

**NEW YORK METS**

| NO. | PLAYER | MINT |
|---|---|---|
| 74 | Rick Aguilera (R) | .75 |
| 75 | Wally Backman | .05 |
| 76 | Gary Carter | .30 |
| 77 | Ron Darling | .15 |
| 78 | Len Dykstra (R) | 3.00 |
| 79 | Sid Fernandez | .15 |
| 80 | George Foster | .15 |
| 81 | Dwight Gooden | 2.00 |
| 82 | Tom Gorman | .05 |
| 83 | Danny Heep | .05 |
| 84 | Keith Hernandez | .25 |
| 85 | Howard Johnson | .75 |
| 86 | Ray Knight | .05 |
| 87 | Terry Leach | .15 |
| 88 | Ed Lynch | .05 |
| 89 | Roger McDowell (R) | .35 |
| 90 | Jesse Orosco | .05 |
| 91 | Tom Paciorek | .05 |
| 92 | Ronn Reynolds | .15 |
| 93 | Rafael Santana | .05 |
| 94 | Doug Sisk | .05 |
| 95 | Rusty Staub | .10 |
| 96 | Darryl Strawberry | 5.00 |
| 97 | Mookie Wilson | .05 |

**NEW YORK YANKEES**

| NO. | PLAYER | MINT |
|---|---|---|
| 98 | Neil Allen | .05 |
| 99 | Don Baylor | .10 |
| 100 | Dale Berra | .05 |
| 101 | Rich Bordi | .05 |
| 102 | Marty Bystrom | .05 |
| 103 | Joe Cowley | .05 |
| 104 | Brian Fisher (R) | .15 |
| 105 | Ken Griffey | .05 |
| 106 | Ron Guidry | .15 |
| 107 | Ron Hassey | .05 |
| 108 | Rickey Henderson | 2.50 |
| 109 | Dan Mattingly | 4.00 |
| 110 | Bobby Meacham | .06 |
| 111 | John Montefusco | .05 |
| 112 | Phil Niekro | .25 |
| 113 | Mike Pagliarulo | .10 |

| NO. | PLAYER | MINT |
|---|---|---|
| 114 | Dan Pasqua | .20 |
| 115 | Willie Randolph | .05 |
| 116 | Dave Righetti | .10 |
| 117 | Andre Robertson | .05 |
| 118 | Billy Sample | .05 |
| 119 | Bob Shirley | .05 |
| 120 | Ed Whitson | .05 |
| 121 | Dave Winfield | .50 |
| 122 | Butch Wynegar | .05 |

**LOS ANGELES DODGERS**

| NO. | PLAYER | MINT |
|---|---|---|
| 123 | Dave Anderson | .05 |
| 124 | Bob Bailor | .05 |
| 125 | Greg Brock | .05 |
| 126 | Enos Cabell | .05 |
| 127 | Bobby Castillo | .05 |
| 128 | Carlos Diaz | .05 |
| 129 | Mariano Duncan (R) | .35 |
| 130 | Pedro Guerrero | .25 |
| 131 | Orel Hershiser | .75 |
| 132 | Rick Honeycutt | .05 |
| 133 | Ken Howell | .05 |
| 134 | Ken Landreaux | .05 |
| 135 | Bill Madlock | .10 |
| 136 | Candy Maldonado | .10 |
| 137 | Mike Marshall | .10 |
| 138 | Len Matuszek | .05 |
| 139 | Tom Niedenfuer | .05 |
| 140 | Alejandro Pena | .05 |
| 141 | Jerry Reuss | .05 |
| 142 | Bill Russell | .05 |
| 143 | Steve Sax | .20 |
| 144 | Mike Scioscia | .05 |
| 145 | Fernando Valenzuela | .20 |
| 146 | Bob Welch | .10 |
| 147 | Terry Whitfield | .05 |

**CALIFORNIA ANGELS**

| NO. | PLAYER | MINT |
|---|---|---|
| 148 | Juan Beniquez | .05 |
| 149 | Bob Boone | .05 |
| 150 | John Candelaria | .05 |
| 151 | Rod Carew | .75 |
| 152 | Stewart Cliburn (R) | .15 |
| 153 | Doug DeCinces | .10 |
| 154 | Brian Downing | .05 |
| 155 | Ken Forsch | .05 |
| 156 | Craig Gerber (R) | .15 |
| 157 | Bobby Grich | .10 |
| 158 | George Hendrick | .05 |
| 159 | Al Holland | .05 |
| 160 | Reggie Jackson | .75 |
| 161 | Ruppert Jones | .05 |
| 162 | Urbano Lugo (R) | .15 |
| 163 | Kirk McCaskill (R) | .30 |
| 164 | Donnie Moore | .05 |
| 165 | Gary Pettis | .05 |
| 166 | Ron Romanick | .05 |
| 167 | Dick Schofield | .05 |
| 168 | Darly Sconiers | .05 |
| 169 | Jim Slaton | .05 |
| 170 | Don Sutton | .30 |
| 171 | Mike Witt | .10 |

**CINCINNATI REDS**

| NO. | PLAYER | MINT |
|---|---|---|
| 172 | Buddy Bell | .10 |
| 173 | Tom Browning | .30 |
| 174 | Dave Concepcion | .10 |
| 175 | Eric Davis | 2.00 |
| 176 | Bo Diaz | .05 |
| 177 | Nick Esasky | .05 |
| 178 | John Franco | .15 |
| 179 | Tom Hume | .05 |
| 180 | Wayne Krenchicki | .05 |
| 181 | Andy McGaffigan | .05 |
| 182 | Eddie Milner | .05 |
| 183 | Ron Oester | .05 |
| 184 | Dave Parker | .30 |
| 185 | Frank Pastore | .05 |
| 186 | Tony Perez | .30 |
| 187 | Ted Power | .05 |
| 188 | Joe Price | .05 |
| 189 | Gary Redus | .05 |
| 190 | Ron Robinson | .05 |
| 191 | Pete Rose | .75 |
| 192 | Mario Soto | .10 |
| 193 | John Stuper | .05 |
| 194 | Jay Tibbs | .05 |
| 195 | Dave Van Gorder | .05 |
| 196 | Max Venable | .05 |

**CHICAGO WHITE SOX**

| NO. | PLAYER | MINT |
|---|---|---|
| 197 | Juan Agosto | .05 |
| 198 | Harold Baines | .25 |
| 199 | Floyd Bannister | .05 |
| 200 | Britt Burns | .05 |
| 201 | Julio Cruz | .05 |
| 202 | Joel Davis (R) | .15 |
| 203 | Richard Dotson | .05 |
| 204 | Carlton Fisk | .60 |
| 205 | Scott Fletcher | .05 |
| 206 | Ozzie Guillen (R) | 1.00 |
| 207 | Jerry Hairston | .05 |
| 208 | Tim Hulett | .05 |
| 209 | Bob James | .05 |
| 210 | Ron Kittle | .10 |
| 211 | Rudy Law | .05 |
| 212 | Bryan Little | .05 |
| 213 | Gene Nelson | .05 |
| 214 | Reid Nichols | .05 |
| 215 | Luis Salazar | .05 |
| 216 | Tom Seaver | .50 |
| 217 | Dan Spillner | .05 |
| 218 | Bruce Tanner (R) | .15 |
| 219 | Greg Walker | .10 |
| 220 | Dave Wehrmeister | .05 |

**DETROIT TIGERS**

| NO. | PLAYER | MINT |
|---|---|---|
| 221 | Juan Berenguer | .05 |
| 222 | Dave Bergman | .05 |
| 223 | Tom Brookens | .05 |
| 224 | Darrell Evans | .10 |
| 225 | Barbaro Garbey | .05 |
| 226 | Kirk Gibson | .30 |
| 227 | John Grubb | .05 |
| 228 | Willie Hernandez | .15 |
| 229 | Larry Herndon | .05 |
| 230 | Chet Lemon | .05 |
| 231 | Aurelio Lopez | .05 |
| 232 | Jack Morris | .35 |
| 233 | Randy O'Neal | .05 |
| 234 | Lance Parrish | .20 |
| 235 | Dan Petry | .15 |
| 236 | Alex Sanchez | .05 |
| 237 | Bill Scherrer | .05 |
| 238 | Nelson Simmons (R) | .10 |
| 239 | Frank Tanana | .05 |
| 240 | Walt Terrell | .05 |
| 241 | Alan Trammell | .40 |
| 242 | Lou Whitaker | .25 |
| 243 | Milt Wilcox | .05 |

**MONTREAL EXPOS**

| NO. | PLAYER | MINT |
|---|---|---|
| 244 | Hubie Brooks | .10 |
| 245 | Tim Burke (R) | .30 |
| 246 | Andre Dawson | .60 |
| 247 | Mike Fitzgerald | .08 |
| 248 | Terry Francona | .05 |
| 249 | Bill Gullickson | .05 |
| 250 | Joe Hesketh | .10 |
| 251 | Bill Laskey | .05 |
| 252 | Vance Law | .05 |
| 253 | Charlie Lea | .05 |
| 254 | Gary Lucas | .05 |
| 255 | David Palmer | .05 |
| 256 | Tim Raines | .30 |
| 257 | Jeff Reardon | .35 |
| 258 | Bert Roberge | .05 |
| 259 | Dan Schatzeder | .05 |
| 260 | Bryn Smith | .05 |
| 261 | Randy St. Claire | .05 |
| 262 | Scot Thompson | .05 |
| 263 | Tim Wallach | .10 |
| 264 | U.L. Washington | .05 |
| 265 | Mitch Webster (R) | .20 |
| 266 | Herm Winningham (R) | .15 |
| 267 | Floyd Youmans (R) | .20 |

**BALTIMORE ORIOLES**

| NO. | PLAYER | MINT |
|---|---|---|
| 268 | Don Aase | .05 |
| 269 | Mike Boddicker | .10 |
| 270 | Rich Dauer | .05 |
| 271 | Storm Davis | .05 |
| 272 | Rick Dempsey | .05 |
| 273 | Ken Dixon | .05 |
| 274 | Jim Dwyer | .05 |
| 275 | Mike Flanagan | .05 |
| 276 | Wayne Gross | .05 |
| 277 | Lee Lacy | .05 |
| 278 | Fred Lynn | .15 |

| NO. | PLAYER | MINT |
|---|---|---|
| 279 | Tippy Martinez | .05 |
| 280 | Dennis Martinez | .05 |
| 281 | Scott McGregor | .05 |
| 282 | Eddie Murray | .75 |
| 283 | Floyd Rayford | .05 |
| 284 | Cal Ripken, Jr. | 3.00 |
| 285 | Gary Roenicke | .05 |
| 286 | Larry Sheets | .25 |
| 287 | John Shelby | .05 |
| 288 | Nate Snell (R) | .15 |
| 289 | Sammy Stewart | .05 |
| 290 | Alan Wiggins | .05 |
| 291 | Mike Young | .10 |

**HOUSTON ASTROS**

| NO. | PLAYER | MINT |
|---|---|---|
| 292 | Alan Ashby | .05 |
| 293 | Mark Bailey | .05 |
| 294 | Kevin Bass | .05 |
| 295 | Jeff Calhoun (R) | .15 |
| 296 | Jose Cruz | .10 |
| 297 | Glenn Davis | 1.50 |
| 298 | Bill Dawley | .05 |
| 299 | Frank DiPino | .05 |
| 300 | Bill Doran | .05 |
| 301 | Phil Garner | .05 |
| 302 | Jeff Heathcock (R) | .15 |
| 303 | Charlie Kerfeld (R) | .20 |
| 304 | Bob Knepper | .05 |
| 305 | Ron Mathis (R) | .15 |
| 306 | Jerry Mumphrey | .05 |
| 307 | Jim Pankovits | .05 |
| 308 | Terry Puhl | .05 |
| 309 | Craig Reynolds | .05 |
| 310 | Nolan Ryan | 4.00 |
| 311 | Mike Scott | .20 |
| 312 | Dave Smith | .05 |
| 313 | Dickie Thon | .05 |
| 314 | Denny Walling | .05 |

**SAN DIEGO PADRES**

| NO. | PLAYER | MINT |
|---|---|---|
| 315 | Kurt Bevacqua | .05 |
| 316 | Al Bumbry | .05 |
| 317 | Jerry Davis | .05 |
| 318 | Luis DeLeon | .05 |
| 319 | Dave Dravecky | .05 |
| 320 | Tim Flannery | .05 |
| 321 | Steve Garvey | .35 |
| 322 | Goose Gossage | .15 |
| 323 | Tony Gwynn | 1.50 |
| 324 | Andy Hawkins | .05 |
| 325 | LaMarr Hoyt | .05 |
| 326 | Roy Lee Jackson | .05 |
| 327 | Terry Kennedy | .05 |
| 328 | Craig Lefferts | .05 |
| 329 | Carmelo Martinez | .05 |
| 330 | Lance McCullers (R) | .15 |
| 331 | Kevin McReynolds | .25 |
| 332 | Graig Nettles | .10 |
| 333 | Jerry Royster | .05 |
| 334 | Eric Show | .05 |
| 335 | Tim Stoddard | .05 |
| 336 | Garry Templeton | .08 |
| 337 | Mark Thurmond | .05 |
| 338 | Ed Wojna (R) | .15 |

**BOSTON RED SOX**

| NO. | PLAYER | MINT |
|---|---|---|
| 339 | Tony Armas | .10 |
| 340 | Marty Barrett | .05 |
| 341 | Wade Boggs | 2.00 |
| 342 | Dennis Boyd | .10 |
| 343 | Bill Buckner | .10 |
| 344 | Mark Clear | .05 |
| 345 | Roger Clemens | 7.50 |
| 346 | Steve Crawford | .05 |
| 347 | Mike Easler | .05 |
| 348 | Dwight Evans | .20 |
| 349 | Rich Gedman | .08 |
| 350 | Jackie Gutierrez | .05 |
| 351 | Glenn Hoffman | .05 |
| 352 | Bruce Hurst | .10 |
| 353 | Bruce Kison | .05 |
| 354 | Tim Lollar | .05 |
| 355 | Steve Lyons | .05 |
| 356 | Al Nipper | .05 |
| 357 | Bob Ojeda | .05 |
| 358 | Jim Rice | .20 |
| 359 | Bob Stanley | .05 |
| 360 | Mike Trujillo (R) | .10 |

| NO. | PLAYER | MINT |
|-----|--------|------|
| **CHICAGO CUBS** | | |
| 361 | Thad Bosley | .05 |
| 362 | Warren Brusstar | .05 |
| 363 | Ron Cey | .10 |
| 364 | Jody Davis | .07 |
| 365 | Bob Dernier | .05 |
| 366 | Shawon Dunston | .75 |
| 367 | Leon Durham | .15 |
| 368 | Dennis Eckersley | .30 |
| 369 | Ray Fontenot | .05 |
| 370 | George Frazier | .05 |
| 371 | Bill Hatcher | .15 |
| 372 | Dave Lopes | .05 |
| 373 | Gary Matthews | .05 |
| 374 | Ron Meredith (R) | .15 |
| 375 | Keith Moreland | .05 |
| 376 | Reggie Patterson | .05 |
| 377 | Dick Ruthven | .05 |
| 378 | Ryne Sandberg | 3.00 |
| 379 | Scott Sanderson | .05 |
| 380 | Lee Smith | .30 |
| 381 | Lary Sorensen | .05 |
| 382 | Chris Speier | .05 |
| 383 | Rick Sutcliffe | .15 |
| 384 | Steve Trout | .05 |
| 385 | Gary Woods | .05 |
| **MINNESOTA TWINS** | | |
| 386 | Bert Blyleven | .15 |
| 387 | Tom Brunansky | .15 |
| 388 | Randy Bush | .05 |
| 389 | John Butcher | .05 |
| 390 | Ron Davis | .05 |
| 391 | Dave Engle | .05 |
| 392 | Frank Eufemia | .10 |
| 393 | Pete Filson | .05 |
| 394 | Gary Gaetti | .15 |
| 395 | Greg Gagne | .10 |
| 396 | Mickey Hatcher | .05 |
| 397 | Kent Hrbek | .20 |
| 398 | Tim Laudner | .05 |
| 399 | Rick Lysander | .05 |
| 400 | Dave Meier | .05 |
| 401 | Kirby Puckett | 6.00 |
| 402 | Mark Salas | .05 |
| 403 | Ken Schrom | .05 |
| 404 | Roy Smalley | .05 |
| 405 | Mike Smithson | .05 |
| 406 | Mike Stenhouse | .05 |
| 407 | Tim Teufel | .05 |
| 408 | Frank Viola | .30 |
| 409 | Ron Washington | .05 |
| **OAKLAND A'S** | | |
| 410 | Keith Atherton | .05 |
| 411 | Dusty Baker | .05 |
| 412 | Tim Birtsas (R) | .15 |
| 413 | Bruce Bochte | .05 |
| 414 | Chris Codiroli | .05 |
| 415 | Dave Collins | .05 |
| 416 | Mike Davis | .05 |
| 417 | Alfredo Griffin | .05 |
| 418 | Mike Heath | .05 |
| 419 | Steve Henderson | .05 |
| 420 | Donnie Hill | .05 |
| 421 | Jay Howell | .10 |
| 422 | Tommy John | .15 |
| 423 | Dave Kingman | .10 |
| 424 | Bill Krueger | .05 |
| 425 | Rick Langford | .05 |
| 426 | Carney Lansford | .10 |
| 427 | Steve McCatty | .05 |
| 428 | Dwayne Murphy | .05 |
| 429 | Steve Ontiveros (R) | .15 |
| 430 | Tony Phillips | .05 |
| 431 | Jose Rijo | .30 |
| 432 | Mickey Tettleton (R) | 1.00 |
| **PHILADELPHIA PHILLIES** | | |
| 433 | Luis Aguayo | .05 |
| 434 | Larry Andersen | .05 |
| 435 | Steve Carlton | .50 |
| 436 | Don Carman (R) | .15 |
| 437 | Tim Corcoran | .05 |
| 438 | Darren Daulton (R) | .40 |
| 439 | John Denny | .08 |
| 440 | Tom Foley | .05 |
| 441 | Greg Gross | .05 |
| 442 | Kevin Gross | .05 |
| 443 | Von Hayes | .15 |
| 444 | Charles Hudson | .05 |
| 445 | Garry Maddox | .05 |
| 446 | Shane Rawley | .05 |
| 447 | Dave Rucker | .05 |
| 448 | John Russell | .05 |
| 449 | Juan Samuel | .15 |
| 450 | Mike Schmidt | 2.00 |
| 451 | Rick Schu | .05 |
| 452 | Dave Shipanoff (R) | .15 |
| 453 | Dave Stewart | .30 |
| 454 | Jeff Stone | .05 |
| 455 | Kent Tekulve | .05 |
| 456 | Ozzie Virgil | .05 |
| 457 | Glenn Wilson | .10 |
| **SEATTLE MARINERS** | | |
| 458 | Jim Beattie | .05 |
| 459 | Karl Best | .10 |
| 460 | Barry Bonnell | .05 |
| 461 | Phil Bradley | .15 |
| 462 | Ivan Calderon (R) | 2.00 |
| 463 | Al Cowens | .05 |
| 464 | Alvin Davis | .15 |
| 465 | Dave Henderson | .25 |
| 466 | Bob Kearney | .05 |
| 467 | Mark Langston | .50 |
| 468 | Bob Long | .05 |
| 469 | Mike Moore | .05 |
| 470 | Edwin Nunez | .05 |
| 471 | Spike Owen | .05 |
| 472 | Jack Perconte | .05 |
| 473 | Jim Presley | .15 |
| 474 | Donnie Scott | .05 |
| 475 | Bill Swift | .05 |
| 476 | Danny Tartabull | .75 |
| 477 | Gorman Thomas | .10 |
| 478 | Roy Thomas | .05 |
| 479 | Ed VandeBerg | .05 |
| 480 | Frank Wills (R) | .15 |
| 481 | Matt Young | .05 |
| **MILWAUKEE BREWERS** | | |
| 482 | Ray Burris | .05 |
| 483 | Jaime Cocanower | .05 |
| 484 | Cecil Cooper | .15 |
| 485 | Danny Darwin | .05 |
| 486 | Rollie Fingers | .25 |
| 487 | Jim Gantner | .05 |
| 488 | Bob Gibson | .05 |
| 489 | Moose Haas | .05 |
| 490 | Teddy Higuera (R) | .50 |
| 491 | Paul Householder | .05 |
| 492 | Pete Ladd | .05 |
| 493 | Rick Manning | .05 |
| 494 | Bob McClure | .05 |
| 495 | Paul Molitor | .25 |
| 496 | Charlie Moore | .05 |
| 497 | Ben Oglivie | .05 |
| 498 | Randy Ready | .05 |
| 499 | Earnie Riles (R) | .20 |
| 500 | Ed Romero | .05 |
| 501 | Bill Schroeder | .05 |
| 502 | Ray Searage | .05 |
| 503 | Ted Simmons | .10 |
| 504 | Pete Vuckovich | .05 |
| 505 | Rick Waits | .05 |
| 506 | Robin Yount | .75 |
| **ATLANTA BRAVES** | | |
| 507 | Len Barker | .05 |
| 508 | Steve Bedrosian | .15 |
| 509 | Bruce Benedict | .05 |
| 510 | Rick Camp | .05 |
| 511 | Rick Cerone | .05 |
| 512 | Chris Chambliss | .05 |
| 513 | Jeff Dedmon | .05 |
| 514 | Terry Forster | .05 |
| 515 | Gene Garber | .05 |
| 516 | Terry Harper | .05 |
| 517 | Bob Horner | .15 |
| 518 | Glenn Hubbard | .05 |
| 519 | Joe Johnson (R) | .15 |
| 520 | Brad Komminsk | .05 |
| 521 | Rick Mahler | .05 |
| 522 | Dale Murphy | .50 |
| 523 | Ken Oberkfell | .05 |
| 524 | Pascual Perez | .05 |
| 525 | Gerald Perry | .20 |
| 526 | Rafael Ramirez | .05 |
| 527 | Steve Shields (R) | .15 |
| 528 | Zane Smith | .30 |
| 529 | Bruce Sutter | .15 |
| 530 | Milt Thompson (R) | .25 |
| 531 | Claudell Washington | .05 |
| 532 | Paul Zuvella | .05 |
| **S.F. GIANTS** | | |
| 533 | Vida Blue | .05 |
| 534 | Bob Brenly | .05 |
| 535 | Chris Brown (R) | .20 |
| 536 | Chili Davis | .10 |
| 537 | Mark Davis | .10 |
| 538 | Rob Deer | .30 |
| 539 | Dan Driessen | .05 |
| 540 | Scott Garrelts | .15 |
| 541 | Dan Gladden | .05 |
| 542 | Jim Gott | .05 |
| 543 | David Green | .05 |
| 544 | Atlee Hammaker | .05 |
| 545 | Mike Jeffcoat | .05 |
| 546 | Mike Krukow | .05 |
| 547 | Dave LaPoint | .05 |
| 548 | Jeff Leonard | .05 |
| 549 | Greg Minton | .05 |
| 550 | Alex Trevino | .05 |
| 551 | Manny Trillo | .05 |
| 552 | Jose Uribe (R) | .20 |
| 553 | Brad Wellman | .05 |
| 554 | Frank Williams | .05 |
| 555 | Joel Youngblood | .05 |
| **TEXAS RANGERS** | | |
| 556 | Alan Bannister | .05 |
| 557 | Glenn Brummer | .05 |
| 558 | Steve Buechele (R) | .50 |
| 559 | Jose Guzman (R) | .25 |
| 560 | Toby Harrah | .05 |
| 561 | Greg Harris | .05 |
| 562 | Dwayne Henry (R) | .15 |
| 563 | Burt Hooton | .05 |
| 564 | Charlie Hough | .05 |
| 565 | Mike Mason | .05 |
| 566 | Oddibe McDowell | .15 |
| 567 | Dickie Noles | .05 |
| 568 | Pete O'Brien | .15 |
| 569 | Larry Parrish | .05 |
| 570 | Dave Rozema | .05 |
| 571 | Dave Schmidt | .05 |
| 572 | Don Slaught | .05 |
| 573 | Wayne Tolleson | .05 |
| 574 | Duane Walker | .05 |
| 575 | Gary Ward | .05 |
| 576 | Chris Welsh | .05 |
| 577 | Curtis Wilkerson | .05 |
| 578 | George Wright | .05 |
| **CLEVELAND INDIANS** | | |
| 579 | Chris Bando | .05 |
| 580 | Tony Bernazard | .05 |
| 581 | Brett Butler | .15 |
| 582 | Ernie Camacho | .05 |
| 583 | Joe Carter | 1.00 |
| 584 | Carmello Castillo | .05 |
| 585 | Jamie Easterly | .05 |
| 586 | Julio Franco | .50 |
| 587 | Mel Hall | .05 |
| 588 | Mike Hargrove | .05 |
| 589 | Neal Heaton | .05 |
| 590 | Brook Jacoby | .10 |
| 591 | Otis Nixon (R) | .50 |
| 592 | Jerry Reed (R) | .15 |
| 593 | Vern Ruhle | .05 |
| 594 | Pat Tabler | .05 |
| 595 | Rich Thompson (R) | .15 |
| 596 | Andre Thornton | .05 |
| 597 | Dave Von Ohlen | .05 |
| 598 | George Vuckovich | .05 |
| 599 | Tom Waddell | .05 |
| 600 | Curt Wardle (R) | .15 |
| 601 | Jerry Willard | .05 |
| **PITTSBURGH PIRATES** | | |
| 602 | Bill Almon | .05 |
| 603 | Mike Bielecki | .05 |
| 604 | Sid Bream | .05 |
| 605 | Mike Brown | .05 |
| 606 | Pat Clements (R) | .15 |
| 607 | Jose DeLeon | .05 |
| 608 | Denny Gonzalez | .05 |
| 609 | Cecilio Guante | .05 |
| 610 | Steve Kemp | .05 |
| 611 | Sam Khalifa (R) | .15 |
| 612 | Lee Mazzilli | .05 |
| 613 | Larry McWilliams | .05 |
| 614 | Jim Morrison | .05 |
| 615 | Joe Orsulak (R) | .35 |
| 616 | Tony Pena | .10 |
| 617 | Johnny Ray | .10 |
| 618 | Rick Reuschel | .05 |
| 619 | R.J. Reynolds | .05 |
| 620 | Rick Rhoden | .05 |
| 621 | Don Robinson | .05 |
| 622 | Jason Thompson | .05 |
| 623 | Lee Tunnell | .05 |
| 624 | Jim Winn | .05 |
| 625 | Marvell Wynne | .05 |
| **SPECIAL CARDS** | | |
| 626 | Gooden in Action | .60 |
| 627 | Mattingly in Action | 1.25 |
| 628 | Pete Rose—4,192 | .50 |
| 629 | 3,000 Career Hits: Rod Carew | .35 |
| 630 | 300 Career Wins: Tom Seaver, Phil Niekro | .35 |
| 631 | Ouch: Don Baylor | .15 |
| 632 | Instant Offense: Raines and Strawberry | .50 |
| 633 | Shortshops Supreme: Trammell & Ripken | .50 |
| 634 | Boggs and "Hero": Wade Boggs, George Brett | .75 |
| 635 | Braves Dynamic Duo: Horner and Murphy | .30 |
| 636 | Cardinal Ignitors: Coleman & McGee | .50 |
| 637 | Terror on Basepaths: Vince Coleman | .50 |
| 638 | Charlie Hustle and Dr. K: Rose and Gooden | .75 |
| 639 | 1984 and 1985 AL Batting Champs: Mattingly and Boggs | 1.50 |
| 640 | NL West Sluggers: Murphy, Garvey, Parker | .30 |
| 641 | Staff Aces: Valenzuela & Gooden | .35 |
| 642 | Blue Jay Stoppers: Key and Stieb | .10 |
| 643 | AL All-Star Backstops: Fisk & Gedman | .10 |
| 644 | Benito Santiago (R) and Gene Walter (R) | 4.00 |
| 645 | Mike Woodard (R) and Colin Ward (R) | .15 |
| 646 | Kal Daniels (R) and Paul O'Neill (R) | 5.00 |
| 647 | Fred Toliver (R) and Andres Galarraga (R) | 1.00 |
| 648 | Bob Kipper (R) and Curt Ford (R) | .20 |
| 649 | Eric Plunk (R) and Jose Canseco (R) | 40.00 |
| 650 | Gus Polidor (R) and Mark McLemore (R) | .20 |
| 651 | Rob Woodward (R) and Mickey Brantley (R) | .20 |
| 652 | Billy Joe Robidoux (R) and Mark Funderburk (R) | .20 |
| 653 | Cecil Fielder (R) and Cory Snyder | 15.00 |
| 654 | Checklist No. 1 | .08 |
| 655 | Checklist No. 2 | .08 |
| 656 | Checklist No. 3 | .08 |
| 657 | Checklist No. 4 | .08 |
| 658 | Checklist No. 5 | .08 |
| 659 | Checklist No. 6 | .08 |
| 660 | Checklist No. 7 | .08 |

# 1986 Fleer Traded Update.... Complete Set of 132 Cards—Value $35.00

This set updates the main 1986 card set with players who had changed teams during the season, and rookies. This set features Fleer's first card of Jose Canseco, Ruben Sierra, Kevin Mitchell and Will Clark. The set was packaged in a printed box and distributed exclusively through card dealers.

| NO. PLAYER | MINT |
|---|---|
| U1 Mike Aldrete | .15 |
| U2 Andy Allanson | .15 |
| U3 Neil Allen | .07 |
| U4 Joaquin Andujar | .07 |
| U5 Paul Assenmacher | .15 |
| U6 Scott Bailes | .15 |
| U7 Jay Baller | .15 |
| U8 Scott Bankhead | .15 |
| U9 Bill Bathe | .15 |
| U10 Don Baylor | .12 |
| U11 Billy Beane | .15 |
| U12 Steve Bedrosian | .15 |
| U13 Juan Beniquez | .10 |
| U14 Barry Bonds (RR) | 7.50 |
| U15 Bobby Bonilla (RR) | 6.00 |
| U16 Rich Bordi | .07 |
| U17 Bill Campbell | .07 |
| U18 Tom Candiotti | .10 |
| U19 John Cangelosi | .20 |
| U20 Jose Canseco (RR) | 10.00 |
| U21 Chuck Cary | .20 |
| U22 Juan Castillo | .15 |
| U23 Rick Cerone | .07 |
| U24 John Cerutti | .15 |
| U25 Will Clark (RR) | 13.00 |
| U26 Marc Clear | .07 |
| U27 Darnell Coles | .15 |
| U28 Dave Collins | .07 |
| U29 Tim Conroy | .07 |
| U30 Ed Correa | .15 |
| U31 Joe Cowley | .07 |
| U32 Bill Dawley | .07 |
| U33 Rob Deer | .25 |

| NO. PLAYER | MINT |
|---|---|
| U34 John Denny | .07 |
| U35 Jim DeShaies | .20 |
| U36 Doug Drabek | 1.00 |
| U37 Mike Easler | .07 |
| U38 Mark Eichhorn | .15 |
| U39 Dave Engle | .07 |
| U40 Mike Fischlin | .07 |
| U41 Scott Fletcher | .07 |
| U42 Terry Forster | .07 |
| U43 Terry Francona | .07 |
| U44 Andres Galarraga | .35 |
| U45 Lee Guetterman | .15 |
| U46 Bill Gullickson | .07 |
| U47 Jackie Gutierrez | .07 |
| U48 Moose Haas | .07 |
| U49 Bily Hatcher | .15 |
| U50 Mike Heath | .10 |
| U51 Guy Hofman | .07 |
| U52 Tom Hume | .07 |
| U53 Pete Incaviglia (RR) | .75 |
| U54 Dane Iorg | .07 |
| U55 Chris James (RR) | .50 |
| U56 Stan Javier | .20 |
| U57 Tommy John | .15 |
| U58 Tracy Jones | .15 |
| U59 Wally Joyner (RR) | 2.25 |
| U60 Wayne Krenchicki | .07 |
| U61 John Kruk | .50 |
| U62 Mike LaCoss | .07 |
| U63 Pete Ladd | .07 |
| U64 Dave LaPoint | .07 |
| U65 Mike LaValliere | .25 |
| U66 Rudy Law | .07 |

| NO. PLAYER | MINT |
|---|---|
| U67 Dennis Leonard | .07 |
| U68 Steve Lombardozzi | .20 |
| U69 Aurelio Lopez | .07 |
| U70 Miceky Mahler | .07 |
| U71 Candy Maldonado | .20 |
| U72 Roger Mason | .15 |
| U73 Greg Mathews | .20 |
| U74 Andy McGaffigan | .10 |
| U75 Joel McKeon | .15 |
| U76 Kevin Mitchell (RR) | 5.00 |
| U77 Bill Mooneyham | .12 |
| U78 Omar Moreno | .07 |
| U79 Jerry Mumphrey | .07 |
| U80 Al Newman | .12 |
| U81 Phil Niekro | .35 |
| U82 Randy Niemann | .07 |
| U83 Juan Nieves | .20 |
| U84 Bob Ojeda | .20 |
| U85 Rick Ownbey | .07 |
| U86 Tom Paciorek | .07 |
| U87 David Palmer | .07 |
| U88 Jeff Parrett | .15 |
| U89 Pat Perry | .20 |
| U90 Dan Plesac | .20 |
| U91 Darrell Porter | .07 |
| U92 Luis Quinones | .15 |
| U93 Rey Quinonez | .20 |
| U94 Gary Redus | .12 |
| U95 Jeff Reed | .12 |
| U96 Bip Roberts | .40 |
| U97 Billy Joe Robidoux | .20 |
| U98 Gary Roenicke | .07 |
| U99 Ron Roenicke | .07 |

| NO. PLAYER | MINT |
|---|---|
| U100 Angel Salazar | .12 |
| U101 Joe Sambito | .07 |
| U102 Billy Sample | .07 |
| U103 Dave Schmidt | .07 |
| U104 Ken Schrom | .07 |
| U105 Ruben Sierra (RR) | 8.00 |
| U106 Ted Simmons | .10 |
| U107 Sammy Stewart | .07 |
| U108 Kurt Stillwell | .25 |
| U109 Dale Sveum | .20 |
| U110 Tim Teufel | .07 |
| U111 Bob Tewksbury | .20 |
| U112 Andres Thomas | .20 |
| U113 Jason Thompson | .12 |
| U114 Milt Thompson | .07 |
| U115 Rob Thompson | .40 |
| U116 Jay Tibbs | .07 |
| U117 Fred Toliver | .07 |
| U118 Wayne Tolleson | .07 |
| U119 Alex Trevino | .07 |
| U120 Manny Trillo | .07 |
| U121 Ed Vande Berg | .07 |
| U122 Ozzie Virgil | .07 |
| U123 Tony Walker | .20 |
| U124 Gene Walter | .15 |
| U125 Duane Ward | .35 |
| U126 Jerry Willard | .07 |
| U127 Mitch Williams | .40 |
| U128 Reggie Williams | .20 |
| U129 Bobby Witt (RR) | .60 |
| U130 Marvell Wynne | .07 |
| U131 Steve Yeager | .10 |
| U132 Checklist | .15 |

# 1987 Fleer ... Complete Set of 660 Cards—Value $110.00 (Factory Sealed Set—Value $120.00)

Features the rookie cards of Kevin Mitchell, Will Clark, Bo Jackson and Ruben Sierra. The back of each card features a *Scouting Report*. A high gloss version of the set was issued in a tin box.

| NO. PLAYER | MINT |
|---|---|
| **NEW YORK METS** | |
| 1 Rick Aguilera | .25 |
| 2 R. Anderson (R) | .15 |
| 3 Wally Backman | .07 |
| 4 Gary Carter | .25 |
| 5 Ron Darling | .20 |
| 6 Len Dykstra | .50 |
| 7 Kevin Elster (R) | .25 |
| 8 Sid Fernandez | .15 |
| 9 Dwight Gooden | 1.00 |

| NO. PLAYER | MINT |
|---|---|
| 10 Ed Hearn (R) | .15 |
| 11 Danny Heep | .05 |
| 12 Keith Hernandez | .25 |
| 13 Howard Johnson | .40 |
| 14 Ray Knight | .07 |
| 15 Lee Mazzilli | .07 |
| 16 Roger McDowell | .15 |
| 17 Kevin Mitchell (R) | 7.50 |
| 18 Randy Niemann | .05 |
| 19 Bob Ojeda | .15 |

| NO. PLAYER | MINT |
|---|---|
| 20 Jesse Orosco | .07 |
| 21 Rafael Santana | .07 |
| 22 Doug Sisk | .07 |
| 23 Darryl Strawberry | 2.00 |
| 24 Tim Teufel | .07 |
| 25 Mookie Wilson | .07 |
| **BOSTON RED SOX** | |
| 26 Toni Armas | .07 |
| 27 Marty Barrett | .12 |
| 28 Don Baylor | .12 |

| NO. PLAYER | MINT |
|---|---|
| 29 Wade Boggs | 1.50 |
| 30 Oil Can Boyd | .12 |
| 31 Bill Buckner | .08 |
| 32 Roger Clemens | 3.00 |
| 33 Steve Crawford | .07 |
| 34 Dwight Evans | .15 |
| 35 Rich Gedman | .07 |
| 36 Dave Henderson | .20 |
| 37 Bruce Hurst | .10 |
| 38 Tim Lollar | .07 |

| NO. | PLAYER | MINT |
|---|---|---|
| 39 | Al Nipper | .07 |
| 40 | Spike Owen | .07 |
| 41 | Jim Rice | .20 |
| 42 | Ed Romero | .07 |
| 43 | Joe Sambito | .07 |
| 44 | Calvin Schiraldi | .15 |
| 45 | Tom Seaver | .50 |
| 46 | Jeff Sellers (R) | .15 |
| 47 | Bob Stanley | .07 |
| 48 | Sammy Stewart | .07 |
| **HOUSTON ASTROS** | | |
| 49 | Larry Andersen | .05 |
| 50 | Alan Ashby | .05 |
| 51 | Keven Bass | .05 |
| 52 | Jeff Calhoun | .05 |
| 53 | Jose Cruz | .10 |
| 54 | Danny Darwin | .05 |
| 55 | Glenn Davis | .35 |
| 56 | Jim Deshaies (R) | .25 |
| 57 | Bill Doran | .05 |
| 58 | Phil Garner | .05 |
| 59 | Billy Hatcher | .10 |
| 60 | Charlie Kerfeld | .12 |
| 61 | Bob Knepper | .08 |
| 62 | Dave Lopes | .08 |
| 63 | Aurelio Lopez | .05 |
| 64 | Jim Pankovits | .05 |
| 65 | Terry Puhl | .08 |
| 66 | Craig Reynolds | .08 |
| 67 | Nolan Ryan | 3.00 |
| 68 | Mike Scott | .15 |
| 69 | Dave Smith | .05 |
| 70 | Dickie Thon | .05 |
| 71 | Tony Walker (R) | .15 |
| 72 | Denny Walling | .05 |
| **CALIFORNIA ANGELS** | | |
| 73 | Bob Boone | .05 |
| 74 | Rick Burleson | .05 |
| 75 | John Candelaria | .08 |
| 76 | Doug Corbett | .05 |
| 77 | Doug DeCinces | .08 |
| 78 | Brian Downing | .05 |
| 79 | Chuck Finley (R) | 4.00 |
| 80 | Terry Forster | .05 |
| 81 | Bobby Grich | .05 |
| 82 | George Hendrick | .05 |
| 83 | Jack Howell | .10 |
| 84 | Reggie Jackson | .50 |
| 85 | Ruppert Jones | .05 |
| 86 | Wally Joyner (R) | 3.00 |
| 87 | Gary Lucas | .05 |
| 88 | Kirk McCaskill | .12 |
| 89 | Donnie Moore | .05 |
| 90 | Gary Pettis | .05 |
| 91 | Vern Ruhle | .05 |
| 92 | Dick Schofield | .05 |
| 93 | Don Sutton | .20 |
| 94 | Rob Wilfong | .05 |
| 95 | Mike Witt | .12 |
| **NEW YORK YANKEES** | | |
| 96 | Doug Drabek (R) | 2.50 |
| 97 | Mike Easler | .07 |
| 98 | Mike Fischlin | .07 |
| 99 | Brian Fisher | .07 |
| 100 | Ron Guidry | .15 |
| 101 | Rickey Henderson | 2.00 |
| 102 | Tommy John | .15 |
| 103 | Ron Kittle | .10 |
| 104 | Don Mattingly | 2.25 |
| 105 | Bobby Meacham | .07 |
| 106 | Joe Niekro | .12 |
| 107 | Mike Pagliarulo | .15 |
| 108 | Dan Pasqua | .15 |
| 109 | Willie Randolph | .10 |
| 110 | Dennis Rasmussen | .10 |
| 111 | Dave Righetti | .15 |
| 112 | Gary Roenicke | .07 |
| 113 | Rod Scurry | .07 |
| 114 | Bob Shirley | .07 |
| 115 | Joel Skinner | .07 |
| 116 | Tim Stoddard | .07 |
| 117 | Bob Tewksbury (R) | .15 |
| 118 | Wayne Tolleson | .07 |
| 119 | C. Washington | .07 |
| 120 | Dave Winfield | .40 |
| **TEXAS RANGERS** | | |
| 121 | Steve Buechele | .05 |
| 122 | Ed Correa (R) | .20 |
| 123 | Scott Fletcher | .05 |
| 124 | Joe Guzman | .15 |
| 125 | Toby Harrah | .05 |
| 126 | Greg Harris | .05 |
| 127 | Charlie Hough | .05 |
| 128 | Pete Incaviglia (R) | .60 |
| 129 | Mike Mason | .05 |
| 130 | Oddibe McDowell | .15 |
| 131 | Dale Mohorcic (R) | .15 |
| 132 | Pete O'Brien | .10 |
| 133 | Tom Paciorek | .05 |
| 134 | Larry Parrish | .05 |
| 135 | Geno Petralli | .05 |
| 136 | Darrell Porter | .05 |
| 137 | Jeff Russell | .05 |
| 138 | Ruben Sierra (R) | 13.00 |
| 139 | Don Slaught | .05 |
| 140 | Gary Ward | .05 |
| 141 | Curtis Wilkerson | .05 |
| 142 | Mitch Williams (R) | .50 |
| 143 | Bobby Witt (R) | 1.00 |
| **DETROIT TIGERS** | | |
| 144 | Dave Bergman | .05 |
| 145 | Tom Brookens | .05 |
| 146 | Bill Campbell | .05 |
| 147 | Chuck Cary (R) | .15 |
| 148 | Darnell Coles | .05 |
| 149 | Dave Collins | .05 |
| 150 | Darrell Evans | .12 |
| 151 | Kirk Gibson | .30 |
| 152 | John Grubb | .05 |
| 153 | Willie Hernandez | .05 |
| 154 | Larry Herndon | .05 |
| 155 | Eric King (R) | .25 |
| 156 | Chet Lemon | .07 |
| 157 | Dwight Lowry (R) | .15 |
| 158 | Jack Morris | .40 |
| 159 | Randy O'Neal | .05 |
| 160 | Lance Parrish | .15 |
| 161 | Dan Petry | .10 |
| 162 | Pat Sheridan | .05 |
| 163 | Jim Slaton | .05 |
| 164 | Frank Tanana | .05 |
| 165 | Walt Terrell | .05 |
| 166 | Mark Thurmond | .05 |
| 167 | Alan Trammell | .40 |
| 168 | Lou Whitaker | .25 |
| **PHILADELPHIA PHILLIES** | | |
| 169 | Luis Aguayo | .05 |
| 170 | Steve Bedrosian | .15 |
| 171 | Don Carman | .05 |
| 172 | Darren Daulton | .05 |
| 173 | Greg Gross | .05 |
| 175 | Von Hayes | .12 |
| 176 | Charles Hudson | .05 |
| 177 | Tom Hume | .05 |
| 178 | Steve Jeltz | .05 |
| 179 | Mike Maddux (R) | .20 |
| 180 | Shane Rawley | .05 |
| 181 | Gary Redus | .05 |
| 182 | Ron Roenicke | .05 |
| 183 | Bruce Ruffin (R) | .20 |
| 184 | John Russell | .05 |
| 185 | Juan Samuel | .25 |
| 186 | Dan Schatzeder | .05 |
| 187 | Mike Schmidt | 1.50 |
| 188 | Rick Schu | .08 |
| 189 | Jeff Stone | .05 |
| 190 | Kent Tekulve | .05 |
| 191 | Milt Thompson | .05 |
| 192 | Glenn Wilson | .05 |
| **CINCINNATI REDS** | | |
| 193 | Buddy Bell | .10 |
| 194 | Tom Browning | .07 |
| 195 | Sal Butera | .05 |
| 196 | Dave Concepcion | .07 |
| 197 | Kal Daniels | .35 |
| 198 | Eric Davis | 1.00 |
| 199 | John Denny | .05 |
| 200 | Bo Diaz | .05 |
| 201 | Nick Esasky | .05 |
| 202 | John Franco | .10 |
| 203 | Bill Gullickson | .05 |
| 204 | Barry Larkin (R) | 6.00 |
| 205 | Eddie Milner | .05 |
| 206 | Rob Murphy (R) | .15 |
| 207 | Ron Oester | .05 |
| 208 | Dave Parker | .30 |
| 209 | Tony Perez | .20 |
| 210 | Ted Power | .05 |
| 211 | Joe Price | .05 |
| 212 | Ron Robinson | .05 |
| 213 | Pete Rose (Mgr.) | .75 |
| 214 | Mario Soto | .05 |
| 215 | Kurt Stillwell (R) | .35 |
| 216 | Max Venable | .05 |
| 217 | Chris Welsh | .05 |
| 218 | Carl Willis (R) | .15 |
| **TORONTO BLUE JAYS** | | |
| 219 | Jesse Barfield | .15 |
| 220 | George Bell | .40 |
| 221 | Bill Caudill | .05 |
| 222 | John Cerutti (R) | .15 |
| 223 | Jim Clancy | .05 |
| 224 | Mark Eichhorn (R) | .20 |
| 225 | Tony Fernandez | .15 |
| 226 | Damaso Garcia | .07 |
| 227 | Kelly Gruber | .75 |
| 228 | Tom Henke | .10 |
| 229 | Garth Iorg | .05 |
| 230 | Joe Johnson | .07 |
| 231 | Cliff Johnson | .05 |
| 232 | Jimmy Key | .10 |
| 233 | Dennis Lamp | .05 |
| 234 | Rick Leach | .05 |
| 235 | Buck Martinez | .05 |
| 236 | Lloyd Moseby | .07 |
| 237 | Rance Mulliniks | .05 |
| 238 | Dave Stieb | .10 |
| 239 | Willie Upshaw | .05 |
| 240 | Ernie Whitt | .05 |
| **CLEVELAND INDIANS** | | |
| 241 | Andy Allanson (R) | .15 |
| 242 | Scott Bailes (R) | .05 |
| 243 | Chris Bando | .05 |
| 244 | Tony Bernazard | .05 |
| 245 | John Butcher | .05 |
| 246 | Brett Butler | .15 |
| 247 | Ernie Camacho | .05 |
| 248 | Tom Candiotti | .05 |
| 249 | Joe Carter | .75 |
| 250 | Carmen Castillo | .05 |
| 251 | Julio Franco | .40 |
| 252 | Mel Hall | .05 |
| 253 | Brook Jacoby | .05 |
| 254 | Phil Niekro | .20 |
| 255 | Otis Nixon | .05 |
| 256 | Dickie Noles | .05 |
| 257 | Bryan Oelkers | .05 |
| 258 | Ken Schrom | .05 |
| 259 | Don Schulze | .05 |
| 260 | Cory Snyder | .20 |
| 261 | Pat Tabler | .10 |
| 262 | Andre Thornton | .05 |
| 263 | Rich Yett (R) | .10 |
| **SAN FRANCISCO GIANTS** | | |
| 264 | Mike Aldrete (R) | .15 |
| 265 | Juan Berenguer | .05 |
| 266 | Vida Blue | .05 |
| 267 | Bob Brenly | .05 |
| 268 | Chris Brown | .10 |
| 269 | Will Clark (R) | 30.00 |
| 270 | Chili Davis | .10 |
| 271 | Mark Davis | .05 |
| 272 | Kelly Downs (R) | .25 |
| 273 | Scott Garrelts | .05 |
| 274 | Dan Gladden | .05 |
| 275 | Mike Krukow | .05 |
| 276 | Randy Kutcher (R) | .15 |
| 277 | Mike LaCoss | .05 |
| 278 | Jeff Leonard | .05 |
| 279 | Candy Maldonado | .15 |
| 280 | Roger Mason | .05 |
| 281 | Bob Melvin | .05 |
| 282 | Greg Minton | .05 |
| 283 | Jeff Robinson | .05 |
| 284 | Harry Spilman | .05 |
| 285 | Rob Thompson (R) | .35 |
| 286 | Jose Uribe | .05 |
| 287 | Frank Williams | .05 |
| 288 | Joel Youngblood | .05 |
| **ST. LOUIS CARDINALS** | | |
| 289 | Jack Clark | .20 |
| 290 | Vince Coleman | .75 |
| 291 | Tim Conroy | .05 |
| 292 | Danny Cox | .05 |
| 293 | Ken Dayley | .05 |
| 294 | Curt Ford | .08 |
| 295 | Bob Forsch | .05 |
| 296 | Tom Herr | .05 |
| 297 | Ricky Horton | .05 |
| 298 | Clint Hurdle | .05 |
| 299 | Jeff Lahti | .05 |
| 300 | Steve Lake | .05 |
| 301 | Tito Landrum | .05 |
| 302 | Mike LaValliere (R) | .25 |
| 303 | Greg Mathews (R) | .25 |
| 304 | Willie McGee | .15 |
| 305 | Jose Oquendo | .05 |
| 306 | Terry Pendleton | .20 |
| 307 | Pat Perry | .10 |
| 308 | Ozzie Smith | .50 |
| 309 | Ray Soff (R) | .15 |
| 310 | John Tudor | .10 |
| 311 | Andy Van Slyke | .25 |
| 312 | Todd Worrell | .15 |
| **MONTREAL EXPOS** | | |
| 313 | Dann Bilardello | .05 |
| 314 | Hubie Brooks | .10 |
| 315 | Tim Burke | .05 |
| 316 | Andre Dawson | .60 |
| 317 | Mike Fitzgerald | .05 |
| 318 | Tom Foley | .05 |
| 319 | Andres Galarraga | .20 |
| 320 | Joe Hesketh | .05 |
| 321 | Wallace Johnson | .05 |
| 322 | Wayne Krenchicki | .05 |
| 323 | Vance Law | .05 |
| 324 | Dennis Martinez | .05 |
| 325 | Bob McClure | .05 |
| 326 | Andy McGaffigan | .05 |
| 327 | Al Newman (R) | .15 |
| 328 | Tim Raines | .30 |
| 329 | Jeff Reardon | .25 |
| 330 | Luis Rivera (R) | .15 |
| 331 | Bob Sebra (R) | .15 |
| 332 | Bryn Smith | .05 |
| 333 | Jay Tibbs | .05 |
| 334 | Tim Wallach | .05 |
| 335 | Mitch Webster | .08 |
| 336 | John Wohlford | .05 |
| 337 | Floyd Youmans | .10 |
| **MILWAUKEE BREWERS** | | |
| 338 | Chris Bosio (R) | .40 |
| 339 | Glenn Braggs (R) | .40 |
| 340 | Rick Cerone | .05 |
| 341 | Mark Clear | .05 |
| 342 | B. Clutterbuck (R) | .15 |
| 343 | Cecil Cooper | .15 |
| 344 | Rob Deer | .15 |
| 345 | Jim Gantner | .05 |
| 346 | Ted Higuera | .10 |
| 347 | J.H. Johnson | .05 |
| 348 | Tim Leary | .15 |
| 349 | Rick Manning | .05 |
| 350 | Paul Molitor | .25 |
| 351 | Charlie Moore | .05 |
| 352 | Juan Nieves | .10 |
| 353 | Ben Oglivie | .05 |
| 354 | Dan Plesac (R) | .20 |
| 355 | Ernest Riles | .05 |
| 356 | Billy Joe Robidoux | .10 |
| 357 | Bill Schroeder | .05 |
| 358 | Dale Sveum (R) | .15 |
| 359 | Gorman Thomas | .10 |
| 360 | Bill Wegman | .05 |
| 361 | Robin Yount | .75 |
| **KC ROYALS** | | |
| 362 | Steve Balboni | .07 |
| 363 | Scott Bankhead | .10 |
| 364 | Buddy Biancalana | .05 |
| 365 | Bud Black | .05 |
| 366 | George Brett | .75 |
| 367 | Steve Farr | .05 |
| 368 | Mark Gubicza | .05 |
| 369 | Bo Jackson (R) | 18.00 |
| 370 | Danny Jackson | .20 |
| 371 | Mike Kingery (R) | .15 |
| 372 | Rudy Law | .05 |
| 373 | Charlie Leibrandt | .05 |

| NO. | PLAYER | MINT |
|---|---|---|
| 374 | Dennis Leonard | .05 |
| 375 | Hal McRae | .05 |
| 376 | Jorge Orta | .05 |
| 377 | Jamie Quirk | .05 |
| 378 | Dan Quisenberry | .10 |
| 379 | Bret Saberhagen | .30 |
| 380 | Angel Salazar | .05 |
| 381 | Lonnie Smith | .05 |
| 382 | Jim Sundberg | .05 |
| 383 | Frank White | .05 |
| 384 | Willie Wilson | .12 |

**OAKLAND A's**

| NO. | PLAYER | MINT |
|---|---|---|
| 385 | Joaquin Andujar | .05 |
| 386 | Doug Bair | .05 |
| 387 | Dusty Baker | .05 |
| 388 | Bruce Bochte | .05 |
| 389 | Jose Canseco | 10.00 |
| 390 | Chris Codiroli | .05 |
| 391 | Mike Davis | .05 |
| 392 | Alfredo Griffin | .05 |
| 393 | Moose Haas | .05 |
| 394 | Donnie Hill | .05 |
| 395 | Jay Howell | .05 |
| 396 | Dave Kingman | .12 |
| 397 | Carney Lansford | .05 |
| 398 | David Leiper | .12 |
| 399 | B. Mooneyham (R) | .15 |
| 400 | Dwayne Murphy | .05 |
| 401 | Steve Ontiveros | .05 |
| 402 | Tony Phillips | .05 |
| 403 | Eric Plunk | .05 |
| 404 | Jose Rijo | .25 |
| 405 | Terry Steinbach (R) | .75 |
| 406 | Dave Stewart | .30 |
| 407 | Mickey Tettleton | .20 |
| 408 | Dave Von Ohlen | .05 |
| 409 | Jerry Willard | .05 |
| 410 | Curt Young | .05 |

**SAN DIEGO PADRES**

| NO. | PLAYER | MINT |
|---|---|---|
| 411 | Bruce Bochy | .05 |
| 412 | Dave Dravecky | .05 |
| 413 | Tim Flannery | .05 |
| 414 | Steve Garvey | .30 |
| 415 | Goose Gossage | .12 |
| 416 | Tony Gwynn | 1.00 |
| 417 | Andy Hawkins | .05 |
| 418 | LaMarr Hoyt | .05 |
| 419 | Terry Kennedy | .05 |
| 420 | John Kruk (R) | .75 |
| 421 | Dave LaPoint | .05 |
| 422 | Craig Letters | .05 |
| 423 | Carmelo Martinez | .05 |
| 424 | Lance McCullers | .12 |
| 425 | Kevin McReynolds | .20 |
| 426 | Graig Nettles | .10 |
| 427 | Bip Roberts (R) | .50 |
| 428 | Jerry Royster | .05 |
| 429 | Benito Santiago | .75 |
| 430 | Eric Show | .07 |
| 431 | Bob Stoddard | .05 |
| 432 | Garry Templeton | .05 |
| 433 | Gene Walter | .10 |
| 434 | Ed Whitson | .05 |
| 435 | Marvell Wynne | .05 |

**LA DODGERS**

| NO. | PLAYER | MINT |
|---|---|---|
| 436 | Dave Anderson | .05 |
| 437 | Greg Brock | .05 |
| 438 | Enos Cabell | .05 |
| 439 | Mariano Duncan | .12 |
| 440 | Pedro Guerrero | .20 |
| 441 | Orel Hershiser | .30 |
| 442 | Rick Honeycutt | .05 |
| 443 | Ken Howell | .05 |
| 444 | Ken Landreaux | .05 |
| 445 | Bill Madlock | .08 |
| 446 | Mike Marshall | .08 |
| 447 | Len Matuszek | .05 |
| 448 | Tom Niedenfuer | .05 |
| 449 | Alejandro Pena | .05 |
| 450 | Dennis Powell | .05 |
| 451 | Jerry Reuss | .05 |
| 452 | Bill Russell | .05 |
| 453 | Steve Sax | .15 |
| 454 | Mike Scioscia | .05 |
| 455 | Franklin Stubbs | .05 |
| 456 | Alex Trevino | .05 |
| 457 | F. Valenzuela | .15 |
| 458 | Ed Vande Berg | .05 |

| NO. | PLAYER | MINT |
|---|---|---|
| 459 | Bob Welch | .10 |
| 460 | Reggie Williams (R) | .15 |

**BALTIMORE ORIOLES**

| NO. | PLAYER | MINT |
|---|---|---|
| 461 | Don Aase | .05 |
| 462 | Juan Beniquez | .05 |
| 463 | Mike Boddicker | .05 |
| 464 | Juan Bonilla | .05 |
| 465 | Rich Bordi | .05 |
| 466 | Storm Davis | .05 |
| 467 | Rick Dempsey | .05 |
| 468 | Ken Dixon | .05 |
| 469 | Jim Dwyer | .05 |
| 470 | Mike Flanagan | .05 |
| 471 | Jackie Gutierrez | .05 |
| 472 | Brad Havens | .05 |
| 473 | Lee Lacy | .05 |
| 474 | Fred Lynn | .15 |
| 475 | Scott McGregor | .08 |
| 476 | Eddie Murray | .60 |
| 477 | Tom O'Malley | .05 |
| 478 | Cal Ripken, Jr. | 2.00 |
| 479 | Larry Sheets | .10 |
| 480 | John Shelby | .05 |
| 481 | Nate Snell | .05 |
| 482 | Jim Traber | .10 |
| 483 | Mike Young | .05 |

**CHICAGO WHITE SOX**

| NO. | PLAYER | MINT |
|---|---|---|
| 484 | Neil Allen | .05 |
| 485 | Harold Baines | .15 |
| 486 | Floyd Bannister | .05 |
| 487 | Daryl Boston | .05 |
| 488 | Ivan Calderon | .35 |
| 489 | John Cangelosi (R) | .20 |
| 490 | Steve Carlton | .50 |
| 491 | Joe Cowley | .05 |
| 492 | Julio Cruz | .05 |
| 493 | Bill Dawley | .05 |
| 494 | Jose DeLeon | .05 |
| 495 | Richard Dotson | .05 |
| 496 | Carlton Fisk | .50 |
| 497 | Ozzie Guillen | .20 |
| 498 | Jerry Hairston | .05 |
| 499 | Ron Hassey | .05 |
| 500 | Tim Hulett | .05 |
| 501 | Bob James | .05 |
| 502 | Steve Lyons | .05 |
| 503 | Joel McKeon (R) | .15 |
| 504 | Gene Nelson | .05 |
| 505 | Dave Schmidt | .05 |
| 506 | Ray Searage | .05 |
| 507 | Bobby Thigpen (R) | 2.00 |
| 508 | Greg Walker | .05 |

**ATLANTA BRAVES**

| NO. | PLAYER | MINT |
|---|---|---|
| 509 | Jim Acker | .05 |
| 510 | Doyle Alexander | .05 |
| 511 | P. Assenmacher (R) | .15 |
| 512 | Bruce Benedict | .05 |
| 513 | Chris Chambliss | .08 |
| 514 | Jeff Dedmon | .05 |
| 515 | Gene Garber | .05 |
| 516 | Ken Griffey | .08 |
| 517 | Terry Harper | .05 |
| 518 | Bob Horner | .15 |
| 519 | Glenn Hubbard | .05 |
| 520 | Rick Mahler | .05 |
| 521 | Omar Moreno | .05 |
| 522 | Dale Murphy | .40 |
| 523 | Ken Oberkfell | .05 |
| 524 | Ed Olwine (R) | .15 |
| 525 | David Palmer | .05 |
| 526 | Rafael Ramirez | .05 |
| 527 | Billy Sample | .05 |
| 528 | Ted Simmons | .05 |
| 529 | Zane Smith | .05 |
| 530 | Bruce Sutter | .12 |
| 531 | Andres Thomas (R) | .15 |
| 532 | Ozzie Virgil | .05 |

**MINNESOTA TWINS**

| NO. | PLAYER | MINT |
|---|---|---|
| 533 | A. Anderson (R) | .20 |
| 534 | Keith Atherton | .05 |
| 535 | Billy Beane | .05 |
| 536 | Bert Blyleven | .15 |
| 537 | Tom Brunansky | .15 |
| 538 | Randy Bush | .05 |
| 539 | George Frazier | .05 |
| 540 | Gary Gaetti | .15 |
| 541 | Greg Gagne | .05 |
| 542 | Mickey Hatcher | .05 |

| NO. | PLAYER | MINT |
|---|---|---|
| 543 | Neal Heaton | .05 |
| 544 | Kent Hrbek | .20 |
| 545 | Roy Lee Jackson | .05 |
| 546 | Tim Laudner | .05 |
| 547 | Steve Lombardozzi | .05 |
| 548 | Mark Portugal (R) | .25 |
| 549 | Kirby Puckett | 3.00 |
| 550 | Jeff Reed | .05 |
| 551 | Mark Salas | .05 |
| 552 | Roy Smalley | .05 |
| 553 | Mike Smithson | .05 |
| 554 | Frank Viola | .25 |

**CHICAGO CUBS**

| NO. | PLAYER | MINT |
|---|---|---|
| 555 | Thad Bosley | .05 |
| 556 | Ron Cey | .05 |
| 557 | Jody Davis | .10 |
| 558 | Ron Davis | .05 |
| 559 | Bob Dernier | .05 |
| 560 | Frank DiPino | .05 |
| 561 | Shawon Dunston | .30 |
| 562 | Leon Durham | .10 |
| 563 | Dennis Eckersley | .05 |
| 564 | Terry Francona | .05 |
| 565 | Dave Gumpert | .05 |
| 566 | Guy Hoffman | .05 |
| 567 | Ed Lynch | .05 |
| 568 | Gary Matthews | .05 |
| 569 | Keith Moreland | .05 |
| 570 | Jamie Moyer (R) | .15 |
| 571 | Jerry Mumphrey | .05 |
| 572 | Ryne Sandberg | 2.00 |
| 573 | Scott Sanderson | .05 |
| 574 | Lee Smith | .15 |
| 575 | Chris Speier | .05 |
| 576 | Rick Sutcliffe | .07 |
| 577 | Manny Trillo | .05 |
| 578 | Steve Trout | .05 |

**SEATTLE MARINERS**

| NO. | PLAYER | MINT |
|---|---|---|
| 579 | Karl Best | .05 |
| 580 | Scott Bradley | .10 |
| 581 | Phil Bradley | .05 |
| 582 | Mickey Brantley | .05 |
| 583 | Mike Brown | .05 |
| 584 | Alvin Davis | .15 |
| 585 | L. Guetterman (R) | .20 |
| 586 | Mark Huismann | .05 |
| 587 | Bob Kearney | .05 |
| 588 | Pete Ladd | .05 |
| 589 | Mark Langston | .25 |
| 590 | Mike Moore | .05 |
| 591 | Mike Morgan | .05 |
| 592 | John Moses | .05 |
| 593 | Ken Phelps | .05 |
| 594 | Jim Presley | .20 |
| 595 | Rey Quinonez (R) | .20 |
| 596 | Harold Reynolds | .15 |
| 597 | Billy Swift | .15 |
| 598 | Danny Tartabull | .40 |
| 599 | Steve Yeager | .05 |
| 600 | Matt Young | .05 |

**PITTSBURGH PIRATES**

| NO. | PLAYER | MINT |
|---|---|---|
| 601 | Bill Almon | .05 |
| 602 | Rafael Belliard (R) | .25 |
| 603 | Mike Bielecki | .05 |
| 604 | Barry Bonds (R) | 12.00 |
| 605 | Bobby Bonilla (R) | 10.00 |
| 606 | Sid Bream | .05 |
| 607 | Mike Brown | .05 |
| 608 | Pat Clements | .05 |
| 609 | Mike Diaz (R) | .15 |
| 610 | Cecilio Guante | .05 |
| 611 | Barry Jones (R) | .20 |
| 612 | Bob Kipper | .05 |
| 613 | Larry McWilliams | .05 |
| 614 | Jim Morrison | .05 |
| 615 | Joe Orsulak | .05 |
| 616 | Junior Ortiz | .05 |
| 617 | Tony Pena | .05 |
| 618 | Johnny Ray | .05 |
| 619 | Rick Reuschel | .05 |
| 620 | R.J. Reynolds | .05 |
| 621 | Rick Rhoden | .05 |
| 622 | Don Robinson | .05 |
| 623 | Bob Walk | .05 |
| 624 | Jim Winn | .05 |

**SPECIAL CARDS**

| NO. | PLAYER | MINT |
|---|---|---|
| 625 | Youthful Power: | .60 |
| | P. Incaviglia, J. Canseco | |

| NO. | PLAYER | MINT |
|---|---|---|
| 626 | 300 Game Winners: | .15 |
| | D. Sutton, P. Niekro | |
| 627 | A.L. Firemen: | .15 |
| | D. Righetti, D. Asse | |
| 628 | Rookie All-Stars: | 1.25 |
| | W. Joyner, J. Canseco | |
| 629 | Magic Mets: | .50 |
| | G. Carter, S. Fernandez, | |
| | D. Gooden, K. Hernandez, | |
| | D. Strawberry | |
| 630 | N.L. Best Righties: | .15 |
| | M. Scott, M. Krukow | |
| 631 | Sensational Southpaws: | .15 |
| | F. Venezuela, J. Franco | |
| 632 | 4 HR's in Game: | .15 |
| | Bob Horner | |
| 633 | Pitcher's Nightmare: | .60 |
| | J. Canseco, J. Rice, | |
| | K. Puckett | |
| 634 | All-Star Battery: | .30 |
| | G. Carter, R. Clemens | |
| 635 | 4,000 Strikeouts: | .20 |
| | S. Carlton | |
| 636 | Big Bats at First Sack: | .20 |
| | G. Davis, E. Murray | |
| 637 | On Base: | .25 |
| | W. Boggs, K. Hernandez | |
| 638 | Sluggers from Left Side: | 1.00 |
| | D. Mattingly, | |
| | D. Strawberry | |
| 639 | Former MVP's: | .20 |
| | D. Parker, R. Sandberg | |
| 640 | Dr. K. & Super K: | .75 |
| | D. Gooden, R. Clemens | |
| 641 | A.L. West Stoppers: | .15 |
| | M. Witt, C. Hough | |
| 642 | Doubles & Triples: | .15 |
| | J. Samuel, T. Raines | |
| 643 | Outfielders with Punch: | .15 |
| | H. Baines, J. Barfield | |

**No. 644 to 653—Major League Prospects**

| NO. | PLAYER | MINT |
|---|---|---|
| 644 | D. Clark (R) and | |
| | G. Swindell (R) | 1.25 |
| 645 | Ron Karkovice (R) and | |
| | Russ Morman (R) | .20 |
| 646 | Devon White (R) and | |
| | Willie Fraser (R) | 1.25 |
| 647 | Mike Stanley (R) and | |
| | Jerry Browne (R) | .30 |
| 648 | Dave Magadan (R) and | |
| | Phil Lombardi (R) | 2.00 |
| 649 | Jose Gonzalez (R) and | |
| | Ralph Bryant (R) | .20 |
| 650 | Jimmy Jones (R) and | |
| | Randy Asadoor (R) | .25 |
| 651 | Tracy Jones (R) and | |
| | Marvin Freeman (R) | .20 |
| 652 | John Stefero (R) and | |
| | Kevin Seitzer (R) | 1.25 |
| 653 | Rob Nelson (R) and | |
| | Steve Fireovid (R) | .15 |
| 654 | Checklist No. 1 | |
| 655 | Checklist No. 2 | |
| 656 | Checklist No. 3 | |
| 657 | Checklist No. 4 | |
| 658 | Checklist No. 5 | |
| 659 | Checklist No. 6 | |
| 660 | Checklist No. 7 | |

# 1987 Fleer Traded Update . . . Complete Set of 132 Cards—Value $17.00

This set updates the main 1987 card set with players who had changed teams during the season, and rookies. This set features Fleer's first card of Ellis Burks, Mike Greenwell, Mark McGwire, and Matt Williams. The set was packaged in a printed box and distributed exclusively through card dealers. A high gloss version of the set was issued in a tin box.

| NO. PLAYER | MINT | NO. PLAYER | MINT | NO. PLAYER | MINT | NO. PLAYER | MINT |
|---|---|---|---|---|---|---|---|
| U1 Scott Bankhead | .07 | U34 Ken Gerhart | .10 | U67 Mike Loynd | .10 | U100 Randy Ready | .07 |
| U2 Eric Bell | .10 | U35 Jim Gott | .07 | U68 Greg Maddux (RR) | .75 | U101 Jeff Reardon | .15 |
| U3 Juan Beniquez | .07 | U36 Dan Gladden | .07 | U69 Bill Madlock | .07 | U102 Gary Redus | .07 |
| U4 Juan Berenguer | .07 | U37 Mike Greenwell (RR) | 2.00 | U70 Dave Magadan | .30 | U103 Rick Rhoden | .10 |
| U5 Mike Birkbeck | .10 | U38 Cecilio Guante | .07 | U71 Joe Magrane (RR) | .25 | U104 Wally Ritchie | .12 |
| U6 Randy Bockus | .10 | U39 Albert Hall | .07 | U72 Fred Manrique | .10 | U105 Jeff Robinson (RR) | .15 |
| U7 Rod Booker | .07 | U40 Atlee Hammaker | .07 | U73 Mike Mason | .07 | U106 Mark Salas | .07 |
| U8 Thad Bosley | .07 | U41 Mickey Hatcher | .07 | U74 Lloyd McClendon | .20 | U107 Dave Schmidt | .07 |
| U9 Greg Brock | .10 | U42 Mike Heath | .07 | U75 Fred McGriff (RR) | 2.50 | U108 Kevin Seitzer | .15 |
| U10 Bob Brower | .10 | U43 Neal Heaton | .07 | U76 Mark McGwire (RR) | 2.50 | U109 John Shelby | .07 |
| U11 Chris Brown | .10 | U44 Mike Henneman | .30 | U77 Mark McLemore | .07 | U110 John Smiley (RR) | .75 |
| U12 Jerry Browne | .07 | U45 Guy Hoffman | .07 | U78 Kevin McReynolds | .15 | U111 Lary Sorensen | .07 |
| U13 Ralph Bryant | .07 | U46 Charlie Hudson | .07 | U79 Dave Meads | .15 | U112 Chris Speier | .07 |
| U14 De Wayne Buice | .10 | U47 Chuck Jackson | .15 | U80 Greg Minton | .12 | U113 Randy St. Claire | .07 |
| U15 Ellis Burks (RR) | 2.00 | U48 Mike Jackson | .20 | U81 John Mitchell | .12 | U114 Jim Sundberg | .07 |
| U16 Casey Candaele | .10 | U49 Reggie Jackson | .50 | U82 Kevin Mitchell | 1.50 | U115 B.J. Surhoff (RR) | .20 |
| U17 Steve Carlton | .25 | U50 Chris James | .15 | U83 John Morris | .10 | U116 Greg Swindell | .30 |
| U18 Juan Castillo | .07 | U51 Dian James | .15 | U84 Jeff Musselman | .20 | U117 Danny Tartabull | .25 |
| U19 Chuck Crim | .15 | U52 Stan Javier | .07 | U85 Randy Myers (RR) | .20 | U118 Dorn Taylor | .10 |
| U20 Mark Davidson | .15 | U53 Stan Jefferson | .10 | U86 Gene Nelson | .07 | U119 Lee Tunnell | .07 |
| U21 Mark Davis | .15 | U54 Jimmy Jones | .10 | U87 Joe Niekro | .15 | U120 Ed Vande Berg | .07 |
| U22 Storm Davis | .15 | U55 Tracy Jones | .10 | U88 Tom Nieto | .07 | U121 Andy Van Slyke | .20 |
| U23 Bill Dawley | .07 | U56 Terry Kennedy | .07 | U89 Reid Nichols | .07 | U122 Gary Ward | .07 |
| U24 Andre Dawson | .35 | U57 Mike Kingery | .07 | U90 Matt Nokes (RR) | .50 | U123 Devon White | .25 |
| U25 Brian Dayett | .07 | U58 Ray Knight | .07 | U91 Dickie Noles | .07 | U124 Alan Wiggins | .07 |
| U26 Rick Dempsey | .07 | U59 Gene Larkin | .25 | U92 Edwin Nunez | .07 | U125 Bill Wilkinson | .12 |
| U27 Ken Dowell | .12 | U60 Mike La Valliere | .07 | U93 Jose Nunez | .15 | U126 Jim Winn | .07 |
| U28 Dave Dravecky | .07 | U61 Jack Lazorko | .12 | U94 Paul O'Neill | .30 | U127 Frank Williams | .07 |
| U29 Mike Dunne (RR) | .15 | U62 Terry Leach | .12 | U95 Jim Paciorek | .15 | U128 Kenny Williams (RR) | .15 |
| U30 Dennis Eckersley | .25 | U63 Rick Leach | .07 | U96 Lance Parrish | .20 | U129 Matt Williams (RR) | 5.00 |
| U31 Cecil Fielder | 2.50 | U64 Craig Lefferts | .07 | U97 Bill Pecota | .15 | U130 Herm Winningham | .07 |
| U32 Brian Fisher | .07 | U65 Jim Lindeman (RR) | .15 | U98 Tony Pena | .07 | U131 Matt Young | .07 |
| U33 Willie Fraser | .07 | U66 Bill Long | .15 | U99 Luis Polonia | .40 | U132 Checklist | .08 |

# 1988 Fleer . . . Complete Set of 660 Cards—Value $45.00 (Factory Sealed Set—Value $50.00)

Features the rookie cards of Mark Grace, Gregg Jefferies, Ellis Burks and Matt Williams. A new feature on the back of the card is "At Their Best." It reveals the player's record regarding day/night and home/road games.

| NO. PLAYER | MINT | NO. PLAYER | MINT | NO. PLAYER | MINT | NO. PLAYER | MINT |
|---|---|---|---|---|---|---|---|
| **MINNESOTA TWINS** | | 8 Mark Davidson (R) | .15 | 16 Steve Lombardozzi | .05 | 24 Les Straker (R) | .15 |
| 1 Keith Atherton | .05 | 9 George Frazier | .05 | 17 Al Newman | .05 | 25 Frank Viola | .15 |
| 2 Don Baylor | .08 | 10 Gary Gaetti | .15 | 18 Joe Niekro | .08 | **ST. LOUIS CARDINALS** | |
| 3 Juan Berenguer | .05 | 11 Greg Gagne | .05 | 19 Kirby Puckett | .50 | 26 Jk. Clark | .15 |
| 4 Bert Blyleven | .10 | 12 Dan Gladden | .05 | 20 Jeff Reardon | .15 | 27 Vince Coleman | .20 |
| 5 Tom Brunansky | .15 | 13 Kent Hrbek | .15 | 21 Dan Schatzader | .05 | 28 Danny Cox | .05 |
| 6 Randy Bush | .05 | 14 Gene Larkin (R) | .20 | 22 Roy Smalley | .05 | 29 Bill Dawley | .05 |
| 7 Steve Carlton | .20 | 15 Tim Laudner | .05 | 23 Mike Smithson | .05 | 30 Ken Dayley | .05 |

| NO. | PLAYER | MINT |
|---|---|---|
| 31 | Doug DeCinces | .05 |
| 32 | Curt Ford | .05 |
| 33 | Bob Forsch | .05 |
| 34 | David Green | .05 |
| 35 | Tom Herr | .05 |
| 36 | Ricky Horton | .05 |
| 37 | Lance Johnson (R) | .30 |
| 38 | Steve Lake | .05 |
| 39 | Jim Lindeman | .12 |
| 40 | Joe Magrane (R) | .20 |
| 41 | Greg Mathews | .05 |
| 42 | Willie McGee | .15 |
| 43 | Jose Oquendo | .05 |
| 44 | Jose Oquendo | .05 |
| 45 | Tony Pena | .05 |
| 46 | Terry Pendleton | .15 |
| 47 | Ozzie Smith | .25 |
| 48 | John Tudor | .10 |
| 49 | Lee Tunnell | .05 |
| 50 | Todd Worrell | .10 |

**DETROIT TIGERS**

| NO. | PLAYER | MINT |
|---|---|---|
| 51 | Doyle Alexander | .05 |
| 52 | Dave Bergman | .05 |
| 53 | Tom Brookens | .05 |
| 54 | Darrell Evans | .05 |
| 55 | Kirk Gibson | .15 |
| 56 | Mike Heath | .05 |
| 57 | Mike Henneman (R) | .25 |
| 58 | Willie Hernandez | .10 |
| 59 | Larry Herndon | .05 |
| 60 | Eric King | .05 |
| 61 | Chet Lemon | .05 |
| 62 | Scott Lusader (R) | .10 |
| 63 | Bill Madlock | .15 |
| 64 | Jack Morris | .15 |
| 65 | Jim Morrison | .05 |
| 66 | Matt Nokes (R) | .50 |
| 67 | Dan Petry | .05 |
| 68 | Jeff Robinson (R) | .10 |
| 68 | J. Robinson (error) | .35 |
| 69 | Pat Sheridan | .05 |
| 70 | Nate Snell | .05 |
| 71 | Frank Tanana | .05 |
| 72 | Walt Terrell | .05 |
| 73 | Mark Thurmond | .05 |
| 74 | Alan Trammell | .20 |
| 75 | Lou Whitaker | .10 |

**SAN FRANCISCO GIANTS**

| NO. | PLAYER | MINT |
|---|---|---|
| 76 | Mike Aldrete | .05 |
| 77 | Bob Brenly | .05 |
| 78 | Will Clark | 3.50 |
| 79 | Chili Davis | .10 |
| 80 | Kelly Downs | .05 |
| 81 | Dave Dravecky | .05 |
| 82 | Scott Garrelts | .05 |
| 83 | Atlee Hammaker | .05 |
| 84 | Dave Henderson | .15 |
| 85 | Mike Krukow | .05 |
| 86 | Mike LaCoss | .05 |
| 87 | Craig Lefferts | .05 |
| 88 | Jeff Leonard | .10 |
| 89 | Candy Maldonado | .10 |
| 90 | Bob Melvin | .05 |
| 91 | Ed Milner | .05 |
| 92 | Kevin Mitchell | .75 |
| 93 | Jon Perlman (R) | .10 |
| 94 | Rick Reuschel | .05 |
| 95 | Don Robinson | .05 |
| 96 | Chris Speier | .05 |
| 97 | Harry Spilman | .05 |
| 98 | Robbie Thompson | .05 |
| 99 | Jose Uribe | .05 |
| 100 | Mark Wasinger (R) | .15 |
| 101 | Matt Williams (R) | 5.00 |

**TORONTO BLUE JAYS**

| NO. | PLAYER | MINT |
|---|---|---|
| 102 | Jesse Barfield | .15 |
| 103 | George Bell | .20 |
| 104 | Juan Beniquez | .05 |
| 105 | John Cerutti | .05 |
| 106 | Jim Clancy | .05 |
| 107 | Rob Ducey (R) | .10 |
| 108 | Mark Eichhorn | .05 |
| 109 | Tony Fernandez | .12 |
| 110 | Cecil Fielder | .75 |
| 111 | Kelly Gruber | .25 |
| 112 | Tom Henke | .05 |
| 113 | Garth Iorg | .05 |
| 114 | Jimmy Key | .10 |

| NO. | PLAYER | MINT |
|---|---|---|
| 115 | Rick Leach | .05 |
| 116 | Manny Lee | .08 |
| 117 | Nelson Liriano (R) | .10 |
| 118 | Fred McGriff | 2.00 |
| 119 | Lloyd Moseby | .10 |
| 120 | Rance Mulliniks | .05 |
| 121 | Jeff Musselman | .10 |
| 122 | Jose Nunez | .10 |
| 123 | Dave Stieb | .05 |
| 124 | Willie Upshaw | .05 |
| 125 | Duane Ward | .10 |
| 126 | Ernie Whitt | .05 |

**NEW YORK METS**

| NO. | PLAYER | MINT |
|---|---|---|
| 127 | Rick Aguilera | .05 |
| 128 | Wally Backman | .05 |
| 129 | Mark Carreon (R) | .20 |
| 130 | Gary Carter | .15 |
| 131 | David Cone | .40 |
| 132 | Ron Darling | .10 |
| 133 | Len Dykstra | .15 |
| 134 | Sid Fernandez | .08 |
| 135 | Dwight Gooden | .30 |
| 136 | Keith Hernandez | .10 |
| 137 | Gregg Jefferies (R) | 2.50 |
| 138 | Howard Johnson | .35 |
| 139 | Terry Leach | .05 |
| 140 | Barry Lyons (R) | .10 |
| 141 | Dave Magadan | .10 |
| 142 | Roger McDowell | .05 |
| 143 | Kevin McReynolds | .15 |
| 144 | Keith Miller (R) | .20 |
| 145 | John Mitchell (R) | .15 |
| 146 | Randy Myers | .10 |
| 147 | Bob Ojeda | .10 |
| 148 | Jesse Orosco | .05 |
| 149 | Rafael Santana | .05 |
| 150 | Doug Sisk | .05 |
| 151 | Darryl Strawberry | .75 |
| 152 | Tim Teufel | .05 |
| 153 | Gene Walter | .05 |
| 154 | Mookie Wilson | .08 |

**MILWAUKEE BREWERS**

| NO. | PLAYER | MINT |
|---|---|---|
| 155 | Jay Aldrich (R) | .10 |
| 156 | Chris Bosio | .05 |
| 157 | Glenn Braggs | .10 |
| 158 | Greg Brock | .05 |
| 159 | Juan Castillo | .08 |
| 160 | Mark Clear | .05 |
| 161 | Cecil Cooper | .08 |
| 162 | Chuck Crim (R) | .10 |
| 163 | Rob Deer | .10 |
| 164 | Mike Felder | .05 |
| 165 | Jim Gantner | .05 |
| 166 | Ted Higuera | .10 |
| 167 | Steve Kiefer | .05 |
| 168 | Rick Manning | .05 |
| 169 | Paul Molitor | .15 |
| 170 | Juan Nieves | .10 |
| 171 | Dan Plesac | .08 |
| 172 | Earnest Riles | .05 |
| 173 | Bill Schroeder | .05 |
| 174 | Steve Stanicek (R) | .05 |
| 175 | B.J. Surhoff | .10 |
| 176 | Dale Sveum | .10 |
| 177 | Bill Wegman | .08 |
| 178 | Robin Yount | .05 |

**MONTREAL EXPOS** .30

| NO. | PLAYER | MINT |
|---|---|---|
| 179 | Hubie Brooks | |
| 180 | Tim Burke | .10 |
| 181 | Casey Candaele | .05 |
| 182 | Mike Fitzgerald | .10 |
| 183 | Tom Foley | .05 |
| 184 | Andres Galarraga | .05 |
| 185 | Neal Heaton | .10 |
| 186 | Wallace Johnson | .05 |
| 187 | Vance Law | .05 |
| 188 | Dennis Martinez | .08 |
| 189 | Bob McClure | .05 |
| 190 | Andy McGaffigan | .05 |
| 191 | Reid Nichols | .05 |
| 192 | Pascual Perez | .05 |
| 193 | Tim Raines | .20 |
| 194 | Jeff Reed | .05 |
| 195 | Bob Sebra | .05 |
| 196 | Bryn Smith | .05 |
| 197 | Randy St. Claire | .05 |
| 198 | Tim Wallach | .10 |

| NO. | PLAYER | MINT |
|---|---|---|
| 199 | Mitch Webster | .05 |
| 200 | Herm Winningham | .05 |
| 201 | Floyd Youmans | .08 |

**N.Y. YANKEES**

| NO. | PLAYER | MINT |
|---|---|---|
| 202 | Brad Arnsberg (R) | .10 |
| 203 | Rick Cerone | .05 |
| 204 | Pat Clements | .05 |
| 205 | Henry Cotto | .05 |
| 206 | Mike Easler | .05 |
| 207 | Ron Guidry | .10 |
| 208 | Bill Gullickson | .05 |
| 209 | Rickey Henderson | .50 |
| 210 | Charles Hudson | .05 |
| 211 | Tommy John | .10 |
| 212 | Roberto Kelly (R) | 1.25 |
| 213 | Ron Kittle | .08 |
| 214 | Don Mattingly | .60 |
| 215 | Bobby Meacham | .05 |
| 216 | Mike Pagliarulo | .15 |
| 217 | Dan Pasqua | .10 |
| 218 | Willie Randolph | .12 |
| 219 | Rick Rhoden | .05 |
| 220 | Dave Righetti | .10 |
| 221 | Jerry Royster | .05 |
| 222 | Tim Stoddard | .05 |
| 223 | Wayne Tolleson | .05 |
| 224 | Gary Ward | .05 |
| 225 | Claudell Washington | .05 |
| 226 | Dave Winfield | .20 |

**CINCINNATI REDS**

| NO. | PLAYER | MINT |
|---|---|---|
| 227 | Buddy Bell | .15 |
| 228 | Tom Browning | .05 |
| 229 | Dave Concepcion | .05 |
| 230 | Kal Daniels | .10 |
| 231 | Eric Davis | .30 |
| 232 | Bo Diaz | .05 |
| 233 | Nick Esasky | .05 |
| 234 | John Franco | .08 |
| 235 | Guy Hoffman | .05 |
| 236 | Tom Hume | .05 |
| 237 | Tracy Jones | .10 |
| 238 | Bill Landrum (R) | .20 |
| 239 | Barry Larkin | .75 |
| 240 | Terry McGriff | .12 |
| 241 | Rob Murphy | .05 |
| 242 | Ron Oester | .05 |
| 243 | Dave Parker | .15 |
| 244 | Pat Perry | .05 |
| 245 | Ted Power | .05 |
| 246 | Dennis Rasmussen | .05 |
| 247 | Ron Robinson | .05 |
| 248 | Kurt Stillwell | .08 |
| 249 | Jeff Treadway | .40 |
| 250 | Frank Williams | .05 |

**K.C. ROYALS**

| NO. | PLAYER | MINT |
|---|---|---|
| 251 | Steve Balboni | .05 |
| 252 | Bud Black | .05 |
| 253 | Thad Bosley | .05 |
| 254 | George Brett | .35 |
| 255 | John Davis (R) | .15 |
| 256 | Steve Farr | .05 |
| 257 | Gene Garber | .05 |
| 258 | Jerry Gleaton | .05 |
| 259 | Mark Gubicza | .05 |
| 260 | Bo Jackson | 3.00 |
| 261 | Danny Jackson | .10 |
| 262 | Ross Jones (R) | .12 |
| 263 | Charlie Leibrandt | .05 |
| 264 | Bill Pecota (R) | .15 |
| 265 | Melido Perez (R) | .25 |
| 266 | Jamie Quirk | .05 |
| 267 | Dan Quisenberry | .10 |
| 268 | Bret Saberhagen | .05 |
| 269 | Angel Salazar | .10 |
| 270 | Kevin Seitzer | .20 |
| 271 | Danny Tartabull | .15 |
| 272 | Gary Thurman (R) | .05 |
| 273 | Frank White | .10 |
| 274 | Willie Wilson | |

**OAKLAND A'S** .05

| NO. | PLAYER | MINT |
|---|---|---|
| 275 | Tony Bernazard | 3.00 |
| 276 | Jose Canseco | .05 |
| 277 | Mike Davis | .05 |
| 278 | Storm Davis | .15 |
| 279 | Dennis Eckersley | .05 |
| 280 | Alfredo Griffin | .05 |
| 281 | Rick Honeycutt | .05 |

| NO. | PLAYER | MINT |
|---|---|---|
| 282 | Jay Howell | .05 |
| 283 | Reggie Jackson | .30 |
| 284 | Dennis Lamp | .05 |
| 285 | Carney Lansford | .05 |
| 286 | Mark McGwire | 1.25 |
| 287 | Dwayne Murphy | .05 |
| 288 | Gene Nelson | .05 |
| 289 | Steve Ontiveros | .05 |
| 290 | Tony Philips | .05 |
| 291 | Eric Plunk | .05 |
| 292 | Luis Polonia (R) | .50 |
| 293 | Rick Rodriguez (R) | .15 |
| 294 | Terry Steinbach | .15 |
| 295 | Dave Stewart | .15 |
| 296 | Curt Young | .05 |

**PHILADELPHIA PHILLIES**

| NO. | PLAYER | MINT |
|---|---|---|
| 297 | Luis Aguayo | .05 |
| 298 | Steve Bedrosian | .05 |
| 299 | Jeff Calhoun | .05 |
| 300 | Don Carman | .05 |
| 301 | Todd Frohwirth (R) | .15 |
| 302 | Greg Gross | .05 |
| 303 | Kevin Gross | .05 |
| 304 | Von Hayes | .05 |
| 305 | Keith Hughes | .12 |
| 306 | Mike Jackson (R) | .15 |
| 307 | Chris James | .10 |
| 308 | Steve Jeltz | .05 |
| 309 | Mike Maddux | .05 |
| 310 | Lance Parrish | .12 |
| 311 | Shane Rawley | .05 |
| 312 | Wally Ritchie (R) | .15 |
| 313 | Bruce Ruffin | .05 |
| 314 | Juan Samuel | .10 |
| 315 | Mike Schmidt | .75 |
| 316 | Rick Schu | .05 |
| 317 | Jeff Stone | .05 |
| 318 | Kent Tekulve | .05 |
| 319 | Milt Thompson | .05 |
| 320 | Glenn Wilson | .08 |

**PITTSBURGH PIRATES**

| NO. | PLAYER | MINT |
|---|---|---|
| 321 | Rafael Belliard | .05 |
| 322 | Barry Bonds | 1.25 |
| 323 | Bobby Bonilla | 1.00 |
| 324 | Sid Bream | .05 |
| 325 | John Cangelosi | .05 |
| 326 | Mike Diaz | .05 |
| 327 | Doug Drabek | .25 |
| 328 | Mike Dunne | .10 |
| 329 | Brian Fisher | .05 |
| 330 | Brett Gideon (R) | .15 |
| 331 | Terry Harper | .05 |
| 332 | Bob Kipper | .05 |
| 333 | Mike LaValliere | .05 |
| 334 | Jose Lind (R) | .50 |
| 335 | Junior Ortiz | .05 |
| 336 | Vincente Palacios (R) | .15 |
| 337 | Bob Patterson (R) | .15 |
| 338 | Al Pedrique (R) | .15 |
| 339 | R.J. Reynolds | .05 |
| 340 | John Smiley (R) | 1.00 |
| 341 | Andy Van Slyke | .15 |
| 342 | Bob Walk | .05 |

**BOSTON RED SOX**

| NO. | PLAYER | MINT |
|---|---|---|
| 343 | Marty Barrett | .10 |
| 344 | Todd Benzinger (R) | .35 |
| 345 | Wade Boggs | .40 |
| 346 | Tom Bolton (R) | .15 |
| 347 | Oil Can Boyd | .05 |
| 348 | Ellis Burks (R) | 2.50 |
| 349 | Roger Clemens | 1.00 |
| 350 | Steve Crawford | .10 |
| 351 | Dwight Evans | .10 |
| 352 | Wes Gardner (R) | .10 |
| 353 | Rich Gedman | .05 |
| 354 | Mike Greenwell | 1.25 |
| 355 | Sam Horn (R) | .25 |
| 356 | Bruce Hurst | .10 |
| 357 | John Marzano | .10 |
| 358 | Al Nipper | .05 |
| 359 | Spike Owen | .05 |
| 360 | Jody Reed (R) | .60 |
| 361 | Jim Rice | .15 |
| 362 | Ed Romero | .05 |
| 363 | Kevin Romine | .10 |
| 364 | Joe Sambito | .05 |
| 365 | Calvin Schiraldi | .05 |

| NO. | PLAYER | MINT |
|---|---|---|
| 366 | Jeff Sellers | .05 |
| 367 | Bob Stanley | .05 |

**SEATTLE MARINERS**

| NO. | PLAYER | MINT |
|---|---|---|
| 368 | Scott Bankhead | .05 |
| 369 | Phil Bradley | .08 |
| 370 | Scott Bradley | .05 |
| 371 | Mickey Brantley | .10 |
| 372 | Mike Campbell (R) | .15 |
| 373 | Alvin Davis | .15 |
| 374 | Lee Guetterman | .05 |
| 375 | Dave Hengel (R) | .15 |
| 376 | Mike Kingery | .05 |
| 377 | Mark Langston | .15 |
| 378 | Edgar Martinez (R) | 1.50 |
| 379 | Mike Moore | .05 |
| 380 | Mike Morgan | .05 |
| 381 | John Moses | .05 |
| 382 | Donnell Nixon (R) | .15 |
| 383 | Edwin Nunez | .05 |
| 384 | Ken Phelps | .05 |
| 385 | Jim Presley | .05 |
| 386 | Rey Quinones | .05 |
| 387 | Jerry Reed | .05 |
| 388 | Harold Reynolds | .05 |
| 389 | Dave Valle | .08 |
| 390 | Bill Wilkinson (R) | .15 |

**CHICAGO WHITE SOX**

| NO. | PLAYER | MINT |
|---|---|---|
| 391 | Harold Baines | .10 |
| 392 | Floyd Bannister | .05 |
| 393 | Daryl Boston | .05 |
| 394 | Ivan Calderon | .12 |
| 395 | Jose DeLeon | .05 |
| 396 | Richard Dotson | .05 |
| 397 | Carlton Fisk | .30 |
| 398 | Ozzie Guillen | .05 |
| 399 | Ron Hassey | .05 |
| 400 | Donnie Hill | .05 |
| 401 | Bob James | .05 |
| 402 | Dave LaPoint | .05 |
| 403 | Bill Lindsey (R) | .15 |
| 404 | Bill Long (R) | .15 |
| 405 | Steve Lyons | .05 |
| 406 | Fred Manrique (R) | .15 |
| 407 | Jack McDowell (R) | 1.25 |
| 408 | Gary Redus | .05 |
| 409 | Ray Searage | .05 |
| 410 | Bobby Thigpen | .15 |
| 411 | Greg Walker | .05 |
| 412 | Kenny Williams (R) | .15 |
| 413 | Jim Winn | .05 |

**CHICAGO CUBS**

| NO. | PLAYER | MINT |
|---|---|---|
| 414 | Jody Davis | .05 |
| 415 | Andre Dawson | .30 |
| 416 | Brian Dayett | .05 |
| 417 | Bob Dernier | .05 |
| 418 | Frank DiPino | .05 |
| 419 | Shawon Dunston | .15 |
| 420 | Leon Durham | .10 |
| 421 | Les Lancaster (R) | .15 |
| 422 | Ed Lynch | .05 |
| 423 | Greg Maddux | .60 |
| 424 | Dave Martinez | .15 |
| 425 | K. Moreland (error) (photo of Jody Davis) | 2.50 |
| 425 | K. Moreland (correct) | .15 |
| 426 | Jamie Moyer | .05 |
| 427 | Jerry Mumphrey | .05 |
| 428 | Paul Noce (R) | .15 |
| 429 | Rafael Palmeiro | 1.50 |
| 430 | Wade Rowdon | .10 |
| 431 | Ryne Sandberg | .75 |
| 432 | Scott Sanderson | .05 |
| 433 | Lee Smith | .15 |
| 434 | Jim Sundberg | .05 |
| 435 | Rick Sutcliffe | .10 |
| 436 | Manny Trillo | .05 |

**HOUSTON ASTROS**

| NO. | PLAYER | MINT |
|---|---|---|
| 437 | Juan Agosto | .05 |
| 438 | Larry Andersen | .05 |
| 439 | Alan Ashby | .05 |
| 440 | Kevin Bass | .05 |
| 441 | Ken Caminiti (R) | .40 |
| 442 | Rocky Childress (R) | .15 |
| 443 | Jose Cruz | .05 |
| 444 | Danny Darwin | .05 |
| 445 | Glenn Davis | .15 |
| 446 | Jim Deshaies | .05 |
| 447 | Bill Doran | .05 |
| 448 | Ty Gainey | .05 |
| 449 | Billy Hatcher | .10 |
| 450 | Jeff Heathcock | .05 |
| 451 | Bob Knepper | .05 |
| 452 | Rob Mallicoat (R) | .15 |
| 453 | Dave Meads (R) | .15 |
| 454 | Craig Reynolds | .05 |
| 455 | Nolan Ryan | 1.50 |
| 456 | Mike Scott | .15 |
| 457 | Dave Smith | .05 |
| 458 | Denny Walling | .05 |
| 459 | Robbie Wine (R) | .15 |
| 460 | Gerald Young (R) | .15 |

**TEXAS RANGERS**

| NO. | PLAYER | MINT |
|---|---|---|
| 461 | Bob Brower | .10 |
| 462 | J. Browne (error) (photo of Bob Brower) | 2.50 |
| 462 | J. Browne (correct) | .15 |
| 463 | Steve Buechele | .05 |
| 464 | Edwin Correa | .05 |
| 465 | Cecil Espy (R) | .15 |
| 466 | Scott Fletcher | .05 |
| 467 | Jose Guzman | .05 |
| 468 | Greg Harris | .05 |
| 469 | Charlie Hough | .05 |
| 470 | Pete Incaviglia | .10 |
| 471 | Paul Kilgus (R) | .15 |
| 472 | Mike Loynd | .08 |
| 473 | Oddibe McDowell | .10 |
| 474 | Dale Mohorcic | .05 |
| 475 | Pete O'Brien | .10 |
| 476 | Larry Parrish | .05 |
| 477 | Geno Petralli | .05 |
| 478 | Jeff Russell | .05 |
| 479 | Ruben Sierra | 1.25 |
| 480 | Mike Stanley | .05 |
| 481 | Curtis Wilkerson | .05 |
| 482 | Mitch Williams | .05 |
| 483 | Bobby Witt | .15 |

**CALIFORNIA ANGELS**

| NO. | PLAYER | MINT |
|---|---|---|
| 484 | Tony Armas | .05 |
| 485 | Bob Boone | .05 |
| 486 | Bill Buckner | .05 |
| 487 | DeWayne Buice (R) | .15 |
| 488 | Brian Downing | .05 |
| 489 | Chuck Finley | .35 |
| 490 | Willie Fraser | .05 |
| 491 | Jack Howell | .05 |
| 492 | Ruppert Jones | .05 |
| 493 | Wally Joyner | .35 |
| 494 | Jack Lazorko | .10 |
| 495 | Gary Lucas | .05 |
| 496 | Kirk McCaskill | .05 |
| 497 | Mark McLemore | .05 |
| 498 | Darrell Miller | .05 |
| 499 | Greg Minton | .05 |
| 500 | Donnie Moore | .05 |
| 501 | Gus Polidor | .05 |
| 502 | Johnny Ray | .05 |
| 503 | Mark Ryal | .05 |
| 504 | Dick Schofield | .05 |
| 505 | Don Sutton | .15 |
| 506 | Devon White | .15 |
| 507 | Mike Witt | .10 |

**LOS ANGELES DODGERS**

| NO. | PLAYER | MINT |
|---|---|---|
| 508 | Dave Anderson | .05 |
| 509 | Tim Belcher | .20 |
| 510 | Ralph Bryant | .05 |
| 511 | Tim Crews (R) | .15 |
| 512 | Mike Devereaux (R) | .30 |
| 513 | Mariano Duncan | .05 |
| 514 | Pedro Guerrero | .15 |
| 515 | Jeff Hamilton | .15 |
| 516 | Mickey Hatcher | .05 |
| 517 | Brad Havens | .05 |
| 518 | Orel Hershiser | .20 |
| 519 | Shawn Hillegas (R) | .15 |
| 520 | Ken Howell | .05 |
| 521 | Tim Leary | .05 |
| 522 | Mike Marshall | .10 |
| 523 | Steve Sax | .15 |
| 524 | Mike Scioscia | .05 |
| 525 | Mike Sharperson | .05 |
| 526 | John Shelby | .05 |
| 527 | Franklin Stubbs | .05 |
| 528 | Fernando Valenzuela | .15 |
| 529 | Bob Welch | .05 |
| 530 | Matt Young | .05 |

**ATLANTA BRAVES**

| NO. | PLAYER | MINT |
|---|---|---|
| 531 | Jim Acker | .05 |
| 532 | Paul Assenmacher | .05 |
| 533 | Jeff Blauser (R) | .35 |
| 534 | Joe Boever (R) | .15 |
| 535 | Martin Clary | .05 |
| 536 | Kevin Coffman | .15 |
| 537 | Jeff Dedmon | .05 |
| 538 | Ron Gant (R) | 5.00 |
| 539 | Tom Glavine (R) | 3.00 |
| 540 | Ken Griffey | .05 |
| 541 | Al Hall | .05 |
| 542 | Glenn Hubbard | .05 |
| 543 | Dion James | .05 |
| 544 | Dale Murphy | .25 |
| 545 | Ken Oberkfell | .05 |
| 546 | David Palmer | .05 |
| 547 | Gerald Perry | .15 |
| 548 | Charlie Puleo | .05 |
| 549 | Ted Simmons | .05 |
| 550 | Zane Smith | .05 |
| 551 | Andres Thomas | .05 |
| 552 | Ozzie Virgil | .05 |

**BALTIMORE ORIOLES**

| NO. | PLAYER | MINT |
|---|---|---|
| 553 | Don Aase | .05 |
| 554 | Jeff Ballard (R) | .15 |
| 555 | Eric Bell | .05 |
| 556 | Mike Boddicker | .05 |
| 557 | Ken Dixon | .05 |
| 558 | Jim Dwyer | .05 |
| 559 | Ken Gehart | .05 |
| 560 | Rene Gonzales (R) | .15 |
| 561 | Mike Griffin | .05 |
| 562 | John Hayban | .10 |
| 563 | Terry Kennedy | .05 |
| 564 | Ray Knight | .05 |
| 565 | Lee Lacy | .05 |
| 566 | Fred Lynn | .15 |
| 567 | Eddie Murray | .25 |
| 568 | Tom Niedenfuer | .05 |
| 569 | Bill Ripken (R) | .20 |
| 570 | Cal Ripken, Jr. | 1.00 |
| 571 | Dave Schmidt | .05 |
| 572 | Larry Sheets | .10 |
| 573 | Pete Stanicek (R) | .15 |
| 574 | Mark Williamson (R) | .15 |
| 575 | Mike Young | .05 |

**SAN DIEGO PADRES**

| NO. | PLAYER | MINT |
|---|---|---|
| 576 | Shawn Abner | .10 |
| 577 | Greg Booker | .05 |
| 578 | Chris Brown | .10 |
| 579 | Keith Comstock (R) | .15 |
| 580 | Joey Cora (R) | .15 |
| 581 | Mark Davis | .10 |
| 582 | Tim Flannery | .05 |
| 583 | Goose Gossage | .10 |
| 584 | Mark Grant | .05 |
| 585 | Tony Gwynn | .40 |
| 586 | Andy Hawkins | .05 |
| 587 | Stan Jefferson | .15 |
| 588 | Jimmy Jones | .05 |
| 589 | John Kruk | .10 |
| 590 | Shane Mack | .25 |
| 591 | Carmelo Martinez | .05 |
| 592 | Lance McCullers | .05 |
| 593 | Eric Nolte (R) | .15 |
| 594 | Randy Ready | .05 |
| 595 | Luis Salazar | .05 |
| 596 | Benito Santiago | .25 |
| 597 | Eric Show | .05 |
| 598 | Garry Templeton | .05 |
| 599 | Ed Whitson | .05 |

**CLEVELAND INDIANS**

| NO. | PLAYER | MINT |
|---|---|---|
| 600 | Scott Bailes | .05 |
| 601 | Chris Bando | .05 |
| 602 | Jay Bell (R) | .75 |
| 603 | Brett Butler | .15 |
| 604 | Tom Candiotti | .10 |
| 605 | Joe Carter | .30 |
| 606 | Carmen Castillo | .05 |
| 607 | Brian Dorsett (R) | .15 |
| 608 | John Farrell (R) | .15 |
| 609 | Julio Franco | .20 |
| 610 | Mel Hall | .05 |
| 611 | Tommy Hinzo (R) | .15 |
| 612 | Brook Jacoby | .10 |
| 613 | Doug Jones (R) | .30 |
| 614 | Ken Schrom | .05 |
| 615 | Cory Snyder | .20 |
| 616 | Sammy Stewart | .05 |
| 617 | Greg Swindell | .15 |
| 618 | Pat Tabler | .05 |
| 619 | Ed Vande Berg | .05 |
| 620 | Eddie Williams (R) | .15 |
| 621 | Rich Yett | .05 |

**SPECIAL CARDS**

| NO. | PLAYER | MINT |
|---|---|---|
| 622 | Slugging Sophomores | .20 |
| 623 | Dominican Dynamite | .10 |
| 624 | Oakland's Power Team | .50 |
| 625 | Classic Relief | .10 |
| 626 | All Star Righties | .10 |
| 627 | Game Closers | .10 |
| 628 | Masters of Double Play | .20 |
| 629 | Rookie Record Setter | .35 |
| 630 | Changing the Guard | .25 |
| 631 | N.L. Batting Champs | .20 |
| 632 | Pitching Magic | .10 |
| 633 | Big Bats At First | .15 |
| 634 | Hitting King and Thief | .20 |
| 635 | Slugging Shortstop | .20 |
| 636 | Tried and True Sluggers | .20 |
| 637 | Crunch Time | .30 |
| 638 | A.L. All Stars | .15 |
| 639 | N.L. All-Stars | .15 |
| 640 | The "O's" Brothers | .20 |

**No. 641 to 653—**
**Major League Prospects**

| NO. | PLAYER | MINT |
|---|---|---|
| 641 | Mark Grace (R) and Darrin Jackson (R) | 5.00 |
| 642 | Damon Berryhill (R) and Jeff Montgomery (R) | .40 |
| 643 | Felix Fermin (R) and Jessie Reid (R) | .20 |
| 644 | Greg Myers (R) and Greg Tabor (R) | .20 |
| 645 | Joey Meyer and Jim Eppard (R) | .15 |
| 646 | Adam Peterson (R) and Randy Velarde (R) | .15 |
| 647 | Peter Smith (R) and Chris Gwynn (R) | .20 |
| 648 | Tom Newell (R) and Greg Jelks (R) | .15 |
| 649 | Mario Diaz (R) and Clay Parker (R) | .15 |
| 650 | Jack Savage (R) and Todd Simmons (R) | .15 |
| 651 | John Burkett (R) and Kirt Manwaring (R) | .35 |
| 652 | Dave Otto (R) and Walt Weiss (R) | .50 |
| 653 | Jeff King (R) and Randell Byers (R) | .20 |
| 654 | Checklist No. 1 | .08 |
| 655 | Checklist No. 2 | .08 |
| 656 | Checklist No. 3 | .08 |
| 657 | Checklist No. 4 | .08 |
| 658 | Checklist No. 5 | .08 |
| 659 | Checklist No. 6 | .08 |
| 660 | Checklist No. 7 | .08 |

# 1988 Fleer Traded Update . . . Complete Set of 132 Cards—Value $13.00

This set updates the main 1988 card set with players who had changed teams during the season, and rookies. This set features Fleer's first card of Chris Sabo and Ricky Jordan. This set was packaged in a printed box and distributed primarily through card dealers. For the first time Fleer arranged the cards of its update set in alphabetical order, by team.

| NO. | PLAYER | MINT |
|---|---|---|
| U1 | Jose Bautista | .10 |
| U2 | Jose Orsulak | .08 |
| U3 | Doug Sisk | .07 |
| U4 | Craig Worthington | .12 |
| U5 | Mike Boddiker | .07 |
| U6 | Rick Cerone | .07 |
| U7 | Larry Parrish | .07 |
| U8 | Lee Smith | .10 |
| U9 | Mike Smithson | .07 |
| U10 | John Trautwein | .08 |
| U11 | Sherman Corbett | .10 |
| U12 | Chili Davis | .10 |
| U13 | Jim Eppard | .10 |
| U14 | Bryan Harvey (RR) | .50 |
| U15 | John Davis | .07 |
| U16 | Dave Gallagher | .15 |
| U17 | Ricky Horton | .07 |
| U18 | Dan Pasqua | .07 |
| U19 | Melido Perez | .15 |
| U20 | Jose Segura | .10 |
| U21 | Andy Allanson | .07 |
| U22 | John Perlman | .07 |
| U23 | Domingo Ramos | .07 |
| U24 | Rick Rodriquez | .07 |
| U25 | Willie Upshaw | .10 |
| U26 | Phil Gibson | .10 |
| U27 | Don Heinkel | .10 |
| U28 | Ray Knight | .07 |
| U29 | Gary Pettis | .07 |
| U30 | Luis Salazar | .07 |
| U31 | Mike MacFarlane | .15 |
| U32 | Jeff Montgomery | .10 |
| U33 | Ted Power | .07 |

| NO. | PLAYER | MINT |
|---|---|---|
| U34 | Israel Sanchez | .10 |
| U35 | Kurt Stillwelll | .12 |
| U36 | Pat Tabler | .07 |
| U37 | Don August | .10 |
| U38 | Darryl Hamilton | .20 |
| U39 | Jeff Leonard | .07 |
| U40 | Joey Meyer | .10 |
| U41 | Allan Anderson | .07 |
| U42 | Brian Harper | .07 |
| U43 | Tom Herr | .07 |
| U44 | Charlie Lea | .07 |
| U45 | John Moses | .07 |
| U46 | John Candelaria | .10 |
| U47 | Jack Clark | .12 |
| U48 | Richard Dotson | .07 |
| U49 | Al Leiter | .10 |
| U50 | Rafael Santana | .07 |
| U51 | Dons Slaught | .07 |
| U52 | Todd Burns | .12 |
| U53 | Dave Henderson | .10 |
| U54 | Doug Jennings | .10 |
| U55 | Dave Parker | .20 |
| U56 | Walt Weiss | .15 |
| U57 | Bob Welch | .07 |
| U58 | Henry Cotto | .07 |
| U59 | Mario Diaz | .07 |
| U60 | Mike Jackson | .07 |
| U61 | Bill Swift | .07 |
| U62 | Jose Cecena | .12 |
| U63 | Ray Haywad | .12 |
| U64 | Jim Steels | .12 |
| U65 | Pat Borders | .30 |
| U66 | Sil Campusano | .15 |

| NO. | PLAYER | MINT |
|---|---|---|
| U67 | Mike Flanagan | .07 |
| U68 | Todd Stottlemyre | .75 |
| U69 | David Wells | .15 |
| U70 | Jose Alvarez | .15 |
| U71 | Paul Runge | .07 |
| U72 | Cesar Jimenez | .15 |
| U73 | Pete Smith | .15 |
| U74 | John Smoltz (RR) | 2.00 |
| U75 | Damon Berryhill | .10 |
| U76 | Goose Gossage | .07 |
| U77 | Mark Grace | 2.00 |
| U78 | Darrin Jackson | .10 |
| U79 | Vance Law | .07 |
| U80 | Jeff Pico | .10 |
| U81 | Gary Varsho | .15 |
| U82 | Tim Birtsas | .07 |
| U83 | Rob Dibble (RR) | 1.00 |
| U84 | Danny Jackson | .10 |
| U85 | Paul O'Neill | .12 |
| U86 | Jose Rijo | .07 |
| U87 | Chris Sabo (RR) | 2.00 |
| U88 | John Fishel | .10 |
| U89 | Craig Biggio (RR) | 1.00 |
| U90 | Terry Puhl | .07 |
| U91 | Rafael Ramirez | .07 |
| U92 | Louie Meadows | .15 |
| U93 | Kirk Gibson | .10 |
| U94 | Alfredo Griffin | .07 |
| U95 | Jay Howell | .12 |
| U96 | Jesse Orosco | .07 |
| U97 | Alejandro Pena | .07 |
| U98 | Tracy Woodson | .12 |
| U99 | John Dopson | .10 |

| NO. | PLAYER | MINT |
|---|---|---|
| U100 | Brian Holman | .35 |
| U101 | Rex Hudler | .15 |
| U102 | Jeff Parrett | .07 |
| U103 | Nelson Santovenia | .10 |
| U104 | Kevin Elster | .10 |
| U105 | Jeff Innis | .10 |
| U106 | Mackey Sasser | .15 |
| U107 | Phil Bradley | .07 |
| U108 | Danny Clay | .07 |
| U109 | Greg Harris | .07 |
| U110 | Ricky Jordan (RR) | .35 |
| U111 | David Palmer | .07 |
| U112 | Jim Gott | .07 |
| U113 | Tommy Gregg | .10 |
| U114 | Barry Jones | .07 |
| U115 | Randy Miligan (RR) | .30 |
| U116 | Luis Alicea | .10 |
| U117 | Tom Brunansky | .10 |
| U118 | John Costello | .10 |
| U119 | Jose DeLeon | .07 |
| U120 | Bob Horner | .07 |
| U121 | Scott Terry | .10 |
| U122 | Roberto Alomar (RR) | 3.00 |
| U123 | Dave Leiper | .07 |
| U124 | Keith Moreland | .07 |
| U125 | Mark Parent | .10 |
| U126 | Dennis Rasmussen | .07 |
| U127 | Randy Bockus | .07 |
| U128 | Brett Butler | .12 |
| U129 | Donnell Nixon | .07 |
| U130 | Ernest Riles | .07 |
| U131 | Roger Samuels | .10 |
| U132 | Checklist | .07 |

# 1989 Fleer . . . Complete Set of 660 Cards—Value $28.00

(Factory Sealed Set—Value $30.00)

Features the rookie cards of Gary Sheffield, Tom Gordon, Sandy Alomar, Jr. and Ken Griffey, Jr. A new feature on the back is a comparison of each player's statistics before and after the All-Star break.

| NO. | PLAYER | MINT |
|---|---|---|
| **OAKLAND A'S** | | |
| 1 | Don Baylor | .08 |
| 2 | Lance Blankenship (R) | .10 |
| 3 | Todd Burns (R) | .10 |
| 4 | Greg Cadaret | .10 |
| 5 | Jose Canseco | .50 |
| 6 | Storm Davis | .05 |
| 7 | Dennis Eckersley | .12 |

| NO. | PLAYER | MINT |
|---|---|---|
| 8 | Mike Gallego | .05 |
| 9 | Ron Hassey | .05 |
| 10 | Dave Henderson | .08 |
| 11 | Rick Honeycutt | .05 |
| 12 | Glenn Hubbard | .05 |
| 13 | Stan Javier | .05 |
| 14 | Doug Jennings (R) | .10 |
| 15 | Felix Jose (R) | 1.00 |

| NO. | PLAYER | MINT |
|---|---|---|
| 16 | Carney Lanstord | .05 |
| 17 | Mark McGwire | .20 |
| 18 | Gene Nelson | .05 |
| 19 | Dave Parker | .10 |
| 20 | Eric Plunk | .05 |
| 21 | Luis Polonia | .05 |
| 22 | Terry Steinbach | .15 |
| 23 | Dave Stewart | .15 |

| NO. | PLAYER | MINT |
|---|---|---|
| 24 | Walt Weiss | .10 |
| 25 | Bob Welch | .08 |
| 26 | Curt Young | .05 |
| **NEW YORK METS** | | |
| 27 | Rick Aguilera | .05 |
| 28 | Wally Backman | .05 |
| 29 | Mark Carreon | .05 |
| 30 | Gary Carter | .15 |

| NO. | PLAYER | MINT |
|-----|--------|------|
| 31 | Dave Cone | .10 |
| 32 | Ron Darling | .10 |
| 33 | Len Dykstra | .10 |
| 34 | Kevin Elster | .08 |
| 35 | Sid Fernandez | .10 |
| 36 | Dwight Gooden | .20 |
| 37 | Keith Hernandez | .15 |
| 38 | Gregg Jefferies | .35 |
| 39 | Howard Johnson | .15 |
| 40 | Terry Leach | .05 |
| 41 | Dave Magadan | .10 |
| 42 | Bob McClure | .05 |
| 43 | Roger McDowell | .05 |
| 44 | Kevin McReynolds | .10 |
| 45 | Keith Miller | .05 |
| 46 | Randy Myers | .08 |
| 47 | Bob Ojeda | .08 |
| 48 | Mackey Sasser | .10 |
| 49 | Darryl Strawberry | .35 |
| 50 | Tim Teufel | .05 |
| 51 | Dave West (R) | .15 |
| 52 | Mookie Wilson | .08 |

**LOS ANGELES DODGERS**

| NO. | PLAYER | MINT |
|-----|--------|------|
| 53 | Dave Anderson | .05 |
| 54 | Tim Belcher | .10 |
| 55 | Mike Davis | .05 |
| 56 | Mike Devereaux | .05 |
| 57 | Kirk Gibson | .10 |
| 58 | Alfredo Griffin | .05 |
| 59 | Chris Gwynn | .10 |
| 60 | Jeff Hamilton | .05 |
| 61 | Danny Heep | .08 |
| 62 | Orel Hershiser | .12 |
| 63 | Brian Holton | .05 |
| 64 | Jay Howell | .08 |
| 65 | Tim Leary | .10 |
| 66 | Mike Marshall | .08 |
| 67 | Ramon Martinez (R) | 2.00 |
| 68 | Jess Orosco | .05 |
| 69 | Alejandro Pena | .08 |
| 70 | Steve Sax | .12 |
| 71 | Mike Scioscia | .05 |
| 72 | Mike Sharperson | .05 |
| 73 | John Shelby | .05 |
| 74 | Franklin Stubbs | .05 |
| 75 | John Tudor | .05 |
| 76 | Fernando Velenzuela | .12 |
| 77 | Tracy Woodson | .10 |

**BOSTON RED SOX**

| NO. | PLAYER | MINT |
|-----|--------|------|
| 78 | Marty Barrett | .05 |
| 79 | Todd Benzinger | .10 |
| 80 | Mike Boddicker | .08 |
| 81 | Wade Boggs | .25 |
| 82 | "Oil Can" Boyd | .08 |
| 83 | Ellis Burks | .20 |
| 84 | Rick Cerone | .05 |
| 85 | Roger Clemens | .35 |
| 86 | Steve Curry (R) | .10 |
| 87 | Dwight Evans | .15 |
| 88 | Wes Gardner | .05 |
| 89 | Rich Gedman | .05 |
| 90 | Mike Greenwell | .20 |
| 91 | Bruce Hurst | .10 |
| 92 | Dennis Lamp | .05 |
| 93 | Spike Owen | .05 |
| 94 | Larry Parrish | .10 |
| 95 | Carlos Quintana (R) | .30 |
| 96 | Jody Reed | .10 |
| 97 | Jim Rice | .10 |
| 98 | Kevin Romine | .10 |
| 98 | K. Romine (error) | .35 |
| 99 | Lee Smith | .08 |
| 100 | Mike Smithson | .05 |
| 101 | Bob Stanley | .05 |

**MINNESOTA TWINS**

| NO. | PLAYER | MINT |
|-----|--------|------|
| 102 | Allan Anderson | .08 |
| 103 | Keith Atherton | .05 |
| 104 | Juan Berenguer | .05 |
| 105 | Bert Blyleven | .10 |
| 106 | Eric Bullock | .10 |
| 107 | Randy Bush | .05 |
| 108 | John Christensen | .05 |
| 109 | Mark Davidson | .05 |
| 110 | Gary Gaetti | .08 |
| 111 | Greg Gagne | .05 |
| 112 | Dan Gladden | .05 |
| 113 | German Gonzalez (R) | .10 |
| 114 | Brian Harper | .05 |
| 115 | Tom Herr | .05 |

| NO. | PLAYER | MINT |
|-----|--------|------|
| 116 | Kent Hrbek | .15 |
| 117 | Gene Larken | .05 |
| 118 | Tim Laudner | .05 |
| 119 | Charlie Lea | .05 |
| 120 | Steve Lombardozzi | .05 |
| 121 | J. Moses (Phoenix) | .20 |
| 121 | J. Moses (Tempe) | .40 |
| 122 | Al Newman | .05 |
| 123 | Mark Portugal | .05 |
| 124 | Kirby Puckett | .35 |
| 125 | Jeff Reardon | .08 |
| 126 | Fred Toliver | .05 |
| 127 | Frank Viola | .10 |

**DETROIT TIGERS**

| NO. | PLAYER | MINT |
|-----|--------|------|
| 128 | Doyle Alexander | .05 |
| 129 | Dave Bergman | .05 |
| 130 | Tom Brookens | .08 |
| 130 | T. Brookens (error) | .75 |
| 131 | Paul Gibson (R) | .12 |
| 132 | Mike Heath | .10 |
| 132 | M. Heath (error) | .75 |
| 133 | Don Heinkel (R) | .12 |
| 134 | Mike Henneman | .05 |
| 135 | Guillermo Hernandez | .05 |
| 136 | Eric King | .05 |
| 137 | Chet Lemon | .05 |
| 138 | Fred Lynn | .08 |
| 139 | Jack Morris | .10 |
| 140 | Matt Nokes | .10 |
| 141 | Gary Pettis | .05 |
| 142 | Ted Power | .05 |
| 143 | Jeff M. Robinson | .10 |
| 144 | Luis Salazar | .05 |
| 145 | Steve Searcy (R) | .12 |
| 146 | Pat Sheridan | .05 |
| 147 | Frank Tanana | .08 |
| 148 | Alan Trammell | .15 |
| 149 | Walt Terrell | .05 |
| 150 | Jim Walewander | .10 |
| 151 | Lou Whitaker | .08 |

**CINCINNATI REDS**

| NO. | PLAYER | MINT |
|-----|--------|------|
| 152 | Tim Birtsas | .05 |
| 153 | Tom Browning | .08 |
| 154 | Keith Brown (R) | .10 |
| 155 | Norm Charlton (R) | .20 |
| 156 | Dave Concepcion | .05 |
| 157 | Kal Daniels | .10 |
| 158 | Eric Davis | .20 |
| 159 | Bo Diaz | .05 |
| 160 | Rob Dibble (R) | .40 |
| 161 | Nick Esasky | .10 |
| 162 | John Franco | .08 |
| 163 | Danny Jackson | .12 |
| 164 | Barry Larkin | .20 |
| 165 | Rob Murphy | .05 |
| 166 | Paul O'Neil | .10 |
| 167 | Jeff Reed | .10 |
| 168 | Jose Rijo | .08 |
| 169 | Ron Robinson | .08 |
| 170 | Chris Sabo (R) | .75 |
| 171 | Candy Sierra (R) | .10 |
| 172 | Van Snider (R) | .10 |
| 173 | Jeff Treadway | .08 |
| 174 | Frank Williams | .05 |
| 175 | Herm Winningham | .05 |

**MILWAUKEE BREWERS**

| NO. | PLAYER | MINT |
|-----|--------|------|
| 176 | Jim Adduci | .08 |
| 177 | Don August | .10 |
| 178 | Mike Birkbeck | .05 |
| 179 | Chris Bosio | .05 |
| 180 | Glenn Braggs | .05 |
| 181 | Greg Brock | .05 |
| 182 | Mark Clear | .05 |
| 183 | Chuck Crim | .05 |
| 184 | Rob Deer | .08 |
| 185 | Tom Filer | .05 |
| 186 | Jim Gantner | .05 |
| 187 | Darryl Hamilton (R) | .15 |
| 188 | Ted Higuera | .10 |
| 189 | Odell Jones | .05 |
| 190 | Jeffrey Leonard | .05 |
| 191 | Joey Meyer | .05 |
| 192 | Paul Mirabella | .05 |
| 193 | Paul Molitor | .10 |
| 194 | Charlie O'Brien | .08 |
| 195 | Dan Plesac | .05 |
| 196 | Gary Sheffield (R) | .50 |
| 197 | B.J. Surhoff | .08 |
| 198 | Dale Sveum | .05 |

| NO. | PLAYER | MINT |
|-----|--------|------|
| 199 | Bill Wegman | .05 |
| 200 | Robin Yount | .15 |

**PITTSBURGH PIRATES**

| NO. | PLAYER | MINT |
|-----|--------|------|
| 201 | Rafael Belliard | .05 |
| 202 | Barry Bonds | .30 |
| 203 | Bobby Bonilla | .25 |
| 204 | Sid Bream | .05 |
| 205 | Benny Distefano | .10 |
| 206 | Doug Drabek | .10 |
| 207 | Mike Dunne | .05 |
| 208 | Felix Fermin | .05 |
| 209 | Brian Fisher | .05 |
| 210 | Jim Gott | .05 |
| 211 | Bob Kipper | .05 |
| 212 | Dave LaPoint | .05 |
| 213 | Mike LaValliere | .05 |
| 214 | Jose Lind | .05 |
| 215 | Junior Ortiz | .05 |
| 216 | Vincente Palacios | .05 |
| 217 | Tom Prince | .10 |
| 218 | Gary Redus | .05 |
| 219 | R.J. Reynolds | .05 |
| 220 | Jeff Robinson | .05 |
| 221 | John Smiley | .08 |
| 222 | Andy Van Slyke | .15 |
| 223 | Bob Walk | .05 |
| 224 | Glenn Wilson | .05 |

**TORONTO BLUE JAYS**

| NO. | PLAYER | MINT |
|-----|--------|------|
| 225 | Jesse Barfield | .12 |
| 226 | George Bell | .15 |
| 227 | Pat Borders (R) | .20 |
| 228 | John Cerutti | .05 |
| 229 | Jim Clancy | .05 |
| 230 | Mark Eichhorn | .05 |
| 231 | Tony Fernandez | .10 |
| 232 | Cecil Fielder | .30 |
| 233 | Mike Flanagan | .05 |
| 234 | Kelly Gruber | .15 |
| 235 | Tom Henke | .05 |
| 236 | Jimmy Key | .15 |
| 237 | Rick Leach | .05 |
| 238 | Manny Lee | .05 |
| 239 | Nelson Liriano | .05 |
| 240 | Fred McGriff | .25 |
| 241 | Lloyd Moseby | .12 |
| 242 | Rance Mulliniks | .05 |
| 243 | Jeff Musselman | .05 |
| 244 | Dave Stieb | .08 |
| 245 | Todd Stottlemyre | .20 |
| 246 | Duane Ward | .05 |
| 247 | David Wells | .10 |
| 248 | Ernie Whitt | .05 |

**NEW YORK YANKEES**

| NO. | PLAYER | MINT |
|-----|--------|------|
| 249 | Luis Aguayo | .05 |
| 250 | Neil Allen (N.Y.) | .15 |
| 250 | Neil Allen (Fla.) | .75 |
| 251 | John Candelaria | .08 |
| 252 | Jack Clark | .10 |
| 253 | Richard Dotson | .08 |
| 254 | Rickey Henderson | .40 |
| 255 | Tommy John | .10 |
| 256 | Roberto Kelly | .15 |
| 257 | Al Leiter | .10 |
| 258 | Don Mattingly | .30 |
| 259 | Dale Mohorcic | .05 |
| 260 | Hal Morris (R) | 2.50 |
| 261 | Scott Nielsen | .05 |
| 262 | Mike Pagliarulo | .10 |
| 263 | Hipolito Peno (R) | .15 |
| 264 | Ken Phelps | .05 |
| 265 | Willie Randolph | .08 |
| 266 | Rick Rhoden | .05 |
| 267 | Dave Righetti | .10 |
| 268 | Rafael Santana | .05 |
| 269 | Steve Shields | .05 |
| 270 | Joel Skinner | .05 |
| 271 | Don Slaught | .05 |
| 272 | Claudell Washington | .05 |
| 273 | Gary Ward | .05 |
| 274 | Dave Winfield | .15 |

**KC ROYALS**

| NO. | PLAYER | MINT |
|-----|--------|------|
| 275 | Luis Aquino | .05 |
| 276 | Floyd Bannister | .05 |
| 277 | George Brett | .20 |
| 278 | Bill Buckner | .08 |
| 279 | Nick Capra (R) | .15 |
| 280 | Jose DeJesus (R) | .15 |
| 281 | Steve Farr | .05 |

| NO. | PLAYER | MINT |
|-----|--------|------|
| 282 | Jerry Don Gleaton | .05 |
| 283 | Mark Gubicza | .10 |
| 284 | Tom Gordon (R) | .30 |
| 285 | Bo Jackson | .50 |
| 286 | Charlie Leibrandt | .08 |
| 287 | Mike MacFarlane (R) | .12 |
| 288 | Jeff Montgomery | .05 |
| 289 | Bill Pecota | .05 |
| 290 | Jamie Quirk | .05 |
| 291 | Bret Saberhagen | .12 |
| 292 | Kevin Seitzer | .15 |
| 293 | Kurt Stillwell | .05 |
| 294 | Pat Tabler | .08 |
| 295 | Danny Tartabull | .15 |
| 296 | Gary Thurman | .05 |
| 297 | Frank White | .05 |
| 298 | Willie Wilson | .08 |

**SAN DIEGO PADRES**

| NO. | PLAYER | MINT |
|-----|--------|------|
| 299 | Roberto Alomar | .75 |
| 300 | Sandy Alomar Jr. (R) | .60 |
| 301 | Chris Brown | .08 |
| 302 | Mike Brumley | .10 |
| 303 | Mark Davis | .10 |
| 304 | Mark Grant | .05 |
| 305 | Tony Gwynn | .20 |
| 306 | Greg W. Harris (R) | .20 |
| 307 | Andy Hawkins | .05 |
| 308 | Jimmy Jones | .05 |
| 309 | John Kruk | .10 |
| 310 | Dave Leiper | .05 |
| 311 | Carmelo Martinez | .05 |
| 312 | Lance McCullers | .08 |
| 313 | Keith Moreland | .05 |
| 314 | Dennis Rasmussen | .05 |
| 315 | Randy Ready | .05 |
| 316 | Benito Santiago | .15 |
| 317 | Eric Show | .05 |
| 318 | Todd Simmons | .05 |
| 319 | Garry Templeton | .05 |
| 320 | Dickie Thon | .05 |
| 321 | Ed Whitson | .05 |
| 322 | Marvell Wynne | .05 |

**SF GIANTS**

| NO. | PLAYER | MINT |
|-----|--------|------|
| 323 | Mike Aldrete | .05 |
| 324 | Bret Butler | .05 |
| 325 | Will Clark | .50 |
| 326 | Kelly Downs | .05 |
| 327 | Dave Dravecky | .05 |
| 328 | Scott Garrelts | .05 |
| 329 | Atlee Hammaker | .05 |
| 330 | Charlie Hayes (R) | .15 |
| 331 | Mike Krukow | .08 |
| 332 | Craig Lefferts | .05 |
| 333 | Candy Maldonado | .10 |
| 334 | Kirt Manwaring | .05 |
| 335 | Bob Melvin | .05 |
| 336 | Kevin Mitchell | .25 |
| 337 | Donell Nixon | .05 |
| 338 | Tony Perezchica (R) | .12 |
| 339 | Joe Price | .05 |
| 340 | Rick Reuschel | .05 |
| 341 | Ernest Riles | .05 |
| 342 | Don Robinson | .05 |
| 343 | Chris Speier | .05 |
| 344 | Robby Thompson | .05 |
| 345 | Jose Uribe | .08 |
| 346 | Matt Williams | .25 |
| 347 | Trevor Wilson (R) | .12 |

**HOUSTON ASTROS**

| NO. | PLAYER | MINT |
|-----|--------|------|
| 348 | Juan Agosto | .05 |
| 349 | Larry Anderson | .10 |
| 350 | Alan Ashby | .05 |
| 351 | Kevin Bass | .08 |
| 352 | Buddy Bell | .08 |
| 353 | Craig Biggio (R) | .75 |
| 354 | Danny Darwin | .05 |
| 355 | Glenn Davis | .10 |
| 356 | Jim Deshaies | .05 |
| 357 | Bill Doran | .08 |
| 358 | John Fisher (R) | .20 |
| 359 | Billy Hatcher | .05 |
| 360 | Bob Knepper | .05 |
| 361 | Louie Meadows (R) | .15 |
| 362 | Dave Meads | .05 |
| 363 | Jim Pankovits | .05 |
| 364 | Terry Puhl | .05 |
| 365 | Rafael Ramirez | .05 |

| NO. | PLAYER | MINT |
|---|---|---|
| 366 | Craig Reynolds | .05 |
| 367 | Mike Scott | .15 |
| 368 | Nolan Ryan | .60 |
| 369 | Dave Smith | .05 |
| 370 | Gerald Young | .08 |

**MONTREAL EXPOS**

| NO. | PLAYER | MINT |
|---|---|---|
| 371 | Hubie Brooks | .05 |
| 372 | Tim Burke | .05 |
| 373 | John Dopson (R) | .12 |
| 374 | Mike Fitzgerald | .05 |
| 375 | Tom Foley | .05 |
| 376 | Andres Galarraga | .10 |
| 377 | Neal Heaton | .05 |
| 378 | Joe Hesketh | .05 |
| 379 | Brian Holman (R) | .20 |
| 380 | Rex Hudler | .10 |
| 381 | Randy Johnson (R) | .35 |
| 382 | Wallace Johnson | .05 |
| 383 | Tracy Jones | .05 |
| 384 | Dave Martinez | .05 |
| 385 | Dennis Martinez | .05 |
| 386 | Andy McGaffigan | .05 |
| 387 | Otis Nixon | .05 |
| 388 | Johnny Padres (R) | .12 |
| 389 | Jeff Parrett | .08 |
| 390 | Pascual Perez | .05 |
| 391 | Tim Raines | .12 |
| 392 | Luis Rivera | .05 |
| 393 | Nelson Santovenia (R) | .12 |
| 394 | Bryn Smith | .05 |
| 395 | Tim Wallach | .08 |

**CLEVELAND INDIANS**

| NO. | PLAYER | MINT |
|---|---|---|
| 396 | Andy Allanson | .05 |
| 397 | Rod Allen (R) | .12 |
| 398 | Scott Bailes | .05 |
| 399 | Tom Candiotti | .08 |
| 400 | Joe Carter | .15 |
| 401 | Carmen Castillo | .05 |
| 402 | Dave Clark | .10 |
| 403 | John Farrell | .10 |
| 404 | Julio Franco | .10 |
| 405 | Don Gordon | .10 |
| 406 | Mel Hall | .05 |
| 407 | Brad Havens | .05 |
| 408 | Brook Jacoby | .05 |
| 409 | Doug Jones | .05 |
| 410 | Jeff Kaiser (R) | .10 |
| 411 | Luis Medina (R) | .12 |
| 412 | Cory Snyder | .08 |
| 413 | Greg Swindell | .08 |
| 414 | Ron Tingley | .08 |
| 415 | Willie Upshaw | .05 |
| 416 | Ron Washington | .05 |
| 417 | Rich Yett | .05 |

**CHICAGO CUBS**

| NO. | PLAYER | MINT |
|---|---|---|
| 418 | Damon Berryhill | .10 |
| 419 | Mike Bielecki | .05 |
| 420 | Doug Dascenzo (R) | .12 |
| 421 | Jody Davis | .05 |
| 422 | Andre Dawson | .15 |
| 423 | Frank Dipino | .05 |
| 424 | Shawon Dunston | .10 |
| 425 | "Goose" Gossage | .08 |
| 426 | Mark Grace | .50 |
| 427 | Mike Harkey (R) | .15 |
| 428 | Darrin Jackson | .08 |
| 429 | Les Lancaster | .05 |
| 430 | Vance Law | .05 |
| 431 | Greg Maddux | .10 |
| 432 | Jamie Moyer | .05 |
| 433 | Al Nipper | .05 |
| 434 | Rafael Palmeiro | .15 |
| 435 | Pat Perry | .05 |
| 436 | Jeff Pico (R) | .10 |
| 437 | Ryne Sandberg | .35 |
| 438 | Calvin Schiraldi | .05 |
| 439 | Rick Sutcliffe | .10 |
| 440 | Manny Trillo | .05 |
| 441 | Gary Varsho (R) | .12 |
| 442 | Mitch Webster | .05 |

**ST. LOUIS CARDINALS**

| NO. | PLAYER | MINT |
|---|---|---|
| 443 | Luis Alicea (R) | .12 |
| 444 | Tom Brunansky | .08 |
| 445 | Vince Coleman | .15 |
| 446 | John Costello (R) | .10 |
| 447 | Danny Cox | .05 |
| 448 | Ken Dayley | .05 |
| 449 | Jose Deleon | .05 |
| 450 | Curt Ford | .05 |
| 451 | Pedro Guerrero | .10 |
| 452 | Bob Horner | .05 |
| 453 | Tim Jones (R) | .12 |
| 454 | Steve Lake | .05 |
| 455 | Joe Magrane | .10 |
| 456 | Greg Mathews | .05 |
| 457 | Willie McGee | .08 |
| 458 | Larry McWilliams | .05 |
| 459 | Jose Oquendo | .05 |
| 460 | Tony Pena | .08 |
| 461 | Terry Pendleton | .10 |
| 462 | Steve Peters (R) | .10 |
| 463 | Ozzie Smith | .15 |
| 464 | Scott Terry | .05 |
| 465 | Denny Walling | .05 |
| 466 | Todd Worrell | .08 |

**CALIFORNIA ANGELS**

| NO. | PLAYER | MINT |
|---|---|---|
| 467 | Tony Armas | .05 |
| 468 | Dante Bichette (R) | .30 |
| 469 | Bob Boone | .05 |
| 470 | Terry Clark (R) | .10 |
| 471 | Stew Cliburn | .05 |
| 472 | Mike Cook (R) | .10 |
| 473 | Sherman Corbett (R) | .10 |
| 474 | Chili Davis | .08 |
| 475 | Brian Downing | .08 |
| 476 | Jim Eppard | .05 |
| 477 | Chuck Finley | .15 |
| 478 | Willie Fraser | .05 |
| 479 | Bryan Harvey (R) | .30 |
| 480 | Jack Howell | .08 |
| 481 | Wally Joyner | .15 |
| 482 | Jack Lazorko | .05 |
| 483 | Kirk McCaskill | .05 |
| 484 | Mark McLemore | .05 |
| 485 | Greg Minton | .05 |
| 486 | Dan Petry | .05 |
| 487 | Johnny Ray | .10 |
| 488 | Dick Schofield | .05 |
| 489 | Devon White | .10 |
| 490 | Mike Witt | .08 |

**CHICAGO WHITE SOX**

| NO. | PLAYER | MINT |
|---|---|---|
| 491 | Harold Baines | .10 |
| 492 | Daryl Boston | .05 |
| 493 | Ivan Calderon | .10 |
| 494 | Mike Diaz | .05 |
| 495 | Carlton Fisk | .15 |
| 496 | Dave Gallagher (R) | .12 |
| 497 | Ozzie Guillen | .08 |
| 498 | Shawn Hillegas | .05 |
| 499 | Lance Johnson | .05 |
| 500 | Barry Jones | .05 |
| 501 | Bill Long | .05 |
| 502 | Steve Lyons | .05 |
| 503 | Fred Manrique | .05 |
| 504 | Jack McDowell | .20 |
| 505 | Donn Pall | .10 |
| 506 | Kelly Paris | .05 |
| 507 | Dan Pasqua | .08 |
| 508 | Ken Patterson (R) | .10 |
| 509 | Melido Perez | .10 |
| 510 | Jerry Reuss | .05 |
| 511 | Mark Salas | .05 |
| 512 | Bobby Thigpen | .05 |
| 513 | Mike Woodard | .05 |

**TEXAS RANGERS**

| NO. | PLAYER | MINT |
|---|---|---|
| 514 | Bob Brower | .05 |
| 515 | Steve Buechele | .05 |
| 516 | Jose Cecena (R) | .10 |
| 517 | Cecil Espy | .05 |
| 518 | Scott Fletcher | .05 |
| 519 | Cecilio Guante | .05 |
| 520 | Jose Guman | .05 |
| 521 | Ray Hayward | .05 |
| 522 | Charlie Hough | .08 |
| 523 | Pete Incaviglia | .10 |
| 524 | Mike Jeffcoat | .05 |
| 525 | Paul Kilgus | .05 |
| 526 | Chad Kreuter (R) | .10 |
| 527 | Jeff Kunkel | .05 |
| 528 | Oddibe McDowell | .08 |
| 529 | Pete O'Brien | .10 |
| 530 | Geno Petralli | .05 |
| 531 | Jeff Russell | .05 |
| 532 | Ruben Sierra | .25 |
| 533 | Mike Stanley | .05 |
| 534 | Ed VandeBerg | .05 |
| 535 | Curtis Wilkerson | .05 |
| 536 | Mitch Williams | .05 |
| 537 | Bobby Witt | .05 |

**SEATTLE MARINERS**

| NO. | PLAYER | MINT |
|---|---|---|
| 538 | Steve Balboni | .05 |
| 539 | Scott Bankhead | .05 |
| 540 | Scott Bradley | .05 |
| 541 | Mickey Brantley | .08 |
| 542 | Jay Buhner | .20 |
| 543 | Mike Campbell | .05 |
| 544 | Darnell Coles | .05 |
| 545 | Henry Cotto | .05 |
| 546 | Alvin Davis | .08 |
| 547 | Mario Diaz | .05 |
| 548 | Ken Griffey Jr. (R) | 10.00 |
| 549 | Erik Hanson (R) | .75 |
| 550 | Mike Jackson | .05 |
| 551 | Mark Langston | .12 |
| 552 | Edgar Martinez | .20 |
| 553 | Bill McGuire (R) | .15 |
| 554 | Mike Moore | .05 |
| 555 | Jim Presley | .05 |
| 556 | Rey Quinones | .05 |
| 557 | Jerry Reed | .05 |
| 558 | Harold Reynolds | .08 |
| 559 | Mike Schooler (R) | .15 |
| 560 | Bill Swift | .05 |
| 561 | Dave Valle | .05 |

**PHILADELPHIA PHILLIES**

| NO. | PLAYER | MINT |
|---|---|---|
| 562 | Steve Bedrosian | .08 |
| 563 | Phil Bradley | .08 |
| 564 | Don Carman | .05 |
| 565 | Bob Dernier | .05 |
| 566 | Marvin Freeman | .05 |
| 567 | Todd Frohwirth | .05 |
| 568 | Greg Gross | .05 |
| 569 | Kevin Gross | .05 |
| 570 | Greg Harris | .12 |
| 571 | Von Hayes | .08 |
| 572 | Chris James | .08 |
| 573 | Steve Jeltz | .05 |
| 574 | Ron Jones (R) | .10 |
| 575 | Ricky Jordan (R) | .20 |
| 576 | Mike Maddux | .05 |
| 577 | David Palmer | .05 |
| 578 | Lance Parrish | .10 |
| 579 | Shane Rawley | .05 |
| 580 | Bruce Ruffin | .05 |
| 581 | Juan Samuel | .10 |
| 582 | Mike Schmidt | .35 |
| 583 | Kent Tekulve | .05 |
| 584 | Milt Thompson | .05 |

**ATLANTA BRAVES**

| NO. | PLAYER | MINT |
|---|---|---|
| 585 | Jose Alvarez (R) | .10 |
| 586 | Paul Assenmacher | .05 |
| 587 | Bruce Benedict | .05 |
| 588 | Jeff Blauser | .05 |
| 589 | Terry Blockner (R) | .10 |
| 590 | Ron Gant | .50 |
| 591 | Tom Glavine | .40 |
| 592 | Tommy Gregg | .10 |
| 593 | Albert Hall | .05 |
| 594 | Dion James | .05 |
| 595 | Rich Mahler | .05 |
| 596 | Dale Murphy | .15 |
| 597 | Gerald Perry | .12 |
| 598 | Charlie Puleo | .05 |
| 599 | Ted Simmons | .05 |
| 600 | Pete Smith | .08 |
| 601 | Zane Smith | .05 |
| 602 | John Smoltz (R) | .75 |
| 603 | Bruce Sutter | .08 |
| 604 | Andres Thomas | .05 |
| 605 | Ozzie Virgil | .05 |

**BALTIMORE ORIOLES**

| NO. | PLAYER | MINT |
|---|---|---|
| 606 | Brady Anderson (R) | .10 |
| 607 | Jeff Ballard | .05 |
| 608 | Jose Bautista (R) | .10 |
| 609 | Ken Gerhart | .05 |
| 610 | Terry Kennedy | .05 |
| 611 | Eddie Murray | .20 |
| 612 | Carl Nichols | .10 |
| 613 | Tom Niedenfuer | .05 |
| 614 | Joe Orsulak | .05 |
| 615 | Oswaldo Perraza (R) | .10 |
| 616 | Billy Ripken (obscenity blocked out in black) | .30 |
| 616 | Billy Ripken (obscenity on bat) | 10.00 |
| 616 | Billy Ripken (obscenity blocked out in white) | 27.00 |
| 617 | Cal Ripken Jr. | .35 |
| 618 | Dave Schmidt | .10 |
| 619 | Rich Schu | .05 |
| 620 | Larry Sheets | .05 |
| 621 | Doug Sisk | .05 |
| 622 | Pete Stanicek | .05 |
| 623 | Mickey Tettleton | .05 |
| 624 | Jay Tibbs | .05 |
| 625 | Jim Traber | .05 |
| 626 | Mark Williamson | .05 |
| 627 | Craig Worthington (R) | .10 |

**SPECIAL CARDS**

| NO. | PLAYER | MINT |
|---|---|---|
| 628 | Speed/Power | .25 |
| 629 | Pitcher Perfect | .08 |
| 630 | Like Father-Like Son | .30 |
| 631 | N.L. All Stars | .15 |
| 632 | Homeruns-Coast to Coast | .35 |
| 633 | Hot Corners-Hot Hitters | .20 |
| 634 | Triple A's | .25 |
| 635 | Dual Heat | .10 |
| 636 | N.L. Pitching Power | .15 |
| 637 | Cannon Arms | .15 |
| 638 | Double Trouble | .15 |
| 639 | Power Center | .20 |

**No. 640 to 653— Major League Prospects**

| NO. | PLAYER | MINT |
|---|---|---|
| 640 | S. Wilson (R)/C. Drew (R) | .15 |
| 641 | K.Brown (R)/K. Reimer (R) | .50 |
| 642 | B.Pounders (R)/J.Clark (R) | .40 |
| 643 | M. Capel (R)/D. Hall | .15 |
| 644 | J.Girardi (R)/R. Roomes (R) | .15 |
| 645 | L. Harris (R)/M. Brown (R) | .30 |
| 646 | L.Santos (R)/J.Campbell (R) | .15 |
| 647 | R.Kramer (R)/M.Garcia (R) | .15 |
| 648 | T.Lovullo (R)/R.Palacios (R) | .15 |
| 649 | J. Corsi (R)/B. Milacki (R) | .20 |
| 650 | G.Hall (R)/M.Rochford (R) | .15 |
| 651 | T.Taylor (R)/V.Lovelace (R) | .15 |
| 652 | K. Hill (R)/D. Cook (R) | .35 |
| 653 | S. Service (R)/S. Turner (R) | .15 |
| 654 | Checklist No. 1 | .08 |
| 655 | Checklist No. 2 | .08 |
| 656 | Checklist No. 3 | .08 |
| 657 | Checklist No. 4 | .08 |
| 658 | Checklist No. 5 | .08 |
| 659 | Checklist No. 6 | .08 |
| 660 | Checklist No. 7 | .08 |

# 1989 Fleer Traded Update . . . Complete Set of 132 Cards—Value $15.00

This set updates the main 1989 card set with players who had changed teams during the season, and rookies. This set features the first card of Jim Abbott, Greg Vaughn, Jerome Walton and Todd Zeile. The set was packaged in a printed box and distributed primarily through card hobby dealers.

| NO. PLAYER | MINT |
|---|---|
| U1 Phil Bradley | .06 |
| U2 Mike Devereaux | .08 |
| U3 Steve Finley (R) | .40 |
| U4 Kevin Hickey | .06 |
| U5 Brian Holton | .08 |
| U6 Bob Milacki | .15 |
| U7 Randy Milligan | .10 |
| U8 John Dopson | .06 |
| U9 Nick Esasky | .10 |
| U10 Rob Murphy | .06 |
| U11 Jim Abbott (R) | 1.25 |
| U12 Bert Blyleven | .06 |
| U13 Jeff Manto (R) | .25 |
| U14 Bob McClure | .06 |
| U15 Lance Parrish | .06 |
| U16 Lee Stevens (R) | .60 |
| U17 Claudell Washington | .06 |
| U18 Mark Davis | .06 |
| U19 Erick King | .06 |
| U20 Ron Kittle | .06 |
| U21 Matt Murullo (R) | .12 |
| U22 Steve Rosenberg (R) | .10 |
| U23 Robin Ventura (R) | 2.00 |
| U24 Keith Atherton | .06 |
| U25 Joey Belle (R) | 1.50 |
| U26 Jerry Browne | .06 |
| U27 Felix Fermin | .06 |
| U28 Brad Komminsk | .06 |
| U29 Pete O'Brien | .06 |
| U30 Mike Brumley | .06 |
| U31 Tracy Jones | .06 |
| U32 Mike Schwabe | .10 |
| U33 Gary Ward | .06 |

| NO. PLAYER | MINT |
|---|---|
| U34 Frank Williams | .06 |
| U35 Kevin Appier (R) | .50 |
| U36 Bob Boone | .06 |
| U37 Luis del los Santos | .10 |
| U38 Jim Eisenreich | .10 |
| U39 Jaime Navarro (R) | .30 |
| U40 Bill Spiers (R) | .12 |
| U41 Greg Vaughn (R) | 1.50 |
| U42 Randy Veres | .12 |
| U43 Wally Backman | .06 |
| U44 Shane Rawley | .06 |
| U45 Steve Balboni | .06 |
| U46 Jesse Barfield | .06 |
| U47 Alvaro Espinosa | .10 |
| U48 Bob Geren | .10 |
| U49 Mel Hall | .06 |
| U50 Andy Hawkins | .06 |
| U51 Hensley Muelens (R) | .50 |
| U52 Steve Sax | .12 |
| U53 Deion Sanders (R) | .50 |
| U54 Rickey Henderson | .35 |
| U55 Mike Moore | .06 |
| U56 Tony Phillips | .06 |
| U57 Greg Briley (R) | .20 |
| U58 Gene Harris | .10 |
| U59 Randy Johnson | .06 |
| U60 Jeffrey Leonard | .06 |
| U61 Dennis Powell | .06 |
| U62 Omar Vizquel (R) | .12 |
| U63 Kevin Brown | .10 |
| U64 Julio Franco | .15 |
| U65 Jamie Moyer | .06 |
| U66 Rafael Palmeiro | .15 |

| NO. PLAYER | MINT |
|---|---|
| U67 Nolan Ryan | 1.50 |
| U68 F. Cabrera (R) | .30 |
| U69 Junior Felix (R) | .25 |
| U70 Al Leiter | .06 |
| U71 Alex Sanchez | .12 |
| U72 Geronimo Berroa | .08 |
| U73 Derek Lilliquist (R) | .12 |
| U74 Lonnie Smith | .08 |
| U75 Jeff Treadway | .06 |
| U76 Paul Kilgus | .06 |
| U77 Lloyd McClendon | .08 |
| U78 Scott Sanderson | .06 |
| U79 Dwight Smith (R) | .20 |
| U80 Jerome Walton (R) | .50 |
| U81 Mitch Williams | .15 |
| U82 Steve Wilson | .10 |
| U83 Todd Benzinger | .06 |
| U84 Ken Griffey | .15 |
| U85 Rick Mahler | .06 |
| U86 Rolando Roomes | .10 |
| U87 Scott Scudder (R) | .20 |
| U88 Jim Clancy | .06 |
| U89 Rick Rhoden | .06 |
| U90 Dan Schatzeder | .06 |
| U91 Mike Morgan | .06 |
| U92 Eddie Murray | .15 |
| U93 Willie Randolph | .06 |
| U94 Ray Searage | .06 |
| U95 Mike Aldrete | .06 |
| U96 Kevin Gross | .06 |
| U97 Mark Langston | .12 |
| U98 Spike Owen | .06 |
| U99 Zane Smith | .06 |

| NO. PLAYER | MINT |
|---|---|
| U100 Don Aase | .06 |
| U101 Barry Lyons | .06 |
| U102 Juan Samuel | .06 |
| U103 Wally Whitehurst (R) | .12 |
| U104 Dennis Cook | .10 |
| U105 Lenny Dykstra | .10 |
| U106 Charlie Hayes | .10 |
| U107 Tommy Herr | .06 |
| U108 Ken Howell | .06 |
| U109 John Kruk | .06 |
| U110 Roger McDowell | .06 |
| U111 Terry Mulholland | .10 |
| U112 Jeff Parrett | .06 |
| U113 Neal Heaton | .06 |
| U114 Jeff King | .12 |
| U115 Randy Kramer | .06 |
| U116 Bill Landrum | .06 |
| U117 Cris Carpenter | .10 |
| U118 Frank DiPino | .06 |
| U119 Ken Hill | .10 |
| U120 Dan Quisenberry | .06 |
| U121 Milt Thompson | .06 |
| U122 Todd Zeile (R) | 1.25 |
| U123 Jack Clark | .12 |
| U124 Bruce Hurst | .06 |
| U125 Mark Parent | .06 |
| U126 Bib Roberts | .06 |
| U127 Jeff Brantley (R) | .20 |
| U128 Terry Kennedy | .06 |
| U129 Mike LaCoss | .06 |
| U130 Greg Litton (R) | .15 |
| U131 Mike Schmidt | 1.00 |
| U132 Checklist | .06 |

# 1990 Fleer . . . Complete Set of 660 Cards—Value $20.00   (Factory Sealed Set—Value $22.00)

A new feature is a 10 card subset "Players of the Decade." New features on the back are "Vital Signs" and some cards feature "Did You Know."

| NO. PLAYER | MINT |
|---|---|
| **OAKLAND A'S** | |
| 1 Lance Blankenship | .08 |
| 2 Todd Burns | .05 |
| 3 Jose Canseco | .40 |
| 4 Jim Corsi | .06 |
| 5 Storm Davis | .06 |
| 6 Dennis Eckersley | .10 |
| 7 Mike Gallego | .08 |

| NO. PLAYER | MINT |
|---|---|
| 8 Ron Hassey | .06 |
| 9 Dave Henderson | .08 |
| 10 Rickey Henderson | .25 |
| 11 Rick Honeycutt | .06 |
| 12 Stan Javier | .06 |
| 13 Felix Jose | .20 |
| 14 Carney Lansford | .08 |
| 15 Mark McGwire | .15 |

| NO. PLAYER | MINT |
|---|---|
| 16 Mike Moore | .08 |
| 17 Gene Nelson | .06 |
| 18 Dave Parker | .10 |
| 19 Tony Phillips | .06 |
| 20 Terry Steinbach | .15 |
| 21 Dave Stewart | .10 |
| 22 Walt Weiss | .10 |
| 23 Bob Welch | .06 |

| NO. PLAYER | MINT |
|---|---|
| 24 Curt Young | .06 |
| **CHICAGO CUBS** | |
| 25 Paul Assenmacher | .06 |
| 26 Damon Beryhill | .08 |
| 27 Mike Bielecki | .06 |
| 28 Kevin Blankenship | .08 |
| 29 Andre Dawson | .12 |
| 30 Shawon Dunston | .08 |

| NO. | PLAYER | MINT |
|---|---|---|
| 31 | Joe Girardi | .10 |
| 32 | Mark Grace | .15 |
| 33 | Mike Harkey | .10 |
| 34 | Paul Kilgus | .06 |
| 35 | Les Lancaster | .06 |
| 36 | Vance Law | .06 |
| 37 | Greg Maddux | .10 |
| 38 | Lloyd McClendon | .06 |
| 39 | Jeff Pico | .06 |
| 40 | Ryne Sandberg | .25 |
| 41 | Scott Sanderson | .06 |
| 42 | Dwight Smith | .10 |
| 43 | Rick Sutcliffe | .06 |
| 44 | Jerome Walton | .10 |
| 45 | Mitch Webster | .06 |
| 46 | Curt Wilkerson | .06 |
| 47 | Dean Wilkins (R) | .12 |
| 48 | Mitch Williams | .08 |
| 49 | Steve Wilson | .08 |

**SAN FRANCISCO GIANTS**

| NO. | PLAYER | MINT |
|---|---|---|
| 50 | Steve Bedrosian | .06 |
| 51 | Mike Benjamin (R) | .15 |
| 52 | Jeff Brantley | .10 |
| 53 | Brett Butler | .06 |
| 54 | Will Clark | .25 |
| 55 | Kelly Downs | .08 |
| 56 | Scott Garrelts | .08 |
| 57 | Atlee Hammaker | .06 |
| 58 | Terry Kennedy | .06 |
| 59 | Mike LaCoss | .06 |
| 60 | Craig Lefferts | .06 |
| 61 | Greg Litton | .10 |
| 62 | Candy Maldonado | .06 |
| 63 | Kirt Manwaring | .08 |
| 64 | Randy McCament (R) | .12 |
| 65 | Kevin Mitchell | .15 |
| 66 | Donell Nixon | .06 |
| 67 | Ken Oberkfell | .06 |
| 68 | Rick Reuschel | .08 |
| 69 | Ernest Riles | .06 |
| 70 | Don Robinson | .06 |
| 71 | Pat Sheridan | .06 |
| 72 | Chris Speier | .06 |
| 73 | Robby Thompson | .10 |
| 74 | Jose Uribe | .06 |
| 75 | Matt Williams | .15 |

**TORONTO BLUE JAYS**

| NO. | PLAYER | MINT |
|---|---|---|
| 76 | George Bell | .10 |
| 77 | Pat Borders | .06 |
| 78 | John Cerutti | .06 |
| 79 | Junior Felix | .10 |
| 80 | Tony Fernandez | .10 |
| 81 | Mike Flanagan | .06 |
| 82 | Mauro Gozzo (R) | .12 |
| 83 | Kelly Gruber | .10 |
| 84 | Tom Henke | .06 |
| 85 | Jimmy Key | .08 |
| 86 | Manny Lee | .06 |
| 87 | Nelson Liriano | .06 |
| 88 | Lee Mazzilli | .06 |
| 89 | Fred McGriff | .12 |
| 90 | Lloyd Moseby | .06 |
| 91 | Rance Mulliniks | .06 |
| 92 | Alex Sanchez | .08 |
| 93 | Dave Stieb | .06 |
| 94 | Todd Stottlemyre | .10 |
| 95 | Duane Ward | .06 |
| 96 | David Wells | .06 |
| 97 | Ernie Whitt | .06 |
| 98 | Frank Wills | .06 |
| 99 | Mookie Wilson | .08 |

**KANSAS CITY ROYALS**

| NO. | PLAYER | MINT |
|---|---|---|
| 100 | Kevin Appier | .15 |
| 101 | Luis Aquino | .06 |
| 102 | Bob Boone | .06 |
| 103 | George Brett | .15 |
| 104 | Jose DeJesus | .06 |
| 105 | Luis de los Santos | .06 |
| 106 | Jim Eisenreich | .06 |
| 107 | Steve Farr | .06 |
| 108 | Tom Gordon | .10 |
| 109 | Mark Gubicza | .06 |
| 110 | Bo Jackson | .35 |
| 111 | Terry Leach | .06 |

| NO. | PLAYER | MINT |
|---|---|---|
| 112 | Charlie Leibrandt | .06 |
| 113 | Rich Luecken (R) | .12 |
| 114 | Mike Macfarlane | .06 |
| 115 | Jeff Montgomery | .08 |
| 116 | Bret Saberhagen | .10 |
| 117 | Kevin Seitzer | .08 |
| 118 | Kurt Stillwell | .06 |
| 119 | Pat Tabler | .06 |
| 120 | Danny Tartabull | .06 |
| 121 | Gary Thurman | .06 |
| 122 | Frank White | .06 |
| 123 | Willie Wilson | .08 |
| 124 | Matt Winters (R) | .12 |

**CALIFORNIA ANGELS**

| NO. | PLAYER | MINT |
|---|---|---|
| 125 | Jim Abbott | .20 |
| 126 | Tony Armas | .06 |
| 127 | Dante Bichette | .08 |
| 128 | Bert Blyleven | .08 |
| 129 | Chili Davis | .06 |
| 130 | Brian Downing | .06 |
| 131 | Mike Fetters (R) | .12 |
| 132 | Chuck Finley | .08 |
| 133 | Willie Fraser | .06 |
| 134 | Bryan Harvey | .06 |
| 135 | Jack Howell | .06 |
| 136 | Wally Joyner | .10 |
| 137 | Jeff Manto | .10 |
| 138 | Kirk McCaskill | .08 |
| 139 | Bob McClure | .06 |
| 140 | Greg Minton | .06 |
| 141 | Lance Parrish | .08 |
| 142 | Dan Petry | .06 |
| 143 | Johnny Ray | .08 |
| 144 | Dick Schofield | .06 |
| 145 | Lee Stevens | .15 |
| 146 | Claudell Washington | .06 |
| 147 | Devon White | .10 |
| 148 | Mike Witt | .08 |

**SAN DIEGO PADRES**

| NO. | PLAYER | MINT |
|---|---|---|
| 149 | Roberto Alomar | .15 |
| 150 | Sandy Alomar, Jr. | .12 |
| 151 | Andy Benes | .20 |
| 152 | Jack Clark | .08 |
| 153 | Pat Clements | .06 |
| 154 | Joey Cora | .06 |
| 155 | Mark Davis | .08 |
| 156 | Mark Grant | .06 |
| 157 | Tony Gwynn | .15 |
| 158 | Greg Harris | .06 |
| 159 | Bruce Hurst | .06 |
| 160 | Darrin Jackson | .06 |
| 161 | Chris James | .06 |
| 162 | Carmelo Martinez | .06 |
| 163 | Mike Pagliarulo | .08 |
| 164 | Mark Parent | .06 |
| 165 | Dennis Rasmussen | .06 |
| 166 | Bip Roberts | .06 |
| 167 | Benito Santiago | .10 |
| 168 | Calvin Schiraldi | .06 |
| 169 | Eric Show | .06 |
| 170 | Garry Templeton | .06 |
| 171 | Ed Whitson | .06 |

**BALTIMORE ORIOLES**

| NO. | PLAYER | MINT |
|---|---|---|
| 172 | Brady Anderson | .06 |
| 173 | Jeff Ballard | .08 |
| 174 | Phil Bradley | .08 |
| 175 | Mike Devereaux | .08 |
| 176 | Steve Finley | .12 |
| 177 | Pete Harnisch | .10 |
| 178 | Kevin Hickey | .10 |
| 179 | Brian Holton | .06 |
| 180 | Ben McDonald (R) | .75 |
| 181 | Bob Melvin | .06 |
| 182 | Bob Milacki | .10 |
| 183 | Randy Milligan | .08 |
| 184 | Gregg Olson | .12 |
| 185 | Joe Orsulak | .06 |
| 186 | Bill Ripken | .08 |
| 187 | Cal Ripken, Jr. | .30 |
| 188 | Dave Schmidt | .08 |
| 189 | Larry Sheets | .05 |
| 190 | Mickey Tettleton | .06 |
| 191 | Mark Thurmond | .06 |
| 192 | Jay Tibbs | .06 |

| NO. | PLAYER | MINT |
|---|---|---|
| 193 | Jim Traber | .06 |
| 194 | Mark Williamson | .06 |
| 195 | Craig Worthington | .10 |

**NEW YORK METS**

| NO. | PLAYER | MINT |
|---|---|---|
| 196 | Don Aase | .06 |
| 197 | Blaine Beatty (R) | .15 |
| 198 | Mark Carreon | .06 |
| 199 | Gary Carter | .10 |
| 200 | David Cone | .10 |
| 201 | Ron Darling | .10 |
| 202 | Kevin Elster | .08 |
| 203 | Sid Fernandez | .08 |
| 204 | Dwight Gooden | .15 |
| 205 | Keith Hernandez | .10 |
| 206 | Jeff Innis | .10 |
| 207 | Gregg Jefferies | .10 |
| 208 | Howard Johnson | .10 |
| 209 | Barry Lyons | .06 |
| 210 | Dave Magadan | .06 |
| 211 | Kevin McReynolds | .10 |
| 212 | Jeff Musselman | .06 |
| 213 | Randy Myers | .10 |
| 214 | Bob Ojeda | .06 |
| 215 | Juan Samuel | .08 |
| 216 | Mackey Sasser | .06 |
| 217 | Darryl Strawberry | .25 |
| 218 | Tim Teufel | .06 |
| 219 | Frank Viola | .10 |

**HOUSTON ASTROS**

| NO. | PLAYER | MINT |
|---|---|---|
| 220 | Juan Agosto | .06 |
| 221 | Larry Andersen | .06 |
| 222 | Eric Anthony (R) | .20 |
| 223 | Kevin Bass | .06 |
| 224 | Craig Biggio | .10 |
| 225 | Ken Caminiti | .06 |
| 226 | Jim Clancy | .06 |
| 227 | Danny Darwin | .06 |
| 228 | Glenn Davis | .10 |
| 229 | Jim Deshaies | .06 |
| 230 | Bill Doran | .06 |
| 231 | Bob Forsch | .10 |
| 232 | Brian Meyer | .08 |
| 233 | Terry Puhl | .06 |
| 234 | Rafael Ramirez | .06 |
| 235 | Rick Rhoden | .06 |
| 236 | Dan Schatzeder | .06 |
| 237 | Mike Scott | .06 |
| 238 | Dave Smith | .08 |
| 239 | Alex Trevino | .06 |
| 240 | Glenn Wilson | .06 |
| 241 | Gerald Young | .06 |

**ST. LOUIS CARDINALS**

| NO. | PLAYER | MINT |
|---|---|---|
| 242 | Tom Brunansky | .06 |
| 243 | Cris Carpenter | .06 |
| 244 | Alex Cole (R) | .35 |
| 245 | Vince Coleman | .10 |
| 246 | John Costello | .08 |
| 247 | Ken Dayley | .06 |
| 248 | Jose DeLeon | .06 |
| 249 | Frank Depino | .06 |
| 250 | Pedro Guerrero | .06 |
| 251 | Ken Hill | .08 |
| 252 | Joe Magrane | .06 |
| 253 | Willie McGee | .08 |
| 254 | John Morris | .06 |
| 255 | Jose Oquendo | .06 |
| 256 | Tony Pena | .08 |
| 257 | Terry Pendleton | .06 |
| 258 | Ted Power | .06 |
| 259 | Dan Quisenberry | .06 |
| 260 | Ozzie Smith | .10 |
| 261 | Scott Terry | .06 |
| 262 | Milt Thompson | .06 |
| 263 | Denny Walling | .06 |
| 264 | Todd Worrell | .08 |
| 265 | Todd Zeile | .35 |

**BOSTON RED SOX**

| NO. | PLAYER | MINT |
|---|---|---|
| 266 | Marty Barrett | .06 |
| 267 | Mike Boddicker | .08 |
| 268 | Wade Boggs | .15 |
| 269 | Ellis Burks | .10 |
| 270 | Rick Cerone | .06 |
| 271 | Roger Clemens | .25 |
| 272 | John Dopson | .08 |

| NO. | PLAYER | MINT |
|---|---|---|
| 273 | Nick Esasky | .08 |
| 274 | Dwight Evans | .10 |
| 275 | Wes Gardner | .08 |
| 276 | Rich Gedman | .06 |
| 277 | Mike Greenwell | .15 |
| 278 | Danny Heep | .06 |
| 279 | Eric Hetzel | .08 |
| 280 | Dennis Lamp | .06 |
| 281 | Rob Murphy | .06 |
| 282 | Joe Price | .06 |
| 283 | Carlos Quintana | .10 |
| 284 | Jody Reed | .06 |
| 285 | Luis Rivera | .06 |
| 286 | Kevin Romine | .06 |
| 287 | Lee Smith | .08 |
| 288 | Mike Smithson | .06 |
| 289 | Bob Stanley | .06 |

**TEXAS RANGERS**

| NO. | PLAYER | MINT |
|---|---|---|
| 290 | Harold Baines | .08 |
| 291 | Kevin Brown | .08 |
| 292 | Steve Buechele | .06 |
| 293 | Scott Coolbaugh (R) | .12 |
| 294 | Jack Daugherty (R) | .12 |
| 295 | Cecil Espy | .06 |
| 296 | Julio Franco | .08 |
| 297 | Juan Gonzalez (R) | 2.00 |
| 298 | Cecilio Guante | .05 |
| 299 | Drew Hall | .06 |
| 300 | Charlie Hough | .06 |
| 301 | Pete Incaviglia | .12 |
| 302 | Mike Jeffcoat | .06 |
| 303 | Chad Kreuter | .06 |
| 304 | Jeff Kunkel | .06 |
| 305 | Rich Leach | .06 |
| 306 | Fred Manrique | .06 |
| 307 | Jamie Moyer | .06 |
| 308 | Rafael Palmeiro | .10 |
| 309 | Geno Petralli | .06 |
| 310 | Kevin Reimer | .08 |
| 311 | Kenny Rogers | .10 |
| 312 | Jeff Russell | .06 |
| 313 | Nolan Ryan | .50 |
| 314 | Ruben Sierra | .15 |
| 315 | Bobby Witt | .08 |

**MILWAUKEE BREWERS**

| NO. | PLAYER | MINT |
|---|---|---|
| 316 | Chris Bosio | .06 |
| 317 | Glenn Braggs | .06 |
| 318 | Greg Brock | .06 |
| 319 | Chuck Crim | .06 |
| 320 | Rob Deer | .06 |
| 321 | Mike Felder | .06 |
| 322 | Tom Filer | .06 |
| 323 | Tony Fossas (R) | .10 |
| 324 | Jim Gantner | .06 |
| 325 | Darryl Hamilton | .06 |
| 326 | Ted Higuera | .06 |
| 327 | Mark Knudson | .10 |
| 328 | Bill Krueger | .06 |
| 329 | Tim McIntosh (R) | .15 |
| 330 | Paul Molitor | .10 |
| 331 | Jamie Navarro | .10 |
| 332 | Charlie O'Brien | .06 |
| 333 | Jeff Peterek (R) | .10 |
| 334 | Dan Plesac | .06 |
| 335 | Jerry Reuss | .06 |
| 336 | Gary Sheffield | .10 |
| 337 | Billy Spiers | .10 |
| 338 | B.J. Surhoff | .06 |
| 339 | Greg Vaughn | .50 |
| 340 | Robin Yount | .15 |

**MONTREAL EXPOS**

| NO. | PLAYER | MINT |
|---|---|---|
| 341 | Hubie Brooks | .06 |
| 342 | Tim Burke | .06 |
| 343 | Mike Fitzgerald | .06 |
| 344 | Tom Foley | .06 |
| 345 | Andres Galarraga | .10 |
| 346 | Damaso Garcia | .06 |
| 347 | Marquis Grissom (R) | .40 |
| 348 | Kevin Gross | .06 |
| 349 | Joe Hesketh | .06 |
| 350 | Jeff Huson (R) | .12 |
| 351 | Wallace Johnson | .06 |
| 352 | Mark Langston | .10 |
| 353 | Dave Martinez | .06 |

| NO. | PLAYER | MINT |
|-----|--------|------|
| 354 | Dennis Martinez | .06 |
| 355 | Andy McGaffigan | .06 |
| 356 | Otis Nixon | .06 |
| 357 | Spike Owen | .06 |
| 358 | Pascual Perez | .06 |
| 359 | Tim Raines | .10 |
| 360 | Nelson Santovenia | .08 |
| 361 | Bryn Smith | .06 |
| 362 | Zane Smith | .06 |
| 363 | Larry Walker (R) | .25 |
| 364 | Tim Wallach | .06 |

**MINNESOTA TWINS**

| NO. | PLAYER | MINT |
|-----|--------|------|
| 365 | Rick Aguilera | .06 |
| 366 | Allan Anderson | .08 |
| 367 | Wally Backman | .06 |
| 368 | Doug Baker | .06 |
| 369 | Juan Berenguer | .06 |
| 370 | Randy Bush | .06 |
| 371 | Carmen Castillo | .06 |
| 372 | Mike Dyer (R) | .12 |
| 373 | Gary Gaetti | .10 |
| 374 | Greg Gagne | .06 |
| 375 | Dan Gladden | .06 |
| 376 | German Gonzalez | .06 |
| 377 | Brian Harper | .06 |
| 378 | Kent Hrbek | .10 |
| 379 | Gene Larkin | .06 |
| 380 | Tim Laudner | .06 |
| 381 | John Moses | .06 |
| 382 | Al Newman | .06 |
| 383 | Kirby Puckett | .20 |
| 384 | Shane Rawley | .06 |
| 385 | Jeff Reardon | .08 |
| 386 | Roy Smith | .06 |
| 387 | Gary Wayne | .08 |
| 388 | Dave West | .08 |

**LOS ANGELES DODGERS**

| NO. | PLAYER | MINT |
|-----|--------|------|
| 389 | Tim Belcher | .08 |
| 390 | Tim Crews | .06 |
| 391 | Mike Davis | .06 |
| 392 | Rick Dempsey | .06 |
| 393 | Kirk Gibson | .10 |
| 394 | Jose Gonzalez | .06 |
| 395 | Alfredo Griffin | .08 |
| 396 | Jeff Hamilton | .06 |
| 397 | Lenny Harris | .06 |
| 398 | Mickey Hatcher | .06 |
| 399 | Orel Hershiser | .10 |
| 400 | Jay Howell | .08 |
| 401 | Mike Marshall | .08 |
| 402 | Ramon Martinez | .25 |
| 403 | Mike Morgan | .06 |
| 404 | Eddie Murray | .10 |
| 405 | Alejandro Pena | .08 |
| 406 | Willie Randolph | .12 |
| 407 | Mike Scioscia | .08 |
| 408 | Ray Searage | .06 |
| 409 | Fernando Valenzuela | .10 |
| 410 | Jose Vizcaino (R) | .15 |
| 411 | John Wetteland | .08 |

**CINCINNATI REDS**

| NO. | PLAYER | MINT |
|-----|--------|------|
| 412 | Jack Armstrong | .08 |
| 413 | Todd Benzinger | .08 |
| 414 | Tim Birtsas | .06 |
| 415 | Tom Browning | .06 |
| 416 | Norm Charlton | .06 |
| 417 | Eric Davis | .15 |
| 418 | Rob Dibble | .10 |
| 419 | John Franco | .08 |
| 420 | Ken Griffey, Sr. | .12 |
| 421 | Chris Hammond (R) | .30 |
| 422 | Danny Jackson | .10 |
| 423 | Barry Larkin | .12 |
| 424 | Tim Leary | .08 |
| 425 | Rick Mahler | .06 |
| 426 | Joe Oliver | .10 |
| 427 | Paul O'Neill | .06 |
| 428 | Luis Quinones | .06 |
| 429 | Jeff Reed | .06 |
| 430 | Jose Rijo | .06 |
| 431 | Ron Robinson | .06 |
| 432 | Rolando Roomes | .08 |
| 433 | Chris Sabo | .12 |
| 434 | Scott Scudder | .08 |
| 435 | Herm Winningham | .06 |

**NEW YORK YANKEES**

| NO. | PLAYER | MINT |
|-----|--------|------|
| 436 | Steve Balboni | .06 |
| 437 | Jesse Barfield | .06 |
| 438 | Mike Blowers (R) | .12 |
| 439 | Tom Brookens | .06 |
| 440 | Greg Cadaret | .06 |
| 441 | Alvaro Espinoza | .06 |
| 442 | Bob Geren | .08 |
| 443 | Lee Guetterman | .06 |
| 444 | Mel Hall | .06 |
| 445 | Andy Hawkins | .06 |
| 446 | Roberto Kelly | .12 |
| 447 | Don Mattingly | .25 |
| 448 | Lance McCullers | .06 |
| 449 | Hensley Meulens | .15 |
| 450 | Dale Mohorcic | .06 |
| 451 | Clay Parker | .06 |
| 452 | Eric Plunk | .06 |
| 453 | Dave Righetti | .10 |
| 454 | Deion Sanders | .15 |
| 455 | Steve Sax | .12 |
| 456 | Don Slaught | .06 |
| 457 | Walt Terrell | .06 |
| 458 | Dave Winfield | .12 |

**PITTSBURGH PIRATES**

| NO. | PLAYER | MINT |
|-----|--------|------|
| 459 | Jay Bell | .06 |
| 460 | Rafael Belliard | .06 |
| 461 | Barry Bonds | .15 |
| 462 | Bobby Bonilla | .15 |
| 463 | Sid Bream | .06 |
| 464 | Benny Distefano | .06 |
| 465 | Doug Drabek | .06 |
| 466 | Jim Gott | .06 |
| 467 | Billy Hatcher | .06 |
| 468 | Neal Heaton | .06 |
| 469 | Jeff King | .08 |
| 470 | Bob Kipper | .06 |
| 471 | Randy Kramer | .06 |
| 472 | Bill Landrum | .06 |
| 473 | Mike LaValliere | .06 |
| 474 | Jose Lind | .06 |
| 475 | Junior Ortiz | .06 |
| 476 | Gary Redus | .06 |
| 477 | Rick Reed (R) | .15 |
| 478 | R.J. Reynolds | .06 |
| 479 | Jeff Robinson | .10 |
| 480 | John Smiley | .08 |
| 481 | Andy Van Slyke | .08 |
| 482 | Bob Walk | .06 |

**CLEVELAND INDIANS**

| NO. | PLAYER | MINT |
|-----|--------|------|
| 483 | Andy Allanson | .06 |
| 484 | Scott Bailes | .06 |
| 485 | Joey Belle | .50 |
| 486 | Bud Black | .06 |
| 487 | Jerry Browne | .06 |
| 488 | Tom Candiotti | .06 |
| 489 | Joe Carter | .10 |
| 490 | David Clark | .06 |
| 491 | John Farrell | .08 |
| 492 | Felix Fermin | .06 |
| 493 | Brook Jacoby | .06 |
| 494 | Dion James | .06 |
| 495 | Doug Jones | .06 |
| 496 | Brad Komminsk | .06 |
| 497 | Rod Nichols | .10 |
| 498 | Pete O'Brien | .12 |
| 499 | Steven Ofin (R) | .12 |
| 500 | Jesse Orosco | .06 |
| 501 | Joel Skinner | .06 |
| 502 | Cory Snyder | .10 |
| 503 | Greg Swindell | .10 |
| 504 | Rich Yett | .06 |

**SEATTLE MARINERS**

| NO. | PLAYER | MINT |
|-----|--------|------|
| 505 | Scott Bankhead | .06 |
| 506 | Scott Bradley | .06 |
| 507 | Greg Briley | .10 |
| 508 | Jay Buhner | .08 |
| 509 | Darnell Coles | .06 |
| 510 | Keith Comstock | .06 |
| 511 | Henry Cotto | .06 |
| 512 | Alvin Davis | .12 |
| 513 | Ken Griffey, Jr. | 1.50 |
| 514 | Erik Hanson | .08 |
| 515 | Gene Harris | .08 |
| 516 | Brian Holman | .06 |

| NO. | PLAYER | MINT |
|-----|--------|------|
| 517 | Mike Jackson | .06 |
| 518 | Randy Johnson | .10 |
| 519 | Jeffrey Leonard | .06 |
| 520 | Edgar Martinez | .08 |
| 521 | Dennis Powell | .06 |
| 522 | Jim Presley | .06 |
| 523 | Jerry Reed | .06 |
| 524 | Harold Reynolds | .06 |
| 525 | Mike Schooler | .10 |
| 526 | Bill Swift | .06 |
| 527 | David Valle | .06 |
| 528 | Omar Vizquel | .08 |

**CHICAGO WHITE SOX**

| NO. | PLAYER | MINT |
|-----|--------|------|
| 529 | Ivan Calderon | .06 |
| 530 | Carlton Fisk | .12 |
| 531 | Scott Fletcher | .06 |
| 532 | Dave Gallagher | .06 |
| 533 | Ozzie Guillen | .08 |
| 534 | Greg Hibbard (R) | .20 |
| 535 | Shawn Hillegas | .06 |
| 536 | Lance Johnson | .06 |
| 537 | Eric King | .06 |
| 538 | Ron Kittle | .06 |
| 539 | Steve Lyons | .06 |
| 540 | Carlos Martinez | .10 |
| 541 | Tom McCarthy | .10 |
| 542 | Matt Merullo | .10 |
| 543 | Donn Pall | .06 |
| 544 | Dan Pasqua | .06 |
| 545 | Ken Patterson | .06 |
| 546 | Melido Perez | .06 |
| 547 | Steve Rosenberg | .06 |
| 548 | Sammy Sosa (R) | .25 |
| 549 | Bobby Thigpen | .06 |
| 550 | Robin Ventura | .50 |
| 551 | Greg Walker | .06 |

**PHILADELPHIA PHILLIES**

| NO. | PLAYER | MINT |
|-----|--------|------|
| 552 | Don Carman | .06 |
| 553 | Pat Combs | .08 |
| 554 | Dennis Cook | .06 |
| 555 | Darren Daulton | .06 |
| 556 | Lenny Dykstra | .08 |
| 557 | Curt Ford | .06 |
| 558 | Charlie Hayes | .06 |
| 559 | Von Hayes | .08 |
| 560 | Tom Herr | .08 |
| 561 | Ken Howell | .06 |
| 562 | Steve Jeltz | .06 |
| 563 | Ron Jones | .06 |
| 564 | Ricky Jordan | .08 |
| 565 | John Kruk | .06 |
| 566 | Steve Lake | .06 |
| 567 | Roger McDowell | .06 |
| 568 | Terry Mulholland | .06 |
| 569 | Dwayne Murphy | .06 |
| 570 | Jeff Parrett | .06 |
| 571 | Randy Ready | .06 |
| 572 | Bruce Ruffin | .06 |
| 573 | Dickie Thon | .06 |

**ATLANTA BRAVES**

| NO. | PLAYER | MINT |
|-----|--------|------|
| 574 | Jose Alvarez | .06 |
| 575 | Geronimo Berroa | .10 |
| 576 | Jeff Blauser | .06 |
| 577 | Joe Boever | .06 |
| 578 | Marty Clary | .06 |
| 579 | Jody Davis | .06 |
| 580 | Mark Eichhorn | .06 |
| 581 | Darrell Evans | .06 |
| 582 | Ron Gant | .25 |
| 583 | Tom Glavine | .12 |
| 584 | Tommy Greene (R) | .25 |
| 585 | Tommy Gregg | .06 |
| 586 | David Justice (R) | 2.50 |
| 587 | Mark Lemke | .08 |
| 588 | Derek Lilliquist | .10 |
| 589 | Oddibe McDowell | .06 |
| 590 | Ken Mercker (R) | .15 |
| 591 | Dale Murphy | .12 |
| 592 | Gerald Perry | .06 |
| 593 | Lonnie Smith | .06 |
| 594 | Pete Smith | .06 |
| 595 | John Smoltz | .15 |
| 596 | Mike Stanton (R) | .12 |
| 597 | Andres Thomas | .06 |
| 598 | Jeff Treadway | .06 |

**DETROIT TIGERS**

| NO. | PLAYER | MINT |
|-----|--------|------|
| 599 | Doyle Alexander | .08 |
| 600 | Dave Bergman | .06 |
| 601 | Brian Dubois (R) | .12 |
| 602 | Paul Gibson | .06 |
| 603 | Mike Heath | .06 |
| 604 | Mike Henneman | .06 |
| 605 | Guillermo Hernandez | .06 |
| 606 | Shawn Holman (R) | .12 |
| 607 | Tracy Jones | .06 |
| 608 | Chet Lemon | .06 |
| 609 | Fred Lynn | .08 |
| 610 | Jack Morris | .08 |
| 611 | Matt Nokes | .10 |
| 612 | Gary Pettis | .06 |
| 613 | Kevin Ritz (R) | .12 |
| 614 | Jeff Robinson | .08 |
| 615 | Steve Searcy | .08 |
| 616 | Frank Tanana | .06 |
| 617 | Alan Trammell | .08 |
| 618 | Gary Ward | .06 |
| 619 | Lou Whitaker | .08 |
| 620 | Frank Williams | .06 |

**PLAYERS OF THE DECADE**

| NO. | PLAYER | MINT |
|-----|--------|------|
| 621 | 1980—G. Brett (correct) | .12 |
| 621 | 1980—G. Brett (error) | 2.00 |
| 622 | 1981—F. Valenzuela | .10 |
| 623 | 1982—Dale Murphy | .10 |
| 624 | C. Ripken (error) misspelled Ripkin | 2.50 |
| 624 | C. Ripken (correct) | .15 |
| 625 | 1984—Ryne Sandberg | .15 |
| 626 | 1985—Don Mattingly | .20 |
| 627 | 1986—Roger Clemens | .15 |
| 628 | 1987—George Bell | .10 |
| 629 | 1988—Jose Canseco | .20 |
| 630 | W. Clark (error) 32 Total Bases | 1.75 |
| 630 | W. Clark (correct) 321 Total Bases | .15 |

**SPECIAL CARDS**

| NO. | PLAYER | MINT |
|-----|--------|------|
| 631 | Game Savers | .15 |
| 632 | Boston Igniters | .20 |
| 633 | Starter & Stopper | .15 |
| 634 | League's Best Shortstops | .15 |
| 635 | Human Dynamos | .25 |
| 636 | 300 Strikeout Club | .20 |
| 637 | Dynamic Duo | .25 |
| 638 | A.L. All-Stars | .20 |
| 639 | N.L. East Rivals | .25 |

**No. 640 to 653—**
**Major League Prospects**

| NO. | PLAYER | MINT |
|-----|--------|------|
| 640 | R. Seanez (R) and C. Charland (R) | .15 |
| 641 | G. Canale (R) and K. Mass (R) | 1.25 |
| 642 | K. Mann (R) and D. Hansen (R) | .30 |
| 643 | G. Smith (R) and S. Tate (R) | .12 |
| 644 | T. Drees (R) and D. Howitt (R) | .15 |
| 645 | M. Roesler (R) and D. May (R) | .25 |
| 646 | S. Hemond (R) and M. Gardner (R) | .20 |
| 647 | J. Orlan (R) and S. Leuis (R) | .20 |
| 648 | R. Monteleone (R) and D. Williams (R) | .12 |
| 649 | M. Huff (R) and S. Frey (R) | .20 |
| 650 | C. McElroy (R) and M. Alou (R) | .25 |
| 651 | B. Rose (R) and M. Hartley (R) | .15 |
| 652 | M. Kinzer (R) and W. Edwards (R) | .15 |
| 653 | D. Deshields (R) and J. Grimsley (R) | .50 |
| 654 | Checklist No. 1 | .10 |
| 655 | Checklist No. 2 | .10 |
| 656 | Checklist No. 3 | .10 |
| 657 | Checklist No. 4 | .10 |
| 658 | Checklist No. 5 | .10 |
| 659 | Checklist No. 6 | .10 |
| 660 | Checklist No. 7 | .10 |

## 1990 Fleer Traded Update. . . . Complete Set of 132 Cards—Value $12.00

This set updates the main 1990 card set with players who had changed teams during the season, and rookies. The set features the first card of Alex Fernandez, Frank Thomas and John Olerud.

| NO. | PLAYER | MINT |
|---|---|---|
| 1 | Steve Avery | 1.00 |
| 2 | Francisco Cabrera | .10 |
| 3 | Nick Esasky | .05 |
| 4 | Jim Kremers (R) | .12 |
| 5 | Greg Olson (R) | .20 |
| 6 | Jim Presley | .05 |
| 7 | Shawn Boskie (R) | .12 |
| 8 | Joe Kraemer (R) | .10 |
| 9 | Luis Salazer | .05 |
| 10 | H. Villanueva (R) | .15 |
| 11 | Glenn Braggs | .05 |
| 12 | Mariano Duncan | .05 |
| 13 | Billy Hatcher | .05 |
| 14 | Tim Layana (R) | .12 |
| 15 | Hal Morris | .30 |
| 16 | Javier Ortiz (R) | .12 |
| 17 | Dave Rohde (R) | .12 |
| 18 | Eric Yelding | .05 |
| 19 | Hubie Brooks | .05 |
| 20 | Kal Daniels | .08 |
| 21 | Dave Hansen | .20 |
| 22 | Mike Hartley | .05 |
| 23 | Stan Javier | .05 |
| 24 | Jose Offerman (R) | .25 |
| 25 | Juan Samuel | .05 |
| 26 | Dennis Boyd | .05 |
| 27 | Delino DeShields | .35 |
| 28 | Steve Frey | .05 |
| 29 | Mark Gardner | .05 |
| 30 | Chris Nabholz (R) | .20 |
| 31 | Bill Sampen (R) | .15 |
| 32 | Dave Schmidt | .05 |
| 33 | Daryl Boston | .05 |

| NO. | PLAYER | MINT |
|---|---|---|
| 34 | Chuck Carr (R) | .10 |
| 35 | John Franco | .05 |
| 36 | Todd Hundley (R) | .30 |
| 37 | Julio Machado (R) | .10 |
| 38 | Alejandro Pena | .05 |
| 39 | Darren Reed (R) | .12 |
| 40 | Kelvin Torve | .10 |
| 41 | Darrel Akerfelds | .10 |
| 42 | Jose DeJesus | .10 |
| 43 | Dave Hollins (R) | .30 |
| 44 | Carmelo Martinez | .05 |
| 45 | Brad Moore | .10 |
| 46 | Dale Murphy | .12 |
| 47 | Wally Backman | .05 |
| 48 | Stan Belinda (R) | .10 |
| 49 | Bob Patterson | .05 |
| 50 | Ted Power | .05 |
| 51 | Don Slaught | .05 |
| 52 | Geronimo Pena | .15 |
| 53 | Lee Smith | .05 |
| 54 | John Tudor | .05 |
| 55 | Joe Carter | .10 |
| 56 | Tom Howard | .15 |
| 57 | Craig Lefferts | .05 |
| 58 | Rafael Valdez (R) | .12 |
| 59 | Dave Anderson | .05 |
| 60 | Kevin Bass | .05 |
| 61 | John Burkett | .15 |
| 62 | Gary Carter | .10 |
| 63 | Rick Parker (R) | .12 |
| 64 | Trevor Wilson | .10 |
| 65 | Chris Hoiles (R) | .20 |
| 66 | Tim Hulett | .05 |

| NO. | PLAYER | MINT |
|---|---|---|
| 67 | Dave Johnson | .10 |
| 68 | Curt Schilling | .10 |
| 69 | David Sequi (R) | .20 |
| 70 | Tom Brunansky | .05 |
| 71 | Greg Harris | .05 |
| 72 | Dana Kiecker (R) | .12 |
| 73 | Tim Naehring (R) | .25 |
| 74 | Tony Pena | .05 |
| 75 | Jeff Reardon | .05 |
| 76 | Jerry Reed | .05 |
| 77 | Mark Eichhorn | .05 |
| 78 | Mark Langston | .10 |
| 79 | John Orton | .05 |
| 80 | Luis Polonia | .05 |
| 81 | Dave Winfield | .12 |
| 82 | Cliff Young (R) | .10 |
| 83 | Wayne Edwards | .10 |
| 84 | A. Fernandez (R) | .75 |
| 85 | Craig Grebeck (R) | .12 |
| 86 | Scott Radinsky (R) | .12 |
| 87 | Frank Thomas (R) | 5.00 |
| 88 | Beau Allred (R) | .15 |
| 89 | Sandy Alomar, Jr. | .12 |
| 90 | Carlos Baerga (R) | .35 |
| 91 | Kevin Bearse | .10 |
| 92 | Chris James | .05 |
| 93 | Candy Maldonado | .05 |
| 94 | Jeff Manto | .05 |
| 95 | Cecil Fielder | .30 |
| 96 | Travis Fryman (R) | 1.00 |
| 97 | Lloyd Moseby | .05 |
| 98 | Edwin Nunez | .05 |
| 99 | Tony Phillips | .05 |

| NO. | PLAYER | MINT |
|---|---|---|
| 100 | Larry Sheets | .05 |
| 101 | Mark Davis | .05 |
| 102 | Storm Davis | .05 |
| 103 | Gerald Perry | .05 |
| 104 | T. Shumpert (R) | .15 |
| 105 | Edgar Diaz (R) | .10 |
| 106 | Dave Parker | .10 |
| 107 | T. Drummond (R) | .10 |
| 108 | Junior Ortiz | .12 |
| 109 | Park Pittman (R) | .15 |
| 110 | Kevin Tapani (R) | .30 |
| 111 | Oscar Azocar (R) | .12 |
| 112 | Jim Leyritz (R) | .10 |
| 113 | Kevin Maas (R) | 1.00 |
| 114 | Alan Mills (R) | .12 |
| 115 | Matt Nokes | .05 |
| 116 | Pascual Perez | .05 |
| 117 | Ozzie Canseco | .15 |
| 118 | Scott Sanderson | .05 |
| 119 | Tino Martinez | .60 |
| 120 | Jeff Schaefer (R) | .10 |
| 121 | Matt Young | .05 |
| 122 | Brian Bohanon (R) | .12 |
| 123 | Jeff Huson | .05 |
| 124 | Ramon Manon (R) | .10 |
| 125 | Gary Mielke (R) | .10 |
| 126 | Willie Blair (R) | .10 |
| 127 | Glenallen Hill | .10 |
| 128 | John Olerud (R) | 1.00 |
| 129 | Luis Sojo (R) | .12 |
| 130 | Mark Whiten (R) | .50 |
| 131 | Nolan Ryan | .75 |
| 132 | Checklist | .05 |

## 1991 Fleer. . . . Complete Set of 720 Cards—Value $25.00

The set was increased from 660 to 720 cards. Fleer introduced two new subsets—12 Pro-Vision sports art cards are in rack and wax packs, and 10 All Star cards are in cello packs. Fleer announced a new policy of not creating variations by reprinting minor errors.

| NO. | PLAYER | MINT |
|---|---|---|
| **OAKLAND A's** | | |
| 1 | Tony Afenir (R) | .12 |
| 2 | Harold Baines | .05 |
| 3 | Lance Blankenship | .05 |
| 4 | Todd Burns | .05 |
| 5 | Jose Canseco | .25 |
| 6 | Dennis Eckersley | .10 |

| NO. | PLAYER | MINT |
|---|---|---|
| 7 | Mike Gallego | .05 |
| 8 | Ron Hassey | .05 |
| 9 | Dave Henderson | .08 |
| 10 | Rickey Henderson | .20 |
| 11 | Rick Honeycutt | .05 |
| 12 | Doug Jennings | .05 |
| 13 | Joe Klink | .08 |

| NO. | PLAYER | MINT |
|---|---|---|
| 14 | Carney Lansford | .05 |
| 15 | Darren Lewis | .15 |
| 16 | Willie McGee | .10 |
| 17 | Mark McGwire | .15 |
| 18 | Mike Moore | .05 |
| 19 | Gene Nelson | .05 |
| 20 | Dave Otto | .05 |

| NO. | PLAYER | MINT |
|---|---|---|
| 21 | Jamie Quirk | .05 |
| 22 | Willie Randolph | .05 |
| 23 | Scott Sanderson | .05 |
| 24 | Terry Steinbach | .05 |
| 25 | Dave Stewart | .12 |
| 26 | Walt Weiss | .05 |
| 27 | Bob Welch | .05 |

| NO. | PLAYER | MINT |
|---|---|---|
| 28 | Curt Young | .05 |

**PITTSBURGH PIRATES**

| NO. | PLAYER | MINT |
|---|---|---|
| 29 | Wally Backman | .05 |
| 30 | Stan Belinda | .05 |
| 31 | Jay Bell | .05 |
| 32 | Rafael Belliard | .05 |
| 33 | Barry Bonds | .15 |
| 34 | Bobby Bonilla | .15 |
| 35 | Sid Bream | .05 |
| 36 | Doug Drabek | .08 |
| 37 | Carlos Garcia (R) | .12 |
| 38 | Neal Heaton | .05 |
| 39 | Jeff King | .05 |
| 40 | Bob Kipper | .05 |
| 41 | Bill Landrum | .05 |
| 42 | Mike LaValliere | .05 |
| 43 | Jose Lind | .05 |
| 44 | Carmelo Martinez | .05 |
| 45 | Bob Patterson | .05 |
| 46 | Ted Power | .05 |
| 47 | Gary Redus | .05 |
| 48 | R. J. Reynolds | .05 |
| 49 | Don Slaught | .05 |
| 50 | John Smiley | .05 |
| 51 | Zane Smith | .05 |
| 52 | Randy Tomlin (R) | .20 |
| 53 | Andy Van Slyke | .08 |
| 54 | Bob Walk | .05 |

**CINCINNATI REDS**

| NO. | PLAYER | MINT |
|---|---|---|
| 55 | Jack Armstrong | .08 |
| 56 | Todd Benzinger | .08 |
| 57 | Glenn Braggs | .05 |
| 58 | Keith Brown | .05 |
| 59 | Tom Browning | .05 |
| 60 | Norm Charlton | .05 |
| 61 | Eric Davis | .15 |
| 62 | Rob Dibble | .05 |
| 63 | Bill Doran | .05 |
| 64 | Mariano Duncan | .05 |
| 65 | Chris Hammond | .05 |
| 66 | Billy Hatcher | .05 |
| 67 | Danny Jackson | .05 |
| 68 | Barry Larkin | .10 |
| 69 | Tim Layana | .05 |
| 70 | Terry Lee (R) | .12 |
| 71 | Rick Mahler | .05 |
| 72 | Hal Morris | .12 |
| 73 | Randy Myers | .05 |
| 74 | Ron Oester | .05 |
| 75 | Joe Oliver | .05 |
| 76 | Paul O'Neill | .05 |
| 77 | Luis Quinones | .05 |
| 78 | Jeff Reed | .05 |
| 79 | Jose Rijo | .05 |
| 80 | Chris Sabo | .10 |
| 81 | Scott Scudder | .05 |
| 82 | Herm Winningham | .05 |

**BOSTON RED SOX**

| NO. | PLAYER | MINT |
|---|---|---|
| 83 | Larry Anderson | .05 |
| 84 | Marty Barrett | .05 |
| 85 | Mike Boddicker | .08 |
| 86 | Wade Boggs | .15 |
| 87 | Tom Bolton | .05 |
| 88 | Tom Brunansky | .08 |
| 89 | Ellis Burks | .10 |
| 90 | Roger Clemens | .20 |
| 91 | Scott Cooper | .15 |
| 92 | John Dopson | .05 |
| 93 | Dwight Evans | .05 |
| 94 | Wes Gardner | .05 |
| 95 | Jeff Gray (R) | .12 |
| 96 | Mike Greenwell | .10 |
| 97 | Greg Harris | .05 |
| 98 | Daryl Irvine (R) | .12 |
| 99 | Dana Klecker | .05 |
| 100 | Randy Kutcher | .05 |
| 101 | Dennis Lamp | .05 |
| 102 | Mike Marshall | .05 |
| 103 | John Marzano | .05 |
| 104 | Rob Murphy | .05 |
| 105 | Tim Naehring | .10 |
| 106 | Tony Pena | .05 |
| 107 | Phil Plantier (R) | 1.00 |

| NO. | PLAYER | MINT |
|---|---|---|
| 108 | Carlos Quintana | .08 |
| 109 | Jeff Reardon | .05 |
| 110 | Jerry Reed | .05 |
| 111 | Jody Reed | .05 |
| 112 | Luis Rivera | .05 |
| 113 | Kevin Romina | .05 |

**CHICAGO WHITE SOX**

| NO. | PLAYER | MINT |
|---|---|---|
| 114 | Phil Bradley | .05 |
| 115 | Ivan Calderon | .05 |
| 116 | Wayne Edwards | .05 |
| 117 | Alex Fernandez | .15 |
| 118 | Carlton Fisk | .10 |
| 119 | Scott Fletcher | .05 |
| 120 | Craig Grebeck | .05 |
| 121 | Ozzie Gulilen | .05 |
| 122 | Greg Hibbard | .05 |
| 123 | Lance Johnson | .05 |
| 124 | Barry Jones | .05 |
| 125 | Ron Karkovice | .05 |
| 126 | Eric King | .05 |
| 127 | Steve Lyons | .05 |
| 128 | Carlos Martinez | .05 |
| 129 | Jack McDowell | .05 |
| 130 | Donn Pall | .05 |
| 131 | Dan Pasqua | .05 |
| 132 | Ken Patterson | .05 |
| 133 | Melido Perez | .05 |
| 134 | Adam Peterson | .05 |
| 135 | Scott Radinsky | .05 |
| 136 | Sammy Sosa | .10 |
| 137 | Bobby Thigpen | .08 |
| 138 | Frank Thomas | 1.00 |
| 139 | Robin Ventura | .15 |

**NEW YORK METS**

| NO. | PLAYER | MINT |
|---|---|---|
| 140 | Daryl Boston | .05 |
| 141 | Chuck Carr | .05 |
| 142 | Mark Carreon | .05 |
| 143 | David Cone | .08 |
| 144 | Ron Darling | .05 |
| 145 | Kevin Elster | .05 |
| 146 | Sid Fernandez | .05 |
| 147 | John Franco | .05 |
| 148 | Dwight Gooden | .15 |
| 149 | Tom Herr | .05 |
| 150 | Todd Hundley | .10 |
| 151 | Gregg Jefferies | .10 |
| 152 | Howard Johnson | .08 |
| 153 | Dave Madagan | .05 |
| 154 | Kevin McReynolds | .08 |
| 155 | Keith Miller | .05 |
| 156 | Bob Ojeda | .05 |
| 157 | Tom O'Malley | .05 |
| 158 | Alejandro Pena | .05 |
| 159 | Darren Reed | .05 |
| 160 | Mackey Sasser | .05 |
| 161 | Darryl Strawberry | .20 |
| 162 | Tim Teufel | .05 |
| 163 | Kelvin Torve | .05 |
| 164 | Julio Valera | .10 |
| 165 | Frank Viola | .10 |
| 166 | Wally Whitehurst | .05 |

**TORONTO BLUE JAYS**

| NO. | PLAYER | MINT |
|---|---|---|
| 167 | Jim Acker | .05 |
| 168 | Derek Bell | .25 |
| 169 | George Bell | .08 |
| 170 | Willie Blair | .05 |
| 171 | Pat Borders | .05 |
| 172 | John Cerutti | .05 |
| 173 | Junior Felix | .10 |
| 174 | Tony Fernandez | .05 |
| 175 | Kelly Gruber | .08 |
| 176 | Tom Henke | .05 |
| 177 | Glenallen Hill | .05 |
| 178 | Jimmy Key | .05 |
| 179 | Manny Lee | .05 |
| 180 | Fred McGriff | .10 |
| 181 | Rance Mulliniks | .05 |
| 182 | Greg Myers | .05 |
| 183 | John Olerud | .12 |
| 184 | Luis Solo | .05 |
| 185 | Dave Stieb | .08 |
| 186 | Todd Stottlemyre | .05 |
| 187 | Duane Ward | .05 |
| 188 | David Wells | .05 |

| NO. | PLAYER | MINT |
|---|---|---|
| 189 | Mark Whiten | .20 |
| 190 | Ken Williams | .05 |
| 191 | Frank Wills | .05 |
| 192 | Mookie Wilson | .05 |

**LOS ANGELES DODGERS**

| NO. | PLAYER | MINT |
|---|---|---|
| 193 | Don Aase | .05 |
| 194 | Tim Belcher | .05 |
| 195 | Hubie Brooks | .05 |
| 196 | Dennis Cook | .05 |
| 197 | Tim Crews | .05 |
| 198 | Kal Daniels | .08 |
| 199 | Kirk Gibson | .10 |
| 200 | Jim Gott | .05 |
| 201 | Alfredo Griffin | .05 |
| 202 | Chris Gwynn | .05 |
| 203 | Dave Hansen | .05 |
| 204 | Lenny Harris | .05 |
| 205 | Mike Hartley | .05 |
| 206 | Mickey Hatcher | .05 |
| 207 | Carlos Hernandez | .08 |
| 208 | Orel Hershiser | .10 |
| 209 | Jay Howell | .05 |
| 210 | Mike Huff | .05 |
| 211 | Stan Javier | .05 |
| 212 | Ramon Martinez | .15 |
| 213 | Mike Morgan | .05 |
| 214 | Eddie Murray | .12 |
| 215 | Jim Niediinger (R) | .15 |
| 216 | Jose Offerman | .10 |
| 217 | Jim Poole | .10 |
| 218 | Juan Samuel | .05 |
| 219 | Mike Scioscia | .05 |
| 220 | Ray Searage | .05 |
| 221 | Mike Sharperson | .05 |
| 222 | Fernando Valenzuela | .10 |
| 223 | Jose Vizcaino | .05 |

**MONTREAL EXPOS**

| NO. | PLAYER | MINT |
|---|---|---|
| 224 | Mike Aldrete | .05 |
| 225 | Scott Anderson (R) | .12 |
| 226 | Dennis Boyd | .05 |
| 227 | Tim Burke | .05 |
| 228 | Delino DeShields | .10 |
| 229 | Mike Fitzgerald | .05 |
| 230 | Tom Foley | .05 |
| 231 | Steve Frey | .05 |
| 232 | Andres Galarraga | .08 |
| 233 | Mark Gardner | .05 |
| 234 | Marquis Grissom | .10 |
| 235 | Kevin Gross | .05 |
| 236 | Drew Hall | .05 |
| 237 | Dave Martinez | .05 |
| 238 | Dennis Martinez | .05 |
| 239 | Dale Mohorcic | .05 |
| 240 | Chris Nabholz | .05 |
| 241 | Otis Nixon | .05 |
| 242 | Junior Noboa | .05 |
| 243 | Spike Owen | .05 |
| 244 | Tim Raines | .08 |
| 245 | Mal Rojas | .05 |
| 246 | Scott Ruskin | .08 |
| 247 | Bill Sampen | .05 |
| 248 | Nelson Santovenia | .05 |
| 249 | Dave Schmidt | .05 |
| 250 | Larry Walker | .08 |
| 251 | Tim Wallach | .05 |

**SAN FRANCISCO GIANTS**

| NO. | PLAYER | MINT |
|---|---|---|
| 252 | Dave Anderson | .05 |
| 253 | Kevin Bass | .05 |
| 254 | Steve Bedrosian | .05 |
| 255 | Jeff Brantley | .05 |
| 256 | John Burkett | .05 |
| 257 | Brett Butler | .05 |
| 258 | Cary Carter | .10 |
| 259 | Will Clark | .20 |
| 260 | Steve Decker (R) | .20 |
| 261 | Kelly Downs | .05 |
| 262 | Scott Garreits | .05 |
| 263 | Terry Kennedy | .05 |
| 264 | Mike LaCoss | .05 |
| 265 | Mark Leonard (R) | .15 |
| 266 | Greg Litton | .05 |
| 267 | Kevin Mitchell | .10 |
| 268 | Randy O'Neal | .05 |
| 269 | Rick Parker | .05 |

| NO. | PLAYER | MINT |
|---|---|---|
| 270 | Rick Reuschel | .05 |
| 271 | Ernest Rlles | .05 |
| 272 | Don Robinson | .05 |
| 273 | Robby Thompson | .05 |
| 274 | Mark Thurmond | .05 |
| 275 | Jose Uribe | .05 |
| 276 | Matt Williams | .10 |
| 277 | Trevor Wilson | .05 |

**TEXAS RANGERS**

| NO. | PLAYER | MINT |
|---|---|---|
| 278 | Gerald Alexander (R) | .10 |
| 279 | Brad Arnsberg | .05 |
| 280 | Kevin Belcher (R) | .12 |
| 281 | Joe Bitker (R) | .12 |
| 282 | Kevin Brown | .05 |
| 283 | Steve Buechele | .05 |
| 284 | Jack Daugherty | .05 |
| 285 | Julio Franco | .08 |
| 286 | Juan Gonzalez | .25 |
| 287 | Bill Haselman (R) | .12 |
| 288 | Charlie Hough | .05 |
| 289 | Jeff Huson | .05 |
| 290 | Peter Incaviglia | .05 |
| 291 | Mike Jeffcoat | .05 |
| 292 | Jeff Kunkel | .05 |
| 293 | Gary Mielke | .05 |
| 294 | Jamie Moyer | .05 |
| 295 | Rafael Palmeiro | .08 |
| 296 | Geno Petralli | .05 |
| 297 | Gary Pettis | .05 |
| 298 | Kevin Reimer | .08 |
| 299 | Kenny Rogers | .05 |
| 300 | Jeff Russell | .05 |
| 301 | John Russell | .05 |
| 302 | Nolan Ryan | .30 |
| 303 | Ruben Sierra | .10 |
| 304 | Bobby Witt | .05 |

**CALIFORNIA ANGELS**

| NO. | PLAYER | MINT |
|---|---|---|
| 305 | Jim Abbott | .10 |
| 306 | Kent Anderson | .05 |
| 307 | Dante Bichette | .05 |
| 308 | Bert Blyleven | .05 |
| 309 | Chili Davis | .05 |
| 310 | Brian Downing | .05 |
| 311 | Mark Eichhorn | .05 |
| 312 | Mike Fetters | .05 |
| 313 | Chuck Finley | .08 |
| 314 | Willie Fraser | .05 |
| 315 | Bryan Harvey | .05 |
| 316 | Donnie Hill | .05 |
| 317 | Wally Joyner | .10 |
| 318 | Mark Langston | .10 |
| 319 | Kirk McCaskill | .05 |
| 320 | John Orton | .05 |
| 321 | Lance Parrish | .05 |
| 322 | Luis Polonia | .05 |
| 323 | Johnny Ray | .05 |
| 324 | Bobby Rose | .05 |
| 325 | Dick Schofield | .05 |
| 326 | Rick Schu | .05 |
| 327 | Lee Stevens | .08 |
| 328 | Devon White | .05 |
| 329 | Dave Winfield | .12 |
| 330 | Cliff Young | .05 |

**DETROIT TIGERS**

| NO. | PLAYER | MINT |
|---|---|---|
| 331 | Dave Bergman | .05 |
| 332 | Phil Clark (R) | .15 |
| 333 | Darnell Coles | .05 |
| 334 | Milt Coyler | .05 |
| 335 | Cecil Fielder | .15 |
| 336 | Travis Fryman | .35 |
| 337 | Paul Gibson | .05 |
| 338 | Jerry Don Gleaton | .05 |
| 339 | Mike Heath | .05 |
| 340 | Mike Henneman | .05 |
| 341 | Chet Lemon | .05 |
| 342 | Lance McCullers | .05 |
| 343 | Jack Morris | .08 |
| 344 | Lloyd Moseby | .05 |
| 345 | Edwin Nunez | .05 |
| 346 | Clay Parker | .05 |
| 347 | Dan Petry | .05 |
| 348 | Tony Phillips | .05 |
| 349 | Jeff Robinson | .05 |
| 350 | Mark Salas | .05 |

| NO. | PLAYER | MINT |
|---|---|---|
| 351 | Mike Schwabe | .05 |
| 352 | Larry Sheets | .05 |
| 353 | John Shelby | .05 |
| 354 | Frank Tanana | .05 |
| 355 | Alan Trammell | .08 |
| 356 | Gary Ward | .05 |
| 357 | Lou Whitaker | .05 |
| **CLEVELAND INDIANS** | | |
| 358 | Beau Allred | .05 |
| 359 | Sandy Alomar, Jr. | .10 |
| 360 | Carlos Baerga | .10 |
| 361 | Kevin Bearse | .05 |
| 362 | Tom Brookens | .05 |
| 363 | Jerry Browne | .05 |
| 364 | Tom Candiotti | .05 |
| 365 | Alex Cole | .08 |
| 366 | John Farrell | .05 |
| 367 | Felix Fermin | .05 |
| 368 | Keith Hernandez | .05 |
| 369 | Brook Jacoby | .05 |
| 370 | Chris James | .05 |
| 371 | Dion James | .05 |
| 372 | Doug Jones | .05 |
| 373 | Candy Maldonado | .05 |
| 374 | Steve Olin | .05 |
| 375 | Jesse Orosco | .05 |
| 376 | Rudy Seanez | .05 |
| 377 | Joel Skinner | .05 |
| 378 | Cory Snyder | .05 |
| 379 | Greg Swindell | .05 |
| 380 | Sergio Valdez | .05 |
| 381 | Mike Walker | .08 |
| 382 | Colby Ward (R) | .12 |
| 383 | Turner Ward (R) | .15 |
| 384 | Mitch Webster | .05 |
| 385 | Kevin Wickander | .05 |
| **PHILADELPHIA PHILLIES** | | |
| 386 | Darrel Akerfelds | .05 |
| 387 | Joe Boever | .05 |
| 388 | Rod Booker | .05 |
| 389 | Sid Campusano | .05 |
| 390 | Don Carman | .05 |
| 391 | Wes Chamberlain (R) | .40 |
| 392 | Pat Combs | .05 |
| 393 | Darren Daulton | .05 |
| 394 | Jose DeJesus | .05 |
| 395 | Len Dykstra | .10 |
| 396 | Jason Grimsley | .05 |
| 397 | Charlie Hayes | .05 |
| 398 | Von Hayes | .05 |
| 399 | David Hollins | .10 |
| 400 | Ken Howell | .05 |
| 401 | Ricky Jordan | .05 |
| 402 | John Kruk | .05 |
| 403 | Steve Lake | .05 |
| 404 | Chuck Malone | .05 |
| 405 | Roger McDowell | .05 |
| 406 | Chuck McElroy | .05 |
| 407 | Mickey Morandini | .10 |
| 408 | Terry Mulholland | .05 |
| 409 | Dale Murphy | .10 |
| 410 | Randy Ready | .05 |
| 411 | Bruce Ruffin | .05 |
| **CHICAGO CUBS** | | |
| 412 | Dickie Thon | .05 |
| 413 | Paul Assenmacher | .05 |
| 414 | Damon Berryhill | .05 |
| 415 | Mike Bielecki | .05 |
| 416 | Shawn Boskie | .05 |
| 417 | Dave Clark | .05 |
| 418 | Doug Dascenzo | .05 |
| 419 | Andre Dawson | .12 |
| 420 | Shawon Dunston | .10 |
| 421 | Joe Girardi | .05 |
| 422 | Mark Grace | .08 |
| 423 | Mike Harkey | .05 |
| 424 | Les Lancaster | .05 |
| 425 | Bill Long | .05 |
| 426 | Greg Maddux | .05 |
| 427 | Derrick May | .10 |
| 428 | Jeff Pico | .05 |
| 429 | Domingo Ramos | .05 |
| 430 | Luis Salazar | .05 |
| 431 | Ryne Sandberg | .20 |
| 432 | Dwight Smith | .05 |
| 433 | Greg Smith | .05 |
| 434 | Rick Sutcliffe | .05 |
| 435 | Gary Varsho | .05 |
| 436 | Hector Villanueva | .10 |
| 437 | Jerome Walton | .10 |
| 438 | Curtis Wilkerson | .05 |
| 439 | Mitch Williams | .05 |
| 440 | Steve Wilson | .05 |
| 441 | Marvell Wynne | .05 |
| **SEATTLE MARINERS** | | |
| 442 | Scott Bankhead | .05 |
| 443 | Scott Bradley | .05 |
| 444 | Greg Briley | .05 |
| 445 | Mike Brumley | .05 |
| 446 | Jay Buhner | .05 |
| 447 | Dave Burba (R) | .12 |
| 448 | Henry Cotto | .05 |
| 449 | Alvin Davis | .05 |
| 450 | Ken Griffey Jr. | .75 |
| 451 | Erik Hanson | .05 |
| 452 | Gene Harris | .05 |
| 453 | Brian Holman | .05 |
| 454 | Mike Jackson | .05 |
| 455 | Randy Johnson | .05 |
| 456 | Jeffrey Leonard | .05 |
| 457 | Edgar Martinez | .05 |
| 458 | Tino Martinez | .15 |
| 459 | Pete O'Brien | .05 |
| 460 | Harold Reynolds | .05 |
| 461 | Mike Schooler | .05 |
| 462 | Bill Swift | .05 |
| 463 | David Valle | .05 |
| 464 | Omar Vizquel | .05 |
| 465 | Matt Young | .05 |
| **BALTIMORE ORIOLES** | | |
| 466 | Brady Anderson | .05 |
| 467 | Jeff Ballard | .05 |
| 468 | Juan Bell | .05 |
| 469 | Mike Devereaux | .05 |
| 470 | Steve Finley | .05 |
| 471 | Dave Gallagher | .05 |
| 472 | Leo Gomez | .20 |
| 473 | Rene Gonzales | .05 |
| 474 | Peter Harnisch | .05 |
| 475 | Kevin Hickey | .05 |
| 476 | Chris Holles | .10 |
| 477 | Sam Horn | .05 |
| 478 | Tim Hulett | .05 |
| 479 | Dave Johnson | .05 |
| 480 | Ron Kittle | .05 |
| 481 | Ben McDonald | .10 |
| 482 | Bob Melvin | .05 |
| 483 | Bob Milacki | .05 |
| 484 | Randy Milligan | .05 |
| 485 | John Mitchell | .05 |
| 486 | Gregg Olson | .10 |
| 487 | Joe Orsulak | .05 |
| 488 | Joe Price | .05 |
| 489 | Bill Ripken | .05 |
| 490 | Cal Ripken Jr. | .20 |
| 491 | Curt Schilling | .05 |
| 492 | David Segui | .05 |
| 493 | Anthony Telford (R) | .12 |
| 494 | Mickey Tettleton | .05 |
| 495 | Mark Williamson | .05 |
| 496 | Craig Worthington | .05 |
| **HOUSTON ASTROS** | | |
| 497 | Juan Agosto | .05 |
| 498 | Eric Anthony | .10 |
| 499 | Craig Biggio | .08 |
| 500 | Ken Caminiti | .05 |
| 501 | Casey Candaele | .05 |
| 502 | Andujar Cedeno | .30 |
| 503 | Danny Darwin | .05 |
| 504 | Mark Davidson | .05 |
| 505 | Glenn Davis | .10 |
| 506 | Jim Deshales | .05 |
| 507 | Luis Gonzalez (R) | .40 |
| 508 | Bill Gullickson | .05 |
| 509 | Xavier Hernandez | .08 |
| 510 | Brian Meyer | .05 |
| 511 | Ken Oberkfell | .05 |
| 512 | Mark Portugal | .05 |
| 513 | Rafael Ramirez | .05 |
| 514 | Karl Rhodes | .10 |
| 515 | Mike Scott | .05 |
| 516 | Mike Simms (R) | .10 |
| 517 | Dave Smith | .05 |
| 518 | Franklin Stubbs | .05 |
| 519 | Glenn Wilson | .05 |
| 520 | Eric Yelding | .05 |
| 521 | Gerald Young | .05 |
| **SAN DIEGO PADRES** | | |
| 522 | Shawn Abner | .05 |
| 523 | Roberto Alomar | .08 |
| 524 | Andy Benes | .10 |
| 525 | Joe Carter | .08 |
| 526 | Jack Clark | .10 |
| 527 | Joey Cora | .05 |
| 528 | Paul Farles (R) | .10 |
| 529 | Tony Gwynn | .15 |
| 530 | Atles Hammaker | .05 |
| 531 | Greg Harris | .05 |
| 532 | Thomas Howard | .05 |
| 533 | Bruce Hurst | .05 |
| 534 | Craig Lefferts | .05 |
| 535 | Derek Lilliquist | .05 |
| 536 | Fred Lynn | .05 |
| 537 | Mike Pagliarulo | .05 |
| 538 | Mark Parent | .05 |
| 539 | Dennis Rasmussen | .05 |
| 540 | Bip Roberts | .05 |
| 541 | Richard Rodriguez | .05 |
| 542 | Benito Santiago | .10 |
| 543 | Calvin Schiraldi | .05 |
| 544 | Eric Show | .05 |
| 545 | Phil Stephenson | .05 |
| 546 | Garry Templeton | .05 |
| 547 | Ed Whitson | .05 |
| 548 | Eddie Williams | .05 |
| **KANSAS CITY ROYALS** | | |
| 549 | Kevin Appier | .05 |
| 550 | Luis Aquino | .05 |
| 551 | Bob Boone | .05 |
| 552 | George Brett | .12 |
| 553 | Jeff Conine (R) | .15 |
| 554 | Steve Crawford | .05 |
| 555 | Mark Davis | .05 |
| 556 | Storm Davis | .05 |
| 557 | Jim Elsenreich | .05 |
| 558 | Steve Farr | .05 |
| 559 | Tom Gordon | .10 |
| 560 | Mark Gubicza | .05 |
| 561 | Bo Jackson | .25 |
| 562 | Mike Macfarlane | .05 |
| 563 | Brian McRae (R) | .40 |
| 564 | Jeff Montgomery | .05 |
| 565 | Bill Pecota | .05 |
| 566 | Gerald Perry | .05 |
| 567 | Bret Saberhagen | .10 |
| 568 | Jeff Schultz (R) | .12 |
| 569 | Kevin Seltzer | .05 |
| 570 | Terry Shumpert | .05 |
| 571 | Kurt Stillwell | .05 |
| 572 | Danny Tartabull | .05 |
| 573 | Gary Thurman | .05 |
| 574 | Frank White | .05 |
| 575 | Willie Wilson | .05 |
| **MILWAUKEE BREWERS** | | |
| 576 | Chris Boslo | .05 |
| 577 | Greg Brock | .05 |
| 578 | George Canale | .05 |
| 579 | Chuck Crim | .05 |
| 580 | Rob Deer | .05 |
| 581 | Edgar Diaz | .05 |
| 582 | Tom Edens (R) | .12 |
| 583 | Mike Felder | .05 |
| 584 | Jim Gantner | .05 |
| 585 | Darryl Hamilton | .05 |
| 586 | Ted Higuera | .05 |
| 587 | Mark Knudson | .05 |
| 588 | Bill Krueger | .05 |
| 589 | Tim McIntosh | .08 |
| 590 | Paul Mirabella | .05 |
| 591 | Paul Molitor | .10 |
| 592 | Jaime Navarro | .05 |
| 593 | Dave Parker | .12 |
| 594 | Dan Plesac | .05 |
| 595 | Ron Robinson | .05 |
| 596 | Gary Sheffield | .10 |
| 597 | Bill Spiers | .05 |
| 598 | B.J. Surhoff | .05 |
| 599 | Greg Vaughn | .10 |
| 600 | Randy Veres | .05 |
| 601 | Robin Yount | .15 |
| **MINNESOTA TWINS** | | |
| 602 | Rick Aguilera | .05 |
| 603 | Allan Anderson | .05 |
| 604 | Juan Berenguer | .05 |
| 605 | Randy Bush | .05 |
| 606 | Carmen Castillo | .05 |
| 607 | Tim Drummond | .05 |
| 608 | Scott Erickson | .60 |
| 609 | Gary Gaetti | .05 |
| 610 | Greg Gagne | .05 |
| 611 | Dan Gladden | .05 |
| 612 | Mark Guthrie | .10 |
| 613 | Brian Harper | .05 |
| 614 | Kent Hrbek | .10 |
| 615 | Gene Larkin | .05 |
| 616 | Terry Leach | .05 |
| 617 | Nelson Liriano | .05 |
| 618 | Shane Mack | .05 |
| 619 | John Moses | .05 |
| 620 | Pedro Munoz (R) | .15 |
| 621 | Al Newman | .05 |
| 622 | Junior Ortiz | .05 |
| 623 | Kirby Puckett | .15 |
| 624 | Roy Smith | .05 |
| 625 | Kevin Tapani | .05 |
| 626 | Gary Wayne | .05 |
| 627 | David West | .05 |
| **ST. LOUIS CARDINALS** | | |
| 628 | Cris Carpenter | .05 |
| 629 | Vince Coleman | .10 |
| 630 | Ken Dayley | .05 |
| 631 | Jose DeLeon | .05 |
| 632 | Frank DiPino | .05 |
| 633 | Bernard Gilkey | .15 |
| 634 | Pedro Guerrero | .10 |
| 635 | Ken Hill | .05 |
| 636 | Felix Jose | .08 |
| 637 | Ray Lankford | .35 |
| 638 | Joe Magrane | .05 |
| 639 | Tom Niedenfuer | .05 |
| 640 | Jose Oquendo | .05 |
| 641 | Tom Pagnozzi | .05 |
| 642 | Terry Pendleton | .08 |
| 643 | Mike Perez (R) | .10 |
| 644 | Bryn Smith | .05 |
| 645 | Lee Smith | .05 |
| 646 | Ozzie Smith | .10 |
| 647 | Scott Terry | .05 |
| 648 | Bob Tewksbury | .05 |
| 649 | Milt Thompson | .05 |
| 650 | John Tudor | .05 |
| 651 | Denny Walling | .05 |
| 652 | Craig Wilson (R) | .12 |
| 653 | Todd Worrell | .05 |
| 654 | Todd Zelle | .10 |
| **NEW YORK YANKEES** | | |
| 655 | Oscar Azocar | .08 |
| 656 | Steve Balboni | .05 |
| 657 | Jesse Barfield | .05 |
| 658 | Greg Cadaret | .05 |
| 659 | Chuck Cary | .05 |
| 660 | Rick Cerone | .05 |
| 661 | David Elland | .05 |
| 662 | Alvaro Espinoza | .05 |
| 663 | Bob Geren | .05 |
| 664 | Lee Guetterman | .05 |
| 665 | Mel Hall | .05 |
| 666 | Andy Hawkins | .05 |
| 667 | Jimmy Jones | .05 |
| 668 | Roberto Kelly | .10 |
| 669 | Dave LaPoint | .05 |
| 670 | Tim Leary | .05 |
| 671 | Jim Leyritz | .10 |
| 672 | Kevin Maas | .15 |
| 673 | Don Mattingly | .15 |
| 674 | Matt Nokes | .05 |

| NO. | PLAYER | MINT |
|---|---|---|
| 675 | Pascual Perez | .05 |
| 676 | Eric Plunk | .05 |
| 677 | Dave Righetti | .05 |
| 678 | Jeff Robinson | .05 |
| 679 | Steve Sax | .05 |
| 680 | Mike Witt | .05 |
| **ATLANTA BRAVES** | | |
| 681 | Steve Avery | .20 |
| 682 | Mike Bell (R) | .12 |
| 683 | Jeff Blauser | .05 |
| 684 | Francisco Cabrera | .05 |
| 685 | Tony Castillo | .05 |
| 686 | Marty Clary | .05 |
| 687 | Nick Esasky | .05 |
| 688 | Ron Gant | .12 |
| 689 | Tom Glavine | .10 |
| 690 | Mark Grant | .05 |
| 691 | Tommy Gregg | .05 |
| 692 | Dwayne Henry | .05 |
| 693 | Dave Justice | .45 |
| 694 | Jimmy Kremers | .05 |
| 695 | Charlie Leibrandt | .05 |
| 696 | Mark Lemke | .05 |
| 697 | Oddible McMcDowell | .05 |

| NO. | PLAYER | MINT |
|---|---|---|
| 698 | Greg Olson | .08 |
| 699 | Jeff Parrett | .05 |
| 700 | Jim Presley | .05 |
| 701 | Victor Rosario (R) | .12 |
| 702 | Lonnie Smith | .05 |
| 703 | Pete Smith | .05 |
| 704 | John Smoltz | .05 |
| 705 | Mike Stanton | .05 |
| 706 | Andres Thomas | .05 |
| 707 | Jeff Treadway | .05 |
| 708 | Jim Vatcher (R) | .12 |
| **SPECIAL CARDS** | | |
| 709 | Home Run Kings— Sandberg, Fielder | .15 |
| 710 | Second Generation Stars—Bonds, Griffey Jr. | .30 |
| 711 | NLCS Team Leaders— Bonilla, Larkin | .08 |
| 712 | Top Games Savers— Thigpen, Franco | .10 |
| 713 | Chicago's 100 Club— Dawson, Sandberg | .10 |
| 714 | Checklists—Athletics, Pirates, Reds, Red Sox | .07 |

| NO. | PLAYER | MINT |
|---|---|---|
| 715 | Checklists—White Sox, Mets, Blue Jays, Dodgers | .07 |
| 716 | Checklists—Giants, Rangers, Angels, Expos | .07 |
| 717 | Checklists—Tigers, Indians, Phillies, Cubs | .07 |
| 718 | Checklists—Mariners, Orioles, Astros, Padres | .07 |
| 719 | Checklists—Royals, Brewers, Twins, Cardinals | .07 |
| 720 | Checklists—Yankees, Braves, Super Stars | .07 |
| **No. 1 to 10—All Stars Insert** | | |
| 1 | Ryne Sandberg | 3.00 |
| 2 | Barry Larkin | .75 |
| 3 | Matt Williams | 1.25 |
| 4 | Cecil Fielder | 1.50 |
| 5 | Barry Bonds | 2.00 |
| 6 | Rickey Henderson | 2.50 |
| 7 | Ken Griffey, Jr. | 5.00 |
| 8 | Jose Canseco | 3.00 |
| 9 | Benito Santiago | .75 |
| 10 | Roger Clemens | 2.50 |

| NO. | PLAYER | MINT |
|---|---|---|
| **No. 1 to 12—Pro Visions** | | |
| 1 | Kirby Puckett | .40 |
| 2 | Will Clark | .60 |
| 3 | Ruben Sierra | .25 |
| 4 | Mark McGwire | .30 |
| 5 | Bo Jackson | .75 |
| 6 | Jose Canseco | 1.00 |
| 7 | Dwight Gooden | .35 |
| 8 | Mike Greenwell | .25 |
| 9 | Roger Clemens | .50 |
| 10 | Eric Davis | .35 |
| 11 | Don Mattingly | .35 |
| 12 | Darryl Strawberry | .45 |
| **No. 1F to 4F—Pro Visions** | | |
| 1F | Barry Bonds | .75 |
| 2F | Rickey Henderson | 1.00 |
| 3F | Ryne Sandberg | 1.00 |
| 4F | Dave Stewart | .30 |

## 1991 Fleer Traded Update . . . Complete Set of 132 Cards—Value $12.00

Updates the main 1991 card set with players who had changed teams during the season, and rookies. Features the rookie cards of Ivan Rodriguez and Jeff Bagwell

| NO. | PLAYER | MINT |
|---|---|---|
| U1 | Glenn Davis | .08 |
| U2 | Dwight Evans | .05 |
| U3 | Jose Mesa | .05 |
| U4 | Jack Clark | .10 |
| U5 | Danny Darwin | .05 |
| U6 | Steve Lyons | .05 |
| U7 | Mo Vaughn | .50 |
| U8 | Floyd Bannister | .05 |
| U9 | Gary Gaetti | .05 |
| U10 | Dave Parker | .10 |
| U11 | Joey Cora | .05 |
| U12 | Charlie Hough | .05 |
| U13 | Matt Merullo | .05 |
| U14 | Warren Newson (R) | .20 |
| U15 | Tim Raines | .10 |
| U16 | Albert Belle | .15 |
| U17 | Glenallen Hill | .05 |
| U18 | Shawn Hillegas | .05 |
| U19 | Mark Lewis | .15 |
| U20 | Charles Nagy | .08 |
| U21 | Mark Whiten | .15 |
| U22 | John Cerutti | .05 |
| U23 | Rob Deer | .05 |
| U24 | Mickey Tettleton | .05 |
| U25 | Warren Cromartie | .05 |
| U26 | Kirk Gibson | .05 |
| U27 | David Howard (R) | .12 |
| U28 | Brent Mayne | .08 |
| U29 | Dante Bichette | .05 |
| U30 | Mark Lee (R) | .12 |
| U31 | Julio Machado | .05 |
| U32 | Edwin Nunez | .05 |
| U33 | Willie Randolph | .08 |

| NO. | PLAYER | MINT |
|---|---|---|
| U34 | Franklin Stubbs | .05 |
| U35 | Bill Wegman | .05 |
| U36 | Chili Davis | .05 |
| U37 | Chuck Knoblauch | .30 |
| U38 | Scott Leius | .10 |
| U39 | Jack Morris | .08 |
| U40 | Mike Pagliarulo | .05 |
| U41 | Lenny Webster | .10 |
| U42 | John Habyan | .05 |
| U43 | Steve Howe | .05 |
| U44 | Jeff Johnson (R) | .15 |
| U45 | Scott Kamieniecki (R) | .20 |
| U46 | Pat Kelly (R) | .25 |
| U47 | Hensley Meulens | .15 |
| U48 | Wade Taylor (R) | .15 |
| U49 | Bernie Williams | .25 |
| U50 | Kirk Dressendorfer (R) | .30 |
| U51 | Ernest Riles | .05 |
| U52 | Rich DeLucia (R) | .12 |
| U53 | Tracy Jones | .05 |
| U54 | Bill Kruger | .05 |
| U55 | Alonzo Powell (R) | .15 |
| U56 | Jeff Schaefer | .05 |
| U57 | Russ Swan | .05 |
| U58 | John Barfield (R) | .12 |
| U59 | Rich Gossage | .05 |
| U60 | Jose Guzman | .05 |
| U61 | Dean Palmer | .30 |
| U62 | Ivan Rodriguez (R) | 1.50 |
| U63 | Roberto Alomar | .15 |
| U64 | Tom Candiotti | .05 |
| U65 | Joe Carter | .10 |
| U66 | Ed Sprague | .10 |

| NO. | PLAYER | MINT |
|---|---|---|
| U67 | Pat Tabler | .05 |
| U68 | Mike Timilin (R) | .15 |
| U69 | Devon White | .05 |
| U70 | Rafael Belliard | .05 |
| U71 | Juan Berenguer | .05 |
| U72 | Sid Bream | .05 |
| U73 | Marvin Freeman | .05 |
| U74 | Kent Mercker | .05 |
| U75 | Otis Nixon | .08 |
| U76 | Terry Pendleton | .08 |
| U77 | George Bell | .08 |
| U78 | Danny Jackson | .05 |
| U79 | Chuck McElroy | .05 |
| U80 | Gary Scott (R) | .25 |
| U81 | Heathcliff Slocumb (R) | .12 |
| U82 | Dave Smith | .05 |
| U83 | Rick Wilkins (R) | .15 |
| U84 | Freddie Benavides (R) | .15 |
| U85 | Ted Power | .05 |
| U86 | Mo Sanford (R) | .20 |
| U87 | Jeff Bagwell (R) | 3.00 |
| U88 | Steve Finley | .05 |
| U89 | Pete Harnisch | .05 |
| U90 | Darryl Kile | .12 |
| U91 | Brett Butler | .08 |
| U92 | John Candelaria | .05 |
| U93 | Gary Carter | .08 |
| U94 | Kevin Gross | .05 |
| U95 | Bob Ojeda | .05 |
| U96 | Darryl Strawberry | .20 |
| U97 | Ivan Calderon | .05 |
| U98 | Ron Hassey | .05 |
| U99 | Gilberto Reyes | .05 |

| NO. | PLAYER | MINT |
|---|---|---|
| U100 | Hubie Brooks | .05 |
| U101 | Rick Cerone | .05 |
| U102 | Vince Coleman | .10 |
| U103 | Jeff Innis | .05 |
| U104 | Pete Schourek (R) | .15 |
| U105 | Andy Ashby (R) | .15 |
| U106 | Wally Backman | .05 |
| U107 | Darrin Fletcher | .08 |
| U108 | Tommy Greene | .05 |
| U109 | John Morris | .05 |
| U110 | Mitch Williams | .05 |
| U111 | Lloyd McClendon | .05 |
| U112 | Orlando Merced (R) | .30 |
| U113 | Vicente Palacios | .05 |
| U114 | Gary Varsho | .05 |
| U115 | John Wehner (R) | .25 |
| U116 | Rex Hudler | .05 |
| U117 | Tim Jones | .05 |
| U118 | Geronimo Pena | .05 |
| U119 | Gerald Perry | .05 |
| U120 | Larry Andersen | .05 |
| U121 | Jerald Clark | .05 |
| U122 | Scott Coolbaugh | .05 |
| U123 | Tony Fernandez | .05 |
| U124 | Darrin Jackson | .05 |
| U125 | Fred McGriff | .10 |
| U126 | Jose Mota (R) | .15 |
| U127 | Tim Teufel | .05 |
| U128 | Bud Black | .08 |
| U129 | Mike Felder | .05 |
| U130 | Willie McGee | .10 |
| U131 | Dave Righetti | .05 |
| U132 | Checklist | .05 |

High quality, glossy card stock. 10 Ultra Gold cards were inserted randomly in wax packs. Features the rookie card of Phil Plantier.

| NO. | PLAYER | MINT |
|---|---|---|
| **ATLANTA BRAVES** | | |
| 1 | Steve Avery | 2.00 |
| 2 | Jeff Blauser | .08 |
| 3 | Francisco Cabrera | .08 |
| 4 | Ron Gant | .25 |
| 5 | Tom Glavine | .25 |
| 6 | Tommy Gregg | .08 |
| 7 | Dave Justice | 2.50 |
| 8 | Oddibe McDowell | .08 |
| 9 | Greg Olson | .08 |
| 10 | Terry Pendleton | .15 |
| 11 | Lonnie Smith | .08 |
| 12 | John Smoltz | .15 |
| 13 | Jeff Treadway | .08 |
| **BALTIMORE ORIOLES** | | |
| 14 | Glenn Davis | .10 |
| 15 | Mike Devereaux | .08 |
| 16 | Leo Gomez | .50 |
| 17 | Chris Hoiles | .15 |
| 18 | Dave Johnson | .08 |
| 19 | Ben McDonald | .20 |
| 20 | Randy Milligan | .08 |
| 21 | Gregg Olson | .12 |
| 22 | Joe Orsulak | .08 |
| 23 | Bill Ripken | .08 |
| 24 | Cal Ripken, Jr. | .75 |
| 25 | David Segui | .15 |
| 26 | Craig Worthington | .08 |
| **BOSTON RED SOX** | | |
| 27 | Wade Boggs | .25 |
| 28 | Tom Bolton | .08 |
| 29 | Tom Brunansky | .08 |
| 30 | Ellis Burks | .15 |
| 31 | Roger Clemens | .50 |
| 32 | Mike Greenwell | .15 |
| 33 | Greg Harris | .08 |
| 34 | Daryl Irvine (R) | .15 |
| 35 | Mike Marshall | .08 |
| 36 | Tim Naehring | .15 |
| 37 | Tony Pena | .08 |
| 38 | Phil Plantier (R) | 4.00 |
| 39 | Carlos Quintana | .08 |
| 40 | Jeff Reardon | .08 |
| 41 | Jody Reed | .08 |
| 42 | Luis Rivera | .08 |
| **CALIFORNIA ANGELS** | | |
| 43 | Jim Abbott | .25 |
| 44 | Chuck Finley | .15 |
| 45 | Bryan Harvey | .08 |
| 46 | Donnie Hill | .08 |
| 47 | Jack Howell | .08 |
| 48 | Wally Joyner | .15 |
| 49 | Mark Langston | .12 |
| 50 | Kirk McCaskill | .08 |
| 51 | Lance Parrish | .08 |
| 52 | Dick Schofield | .08 |
| 53 | Lee Stevens | .25 |
| 54 | Dave Winfield | .20 |
| **CHICAGO CUBS** | | |
| 55 | George Bell | .15 |
| 56 | Damon Berryhill | .08 |
| 57 | Mike Bielecki | .08 |
| 58 | Andre Dawson | .20 |
| 59 | Shawon Dunston | .10 |
| 60 | Joe Girardi | .12 |
| 61 | Mark Grace | .15 |

| NO. | PLAYER | MINT |
|---|---|---|
| 62 | Mike Harkey | .08 |
| 63 | Les Lancaster | .08 |
| 64 | Greg Maddux | .08 |
| 65 | Derrick May | .12 |
| 66 | Ryne Sandberg | .50 |
| 67 | Luis Salazar | .08 |
| 68 | Dwight Smith | .08 |
| 69 | Hector Villanueva | .08 |
| 70 | Jerome Walton | .10 |
| 71 | Mitch Williams | .08 |
| **CHICAGO WHITE SOX** | | |
| 72 | Carlton Fisk | .25 |
| 73 | Scott Fletcher | .08 |
| 74 | Ozzie Guillen | .08 |
| 75 | Greg Hibbard | .08 |
| 76 | Lance Johnson | .08 |
| 77 | Steve Lyons | .08 |
| 78 | Jack McDowell | .12 |
| 79 | Dan Pasqua | .08 |
| 80 | Melido Perez | .08 |
| 81 | Tim Raines | .12 |
| 82 | Sammy Sosa | .10 |
| 83 | Cory Snyder | .08 |
| 84 | Bobby Thigpen | .08 |
| 85 | Frank Thomas | 5.00 |
| 86 | Robin Ventura | .50 |
| **CINCINNATI REDS** | | |
| 87 | Todd Benzinger | .08 |
| 88 | Glenn Braggs | .08 |
| 89 | Tom Browning | .08 |
| 90 | Norm Charlton | .08 |
| 91 | Eric Davis | .20 |
| 92 | Rob Dibble | .12 |
| 93 | Bill Doran | .08 |
| 94 | Mariano Duncan | .08 |
| 95 | Billy Hatcher | .08 |
| 96 | Barry Larkin | .15 |
| 97 | Randy Myers | .08 |
| 98 | Hal Morris | .15 |
| 99 | Joe Oliver | .08 |
| 100 | Paul O'Neill | .08 |
| 101 | Jeff Reed | .08 |
| 102 | Jose Rijo | .08 |
| 103 | Chris Sabo | .12 |
| **CLEVELAND INDIANS** | | |
| 104 | Beau Allred | .15 |
| 105 | Sandy Alomar, Jr. | .12 |
| 106 | Carlos Baerga | .25 |
| | wrong no.-103 | |
| 107 | Albert Belle | .50 |
| 108 | Jerry Browne | .08 |
| 109 | Tom Candiotti | .08 |
| 110 | Alex Cole | .12 |
| 111 | John Farrell | .08 |
| 112 | Felix Fermin | .08 |
| 113 | Brook Jacoby | .08 |
| 114 | Chris James | .08 |
| 115 | Doug Jones | .08 |
| 116 | Steve Olin | .08 |
| 117 | Greg Swindell | .08 |
| 118 | Turner Ward (R) | .20 |
| 119 | Mitch Webster | .08 |
| **DETROIT TIGERS** | | |
| 120 | Dave Bergman | .08 |
| 121 | Cecil Fielder | .35 |
| 122 | Travis Fryman | 1.50 |

| NO. | PLAYER | MINT |
|---|---|---|
| 123 | Mike Henneman | .08 |
| 124 | Lloyd Moseby | .08 |
| 125 | Dan Petry | .08 |
| 126 | Tony Phllips | .08 |
| 127 | Mark Salas | .08 |
| 128 | Frank Tanana | .08 |
| 129 | Alan Trammell | .15 |
| 130 | Lou Whitaker | .08 |
| **HOUSTON ASTROS** | | |
| 131 | Eric Anthony | .12 |
| 132 | Craig Biggio | .12 |
| 133 | Ken Caminiti | .08 |
| 134 | Casey Candaele | .08 |
| 135 | Andujar Cedeno | .75 |
| 136 | Mark Davidson | .08 |
| 137 | Jim Deshaies | .08 |
| 138 | Mark Portugal | .08 |
| 139 | Rafael Ramirez | .08 |
| 140 | Mike Scott | .08 |
| 141 | Eric Yelding | .08 |
| 142 | Gerald Young | .08 |
| **KANSAS CITY ROYALS** | | |
| 143 | Kevin Appier | .08 |
| 144 | George Brett | .25 |
| 145 | Jeff Conine | .20 |
| 146 | Jim Eisenreich | .08 |
| 147 | Tom Gordon | .10 |
| 148 | Mark Gubicza | .08 |
| 149 | Bo Jackson | .50 |
| 150 | Brent Mayne | .20 |
| 151 | Mike Macfarlane | .08 |
| 152 | Brian McRae (R) | 1.00 |
| 153 | Jeff Montgomery | .08 |
| 154 | Bret Saberhagen | .12 |
| 155 | Kevin Seitzer | .08 |
| 156 | Terry Shumpert | .08 |
| 157 | Kurt Stillwell | .08 |
| 158 | Danny Tartabull | .10 |
| **LOS ANGELES DODGERS** | | |
| 159 | Tim Belcher | .08 |
| 160 | Kal Daniels | .10 |
| 161 | Alfredo Griffin | .08 |
| 162 | Lenny Harris | .08 |
| 163 | Jay Howell | .08 |
| 164 | Ramon Martinez | .25 |
| 165 | Mike Morgan | .08 |
| 166 | Eddie Murray | .15 |
| 167 | Jose Offerman | .10 |
| 168 | Juan Samuel | .08 |
| 169 | Mike Scioscia | .08 |
| 170 | Mike Sharperson | .08 |
| 171 | Darryl Strawberry | .35 |
| **MILWAUKEE BREWERS** | | |
| 172 | Greg Brock | .08 |
| 173 | Chuck Crim | .08 |
| 174 | Jim Gantner | .08 |
| 175 | Ted Higuera | .08 |
| 176 | Mark Knudson | .08 |
| 177 | Tim McIntosh | .08 |
| 178 | Paul Molitor | .10 |
| 179 | Dan Plesac | .08 |
| 180 | Gary Sheffield | .10 |
| 181 | Bill Spiers | .08 |
| 182 | B.J. Surhoff | .08 |
| 183 | Greg Vaughn | .15 |
| 184 | Robin Yount | .20 |

| NO. | PLAYER | MINT |
|---|---|---|
| **MINNESOTA TWINS** | | |
| 185 | Rick Aguilera | .08 |
| 186 | Greg Gagne | .08 |
| 187 | Dan Gladden | .08 |
| 188 | Brian Harper | .08 |
| 189 | Kent Hrbek | .08 |
| 190 | Gene Larkin | .08 |
| 191 | Shane Mack | .08 |
| 192 | Pedro Munoz (R) | .50 |
| 193 | Al Newman | .08 |
| 194 | Junior Ortiz | .08 |
| 195 | Kirby Puckett | .20 |
| 196 | Kevin Tapani | .08 |
| **MONTREAL EXPOS** | | |
| 197 | Dennis Boyd | .08 |
| 198 | Tim Burke | .08 |
| 199 | Ivan Calderon | .08 |
| 200 | Delino DeShields | .15 |
| 201 | Mike Fitgerald | .08 |
| 202 | Steve Frey | .10 |
| 203 | Andres Galarraga | .08 |
| 204 | Marquis Grisson | .15 |
| 205 | Dave Martinez | .08 |
| 206 | Dennis Martinez | .08 |
| 207 | Junior Noboa | .08 |
| 208 | Spike Owen | .08 |
| 209 | Scott Ruskin | .10 |
| 210 | Tim Wallach | .08 |
| **NEW YORK METS** | | |
| 211 | Daryl Boston | .08 |
| 212 | Vince Coleman | .12 |
| 213 | David Cone | .10 |
| 214 | Ron Darling | .08 |
| 215 | Kevin Elster | .08 |
| 216 | Sid Fernandez | .08 |
| 217 | John Franco | .08 |
| 218 | Dwight Gooden | .20 |
| 219 | Tom Herr | .08 |
| 220 | Tod Hundley | .08 |
| 221 | Gregg Jefferies | .08 |
| 222 | Howard Johnson | .15 |
| 223 | Dave Magadan | .08 |
| 224 | Kevin McReynolds | .10 |
| 225 | Keith Miller | .08 |
| 226 | Mackey Sasser | .08 |
| 227 | Frank Viola | .10 |
| **NEW YORK YANKEES** | | |
| 228 | Jesse Barfield | .08 |
| 229 | Greg Cadaret | .08 |
| 230 | Alvaro Espinoza | .08 |
| 231 | Bob Geren | .08 |
| 232 | Lee Guetterman | .08 |
| 233 | Mel Hall | .08 |
| 234 | Andy Hawkins | .08 |
| 235 | Roberto Kelly | .10 |
| 236 | Tim Leary | .08 |
| 237 | Jim Leyritz | .08 |
| 238 | Kevin Maas | .25 |
| 239 | Don Mattingly | .25 |
| 240 | Hensley Meulens | .08 |
| 241 | Eric Plunk | .08 |
| 242 | Steve Sax | .10 |
| **OAKLAND ATHLETICS** | | |
| 243 | Todd Burns | .08 |
| 244 | Jose Canseco | .75 |
| 245 | Dennis Eckersley | .10 |
| 246 | Mike Gallego | .08 |

| NO. | PLAYER | MINT |
|---|---|---|
| 247 | Dave Henderson | .10 |
| 248 | Rickey Henderson | .50 |
| 249 | Rick Honeycutt | .08 |
| 250 | Carney Lansford | .08 |
| 251 | Mark McGwire | .15 |
| 252 | Mike Moore | .08 |
| 253 | Terry Steinbach | .08 |
| 254 | Dave Stewart | .12 |
| 255 | Walt Weiss | .08 |
| 256 | Bob Welch | .08 |
| 257 | Curt Young | .08 |

**PHILADELPHIA PHILLIES**

| NO. | PLAYER | MINT |
|---|---|---|
| 258 | Wes Chamberlain (R) | 1.00 |
| 259 | Pat Combs | .08 |
| 260 | Darren Daulton | .08 |
| 261 | Jose DeJesus | .08 |
| 262 | Len Dykstra | .10 |
| 263 | Charlie Hayes | .08 |
| 264 | Von Hayes | .08 |
| 265 | Ken Howell | .08 |
| 266 | John Kruk | .08 |
| 267 | Roger McDowell | .08 |
| 268 | Mickey Morandini | .15 |
| 269 | Terry Mulholland | .08 |
| 270 | Dale Murphy | .15 |
| 271 | Randy Ready | .08 |
| 272 | Dickie Thon | .08 |

**PITTSBURGH PIRATES**

| NO. | PLAYER | MINT |
|---|---|---|
| 273 | Stan Belinda | .08 |
| 274 | Jay Bell | .08 |
| 275 | Barry Bonds | .30 |
| 276 | Bobby Bonilla | .20 |
| 277 | Doug Drabek | .08 |
| 278 | Carlos Garcia (R) | .20 |
| 279 | Neal Heaton | .08 |
| 280 | Jeff King | .08 |
| 281 | Bill Landrum | .08 |
| 282 | Mike LaValliere | .08 |
| 283 | Jose Lind | .08 |
| 284 | Orlando Merced (R) | .75 |
| 285 | Gary Redus | .08 |
| 286 | Don Slaught | .08 |
| 287 | Andy Van Slyke | .10 |

**ST. LOUIS CARDINALS**

| NO. | PLAYER | MINT |
|---|---|---|
| 288 | Jose DeLeon | .08 |
| 289 | Pedro Guerrero | .10 |
| 290 | Ray Lankford | .50 |
| 291 | Joe Magrane | .08 |
| 292 | Jose Oquendo | .08 |
| 293 | Tom Pagnozzi | .08 |
| 294 | Bryn Smith | .08 |
| 295 | Lee Smith | .08 |
| 296 | Ozzie Smith | .25 |
| 297 | Milt Thompson | .08 |
| 298 | Craig Wilson (R) | .15 |
| 299 | Todd Zeile | .20 |

**SAN DIEGO PADRES**

| NO. | PLAYER | MINT |
|---|---|---|
| 300 | Shawn Abner | .08 |
| 301 | Andy Benes | .15 |
| 302 | Paul Farie (R) | .15 |
| 303 | Tony Gwynn | .25 |
| 304 | Greg Harris | .08 |
| 305 | Thomas Howard | .08 |
| 306 | Bruce Hurst | .08 |
| 307 | Craig Lefferts | .08 |
| 308 | Fred McGriff | .20 |
| 309 | Dennis Rasmussen | .08 |
| 310 | Bip Roberts | .08 |
| 311 | Benito Santiago | .10 |
| 312 | Garry Templeton | .08 |
| 313 | Ed Whitson | .08 |

**SAN FRANCISCO GIANTS**

| NO. | PLAYER | MINT |
|---|---|---|
| 314 | Dave Anderson | .08 |
| 315 | Kevin Bass | .08 |
| 316 | Jeff Brantley | .08 |
| 317 | John Burkett | .08 |
| 318 | Will Clark | .65 |
| 319 | Steve Decker (R) | .35 |
| 320 | Scott Garrelts | .08 |
| 321 | Terry Kennedy | .08 |
| 322 | Mark Leonard (R) | .20 |
| 323 | Darren Lewis | .50 |
| 324 | Greg Litton | .08 |
| 325 | Willie McGee | .10 |
| 326 | Kevin Mitchell | .15 |
| 327 | Don Robinson | .08 |
| 328 | Andres Santana | .25 |
| 329 | Robby Thompson | .08 |

| NO. | PLAYER | MINT |
|---|---|---|
| 330 | Jose Uribe | .08 |
| 331 | Matt Williams | .20 |

**SEATTLE MARINERS**

| NO. | PLAYER | MINT |
|---|---|---|
| 332 | Scott Bradley | .08 |
| 333 | Henry Cotto | .08 |
| 334 | Alvin Davis | .08 |
| 335 | Ken Griffey | .08 |
| 336 | Ken Grifey, Jr. | 3.00 |
| 337 | Erik Hanson | .10 |
| 338 | Brian Holman | .08 |
| 339 | Randy Johnson | .08 |
| 340 | Edgar Martinez | .10 |
| 341 | Tino Martinez | .25 |
| 342 | Pete O'Brien | .08 |
| 343 | Harold Reynolds | .08 |
| 344 | David Valle | .08 |
| 345 | Omar Vizquel | .08 |

**TEXAS RANGERS**

| NO. | PLAYER | MINT |
|---|---|---|
| 346 | Brad Arnsberg | .08 |
| 347 | Kevin Brown | .08 |
| 348 | Julio Franco | .12 |
| 349 | Jeff Huson | .08 |
| 350 | Rafael Palmeiro | .15 |
| 351 | Geno Petralli | .08 |
| 352 | Gary Pettis | .08 |
| 353 | Kenny Rogers | .08 |
| 354 | Jeff Russell | .08 |
| 355 | Nolan Ryan | 1.00 |
| 356 | Ruben Sierra | .25 |
| 357 | Bobby Witt | .08 |

**TORONTO BLUE JAYS**

| NO. | PLAYER | MINT |
|---|---|---|
| 358 | Roberto Alomar | .20 |
| 359 | Pat Borders | .08 |
| 360 | Joe Carter | .20 |
| 361 | Kelly Gruber | .10 |
| 362 | Tom Henke | .08 |
| 363 | Glenallen Hill | .08 |
| 364 | Jimmy Key | .08 |
| 365 | Manny Lee | .08 |
| 366 | Rance Muiliniks | .08 |
| 367 | John Olerud | .25 |
| 368 | Dave Stieb | .08 |
| 369 | Duane Ward | .08 |
| 370 | David Wells | .08 |

| NO. | PLAYER | MINT |
|---|---|---|
| 371 | Mark Whiten | .25 |
| 372 | Mookie Wilson | .08 |

**ULTRA PROSPECTS™**

| NO. | PLAYER | MINT |
|---|---|---|
| 373 | Willie Banks | .35 |
| 374 | Steve Carter | .12 |
| 375 | Scott Chiamparino | .15 |
| 376 | Steve Chitren (R) | .15 |
| 377 | Darrin Fletcher | .15 |
| 378 | Rich Garces (R) | .15 |
| 379 | Reggie Jefferson | .75 |
| 380 | Eric Karros (R) | 1.00 |
| 381 | Pat Kelly (R) | .50 |
| 382 | Chuck Knoblauch | 2.00 |
| 383 | Denny Neagle (R) | .50 |
| 384 | Dan Opperman (R) | .75 |
| 385 | John Ramos (R) | .30 |
| 386 | Henry Rodriguez (R) | .25 |
| 387 | Maurice Vaughn | 1.50 |
| 388 | Gerald Williams (R) | .50 |
| 389 | Mike York (R) | .20 |
| 390 | Eddie Zosky | .25 |

**GREAT PERFORMANCES**

| NO. | PLAYER | MINT |
|---|---|---|
| 391 | Barry Bonds | .20 |
| 392 | Cecil Fielder | .25 |
| 393 | Rickey Henderson | .30 |
| 394 | Dave Justice | .75 |
| 395 | Nolan Ryan | .50 |
| 396 | Bobby Thigpen | .12 |
| 397 | Checklist | .08 |
| 398 | Checklist | .08 |
| 399 | Checklist | .08 |
| 400 | Checklist | .08 |

**No. 1 to 10—Ultra Gold**

| NO. | PLAYER | MINT |
|---|---|---|
| 1 | Barry Bonds | 1.00 |
| 2 | Will Clark | 1.50 |
| 3 | Will Cordero | .50 |
| 4 | Ken Griffey, Jr. | 3.00 |
| 5 | Rickey Henderson | 1.50 |
| 6 | Bo Jackson | 1.50 |
| 7 | Ramon Martinez | .75 |
| 8 | Kirby Puckett | 1.25 |
| 9 | Chris Sabo | .50 |
| 10 | Ryne Sandberg | 1.50 |

## 1991 Fleer Ultra Update . . . Complete Set of 120 Cards—Value—$25.00

Updates the Fleer Ultra card set with players who had changed teams during the season, and rookies. Features the rookie cards of Jeff Bagwell and Ivan Rodriguez.

| NO. | PLAYER | MINT |
|---|---|---|
| U1 | Dwight Evans | .08 |
| U2 | Chito Martinez (R) | 1.50 |
| U3 | Bob Melvin | .06 |
| U4 | Mike Mussina (R) | .60 |
| U5 | Jack Clark | .10 |
| U6 | Dana Kiecker | .06 |
| U7 | Steve Lyons | .06 |
| U8 | Cary Gaetti | .06 |
| U9 | Dave Gallagher | .06 |
| U10 | Dave Parker | .20 |

| NO. | PLAYER | MINT |
|---|---|---|
| U11 | Luis Polonia | .06 |
| U12 | Luis Sojo | .06 |
| U13 | Wilson Alvarez | .06 |
| U14 | Alex Fernandez | .35 |
| U15 | Craig Grebeck | .06 |
| U16 | Ron Karkovice | .06 |
| U17 | Warren Newson(R) | .30 |
| U18 | Scott Radinsky | .06 |
| U19 | Glenallen Hill | .06 |
| U20 | Charles Nagy | .10 |

| NO. | PLAYER | MINT |
|---|---|---|
| U21 | Mark Whiten | .30 |
| U22 | Milt Cuyler | .20 |
| U23 | Paul Gibson | .06 |
| U24 | Mickey Tettleton | .06 |
| U25 | Todd Benzinger | .06 |
| U26 | Storm Davis | .06 |
| U27 | Kirk Gibson | .10 |
| U28 | Bill Pecota | .06 |
| U29 | Gary Thurman | .06 |
| U30 | Darryl Hamilton | .06 |

| NO. | PLAYER | MINT |
|---|---|---|
| U31 | Jaime Navarro | .06 |
| U32 | Willie Randolph | .08 |
| U33 | Bill Wegman | .06 |
| U34 | Randy Bush | .06 |
| U35 | Chili Davis | .06 |
| U36 | Scott Erickson | 2.00 |
| U37 | Chuck Knoblauch | 1.00 |
| U38 | Scott Leius | .10 |
| U39 | Jack Morris | .10 |
| U40 | John Habyan | .06 |

| NO. | PLAYER | MINT | NO. | PLAYER | MINT | NO. | PLAYER | MINT | NO. | PLAYER | MINT |
|-----|--------|------|-----|--------|------|-----|--------|------|-----|--------|------|
| U41 | Pat Kelly | .50 | U61 | Bob MacDonald (R) | .15 | U81 | Steve Finley | .06 | U101 | Mitch Williams | .06 |
| U42 | Matt Nokes | .06 | U62 | Greg Myers | .06 | U82 | Luis Gonzalez (R) | 1.00 | U102 | John Smiley | .06 |
| U43 | Scott Sanderson | .06 | U63 | Ed Sprago | .15 | U83 | Pete Harnisch | .06 | U103 | Randy Tomlin (R) | .40 |
| U44 | Bernie Williams | .30 | U64 | Devon White | .06 | U84 | Darryl Kile | .15 | U104 | Gary Varsho | .06 |
| U45 | Harold Baines | .06 | U65 | Rafael Belliard | .06 | U85 | Brett Butler | .06 | U105 | Cris Carpenter | .06 |
| U46 | Brook Jacoby | .06 | U66 | Juan Berenguer | .06 | U86 | Gary Carter | .10 | U106 | Ken Hill | .06 |
| U47 | Ernest Riles | .06 | U67 | Brian Hunter (R) | 1.25 | U87 | Tim Crews | .06 | U107 | Felix Jose | .12 |
| U48 | Willie Wilson | .06 | U68 | Kent Mercker | .06 | U88 | Orel Hershiser | .10 | U108 | Omar Olivares (R) | .15 |
| U49 | Jay Buhner | .10 | U69 | Otis Nixon | .10 | U89 | Bob Ojeda | .06 | U109 | Gerald Perry | .06 |
| U50 | Rich DeLucia (R) | .25 | U70 | Danny Jackson | .06 | U90 | Bret Barberie (R) | .40 | U110 | Jerald Clark | .06 |
| U51 | Mike Jackson | .06 | U71 | Chuck McElroy | .06 | U91 | Barry Jones | .06 | U111 | Tony Fernandez | .06 |
| U52 | Bill Krueger | .06 | U72 | Gary Scott (R) | .50 | U92 | Gilberto Reves | .06 | U112 | Darrin Jackson | .06 |
| U53 | Bill Swift | .06 | U73 | Heathcliff Slocumb (R) | .15 | U93 | Larry Walker | .10 | U113 | Mike Maddux | .06 |
| U54 | Brian Downing | .06 | U74 | Chico Walker | .06 | U94 | Hubie Brooks | .06 | U114 | Tim Teufel | .06 |
| U55 | Juan Gonzalez | 2.25 | U75 | Rick Wilkins (R) | .40 | U95 | Tim Burke | .06 | U115 | Bud Black | .06 |
| U56 | Dean Palmer | .75 | U76 | Chris Hammond | .12 | U96 | Rick Cerone | .06 | U116 | Kelly Downs | .06 |
| U57 | Kevin Reimer | .06 | U77 | Luis Quinones | .06 | U97 | Jeff Innis | .06 | U117 | Mike Felder | .06 |
| U58 | Ivan Rodriguez (R) | 3.50 | U78 | Herm Winningham | .06 | U98 | Wally Backman | .06 | U118 | Willie McGee | .12 |
| U59 | Tony Candiotti | .06 | U79 | Jeff Bagwell (R) | 5.00 | U99 | Tommy Greene | .12 | U119 | Trevor Wilson | .06 |
| U60 | Juan Guzman (R) | 1.00 | U80 | Jim Corsi | .06 | U100 | Ricky Jordan | .08 | U120 | Checklist | .06 |

## 1992 Fleer . . . Complete Set of 720 Cards—Value $65.00

Improvements included smooth card stock on both sides, larger photos on the back and more action photos. A new tamper proof poly wrapper replaced the wax wrapper. A new 6-card subset was Pro-Vision art cards. 24 limited gold foil All-Star Cards were randomly inserted in foil packs. 12 limited gold foil Roger Clemens cards (over 2,000 were autographed) were randomly inserted in all packs. A 3-card Roger Clemens subset was available only by a mail offer. Production was significantly reduced with the original factory cost increasing about 50%.

| NO. | PLAYER | MINT | NO. | PLAYER | MINT | NO. | PLAYER | MINT | NO. | PLAYER | MINT |
|-----|--------|------|-----|--------|------|-----|--------|------|-----|--------|------|
| **BALTIMORE ORIOLES** | | | 35 | Ellis Burks | .08 | 70 | Luis Sojo | .05 | 104 | Carlos Baerga | .12 |
| 1 | Brady Anderson | .05 | 36 | Jack Clark | .05 | 71 | Lee Stevens | .05 | 105 | Albert Belle | .15 |
| 2 | Jose Bautista | .05 | 37 | Roger Clemens | .20 | 72 | Dave Winfield | .12 | 106 | Willie Blair | .05 |
| 3 | Juan Bell | .05 | 38 | Danny Darwin | .05 | 73 | Cliff Young | .05 | 107 | Jerry Browne | .05 |
| 4 | Glenn Davis | .08 | 39 | Mike Greenwell | .10 | **CHICAGO WHITE SOX** | | | 108 | Alex Cole | .05 |
| 5 | Mike Devereaux | .05 | 40 | Joe Hesketh | .05 | 74 | Wilson Alvarez | .10 | 109 | Felix Fermin | .05 |
| 6 | Dwight Evans | .05 | 41 | Daryl Irvine | .05 | 75 | Esteban Beltre (R) | .15 | 110 | Glenallen Hill | .05 |
| 7 | Mike Flanagan | .05 | 42 | Dennis Lamp | .05 | 76 | Joey Cora | .05 | 111 | Shawn Hillegas | .05 |
| 8 | Leo Gomez | .12 | 43 | Tony Pena | .05 | 77 | Brian Drahman | .08 | 112 | Chris James | .05 |
| 9 | Chris Hoiles | .05 | 44 | Phil Plantier | .75 | 78 | Alex Fernandez | .12 | 113 | Reggie Jefferson | .15 |
| 10 | Sam Horn | .05 | 45 | Carlos Quintana | .05 | 79 | Carlton Fisk | .12 | 114 | Doug Jones | .05 |
| 11 | Tim Hulett | .05 | 46 | Jeff Reardon | .05 | 80 | Scott Fletcher | .05 | 115 | Eric King | .05 |
| 12 | Dave Johnson | .05 | 47 | Jody Reed | .05 | 81 | Craig Grebeck | .05 | 116 | Mark Lewis | .20 |
| 13 | Chito Martinez | .30 | 48 | Luis Rivera | .05 | 82 | Ozzie Guillen | .05 | 117 | Carlos Martinez | .05 |
| 14 | Ben McDonald | .08 | 49 | Mo Vaughn | .35 | 83 | Greg Hibbard | .05 | 118 | Charles Nagy | .05 |
| 15 | Bob Melvin | .05 | **CALIFORNIA ANGELS** | | | 84 | Charlie Hough | .05 | 119 | Rod Nichols | .05 |
| 16 | Luis Mercedes | .20 | 50 | Jim Abbott | .15 | 85 | Mike Huff | .05 | 120 | Steve Olin | .05 |
| 17 | Jose Mesa | .05 | 51 | Kyle Abbott | .15 | 86 | Bo Jackson | .30 | 121 | Jesse Orosco | .05 |
| 18 | Bob Milacki | .05 | 52 | Ruben Amaro | .08 | 87 | Lance Johnson | .05 | 122 | Rudy Seanez | .05 |
| 19 | Randy Milligan | .05 | 53 | Scott Bailes | .05 | 88 | Ron Karkovice | .05 | 123 | Joel Skinner | .05 |
| 20 | Mike Mussina | .15 | 54 | Chris Beasley | .08 | 89 | Jack McDowell | .05 | 124 | Greg Swindell | .05 |
| 21 | Gregg Olson | .05 | 55 | Mark Eichhorn | .05 | 90 | Matt Merullo | .05 | 125 | Jim Thome | .50 |
| 22 | Jose Orsulak | .05 | 56 | Mike Fetters | .05 | 91 | Warren Newson | .08 | 126 | Mark Whiten | .15 |
| 23 | Jim Poole | .05 | 57 | Chuck Finley | .05 | 92 | Donn Pall | .05 | **DETROIT TIGERS** | | |
| 24 | Arthur Rhodes | .25 | 58 | Gary Gaetti | .05 | 93 | Dan Pasqua | .05 | 127 | Scott Aldred | .05 |
| 25 | Billy Ripken | .05 | 59 | Dave Gallagher | .05 | 94 | Ken Patterson | .05 | 128 | Andy Allanson | .05 |
| 26 | Cal Ripken, Jr. | .35 | 60 | Donnie Hill | .05 | 95 | Melido Perez | .05 | 129 | John Cerutti | .05 |
| 27 | David Segui | .05 | 61 | Bryan Harvey | .05 | 96 | Scott Radinsky | .05 | 130 | Milt Cuyler | .08 |
| 28 | Roy Smith | .05 | 62 | Wally Joyner | .08 | 97 | Tim Raines | .08 | 131 | Mike Dalton | .08 |
| 29 | Anthony Telford | .05 | 63 | Mark Langston | .05 | 98 | Sammy Sosa | .05 | 132 | Rob Deer | .05 |
| 30 | Mark Williamson | .05 | 64 | Kirk McCaskill | .05 | 99 | Bobby Thigpen | .05 | 133 | Cecil Fielder | .20 |
| 31 | Craig Worthington | .05 | 65 | John Orton | .05 | 100 | Frank Thomas | 1.25 | 134 | Travis Fryman | .25 |
| **BOSTON RED SOX** | | | 66 | Lance Parrish | .05 | 101 | Robin Ventura | .20 | 135 | Dan Gakeler | .08 |
| 32 | Wade Boggs | .20 | 67 | Luis Polonia | .05 | **CLEVELAND INDIANS** | | | 136 | Paul Gibson | .05 |
| 33 | Tom Bolton | .05 | 68 | Bobby Rose | .05 | 102 | Mike Aldrete | .05 | 137 | Bill Gullickson | .05 |
| 34 | Tom Brunansky | .05 | 69 | Dick Schofield | .05 | 103 | Sandy Alomar, Jr. | .08 | 138 | Mike Henneman | .05 |

| NO. | PLAYER | MINT |
|-----|--------|------|
| 139 | Pete Incaviglia | .05 |
| 140 | Mark Leiter | .05 |
| 141 | Scott Livingstone | .15 |
| 142 | Lloyd Moseby | .05 |
| 143 | Tony Phillips | .05 |
| 144 | Mark Salas | .05 |
| 145 | Frank Tanana | .05 |
| 146 | Walt Terrell | .05 |
| 147 | Mickey Tettleton | .05 |
| 148 | Alan Trammell | .08 |
| 149 | Lou Whitaker | .05 |

**KANSAS CITY ROYALS**

| NO. | PLAYER | MINT |
|-----|--------|------|
| 150 | Kevin Appier | .05 |
| 151 | Luis Aquino | .05 |
| 152 | Todd Benzinger | .05 |
| 153 | Mike Boddicker | .05 |
| 154 | George Brett | .15 |
| 155 | Storm Davis | .05 |
| 156 | Jim Eisenreich | .05 |
| 157 | Kirk Gibson | .05 |
| 158 | Tom Gordon | .05 |
| 159 | Mark Gubicza | .05 |
| 160 | David Howard | .05 |
| 161 | Mike Macfarlane | .05 |
| 162 | Brent Mayne | .05 |
| 163 | Brian McRae | .20 |
| 164 | Jeff Montgomery | .05 |
| 165 | Bill Pecota | .05 |
| 166 | Harvey Pulliam | .25 |
| 167 | Bret Saberhagen | .12 |
| 168 | Kevin Seitzer | .05 |
| 169 | Terry Shumpert | .05 |
| 170 | Kurt Stillwell | .05 |
| 171 | Danny Tartabull | .08 |
| 172 | Gary Thurman | .05 |

**MILWAUKEE BREWERS**

| NO. | PLAYER | MINT |
|-----|--------|------|
| 173 | Dante Bichette | .05 |
| 174 | Kevin Brown | .05 |
| 175 | Chuck Crim | .05 |
| 176 | Jim Gantner | .05 |
| 177 | Darryl Hamilton | .05 |
| 178 | Ted Higuera | .05 |
| 179 | Darren Holmes | .08 |
| 180 | Mark Lee | .05 |
| 181 | Julio Machado | .05 |
| 182 | Paul Molitor | .08 |
| 183 | Jaime Navarro | .05 |
| 184 | Edwin Nunez | .05 |
| 185 | Dan Plesac | .05 |
| 186 | Willie Randolph | .08 |
| 187 | Ron Robinson | .05 |
| 188 | Gary Sheffield | .08 |
| 189 | Bill Spiers | .05 |
| 190 | B.J. Surhoff | .05 |
| 191 | Dale Sveum | .05 |
| 192 | Greg Vaughn | .10 |
| 193 | Bill Wegman | .05 |
| 194 | Robin Yount | .12 |

**MINNESOTA TWINS**

| NO. | PLAYER | MINT |
|-----|--------|------|
| 195 | Rick Aguilera | .05 |
| 196 | Allan Anderson | .05 |
| 197 | Steve Bedrosian | .05 |
| 198 | Randy Bush | .05 |
| 199 | Larry Casian | .05 |
| 200 | Chili Davis | .05 |
| 201 | Scott Erickson | .30 |
| 202 | Greg Gagne | .05 |
| 203 | Dan Gladden | .05 |
| 204 | Brian Harper | .05 |
| 205 | Kent Hrbek | .05 |
| 206 | Chuck Knoblauch | .50 |
| 207 | Gene Larkin | .05 |
| 208 | Terry Leach | .05 |
| 209 | Scott Leius | .05 |
| 210 | Shane Mack | .05 |
| 211 | Jack Morris | .08 |
| 212 | Pedro Munoz | .12 |
| 213 | Denny Neagle | .25 |
| 214 | Al Newman | .05 |
| 215 | Junior Ortiz | .05 |
| 216 | Mike Pagliarulo | .05 |
| 217 | Kirby Puckett | .20 |
| 218 | Paul Sorrento | .05 |
| 219 | Kevin Tapani | .08 |

| NO. | PLAYER | MINT |
|-----|--------|------|
| 220 | Lenny Webster | .05 |

**N.Y. YANKEES**

| NO. | PLAYER | MINT |
|-----|--------|------|
| 221 | Jesse Barfield | .05 |
| 222 | Greg Cadaret | .05 |
| 223 | Dave Eiland | .05 |
| 224 | Alvaro Espinoza | .05 |
| 225 | Steve Farr | .05 |
| 226 | Bob Geren | .05 |
| 227 | Lee Guetterman | .05 |
| 228 | John Habyan | .05 |
| 229 | Mel Hall | .05 |
| 230 | Steve Howe | .05 |
| 231 | Mike Humphreys | .08 |
| 232 | Scott Kamieniecki | .05 |
| 233 | Pat Kelly | .15 |
| 234 | Roberto Kelly | .08 |
| 235 | Tim Leary | .05 |
| 236 | Kevin Maas | .15 |
| 237 | Don Mattingly | .20 |
| 238 | Hensley Meulens | .05 |
| 239 | Matt Nokes | .05 |
| 240 | Pascual Perez | .05 |
| 241 | Eric Plunk | .05 |
| 242 | John Ramos | .15 |
| 243 | Scott Sanderson | .05 |
| 244 | Steve Sax | .05 |
| 245 | Wade Taylor | .08 |
| 246 | Randy Velarde | .05 |
| 247 | Bernie Williams | .15 |

**OAKLAND ATHLETICS**

| NO. | PLAYER | MINT |
|-----|--------|------|
| 248 | Troy Afenir | .05 |
| 249 | Harod Baines | .05 |
| 250 | Lance Blankenship | .05 |
| 251 | Mike Bordick | .08 |
| 252 | Jose Canseco | .30 |
| 253 | Steve Chitren | .05 |
| 254 | Ron Darling | .05 |
| 255 | Dennis Eckersley | .10 |
| 256 | Mike Gallego | .05 |
| 257 | Dave Henderson | .05 |
| 258 | Rickey Henderson | .35 |
| 259 | Rick Honeycutt | .05 |
| 260 | Brook Jacoby | .05 |
| 261 | Carney Lansford | .05 |
| 262 | Mark McGwire | .12 |
| 263 | Mike Moore | .05 |
| 264 | Gene Nelson | .05 |
| 265 | Jamie Quirk | .05 |
| 266 | Joe Slusarski | .05 |
| 267 | Terry Steinbach | .05 |
| 268 | Dave Stewart | .08 |
| 269 | Todd Van Poppel | .75 |
| 270 | Walt Weiss | .05 |
| 271 | Bob Welch | .05 |
| 272 | Curt Young | .05 |

**SEATTLE MARINERS**

| NO. | PLAYER | MINT |
|-----|--------|------|
| 273 | Scott Bradley | .05 |
| 274 | Greg Briley | .05 |
| 275 | Jay Buhner | .08 |
| 276 | Henry Cotto | .05 |
| 277 | Alvin Davis | .05 |
| 278 | Rich DeLucia | .05 |
| 279 | Ken Griffey, Jr. | .75 |
| 280 | Erik Hanson | .05 |
| 281 | Brian Holman | .05 |
| 282 | Mike Jackson | .05 |
| 283 | Randy Johnson | .05 |
| 284 | Tracy Jones | .05 |
| 285 | Bill Krueger | .05 |
| 286 | Edgar Martinez | .05 |
| 287 | Tino Martinez | .15 |
| 288 | Rob Murphy | .05 |
| 289 | Pete O'Brien | .05 |
| 290 | Alonzo Powell | .05 |
| 291 | Harold Reynolds | .05 |
| 292 | Mike Schooler | .05 |
| 293 | Russ Swan | .05 |
| 294 | Bill Swift | .05 |
| 295 | Dave Valle | .05 |
| 296 | Omar Vizquel | .05 |

**TEXAS RANGERS**

| NO. | PLAYER | MINT |
|-----|--------|------|
| 297 | Gerald Alexander | .05 |
| 298 | Brad Arnsberg | .05 |
| 299 | Kevin Brown | .05 |

| NO. | PLAYER | MINT |
|-----|--------|------|
| 300 | Jack Daugherty | .05 |
| 301 | Mario Diaz | .05 |
| 302 | Brian Downing | .05 |
| 303 | Julio Franco | .08 |
| 304 | Juan Gonzalez | .30 |
| 305 | Rich Gossage | .05 |
| 306 | Jose Guzman | .05 |
| 307 | Jose Hernandez (R) | .15 |
| 308 | Jeff Huson | .05 |
| 309 | Mike Jeffcoat | .05 |
| 310 | Terry Mathews | .05 |
| 311 | Rafael Palmeiro | .10 |
| 312 | Dean Palmer | .15 |
| 313 | Geno Petralli | .05 |
| 314 | Gary Pettis | .05 |
| 315 | Kevin Reimer | .05 |
| 316 | Ivan Rodriguez | 1.00 |
| 317 | Kenny Rogers | .05 |
| 318 | Wayne Rosenthal (R) | .15 |
| 319 | Jeff Russell | .05 |
| 320 | Nolan Ryan | .40 |
| 321 | Ruben Sierra | .15 |
| 322 | Jim Acker | .05 |

**TORONTO BLUE JAYS**

| NO. | PLAYER | MINT |
|-----|--------|------|
| 323 | Roberto Alomar | .15 |
| 324 | Derek Bell | .30 |
| 325 | Pat Borders | .05 |
| 326 | Tom Candiotti | .05 |
| 327 | Joe Carter | .12 |
| 328 | Rob Ducey | .05 |
| 329 | Kelly Gruber | .05 |
| 330 | Juan Guzman | .75 |
| 331 | Tom Henke | .05 |
| 332 | Jimmy Key | .05 |
| 333 | Manny Lee | .05 |
| 334 | Al Leiter | .05 |
| 335 | Bob MacDonald | .08 |
| 336 | Candy Maldonado | .05 |
| 337 | Rance Mulliniks | .05 |
| 338 | Grey Myers | .05 |
| 339 | John Olerud | .15 |
| 340 | Ed Sprague | .10 |
| 341 | Dave Stieb | .05 |
| 342 | Todd Stottlemyre | .05 |
| 343 | Mike Timlin | .05 |
| 344 | Duane Ward | .05 |
| 345 | David Wells | .05 |
| 346 | Devon White | .05 |
| 347 | Mookie Wilson | .05 |
| 348 | Eddie Zosky | .08 |

**ATLANTA BRAVES**

| NO. | PLAYER | MINT |
|-----|--------|------|
| 349 | Steve Avery | .25 |
| 350 | Mike Bell | .05 |
| 351 | Rafael Belliard | .05 |
| 352 | Juan Berenguer | .05 |
| 353 | Jeff Blauser | .05 |
| 354 | Sid Bream | .05 |
| 355 | Francisco Cabrera | .05 |
| 356 | Marvin Freeman | .05 |
| 357 | Ron Gant | .15 |
| 358 | Tom Glavine | .12 |
| 359 | Brian Hunter | .50 |
| 360 | Dave Justice | .50 |
| 361 | Charlie Leibrandt | .05 |
| 362 | Mark Lemke | .05 |
| 363 | Kent Mercker | .05 |
| 364 | Keith Mitchell | .20 |
| 365 | Greg Olson | .05 |
| 366 | Terry Pendleton | .08 |
| 367 | A. Reynoso (R) | .15 |
| 368 | Deion Sanders | .10 |
| 369 | Lonnie Smith | .05 |
| 370 | Pete Smith | .05 |
| 371 | John Smoltz | .10 |
| 372 | Mike Stanton | .05 |
| 373 | Jeff Treadway | .05 |
| 374 | Mark Wohlers | .25 |

**CHICAGO CUBS**

| NO. | PLAYER | MINT |
|-----|--------|------|
| 375 | Paul Assenmacher | .05 |
| 376 | George Bell | .08 |
| 377 | Shawn Boskie | .05 |
| 378 | Frank Castillo | .05 |
| 379 | Andre Dawson | .15 |
| 380 | Shawon Dunston | .05 |

| NO. | PLAYER | MINT |
|-----|--------|------|
| 381 | Mark Grace | .10 |
| 382 | Mike Harkey | .05 |
| 383 | Danny Jackson | .05 |
| 384 | Les Lancaster | .05 |
| 385 | Cedric Landrum | .10 |
| 386 | Greg Maddux | .05 |
| 387 | Derrick May | .05 |
| 388 | Chuck McElroy | .05 |
| 389 | Ryne Sandberg | .35 |
| 390 | Heathcliff Slocumb | .05 |
| 391 | Dave Smith | .05 |
| 392 | Dwight Smith | .05 |
| 393 | Rick Sutcliffe | .05 |
| 394 | Hector Villanueva | .05 |
| 395 | Chico Walker | .05 |
| 396 | Jerome Walton | .05 |
| 397 | Rick Wilkins | .10 |

**CINCINNATI REDS**

| NO. | PLAYER | MINT |
|-----|--------|------|
| 398 | Jack Armstrong | .05 |
| 399 | Freddie Benavides | .05 |
| 400 | Glenn Braggs | .05 |
| 401 | Tom Browning | .05 |
| 402 | Norm Charlton | .05 |
| 403 | Eric Davis | .10 |
| 404 | Rob Dibble | .05 |
| 405 | Bill Doran | .05 |
| 406 | Mariano Duncan | .05 |
| 407 | Kip Gross (R) | .20 |
| 408 | Chris Hammond | .08 |
| 409 | Billy Hatcher | .05 |
| 410 | Chris Jones | .05 |
| 411 | Barry Larkin | .10 |
| 412 | Hal Morris | .10 |
| 413 | Randy Myers | .05 |
| 414 | Joe Oliver | .05 |
| 415 | Paul O'Neill | .05 |
| 416 | Ted Power | .05 |
| 417 | Luis Quinones | .05 |
| 418 | Jeff Reed | .05 |
| 419 | Jose Rijo | .05 |
| 420 | Chris Sabo | .08 |
| 421 | Reggie Sanders | .20 |
| 422 | Scott Scudder | .05 |
| 423 | Glenn Sutko | .05 |

**HOUSTON ASTROS**

| NO. | PLAYER | MINT |
|-----|--------|------|
| 424 | Eric Anthony | .05 |
| 425 | Jeff Bagwell | 1.00 |
| 426 | Craig Biggio | .05 |
| 427 | Ken Caminiti | .05 |
| 428 | Casey Candaele | .05 |
| 429 | Mike Capel | .05 |
| 430 | Andujar Cedeno | .20 |
| 431 | Jim Corsi | .05 |
| 432 | Mark Davidson | .05 |
| 433 | Steve Finley | .05 |
| 434 | Luis Gonzalez | .15 |
| 435 | Pete Harnisch | .05 |
| 436 | Dwayne Henry | .05 |
| 437 | Xavier Hernandez | .05 |
| 438 | Jimmy Jones | .05 |
| 439 | Darryl Kile | .08 |
| 440 | Rob Mallicoat | .05 |
| 441 | Andy Mota | .10 |
| 442 | Al Osuna | .05 |
| 443 | Mark Portugal | .05 |
| 444 | Scott Servais | .08 |
| 445 | Mike Simms | .08 |
| 446 | Gerald Young | .05 |

**LOS ANGELES DODGERS**

| NO. | PLAYER | MINT |
|-----|--------|------|
| 447 | Tim Belcher | .05 |
| 448 | Brett Butler | .05 |
| 449 | John Candelaria | .05 |
| 450 | Gary Carter | .08 |
| 451 | Dennis Cook | .05 |
| 452 | Tim Crews | .05 |
| 453 | Kal Daniels | .05 |
| 454 | Jim Gott | .05 |
| 455 | Alfredo Griffin | .05 |
| 456 | Kevin Gross | .05 |
| 457 | Chris Gwynn | .05 |
| 458 | Lenny Harris | .05 |
| 459 | Orel Hershiser | .08 |
| 460 | Jay Howell | .05 |
| 461 | Stan Javier | .05 |

| NO. | PLAYER | MINT |
|---|---|---|
| 462 | Eric Karros | .20 |
| 463 | Ramon Martinez | .15 |
| 464 | Roger McDowell | .05 |
| 465 | Mike Morgan | .05 |
| 466 | Eddie Murray | .10 |
| 467 | Jose Offerman | .08 |
| 468 | Bob Ojeda | .05 |
| 469 | Juan Samuel | .05 |
| 470 | Mike Scioscia | .05 |
| 471 | Darryl Strawberry | .25 |

**MONTREAL EXPOS**

| NO. | PLAYER | MINT |
|---|---|---|
| 472 | Bret Barberie | .15 |
| 473 | Brian Barnes | .05 |
| 474 | Eric Bullock | .05 |
| 475 | Ivan Calderon | .05 |
| 476 | Delino DeShields | .08 |
| 477 | Jeff Fassero | .05 |
| 478 | Mike Fitzgerald | .05 |
| 479 | Steve Frey | .05 |
| 480 | Andres Galarraga | .05 |
| 481 | Mark Gardner | .05 |
| 482 | Marquis Grissom | .08 |
| 483 | Chris Haney | .08 |
| 484 | Barry Jones | .05 |
| 485 | Dave Martinez | .05 |
| 486 | Dennis Martinez | .05 |
| 487 | Chris Nabholz | .05 |
| 488 | Spike Owen | .05 |
| 489 | Gilberto Reyes | .05 |
| 490 | Mel Rojas | .05 |
| 491 | Scott Ruskin | .05 |
| 492 | Bill Sampen | .05 |
| 493 | Larry Walker | .05 |
| 494 | Tim Wallach | .05 |

**NEW YORK METS**

| NO. | PLAYER | MINT |
|---|---|---|
| 495 | Daryl Boston | .05 |
| 496 | Hubie Brooks | .05 |
| 497 | Tim Burke | .05 |
| 498 | Mark Carreon | .05 |
| 499 | Tony Castillo | .05 |
| 500 | Vince Coleman | .08 |
| 501 | David Cone | .08 |
| 502 | Kevin Elster | .05 |
| 503 | Sid Fernandez | .05 |
| 504 | John Franco | .05 |
| 505 | Dwight Gooden | .15 |
| 506 | Todd Hundley | .10 |
| 507 | Jeff Innis | .05 |
| 508 | Gregg Jefferies | .10 |
| 509 | Howard Johnson | .08 |
| 510 | Dave Magaden | .05 |
| 511 | T. McDaniel (R) | .12 |
| 512 | Kevin McReynolds | .08 |
| 513 | Keith Miller | .05 |
| 514 | Charlie O'Brien | .05 |
| 515 | Mackey Sasser | .05 |
| 516 | Pete Schourek | .05 |
| 517 | Julio Valera | .05 |
| 518 | Frank Viola | .05 |
| 519 | Wally Whitehurst | .05 |
| 520 | Anthony Young | .20 |

**PHILADELPHIA PHILLIES**

| NO. | PLAYER | MINT |
|---|---|---|
| 521 | Andy Ashby | .15 |
| 522 | Kim Batiste | .15 |
| 523 | Joe Boever | .05 |
| 524 | Wes Chamberlain | .20 |
| 525 | Pat Combs | .05 |
| 526 | Danny Cox | .05 |
| 527 | Darren Daulton | .05 |
| 528 | Jose DeJesus | .05 |
| 529 | Lenny Dykstra | .08 |

| NO. | PLAYER | MINT |
|---|---|---|
| 530 | Darrin Fletcher | .05 |
| 531 | Tommy Greene | .05 |
| 532 | Jason Grimsley | .05 |
| 533 | Charlies Hayes | .05 |
| 534 | Von Hayes | .08 |
| 535 | Dave Hollins | .05 |
| 536 | Ricky Jordan | .08 |
| 537 | John Kruk | .05 |
| 538 | Jim Lindeman | .05 |
| 539 | Mickey Morandini | .05 |
| 540 | Terry Mulholland | .05 |
| 541 | Dale Murphy | .10 |
| 542 | Randy Ready | .05 |
| 543 | Wally Ritchie | .05 |
| 544 | Bruce Ruffin | .05 |
| 545 | Steve Searcy | .05 |
| 546 | Dickie Thon | .05 |
| 547 | Mitch Williams | .05 |

**PITTSBURGH PIRATES**

| NO. | PLAYER | MINT |
|---|---|---|
| 548 | Stan Belinda | .05 |
| 549 | Jay Bell | .05 |
| 550 | Barry Bonds | .20 |
| 551 | Bobby Bonilla | .15 |
| 552 | Steve Buechele | .05 |
| 553 | Doug Drabek | .08 |
| 554 | Neal Heaton | .05 |
| 555 | Jeff King | .05 |
| 556 | Bob Kipper | .05 |
| 557 | Bill Landrum | .05 |
| 558 | Mike LaValliere | .05 |
| 559 | Jose Lind | .05 |
| 560 | Lloyd McClendon | .05 |
| 561 | Orlando Merced | .20 |
| 562 | Bob Patterson | .05 |
| 563 | Joe Redfield (R) | .15 |
| 564 | Gary Redus | .05 |
| 565 | Rosario Rodriguez | .08 |
| 566 | Don Slaught | .05 |
| 567 | John Smiley | .05 |
| 568 | Zane Smith | .05 |
| 569 | Randy Tomlin | .05 |
| 570 | Andy Van Slyke | .10 |
| 571 | Gary Varsho | .05 |
| 572 | Bob Walk | .05 |
| 573 | John Wehner | .15 |

**ST LOUIS CARDINALS**

| NO. | PLAYER | MINT |
|---|---|---|
| 574 | Juan Agosto | .05 |
| 575 | Cris Carpenter | .05 |
| 576 | Jose DeLeon | .05 |
| 577 | Rich Gedman | .05 |
| 578 | Bernard Gilkey | .08 |
| 579 | Pedro Guerrero | .05 |
| 580 | Ken Hill | .05 |
| 581 | Rex Hudler | .05 |
| 582 | Felix Jose | .08 |
| 583 | Ray Lankford | .12 |
| 584 | Omar Olivares | .05 |
| 585 | Jose Oquendo | .05 |
| 586 | Tom Pagnozzi | .05 |
| 587 | Geronimo Pena | .05 |
| 588 | Mike Perez | .05 |
| 589 | Gerald Perry | .05 |
| 590 | Bryan Smith | .10 |
| 591 | Lee Smith | .05 |
| 592 | Ozzie Smith | .10 |
| 593 | Scott Terry | .05 |
| 594 | Bob Tewksbury | .05 |
| 595 | Milt Thompson | .05 |
| 596 | Todd Zeile | .10 |

**SAN DIEGO PADRES**

| NO. | PLAYER | MINT |
|---|---|---|
| 597 | Larry Anderson | .05 |

| NO. | PLAYER | MINT |
|---|---|---|
| 598 | Oscar Azocar | .05 |
| 599 | Andy Benes | .08 |
| 600 | Ricky Bones | .05 |
| 601 | Jerald Clark | .05 |
| 602 | Pat Clements | .05 |
| 603 | Paul Faries | .05 |
| 604 | Tony Fernandez | .05 |
| 605 | Tony Gwynn | .15 |
| 606 | Greg Harris | .05 |
| 607 | Thomas Howard | .05 |
| 608 | Bruce Hurst | .05 |
| 609 | Darrin Jackson | .05 |
| 610 | Tom Lampkin | .05 |
| 611 | Craig Lefferts | .05 |
| 612 | Jim Lewis (R) | .15 |
| 613 | Mike Maddux | .05 |
| 614 | Fred McGriff | .10 |
| 615 | Jose Melendez | .08 |
| 616 | Jose Mota | .05 |
| 617 | Dennis Rasmussen | .05 |
| 618 | Bib Roberts | .05 |
| 619 | Rich Rodriguez | .05 |
| 620 | Benito Santiago | .08 |
| 621 | Craig Shipley (R) | .12 |
| 622 | Tim Teufel | .05 |
| 623 | Kevin Ward (R) | .12 |
| 624 | Ed Whitson | .05 |

**SAN FRANCISCO GIANTS**

| NO. | PLAYER | MINT |
|---|---|---|
| 625 | Dave Anderson | .05 |
| 626 | Kevin Bass | .05 |
| 627 | Rod Beck (R) | .15 |
| 628 | Bud Black | .05 |
| 629 | Jeff Brantley | .05 |
| 630 | John Burkett | .05 |
| 631 | Will Clark | .25 |
| 632 | Royce Clayton | .20 |
| 633 | Steve Decker | .15 |
| 634 | Kelly Downs | .05 |
| 635 | Mike Felder | .05 |
| 636 | Scott Garrelts | .05 |
| 637 | Eric Gunderson | .05 |
| 638 | B. Hickerson (R) | .15 |
| 639 | Darren Lewis | .12 |
| 640 | Greg Litton | .05 |
| 641 | Kirt Manwaring | .05 |
| 642 | Paul McClellan | .08 |
| 643 | Willie McGee | .05 |
| 644 | Kevin Mitchell | .12 |
| 645 | Francisco Oliveras | .05 |
| 646 | Mike Remlinger | .05 |
| 647 | Dave Righetti | .05 |
| 648 | Robby Thompson | .05 |
| 649 | Jose Uribe | .05 |
| 650 | Matt Williams | .12 |
| 651 | Trevor Wilson | .05 |

**No. 652 to 680—Prospects**

| NO. | PLAYER | MINT |
|---|---|---|
| 652 | Tom Goodwin | .15 |
| 653 | Terry Bross | .05 |
| 654 | M. Christopher (R) | .12 |
| 655 | Kenny Lofton | .35 |
| 656 | Chris Cron (R) | .15 |
| 657 | Willie Banks | .15 |
| 658 | Pat Rice (R) | .15 |
| 659 | Rob Mauer (R) | .40 |
| 660 | Don Harris | .10 |
| 661 | Henry Rodriguez | .10 |
| 662 | Cliff Brantley (R) | .25 |
| 663 | Mike Linskey | .05 |
| 664 | Gary Disarcina | .05 |
| 665 | Gil Heredia (R) | .15 |
| 666 | Vinny Castilla (R) | .15 |

| NO. | PLAYER | MINT |
|---|---|---|
| 667 | Paul Abbott | .05 |
| 668 | Monty Fariss | .10 |
| 669 | Jarvis Brown (R) | .15 |
| 670 | Wayne Kirby (R) | .15 |
| 671 | Scott Brosius (R) | .15 |
| 672 | Bob Hamilton | .05 |
| 673 | Joel Johnston | .12 |
| 674 | Tim Spehr | .08 |
| 675 | Jeff Gardner (R) | .12 |
| 676 | Rico Rossy (R) | .15 |
| 677 | Roberto Hernandez | .20 |
| 678 | Ted Wood (R) | .40 |
| 679 | Cal Eldred | .08 |
| 680 | Sean Berry | .10 |

**No. 681 to 687—Record Setters**

| NO. | PLAYER | MINT |
|---|---|---|
| 681 | Rickey Henderson | .15 |
| 682 | Nolan Ryan | .35 |
| 683 | Dennis Martinez | .08 |
| 684 | Wilson Alvarez | .08 |
| 685 | Joe Carter | .08 |
| 686 | Dave Winfield | .12 |
| 687 | David Cone | .08 |

**No. 688 to 697—League Leaders**

| NO. | PLAYER | MINT |
|---|---|---|
| 688 | Jose Canseco | .15 |
| 689 | Howard Johnson | .08 |
| 690 | Julio Franco | .08 |
| 691 | Terry Pendleton | .08 |
| 692 | Cecil Fielder | .15 |
| 693 | Scott Erickson | .20 |
| 694 | Tom Glavine | .08 |
| 695 | Dennis Martinez | .08 |
| 696 | Bryan Harvey | .08 |
| 697 | Lee Smith | .08 |

**No. 698 to 707—Super Star Specials**

| NO. | PLAYER | MINT |
|---|---|---|
| 698 | Super Siblings: Roberto & Sandy Alomar, Jr. | .10 |
| 699 | The Indispensables: Bonilla & Clark | .20 |
| 700 | Teamwork: Mark Wohlers, Kent Mercker & Alejandro Pena | .15 |
| 701 | Tiger Tandems: S. Jones, B. Jackson, G. Olson, F. Thomas | .08 |
| 702 | The Ignitors: Molitor & Butler | .35 |
| 703 | The Indispensables II: Ripken, & Carter | .15 |
| 704 | Power Packs: Larkin & Puckett | .15 |
| 705 | Today and Tomorrow: Vaughn & Fielder | .15 |
| 706 | Teenage Sensations: Martinez & Guillen | .10 |
| 707 | Designated Hitters: Baines & Boggs | .08 |

**No. 708 to 714—Pro Visions**

| NO. | PLAYER | MINT |
|---|---|---|
| 708 | Robin Yount | .25 |
| 709 | Ken Griffey, Jr. | .75 |
| 710 | Nolan Ryan | .50 |
| 711 | Cal Ripken, Jr. | .50 |
| 712 | Frank Thomas | 1.25 |
| 713 | Dave Justice | .50 |
| 714 | Checklist | .08 |

**No. 715 to 720—Checklist**

| NO. | PLAYER | MINT |
|---|---|---|
| 715 | Checklist | .07 |
| 716 | Checklist | .07 |
| 717 | Checklist | .07 |
| 718 | Checklist | .07 |
| 719 | Checklist | .07 |
| 720 | Checklist | .07 |

# 1990 Leaf . . . Series One Set of 264 Cards—Value $125.00
## Series Two Set of 264 Cards—Value $170.00

Leaf, the parent company of Donruss produced this limited printing, upscale baseball card set. There was an ultra gloss finish on front and back with 5-color photo clarity. The cards were issued late in the year—July (series one) and September (series two). Leaf previously issued baseball cards in 1948 and 1960. From 1985 to 1988 Leaf issued a set for the Canadian market. Features the rookie cards of Dave Justice, John Olerud, Frank Thomas and Kevin Maas.

JOHN OLERUD     BEN McDONALD     DAVE JUSTICE     FRANK THOMAS     KEVIN MAAS

| NO. | PLAYER | MINT | NO. | PLAYER | MINT | NO. | PLAYER | MINT | NO. | PLAYER | MINT |
|---|---|---|---|---|---|---|---|---|---|---|---|
| | **SERIES NO. 1** | | 62 | Mark McGwire | .65 | 124 | Jerome Walton | .35 | 186 | Spike Owen | .15 |
| 1 | The Leaf Set | .15 | 63 | Bert Blyleven | .15 | 125 | Bo Jackson | 3.00 | 187 | Cory Snyder | .15 |
| 2 | Mike Henneman | .15 | 64 | Bob Walk | .15 | 126 | Harold Baines | .25 | 188 | Fred Lynn | .25 |
| 3 | Steve Bedrosian | .15 | 65 | Mickey Tettleton | .15 | 127 | Scott Bankhead | .15 | 189 | Eric Davis | .50 |
| 4 | Mike Scott | .20 | 66 | Sid Fernandez | .15 | 128 | Ozzie Guillen | .15 | 190 | Dave Parker | .40 |
| 5 | Allan Anderson | .15 | 67 | Terry Kennedy | .15 | 129 | Jose Oquendo | .15 | 191 | Jeff Blauser | .15 |
| 6 | Rick Sutcliffe | .20 | 68 | Fernando Valenzuela | .30 | 130 | John Dopson | .15 | 192 | Matt Nokes | .15 |
| 7 | Gregg Olson | .60 | 69 | Don Mattingly | 1.50 | 131 | Charlie Hayes | .30 | 193 | Delino DeShields (R) | 3.00 |
| 8 | Kevin Elster | .15 | 70 | Paul O'Neill | .15 | 132 | Fred McGriff | .75 | 194 | Scott Sanderson | .15 |
| 9 | Pete O'Brien | .15 | 71 | Robin Yount | 1.00 | 133 | Chet Lemon | .15 | 195 | Lance Parrish | .40 |
| 10 | Carlton Fisk | 1.00 | 72 | Bret Saberhagen | .30 | 134 | Gary Carter | .25 | 196 | Bobby Bonilla | 1.00 |
| 11 | Joe Magrane | .15 | 73 | Geno Petralli | .15 | 135 | Rafael Ramirez | .15 | 197 | Cal Ripken, Jr. | 2.50 |
| 12 | Roger Clemens | 1.50 | 74 | Brook Jacoby | .15 | 136 | Shane Mack | .15 | 198 | Kevin McReynolds | .30 |
| 13 | Tom Glavine | 1.00 | 75 | Roberto Alomar | 1.25 | 137 | Mark Grace | .50 | 199 | Robby Thompson | .15 |
| 14 | Tom Gordon | .25 | 76 | Devon White | .15 | 138 | Phil Bradley | .15 | 200 | Tim Belcher | .15 |
| 15 | Todd Benzinger | .15 | 77 | Jose Lind | .15 | 139 | Dwight Gooden | .60 | 201 | Jesse Barfield | .20 |
| 16 | Hubie Brooks | .25 | 78 | Pat Combs | .25 | 140 | Harold Reynolds | .15 | 202 | Mariano Duncan | .15 |
| 17 | Roberto Kelly | .30 | 79 | Dave Stieb | .20 | 141 | Scott Fletcher | .15 | 203 | Bill Spiers | .30 |
| 18 | Barry Larkin | .50 | 80 | Tim Wallach | .15 | 142 | Ozzie Smith | .75 | 204 | Frank White | .15 |
| 19 | Mike Boddicker | .25 | 81 | Dave Stewart | .30 | 143 | Mike Greenwell | .60 | 205 | Julio Franco | .35 |
| 20 | Roger McDowell | .15 | 82 | Eric Anthony (R) | .50 | 144 | Pete Smith | .15 | 206 | Greg Swindell | .15 |
| 21 | Nolan Ryan | 7.00 | 83 | Randy Bush | .15 | 145 | Mark Gubicza | .15 | 207 | Benito Santiago | .30 |
| 22 | John Farrell | .15 | 84 | Checklist No. 1 | .30 | 146 | Chris Sabo | .50 | 208 | Johnny Ray | .15 |
| 23 | Bruce Hurst | .15 | 85 | Jaime Navarro | .30 | 147 | Ramon Martinez | 4.50 | 209 | Gary Redus | .15 |
| 24 | Wally Joyner | .35 | 86 | Tommy Gregg | .15 | 148 | Tim Leary | .15 | 210 | Jeff Parrett | .15 |
| 25 | Greg Maddux | .15 | 87 | Frank Tanana | .15 | 149 | Randy Myers | .20 | 211 | Jimmy Key | .15 |
| 26 | Chris Bosio | .15 | 88 | Omar Vizquel | .25 | 150 | Jody Reed | .15 | 212 | Tim Raines | .35 |
| 27 | John Cerutti | .15 | 89 | Ivan Calderon | .15 | 151 | Bruce Ruffin | .15 | 213 | Carney Lansford | .15 |
| 28 | Tim Burke | .15 | 90 | Vince Coleman | .35 | 152 | Jeff Russell | .15 | 214 | Gerald Young | .15 |
| 29 | Dennis Eckersley | .30 | 91 | Barry Bonds | 1.00 | 153 | Doug Jones | .15 | 215 | Gene Larkin | .15 |
| 30 | Glenn Davis | .25 | 92 | Randy Milligan | .20 | 154 | Tony Gwynn | 1.50 | 216 | Dan Plesac | .15 |
| 31 | Jim Abbott | 1.50 | 93 | Frank Viola | .30 | 155 | Mark Langston | .35 | 217 | Lonnie Smith | .15 |
| 32 | Mike LaValliere | .15 | 94 | Matt Williams | .60 | 156 | Mitch Williams | .15 | 218 | Alan Trammell | .50 |
| 33 | Andres Thomas | .15 | 95 | Alfredo Griffin | .15 | 157 | Gary Sheffield | .35 | 219 | Jeffrey Leonard | .15 |
| 34 | Lou Whitaker | .15 | 96 | Steve Sax | .15 | 158 | Tom Henke | .15 | 220 | Sammy Sosa (R) | 1.50 |
| 35 | Alvin Davis | .15 | 97 | Gary Gaetti | .15 | 159 | Oil Can Boyd | .15 | 221 | Todd Zeile | 1.50 |
| 36 | Melido Perez | .15 | 98 | Ryne Sandberg | 2.50 | 160 | Rickey Henderson | 2.00 | 222 | Bill Landrum | .15 |
| 37 | Craig Biggio | .60 | 99 | Danny Tartabull | .35 | 161 | Bill Doran | .15 | 223 | Mike Devereaux | .15 |
| 38 | Rick Aguilera | .15 | 100 | Rafael Palmeiro | .75 | 162 | Chuck Finley | .40 | 224 | Mike Marshall | .15 |
| 39 | Pete Harnisch | .40 | 101 | Jesse Orosco | .15 | 163 | Jeff King | .20 | 225 | Jose Uribe | .15 |
| 40 | David Cone | .25 | 102 | Garry Templeton | .15 | 164 | Nick Esasky | .15 | 226 | Juan Samuel | .15 |
| 41 | Scott Garrelts | .15 | 103 | Frank DiPino | .15 | 165 | Cecil Fielder | 2.00 | 227 | Mel Hall | .15 |
| 42 | Jay Howell | .15 | 104 | Tony Pena | .15 | 166 | Dave Valle | .15 | 228 | Kent Hrbek | .20 |
| 43 | Eric King | .15 | 105 | Dickie Thon | .15 | 167 | Robin Ventura | 7.50 | 229 | Shawon Dunston | .35 |
| 44 | Pedro Guerrero | .30 | 106 | Kelly Gruber | .30 | 168 | Jim Deshaies | .15 | 230 | Kevin Seitzer | .15 |
| 45 | Mike Bielecki | .15 | 107 | Marquis Grissom (R) | 2.50 | 169 | Juan Berenguer | .15 | 231 | Pete Incaviglia | .25 |
| 46 | Bob Boone | .15 | 108 | Jose Canseco | 2.50 | 170 | Craig Worthington | .20 | 232 | Sandy Alomar | .50 |
| 47 | Kevin Brown | .25 | 109 | Mike Blowers (R) | .30 | 171 | Gregg Jefferies | .40 | 233 | Rip Roberts | .15 |
| 48 | Jerry Browne | .15 | 110 | Tom Browning | .15 | 172 | Will Clark | 3.00 | 234 | Scott Terry | .15 |
| 49 | Mike Scioscia | .15 | 111 | Greg Vaughn | 4.00 | 173 | Kirk Gibson | .25 | 235 | Dwight Evans | .25 |
| 50 | Chuck Cary | .15 | 112 | Oddibe McDowell | .15 | 174 | Checklist No. 2 | .25 | 236 | Ricky Jordan | .20 |
| 51 | Wade Boggs | 1.25 | 113 | Gary Ward | .15 | 175 | Bobby Thigpen | .20 | 237 | John Olerud (R) | 5.00 |
| 52 | Von Hayes | .15 | 114 | Jay Buhner | .15 | 176 | John Tudor | .15 | 238 | Zane Smith | .15 |
| 53 | Tony Fernandez | .15 | 115 | Eric Show | .15 | 177 | Andre Dawson | .60 | 239 | Walt Weiss | .15 |
| 54 | Dennis Martinez | .15 | 116 | Bryan Harvey | .15 | 178 | George Brett | 1.00 | 240 | Alvaro Espinoza | .15 |
| 55 | Tom Candiotti | .15 | 117 | Andy Van Slyke | .30 | 179 | Steve Buechele | .15 | 241 | Billy Hatcher | .15 |
| 56 | Andy Benes | 1.00 | 118 | Jeff Ballard | .15 | 180 | Joey Belle | 5.00 | 242 | Paul Molitor | .35 |
| 57 | Rob Dibble | .25 | 119 | Barry Lyons | .15 | 181 | Eddie Murray | .75 | 243 | Dale Murphy | .50 |
| 58 | Chuck Crim | .15 | 120 | Kevin Mitchell | .75 | 182 | Bob Geren | .20 | 244 | Dave Bergman | .15 |
| 59 | John Smoltz | 1.25 | 121 | Mike Gallego | .15 | 183 | Rob Murphy | .15 | 245 | Ken Griffey, Jr. | 20.00 |
| 60 | Mike Heath | .15 | 122 | Dave Smith | .15 | 184 | Tom Herr | .15 | 246 | Ed Whitson | .15 |
| 61 | Kevin Gross | .15 | 123 | Kirby Puckett | 1.50 | 185 | George Bell | .50 | 247 | Kirk McCaskill | .15 |

| NO. | PLAYER | MINT |
|---|---|---|
| 248 | Jay Bell | .15 |
| 249 | Ben McDonald (R) | 4.00 |
| 250 | Darryl Strawberry | 2.00 |
| 251 | Brett Butler | .15 |
| 252 | Terry Steinbach | .15 |
| 253 | Ken Caminiti | .15 |
| 254 | Dan Gladden | .15 |
| 255 | Dwight Smith | .25 |
| 256 | Kurt Stillwell | .15 |
| 257 | Ruben Sierra | 1.50 |
| 258 | Mike Schooler | .30 |
| 259 | Lance Johnson | .15 |
| 260 | Terry Pendleton | .30 |
| 261 | Ellis Burks | .40 |
| 262 | Len Dykstra | .35 |
| 263 | Mookie Wilson | .15 |
| 264 | Checklist No. 3 | .50 |
| **SERIES NO. 2** | | |
| 265 | Ryan "No Hit King" | 5.00 |
| 266 | Brian DuBois (R) | .30 |
| 267 | Don Robinson | .15 |
| 268 | Glenn Wilson | .15 |
| 269 | Kevin Tapani (R) | 2.00 |
| 270 | Marvell Wynne | .15 |
| 271 | Billy Ripken | .15 |
| 272 | Howard Johnson | .50 |
| 273 | Brian Holman | .25 |
| 274 | Dan Pasqua | .15 |
| 275 | Ken Dayley | .15 |
| 276 | Jeff Reardon | .15 |
| 277 | Jim Presley | .15 |
| 278 | Jim Eisenreich | .15 |
| 279 | Danny Jackson | .15 |
| 280 | Orel Hershiser | .30 |
| 281 | Andy Hawkins | .15 |
| 282 | Jose Rijo | .15 |
| 283 | Luis Rivera | .15 |
| 284 | John Kruk | .20 |
| 285 | Jeff Huson (R) | .30 |
| 286 | Joel Skinner | .15 |
| 287 | Jack Clark | .30 |
| 288 | Chili Davis | .15 |
| 289 | Joe Girardi | .20 |
| 290 | B.J. Surhoff | .15 |
| 291 | Luis Sojo (R) | .35 |
| 292 | Tom Foley | .15 |
| 293 | Mike Moore | .15 |
| 294 | Ken Oberkfell | .15 |
| 295 | Luis Polonia | .15 |
| 296 | Doug Drabek | .30 |
| 297 | Dave Justice (R) | 40.00 |
| 298 | Paul Gibson | .15 |
| 299 | Edgar Martinez | .50 |
| 300 | Frank Thomas (R) | 65.00 |
| 301 | Eric Yelding | .30 |
| 302 | Greg Gagne | .15 |
| 303 | Brad Komminsk | .15 |
| 304 | Ron Darling | .20 |
| 305 | Kevin Bass | .15 |
| 306 | Jeff Hamilton | .15 |
| 307 | Ron Karkovice | .15 |
| 308 | Milt Thompson | .15 |
| 309 | Mike Harkey | .30 |
| 310 | Mel Stottlemyre | .20 |
| 311 | Kenny Rogers | .25 |
| 312 | Mitch Webster | .15 |
| 313 | Kal Daniels | .30 |
| 314 | Matt Nokes | .15 |
| 315 | Dennis Lamp | .15 |
| 316 | Ken Howell | .15 |

| NO. | PLAYER | MINT |
|---|---|---|
| 317 | Glenallen Hill | .25 |
| 318 | Dave Martinez | .15 |
| 319 | Chris James | .15 |
| 320 | Mike Pagliarulo | .15 |
| 321 | Hal Morris | 4.00 |
| 322 | Rob Deer | .15 |
| 323 | Greg Olson (R) | .50 |
| 324 | Tony Phillips | .15 |
| 325 | Larry Walker (R) | .75 |
| 326 | Ron Hassey | .15 |
| 327 | Jack Howell | .15 |
| 328 | John Smiley | .15 |
| 329 | Steve Finley | .50 |
| 330 | Dave Magadan | .15 |
| 331 | Greg Litton | .30 |
| 332 | Mickey Hatcher | .15 |
| 333 | Lee Guetterman | .15 |
| 334 | Norm Charlton | .25 |
| 335 | Edgar Diaz | .25 |
| 336 | Willie Wilson | .15 |
| 337 | Bobby Witt | .15 |
| 338 | Candy Maldonado | .15 |
| 339 | Craig Lefferts | .15 |
| 340 | Dante Bichette | .35 |
| 341 | Wally Backman | .15 |
| 342 | Dennis Cook | .15 |
| 343 | Pat Borders | .20 |
| 344 | Wallace Johnson | .15 |
| 345 | Willie Randolph | .20 |
| 346 | Danny Darwin | .15 |
| 347 | Al Newman | .15 |
| 348 | Mark Knudson | .15 |
| 349 | Joe Boever | .15 |
| 350 | Larry Sheets | .15 |
| 351 | Mike Jackson | .15 |
| 352 | Wayne Edwards (R) | .30 |
| 353 | Bernard Gilkey (R) | 1.50 |
| 354 | Don Slaught | .15 |
| 355 | Joe Orsulak | .15 |
| 356 | John Franco | .15 |
| 357 | Jeff Brantley | .20 |
| 358 | Mike Morgan | .15 |
| 359 | Deion Sanders | .75 |
| 360 | Terry Leach | .15 |
| 361 | Les Lancaster | .15 |
| 362 | Storm Davis | .15 |
| 363 | Scott Coolbaugh (R) | .40 |
| 364 | Checklist No. 4 | .25 |
| 365 | Cecilio Guante | .15 |
| 366 | Joey Cora | .15 |
| 367 | Willie McGee | .30 |
| 368 | Jerry Reed | .15 |
| 369 | Darren Daulton | .15 |
| 370 | Manny Lee | .15 |
| 371 | Mark Gardner (R) | .50 |
| 372 | Rick Honeycutt | .15 |
| 373 | Steve Balboni | .15 |
| 374 | Jack Armstrong | .20 |
| 375 | Charlie O'Brien | .15 |
| 376 | Ron Gant | 1.25 |
| 377 | Lloyd Moseby | .15 |
| 378 | Gene Harris | .30 |
| 379 | Joe Carter | .60 |
| 380 | Scott Bailes | .15 |
| 381 | R.J. Reynolds | .15 |
| 382 | Bob Melvin | .15 |
| 383 | Tim Teufel | .15 |
| 384 | John Burkett | .40 |
| 385 | Felix Jose | 3.00 |
| 386 | Larry Andersen | .15 |

| NO. | PLAYER | MINT |
|---|---|---|
| 387 | David West | .15 |
| 388 | Luis Salazar | .15 |
| 389 | Mike Macfarlane | .15 |
| 390 | Charlie Hough | .15 |
| 391 | Greg Briley | .30 |
| 392 | Donn Pall | .15 |
| 393 | Bryn Smith | .15 |
| 394 | Carlos Quintana | .50 |
| 395 | Steve Lake | .15 |
| 396 | Mark Whiten (R) | 3.00 |
| 397 | Edwin Nunez | .15 |
| 398 | Rick Parker (R) | .30 |
| 399 | Mark Portugal | .15 |
| 400 | Roy Smith | .15 |
| 401 | Hector Villanueva (R) | .30 |
| 402 | Bob Milacki | .15 |
| 403 | Alejandro Pena | .15 |
| 404 | Scott Bradley | .15 |
| 405 | Ron Kittle | .15 |
| 406 | Bob Tewksbury | .15 |
| 407 | Wes Gardner | .15 |
| 408 | Ernie Whitt | .15 |
| 409 | Terry Shumpert (R) | .35 |
| 410 | Tim Layana (R) | .30 |
| 411 | Chris Gwynn | .15 |
| 412 | Jeff Robinson | .15 |
| 413 | Scott Scudder | .35 |
| 414 | Kevin Romine | .15 |
| 415 | Jose DeJesus | .25 |
| 416 | Mike Jeffcoat | .15 |
| 417 | Rudy Seanez (R) | .30 |
| 418 | Mike Dunne | .15 |
| 419 | Dick Schofield | .15 |
| 420 | Steve Wilson | .20 |
| 421 | Bill Krueger | .15 |
| 422 | Junior Felix | .30 |
| 423 | Drew Hall | .15 |
| 424 | Curt Young | .15 |
| 425 | Franklin Stubbs | .15 |
| 426 | Dave Winfield | .50 |
| 427 | Rick Reed (R) | .25 |
| 428 | Charlie Leibrandt | .15 |
| 429 | Jeff Robinson | .15 |
| 430 | Erik Hanson | .75 |
| 431 | Barry Jones | .15 |
| 432 | Alex Trevino | .15 |
| 433 | John Moses | .15 |
| 434 | Dave Johnson (R) | .30 |
| 435 | Mackey Sasser | .15 |
| 436 | Rick Leach | .15 |
| 437 | Lenny Harris | .25 |
| 438 | Carlos Martinez | .15 |
| 439 | Rex Hudler | .15 |
| 440 | Domingo Ramos | .15 |
| 441 | Gerald Perry | .15 |
| 442 | Jeff Russell | .15 |
| 443 | Carlos Baerga (R) | 2.00 |
| 444 | Checklist No. 5 | .30 |
| 445 | Stan Javier | .15 |
| 446 | Kevin Maas (R) | 6.00 |
| 447 | Tom Brunansky | .20 |
| 448 | Carmelo Martinez | .15 |
| 449 | Willie Blair | .30 |
| 450 | Andres Galarraga | .20 |
| 451 | Bud Black | .15 |
| 452 | Greg Harris | .35 |
| 453 | Joe Oliver | .30 |
| 454 | Greg Brock | .15 |
| 455 | Jeff Treadway | .15 |
| 456 | Lance McCullers | .15 |
| 457 | Dave Schmidt | .15 |

| NO. | PLAYER | MINT |
|---|---|---|
| 458 | Todd Burns | .15 |
| 459 | Max Venable | .15 |
| 460 | Neal Heaton | .15 |
| 461 | Mark Williamson | .15 |
| 462 | Keith Miller | .15 |
| 463 | Mike LaCoss | .15 |
| 464 | Jose Offerman (R) | 1.25 |
| 465 | Jim Leyritz (R) | .30 |
| 466 | Glenn Braggs | .15 |
| 467 | Ron Robinson | .15 |
| 468 | Mark Davis | .15 |
| 469 | Gary Pettis | .15 |
| 470 | Keith Hernandez | .15 |
| 471 | Dennis Rasmussen | .15 |
| 472 | Mark Eichhorn | .15 |
| 473 | Ted Power | .15 |
| 474 | Terry Mulholland | .15 |
| 475 | Todd Stottlemyre | .30 |
| 476 | Jerry Goff | .25 |
| 477 | Gene Nelson | .15 |
| 478 | Rich Gedman | .15 |
| 479 | Brian Harper | .15 |
| 480 | Mike Felder | .15 |
| 481 | Steve Avery | 12.00 |
| 482 | Jack Morris | .35 |
| 483 | Randy Johnson | .65 |
| 484 | Scott Radinsky (R) | .35 |
| 485 | Jose DeLeon | .15 |
| 486 | Stan Belinda (R) | .40 |
| 487 | Brian Holton | .15 |
| 488 | Mark Carreon | .15 |
| 489 | Trevor Wilson | .25 |
| 490 | Mike Sharperson | .15 |
| 491 | Alan Mills (R) | .35 |
| 492 | John Candelaria | .15 |
| 493 | Paul Assenmacher | .15 |
| 494 | Steve Crawford | .15 |
| 495 | Brad Arnsberg (R) | .15 |
| 496 | Sergio Valdez (R) | .30 |
| 497 | Mark Parent | .15 |
| 498 | Tom Pagnozzi | .15 |
| 499 | Greg Harris | .15 |
| 500 | Randy Ready | .15 |
| 501 | Duane Ward | .15 |
| 502 | Nelson Santovenia | .15 |
| 503 | Joe Klink (R) | .35 |
| 504 | Eric Plunk | .15 |
| 505 | Jeff Reed | .15 |
| 506 | Ted Higuera | .15 |
| 507 | Joe Hesketh | .15 |
| 508 | Dan Petry | .15 |
| 509 | Matt Young | .15 |
| 510 | Jerald Clark | .40 |
| 511 | John Orton (R) | .25 |
| 512 | Scott Ruskin (R) | .35 |
| 513 | Chris Hoiles (R) | .50 |
| 514 | Daryl Boston | .15 |
| 515 | Francisco Oliveras | .25 |
| 516 | Ozzie Canseco | .35 |
| 517 | Xavier Hernandez (R) | .30 |
| 518 | Fred Manrique | .15 |
| 519 | Shawn Boskie (R) | .35 |
| 520 | Jeff Montgomery | .15 |
| 521 | Jack Daugherty (R) | .30 |
| 522 | Keith Comstock | .15 |
| 523 | Greg Hibbard (R) | .50 |
| 524 | Lee Smith | .15 |
| 525 | Dana Kiecker (R) | .25 |
| 526 | Darrel Akerfelds | .15 |
| 527 | Greg Myers | .15 |
| 528 | Checklist No. 6 | .30 |

# 1991 Leaf . . . Series One Set of 264 Cards—Value $40.00
## Series Two Set of 264 Cards—Value $45.00

Features an ultra gloss finish on front and back. Issued late in the year. Features the rookie cards of Wes Chamberlain and Brian McRae.

SCOTT ERICKSON P

JUAN GONZALEZ CF

WES CHAMBERLAIN OF

TRAVIS FRYMAN 3B

FRANK THOMAS 1B

| NO. | PLAYER | MINT |
|---|---|---|
| **SERIES NO. 1 (1 to 264)** | | |
| 1 | The Leaf Card | .10 |
| 2 | Kurt Stillwell | .10 |
| 3 | Bobby Witt | .10 |
| 4 | Tony Phillips | .10 |
| 5 | Scott Garrelts | .10 |
| 6 | Greg Swindell | .10 |
| 7 | Billy Ripken | .10 |
| 8 | Dave Martinez | .10 |
| 9 | Kelly Gruber | .15 |
| 10 | Juan Samuel | .10 |
| 11 | Brian Holman | .10 |
| 12 | Craig Biggio | .20 |
| 13 | Lonnie Smith | .10 |
| 14 | Ron Robinson | .10 |
| 15 | Mike LaValliere | .10 |
| 16 | Mark Davis | .10 |
| 17 | Jack Daugherty | .10 |
| 18 | Mike Henneman | .10 |
| 19 | Mike Greenwell | .25 |
| 20 | Dave Magadan | .10 |
| 21 | Mark Williamson | .10 |
| 22 | Marquis Grissom | .25 |
| 23 | Pat Borders | .10 |
| 24 | Mike Scioscia | .10 |
| 25 | Shawon Dunston | .12 |
| 26 | Randy Bush | .10 |
| 27 | John Smoltz | .20 |
| 28 | Chuck Crim | .10 |
| 29 | Don Slaught | .10 |
| 30 | Mike Macfarlane | .10 |
| 31 | Wally Joyner | .20 |
| 32 | Pat Combs | .10 |
| 33 | Tony Pena | .10 |
| 34 | Howard Johnson | .25 |
| 35 | Leo Gomez | .75 |
| 36 | Spike Owen | .10 |
| 37 | Eric Davis | .30 |
| 38 | Roberto Kelly | .15 |
| 39 | Jerome Walton | .15 |
| 40 | Shane Mack | .10 |
| 41 | Kent Mercker | .10 |
| 42 | B. J. Surhoff | .10 |
| 43 | Jerry Browne | .10 |
| 44 | Lee Smith | .10 |
| 45 | Chuck Finley | .20 |
| 46 | Terry Mulholland | .10 |
| 47 | Tom Bolton | .10 |
| 48 | Tom Herr | .10 |
| 49 | Jim Deshaies | .10 |
| 50 | Walt Weiss | .10 |
| 51 | Hal Morris | .25 |
| 52 | Lee Guetterman | .10 |
| 53 | Paul Assenmacher | .10 |
| 54 | Brian Harper | .10 |
| 55 | Paul Gibson | .10 |
| 56 | John Burkett | .10 |
| 57 | Doug Jones | .10 |
| 58 | Jose Qquendo | .10 |
| 59 | Dick Schofield | .10 |
| 60 | Dickie Thon | .10 |
| 61 | Ramon Martinez | .50 |
| 62 | Jay Buhner | .10 |
| 63 | Mark Portugal | .10 |
| 64 | Bob Welch | .10 |
| 65 | Chris Sabo | .20 |

| NO. | PLAYER | MINT |
|---|---|---|
| 66 | Chuck Cary | .10 |
| 67 | Mark Langston | .20 |
| 68 | Joe Boever | .10 |
| 69 | Jody Reed | .10 |
| 70 | Alejandro Pena | .10 |
| 71 | Jeff King | .10 |
| 72 | Tom Pagnozzi | .10 |
| 73 | Joe Oliver | .10 |
| 74 | Mike Witt | .10 |
| 75 | Hector Villanueva | .10 |
| 76 | Dan Gladden | .10 |
| 77 | Dave Justice | 4.00 |
| 78 | Mike Gallego | .10 |
| 79 | Tom Candiotti | .10 |
| 80 | Ozzie Smith | .35 |
| 81 | Luis Polonia | .10 |
| 82 | Randy Ready | .10 |
| 83 | Greg Harris | .10 |
| 84 | Checklist | .25 |
| 85 | Kevin Mitchell | .30 |
| 86 | Mark McLemore | .10 |
| 87 | Terry Steinbach | .10 |
| 88 | Tom Browning | .10 |
| 89 | Matt Nokes | .10 |
| 90 | Mike Harkey | .10 |
| 91 | Omar Vizquel | .10 |
| 92 | Dave Bergman | .10 |
| 93 | Matt Williams | .25 |
| 94 | Steve Olin | .10 |
| 95 | Craig Wilson (R) | .20 |
| 96 | Dave Stieb | .10 |
| 97 | Ruben Sierra | .50 |
| 98 | Jay Howell | .10 |
| 99 | Scott Bradley | .10 |
| 100 | Eric Yelding | .10 |
| 101 | Rickey Henderson | .75 |
| 102 | Jeff Reed | .10 |
| 103 | Jimmy Key | .10 |
| 104 | Terry Shumpert | .10 |
| 105 | Kenny Rogers | .10 |
| 106 | Cecil Fielder | .60 |
| 107 | Robby Thompson | .10 |
| 108 | Alex Cole | .10 |
| 109 | Randy Milligan | .10 |
| 110 | Andres Galarraga | .10 |
| 111 | Bill Spiers | .10 |
| 112 | Kal Daniels | .20 |
| 113 | Henry Cotto | .10 |
| 114 | Casey Candaele | .10 |
| 115 | Jeff Blauser | .10 |
| 116 | Robin Yount | .35 |
| 117 | Ben McDonald | .30 |
| 118 | Bret Saberhagen | .10 |
| 119 | Juan Gonzalez | 4.00 |
| 120 | Lou Whitaker | .10 |
| 121 | Ellis Burks | .20 |
| 122 | Charlie O'Brien | .10 |
| 123 | John Smiley | .10 |
| 124 | Tim Burke | .10 |
| 125 | John Olerud | .30 |
| 126 | Eddie Murray | .40 |
| 127 | Greg Maddux | .10 |
| 128 | Kevin Tapani | .20 |
| 129 | Ron Gant | .30 |
| 130 | Jay Bell | .10 |
| 131 | Chris Hoiles | .15 |

| NO. | PLAYER | MINT |
|---|---|---|
| 132 | Tom Gordon | .15 |
| 133 | Kevin Seitzer | .10 |
| 134 | Jeff Huson | .10 |
| 135 | Jerry Don Gleaton | .10 |
| 136 | Jeff Brantley | .10 |
| 137 | Felix Fermin | .10 |
| 138 | Mike Devereaux | .10 |
| 139 | Delino DeShields | .30 |
| 140 | David Wells | .10 |
| 141 | Tim Crews | .10 |
| 142 | Erik Hanson | .10 |
| 143 | Mark Davidson | .10 |
| 144 | Tommy Gregg | .10 |
| 145 | Jim Gantner | .10 |
| 146 | Jose Lind | .10 |
| 147 | Danny Tartabull | .10 |
| 148 | Geno Petralli | .10 |
| 149 | Travis Fryman | 2.00 |
| 150 | Tim Naehring | .10 |
| 151 | Kevin McReynolds | .10 |
| 152 | Joe Orsulak | .10 |
| 153 | Steve Frey | .10 |
| 154 | Duane Ward | .10 |
| 155 | Stan Javier | .10 |
| 156 | Damon Berryhill | .10 |
| 157 | Gene Larkin | .10 |
| 158 | Greg Olson | .10 |
| 159 | Mark Knudson | .10 |
| 160 | Carmelo Martinez | .10 |
| 161 | Storm Davis | .10 |
| 162 | Jim Abbott | .25 |
| 163 | Len Dykstra | .15 |
| 164 | Tom Brunansky | .10 |
| 165 | Dwight Gooden | .25 |
| 166 | Jose Mesa | .10 |
| 167 | Oil Can Boyd | .10 |
| 168 | Barry Larkin | .30 |
| 169 | Scott Sanderson | .10 |
| 170 | Mark Grace | .25 |
| 171 | Mark Guthrie | .10 |
| 172 | Tom Glavine | .30 |
| 173 | Gary Sheffield | .15 |
| 174 | Checklist | .20 |
| 175 | Chris James | .10 |
| 176 | Milt Thompson | .10 |
| 177 | Donnie Hill | .10 |
| 178 | Wes Chamberlain (R) | 2.00 |
| 179 | John Marzano | .10 |
| 180 | Frank Viola | .15 |
| 181 | Eric Anthony | .10 |
| 182 | Jose Canseco | 1.00 |
| 183 | Scott Scudder | .10 |
| 184 | Dave Eiland | .10 |
| 185 | Luis Salazar | .10 |
| 186 | Pedro Munoz (R) | .75 |
| 187 | Steve Searcy | .10 |
| 188 | Don Robinson | .10 |
| 189 | Sandy Alomar | .15 |
| 190 | Jose DeLeon | .10 |
| 191 | John Orton | .10 |
| 192 | Darren Daulton | .10 |
| 193 | Mike Morgan | .10 |
| 194 | Greg Briley | .10 |
| 195 | Karl Rhodes | .10 |
| 196 | Harold Baines | .10 |
| 197 | Bill Doran | .10 |

| NO. | PLAYER | MINT |
|---|---|---|
| 198 | Alvaro Espinoza | .10 |
| 199 | Kirk McCaskill | .10 |
| 200 | Jose DeJesus | .10 |
| 201 | Jack Clark | .10 |
| 202 | Daryl Boston | .10 |
| 203 | Randy Tomlin (R) | .50 |
| 204 | Pedro Guerrero | .15 |
| 205 | Billy Hatcher | .10 |
| 206 | Tim Leary | .10 |
| 207 | Ryne Sandberg | .75 |
| 208 | Kirby Puckett | .50 |
| 209 | Chrlies Leibrandt | .10 |
| 210 | Rick Honeycutt | .10 |
| 211 | Joel Skinner | .10 |
| 212 | Rex Hudler | .10 |
| 213 | Bryan Harvey | .10 |
| 214 | Charlie Hayes | .10 |
| 215 | Matt Young | .10 |
| 216 | Terry Kennedy | .10 |
| 217 | Carl Nichols | .10 |
| 218 | Mike Moore | .10 |
| 219 | Paul O'Neill | .10 |
| 220 | Steve Sax | .10 |
| 221 | Shawn Boskie | .10 |
| 222 | Rich DeLucia (R) | .35 |
| 223 | Lloyd Moseby | .10 |
| 224 | Mike Kingery | .10 |
| 225 | Carlos Baerga | .30 |
| 226 | Bryn Smith | .10 |
| 227 | Todd Stottlemyre | .20 |
| 228 | Julio Franco | .20 |
| 229 | Jim Gott | .10 |
| 230 | Mike Schooler | .10 |
| 231 | Steve Finley | .10 |
| 232 | Dave Henderson | .10 |
| 233 | Luis Quinones | .10 |
| 234 | Mark Whiten | .40 |
| 235 | Brian McRae (R) | 1.50 |
| 236 | Rich Gossage | .10 |
| 237 | Rob Deer | .10 |
| 238 | Will Clark | .75 |
| 239 | Albert Belle | .50 |
| 240 | Bob Melvin | .10 |
| 241 | Larry Walker | .10 |
| 242 | Dante Bichette | .10 |
| 243 | Orel Hershiser | .20 |
| 244 | Pete O'Brien | .10 |
| 245 | Pete Harnisch | .10 |
| 246 | Jeff Treadway | .10 |
| 247 | Julio Machado | .10 |
| 248 | Dave Johnson | .10 |
| 249 | Kirk Gibson | .15 |
| 250 | Kevin Brown | .10 |
| 251 | Milt Cuyler | .50 |
| 252 | Jeff Reardon | .10 |
| 253 | David Cone | .10 |
| 254 | Gary Redus | .10 |
| 255 | Junior Noboa | .10 |
| 256 | Greg Myers | .10 |
| 257 | Dennis Cook | .10 |
| 258 | Joe Girardi | .10 |
| 259 | Allan Anderson | .10 |
| 260 | Paul Marak (R) | .20 |
| 261 | Barry Bonds | .50 |
| 262 | Juan Bell | .10 |
| 263 | Russ Morman | .10 |

| NO. | PLAYER | MINT |
|-----|--------|------|
| 264 | Checklist | .15 |
| **SERIES NO. 2 (No. 265 to 528)** | | |
| 265 | Jerald Clark | .10 |
| 266 | Dwight Evans | .10 |
| 267 | Roberto Alomar | .30 |
| 268 | Danny Jackson | .10 |
| 269 | Brian Downing | .10 |
| 270 | John Cerutti | .10 |
| 271 | Robin Ventura | 1.00 |
| 272 | Gerald Perry | .10 |
| 273 | Wade Boggs | .50 |
| 274 | Dennis Martinez | .10 |
| 275 | Andy Benes | .20 |
| 276 | Tony Fossas | .10 |
| 277 | Franklin Stubbs | .10 |
| 278 | John Kruk | .10 |
| 279 | Kevin Gross | .10 |
| 280 | Von Hayes | .10 |
| 281 | Frank Thomas | 7.50 |
| 282 | Rob Dibble | .10 |
| 283 | Mel Hall | .10 |
| 284 | Rick Mahler | .10 |
| 285 | Dennis Eckersley | .20 |
| 286 | Bernard Gilkey | .20 |
| 287 | Dan Plesac | .10 |
| 288 | Jason Grimsley | .10 |
| 289 | Mark Lewis | .75 |
| 290 | Tony Gwynn | .50 |
| 291 | Jeff Russell | .10 |
| 292 | Curt Schilling | .10 |
| 293 | Pascual Perez | .10 |
| 294 | Jack Morris | .20 |
| 295 | Hubie Brooks | .10 |
| 296 | Alex Fernandez | .50 |
| 297 | Harold Reynolds | .10 |
| 298 | Craig Worthington | .10 |
| 299 | Willie Wilson | .10 |
| 300 | Mike Maddux | .10 |
| 301 | Dave Righetti | .10 |
| 302 | Paul Molitor | .15 |
| 303 | Gary Gaetti | .10 |
| 304 | Terry Pendleton | .15 |
| 305 | Kevin Elster | .10 |
| 306 | Scott Fletcher | .10 |
| 307 | Jeff Robinson | .10 |
| 308 | Jesse Barfield | .10 |
| 309 | Mike LaCoss | .10 |
| 310 | Andy Van Slyke | .20 |
| 311 | Glenallen Hill | .10 |
| 312 | Bud Black | .10 |
| 313 | Kent Hrbek | .10 |
| 314 | Tim Teufel | .10 |
| 315 | Tony Fernandez | .10 |
| 316 | Beau Allred | .20 |
| 317 | Curtis Wilkerson | .10 |
| 318 | Bill Sampen | .10 |
| 319 | Randy Johnson | .10 |
| 320 | Mike Heath | .10 |
| 321 | Sammy Sosa | .15 |
| 322 | Mickey Tettleton | .10 |
| 323 | Jose Vizcaino | .10 |
| 324 | John Candelaria | .10 |
| 325 | Dave Howard (R) | .30 |
| 326 | Jose Rijo | .10 |
| 327 | Todd Zeile | .30 |
| 328 | Gene Nelson | .10 |
| 329 | Dwayne Henry | .10 |
| 330 | Mike Boddicker | .10 |
| 331 | Ozzie Guillen | .10 |
| 332 | Sam Horn | .10 |
| 333 | Wally Whitehurst | .10 |
| 334 | Dave Parker | .15 |
| 335 | George Brett | .40 |
| 336 | Bobby Thigpen | .10 |

| NO. | PLAYER | MINT |
|-----|--------|------|
| 337 | Ed Whitson | .10 |
| 338 | Ivan Calderon | .10 |
| 339 | Mike Pagliarulo | .10 |
| 340 | Jack McDowell | .20 |
| 341 | Dana Kiecker | .10 |
| 342 | Fred McGriff | .30 |
| 343 | Mark Lee (R) | .20 |
| 344 | Alfredo Griffin | .10 |
| 345 | Scott Bankhead | .10 |
| 346 | Darrin Jackson | .10 |
| 347 | Rafael Palmeiro | .35 |
| 348 | Steve Farr | .10 |
| 349 | Hensley Meulens | .15 |
| 350 | Danny Cox | .10 |
| 351 | Alan Trammell | .20 |
| 352 | Edwin Nunez | .10 |
| 353 | Joe Carter | .25 |
| 354 | Eric Show | .10 |
| 355 | Vance Law | .10 |
| 356 | Jeff Gray (R) | .15 |
| 357 | Bobby Bonilla | .40 |
| 358 | Ernest Riles | .10 |
| 359 | Ron Hassey | .10 |
| 360 | Willie McGee | .15 |
| 361 | Mackey Sasser | .10 |
| 362 | Glenn Braggs | .10 |
| 363 | Mario Diaz | .10 |
| 364 | Checklist | .10 |
| 365 | Kevin Bass | .10 |
| 366 | Pete Incaviglia | .10 |
| 367 | Luis Sojo | .10 |
| 368 | Lance Parrish | .10 |
| 369 | Mark Leonard (R) | .30 |
| 370 | Heath Slocumb (R) | .20 |
| 371 | Jimmy Jones | .10 |
| 372 | Ken Griffey, Jr. | 5.00 |
| 373 | Chris Hammond | .10 |
| 374 | Chili Davis | .10 |
| 375 | Joey Cora | .10 |
| 376 | Ken Hill | .10 |
| 377 | Darryl Strawberry | .75 |
| 378 | Ron Darling | .10 |
| 379 | Sid Bream | .10 |
| 380 | Bill Swift | .10 |
| 381 | Shawn Abner | .10 |
| 382 | Eric King | .10 |
| 383 | Mickey Morandini | .20 |
| 384 | Carlton Fisk | .20 |
| 385 | Steve Lake | .10 |
| 386 | Mike Jeffcoat | .10 |
| 387 | Darren Holmes (R) | .25 |
| 388 | Tim Wallach | .10 |
| 389 | George Bell | .25 |
| 390 | Craig Lefferts | .10 |
| 391 | Ernie Whitt | .10 |
| 392 | Felix Jose | .30 |
| 393 | Kevin Mass | .60 |
| 394 | Devon White | .10 |
| 395 | Otis Nixon | .10 |
| 396 | Chuck Knoblauch | 2.50 |
| 397 | Scott Coolbaugh | .10 |
| 398 | Glenn Davis | .15 |
| 399 | Manny Lee | .10 |
| 400 | Andre Dawson | .25 |
| 401 | Scott Chiamparino | .15 |
| 402 | Bill Gullickson | .10 |
| 403 | Lance Johnson | .10 |
| 404 | Juan Agosto | .10 |
| 405 | Danny Darwin | .10 |
| 406 | Barry Jones | .10 |
| 407 | Larry Andersen | .10 |
| 408 | Luis Rivera | .10 |
| 409 | Jaime Navarro | .10 |

| NO. | PLAYER | MINT |
|-----|--------|------|
| 410 | Roger McDowell | .10 |
| 411 | Brett Butler | .10 |
| 412 | Dale Murphy | .15 |
| 413 | Tim Raines | .20 |
| 414 | Norm Charlton | .10 |
| 415 | Greg Cadaret | .10 |
| 416 | Chris Nabholz | .15 |
| 417 | Dave Stewart | .20 |
| 418 | Rich Gedman | .10 |
| 419 | Willie Randolph | .10 |
| 420 | Mitch Williams | .10 |
| 421 | Brook Jacoby | .10 |
| 422 | Greg Harris | .10 |
| 423 | Nolan Ryan | 3.00 |
| 424 | Dave Rohde | .10 |
| 425 | Don Mattingly | .50 |
| 426 | Greg Gagne | .10 |
| 427 | Vince Coleman | .20 |
| 428 | Dan Pasqua | .10 |
| 429 | Alvin Davis | .10 |
| 430 | Cal Ripken | 1.00 |
| 431 | Jamie Quirk | .10 |
| 432 | Benito Santiago | .15 |
| 433 | Jose Uribe | .10 |
| 434 | Candy Maldonado | .10 |
| 435 | Junior Felix | .10 |
| 436 | Deion Sanders | .15 |
| 437 | John Franco | .10 |
| 438 | Greg Hibbard | .10 |
| 439 | Floyd Bannister | .10 |
| 440 | Steve Howe | .10 |
| 441 | Steve Decker (R) | .50 |
| 442 | Vicente Palacios | .10 |
| 443 | Pat Tabler | .10 |
| 444 | Checklist | .10 |
| 445 | Mike Felder | .10 |
| 446 | Al Newman | .10 |
| 447 | Chris Donnels (R) | .60 |
| 448 | Rich Rodriguez (R) | .15 |
| 449 | Turner Ward (R) | .30 |
| 450 | Bob Walk | .10 |
| 451 | Gilberto Reyes | .10 |
| 452 | Mike Jackson | .10 |
| 453 | Rafael Belliard | .10 |
| 454 | Wayne Edwards | .10 |
| 455 | Andy Allanson | .10 |
| 456 | Dave Smith | .10 |
| 457 | Gary Carter | .15 |
| 458 | Warren Cromartie | .10 |
| 459 | Jack Armstrong | .10 |
| 460 | Bob Tewksbury | .10 |
| 461 | Joe Klink | .10 |
| 462 | Xavier Hernandez | .10 |
| 463 | Scott Radinsky | .10 |
| 464 | Jeff Robinson | .10 |
| 465 | Gregg Jefferies | .20 |
| 466 | Denny Neagle (R) | .75 |
| 467 | Carmelo Martinez | .10 |
| 468 | Donn Pall | .10 |
| 469 | Bruce Hurst | .10 |
| 470 | Eric Bullock | .10 |
| 471 | Rick Aguilera | .10 |
| 472 | Charlie Hough | .10 |
| 473 | Carlos Quintana | .10 |
| 474 | Marty Barrett | .10 |
| 475 | Kevin Brown | .10 |
| 476 | Bobby Ojeda | .10 |
| 477 | Edgar Martinez | .10 |
| 478 | Bip Roberts | .10 |
| 479 | Mike Flanagan | .10 |
| 480 | John Habyan | .10 |
| 481 | Larry Casian (R) | .20 |
| 482 | Wally Backman | .10 |

| NO. | PLAYER | MINT |
|-----|--------|------|
| 483 | Doug Dascenzo | .10 |
| 484 | Rick Dempsey | .10 |
| 485 | Ed Sprague | .25 |
| 486 | Steve Chitren (R) | .15 |
| 487 | Mark McGwire | .25 |
| 488 | Roger Clemens | .75 |
| 489 | Orlando Merced (R) | 1.25 |
| 490 | Rene Gonzales | .10 |
| 491 | Mike Stanton | .10 |
| 492 | Al Osuna (R) | .25 |
| 493 | Rick Cerone | .10 |
| 494 | Mariano Duncan | .10 |
| 495 | Zane Smith | .10 |
| 496 | John Morris | .20 |
| 497 | Frank Tanana | .10 |
| 498 | Junior Ortiz | .10 |
| 499 | Dave Winfield | .20 |
| 500 | Gary Varsho | .10 |
| 501 | Chico Walker | .10 |
| 502 | Ken Caminiti | .10 |
| 503 | Ken Griffey, Sr. | .10 |
| 504 | Randy Myers | .10 |
| 505 | Steve Bedrosian | .10 |
| 506 | Cory Snyder | .10 |
| 507 | Cris Carpenter | .10 |
| 508 | Tim Belcher | .10 |
| 509 | Jeff Hamilton | .10 |
| 510 | Steve Avery | 2.00 |
| 511 | Dave Valle | .10 |
| 512 | Tom Lampkin | .10 |
| 513 | Shawn Hillegas | .10 |
| 514 | Reggie Jefferson | 1.25 |
| 515 | Ron Karkovice | .10 |
| 516 | Doug Drabek | .10 |
| 517 | Tom Henke | .10 |
| 518 | Chris Bosio | .10 |
| 519 | Gregg Olson | .15 |
| 520 | Bob Scanlan | .20 |
| 521 | Alonzo Powell (R) | .20 |
| 522 | Jeff Ballard | .10 |
| 523 | Ray Lankford | 1.00 |
| 524 | Tommy Greene | .15 |
| 525 | Mike Timlin (R) | .25 |
| 526 | Juan Berenguer | .10 |
| 527 | Scott Erickson | 4.00 |
| 528 | Checklist | .10 |

**No. BC1 to 26—Gold Bonus**

| No. | Player | Mint |
|-----|--------|------|
| BC1 | Scott Leius | 1.50 |
| BC2 | Luis Gonzalez | 5.00 |
| BC3 | Wilfredo Cordero | 3.00 |
| BC4 | Gary Scott | 3.00 |
| BC5 | Willie Banks | 2.50 |
| BC6 | Arthur Rhodes | 2.50 |
| BC7 | Mo Vaughn | 6.00 |
| BC8 | Henry Rodriguez | 1.50 |
| BC9 | Todd Van Poppel | 7.50 |
| BC10 | Reggie Sanders | 5.00 |
| BC11 | Rico Brogna | 3.00 |
| BC12 | Mike Mussina | 5.00 |
| BC13 | Kirk Dressendorfer | 2.50 |
| BC14 | Jeff Bagwell | 12.50 |
| BC15 | Pete Schourek | 2.00 |
| BC16 | Wade Taylor | 2.00 |
| BC17 | Pat Kelly | 3.00 |
| BC18 | Tim Costo | 2.50 |
| BC19 | Roger Salkeld | 4.00 |
| BC20 | Andujar Cedeno | 4.00 |
| BC21 | Ryan Klesko | 15.00 |
| BC22 | Mike Huff | 1.00 |
| BC23 | Anthony Young | 2.00 |
| BC24 | Eddie Zosky | 3.00 |
| BC25 | Nolan Ryan | 7.50 |
| BC26 | Rickey Henderson | 5.00 |

# 1991 O-Pee-Chee Premier . . . Complete Set of 132 Cards—Value $50.00

O-Pee-Chee (licensed by Topps) previously only issued hockey cards for the Canadian market. The cards were printed in Canada.

| NO. | PLAYER | MINT |
|---|---|---|
| 1 | Roberto Alomor | .40 |
| 2 | Sandy Alomar | .20 |
| 3 | Moises Alou | .10 |
| 4 | Brian Barnes (R) | .30 |
| 5 | Steve Bedrosian | .08 |
| 6 | George Bell | .30 |
| 7 | Juan Bell | .08 |
| 8 | Albert Belle | 1.00 |
| 9 | Bud Black | .08 |
| 10 | Mike Boddicker | .08 |
| 11 | Wade Boggs | .75 |
| 12 | Barry Bonds | .75 |
| 13 | Denis Boucher (R) | .25 |
| 14 | George Brett | .40 |
| 15 | Hubie Brooks | .08 |
| 16 | Brett Butler | .10 |
| 17 | Ivan Calderon | .08 |
| 18 | Jose Canseco | 1.50 |
| 19 | Cary Carter | .15 |
| 20 | Joe Carter | .30 |
| 21 | Jack Clark | .15 |
| 22 | Will Clark | 1.50 |
| 23 | Roger Clemens | 1.00 |
| 24 | Alex Cole | .15 |
| 25 | Vince Coleman | .25 |
| 26 | Jeff Conine (R) | .30 |
| 27 | Milt Cuyler | .50 |
| 28 | Danny Darwin | .08 |
| 29 | Eric Davis | .30 |
| 30 | Glenn Davis | .12 |
| 31 | Andre Dawson | .35 |
| 32 | Ken Dayley | .08 |
| 33 | Steve Decker (R) | .75 |

| NO. | PLAYER | MINT |
|---|---|---|
| 34 | Delino DeShields | .30 |
| 35 | Lance Dickson (R) | .50 |
| 36 | Kirk Dressendorfer (R) | .60 |
| 37 | Shawon Dunston | .15 |
| 38 | Dennis Eckersley | .20 |
| 39 | Dwight Evans | .08 |
| 40 | Howard Farmer | .15 |
| 41 | Junior Felix | .08 |
| 42 | Alex Fernandez | .60 |
| 43 | Tony Fernandez | .08 |
| 44 | Cecil Fielder | 1.00 |
| 45 | Carlton Fisk | .50 |
| 46 | Willie Fraser | .08 |
| 47 | Gary Gaetti | .08 |
| 48 | Andres Galarraga | .08 |
| 49 | Ron Gant | .50 |
| 50 | Kirk Gibson | .15 |
| 51 | Bernard Gilkey | .25 |
| 52 | Leo Gomez | .75 |
| 53 | Rene Gonzales | .08 |
| 54 | Juan Gonzalez | 5.00 |
| 55 | Doc Gooden | .35 |
| 56 | Ken Griffey, Jr. | 6.00 |
| 57 | Kelly Gruber | .15 |
| 58 | Pedro Guerrero | .12 |
| 59 | Tony Gwynn | .75 |
| 60 | Chris Hammond | .15 |
| 61 | Ron Hassey | .08 |
| 62 | Rickey Henderson | 1.50 |
| 63 | Tom Henke | .08 |
| 64 | Orel Hershiser | .25 |
| 65 | Chris Hoiles | .20 |
| 66 | Todd Hundley | .30 |

| NO. | PLAYER | MINT |
|---|---|---|
| 67 | Pete Incaviglia | .08 |
| 68 | Danny Jackson | .08 |
| 69 | Barry Jones | .35 |
| 70 | David Justice | 7.00 |
| 71 | Jimmy Key | .08 |
| 72 | Ray Lankford | 1.00 |
| 73 | Darren Lewis | .75 |
| 74 | Kevin Maas | .75 |
| 75 | Denny Martinez | .10 |
| 76 | Tino Martinez | .50 |
| 77 | Don Mattingly | 1.00 |
| 78 | Willie McGee | .15 |
| 79 | Fred McGriff | .35 |
| 80 | Hensley Meulens | .25 |
| 81 | Kevin Mitchell | .40 |
| 82 | Paul Molitor | .25 |
| 83 | Mickey Morandini | .30 |
| 84 | Jack Morris | .25 |
| 85 | Dale Murphy | .30 |
| 86 | Eddie Murray | .30 |
| 87 | Chris Nabholz | .15 |
| 88 | Tim Naehring | .25 |
| 89 | Otis Nixon | .15 |
| 90 | Jose Offerman | .20 |
| 91 | Bob Ojeda | .08 |
| 92 | John Olerud | .50 |
| 93 | Gregg Olson | .15 |
| 94 | Dave Parker | .20 |
| 95 | Terry Pendleton | .20 |
| 96 | Kirby Puckett | 1.00 |
| 97 | Rock Raines | .25 |
| 98 | Jeff Reardon | .12 |
| 99 | Dave Righetti | .08 |

| NO. | PLAYER | MINT |
|---|---|---|
| 100 | Cal Ripken | 2.00 |
| 101 | Mel Rojas | .15 |
| 102 | Nolan Ryan | 5.00 |
| 103 | Ryne Sandberg | 1.50 |
| 104 | Scott Sanderson | .08 |
| 105 | Benny Santiago | .15 |
| 106 | Pete Schourek (R) | .25 |
| 107 | Gary Scott (R) | .75 |
| 108 | Terry Shumpert | .12 |
| 109 | Ruben Sierra | .75 |
| 110 | Doug Simons | .20 |
| 111 | Dave Smith | .08 |
| 112 | Ozzie Smith | .50 |
| 113 | Cory Snyder | .10 |
| 114 | Luis Sojo | .15 |
| 115 | Dave Stewart | .12 |
| 116 | Dave Stieb | .08 |
| 117 | Darryl Strawberry | 1.00 |
| 118 | Pat Tabler | .08 |
| 119 | Wade Taylor (R) | .35 |
| 120 | Bobby Thigpen | .12 |
| 121 | Frank Thomas | 15.00 |
| 122 | Mike Timlin (R) | .30 |
| 123 | Alan Trammell | .25 |
| 124 | Mo Vaughn | 2.00 |
| 125 | Tim Wallach | .08 |
| 126 | Devon White | .08 |
| 127 | Mark Whiten | .50 |
| 128 | Bernie Williams | 1.00 |
| 129 | Willie Wilson | .08 |
| 130 | Dave Winfield | .30 |
| 131 | Robin Yount | .50 |
| 132 | Checklist | .08 |

# 1988 Score . . . Complete Set of 660 Cards—Value $20.00 (Factory-Sealed Set—Value $25.00)

This was Score's *first* baseball card set. It was issued by the same company that produced the Sportsflic card sets. Features the rookie cards of Gregg Jefferies, Ellis Burks and Matt Williams.

| NO. PLAYER | MINT |
|---|---|
| 1 Don Mattingly | .30 |
| 2 Wade Boggs | .25 |
| 3 Tim Raines | .15 |
| 4 Andre Dawson | .15 |
| 5 Mark McGwire | .40 |
| 6 Kevin Seitzer | .08 |
| 7 Wally Joyner | .15 |
| 8 Jesse Barfield | .08 |
| 9 Pedro Guerrero | .08 |
| 10 Eric Davis | .20 |
| 11 George Brett | .20 |
| 12 Ozzie Smith | .15 |
| 13 Rickey Henderson | .30 |
| 14 Jim Rice | .10 |
| 15 Matt Nokes (R) | .25 |
| 16 Mike Schmidt | .40 |
| 17 Dave Parker | .10 |
| 18 Eddie Murray | .15 |
| 19 Andres Galarraga | .08 |
| 20 Tony Fernandez | .08 |
| 21 Kevin McReynolds | .08 |
| 22 B.J. Surhoff | .08 |
| 23 Pat Tabler | .05 |
| 24 Kirby Puckett | .30 |
| 25 Benito Santiago | .15 |
| 26 Ryn Sandberg | .35 |
| 27 Kelly Downs | .05 |
| 28 Jose Cruz | .05 |
| 29 Pete O'Brien | .08 |
| 30 Mark Langston | .08 |
| 31 Lee Smith | .08 |
| 32 Juan Samuel | .10 |
| 33 Kevin Bass | .08 |
| 34 R.J. Reynolds | .08 |
| 35 Steve Sax | .10 |
| 36 John Kruk | .08 |
| 37 Alan Trammell | .15 |
| 38 Chris Bosio | .05 |
| 39 Brook Jacoby | .08 |
| 40 Willie McGee | .08 |
| 41 Dave Magadan | .08 |
| 42 Fred Lynn | .10 |
| 43 Kent Hrbek | .10 |
| 44 Brian Downing | .05 |
| 45 Jose Canseco | .75 |
| 46 Jim Presley | .05 |
| 47 Mike Stanley | .05 |
| 48 Tony Pena | .05 |
| 49 David Cone | .25 |
| 50 Rick Sutcliffe | .05 |
| 51 Doug Drabeck | .12 |
| 52 Bill Doran | .05 |
| 53 Mike Scioscia | .05 |
| 54 Candy Maldonado | .05 |
| 55 Dave Winfield | .15 |
| 56 Lou Whitaker | .05 |
| 57 Tom Henke | .05 |
| 58 Ken Gerhardt | .08 |
| 59 Glenn Braggs | .08 |
| 60 Julio Franco | .15 |
| 61 Charlie Leibrandt | .05 |
| 62 Gary Gaetti | .05 |
| 63 Bob Boone | .05 |
| 64 Luis Polonia (R) | .25 |
| 65 Dwight Evans | .10 |
| 66 Phil Bradley | .08 |
| 67 Mike Boddicker | .05 |

| NO. PLAYER | MINT |
|---|---|
| 68 Vince Coleman | .15 |
| 69 Howard Johnson | .15 |
| 70 Tim Wallach | .08 |
| 71 Keith Moreland | .05 |
| 72 Barry Larkin | .25 |
| 73 Alan Ashby | .05 |
| 74 Rick Rhoden | .05 |
| 75 Darrell Evans | .08 |
| 76 Dave Stieb | .08 |
| 77 Dan Plesac | .08 |
| 78 Will Clark | .75 |
| 79 Frank White | .05 |
| 80 Joe Carter | .15 |
| 81 Mike Witt | .05 |
| 82 Terry Steinbach | .10 |
| 83 Alvin Davis | .08 |
| 84 Tom Herr | .05 |
| 85 Vance Law | .05 |
| 86 Kal Daniels | .08 |
| 87 Rick Honeycutt | .05 |
| 88 Alfredo Griffin | .05 |
| 89 Bret Saberhagen | .12 |
| 90 Bert Blyleven | .08 |
| 91 Jeff Reardon | .10 |
| 92 Cory Snyder | .08 |
| 93 Greg Walker | .08 |
| 94 Joe Magrane (R) | .15 |
| 95 Rob Deer | .05 |
| 96 Ray Knight | .05 |
| 97 Casey Candaele | .05 |
| 98 John Cerutti | .05 |
| 99 Buddy Bell | .05 |
| 100 Jack Clark | .10 |
| 101 Eric Bell (R) | .10 |
| 102 Willie Wilson | .05 |
| 103 Dave Schmidt | .05 |
| 104 Dennis Eckersley | .10 |
| 105 Don Sutton | .10 |
| 106 Danny Tartabull | .15 |
| 107 Fred McGriff | .75 |
| 108 Les Straker (R) | .12 |
| 109 Lloyd Moseby | .08 |
| 110 Roger Clemens | .35 |
| 111 Glenn Hubbard | .05 |
| 112 Ken Williams (R) | .12 |
| 113 Ruben Sierra | .35 |
| 114 Stan Jefferson | .05 |
| 115 Milt Thompson | .05 |
| 116 Bobby Bonilla | .30 |
| 117 Wayne Tolleson | .05 |
| 118 Matt Williams (R) | 1.50 |
| 119 Chet Lemon | .05 |
| 120 Dale Sveum | .05 |
| 121 Dennis Boyd | .05 |
| 122 Brett Butler | .08 |
| 123 Terry Kennedy | .05 |
| 124 Jack Howell | .05 |
| 125 Curt Young | .05 |
| 126 Dale Valle (error) | .15 |
| 126 Dave Valle (correct) | .08 |
| 127 Curt Wilkerson | .05 |
| 128 Tim Teufel | .05 |
| 129 Ozzie Virgil | .05 |
| 130 Brian Fisher | .05 |
| 131 Lance Parrish | .08 |
| 132 Tom Browning | .05 |
| 133 L. Anderson (error) | .15 |
| 133 L. Anderson (correct) | .08 |

| NO. PLAYER | MINT |
|---|---|
| 134 B. Brenley (error) | .15 |
| 134 B. Brenley (correct) | .08 |
| 135 Mike Marshall | .08 |
| 136 Gerald Perry | .08 |
| 137 Bobby Meacham | .05 |
| 138 Larry Herndon | .05 |
| 139 Fred Manrique (R) | .10 |
| 140 Charlie Hough | .05 |
| 141 Ron Darling | .10 |
| 142 Herm Winningham | .05 |
| 143 Mike Diaz | .05 |
| 144 Mike Jackson (R) | .10 |
| 145 Denny Walling | .05 |
| 146 Rob Thompson | .05 |
| 147 Franklin Stubbs | .05 |
| 148 Albert Hall | .05 |
| 149 Bobby Witt | .10 |
| 150 Lance McCullers | .08 |
| 151 Scott Bradley | .05 |
| 152 Mark McLemore | .08 |
| 153 Tim Laudner | .05 |
| 154 Greg Swindell | .10 |
| 155 Marty Barrett | .05 |
| 156 Mike Heath | .05 |
| 157 Gary Ward | .05 |
| 158 Lee Mazilli (error) | .15 |
| 158 Lee Mazilli (correct) | .05 |
| 159 Tom Foley | .05 |
| 160 Robin Yount | .20 |
| 161 Steve Bedrosian | .08 |
| 162 Bob Walk | .05 |
| 163 Nick Esasky | .05 |
| 164 Ken Caminiti (R) | .15 |
| 165 Jose Uribe | .05 |
| 166 Dave Anderson | .05 |
| 167 Ed Whitson | .05 |
| 168 Ernie Whitt | .05 |
| 169 Cecil Cooper | .10 |
| 170 Mike Pagliarulo | .10 |
| 171 Pat Sheridan | .05 |
| 172 Chris Bando | .05 |
| 173 Lee Lacy | .05 |
| 174 Steve Lombardozzi | .05 |
| 175 Mike Greenwell | .50 |
| 176 Greg Minton | .05 |
| 177 Moose Haas | .05 |
| 178 Mike Kingery | .05 |
| 179 Greg Harris | .05 |
| 180 Bo Jackson | .50 |
| 181 Carmelo Martinez | .05 |
| 182 Alex Trevino | .05 |
| 183 Ron Oester | .05 |
| 184 Danny Darwin | .05 |
| 185 Mike Krukow | .05 |
| 186 Rafael Palmeiro | .50 |
| 187 Tim Burke | .05 |
| 188 Roger McDowell | .05 |
| 189 Garry Templeton | .05 |
| 190 Terry Pendleton | .12 |
| 191 Larry Parrish | .05 |
| 192 Rey Quinones | .05 |
| 193 Joaquin Andujar | .05 |
| 194 Tom Brunansky | .08 |
| 195 Donnie Moore | .05 |
| 196 Dan Pasqual | .08 |
| 197 Jim Gantner | .05 |
| 198 Mark Eichhorn | .05 |

| NO. PLAYER | MINT |
|---|---|
| 199 John Grubb | .05 |
| 200 Bill Ripken (R) | .20 |
| 201 Sam Horn (R) | .15 |
| 202 Todd Worrell | .08 |
| 203 Terry Leach | .05 |
| 204 Garth Iorg | .05 |
| 205 Brian Dayett | .05 |
| 206 Bo Diaz | .05 |
| 207 Craig Reynolds | .05 |
| 208 Brian Holton | .05 |
| 209 Marvelle Wynne | .05 |
| 210 Dave Concepcion | .08 |
| 211 Mike Davis | .05 |
| 212 Devon White | .10 |
| 213 Mickey Brantley | .08 |
| 214 Greg Gagne | .05 |
| 215 Oddibe McDowell | .08 |
| 216 Jimmy Key | .08 |
| 217 Dave Bergman | .05 |
| 218 Calvin Schiraldi | .05 |
| 219 Larry Sheets | .08 |
| 220 Mike Easler | .05 |
| 221 Kurt Stillwell | .08 |
| 222 Chuck Jackson (R) | .12 |
| 223 Dave Martinez | .05 |
| 224 Tim Leary | .05 |
| 225 Steve Garvey | .20 |
| 226 Greg Mathews | .05 |
| 227 Doug Sisk | .05 |
| 228 Dave Henderson | .05 |
| 229 Jimmy Dwyer | .05 |
| 230 Larry Owen | .05 |
| 231 Andre Thornton | .05 |
| 232 Mark Salas | .05 |
| 233 Tom Brookens | .05 |
| 234 Greg Brock | .05 |
| 235 Rance Mulliniks | .05 |
| 236 Bob Brower | .08 |
| 237 Joe Niekro | .10 |
| 238 Scott Bankhead | .05 |
| 239 Doug DeCinces | .05 |
| 240 Tommy John | .10 |
| 241 Rich Gedman | .05 |
| 242 Ted Power | .05 |
| 243 Dave Meads (R) | .12 |
| 244 Jim Sundberg | .05 |
| 245 Ken Oberkfell | .05 |
| 246 Jimmy Jones | .10 |
| 247 Ken Landreaux | .05 |
| 248 Jose Oquendo | .05 |
| 249 John Mitchell (R) | .12 |
| 250 Don Baylor | .05 |
| 251 Scott Fletcher | .05 |
| 252 Al Newman | .05 |
| 253 Carney Lansford | .05 |
| 254 Johnny Ray | .08 |
| 255 Gary Pettis | .05 |
| 256 Ken Phelps | .05 |
| 257 Rick Leach | .05 |
| 258 Tim Stoddard | .05 |
| 259 Ed Romero | .05 |
| 260 Sid Bream | .05 |
| 261 T. Niedenfuer (error) | .15 |
| 261 T. Niedenfuer (cor.) | .05 |
| 262 Rick Dempsey | .05 |
| 263 Lonnie Smith | .05 |
| 264 Bob Forsch | .05 |

| NO. PLAYER | MINT |
|---|---|
| 265 Barry Bonds | .35 |
| 266 Willie Randolph | .10 |
| 267 Mike Ramsey | .08 |
| 268 Don Slaught | .05 |
| 269 Mickey Tettleton | .05 |
| 270 Jerry Reuss | .05 |
| 271 Marc Sullivan | .05 |
| 272 Jim Morrison | .05 |
| 273 Steve Balboni | .05 |
| 274 Dick Schofield | .05 |
| 275 John Tudor | .08 |
| 276 Gene Larkin (R) | .15 |
| 277 Harold Reynolds | .05 |
| 278 Jerry Browne | .05 |
| 279 Willie Upshaw | .05 |
| 280 Ted Higuera | .08 |
| 281 Terry McGriff | .08 |
| 282 Terry Puhl | .05 |
| 283 Mark Wasinger (R) | .12 |
| 284 Luis Salazar | .05 |
| 285 Ted Simmons | .08 |
| 286 John Shelby | .05 |
| 287 John Smiley (R) | .50 |
| 288 Curt Ford | .05 |
| 289 Steve Crawford | .05 |
| 290 Dan Quisenberry | .08 |
| 291 Alan Wiggins | .05 |
| 292 Randy Bush | .05 |
| 293 John Candelaria | .08 |
| 294 Tony Phillips | .05 |
| 295 Mike Morgan | .05 |
| 296 Bill Wegman | .05 |
| 297 T. Francona (error) | .15 |
| 297 T. Francona (correct) | .05 |
| 298 Mickey Hatcher | .05 |
| 299 Andres Thomas | .05 |
| 300 Bob Stanley | .05 |
| 301 Alfredo Pedrique (R) | .12 |
| 302 Jim Lindeman | .10 |
| 303 Wally Backman | .05 |
| 304 Paul O'Neill | .15 |
| 305 Hubie Brooks | .08 |
| 306 Steve Buechele | .05 |
| 307 Bobby Thigpen | .12 |
| 308 George Hendrick | .05 |
| 309 John Moses | .05 |
| 310 Ron Guidry | .08 |
| 311 Bill Schroeder | .05 |
| 312 Jose Nunez (R) | .12 |
| 313 Bud Black | .05 |
| 314 Joe Sambito | .05 |
| 315 Scott McGregor | .05 |
| 316 Rafael Santana | .05 |
| 317 Frank Williams | .05 |
| 318 Mike Fitzgerald | .05 |
| 319 Rick Mahler | .05 |
| 320 Jim Gott | .05 |
| 321 Marinao Duncan | .05 |
| 322 Jose Guzman | .05 |
| 323 Lee Guetterman | .05 |
| 324 Dan Gladden | .05 |
| 325 Gary Carter | .10 |
| 326 Tracy Jones | .08 |
| 327 Floyd Youmans | .05 |
| 328 Bill Dawley | .05 |
| 329 Paul Noce (R) | .12 |
| 330 Angel Salazar | .05 |
| 331 Goose Gossage | .10 |
| 332 George Frazier | .05 |
| 333 Ruppert Jones | .05 |
| 334 Billy Jo Robidoux | .05 |
| 335 Mike Scott | .08 |
| 336 Randy Myers | .08 |
| 337 Bob Sebra | .05 |
| 338 Eric Show | .05 |
| 339 Mitch Williams | .05 |
| 340 Paul Molitor | .12 |
| 341 Gus Polidor | .05 |
| 342 Steve Trout | .05 |
| 343 Jerry Don Gleaton | .05 |
| 344 Bob Knepper | .05 |
| 345 Mitch Webster | .05 |
| 346 John Morris | .05 |
| 347 Andy Hawkins | .05 |
| 348 Dave Leiper | .05 |

| NO. PLAYER | MINT |
|---|---|
| 349 Ernest Riles | .05 |
| 350 Dwight Gooden | .20 |
| 351 Dave Righetti | .08 |
| 352 Pat Dodson | .08 |
| 353 John Habyan | .08 |
| 354 Jim Deshaies | .05 |
| 355 Butch Wynegar | .05 |
| 356 Bryn Smith | .05 |
| 357 Matt Young | .05 |
| 358 Tom Pagnozzi (R) | .12 |
| 359 Floyd Rayford | .05 |
| 360 Darryl Strawberry | .35 |
| 361 Sal Butera | .05 |
| 362 Domingo Ramos | .05 |
| 363 Chris Brown | .08 |
| 364 Jose Gonzalez | .08 |
| 365 Dave Smith | .05 |
| 366 Andy McGaffigan | .05 |
| 367 Stan Javier | .05 |
| 368 Henry Cotto | .05 |
| 369 Mike Birkbeck | .05 |
| 370 Len Dykstra | .10 |
| 371 Dave Collins | .05 |
| 372 Spike Owen | .05 |
| 373 Geno Petralli | .05 |
| 374 Ron Karkovice | .05 |
| 375 Shane Rawley | .05 |
| 376 Dewayne Buice (R) | .12 |
| 377 Bill Pecota (R) | .12 |
| 378 Leon Durham | .05 |
| 379 Ed Olwine | .05 |
| 380 Bruce Hurst | .10 |
| 381 Bob McClure | .05 |
| 382 Mark Thurmond | .05 |
| 383 Buddy Biancalana | .05 |
| 384 Tim Conroy | .05 |
| 385 Tony Gwynn | .25 |
| 386 Greg Gross | .05 |
| 387 Barry Lyons (R) | .10 |
| 388 Mike Felder | .05 |
| 389 Pat Clements | .05 |
| 390 Ken Griffey | .08 |
| 391 Mark Davis | .05 |
| 392 Jose Rijo | .05 |
| 393 Mike Young | .05 |
| 394 Willie Fraser | .08 |
| 395 Dion James | .05 |
| 396 Steve Shields | .08 |
| 397 Randy St. Claire | .05 |
| 398 Danny Jackson | .10 |
| 399 Cecil Fielder | .35 |
| 400 Keith Hernandez | .08 |
| 401 Don Carman | .05 |
| 402 Chuck Crim (R) | .12 |
| 403 Rob Woodward | .05 |
| 404 Junior Ortiz | .05 |
| 405 Glenn Wilson | .05 |
| 406 Ken Howell | .05 |
| 407 Jeff Kunkel | .05 |
| 408 Jeff Reed | .05 |
| 409 Chris James | .10 |
| 410 Zane Smith | .05 |
| 411 Ken Dixon | .05 |
| 412 Rickey Horton | .05 |
| 413 Frank Dipino | .05 |
| 414 Shane Mack | .15 |
| 415 Danny Cox | .05 |
| 416 Andy Van Slyke | .10 |
| 417 Danny Heep | .05 |
| 418 John Cangelosi | .05 |
| 419 J. Christensen (err.) | .15 |
| 419 J. Christensen (cor.) | .05 |
| 420 Joey Cora (R) | .12 |
| 421 Mike Lavalliere | .05 |
| 422 Kelly Gruber | .15 |
| 423 Bruce Benedict | .05 |
| 424 Len Matuszek | .05 |
| 425 Kent Tekulve | .05 |
| 426 Rafael Ramirez | .05 |
| 427 Mike Flanagan | .05 |
| 428 Mike Gallego | .05 |
| 429 Juan Castillo | .05 |
| 430 Neal Heaton | .05 |
| 431 Phil Garner | .05 |
| 432 Mike Dunne | .08 |

| NO. PLAYER | MINT |
|---|---|
| 433 Wallace Johnson | .05 |
| 434 Jack O'Connor | .05 |
| 435 Steve Jeltz | .05 |
| 436 Donnell Nixon (R) | .12 |
| 437 Jack Lazorko | .05 |
| 438 Keith Comstock (R) | .10 |
| 439 Jeff Robinson | .05 |
| 440 Graig Nettles | .10 |
| 441 Mel Hall | .08 |
| 442 Gerald Young (R) | .12 |
| 443 Gary Redus | .05 |
| 444 Charlie Moore | .05 |
| 445 Bill Madlock | .08 |
| 446 Mark Clear | .05 |
| 447 Greg Booker | .05 |
| 448 Rick Schu | .05 |
| 449 Ron Kittle | .08 |
| 450 Dale Murphy | .15 |
| 451 Bob Dernier | .05 |
| 452 Dale Mohorcic | .05 |
| 453 Rafael Belliard | .05 |
| 454 Charlie Puleo | .05 |
| 455 Dwayne Murphy | .05 |
| 456 Jim Eisenreich | .05 |
| 457 David Palmer | .05 |
| 458 Dave Stewart | .10 |
| 459 Pasqual Perez | .05 |
| 460 Glenn Davis | .10 |
| 461 Dan Petry | .08 |
| 462 Jim Winn | .05 |
| 463 Darrell Miller | .05 |
| 464 Mike Moore | .05 |
| 465 Mike LaCoss | .05 |
| 466 Steve Farr | .05 |
| 467 Jerry Mumphrey | .05 |
| 468 Kevin Gross | .05 |
| 469 Bruce Bochy | .05 |
| 470 Orel Hershiser | .12 |
| 471 Eric King | .05 |
| 472 Ellis Burks (R) | .50 |
| 473 Darren Daulton | .05 |
| 474 Mookie Wilson | .05 |
| 475 Frank Viola | .10 |
| 476 Ron Robinson | .05 |
| 477 Bob Melvin | .05 |
| 478 Jeff Musselman | .08 |
| 479 Charlie Kerfeld | .05 |
| 480 Richard Dotson | .05 |
| 481 Kevin Mitchell | .25 |
| 482 Gary Roenicke | .05 |
| 483 Tim Flannery | .05 |
| 484 Rich Yett | .05 |
| 485 Pete Incaviglia | .08 |
| 486 Rick Cerone | .05 |
| 487 Tony Armas | .05 |
| 488 Jerry Reed | .05 |
| 489 Davey Lopes | .05 |
| 490 Frank Tanana | .05 |
| 491 Mike Loynd | .08 |
| 492 Bruce Ruffin | .05 |
| 493 Chris Speier | .05 |
| 494 Tom Hume | .05 |
| 495 Jesse Orosco | .05 |
| 496 Robbie Wine, Jr. (R) | .12 |
| 497 Jeff Montgomery (R) | .20 |
| 498 Jeff Dedmon | .05 |
| 499 Luis Aguayo | .05 |
| 500 Reggie Jackson #1 | .20 |
| 501 Reggie Jackson #2 | .20 |
| 502 Reggie Jackson #3 | .20 |
| 503 Reggie Jackson #4 | .20 |
| 504 Reggie Jackson #5 | .20 |
| 505 Billy Hatcher | .08 |
| 506 Ed Lynch | .05 |
| 507 Willie Hernandez | .05 |
| 508 Jose DeLeon | .05 |
| 509 Joel Youngblood | .05 |
| 510 Bob Welch | .05 |
| 511 Steve Ontiveros | .05 |
| 512 Randy Ready | .05 |
| 513 Juan Nieves | .05 |
| 514 Jeff Russell | .05 |
| 515 Von Hayes | .08 |
| 516 Mark Gubicza | .05 |

| NO. PLAYER | MINT |
|---|---|
| 517 Ken Dayley | .05 |
| 518 Don Aase | .05 |
| 519 Rick Reuschel | .05 |
| 520 Mike Henneman (R) | .15 |
| 521 Rick Aguilera | .05 |
| 522 Jay Howell | .05 |
| 523 Ed Correa | .05 |
| 524 Manny Trillo | .05 |
| 525 Kirk Gibson | .15 |
| 526 Wally Ritchie (R) | .12 |
| 527 Al Nipper | .05 |
| 528 Atlee Hammaker | .05 |
| 529 Shawon Dunston | .10 |
| 530 Jim Clancy | .05 |
| 531 Tom Paciorek | .05 |
| 532 Joel Skinner | .05 |
| 533 Scott Garrelts | .05 |
| 534 Tom O'Malley | .05 |
| 535 John Franco | .10 |
| 536 Paul Kilgus (R) | .12 |
| 537 Darrell Porter | .05 |
| 538 Walt Terrell | .05 |
| 539 Bill Long (R) | .12 |
| 540 George Bell | .15 |
| 541 Jeff Sellers | .05 |
| 542 Joe Boever (R) | .15 |
| 543 Steve Howe | .05 |
| 544 Scott Sanderson | .05 |
| 545 Jack Morris | .10 |
| 546 Todd Benzinger (R) | .20 |
| 547 Steve Henderson | .05 |
| 548 Eddie Milner | .05 |
| 549 Jeff Robinson | .10 |
| 550 Cal Ripken, Jr. | .40 |
| 551 Jody Davis | .08 |
| 552 Kirk McCaskill | .05 |
| 553 Craig Lefferts | .05 |
| 554 Darnell Coles | .05 |
| 555 Phil Niekro | .15 |
| 556 Mike Aldrete | .05 |
| 557 Pat Perry | .05 |
| 558 Juan Agosto | .05 |
| 559 Rob Murphy | .05 |
| 560 Dennis Rasmussen | .05 |
| 561 Manny Lee | .05 |
| 562 Jeff Blauser (R) | .20 |
| 563 Bob Ojeda | .05 |
| 564 Dave Dravecky | .05 |
| 565 Gene Garber | .05 |
| 566 Ron Roenicke | .05 |
| 567 Tommy Hinzo (R) | .12 |
| 568 Eric Nolte (R) | .12 |
| 569 Ed Hearn | .05 |
| 570 Mark Davidson (R) | .12 |
| 571 Jim Walewander (R) | .12 |
| 572 Donnie Hill | .05 |
| 573 Jamie Moyer | .05 |
| 574 Ken Schrom | .05 |
| 575 Nolan Ryan | .40 |
| 576 Jim Acker | .05 |
| 577 Jamie Quirk | .05 |
| 578 Jay Alrich (R) | .12 |
| 579 Claudell Washington | .05 |
| 580 Jeff Leonard | .08 |
| 581 Carmen Castillo | .05 |
| 582 Darryl Boston | .05 |
| 583 Jeff DeWillis (R) | .10 |
| 584 John Marzano (R) | .10 |
| 585 Bill Gullickson | .05 |
| 586 Andy Allanson | .05 |
| 587 Lee Tunnell | .05 |
| 588 Gene Nelson | .05 |
| 589 Dave LaPoint | .05 |
| 590 Harold Baines | .10 |
| 591 Bill Buckner | .05 |
| 592 Carlton Fisk | .20 |
| 593 Rick Manning | .05 |
| 594 Doug Jones (R) | .15 |
| 595 Tom Candiotti | .08 |
| 596 Steve Lake | .05 |
| 597 Jose Lind (R) | .20 |
| 598 Ross Jones (R) | .12 |
| 599 Gary Matthews | .05 |
| 600 Fernando Valenzuela | .10 |

# 1989 Score . . . Complete Set of 660 Cards—Value $20.00 (Factory-Sealed Set—Value $25.00)

Features the rookie cards of Sandy Alomar, Jr., Ricky Jordan, Tom Gordon and Gary Sheffield. The set includes 9 Highlight cards and 32 Rookie Prospect cards.

| NO. | PLAYER | MINT | NO. | PLAYER | MINT | NO. | PLAYER | MINT | NO. | PLAYER | MINT |
|---|---|---|---|---|---|---|---|---|---|---|---|
| 1 | Jose Canseco | .50 | 69 | Steve Sax | .10 | 136 | Howard Johnson | .10 | 204 | Pat Sheridan | .05 |
| 2 | Andre Dawson | .15 | 70 | Rickey Henderson | .30 | 137 | Terry Pendleton | .08 | 205 | Don Baylor | .08 |
| 3 | Mark McGwire | .15 | 71 | Mitch Webster | .05 | 138 | Andy McGaffigan | .05 | 206 | Paul O'Neill | .08 |
| 4 | Benny Santiago | .08 | 72 | Rob Deer | .08 | 139 | Ken Oberkfell | .05 | 207 | Pete Smith | .05 |
| 5 | Rick Reuschel | .05 | 73 | Jim Presley | .05 | 140 | Butch Wynegar | .05 | 208 | Mark McLemore | .05 |
| 6 | Fred McGriff | .20 | 74 | Albert Hall | .05 | 141 | Rob Murphy | .05 | 209 | Henry Cotto | .05 |
| 7 | Kal Daniels | .08 | 75 | G. Brett (correct) | .15 | 142 | Rich Renteria | .10 | 210 | Kirk Gibson | .08 |
| 8 | Gary Gaetti | .10 | 75 | G. Brett (error) | .50 | 143 | Jose Guzman | .05 | 211 | Claudell Washington | .05 |
| 9 | Ellis Burks | .20 | 76 | Brian Downing | .08 | 144 | Andres Galarraga | .08 | 212 | Randy Bush | .05 |
| 10 | Darryl Strawberry | .30 | 77 | Dave Martinez | .05 | 145 | Rick Horton | .05 | 213 | Joe Carter | .12 |
| 11 | Julio Franco | .10 | 78 | Scott Fletcher | .05 | 146 | Frank DiPino | .05 | 214 | Bill Buckner | .08 |
| 12 | Lloyd Moseby | .12 | 79 | Phil Bradley | .08 | 147 | Glenn Braggs | .05 | 215 | Bert Blyleven | .10 |
| 13 | Jeff Pico (R) | .10 | 80 | Ozzie Smith | .15 | 148 | John Kruk | .08 | 216 | Brett Butler | .05 |
| 14 | Johnny Ray | .05 | 81 | Larry Sheets | .05 | 149 | Mike Schmidt | .35 | 217 | Lee Mazzilli | .05 |
| 15 | Cal Ripken, Jr. | .30 | 82 | Mike Aldrete | .05 | 150 | Lee Smith | .08 | 218 | Spike Owen | .05 |
| 16 | Dick Schofield | .05 | 83 | Darnell Coles | .05 | 151 | Robin Yount | .15 | 219 | Bill Swift | .05 |
| 17 | Mel Hall | .05 | 84 | Len Dykstra | .10 | 152 | Mark Eichhorn | .05 | 220 | Tim Wallach | .08 |
| 18 | Bill Ripken | .05 | 85 | Jim Rice | .08 | 153 | DeWayne Buice | .05 | 221 | David Cone | .08 |
| 19 | Brook Jacoby | .05 | 86 | Jeff Treadway | .05 | 154 | B.J. Surhoff | .08 | 222 | Don Carman | .05 |
| 20 | Kirby Puckett | .30 | 87 | Jose Lind | .05 | 155 | Vince Coleman | .10 | 223 | Rich Gossage | .08 |
| 21 | Bill Doran | .08 | 88 | Willie McGee | .08 | 156 | Tony Phillips | .05 | 224 | Bob Walk | .05 |
| 22 | Pete O'Brien | .05 | 89 | Mickey Brantley | .05 | 157 | Willie Fraser | .05 | 225 | Dave Righetti | .10 |
| 23 | Matt Nokes | .08 | 90 | Tony Gwynn | .20 | 158 | Lance McCullers | .08 | 226 | Kevin Bass | .08 |
| 24 | Brian Fisher | .05 | 91 | R.J. Reynolds | .05 | 159 | Greg Gagne | .05 | 227 | Kevin Gross | .05 |
| 25 | Jack Clark | .08 | 92 | Milt Thompson | .05 | 160 | Jesse Barfield | .08 | 228 | Tim Burke | .05 |
| 26 | Gary Petis | .05 | 93 | Kevin McReynolds | .10 | 161 | Mark Langston | .10 | 229 | Rick Mahler | .05 |
| 27 | Dave Valle | .05 | 94 | Eddie Murray | .15 | 162 | Kurt Stillwell | .05 | 230 | Lou Whitaker | .08 |
| 28 | Willie Wilson | .08 | 95 | Lance Parrish | .10 | 163 | Dion James | .05 | 231 | Luis Alicea (R) | .15 |
| 29 | Curt Young | .05 | 96 | Ron Kittle | .08 | 164 | Glenn Davis | .10 | 232 | Roberto Alomar | .50 |
| 30 | Dale Murphy | .15 | 97 | Gerald Young | .08 | 165 | Walt Weiss | .08 | 233 | Bob Boone | .05 |
| 31 | Barry Larkin | .15 | 98 | Ernie Whitt | .05 | 166 | Dave Concepcion | .05 | 234 | Dickie Thon | .05 |
| 32 | Dave Stewart | .08 | 99 | Jeff Reed | .05 | 167 | Alfredo Griffin | .05 | 235 | Shawon Dunston | .10 |
| 33 | Mike LaValliere | .05 | 100 | Don Mattingly | .25 | 168 | Don Heinkel (R) | .10 | 236 | Pete Stanicek | .05 |
| 34 | Glen Hubbard | .05 | 101 | Gerald Perry | .08 | 169 | Luis Rivera | .05 | 237 | Craig Biggio (R) | .35 |
| 35 | Ryne Sandberg | .35 | 102 | Vance Law | .05 | 170 | Shane Rawley | .05 | 238 | Dennis Boyd | .08 |
| 36 | Tony Pena | .08 | 103 | John Shelby | .05 | 171 | Darrell Evans | .05 | 239 | Tom Candiotti | .08 |
| 37 | Greg Walker | .05 | 104 | Chris Sabo (R) | .50 | 172 | Robby Thompson | .05 | 240 | Gary Carter | .08 |
| 38 | Von Hayes | .08 | 105 | Danny Tartabull | .10 | 173 | Jody Davis | .05 | 241 | Mike Stanley | .05 |
| 39 | Kevin Mitchell | .20 | 106 | Glenn Wilson | .05 | 174 | Andy Van Slyke | .12 | 242 | Ken Phelps | .05 |
| 40 | Tim Raines | .10 | 107 | Mark Davidson | .05 | 175 | Wade Boggs | .20 | 243 | Chris Bosio | .05 |
| 41 | Keith Hernandez | .10 | 108 | Dave Parker | .10 | 176 | Garry Templeton | .05 | 244 | Les Straker | .05 |
| 42 | Keith Moreland | .05 | 109 | Eric Davis | .12 | 177 | Gary Redus | .05 | 245 | Dave Smith | .05 |
| 43 | Ruben Sierra | .20 | 110 | Alan Trammell | .10 | 178 | Craig Lefferts | .05 | 246 | John Candelaria | .05 |
| 44 | Chet Lemon | .05 | 111 | Ozzie Virgil | .05 | 179 | Carney Lansford | .08 | 247 | Joe Orsulak | .05 |
| 45 | Willie Randolph | .08 | 112 | Frank Tanana | .08 | 180 | Ron Darling | .10 | 248 | Storm Davis | .05 |
| 46 | Andy Allanson | .05 | 113 | Rafael Ramirez | .05 | 181 | Kirk McCaskill | .05 | 249 | Floyd Bannister | .05 |
| 47 | Candy Maldonado | .10 | 114 | Dennis Martinez | .05 | 182 | Tony Armas | .05 | 250 | Jack Morris | .10 |
| 48 | Sid Bream | .05 | 115 | Jose DeLeon | .05 | 183 | Steve Farr | .05 | 251 | Bret Saberhagen | .10 |
| 49 | Denny Walling | .05 | 116 | Bob Ojeda | .08 | 184 | Tom Brunansky | .08 | 252 | Tom Niedenfuer | .05 |
| 50 | Dave Winfield | .15 | 117 | Doug Drabek | .10 | 185 | Bryan Harvey (R) | .25 | 253 | Neal Heaton | .05 |
| 51 | Alvin Davis | .08 | 118 | Andy Hawkins | .05 | 186 | Mike Marshall | .08 | 254 | Eric Show | .05 |
| 52 | Cory Snyder | .10 | 119 | Greg Maddux | .10 | 187 | Bo Diaz | .05 | 255 | Juan Samuel | .08 |
| 53 | Hubie Brooks | .05 | 120 | Cecil Fielder | .30 | 188 | Willie Upshaw | .05 | 256 | Dale Sveum | .08 |
| 54 | Chili Davis | .08 | 121 | Mike Scioscia | .05 | 189 | Mike Pagliarulo | .10 | 257 | Jim Gott | .05 |
| 55 | Kevin Seitzer | .10 | 122 | Dan Petry | .05 | 190 | Mike Krukow | .08 | 258 | Scott Garrelts | .05 |
| 56 | Jose Uribe | .05 | 123 | Terry Kennedy | .05 | 191 | Tommy Herr | .05 | 259 | Larry McWilliams | .05 |
| 57 | Tony Fernandez | .10 | 124 | Kelly Downs | .05 | 192 | Jim Pankovits | .05 | 260 | Steve Bedrosian | .08 |
| 58 | Tim Teufel | .05 | 125 | Greg Gross | .05 | 193 | Dwight Evans | .08 | 261 | Jack Howell | .08 |
| 59 | Oddibe McDowell | .08 | 126 | Fred Lynn | .08 | 194 | Kelly Gruber | .10 | 262 | Jay Tibbs | .05 |
| 60 | Les Lancaster | .05 | 127 | Barry Bonds | .30 | 195 | Bobby Bonilla | .20 | 263 | Jamie Moyer | .05 |
| 61 | Billy Hatcher | .05 | 128 | Harold Baines | .08 | 196 | Wallace Johnson | .05 | 264 | Doug Sisk | .05 |
| 62 | Dan Gladden | .05 | 129 | Doyle Alexander | .05 | 197 | Dave Stieb | .08 | 265 | Todd Worrell | .08 |
| 63 | Marty Barrett | .05 | 130 | Kevin Elster | .08 | 198 | Pat Borders (R) | .15 | 266 | John Farrell | .05 |
| 64 | Nick Esasky | .10 | 131 | Mike Heath | .05 | 199 | Rafael Palmeiro | .12 | 267 | Dave Collins | .05 |
| 65 | Wally Joyner | .15 | 132 | Teddy Higuera | .05 | 200 | Doc Gooden | .15 | 268 | Sid Fernandez | .08 |
| 66 | Mike Greenwell | .15 | 133 | Charlie Leibrandt | .08 | 201 | Pete Incaviglia | .08 | 269 | Tom Brookens | .05 |
| 67 | Ken Williams | .05 | 134 | Tim Laudner | .05 | 202 | Chris James | .08 | 270 | Shane Mack | .05 |
| 68 | Bob Horner | .05 | 135 | Ray Knight (correct) | .15 | 203 | Marvell Wynne | .05 | 271 | Paul Kilgus | .05 |
|  |  |  | 135 | Ray Knight (error) | .75 |  |  |  |  |  |  |

| NO. | PLAYER | MINT |
|---|---|---|
| 272 | Chuck Crim | .05 |
| 273 | Bob Knepper | .05 |
| 274 | Mike Moore | .05 |
| 275 | Guillermo Hernandez | .05 |
| 276 | Dennis Eckersley | .10 |
| 277 | Craig Nettles | .10 |
| 278 | Rich Dotson | .08 |
| 279 | Larry Herndon | .05 |
| 280 | Gene Larkin | .05 |
| 281 | Roger McDowell | .05 |
| 282 | Greg Swindell | .10 |
| 283 | Juan Agosto | .05 |
| 284 | Jeff Robinson | .15 |
| 285 | Mike Dunne | .05 |
| 286 | Greg Mathews | .05 |
| 287 | Kent Tekulve | .05 |
| 288 | Jerry Mumphrey | .05 |
| 289 | Jack McDowell | .20 |
| 290 | Frank Viola | .08 |
| 291 | Mark Gubicza | .10 |
| 292 | Dave Schmidt | .05 |
| 293 | Mike Henneman | .05 |
| 294 | Jimmy Jones | .05 |
| 295 | Charlie Hough | .08 |
| 296 | Rafael Santana | .05 |
| 297 | Chris Speier | .05 |
| 298 | Mike Witt | .08 |
| 299 | Pascual Perez | .05 |
| 300 | Nolan Ryan | .50 |
| 301 | Mitch Williams | .05 |
| 302 | Mookie Wilson | .08 |
| 303 | Mackey Sasser | .08 |
| 304 | John Cerutti | .05 |
| 305 | Jeff Reardon | .08 |
| 306 | Randy Myers | .08 |
| 307 | Greg Brock | .05 |
| 308 | Bob Welch | .08 |
| 309 | Jeff Robinson | .05 |
| 310 | Harold Reynolds | .08 |
| 311 | Jim Walewander | .05 |
| 312 | Dave Magadan | .10 |
| 313 | Jim Gantner | .05 |
| 314 | Walt Terrell | .05 |
| 315 | Wally Backman | .05 |
| 316 | Luis Salazar | .05 |
| 317 | Rick Rhoden | .05 |
| 318 | Tom Henke | .05 |
| 319 | Mike Macfarlane (R) | .12 |
| 320 | Dan Plesac | .05 |
| 321 | Calvin Schiraldi | .05 |
| 322 | Stan Javier | .05 |
| 323 | Devon White | .10 |
| 324 | Scott Bradley | .05 |
| 325 | Bruce Hurst | .15 |
| 326 | Manny Lee | .05 |
| 327 | Rick Aguilera | .05 |
| 328 | Bruce Ruffin | .05 |
| 329 | Ed Whitson | .05 |
| 330 | Bo Jackson | .50 |
| 331 | Ivan Calderon | .10 |
| 332 | Mickey Hatcher | .05 |
| 333 | Barry Jones | .05 |
| 334 | Ron Hassey | .05 |
| 335 | Bill Wegman | .05 |
| 336 | Damon Berryhill | .08 |
| 337 | Steve Ontiveros | .05 |
| 338 | Dan Pasqua | .08 |
| 339 | Bill Pecota | .05 |
| 340 | Greg Cadaret | .08 |
| 341 | Scott Bankhead | .05 |
| 342 | Ron Guidry | .08 |
| 343 | Danny Heep | .05 |
| 344 | Bob Brower | .05 |
| 345 | Rich Gedman | .05 |
| 346 | Nelson Santovenia (R) | .12 |
| 347 | George Bell | .10 |
| 348 | Ted Power | .05 |
| 349 | Mark Grant | .05 |
| 350 | R. Clemens (correct) | .40 |
| 350 | R. Clemens (error) | 3.50 |
| 351 | Bill Long | .05 |
| 352 | Jay Bell | .10 |
| 353 | Steve Balboni | .05 |
| 354 | Bob Kipper | .05 |
| 355 | Steve Jeltz | .05 |
| 356 | Jesse Orosco | .05 |
| 357 | Bob Dernier | .05 |
| 358 | Mickey Tettleton | .05 |
| 359 | Duane Ward | .05 |
| 360 | Darrin Jackson | .10 |
| 361 | Rey Quinones | .05 |
| 362 | Mark Grace | .30 |
| 363 | Steve Lake | .05 |
| 364 | Pat Perry | .05 |
| 365 | Terry Steinbach | .08 |
| 366 | Alan Ashby | .05 |
| 367 | Jeff Montgomery | .05 |
| 368 | Steve Buechele | .05 |
| 369 | Chris Brown | .08 |
| 370 | Orel Hershiser | .10 |
| 371 | Todd Benzinger | .10 |
| 372 | Ron Gant | .40 |
| 373 | Paul Assenmacher | .05 |
| 374 | Joey Meyer | .08 |
| 375 | Neil Allen | .05 |
| 376 | Mike Davis | .05 |
| 377 | Jeff Parrett | .08 |
| 378 | Jay Howell | .08 |
| 379 | Rafael Belliard | .05 |
| 380 | Luis Polonia | .08 |
| 381 | Keith Atherton | .05 |
| 382 | Kent Hrbek | .08 |
| 383 | Bob Stanley | .05 |
| 384 | Dave LaPoint | .05 |
| 385 | Rance Mulliniks | .05 |
| 386 | Melido Perez | .08 |
| 387 | Doug Jones | .05 |
| 388 | Steve Lyons | .05 |
| 389 | Alejandro Pena | .08 |
| 390 | Frank White | .05 |
| 391 | Pat Tabler | .08 |
| 392 | Eric Plunk | .05 |
| 393 | Mike Maddux | .05 |
| 394 | Allan Anderson | .08 |
| 395 | Bob Brenly | .05 |
| 396 | Rick Cerone | .05 |
| 397 | Scott Terry | .05 |
| 398 | Mike Jackson | .05 |
| 399 | Bobby Thigpen | .05 |
| 400 | Don Sutton | .10 |
| 401 | Cecil Espy | .08 |
| 402 | Junior Ortiz | .05 |
| 403 | Mike Smithson | .05 |
| 404 | Bud Black | .05 |
| 405 | Tom Foley | .05 |
| 406 | Andres Thomas | .05 |
| 407 | Rick Sutcliffe | .10 |
| 408 | Brian Harper | .05 |
| 409 | John Smoley | .08 |
| 410 | Juan Nieves | .05 |
| 411 | Shawn Abner | .05 |
| 412 | Wes Gardner | .05 |
| 413 | Darren Daulton | .05 |
| 414 | Juan Berenguer | .05 |
| 415 | Charles Hudson | .08 |
| 416 | Rick Honeycutt | .05 |
| 417 | Greg Booker | .05 |
| 418 | Tim Belcher | .10 |
| 419 | Don August | .15 |
| 420 | Dale Mohorcic | .05 |
| 421 | Steve Lombardozzi | .05 |
| 422 | Atlee Hammaker | .05 |
| 423 | Jerry Don Gleaton | .05 |
| 424 | Scott Bailes | .05 |
| 425 | Bruce Sutter | .08 |
| 426 | Randy Ready | .05 |
| 427 | Jerry Reed | .05 |
| 428 | Bryn Smith | .05 |
| 429 | Tim Leary | .10 |
| 430 | Mark Clear | .05 |
| 431 | Terry Leach | .05 |
| 432 | John Moses | .05 |
| 433 | Ozzie Guillen | .08 |
| 434 | Gene Nelson | .05 |
| 435 | Gary Ward | .05 |
| 436 | Luis Aguayo | .05 |
| 437 | Fernando Valenzuela | .10 |
| 438 | Jeff Russell | .05 |
| 439 | Cecilio Guante | .05 |
| 440 | Don Robinson | .05 |
| 441 | Rick Anderson | .05 |
| 442 | Tom Glavine | .30 |
| 443 | Daryl Boston | .05 |
| 444 | Joe Price | .05 |
| 445 | Stewart Cliburn | .05 |
| 446 | Manny Trillo | .05 |
| 447 | Joel Skinner | .05 |
| 448 | Charlie Puleo | .05 |
| 449 | Carlton Fisk | .15 |
| 450 | Will Clark | .40 |
| 451 | Otis Nixon | .05 |
| 452 | Rick Schu | .05 |
| 453 | Todd Stottlemyre | .15 |
| 454 | Tim Birtsas | .05 |
| 455 | Dave Gallagher (R) | .10 |
| 456 | Barry Lyons | .05 |
| 457 | Fred Manrique | .05 |
| 458 | Ernest Riles | .05 |
| 459 | Doug Jennings (R) | .10 |
| 460 | Joe Magrane | .10 |
| 461 | Jamie Quirk | .05 |
| 462 | Jack Armstrong (R) | .12 |
| 463 | Bobby Witt | .05 |
| 464 | Keith Miller | .05 |
| 465 | Todd Burns (R) | .10 |
| 466 | John Dopson (R) | .10 |
| 467 | Rich Yett | .05 |
| 468 | Craig Reynolds | .05 |
| 469 | Dave Bergman | .05 |
| 470 | Rex Hudler | .08 |
| 471 | Eric King | .05 |
| 472 | Joaquin Andujar | .05 |
| 473 | Sil Campusano (R) | .10 |
| 474 | Terry Mulholland | .05 |
| 475 | Mike Flanagan | .05 |
| 476 | Greg Harris | .08 |
| 477 | Tommy John | .10 |
| 478 | Dave Anderson | .05 |
| 479 | Fred Toliver | .05 |
| 480 | Jimmy Key | .08 |
| 481 | Donell Nixon | .05 |
| 482 | Mark Portugal | .05 |
| 483 | Tom Pagnozzi | .05 |
| 484 | Jeff Kunkel | .05 |
| 485 | Frank Williams | .05 |
| 486 | Jody Reed | .10 |
| 487 | Roberto Kelly | .15 |
| 488 | Shawn Hillegas | .05 |
| 489 | Jerry Reuss | .05 |
| 490 | Mark Davis | .05 |
| 491 | Jeff Sellers | .05 |
| 492 | Zane Smith | .05 |
| 493 | Al Newman | .05 |
| 494 | Mike Young | .05 |
| 495 | Larry Parrish | .05 |
| 496 | Herm Winningham | .05 |
| 497 | Carmen Castillo | .05 |
| 498 | Joe Hesketh | .05 |
| 499 | Darrell Miller | .05 |
| 500 | Mike LaCoss | .05 |
| 501 | Charlie Lea | .05 |
| 502 | Bruce Benedict | .05 |
| 503 | Chuck Finley | .10 |
| 504 | Brad Wellman | .05 |
| 505 | Tim Crews | .05 |
| 506 | Ken Gerhart | .05 |
| 507 | Brian Holton | .05 |
| 508 | Dennis Lamp | .05 |
| 509 | Bobby Meacham | .05 |
| 510 | Tracy Jones | .05 |
| 511 | Mike Fitzgerald | .05 |
| 512 | Jeff Bittiger (R) | .10 |
| 513 | Tim Flannery | .05 |
| 514 | Ray Hayward | .05 |
| 515 | Dave Leiper | .05 |
| 516 | Rod Scurry | .05 |
| 517 | Carmelo Martinez | .05 |
| 518 | Curtis Wilkerson | .05 |
| 519 | Stan Jefferson | .08 |
| 520 | Dan Quisenberry | .08 |
| 521 | Lloyd McClendon | .08 |
| 522 | Steve Trout | .05 |
| 523 | Larry Andersen | .05 |
| 524 | Don Aase | .05 |
| 525 | Bob Forsch | .05 |
| 526 | Geno Petralli | .05 |
| 527 | Angel Salazar | .05 |
| 528 | Mike Schooler (R) | .12 |
| 529 | Jose Oquendo | .05 |
| 530 | Jay Buhner | .15 |
| 531 | Tom Bolton | .08 |
| 532 | Al Nipper | .05 |
| 533 | Dave Henderson | .08 |
| 534 | John Costello (R) | .12 |
| 535 | Donnie Moore | .05 |
| 536 | Mike Laga | .05 |
| 537 | Mike Gallego | .05 |
| 538 | Jim Clancy | .05 |
| 539 | Joel Youngblood | .05 |
| 540 | Rick Leach | .05 |
| 541 | Kevin Romine | .05 |
| 542 | Mark Salas | .05 |
| 543 | Greg Minton | .05 |
| 544 | Dave Palmer | .05 |
| 545 | Dwayne Murphy | .05 |
| 546 | Jim Deshaies | .05 |
| 547 | Don Gordon | .10 |
| 548 | Ricky Jordan (R) | .20 |
| 549 | Mike Boddicker | .08 |
| 550 | Mike Scott | .08 |
| 551 | Jeff Ballard | .08 |
| 552 | Jose Rijo | .15 |
| 552 | Jose Rijo (error) | .75 |
| 553 | Danny Darwin | .05 |
| 554 | Tom Browning | .08 |
| 555 | Danny Jackson | .08 |
| 556 | Rick Dempsey | .05 |
| 557 | Jeffrey Leonard | .05 |
| 558 | Jeff Musselman | .05 |
| 559 | Ron Robinson | .08 |
| 560 | John Tudor | .05 |
| 561 | Don Slaught | .05 |
| 562 | Dennis Rasmussen | .05 |
| 563 | Brady Anderson (R) | .10 |
| 564 | Pedro Guerrero | .10 |
| 565 | Paul Molitor | .08 |
| 566 | Terry Clark (R) | .15 |
| 567 | Terry Puhl | .05 |
| 568 | Mike Campbell | .05 |
| 569 | Paul Mirabella | .05 |
| 570 | Jeff Hamilton | .05 |
| 571 | Oswald Peraza (R) | .10 |
| 572 | Bob McClure | .05 |
| 573 | Jose Bautista (R) | .10 |
| 574 | Alex Trevino | .05 |
| 575 | John Franco | .08 |
| 576 | Mark Parent (R) | .10 |
| 577 | Nelson Liriano | .05 |
| 578 | Steve Shields | .05 |
| 579 | Odell Jones | .05 |
| 580 | Al Leiter | .10 |
| 581 | Dave Stapleton | .05 |
| 582 | '88 World Series | .15 |
| 583 | Donnie Hill | .05 |
| 584 | Chuck Jackson | .05 |
| 585 | Rene Gonzales | .05 |
| 586 | Tracy Woodson | .08 |
| 587 | Jim Adduci | .08 |
| 588 | Mario Soto | .05 |
| 589 | Jeff Blauser | .05 |
| 590 | Jim Traber | .05 |
| 591 | Jon Perlman | .05 |
| 592 | Mark Williamson | .10 |
| 593 | Dave Meads | .05 |
| 594 | Jim Eisenreich | .05 |
| 595 | P. Gibson (err.) (R) | 1.00 |
| 595 | P. Gibson (cor.) (R) | .12 |
| 596 | Mike Birkbeck | .05 |
| 597 | Terry Francona | .05 |
| 598 | Paul Zuvella | .05 |
| 599 | Franklin Stubbs | .05 |
| 600 | Gregg Jefferies | .30 |
| 601 | John Cangelosi | .05 |

| NO. | PLAYER | MINT |
|-----|--------|------|
| 602 | Mike Sharperson | .05 |
| 603 | Mike Diaz | .05 |
| 604 | Gary Varsho (R) | .10 |
| 605 | Terry Blocker (R) | .10 |
| 606 | Charlie O'Brien | .05 |
| 607 | Jim Eppard | .08 |
| 608 | John Davis | .05 |
| 609 | Ken Griffey, Sr. | .10 |
| 610 | Buddy Bell | .05 |
| 611 | Ted Simmons | .05 |
| 612 | Matt Williams | .20 |
| 613 | Danny Cox | .05 |
| 614 | Al Pedrique | .05 |
| 615 | Ron Oester | .05 |
| 616 | John Smoltz (R) | .60 |
| 617 | Bob Melvin | .05 |
| 618 | Rob Dibble (R) | .25 |

| NO. | PLAYER | MINT |
|-----|--------|------|
| 619 | Kirt Manwaring | .05 |
| **No. 620 to 651 (Rookie Prospects)** | | |
| 620 | Felix Fermin | .10 |
| 621 | Doug Dascenzo (R) | .10 |
| 622 | Bill Brennan (R) | .10 |
| 623 | Carlos Quintana (R) | .35 |
| 624 | Mike Harkey (R) | .15 |
| 625 | Gary Sheffield (R) | .30 |
| 626 | Tom Prince | .10 |
| 627 | Steve Searcy (R) | .12 |
| 628 | Charlie Hayes (R) | .15 |
| 629 | Felix Jose (R) | .75 |
| 630 | Sandy Alomar (R) | .50 |
| 631 | Derek Lilliquist (R) | .12 |
| 632 | Geronimo Berroa | .08 |
| 633 | Luis Medina (R) | .10 |
| 634 | Tom Gordon (R) | .20 |

| NO. | PLAYER | MINT |
|-----|--------|------|
| 635 | Ramon Martinez (R) | 1.00 |
| 636 | Craig Worthington (R) | .10 |
| 637 | Edgar Martinez | .25 |
| 638 | Chad Krueter (R) | .10 |
| 639 | Ron Jones (R) | .10 |
| 640 | Van Snider (R) | .10 |
| 641 | Lance Blankenship (R) | .10 |
| 642 | Dwight Smith (R) | .15 |
| 643 | Cameron Drew (R) | .10 |
| 644 | Jerald Clark (R) | .20 |
| 645 | Randy Johnson (R) | .35 |
| 646 | Norm Charlton (R) | .15 |
| 647 | Todd Frohwirth | .08 |
| 648 | Luis De los Santos (R) | .12 |
| 649 | Tim Jones (R) | .10 |
| 650 | Dave West (R) | .12 |
| 651 | Bob Milacki (R) | .20 |

| NO. | PLAYER | MINT |
|-----|--------|------|
| 652 | Highlight—Wrigley Field—night opener | .12 |
| 653 | Highlight—Hershiser—scoreless inning record | .10 |
| 654 | Highlight—Boggs—6 yrs. consecutive 200 hits | .15 |
| 654 | HL Boggs (error) | 4.00 |
| 655 | Highlight—Canseco 40 hr's, 40 stolen bases | .25 |
| 656 | Highlight—Jones—saves | .05 |
| 657 | Highlight—Henderson—lead off homers | .20 |
| 658 | Highlight—Browning—perfect game | .10 |
| 659 | Highlight—Greenwell—A.L. game-winning record | .10 |
| 660 | Highlight—Red Sox—24 home game-winning streak | .10 |

## 1989 Score Traded & Rookie.... Complete Set of 110 Cards—Value $15.00

Updates the main 1989 card set with players who changed teams during the season, and rookies. Features the first Score card of Jerome Walton, Jim Abbott and Ken Griffey, Jr.

| NO. | PLAYER | MINT |
|-----|--------|------|
| 1 | Rafael Palmeiro | .20 |
| 2 | Nolan Ryan | 1.25 |
| 3 | Jack Clark | .10 |
| 4 | Dave LaPoint | .05 |
| 5 | Mike Moore | .05 |
| 6 | Pete O'Brien | .05 |
| 7 | Jeffrey Leonard | .05 |
| 8 | Rob Murphy | .05 |
| 9 | Tom Herr | .05 |
| 10 | Claudell Washington | .05 |
| 11 | Mike Pagliarulo | .05 |
| 12 | Steve Lake | .05 |
| 13 | Spike Owen | .05 |
| 14 | Andy Hawkins | .05 |
| 15 | Todd Benzinger | .05 |
| 16 | Mookie Wilson | .05 |
| 17 | Bert Blyleven | .10 |
| 18 | Jeff Treadway | .05 |
| 19 | Bruce Hurst | .05 |
| 20 | Steve Sax | .15 |
| 21 | Juan Samuel | .05 |
| 22 | Jesse Barfield | .05 |
| 23 | Carmelo Castillo | .05 |
| 24 | Terry Leach | .05 |
| 25 | Mark Langston | .15 |
| 26 | Eric King | .05 |
| 27 | Steve Balboni | .05 |
| 28 | Len Dykstra | .05 |

| NO. | PLAYER | MINT |
|-----|--------|------|
| 29 | Keith Moreland | .05 |
| 30 | Terry Kennedy | .05 |
| 31 | Eddie Murray | .12 |
| 32 | Mitch Williams | .15 |
| 33 | Jeff Parrett | .05 |
| 34 | Wally Backman | .05 |
| 35 | Julio Franco | .10 |
| 36 | Lance Parrish | .05 |
| 37 | Nick Esasky | .10 |
| 38 | Luis Polonia | .05 |
| 39 | Kevin Gross | .05 |
| 40 | John Dopson | .05 |
| 41 | Willie Randolph | .05 |
| 42 | Jim Clancy | .05 |
| 43 | Tracy Jones | .05 |
| 44 | Phil Bradley | .05 |
| 45 | Milt Thompson | .05 |
| 46 | Chris James | .05 |
| 47 | Scott Fletcher | .05 |
| 48 | Kal Daniels | .10 |
| 49 | Steve Bedrosian | .05 |
| 50 | Rickey Henderson | .30 |
| 51 | Dion James | .05 |
| 52 | Tim Leary | .05 |
| 53 | Roger Mcdowell | .05 |
| 54 | Mel Hall | .05 |
| 55 | Dickie Thon | .05 |

| NO. | PLAYER | MINT |
|-----|--------|------|
| 56 | Zane Smith | .05 |
| 57 | Danny Heep | .05 |
| 58 | Bob McClure | .05 |
| 59 | Brian Holton | .05 |
| 60 | Randy Ready | .05 |
| 61 | Bob Melvin | .05 |
| 62 | Harold Baines | .05 |
| 63 | Lance McCullers | .05 |
| 64 | Jody Davis | .05 |
| 65 | Darrell Evans | .05 |
| 66 | Joel Youngblood | .05 |
| 67 | Frank Viola | .08 |
| 68 | Mike Aldrete | .05 |
| 69 | Greg Cadaret | .05 |
| 70 | John Kruk | .05 |
| 71 | Pat Sheridan | .05 |
| 72 | Oddibe McDowell | .05 |
| 73 | Tom Brookens | .05 |
| 74 | Bob Boone | .05 |
| 75 | Walt Terrell | .05 |
| 76 | Joel Skinner | .05 |
| 77 | Randy Johnson | .05 |
| 78 | Felix Fermin | .05 |
| 79 | Rick Mahler | .05 |
| 80 | Rich Dotson | .05 |
| 81 | Cris Carpenter (R) | .12 |
| 82 | Bill Spiers (R) | .12 |

| NO. | PLAYER | MINT |
|-----|--------|------|
| 83 | Junior Felix (R) | .20 |
| 84 | Joe Girardi (R) | .12 |
| 85 | Jerome Walton (R) | .40 |
| 86 | Greg Litton (R) | .12 |
| 87 | Greg Harris (R) | .20 |
| 88 | Jim Abbott (R) | 1.25 |
| 89 | Kevin Brown | .12 |
| 90 | John Wetteland (R) | .12 |
| 91 | Gary Wayne (R) | .12 |
| 92 | Rich Monteleone (R) | .12 |
| 93 | Bob Geren (R) | .10 |
| 94 | Clay Parker | .10 |
| 95 | Steve Finley (R) | .30 |
| 96 | Gregg Olson (R) | .60 |
| 97 | Ken Patterson (R) | .10 |
| 98 | Ken Hill (R) | .25 |
| 99 | Scott Scudder (R) | .25 |
| 100 | Ken Griffey. Jr. (R) | 6.00 |
| 101 | Jeff Brantley (R) | .25 |
| 102 | Donn Pall (R) | .12 |
| 103 | Carlos Martinez (R) | .20 |
| 104 | Joe Oliver (R) | .30 |
| 105 | Omar Vizquel (R) | .10 |
| 106 | Joey Belle (R) | 2.00 |
| 107 | Kenny Rogers (R) | .15 |
| 108 | Mark Carreon | .08 |
| 109 | Rolando Roomes (R) | .10 |
| 110 | Pete Harnish (R) | .30 |

# 1990 Score . . . Complete Set of 704 Cards—Value $22.00

The set was increased from 660 to 704 cards. New features this year include 22 First Round Draft Pick cards, 13 Dream Team cards (styled after the 1911 T-206 cards), 4 World Series cards and 5 Highlight cards.

| NO. | PLAYER | MINT |
|---|---|---|
| 1 | Don Mattingly | .25 |
| 2 | Cal Ripken, Jr. | .30 |
| 3 | Dwight Evans | .08 |
| 4 | Barry Bonds | .20 |
| 5 | Kevin McReynolds | .08 |
| 6 | Ozzie Guillen | .08 |
| 7 | Terry Kennedy | .05 |
| 8 | Bryan Harvey | .05 |
| 9 | Alan Trammell | .08 |
| 10 | Cory Snyder | .08 |
| 11 | Jody Reed | .05 |
| 12 | Roberto Alomar | .15 |
| 13 | Pedro Guerrero | .08 |
| 14 | Gary Redus | .05 |
| 15 | Marty Barrett | .05 |
| 16 | Ricky Jordan | .08 |
| 17 | Joe Magrane | .08 |
| 18 | Sid Fernandez | .08 |
| 19 | Rich Dotson | .05 |
| 20 | Jack Clark | .08 |
| 21 | Bob Walk | .05 |
| 22 | Ron Karkovice | .05 |
| 23 | Lenny Harris | .08 |
| 24 | Phil Bradley | .08 |
| 25 | Andres Galarraga | .08 |
| 26 | Brian Downing | .05 |
| 27 | Dave Martinez | .05 |
| 28 | Eric King | .05 |
| 29 | Barry Lyons | .05 |
| 30 | Dave Schmidt | .08 |
| 31 | Mike Boddicker | .08 |
| 32 | Tom Foley | .05 |
| 33 | Brady Anderson | .05 |
| 34 | Jim Presley | .05 |
| 35 | Lance Parrish | .08 |
| 36 | Von Hayes | .08 |
| 37 | Lee Smith | .08 |
| 38 | Herm Winningham | .05 |
| 39 | Alejandro Pena | .05 |
| 40 | Mike Scott | .08 |
| 41 | Joe Orsulak | .05 |
| 42 | Rafael Ramirez | .05 |
| 43 | Gerald Young | .08 |
| 44 | Dick Schofield | .05 |
| 45 | Dve Smith | .05 |
| 46 | Dave Magadan | .08 |
| 47 | Dennis Martinez | .05 |
| 48 | Greg Minton | .05 |
| 49 | Milt Thompson | .05 |
| 50 | Orel Hershiser | .08 |
| 51 | Bip Roberts | .05 |
| 52 | Jerry Browne | .08 |
| 53 | Bob Ojeda | .05 |
| 54 | Fernando Valenzuela | .10 |
| 55 | Matt Nokes | .05 |
| 56 | Brook Jacoby | .05 |
| 57 | Frank Tanana | .05 |
| 58 | Scott Fletcher | .05 |
| 59 | Ron Oester | .05 |
| 60 | Bob Boone | .05 |
| 61 | Dan Gladden | .05 |
| 62 | Darnell Coles | .05 |
| 63 | Gregg Olson | .10 |
| 64 | Todd Burns | .05 |

| NO. | PLAYER | MINT |
|---|---|---|
| 65 | Todd Benzinger | .08 |
| 66 | Dale Murphy | .12 |
| 67 | Mike Flanagan | .05 |
| 68 | Jose Oquendo | .05 |
| 69 | Cecil Espy | .05 |
| 70 | Chris Sabo | .10 |
| 71 | Shane Rawley | .05 |
| 72 | Tom Brunansky | .05 |
| 73 | Vance Law | .05 |
| 74 | B.J. Surhoff | .05 |
| 75 | Lou Whitaker | .08 |
| 76 | Ken Caminiti | .05 |
| 77 | Nelson Liriano | .05 |
| 78 | Tommy Gregg | .05 |
| 79 | Don Slaught | .05 |
| 80 | Eddie Murray | .10 |
| 81 | Joe Boever | .05 |
| 82 | Charlie Leibrandt | .05 |
| 83 | Jose Lind | .05 |
| 84 | Tony Phillips | .05 |
| 85 | Mitch Webster | .05 |
| 86 | Dan Plesac | .05 |
| 87 | Rick Mahler | .05 |
| 88 | Steve Lyons | .05 |
| 89 | Tony Fernandez | .10 |
| 90 | Ryne Sandberg | .25 |
| 91 | Nick Esasky | .05 |
| 92 | Luis Salazar | .05 |
| 93 | Pete Incaviglia | .08 |
| 94 | Ivan Calderon | .05 |
| 95 | Jeff Treadway | .05 |
| 96 | Kurt Stillwell | .05 |
| 97 | Gary Sheffield | .08 |
| 98 | Jeffrey Leonard | .05 |
| 99 | Andres Thomas | .05 |
| 100 | Roberto Kelly | .10 |
| 101 | Alvaro Espinoza | .05 |
| 102 | Greg Gagne | .05 |
| 103 | John Farrell | .08 |
| 104 | Willie Wilson | .08 |
| 105 | Glenn Braggs | .05 |
| 106 | Chet Lemon | .05 |
| 107 | J. Moyer (error) | .10 |
| 107 | J. Moyer (correct) | .35 |
| 108 | Chuck Crim | .05 |
| 109 | Dave Valle | .05 |
| 110 | Walt Weiss | .10 |
| 111 | Larry Sheets | .05 |
| 112 | Don Robinson | .05 |
| 113 | Danny Heep | .05 |
| 114 | Carmelo Martinez | .05 |
| 115 | Dave Gallagher | .05 |
| 116 | Mike LaValliere | .05 |
| 117 | Bob McClure | .05 |
| 118 | Rene Gonzales | .05 |
| 119 | Mark Parent | .05 |
| 120 | Wally Joyner | .10 |
| 121 | Mark Gubicza | .05 |
| 122 | Tony Pena | .08 |
| 123 | Carmelo Castillo | .05 |
| 124 | Howard Johnson | .10 |
| 125 | Steve Sax | .08 |
| 126 | Tim Belcher | .08 |
| 127 | Tim Burke | .05 |
| 128 | Al Newman | .05 |

| NO. | PLAYER | MINT |
|---|---|---|
| 129 | Dennis Rasmussen | .05 |
| 130 | Doug Jones | .05 |
| 131 | Fred Lynn | .08 |
| 132 | Jeff Hamilton | .05 |
| 133 | German Gonzalez | .05 |
| 134 | John Morris | .05 |
| 135 | Dave Parker | .10 |
| 136 | Gary Pettis | .05 |
| 137 | Dennis Boyd | .05 |
| 138 | Candy Maldonado | .05 |
| 139 | Rick Cerone | .05 |
| 140 | George Brett | .15 |
| 141 | Dave Clark | .05 |
| 142 | Dickie Thon | .05 |
| 143 | Junior Ortiz | .05 |
| 144 | Don August | .08 |
| 145 | Gary Gaetti | .10 |
| 146 | Kirt Manwaring | .05 |
| 147 | Jeff Reed | .05 |
| 148 | Jose Alvarez | .05 |
| 149 | Mike Schooler | .10 |
| 150 | Mark Grace | .12 |
| 151 | Geronimo Berroa | .07 |
| 152 | Barry Jones | .05 |
| 153 | Geno Petralli | .05 |
| 154 | Jim Deshaies | .05 |
| 155 | Barry Larkin | .12 |
| 156 | Alfredo Griffin | .08 |
| 157 | Tom Henke | .05 |
| 158 | Mike Jeffcoat | .05 |
| 159 | Bob Welch | .05 |
| 160 | Julio Franco | .10 |
| 161 | Henry Cotto | .05 |
| 162 | Terry Steinbach | .10 |
| 163 | Damon Berryhill | .08 |
| 164 | Tim Crews | .05 |
| 165 | Tom Browning | .05 |
| 166 | Fred Manrique | .05 |
| 167 | Harold Reynolds | .05 |
| 168 | R. Hassey (error) | .10 |
| 168 | R. Hassey (correct) | 1.25 |
| 169 | Shawon Dunston | .08 |
| 170 | Bobby Bonilla | .15 |
| 171 | Tom Herr | .05 |
| 172 | Mike Heath | .05 |
| 173 | Rich Gedman | .05 |
| 174 | Bill Ripken | .08 |
| 175 | Pete O'Brien | .08 |
| 176 | L. McClendon (err.) | 1.00 |
| 176 | L. McClendon (cor.) | .10 |
| 177 | Brian Holton | .05 |
| 178 | Jeff Blauser | .05 |
| 179 | Jim Eisenreich | .05 |
| 180 | Bert Blyleven | .08 |
| 181 | Rob Murphy | .05 |
| 182 | Bill Doran | .05 |
| 183 | Curt Ford | .05 |
| 184 | Mike Henneman | .05 |
| 185 | Eric Davis | .15 |
| 186 | Lance McCullers | .05 |
| 187 | Steve Davis (R) | .12 |
| 188 | Bill Wegman | .05 |
| 189 | Brian Harper | .05 |
| 190 | Mike Moore | .08 |
| 191 | Dale Mohorcic | .05 |
| 192 | Tim Wallach | .05 |

| NO. | PLAYER | MINT |
|---|---|---|
| 193 | Keith Hernandez | .08 |
| 194 | Dave Righetti | .10 |
| 195 | Bret Saberhagen | .10 |
| 196 | Paul Kilgus | .05 |
| 197 | Bud Black | .05 |
| 198 | Juan Samuel | .08 |
| 199 | Kevin Seitzer | .10 |
| 200 | Darryl Strawberry | .25 |
| 201 | Dave Stieb | .05 |
| 202 | Charlie Hough | .05 |
| 203 | Jack Morris | .10 |
| 204 | Rance Mulliniks | .05 |
| 205 | Alvin Davis | .08 |
| 206 | Jack Howell | .05 |
| 207 | Ken Patterson | .05 |
| 208 | Terry Pendleton | .05 |
| 209 | Craig Lefferts | .05 |
| 210 | Kevin Brown | .05 |
| 211 | Dan Petry | .05 |
| 212 | Dave Leiper | .05 |
| 213 | Daryl Boston | .05 |
| 214 | Kevin Hickey | .08 |
| 215 | Mike Krukow | .05 |
| 216 | Terry Francona | .05 |
| 217 | Mirk McCaskill | .08 |
| 218 | Scott Bailes | .05 |
| 219 | Bob Forsch | .05 |
| 220 | M. Aldrete (err.) | .10 |
| 220 | M. Aldrete (cor.) | .35 |
| 221 | Steve Buechele | .05 |
| 222 | Jesse Barfield | .05 |
| 223 | Juan Berenguer | .05 |
| 224 | Andy McGaffigan | .05 |
| 225 | Pete Smith | .05 |
| 226 | Mike Witt | .08 |
| 227 | Jay Howell | .08 |
| 228 | Scott Bradley | .05 |
| 229 | Jerome Walton | .10 |
| 230 | Greg Swindell | .10 |
| 231 | Atlee Hammaker | .05 |
| 232 | M. Devereaux (err.) | .10 |
| 232 | M. Devereaux (cor.) | 1.25 |
| 233 | Ken Hill | .08 |
| 234 | Craig Worthington | .08 |
| 235 | Scott Terry | .05 |
| 236 | Brett Butler | .05 |
| 237 | Doyle Alexander | .08 |
| 238 | Dave Anderson | .05 |
| 239 | Bob Milacki | .08 |
| 240 | Dwight Smith | .08 |
| 241 | Otis Nixon | .08 |
| 242 | Pat Tabler | .05 |
| 243 | Derek Lilliquist | .08 |
| 244 | Danny Tartabull | .08 |
| 245 | Wade Boggs | .15 |
| 246 | Scott Garrelts | .08 |
| 247 | Spike Owen | .05 |
| 248 | Norm Charlton | .05 |
| 249 | Gerald Perry | .05 |
| 250 | Nolan Ryan | .50 |
| 251 | Kevin Gross | .05 |
| 252 | Randy Milligan | .05 |
| 253 | Mike LaCoss | .05 |
| 254 | Dave Bergman | .05 |
| 255 | Tony Gwynn | .15 |
| 256 | Felix Fermin | .05 |

| NO. | PLAYER | MINT |
|-----|--------|------|
| 257 | Greg Harris | .10 |
| 258 | Junior Felix | .08 |
| 259 | Mark Davis | .08 |
| 260 | Vince Coleman | .10 |
| 261 | Paul Gibson | .05 |
| 262 | Mitch Williams | .08 |
| 263 | Jeff Russell | .05 |
| 264 | Omar Vizquel | .08 |
| 265 | Andre Dawson | .12 |
| 266 | Storm Davis | .05 |
| 267 | Guillermo Hernandez | .05 |
| 268 | Mike Felder | .05 |
| 269 | Tom Candiotti | .05 |
| 270 | Bruce Hurst | .05 |
| 271 | Fred McGriff | .12 |
| 272 | Glenn Davis | .08 |
| 273 | John Franco | .08 |
| 274 | Rich Yett | .08 |
| 275 | Craig Biggio | .10 |
| 276 | Gene Larkin | .05 |
| 277 | Rob Dibble | .08 |
| 278 | Randy Bush | .05 |
| 279 | Kevin Bass | .05 |
| 280 | Bo Jackson (error) | .35 |
| 280 | Bo Jackson (correct) | .75 |
| 281 | Wally Backman | .05 |
| 282 | Larry Andersen | .05 |
| 283 | Chris Bosio | .05 |
| 284 | Juan Agosto | .05 |
| 285 | Ozzie Smith | .12 |
| 286 | George Bell | .08 |
| 287 | Rex Hudler | .05 |
| 288 | Pat Borders | .05 |
| 289 | Danny Jackson | .10 |
| 290 | Carlton Fisk | .10 |
| 291 | Tracy Jones | .05 |
| 292 | Allan Anderson | .08 |
| 293 | Johnny Ray | .08 |
| 294 | Lee Guetterman | .05 |
| 295 | Paul O'Neill | .05 |
| 296 | Carney Lansford | .08 |
| 297 | Tom Brookens | .05 |
| 298 | Claudell Washington | .05 |
| 299 | Hubie Brooks | .05 |
| 300 | Will Clark | .25 |
| 301 | Kenny Rogers | .10 |
| 302 | Darrell Evans | .05 |
| 303 | Greg Briley | .08 |
| 304 | Donn Pall | .08 |
| 305 | Teddy Higuera | .05 |
| 306 | Dan Pasqua | .05 |
| 307 | Dave Winfield | .10 |
| 308 | Dennis Powell | .05 |
| 309 | Jose DeLeon | .05 |
| 310 | Roger Clemens | .30 |
| 311 | Melido Perez | .05 |
| 312 | Devon White | .08 |
| 313 | Doc Gooden | .15 |
| 314 | Carlos Martinez | .08 |
| 315 | Dennis Eckersley | .08 |
| 316 | Clay Parker | .08 |
| 317 | Rick Honeycutt | .05 |
| 318 | Tim Laudner | .05 |
| 319 | Joe Carter | .10 |
| 320 | Robin Yount | .15 |
| 321 | Felix Jose | .20 |
| 322 | Mickey Tettleton | .05 |
| 323 | Mike Gallego | .05 |
| 324 | Edgar Martinez | .10 |
| 325 | Dave Henderson | .08 |
| 326 | Chili Davis | .05 |
| 327 | Steve Balboni | .05 |
| 328 | Jody Davis | .05 |
| 329 | Shawn Hillegas | .05 |
| 330 | Jim Abbott | .20 |
| 331 | John Dopson | .08 |
| 332 | Mark Williamson | .05 |
| 333 | Jeff Robinson | .08 |
| 334 | John Smiley | .08 |
| 335 | Bobby Thigpen | .05 |
| 336 | Garry Templeton | .05 |
| 337 | Marvell Wynne | .05 |
| 338 | Ken Griffey, Sr. (cor.) | 1.50 |
| 338 | Ken Griffey, Sr. (error) | .15 |
| 339 | Steve Finley | .12 |
| 340 | Ellis Burks | .10 |

| NO. | PLAYER | MINT |
|-----|--------|------|
| 341 | Frank Williams | .05 |
| 342 | Mike Morgan | .05 |
| 343 | Kevin Mitchell | .10 |
| 344 | Joel Youngblood | .05 |
| 345 | Mike Greenwell | .12 |
| 346 | Glenn Wilson | .05 |
| 347 | John Costello | .05 |
| 348 | Wes Gardner | .05 |
| 349 | Jeff Ballard | .08 |
| 350 | Mark Thurmond | .05 |
| 351 | Randy Myers | .08 |
| 352 | Shawn Abner | .05 |
| 353 | Jesse Orosco | .05 |
| 354 | Greg Walker | .05 |
| 355 | Pete Harnisch | .08 |
| 356 | Steve Farr | .05 |
| 357 | Dave LaPoint | .05 |
| 358 | Willie Fraser | .05 |
| 359 | Mickey Hatcher | .08 |
| 360 | Rickey Henderson | .25 |
| 361 | Mike Fitzgerald | .05 |
| 362 | Bill Schroeder | .05 |
| 363 | Mark Carreon | .05 |
| 364 | Ron Jones | .05 |
| 365 | Jeff Montgomery | .08 |
| 366 | Bill Krueger | .05 |
| 367 | John Cangelosi | .05 |
| 368 | Jose Gonzalez | .05 |
| 369 | Greg Hibbard (R) | .15 |
| 370 | John Smoltz | .15 |
| 371 | Jeff Brantley | .08 |
| 372 | Frank White | .05 |
| 373 | Ed Whitson | .05 |
| 374 | Willie McGee | .08 |
| 375 | Jose Canseco | .40 |
| 376 | Randy Ready | .05 |
| 377 | Don Aase | .05 |
| 378 | Tony Armas | .05 |
| 379 | Steve Bedrosian | .05 |
| 380 | Chuck Finley | .10 |
| 381 | Kent Hrbek | .08 |
| 382 | Jim Gantner | .05 |
| 383 | Mel Hall | .05 |
| 384 | Mike Marshall | .08 |
| 385 | Mark McGwire | .12 |
| 386 | Wayne Tolleson | .05 |
| 387 | Brian Holman | .08 |
| 388 | John Wetteland | .15 |
| 389 | Darren Daulton | .05 |
| 390 | Rob Deer | .05 |
| 391 | John Moses | .05 |
| 392 | Todd Worrell | .08 |
| 393 | Chuck Cary | .05 |
| 394 | Stan Javier | .05 |
| 395 | Willie Randolph | .08 |
| 396 | Bill Buckner | .05 |
| 397 | Robby Thompson | .10 |
| 398 | Mike Scioscia | .08 |
| 399 | Lonnie Smith | .05 |
| 400 | Kirby Puckett | .20 |
| 401 | Mark Langston | .10 |
| 402 | Danny Darwin | .05 |
| 403 | Greg Maddux | .08 |
| 404 | Lloyd Moseby | .08 |
| 405 | Rafael Palmeiro | .10 |
| 406 | Chad Kreuter | .05 |
| 407 | Jimmy Key | .08 |
| 408 | Tim Birtsas | .05 |
| 409 | Tim Raines | .12 |
| 410 | Dave Stewart | .10 |
| 411 | Eric Yelding | .08 |
| 412 | Kent Anderson | .05 |
| 413 | Les Lancaster | .05 |
| 414 | Rick Dempsey | .05 |
| 415 | Randy Johnson | .08 |
| 416 | Gary Carter | .08 |
| 417 | Rolando Roomes | .08 |
| 418 | Dan Schatzeder | .05 |
| 419 | Bryn Smith | .05 |
| 420 | Ruben Sierra | .20 |
| 421 | Steve Jeltz | .08 |
| 422 | Ken Oberkfell | .05 |
| 423 | Sid Bream | .05 |
| 424 | Jim Clancy | .05 |
| 425 | Kelly Gruber | .10 |

| NO. | PLAYER | MINT |
|-----|--------|------|
| 426 | Rick Leach | .05 |
| 427 | Lenny Dykstra | .10 |
| 428 | Jeff Pico | .05 |
| 429 | John Cerutti | .05 |
| 430 | David Cone | .10 |
| 431 | Jeff Kunkel | .05 |
| 432 | Luis Aquino | .05 |
| 433 | Ernie Whitt | .05 |
| 434 | Bo Diaz | .05 |
| 435 | Steve Lake | .05 |
| 436 | Pat Perry | .05 |
| 437 | Mike Davis | .05 |
| 438 | Cecilio Guante | .05 |
| 439 | Duane Ward | .05 |
| 440 | Andy Van Slyke | .10 |
| 441 | Gene Nelson | .05 |
| 442 | Luis Polonia | .05 |
| 443 | Kevin Elster | .08 |
| 444 | Keith Moreland | .05 |
| 445 | Roger McDowell | .05 |
| 446 | Ron Darling | .10 |
| 447 | Ernest Riles | .05 |
| 448 | Mookie Wilson | .08 |
| 449 | B. Spiers (correct) | .10 |
| 449 | B. Spiers (error) | 1.00 |
| 450 | Rick Sutcliffe | .05 |
| 451 | Nelson Santovenia | .05 |
| 452 | Andy Allanson | .05 |
| 453 | Bob Melvin | .05 |
| 454 | Benny Santiago | .10 |
| 455 | Jose Uribe | .05 |
| 456 | Bill Landrum | .05 |
| 457 | Bobby Witt | .08 |
| 458 | Kevin Romine | .05 |
| 459 | Lee Mazzilli | .05 |
| 460 | Paul Molitor | .10 |
| 461 | Ramon Martinez | .25 |
| 462 | Frank DiPino | .05 |
| 463 | Walt Terrell | .05 |
| 464 | Bob Geren | .15 |
| 465 | Rick Reuschel | .08 |
| 466 | Mark Grant | .05 |
| 467 | John Kruk | .05 |
| 468 | Gregg Jefferies | .10 |
| 469 | R.J. Reynolds | .05 |
| 470 | Harold Baines | .08 |
| 471 | Dennis Lamp | .05 |
| 472 | Tom Gordon | .08 |
| 473 | Terry Puhl | .05 |
| 474 | Curtis Wilkerson | .05 |
| 475 | Dan Quisenberry | .05 |
| 476 | Oddibe McDowell | .05 |
| 477 | Zane Smith | .05 |
| 478 | Franklin Stubbs | .05 |
| 479 | Wallace Johnson | .05 |
| 480 | Jay Tibbs | .05 |
| 481 | Tom Glavine | .15 |
| 482 | Manny Lee | .05 |
| 483 | Joe Hesketh | .05 |
| 484 | Mike Bielecki | .05 |
| 485 | Greg Brock | .05 |
| 486 | Pascual Perez | .05 |
| 487 | Kirk Gibson | .08 |
| 488 | Scott Sanderson | .05 |
| 489 | Domingo Ramos | .05 |
| 490 | Kal Daniels | .08 |
| 491 | David Wells (correct) | .10 |
| 491 | David Wells (error) | 1.50 |
| 492 | Jerry Reed | .05 |
| 493 | Eric Show | .05 |
| 494 | Mike Pagliarulo | .08 |
| 495 | Ron Robinson | .05 |
| 496 | Brad Komminsk | .05 |
| 497 | Greg Litton | .10 |
| 498 | Chris James | .05 |
| 499 | Luis Quinones | .05 |
| 500 | Frank Viola | .10 |
| 501 | Tim Teufel | .05 |
| 502 | Terry Leach | .05 |
| 503 | Matt Williams | .15 |
| 504 | Tim Leary | .08 |
| 505 | Doug Drabek | .05 |
| 506 | Mariano Duncan | .05 |
| 507 | Charlie Hayes | .05 |
| 508 | Joey Belle | .50 |

| NO. | PLAYER | MINT |
|-----|--------|------|
| 509 | Pat Sheridan | .05 |
| 510 | Mackey Sasser | .05 |
| 511 | Jose Rijo | .05 |
| 512 | Mike Smithson | .05 |
| 513 | Gary Ward | .05 |
| 514 | Dion James | .05 |
| 515 | Jim Gott | .05 |
| 516 | Drew Hall | .05 |
| 517 | Doug Bair | .05 |
| 518 | Scott Scudder | .15 |
| 519 | Rick Aguilera | .05 |
| 520 | Rafael Belliard | .05 |
| 521 | Jay Buhner | .08 |
| 522 | Jeff Reardon | .08 |
| 523 | Steve Rosenberg | .05 |
| 524 | Randy Verlarde | .05 |
| 525 | Jeff Musselman | .05 |
| 526 | Bill Long | .05 |
| 527 | Gary Wayne | .08 |
| 528 | Dave Johnson (R) | .10 |
| 529 | Ron Kittle | .05 |
| 530 | Erik Hanson | .12 |
| 531 | Steve Wilson | .10 |
| 532 | Joey Meyer | .05 |
| 533 | Curt Young | .05 |
| 534 | Kelly Downs | .08 |
| 535 | Joe Girardi | .05 |
| 536 | Lance Blankenship | .05 |
| 537 | Greg Mathews | .05 |
| 538 | Donell Nixon | .05 |
| 539 | Mark Knudson | .08 |
| 540 | Jeff Wetherby (R) | .12 |
| 541 | Darrin Jackson | .05 |
| 542 | Terry Mulholland | .05 |
| 543 | Eric Hetzel | .05 |
| 544 | Rick Reed (R) | .12 |
| 545 | Dennis Cook | .08 |
| 546 | Mike Jackson | .05 |
| 547 | Brian Fisher | .05 |
| 548 | Gene Harris | .08 |
| 549 | Jeff King | .08 |
| 550 | Dave Dravecky | .05 |
| 551 | Randy Kutcher | .05 |
| 552 | Mark Portugal | .05 |
| 553 | Jim Corsi | .08 |
| 554 | Todd Stottlemyre | .08 |
| 555 | Scott Bankhead | .05 |
| 556 | Ken Dayley | .05 |
| 557 | Rick Wrona | .08 |
| 558 | Sammy Sosa (R) | .25 |
| 559 | Keith Miller | .05 |
| 560 | Ken Griffey, Jr. | 2.00 |
| 561 | HL: R. Sandberg (cor.) | .20 |
| 561 | HL: R. Sandberg (error) | 8.00 |
| 562 | Billy Hatcher | .05 |
| 563 | Jay Bell | .05 |
| 564 | Jack Daugherty (R) | .12 |
| 565 | Rich Monteleone | .10 |
| 566 | Bo Jackson (MVP) | .25 |
| 567 | Tony Fossas (R) | .10 |
| 568 | Roy Smith | .05 |
| 569 | Jaime Navarro | .08 |
| 570 | Lance Johnson | .05 |
| 571 | Mike Dyer (R) | .10 |
| 572 | Kevin Ritz (R) | .10 |
| 573 | Dave West | .10 |
| 574 | Gary Mielke (R) | .10 |
| 575 | Scott Lusader | .05 |
| 576 | Joe Oliver | .08 |
| 577 | Sandy Alomar, Jr. | .12 |
| 578 | Andy Benes | .20 |
| 579 | Tim Jones | .05 |
| 580 | Randy McCament (R) | .10 |
| 581 | Curt Schilling | .10 |
| 582 | John Orton (R) | .12 |
| 583 | M. Cuyler (error) | 1.50 |
| 583 | M. Cuyler (correct) | .50 |
| 584 | Eric Anthony (R) | .20 |
| 585 | Greg Vaughn | .50 |
| 586 | Deion Sanders | .20 |
| 587 | Jose DeJesus | .05 |
| 588 | Chip Hale (R) | .10 |
| 589 | John Olerud (R) | 1.00 |
| 590 | Steve Olin | .12 |
| 591 | Marquis Grissom (R) | .50 |
| 592 | Moises Alou (R) | .15 |

| NO. | PLAYER | MINT |
|---|---|---|
| 593 | Mark Lemke | .05 |
| 594 | Dean Palmer (R) | .75 |
| 595 | Robin Ventura | .60 |
| 596 | Tino Martinez | .50 |
| 597 | Mike Huff (R) | .15 |
| 598 | Scott Hemond (R) | .15 |
| 599 | Wally Whitehurst | .08 |
| 600 | Todd Zeile | .30 |
| 601 | Hill Glenallen | .08 |
| 602 | Hal Morris | .40 |
| 603 | Juan Bell | .08 |
| 604 | Bobby Rose (R) | .12 |
| 605 | Matt Merullo | .08 |
| 606 | Kevin Maas (R) | 1.25 |
| 607 | Randy Nosek (R) | .08 |
| 608 | Billy Bates (R) | .10 |
| 609 | Mike Stanton (R) | .12 |
| 610 | Goose Gozzo (R) | .12 |
| 611 | Charles Nagy | .15 |
| 612 | Scott Coolbaugh (R) | .12 |
| 613 | Jose Vizcaino (R) | .12 |
| 614 | Greg Smith (R) | .12 |
| 615 | Jeff Huson (R) | .10 |
| 616 | Mickey Weston (R) | .10 |
| 617 | John Pawlowski | .08 |
| 618 | Joe Skalski (error) | .10 |
| 618 | Joe Skalski (correct) | 1.25 |
| 619 | Bernie Williams (R) | .50 |
| 620 | Shawn Holman (R) | .12 |

| NO. | PLAYER | MINT |
|---|---|---|
| 621 | Gary Eave (R) | .12 |
| 622 | Darrin Fletcher (R) | .15 |
| 623 | Pat Combs | .08 |
| 624 | Mike Blowers (R) | .12 |
| 625 | Kevin Appier | .20 |
| 626 | Pat Austin (R) | .10 |
| 627 | Kelly Mann (R) | .10 |
| 628 | Matt Kinzer (R) | .10 |
| 629 | Chris Hammond (R) | .25 |
| 630 | Dean Wilkins (R) | .12 |
| 631 | Larry Walker (R) | .25 |
| 632 | Blaine Beatty (R) | .12 |
| 633 | T. Barrett (error) | .10 |
| 633 | T. Barrett (correct) | 3.50 |
| 634 | Stan Belinda (R) | .12 |
| 635 | Mike Smith (Tex) (R) | .10 |
| 636 | Hensley Meulens | .12 |
| 637 | Juan Gonzalez (R) | 2.00 |
| 638 | Lenny Webster (R) | .12 |
| 639 | Mark Gardner (R) | .15 |
| 640 | Tommy Greene (R) | .25 |
| 641 | Mike Hartley (R) | .12 |
| 642 | Phil Stephenson (R) | .08 |
| 643 | Kevin Mmahat (R) | .10 |
| 644 | Ed Whited (R) | .12 |
| 645 | Delino DeShields (R) | .35 |
| 646 | Kevin Blankenship | .08 |
| 647 | Paul Sorrento (R) | .12 |
| 648 | Mike Roesler (R) | .10 |

| NO. | PLAYER | MINT |
|---|---|---|
| 649 | Jason Brimsely (R) | .12 |
| 650 | Dave Justice (R) | 2.00 |
| 651 | Scott Cooper (R) | .50 |
| 652 | Dave Eiland | .08 |
| 653 | Mike Munoz (R) | .10 |
| 654 | Jeff Fischer (R) | .10 |
| 655 | Terry Jorgenson (R) | .10 |
| 656 | George Canale (R) | .10 |
| 657 | Brian Dubois (R) | .10 |
| 658 | Carlos Quintana | .08 |
| 659 | Luis De Los Santos | .05 |
| 660 | Jerald Clark | .05 |

**No. 661 to 682—No. 1 Draft Picks**

| NO. | PLAYER | MINT |
|---|---|---|
| 661 | Donald Harris (R) | .12 |
| 662 | Paul Coleman (R) | .20 |
| 663 | Frank Thomas (R) | 5.00 |
| 664 | Brent Mayne (R) | .25 |
| 665 | Eddie Zosky (R) | .40 |
| 666 | Steve Hosey (R) | .15 |
| 667 | Scott Bryant (R) | .20 |
| 668 | Tom Goodwin (R) | .30 |
| 669 | Cal Eldred (R) | .15 |
| 670 | Earl Cunningham (R) | .15 |
| 671 | Alan Zinter (R) | .12 |
| 672 | Chuck Knoblauch (R) | 1.50 |
| 673 | Kyle Abbott (R) | .25 |
| 674 | Roger Salkeld (R) | .60 |
| 675 | Maurice Vaughn (R) | 1.50 |
| 676 | Keith Jones (Kiki) (R) | .15 |

| NO. | PLAYER | MINT |
|---|---|---|
| 677 | Tyler Houston (R) | .15 |
| 678 | Jeff Jackson (R) | .10 |
| 679 | Greg Gohr (R) | .60 |
| 680 | Ben McDonald (R) | 1.25 |
| 681 | Greg Blosser (R) | .30 |
| 682 | Willie Green (R) | .15 |

**No. 683 to 695—Dream Team**

| NO. | PLAYER | MINT |
|---|---|---|
| 683 | Wade Boggs | .10 |
| 684 | Will Clark | .15 |
| 685 | Tony Gwynn | .10 |
| 686 | Rickey Henderson | .20 |
| 687 | Bo Jackson | .20 |
| 688 | Mark Langston | .08 |
| 689 | Barry Larkin | .08 |
| 690 | Kirby Puckett | .12 |
| 691 | Ryne Sandberg | .15 |
| 692 | Mike Scott | .08 |
| 693 | T. Steinbach (err.) | .10 |
| 693 | T. Steinbach (cor.) | .35 |
| 694 | Bobby Thigpen | .08 |
| 695 | Mitch Williams | .08 |

**Special Cards**

| NO. | PLAYER | MINT |
|---|---|---|
| 696 | Nolan Ryan | .30 |
| 697 | Bo Jackson FB/BB | 3.00 |
| 698 | Rickey Henderson | .15 |
| 699 | Will Clark | .15 |

**No. 700 to 703—World Series**

| NO. | PLAYER | MINT |
|---|---|---|
| 700 | WS Games 1,2 | .08 |
| 701 | Candlestick Park | .08 |
| 702 | WS Game 3 | .08 |
| 703 | WS Wrap-up | .08 |
| 704 | HL: Wade Boggs | .10 |

## 1990 Score Traded & Rookie . . . Complete Set of 110 Cards—Value $20.00

Updates the main 1990 card set with players who changed teams during the season, and rookies. Features the first Score card of Eric Lindros.

| NO. | PLAYER | MINT |
|---|---|---|
| 1T | Dave Winfield | .15 |
| 2T | Kevin Bass | .05 |
| 3T | Nick Esasky | .05 |
| 4T | Mitch Webster | .05 |
| 5T | Pascual Perez | .05 |
| 6T | Gary Pettis | .05 |
| 7T | Tony Pena | .05 |
| 8T | Candy Maldonado | .05 |
| 9T | Cecil Fielder | .30 |
| 10T | Carmelo Martinez | .05 |
| 11T | Mark Langston | .08 |
| 12T | Dave Parker | .08 |
| 13T | Don Slaught | .05 |
| 14T | Tony Phillips | .05 |
| 15T | John Franco | .05 |
| 16T | Randy Myers | .05 |
| 17T | Jeff Reardon | .05 |
| 18T | Sandy Alomar Jr. | .10 |
| 19T | Joe Carter | .10 |
| 20T | Fred Lynn | .08 |
| 21T | Storm Davis | .05 |
| 22T | Craig Lefferts | .05 |
| 23T | Pete O'Brien | .05 |
| 24T | Dennis Boyd | .05 |
| 25T | Lloyd Moseby | .05 |
| 26T | Mark Davis | .05 |
| 27T | Tim Leary | .05 |
| 28T | Gerald Perry | .05 |

| NO. | PLAYER | MINT |
|---|---|---|
| 29T | Don Aase | .05 |
| 30T | Ernie Whitt | .05 |
| 31T | Dale Murphy | .08 |
| 32T | Alejandro Pena | .05 |
| 33T | Juan Samuel | .05 |
| 34T | Hubie Brooks | .05 |
| 35T | Gary Carter | .10 |
| 36T | Jim Presley | .05 |
| 37T | Wally Backman | .05 |
| 38T | Matt Nokes | .08 |
| 39T | Dan Petry | .05 |
| 40T | Franklin Stubbs | .05 |
| 41T | Jeff Huson | .05 |
| 42T | Billy Hatcher | .05 |
| 43T | Terry Leach | .05 |
| 44T | Phil Bradley | .05 |
| 45T | Claudell Washington | .05 |
| 46T | Luis Polonia | .05 |
| 47T | Daryl Boston | .05 |
| 48T | Lee Smith | .08 |
| 49T | Tom Brunansky | .08 |
| 50T | Mike Witt | .05 |
| 51T | Willie Randolph | .05 |
| 52T | Stan Javier | .05 |
| 53T | Brad Komminsk | .05 |
| 54T | John Candelaria | .05 |
| 55T | Bryn Smith | .05 |

| NO. | PLAYER | MINT |
|---|---|---|
| 56T | Glenn Braggs | .05 |
| 57T | Keith Hernandez | .05 |
| 58T | Ken Oberkfell | .05 |
| 59T | Steve Jeltz | .05 |
| 60T | Chris James | .05 |
| 61T | Scott Sanderson | .05 |
| 62T | Bill Long | .05 |
| 63T | Rick Cerone | .05 |
| 64T | Scott Bailes | .05 |
| 65T | Larry Sheets | .05 |
| 66T | Junior Ortiz | .05 |
| 67T | Francisco Cabrera | .10 |
| 68T | Gary Disarcina (R) | .12 |
| 69T | Greg Olson (R) | .15 |
| 70T | Beau Allred (R) | .12 |
| 71T | Oscar Azocar (R) | .12 |
| 72T | Kent Mercker (R) | .15 |
| 73T | John Burkett | .12 |
| 74T | Carlos Baerga (R) | .50 |
| 75T | Dave Hollins (R) | .40 |
| 76T | Todd Hundley (R) | .40 |
| 77T | Rick Parker (R) | .10 |
| 78T | Steve Cummings (R) | .10 |
| 79T | Bill Sampen (R) | .12 |
| 80T | Jerry Kutzler (R) | .10 |
| 81T | Derek Bell (R) | 2.00 |
| 82T | Kevin Tapani (R) | .50 |

| NO. | PLAYER | MINT |
|---|---|---|
| 83T | Jim Leyritz (R) | .10 |
| 84T | Ray Lankford (R) | 1.25 |
| 85T | Wayne Edwards (R) | .10 |
| 86T | Frank Thomas | 8.00 |
| 87T | Tim Naehring (R) | .25 |
| 88T | Willie Blair (R) | .10 |
| 89T | Alan Mills (R) | .12 |
| 90T | Scott Radinsky (R) | .12 |
| 91T | Howard Farmer (R) | .12 |
| 92T | Julio Machado (R) | .12 |
| 93T | Rafael Valdez (R) | .12 |
| 94T | Shawn Boskie (R) | .12 |
| 95T | David Sequi (R) | .20 |
| 96T | Chris Hoiles (R) | .20 |
| 97T | D.J. Dozier (R) | .40 |
| 98T | Hector Villanueva (R) | .12 |
| 99T | Eric Gunderson (R) | .12 |
| 100T | Eric Lindros (R) | 6.00 |
| 101T | Dave Otto | .10 |
| 102T | Dana Kiecker (R) | .10 |
| 103T | Tim Drummond (R) | .10 |
| 104T | Mickey Pina (R) | .12 |
| 105T | Craig Grebeck (R) | .10 |
| 106T | Bernard Gilkey (R) | .40 |
| 107T | Tim Layana (R) | .12 |
| 108T | Scott Chiamparino (R) | .20 |
| 109T | Steve Avery (R) | 3.00 |
| 110T | Terry Schumpert (R) | .12 |

## 1991 Score . . . Series One Set of 441 Cards (#1 to 441)—Value $12.50
### Series Two Set of 452 Cards (#442 to 893)—Value $12.50

(Factory-Sealed Set of 900 Cards—Value $30.00)

The set was increased from 704 to 893 cards—the largest baseball card set ever issued. For the first time Score cards were issued in two series—series one contains 441 cards; series two has 452 cards. There are several new subsets for 1991—the Franchise, No-Hit Club, Master Blasters. K-Man and Rifleman. Factory sets include seven bonus cards.

| NO. | PLAYER | MINT |
|-----|--------|------|
| | **SERIES ONE** | |
| 1 | Jose Canseco | .25 |
| 2 | Ken Griffey, Jr. | .75 |
| 3 | Ryne Sandberg | .20 |
| 4 | Nolan Ryan | .30 |
| 5 | Bo Jackson | .25 |
| 6 | Bret Saberhagen | .10 |
| 7 | Will Clark | .20 |
| 8 | Ellis Burks | .08 |
| 9 | Joe Carter | .08 |
| 10 | Rickey Henderson | .20 |
| 11 | Ozzie Guillen | .05 |
| 12 | Wade Boggs | .15 |
| 13 | Jerome Walton | .10 |
| 14 | John Franco | .05 |
| 15 | Ricky Jordan | .05 |
| 16 | Wally Backman | .05 |
| 17 | Rob Dibble | .05 |
| 18 | Glenn Braggs | .05 |
| 19 | Cory Snyder | .08 |
| 20 | Kal Daniels | .08 |
| 21 | Mark Langston | .08 |
| 22 | Kevin Gross | .05 |
| 23 | Don Mattingly | .20 |
| 24 | Dave Righetti | .05 |
| 25 | Roberto Alomar | .08 |
| 26 | Robby Thompson | .05 |
| 27 | Jack McDowell | .08 |
| 28 | Bip Roberts | .05 |
| 29 | Jay Howell | .05 |
| 30 | Dave Stieb | .08 |
| 31 | Johnny Ray | .05 |
| 32 | Steve Sax | .05 |
| 33 | Terry Mulholland | .05 |
| 34 | Lee Guetterman | .05 |
| 35 | Tim Raines | .08 |
| 36 | Scott Fletcher | .05 |
| 37 | Lance Parrish | .05 |
| 38 | Tony Phillips | .05 |
| 39 | Todd Stottlemyre | .05 |
| 40 | Alan Trammell | .08 |
| 41 | Todd Burns | .05 |
| 42 | Mookie Wilson | .05 |
| 43 | Chris Bosio | .05 |
| 44 | Jeffrey Leonard | .05 |
| 45 | Doug Jones | .05 |
| 46 | Mike Scott | .05 |
| 47 | Andy Hawkins | .05 |
| 48 | Harold Reynolds | .05 |
| 49 | Paul Molitor | .08 |
| 50 | John Farrell | .05 |
| 51 | Danny Darwin | .05 |
| 52 | Jeff Blauser | .05 |
| 53 | John Tudor | .05 |
| 54 | Milt Thompson | .05 |
| 55 | Dave Justice | .50 |
| 56 | Greg Olson | .08 |
| 57 | Willie Blair | .05 |
| 58 | Rick Parker | .05 |
| 59 | Shawn Boskie | .05 |
| 60 | Kevin Tapani | .05 |
| 61 | Dave Hollins | .08 |
| 62 | Scott Radinsky | .05 |
| 63 | Francisco Cabrera | .05 |
| 64 | Tim Layana | .05 |
| 65 | Jim Leyritz | .08 |
| 66 | Wayne Edwards | .05 |
| 67 | Lee Stevens | .12 |
| 68 | Bill Sampen | .05 |
| 69 | Craig Grebeck | .05 |
| 70 | John Burkett | .05 |
| 71 | Hector Villanueva | .10 |
| 72 | Oscar Azocar | .10 |
| 73 | Alan Mills | .05 |
| 74 | Carlos Baerga | .10 |
| 75 | Charles Nagy | .10 |
| 76 | Tim Drummond | .05 |
| 77 | Dana Kiecker | .05 |
| 78 | Tom Edens (R) | .10 |
| 79 | Kent Mercker | .05 |
| 80 | Steve Avery | .25 |
| 81 | Lee Smith | .05 |
| 82 | Dave Martinez | .05 |
| 83 | Dave Winfield | .08 |
| 84 | Bill Spiers | .05 |
| 85 | Dan Pasqua | .05 |
| 86 | Randy Milligan | .05 |
| 87 | Tracy Jones | .05 |
| 88 | Greg Myers | .05 |
| 89 | Keith Hernandez | .05 |
| 90 | Todd Benzinger | .08 |
| 91 | Mike Jackson | .05 |
| 92 | Mike Stanley | .05 |
| 93 | Candy Maldonado | .05 |
| 94 | John Kruk | .05 |
| 95 | Cal Ripken, Jr. | .20 |
| 96 | Willie Fraser | .05 |
| 97 | Mike Felder | .05 |
| 98 | Bill Landrum | .05 |
| 99 | Chuck Crim | .05 |
| 100 | Chuck Finley | .08 |
| 101 | Kirt Manwaring | .05 |
| 102 | Jaime Navarro | .05 |
| 103 | Dickie Thon | .05 |
| 104 | Brian Downing | .05 |
| 105 | Jim Abbott | .10 |
| 106 | Tom Brookens | .05 |
| 107 | Darryl Hamilton | .05 |
| 108 | Bryan Harvey | .05 |
| 109 | Greg Harris | .05 |
| 110 | Greg Swindell | .05 |
| 111 | Juan Berenguer | .05 |
| 112 | Mike Heath | .05 |
| 113 | Scott Bracley | .05 |
| 114 | Jack Morris | .08 |
| 115 | Barry Jones | .05 |
| 116 | Kevin Romine | .05 |
| 117 | Garry Templeton | .05 |
| 118 | Scott Sanderson | .05 |
| 119 | Roberto Kelly | .05 |
| 120 | George Brett | .15 |
| 121 | Oddibe McDowell | .05 |
| 122 | Jim Acker | .05 |
| 123 | Bill Swift | .05 |
| 124 | Eric King | .05 |
| 125 | Jay Buhner | .05 |
| 126 | Matt Young | .05 |
| 127 | Alvaro Espinoza | .05 |
| 128 | Greg Hibbard | .05 |
| 129 | Jeff Robinson | .05 |
| 130 | Mike Greenwell | .10 |
| 131 | Dion James | .05 |
| 132 | Donn Pall | .05 |
| 133 | Lloyd Moseby | .05 |
| 134 | Randy Velarde | .05 |
| 135 | Allan Anderson | .05 |
| 136 | Mark Davis | .05 |
| 137 | Eric Davis | .10 |
| 138 | Phil Stephenson | .05 |
| 139 | Felix Fermin | .05 |
| 140 | Pedro Guerrero | .08 |
| 141 | Charlie Hough | .05 |
| 142 | Mike Henneman | .05 |
| 143 | Jeff Montgomery | .05 |
| 144 | Lenny Harris | .05 |
| 145 | Bruce Hurst | .05 |
| 146 | Eric Anthony | .08 |
| 147 | Paul Assenmacher | .05 |
| 148 | Jesse Barfield | .08 |
| 149 | Carlos Quintana | .08 |
| 150 | Dave Stewart | .08 |
| 151 | Roy Smith | .05 |
| 152 | Paul Gibson | .05 |
| 153 | Mickey Hatcher | .05 |
| 154 | Jim Eisenreich | .05 |
| 155 | Kenny Rogers | .05 |
| 156 | Dave Schmidt | .05 |
| 157 | Lance Johnson | .05 |
| 158 | Dave West | .05 |
| 159 | Steve Balboni | .05 |
| 160 | Jeff Brantley | .05 |
| 161 | Craig Biggio | .05 |
| 162 | Brook Jacoby | .05 |
| 163 | Dan Gladden | .05 |
| 164 | Jeff Reardon | .05 |
| 165 | Mark Carreon | .05 |
| 166 | Mel Hall | .05 |
| 167 | Gary Mielke | .05 |
| 168 | Cecil Fielder | .15 |
| 169 | Darrin Jackson | .05 |
| 170 | Rick Aguilera | .05 |
| 171 | Walt Weiss | .05 |
| 172 | Steve Farr | .05 |
| 173 | Jody Reed | .05 |
| 174 | Mike Jeffcoat | .05 |
| 175 | Mark Grace | .08 |
| 176 | Larry Sheets | .05 |
| 177 | Bill Gullickson | .05 |
| 178 | Chris Gwynn | .05 |
| 179 | Melido Perez | .05 |
| 180 | Sid Fernandez | .05 |
| 181 | Tim Burke | .05 |
| 182 | Gary Pettis | .05 |
| 183 | Rob Murphy | .05 |
| 184 | Craig Lefferts | .05 |
| 185 | Howard Johnson | .10 |
| 186 | Ken Caminiti | .05 |
| 187 | Tim Belcher | .05 |
| 188 | Greg Cadaret | .05 |
| 189 | Matt Williams | .10 |
| 190 | Dave Magadan | .08 |
| 191 | Geno Petralli | .05 |
| 192 | Jeff Robinson | .05 |
| 193 | Jim Deshaies | .05 |
| 194 | Willie Randolph | .05 |
| 195 | George Bell | .08 |
| 196 | Hubie Brooks | .05 |
| 197 | Tom Gordon | .10 |
| 198 | Mike Fitzgerald | .05 |
| 199 | Mike Pagliarulo | .05 |
| 200 | Kirby Puckett | .15 |
| 201 | Shawon Dunston | .08 |
| 202 | Dennis Boyd | .05 |
| 203 | Junior Felix | .08 |
| 204 | Alejandro Pena | .05 |
| 205 | Pete Smith | .05 |
| 206 | Tom Glavine | .10 |
| 207 | Luis Salazar | .05 |
| 208 | John Smoltz | .10 |
| 209 | Doug Dascenzo | .05 |
| 210 | Tim Wallach | .05 |
| 211 | Greg Gagne | .05 |
| 212 | Mark Gubicza | .05 |
| 213 | Mark Parent | .05 |
| 214 | Ken Oberkfell | .05 |
| 215 | Gary Carter | .10 |
| 216 | Rafael Palmeiro | .08 |
| 217 | Tom Niedenfuer | .05 |
| 218 | Dave LaPoint | .05 |
| 219 | Jeff Treadway | .05 |
| 220 | Mitch Williams | .05 |
| 221 | Jose DeLeon | .05 |
| 222 | Mike LaValliere | .05 |
| 223 | Darrel Akerfelds | .05 |
| 224 | Kent Anderson | .05 |
| 225 | Dwight Evans | .05 |
| 226 | Gary Redus | .05 |
| 227 | Paul O'Neill | .05 |
| 228 | Marty Barrett | .05 |
| 229 | Tom Browning | .05 |
| 230 | Terry Pendleton | .08 |
| 231 | Jack Armstrong | .05 |
| 232 | Mike Boddicker | .05 |
| 233 | Neal Heaton | .05 |
| 234 | Marquis Grissom | .10 |
| 235 | Bert Blyleven | .05 |
| 236 | Curt Young | .05 |
| 237 | Don Carman | .05 |
| 238 | Charlies Hayes | .05 |
| 239 | Mark Knudson | .05 |
| 240 | Todd Zeille | .08 |
| 241 | Larry Walker | .08 |
| 242 | Jerald Clark | .05 |
| 243 | Jeff Ballard | .05 |
| 244 | Jeff King | .05 |
| 245 | Tom Brunansky | .08 |
| 246 | Darren Daulton | .05 |
| 247 | Scott Terry | .05 |
| 248 | Rob Deer | .05 |

| NO. | PLAYER | MINT |
|-----|--------|------|
| 249 | Brady Anderson | .05 |
| 250 | Lenny Dykstra | .10 |
| 251 | Gerg Harris | .05 |
| 252 | Mike Hartley | .05 |
| 253 | Joey Cora | .05 |
| 254 | Ivan Calderon | .05 |
| 255 | Ted Power | .05 |
| 256 | Sammy Sosa | .08 |
| 257 | Steve Buechele | .05 |
| 258 | Mike Devereaux | .05 |
| 259 | Brad Komminsk | .05 |
| 260 | Teddy Higuera | .05 |
| 261 | Shawn Abner | .05 |
| 262 | Dave Valle | .05 |
| 263 | Jeff Huson | .05 |
| 264 | Edgar Martinez | .08 |
| 265 | Carlton Fisk | .10 |
| 266 | Steve Finley | .05 |
| 267 | John Wetteland | .05 |
| 268 | Kevin Appier | .05 |
| 269 | Steve Lyons | .05 |
| 270 | Mickey Tettleton | .05 |
| 271 | Luis Rivera | .05 |
| 272 | Steve Jeltz | .05 |
| 273 | R.J. Reynolds | .05 |
| 274 | Carlos Martinez | .05 |
| 275 | Dan Plesac | .05 |
| 276 | Mike Morgan | .05 |
| 277 | Jeff Russell | .05 |
| 278 | Pete Incaviglia | .05 |
| 279 | Kevin Seitzer | .05 |
| 280 | Bobby Thigpen | .08 |
| 281 | Stan Javier | .05 |
| 282 | Henry Cotto | .05 |
| 283 | Gary Wayne | .05 |
| 284 | Shane Mack | .05 |
| 285 | Brian Holman | .05 |
| 286 | Gerald Perry | .05 |
| 287 | Steve Crawford | .05 |
| 288 | Nelson Liriano | .05 |
| 289 | Don Aase | .05 |
| 290 | Randy Johnson | .05 |
| 291 | Harold Baines | .05 |
| 292 | Kent Hrbek | .12 |
| 293 | Les Lancaster | .05 |
| 294 | Jeff Musselman | .05 |
| 295 | Kurt Stillwell | .05 |
| 296 | Stan Belinda | .05 |
| 297 | Lou Whitaker | .05 |
| 298 | Glenn Wilson | .05 |
| 299 | Omar Vizquel | .05 |
| 300 | Ramon Martinez | .12 |
| 301 | Dwight Smith | .05 |
| 302 | Tim Crews | .05 |
| 303 | Lance Blankenship | .05 |
| 304 | Sid Bream | .05 |
| 305 | Rafael Ramirez | .05 |
| 306 | Steve Wilson | .05 |
| 307 | Mackey Sasser | .05 |
| 308 | Franklin Stubbs | .05 |
| 309 | Jack Daugherty | .05 |
| 310 | Eddie Murray | .15 |
| 311 | Bob Welch | .05 |
| 312 | Brian Harper | .05 |
| 313 | Lance McCullers | .05 |
| 314 | Dave Smith | .05 |
| 315 | Bobby Bonilla | .15 |
| 316 | Jerry Don Gleaton | .05 |
| 317 | Greg Maddux | .05 |
| 318 | Keith Miller | .05 |
| 319 | Mark Portugal | .05 |
| 320 | Robin Ventura | .15 |
| 321 | Bob Ojeda | .05 |
| 322 | Mike Harkey | .05 |
| 323 | Jay Bell | .05 |
| 324 | Mark McGwire | .12 |
| 325 | Gary Gaetti | .05 |
| 326 | Jeff Pico | .05 |
| 327 | Kevin McReynolds | .08 |
| 328 | Frank Tanana | .05 |
| 329 | Eric Yelding | .05 |
| 330 | Barry Bonds | .15 |

**No. 331 to 379—Rookie Prospects**

| NO. | PLAYER | MINT |
|-----|--------|------|
| 331 | Brian McRae (R) | .40 |
| 332 | Pedro Munoz (R) | .20 |
| 333 | Daryl Irvine (R) | .10 |
| 334 | Chris Hoiles | .08 |
| 335 | Thomas Howard | .08 |
| 336 | Jeff Schulz (R) | .10 |
| 337 | Jeff Manto | .07 |
| 338 | Beau Allred | .07 |
| 339 | Mike Brodick (R) | .10 |
| 340 | Todd Hundley | .10 |
| 341 | Jim Vatcher (R) | .10 |
| 342 | Luis Sojo | .08 |
| 343 | Jose Offerman | .10 |
| 344 | Pete Coachman (R) | .10 |
| 345 | Mike Benjamin | .08 |
| 346 | Ozzie Canseco | .10 |
| 347 | Tim McIntosh | .05 |
| 348 | Phil Plantier (R) | 1.00 |
| 349 | Terry Shumpert | .05 |
| 350 | Darren Lewis | .20 |
| 351 | David Walsh (R) | .12 |
| 352 | Scott Chiamparino | .10 |
| 353 | Julio Valera | .08 |
| 354 | Anthony Telford (R) | .10 |
| 355 | Kevin Wickander | .07 |
| 356 | Tim Naehring | .10 |
| 357 | Jim Poole (R) | .10 |
| 358 | Mark Whiten | .20 |
| 359 | Terry Wells (R) | .10 |
| 360 | Rafael Valdez | .07 |
| 361 | Mel Stottlemyre, Jr. | .07 |
| 362 | David Segui | .08 |
| 363 | Paul Abbott (R) | .10 |
| 364 | Steve Howard | .08 |
| 365 | Karl Rhodes | .08 |
| 366 | Rafael Novoa (R) | .10 |
| 367 | Joe Grahe (R) | .10 |
| 368 | Darren Reed | .07 |
| 369 | Jeff McKnight | .08 |
| 370 | Scott Leius | .10 |
| 371 | Mark Dewey (R) | .10 |
| 372 | Mark Lee (R) | .10 |
| 373 | Rosario Rodriguez (R) | .10 |
| 374 | Chuck McElroy | .07 |
| 375 | Mike Bell (R) | .10 |
| 376 | Mickey Morandini | .10 |
| 377 | Bill Haselman (R) | .10 |
| 378 | Dave Pavlas (R) | .10 |
| 379 | Derrick May | .08 |

**No. 380 to 391—1st Round Draft Pick**

| NO. | PLAYER | MINT |
|-----|--------|------|
| 380 | Jeromy Burnitz (R) | .75 |
| 382 | Alex Fernandez (R) | .15 |
| 382 | Alex Fernandez (R) | .15 |
| 383 | Mike Mussina (R) | .30 |
| 384 | Daniel Smith (R) | .15 |
| 385 | Lance Dickson (R) | .20 |
| 386 | Carl Everett (R) | .25 |
| 387 | Tom Nevers (R) | .15 |
| 388 | Adam Hyzdu (R) | .15 |
| 389 | Todd Van Poppel (R) | 1.00 |
| 390 | Rondell White (R) | .35 |
| 391 | Marc Newfield (R) | 1.00 |

**No. 392 to 401—Score All Star Team**

| NO. | PLAYER | MINT |
|-----|--------|------|
| 392 | Julio Franco | .07 |
| 393 | Wade Boggs | .10 |
| 394 | Ozzie Guillen | .07 |
| 395 | Cecil Fielder | .10 |
| 396 | Ken Griffey, Jr. | .30 |
| 397 | Rickey Henderson | .15 |
| 398 | Jose Canseco | .15 |
| 399 | Roger Clemens | .10 |
| 400 | Sandy Alomar, Jr. | .08 |
| 401 | Bobby Thigpen | .07 |

**No. 402 to 406—Master Blaster**

| NO. | PLAYER | MINT |
|-----|--------|------|
| 402 | Bobby Bonilla | .10 |
| 403 | Eric Davis | .10 |
| 404 | Fred McGriff | .10 |
| 405 | Glenn Davis | .10 |
| 406 | Kevin Mitchell | .10 |

**No. 407 to 411—K-Man**

| NO. | PLAYER | MINT |
|-----|--------|------|
| 407 | Rob Dibble | .07 |
| 408 | Ramon Martinez | .07 |
| 409 | David Cone | .07 |
| 410 | Bobby Witt | .07 |
| 411 | Mark Langston | .07 |

**No. 412 to 416—Rifleman**

| NO. | PLAYER | MINT |
|-----|--------|------|
| 412 | Bo Jackson | .20 |
| 413 | Shawon Dunston | .07 |
| 414 | Jesse Barfield | .07 |
| 415 | Ken Caminiti | .07 |
| 416 | Benny Santiago | .07 |

**No. 417 to 421—1990 Highlights's**

| NO. | PLAYER | MINT |
|-----|--------|------|
| 417 | Nolan Ryan | .25 |
| 418 | Bobby Thigpen | .05 |
| 419 | Ramon Martinez | .10 |
| 420 | Bo Jackson | .20 |
| 421 | Carlton Fisk | .05 |
| 422 | Jimmy Key | .05 |
| 423 | Junior Noboa | .05 |
| 424 | Al Newman | .05 |
| 425 | Pat Borders | .05 |
| 426 | Von Hayes | .05 |
| 427 | Tim Teufel | .05 |
| 428 | Eric Plunk | .05 |
| 429 | John Moses | .05 |
| 430 | Mike Witt | .05 |
| 431 | Otis Nixon | .05 |
| 432 | Tony Fernandez | .05 |
| 433 | Rance Mulliniks | .05 |
| 434 | Dan Petry | .05 |
| 435 | Bob Geren | .05 |
| 436 | Steve Frey | .05 |
| 437 | Jamie Moyer | .05 |
| 438 | Junior Ortiz | .05 |
| 439 | Tom O'Malley | .05 |
| 440 | Pat Combs | .05 |
| 441 | Jose Canseco | 2.50 |

**SERIES NO. 2**

| NO. | PLAYER | MINT |
|-----|--------|------|
| 442 | Alfredo Griffin | .05 |
| 443 | Andres Galarraga | .05 |
| 444 | Bryn Smith | .05 |
| 445 | Andre Dawson | .10 |
| 446 | Juan Samuel | .05 |
| 447 | Mike Aldrete | .05 |
| 448 | Ron Gant | .10 |
| 449 | Fernando Valenzuela | .08 |
| 450 | Vince Coleman | .10 |
| 451 | Kevin Mitchell | .12 |
| 452 | Spike Owen | .05 |
| 453 | Mike Bielecki | .05 |
| 454 | Dennis Martinez | .05 |
| 455 | Brett Butler | .05 |
| 456 | Ron Darling | .05 |
| 457 | Dennis Rasmussen | .05 |
| 458 | Ken Howell | .05 |
| 459 | Steve Bedrosian | .05 |
| 460 | Frank Viola | .08 |
| 461 | Jose Lind | .05 |
| 462 | Chris Sabo | .08 |
| 463 | Dante Bichette | .05 |
| 464 | Rick Mahler | .05 |
| 465 | John Smiley | .05 |
| 466 | Devon White | .05 |
| 467 | John Orton | .05 |
| 468 | Mike Stanton | .05 |
| 469 | Billy Hatcher | .05 |
| 470 | Wally Joyner | .08 |
| 471 | Gene Larkin | .05 |
| 472 | Doug Drabek | .08 |
| 473 | Gary Sheffield | .10 |
| 474 | David Wells | .05 |
| 475 | Andy Van Slyke | .08 |
| 476 | Mike Gallego | .05 |
| 477 | B.J. Surhoff | .05 |
| 478 | Gene Nelson | .05 |
| 479 | Mariano Duncan | .05 |
| 480 | Fred McGriff | .12 |
| 481 | Jerry Browne | .05 |
| 482 | Alvin Davis | .05 |
| 483 | Bill Wegman | .05 |
| 484 | Dave Parker | .08 |
| 485 | Dennis Eckersley | .10 |
| 486 | Erik Hanson | .05 |
| 487 | Bill Ripken | .05 |
| 488 | Tom Candiotti | .05 |
| 489 | Mike Schooler | .05 |
| 490 | Gregg Olson | .08 |
| 491 | Chris James | .05 |
| 492 | Pete Harnisch | .05 |
| 493 | Julio Franco | .08 |
| 494 | Greg Briley | .05 |
| 495 | Ruben Sierra | .10 |
| 496 | Steve Olin | .05 |
| 497 | Mike Fetters | .05 |
| 498 | Mark Williams (R) | .12 |
| 499 | Bob Tewksbury | .05 |
| 500 | Tony Gwynn | .12 |
| 501 | Randy Myers | .05 |
| 502 | Keith Comstock | .05 |
| 503 | Craig Worthington | .05 |
| 504 | Mark Eichhorn | .05 |
| 505 | Barry Larkin | .10 |
| 506 | Dave Johnson | .05 |
| 507 | Bobby Witt | .05 |
| 508 | Joe Orsulak | .05 |
| 509 | Pete O'Brien | .03 |
| 510 | Brad Arnsberg | .05 |
| 511 | Storm Davis | .05 |
| 512 | Bob Milacki | .05 |
| 513 | Bill Pecota | .05 |
| 514 | Glenallen Hill | .05 |
| 515 | Danny Tartabull | .05 |
| 516 | Mike Moore | .05 |
| 517 | Ron Robinson | .05 |
| 518 | Mark Gardner | .05 |
| 519 | Rick Wrona | .05 |
| 520 | Mike Scioscia | .05 |
| 521 | Frank Wills | .05 |
| 522 | Greg Brock | .05 |
| 523 | Jack Clark | .10 |
| 524 | Bruce Ruffin | .05 |
| 525 | Robin Yount | .12 |
| 526 | Tom Foley | .05 |
| 527 | Pat Perry | .05 |
| 528 | Greg Vaughn | .10 |
| 529 | Wally Whitehurst | .05 |
| 530 | Norm Charlton | .05 |
| 531 | Marvell Wynne | .05 |
| 532 | Jim Gantner | .05 |
| 533 | Greg Litton | .05 |
| 534 | Manny Lee | .05 |
| 535 | Scott Bailes | .05 |
| 536 | Charlie Leibrandt | .05 |
| 537 | Roger McDowell | .05 |
| 538 | Andy Benes | .10 |
| 539 | Rick Honeycutt | .05 |
| 540 | Doc Gooden | .15 |
| 541 | Scott Garrelts | .05 |
| 542 | Dave Clark | .05 |
| 543 | Lonnie Smith | .05 |
| 544 | Rick Reuschel | .05 |
| 545 | Delino DeShields | .15 |
| 546 | Mike Sharperson | .05 |
| 547 | Mike Kingery | .05 |
| 548 | Terry Kennedy | .05 |
| 549 | David Cone | .10 |
| 550 | Orel Hershiser | .10 |
| 551 | Matt Nokes | .05 |
| 552 | Eddie Williams | .05 |
| 553 | Frank DiPino | .05 |
| 554 | Fred Lynn | .05 |
| 555 | Alex Cole | .08 |
| 556 | Terry Leach | .05 |
| 557 | Chet Lemon | .05 |
| 558 | Paul Mirabella | .05 |
| 559 | Bill Long | .05 |
| 560 | Phil Bradley | .05 |
| 561 | Duane Ward | .05 |
| 562 | Dave Bergman | .05 |
| 563 | Eric Show | .05 |
| 564 | Xavier Hernandez | .05 |
| 565 | Jeff Parrett | .05 |
| 566 | Chuck Cary | .05 |
| 567 | Ken Hill | .05 |
| 568 | Bob Welch | .08 |
| 569 | John Mitchell | .05 |
| 570 | Travis Fryman | .45 |
| 571 | Derek Lilliquist | .05 |
| 572 | Steve Lake | .05 |
| 573 | John Barfield (R) | .12 |
| 574 | Randy Bush | .05 |

| NO. | PLAYER | MINT |
|---|---|---|
| 575 | Joe Magrane | .05 |
| 576 | Eddie Diaz | .08 |
| 577 | Casey Candaele | .05 |
| 578 | Jesse Orosco | .05 |
| 579 | Tom Henke | .05 |
| 580 | Rick Cerone | .05 |
| 581 | Drew Hall | .05 |
| 582 | Tony Castillo | .05 |
| 583 | Jimmy Jones | .05 |
| 584 | Rick Reed | .05 |
| 585 | Joe Girardi | .05 |
| 586 | Jeff Gray (R) | .10 |
| 587 | Luis Polonia | .05 |
| 588 | Joe Klink | .05 |
| 589 | Rex Hudler | .05 |
| 590 | Kirk McCaskill | .05 |
| 591 | Juan Agosto | .05 |
| 592 | Wes Gardner | .05 |
| 593 | Rich Rodriguez (R) | .10 |
| 594 | Mitch Webster | .05 |
| 595 | Kelly Gruber | .10 |
| 596 | Dale Mohorcic | .05 |
| 597 | Willie McGee | .10 |
| 598 | Bill Krueger | .05 |
| 599 | Bob Walk | .05 |
| 600 | Kevin Maas | .20 |
| 601 | Danny Jackson | .05 |
| 602 | Craig McMurtry | .05 |
| 603 | Curtis Wilkerson | .05 |
| 604 | Adam Peterson | .05 |
| 605 | Sam Horn | .05 |
| 606 | Tommy Gregg | .05 |
| 607 | Ken Dayley | .05 |
| 608 | Carmelo Castillo | .05 |
| 609 | John Shelby | .05 |
| 610 | Don Slaught | .05 |
| 611 | Calvin Schiraldi | .05 |
| 612 | Dennis Lamp | .05 |
| 613 | Andres Thomas | .05 |
| 614 | Jose Gonzalez | .05 |
| 615 | Randy Ready | .05 |
| 616 | Kevin Bass | .08 |
| 617 | Mike Marshall | .05 |
| 618 | Daryl Boston | .05 |
| 619 | Andy McGaffigan | .05 |
| 620 | Joe Oliver | .05 |
| 621 | Jim Gott | .05 |
| 622 | Jose Oquendo | .05 |
| 623 | Jose DeJesus | .05 |
| 624 | Mike Brumley | .05 |
| 625 | John Olerud | .15 |
| 626 | Ernest Riles | .05 |
| 627 | Gene Harris | .05 |
| 628 | Jose Uribe | .05 |
| 629 | Darnell Coles | .05 |
| 630 | Carney Lansford | .05 |
| 631 | Tim Leary | .05 |
| 632 | Tim Hulett | .05 |
| 633 | Kevin Elster | .05 |
| 634 | Tony Fossas | .05 |
| 635 | Francisco Oliveras | .05 |
| 636 | Bob Patterson | .05 |
| 637 | Gary Ward | .05 |
| 638 | Rene Gonzales | .05 |
| 639 | Don Robinson | .05 |
| 640 | Darryl Strawberry | .15 |
| 641 | Dave Anderson | .05 |
| 642 | Scott Scudder | .05 |
| 643 | Reggie Harris | .08 |
| 644 | Dave Henderson | .08 |
| 645 | Ben McDonald | .08 |
| 646 | Bob Kipper | .05 |
| 647 | Hal Morris | .10 |
| 648 | Tim Birtsas | .05 |
| 649 | Steve Searcy | .05 |
| 650 | Dale Murphy | .12 |
| 651 | Ron Oester | .05 |
| 652 | Mike LaCoss | .05 |
| 653 | Ron Jones | .05 |
| 654 | Kelly Downs | .05 |
| 655 | Roger Clemens | .15 |
| 656 | Herm Winningham | .05 |
| 657 | Trevor Wilson | .05 |
| 658 | Jose Rijo | .05 |
| 659 | Dann Bilardello | .05 |
| 660 | Gregg Jefferies | .08 |
| 661 | Doug Drabek | .05 |
| 662 | Randy Myers (AS) | .05 |
| 663 | Benny Santiago (AS) | .05 |
| 664 | Will Clark (AS) | .15 |
| 665 | Ryne Sandberg (AS) | .12 |
| 666 | Barry Larkin (AS) | .05 |
| 667 | Matt Williams (AS) | .10 |
| 668 | Barry Bonds (AS) | .10 |
| 669 | Eric Davis (AS) | .10 |
| 670 | Bobby Bonilla (AS) | .08 |

**No. 671 to 683—1st Round Draft Pick**

| NO. | PLAYER | MINT |
|---|---|---|
| 671 | Chipper Jones (R) | .25 |
| 672 | Eric Christopherson (R) | .15 |
| 673 | Robbie Beckett (R) | .15 |
| 674 | Shane Andrews (R) | .15 |
| 675 | Steve Karsay (R) | .25 |
| 676 | Aaron Holbert (R) | .15 |
| 677 | Donovan Osborne (R) | .15 |
| 678 | Todd Ritchie (R) | .15 |
| 679 | Ron Walden (R) | .15 |
| 680 | Tim Costo (R) | .20 |
| 681 | Dan Wilson (R) | .20 |
| 682 | Kurt Miller (R) | .15 |
| 683 | Mike Lieberthal (R) | .15 |

**No. 684 to 688—K Man**

| NO. | PLAYER | MINT |
|---|---|---|
| 684 | Roger Clemens | .15 |
| 685 | Doc Gooden | .10 |
| 686 | Nolan Ryan | .20 |
| 687 | Frank Viola | .08 |
| 688 | Erik Hanson | .08 |
| 689 | Matt Williams | .10 |
| 690 | Jose Canseco | .15 |
| 691 | Darryl Strawberry | .10 |
| 692 | Bo Jackson | .15 |
| 693 | Cecil Fielder | .10 |

**No. 694 to 698—Rifleman**

| NO. | PLAYER | MINT |
|---|---|---|
| 694 | Sandy Alomar Jr. | .10 |
| 695 | Cory Snyder | .10 |
| 696 | Eric Davis | .10 |
| 697 | Ken Griffey Jr. | .30 |
| 698 | Andy Van Slyke | .08 |

**No. 699 to 707—No Hit Club**

| NO. | PLAYER | MINT |
|---|---|---|
| 699 | Langston/Witt | .05 |
| 700 | Randy Johnson | .05 |
| 701 | Nolan Ryan | .25 |
| 702 | Dave Stewart | .10 |
| 703 | Fernando Valenzuela | .08 |
| 704 | Andy Hawkins | .05 |
| 705 | Melido Perez | .05 |
| 706 | Terry Mulholland | .05 |
| 707 | Dave Stieb | .05 |

**No. 708 to 768—Rookie Prospects**

| NO. | PLAYER | MINT |
|---|---|---|
| 708 | Brian Barnes | .12 |
| 709 | Bernard Gilkey | .15 |
| 710 | Steve Decker (R) | .25 |
| 711 | Paul Faries (R) | .12 |
| 712 | Paul Marak (R) | .12 |
| 713 | Wes Chamberlain (R) | .40 |
| 714 | Kevin Belcher (R) | .12 |
| 715 | Dan Boone | .05 |
| 716 | Steve Adkins (R) | .12 |
| 717 | Geronimo Pena | .08 |
| 718 | Howard Farmer | .08 |
| 719 | Mark Leonard (R) | .15 |
| 720 | Tom Lampkin | .05 |
| 721 | Mike Gardiner (R) | .15 |
| 722 | Jeff Conine (R) | .15 |
| 723 | Efrain Valdez (R) | .12 |
| 724 | Chuck Malone | .08 |
| 725 | Leo Gomez | .25 |
| 726 | Paul McClellan (R) | .15 |
| 727 | Mark Leiter (R) | .12 |
| 728 | Rich DeLucia (R) | .15 |
| 729 | Mel Rojas | .10 |
| 730 | Hector Wagner (R) | .12 |
| 731 | Ray Lankford | .25 |
| 732 | Turner Ward (R) | .15 |
| 733 | Gerald Alexander (R) | .12 |
| 734 | Scott Anderson (R) | .12 |
| 735 | Tony Perezchica | .05 |
| 736 | Jimmy Kremers | .08 |
| 737 | American Flag | .35 |
| 738 | Mike York | .10 |
| 739 | Mike Rochford | .05 |
| 740 | Scott Aldred | .08 |
| 741 | Rico Brogna | .25 |
| 742 | Dave Burba (R) | .12 |
| 743 | Ray Stephens (R) | .12 |
| 744 | Eric Gunderson | .10 |
| 745 | Troy Afenir (R) | .12 |
| 746 | Jeff Shaw | .08 |
| 747 | Orlando Merced (R) | .30 |
| 748 | Omar Olivares (R) | .12 |
| 749 | Jerry Kutzler | .05 |
| 750 | Mo Vaughn | .30 |
| 751 | Matt Stark (R) | .15 |
| 752 | Randy Hennis (R) | .12 |
| 753 | Andujar Cedeno | .30 |
| 754 | Kelvin Torve | .08 |
| 755 | Joe Kraemer | .08 |
| 756 | Phil Clark (R) | .15 |
| 757 | Ed Vosberg (R) | .12 |
| 758 | Mike Perez (R) | .12 |
| 759 | Scott Lewis (R) | .12 |
| 760 | Steve Chitren (R) | .12 |
| 761 | Ray Young (R) | .15 |
| 762 | Andres Santana | .15 |
| 763 | Rodney McCray (R) | .12 |
| 764 | Sean Berry (R) | .15 |
| 765 | Brent Mayne | .05 |
| 766 | Mike Simms (R) | .15 |
| 767 | Glenn Sutko (R) | .12 |
| 768 | Gary DiSarcina | .05 |
| 769 | George Brett (HL) | .12 |
| 770 | Cecil Fielder (HL) | .10 |
| 771 | Jim Presley | .05 |
| 772 | John Dopson | .05 |
| 773 | Bo Jackson (RB) | .25 |
| 774 | Brent Knackert | .10 |
| 775 | Bill Doran | .05 |
| 776 | Dick Schofield | .05 |
| 777 | Nelson Santovenia | .05 |
| 778 | Mark Guthrie | .08 |
| 779 | Mark Lemke | .05 |
| 780 | Terry Steinbach | .05 |
| 781 | Tom Bolton | .05 |
| 782 | Randy Tomlin (R) | .20 |
| 783 | Jeff Kunkel | .05 |
| 784 | Felix Jose | .08 |
| 785 | Rick Sutcliffe | .05 |
| 786 | John Cerutti | .05 |
| 787 | Jose Vizcaino | .05 |
| 788 | Curt Schilling | .05 |
| 789 | Ed Whitson | .05 |
| 790 | Tony Pena | .05 |
| 791 | John Candelaria | .05 |
| 792 | Carmelo Martinez | .05 |
| 793 | Sandy Alomar Jr. | .10 |
| 794 | Jim Neidlinger (R) | .12 |
| 795 | Barry Larkin (WS) | .08 |
| 796 | Paul Sorrento | .05 |
| 797 | Tom Pagnozzi | .05 |
| 798 | Tino Martinez | .15 |
| 799 | Scott Ruskin | .08 |
| 800 | Kirk Gibson | .08 |
| 801 | Walt Terrell | .05 |
| 802 | John Tussell | .05 |
| 803 | Chili Davis | .05 |
| 804 | Chris Nabholz | .10 |
| 805 | Juan Gonzalez | .30 |
| 806 | Ron Hassey | .05 |
| 807 | Todd Worrell | .05 |
| 808 | Tommy Greene | .05 |
| 809 | Joel Skinner | .05 |
| 810 | Benny Santiago | .08 |
| 811 | Pat Tabler | .05 |
| 812 | Scott Erickson | .60 |
| 813 | Moises Alou | .08 |
| 814 | Dale Sveum | .05 |
| 815 | Ryne Sandberg Man of the Year | .20 |
| 816 | Rick Dempsey | .05 |
| 817 | Scott Bankhead | .05 |
| 818 | Jason Grimsley | .05 |
| 819 | Doug Jennings | .05 |
| 820 | Tom Herr | .05 |
| 821 | Rob Ducey | .05 |
| 822 | Luis Quinones | .05 |
| 823 | Greg Minton | .05 |
| 824 | Mark Grant | .05 |
| 825 | Ozzie Smith | .10 |
| 826 | Dave Eiland | .05 |
| 827 | Danny Heep | .05 |
| 828 | Hensely Meulens | .08 |
| 829 | Charlie O'Brien | .05 |
| 830 | Glenn Davis | .08 |
| 831 | John Marzano | .05 |
| 832 | Steve Ontiveros | .05 |
| 833 | Ron Karkovice | .05 |
| 834 | Jerry Goff | .05 |
| 835 | Ken Griffey Sr. | .05 |
| 836 | Kevin Reimer | .10 |
| 837 | Randy Kutcher | .05 |
| 838 | Mike Blowers | .05 |
| 839 | Mike Macfarlane | .05 |
| 840 | Frank Thomas | 1.00 |
| 841 | The Griffeys | 1.00 |
| 842 | Jack Howell | .05 |
| 843 | Mauro Gozzo | .05 |
| 844 | Gerald Young | .05 |
| 845 | Zane Smith | .05 |
| 846 | Kevin Brown | .05 |
| 847 | Sil Campusano | .05 |
| 848 | Larry Andersen | .05 |

**849 to 874—The Franchise**

| NO. | PLAYER | MINT |
|---|---|---|
| 849 | Cal Ripken Jr. | .15 |
| 850 | Roger Clemens | .15 |
| 851 | Sandy Alomar Jr. | .08 |
| 852 | Alan Trammell | .08 |
| 853 | George Brett | .12 |
| 854 | Robin Yount | .12 |
| 855 | Kirby Puckett | .15 |
| 856 | Don Mattingly | .15 |
| 857 | Rickey Henderson | .15 |
| 858 | Ken Griffey Jr. | .75 |
| 859 | Ruben Sierra | .15 |
| 860 | John Olerud | .10 |
| 861 | Dave Justice | .50 |
| 862 | Ryne Sandberg | .15 |
| 863 | Eric Davis | .10 |
| 864 | Darryl Strawberry | .15 |
| 865 | Tim Wallach | .05 |
| 866 | Doc Gooden | .08 |
| 867 | Lenny Dykstra | .05 |
| 868 | Barry Bonds | .08 |
| 869 | Todd Zeile | .10 |
| 870 | Benny Santiago | .08 |
| 871 | Will Clark | .20 |
| 872 | Craig Biggio | .08 |
| 873 | Wally Joyner | .10 |
| 874 | Frank Thomas | .75 |
| 875 | Rickey Henderson (MVP) | .15 |
| 876 | Barry Bonds (MVP) | .10 |
| 877 | Bob Welch (CY) | .05 |
| 878 | Doug Drabek (CY) | .05 |
| 879 | Sandy Alomar Jr. (ROY) | .10 |
| 880 | Dave Justice (ROY) | .25 |
| 881 | Damon Berryhill | .05 |

**No. 882 to 893—Deam Team**

| NO. | PLAYER | MINT |
|---|---|---|
| 882 | Frank Viola | .15 |
| 883 | Dave Stewart | .12 |
| 884 | Doug Jones | .05 |
| 885 | Randy Myers | .05 |
| 886 | Will Clark | .40 |
| 887 | Roberto Alomar | .20 |
| 888 | Barry Larkin | .15 |
| 889 | Wade Boggs | .25 |
| 890 | Rickey Henderson | .75 |
| 891 | Kirby Puckett | .25 |
| 892 | Ken Griffey Jr. | 1.50 |
| 893 | Benny Santiago | .15 |

# 1991 Score Traded & Rookie . . . Complete Set of 110 Cards—Value $12.00

Updates the main 1991 card set with players who changed teams during the season and rookies. The set was packaged in a printed box. Features the rookie cards of Ivan Rodriguez and Jeff Bagwell.

| NO. PLAYER | MINT | NO. PLAYER | MINT | NO. PLAYER | MINT | NO. PLAYER | MINT |
|---|---|---|---|---|---|---|---|
| 1T Bo Jackson | 1.00 | 29T Otis Nixon | .08 | 56T Bill Gullickson | .05 | 83T David Howard (R) | .12 |
| 2T Mike Flanagan | .05 | 30T Brian Downing | .05 | 57T Vince Coleman | .10 | 84T Heath Slocumb (R) | .12 |
| 3T Pete Incaviglia | .05 | 31T Dave Parker | .10 | 58T Fred McGriff | .10 | 85T Mike Timlin (R) | .15 |
| 4T Jack Clark | .10 | 32T John Candelaria | .05 | 59T Franklin Stubbs | .05 | 86T Darryl Kile | .12 |
| 5T Hubie Brooks | .05 | 33T Rob Murphy | .05 | 60T Eric King | .05 | 87T Pete Schourek (R) | .12 |
| 6T Ivan Calderon | .05 | 34T Deion Sanders | .08 | 61T Cory Snyder | .05 | 88T Bruce Walton (R) | .15 |
| 7T Glenn Davis | .05 | 35T Willie Randolph | .08 | 62T Dwight Evans | .05 | 89T Al Osuna (R) | .12 |
| 8T Wally Backman | .05 | 36T Pete Harnisch | .05 | 63T Gerald Perry | .05 | 90T Gary Scott (R) | .25 |
| 9T Dave Smith | .05 | 37T Dante Bichette | .05 | 64T Eric Show | .05 | 91T Doug Simons (R) | .12 |
| 10T Tim Raines | .10 | 38T Garry Templeton | .05 | 65T Shawn Hillegas | .05 | 92T Chris Jones (R) | .20 |
| 11T Joe Carter | .08 | 39T Gary Gaetti | .05 | 66T Tony Fernandez | .05 | 93T Chuck Knoblauch | .35 |
| 12T Sid Bream | .05 | 40T John Cerutti | .05 | 67T Tim Teufel | .05 | 94T Dana Allison (R) | .15 |
| 13T George Bell | .08 | 41T Rick Cerone | .05 | 68T Mitch Webster | .05 | 95T Erik Pappas (R) | .15 |
| 14T Steve Bedrosian | .05 | 42T Mike Pagliarulo | .05 | 69T Mike Heath | .05 | 96T Jeff Bagwell (R) | 3.00 |
| 15T Willie Wilson | .05 | 43T Ron Hassey | .05 | 70T Chili Davis | .05 | 97T Kirk Dressendorfer (R) | .25 |
| 16T Darryl Strawberry | .20 | 44T Roberto Alomar | .08 | 71T Larry Andersen | .05 | 98T Freddie Benavides (R) | .12 |
| 17T Danny Jackson | .05 | 45T Mike Boddicker | .05 | 72T Gary Varsho | .05 | 99T Luis Gonzalez (R) | .50 |
| 18T Kirk Gibson | .10 | 46T Bud Black | .05 | 73T Juan Berenguer | .05 | 100T Wade Taylor (R) | .15 |
| 19T Willie McGee | .10 | 47T Rob Deer | .05 | 74T Jack Morris | .08 | 101T Ed Sprague | .08 |
| 20T Junior Felix | .05 | 48T Devon White | .05 | 75T Barry Jones | .05 | 102T Bob Scanlan (R) | .12 |
| 21T Steve Farr | .05 | 49T Luis Sojo | .05 | 76T Rafael Belliard | .05 | 103T Rick Wilkins (R) | .20 |
| 22T Pat Tabler | .05 | 50T Terry Pendleton | .08 | 77T Andy Hawkins | .05 | 104T Chris Donnels (R) | .25 |
| 23T Brett Butler | .05 | 51T Kevin Gross | .05 | 78T Scott Sanderson | .05 | 105T Joe Slusarski (R) | .12 |
| 24T Danny Darwin | .05 | 52T Mike Huff | .05 | 79T Bob Ojeda | .05 | 106T Mark Lewis | .15 |
| 25T Mickey Tettleton | .05 | 53T Dave Righetti | .05 | 80T Curt Schilling | .05 | 107T Pat Kelly (R) | .25 |
| 26T Gary Carter | .08 | 54T Matt Young | .05 | 81T Brian Drahman (R) | .12 | 108T John Briscoe (R) | .12 |
| 27T Mitch Williams | .05 | 55T Ernest Riles | .05 | 82T Ivan Rodriguez (R) | 1.50 | 109T Luis Lopez (R) | .20 |
| 28T Candy Maldonado | .05 | | | | | 110T Jeff Johnson (R) | .20 |

# 1992 Score . . . Series One Set of 442 Cards (#1 to 442)—Value $15.00

Score announced late in 1991 that the company was sold. 2,495 autographed and 150,000 (5 card set) unsigned Joe D. Maggio cards were randomly inserted in packs. Seven bonus cards were only found in factory sets.

| NO. PLAYER | MINT | NO. PLAYER | MINT | NO. PLAYER | MINT | NO. PLAYER | MINT |
|---|---|---|---|---|---|---|---|
| SERIES ONE—No. 1 to 442 | | 14 Jeff Mongomery | .05 | 28 Dan Gladden | .05 | 42 Rick Aguilera | .05 |
| 1 Ken Griffey Jr. | .50 | 15 Roberto Alomar | .10 | 29 Melido Perez | .05 | 43 Mike Gallego | .05 |
| 2 Nolan Ryan | .35 | 16 Delino DeShields | .08 | 30 Willie Randolph | .05 | 44 Eric Davis | .12 |
| 3 Will Clark | .25 | 17 Steve Bedrosian | .05 | 31 Albert Belle | .10 | 45 George Bell | .08 |
| 4 Dave Justice | .30 | 18 Terry Pendleton | .08 | 32 Dave Winfield | .12 | 46 Tom Brunansky | .05 |
| 5 Dave Henderson | .10 | 19 Mark Carreon | .05 | 33 Jimmy Jones | .05 | 47 Steve Farr | .05 |
| 6 Bret Saberhagen | .10 | 20 Mark McGwire | .12 | 34 Kevin Gross | .05 | 48 Duane Ward | .05 |
| 7 Fred McGriff | .08 | 21 Roger Clemens | .20 | 35 Andres Galarraga | .08 | 49 David Wells | .05 |
| 8 Erik Hanson | .05 | 22 Chuck Crim | .05 | 36 Mike Devereaux | .05 | 50 Cecil Fielder | .12 |
| 9 Darryl Strawberry | .20 | 23 Don Mattingly | .15 | 37 Chris Bosio | .05 | 51 Walt Weiss | .05 |
| 10 Dwight Gooden | .10 | 24 Dickie Thon | .05 | 38 Mike LaValliere | .05 | 52 Todd Zeile | .08 |
| 11 Juan Gonzalez | .20 | 25 Ron Gant | .10 | 39 Gary Gaetti | .05 | 53 Doug Jones | .05 |
| 12 Mark Langston | .08 | 26 Milt Cuyler | .10 | 40 Felix Jose | .05 | 54 Bob Walk | .05 |
| 13 Lonnie Smith | .05 | 27 Mike Macfarlane | .05 | 41 Alvaro Espinoza | .05 | 55 Rafael Palmeiro | .08 |

| NO. | PLAYER | MINT |
|---|---|---|
| 56 | Rob Deer | .05 |
| 57 | Paul O'Neill | .05 |
| 58 | Jeff Reardon | .05 |
| 59 | Randy Ready | .05 |
| 60 | Scott Erickson | .15 |
| 61 | Paul Molitor | .10 |
| 62 | Jack McDowell | .05 |
| 63 | Jim Acker | .05 |
| 64 | Jay Buhner | .05 |
| 65 | Travis Fryman | .12 |
| 66 | Marquis Grissom | .08 |
| 67 | Mike Harkey | .05 |
| 68 | Luis Polonia | .05 |
| 69 | Ken Caminiti | .05 |
| 70 | Chris Sabo | .08 |
| 71 | Gregg Olson | .10 |
| 72 | Carlton Fisk | .12 |
| 73 | Juan Samuel | .05 |
| 74 | Todd Stottlemyre | .05 |
| 75 | Andre Dawson | .10 |
| 76 | Alvin Davis | .05 |
| 77 | Bill Doran | .05 |
| 78 | B.J. Surhoff | .05 |
| 79 | Kirk McCaskill | .05 |
| 80 | Dale Murphy | .10 |
| 81 | Jose DeLeon | .05 |
| 82 | Alex Fernandez | .08 |
| 83 | Ivan Calderon | .05 |
| 84 | Brent Mayne | .05 |
| 85 | Jody Reed | .05 |
| 86 | Randy Tomlin | .08 |
| 87 | Randy Milligan | .05 |
| 88 | Pascual Perez | .05 |
| 89 | Hensley Meulens | .08 |
| 90 | Joe Carter | .10 |
| 91 | Mike Moore | .05 |
| 92 | Ozzie Guillen | .05 |
| 93 | Shawn Hilligas | .05 |
| 94 | Chili Davis | .05 |
| 95 | Vince Coleman | .10 |
| 96 | Jimmy Key | .05 |
| 97 | Billy Ripken | .05 |
| 98 | Dave Smith | .05 |
| 99 | Tom Bolton | .05 |
| 100 | Barry Larkin | .08 |
| 101 | Kenny Rogers | .05 |
| 102 | Mike Boddicker | .05 |
| 103 | Kevin Elster | .05 |
| 104 | Ken Hill | .05 |
| 105 | Charlie Leibrandt | .05 |
| 106 | Pat Combs | .05 |
| 107 | Hubie Brooks | .05 |
| 108 | Julio Franco | .08 |
| 109 | Vicente Palacios | .05 |
| 110 | Kal Daniels | .05 |
| 111 | Bruce Hurst | .05 |
| 112 | Willie McGee | .10 |
| 113 | Ted Power | .05 |
| 114 | Milt Thompson | .05 |
| 115 | Doug Drabek | .05 |
| 116 | Rafael Belliard | .05 |
| 117 | Scott Garrelts | .05 |
| 118 | Terry Mulholland | .05 |
| 119 | Jay Howell | .05 |
| 120 | Danny Jackson | .05 |
| 121 | Scott Ruskin | .05 |
| 122 | Robin Ventura | .12 |
| 123 | Bip Roberts | .05 |
| 124 | Jeff Russell | .05 |
| 125 | Hal Morris | .08 |
| 126 | Teddy Higuera | .05 |
| 127 | Luis Sojo | .05 |
| 128 | Carlos Baerga | .08 |
| 129 | Jeff Ballard | .05 |
| 130 | Tom Gordon | .05 |
| 131 | Sid Bream | .05 |
| 132 | Rance Mulliniks | .05 |
| 133 | Andy Benes | .08 |
| 134 | Mickey Tettleton | .05 |
| 135 | Rich DeLucia | .05 |
| 136 | Tom Pagnozzi | .05 |
| 137 | Harold Baines | .05 |
| 138 | Danny Darwin | .05 |
| 139 | Kevin Bass | .05 |
| 140 | Chris Nabholz | .05 |
| 141 | Pete O'Brien | .05 |
| 142 | Jeff Treadway | .05 |
| 143 | Mickey Morandini | .05 |
| 144 | Eric King | .05 |
| 145 | Danny Tartabull | .08 |
| 146 | Lance Johnson | .05 |
| 147 | Casey Candaele | .05 |
| 148 | Felix Fermin | .05 |
| 149 | Rich Rodriquez | .05 |
| 150 | Dwight Evans | .05 |
| 151 | Joe Klink | .05 |
| 152 | Kevin Reimer | .05 |
| 153 | Orlando Merced | .10 |
| 154 | Mel Hall | .05 |
| 155 | Randy Myers | .05 |
| 156 | Greg Harris | .05 |
| 157 | Jeff Brantley | .05 |
| 158 | Jim Eisenreich | .05 |
| 159 | Luis Rivera | .05 |
| 160 | Cris Carpenter | .05 |
| 161 | Bruce Ruffin | .05 |
| 162 | Omar Vizquel | .05 |
| 163 | Gerald Alexander | .05 |
| 164 | Mark Guthrie | .05 |
| 165 | Scott Lewis | .08 |
| 166 | Bill Sampen | .05 |
| 167 | Dave Anderson | .05 |
| 168 | Kevin McReynolds | .08 |
| 169 | Jose Vizcaino | .05 |
| 170 | Bob Geren | .05 |
| 171 | Mike Morgan | .05 |
| 172 | Jim Gott | .05 |
| 173 | Mike Pagliarulo | .05 |
| 174 | Mike Jeffcoat | .05 |
| 175 | Craig Lefferts | .05 |
| 176 | Steve Finley | .05 |
| 177 | Wally Backman | .05 |
| 178 | Kent Mercker | .05 |
| 179 | John Cerutii | .05 |
| 180 | Jay Bell | .05 |
| 181 | Dale Sveum | .05 |
| 182 | Greg Gagne | .05 |
| 183 | Donnie Hill | .05 |
| 184 | Rex Hudler | .05 |
| 185 | Pat Kelly | .08 |
| 186 | Jeff Robinson | .05 |
| 187 | Jeff Gray | .05 |
| 188 | Jerry Willard | .05 |
| 189 | Carlos Quintana | .05 |
| 190 | Dennis Eckersley | .10 |
| 191 | Kelly Downs | .05 |
| 192 | Gregg Jefferies | .08 |
| 193 | Darrin Fletcher | .05 |
| 194 | Mike Jackson | .05 |
| 195 | Eddie Murray | .12 |
| 196 | Bill Landrum | .05 |
| 197 | Eric Yelding | .05 |
| 198 | Devon White | .05 |
| 199 | Larry Walker | .05 |
| 200 | Ryne Sandberg | .20 |
| 201 | Dave Magadan | .05 |
| 202 | Steve Chitren | .05 |
| 203 | Scott Fletcher | .05 |
| 204 | Dwayne Henry | .05 |
| 205 | Scott Coolbaugh | .05 |
| 206 | Tracy Jones | .05 |
| 207 | Von Hayes | .05 |
| 208 | Bob Melvin | .05 |
| 209 | Scott Scudder | .05 |
| 210 | Luis Gonzalez | .10 |
| 211 | Scott Sanderson | .05 |
| 212 | Chris Donnels | .10 |
| 213 | Heath Slocumb | .05 |
| 214 | Mike Timlin | .08 |
| 215 | Brian Harper | .05 |
| 216 | Juan Berenguer | .05 |
| 217 | Mike Henneman | .05 |
| 218 | Bill Spiers | .05 |
| 219 | Scott Terry | .05 |
| 220 | Frank Viola | .05 |
| 221 | Mark Eichhorn | .05 |
| 222 | Ernest Riles | .05 |
| 223 | Ray Lankford | .08 |
| 224 | Pete Harnisch | .05 |
| 225 | Bobby Bonilla | .10 |
| 226 | Mike Scioscia | .05 |
| 227 | Joel Skinner | .05 |
| 228 | Brian Holman | .05 |
| 229 | Gilberto Reyes | .05 |
| 230 | Matt Williams | .10 |
| 231 | Jaime Navarro | .05 |
| 232 | Jose Rijo | .05 |
| 233 | Atlee Hammaker | .05 |
| 234 | Tim Teufel | .05 |
| 235 | John Kruk | .05 |
| 236 | Kurt Stillwell | .05 |
| 237 | Dan Pasqua | .05 |
| 238 | Tim Crews | .05 |
| 239 | Dave Gallagher | .05 |
| 240 | Leo Gomez | .08 |
| 241 | Steve Avery | .15 |
| 242 | Bill Gullickson | .05 |
| 243 | Mark Portugal | .05 |
| 244 | Lee Guetterman | .05 |
| 245 | Benito Santiago | .05 |
| 246 | Jim Gantner | .05 |
| 247 | Robby Thompson | .05 |
| 248 | Terry Shumpert | .05 |
| 249 | Mike Bell | .05 |
| 250 | Harold Reynolds | .05 |
| 251 | Mike Felder | .05 |
| 252 | Bill Pecota | .05 |
| 253 | Bill Krueger | .05 |
| 254 | Alfredo Griffin | .05 |
| 255 | Lou Whitaker | .05 |
| 256 | Roy Smith | .05 |
| 257 | Jerald Clark | .05 |
| 258 | Sammy Sosa | .05 |
| 259 | Tim Naehring | .05 |
| 260 | Dave Righetti | .05 |
| 261 | Paul Gibson | .05 |
| 262 | Chris James | .05 |
| 263 | Larry Anderson | .05 |
| 264 | Storm Davis | .05 |
| 265 | Jose Lind | .05 |
| 266 | Greg Hibbard | .05 |
| 267 | Norm Charlton | .05 |
| 268 | Paul Kilgus | .05 |
| 270 | Ellis Burks | .08 |
| 271 | Frank Tanana | .05 |
| 272 | Gene Larkin | .05 |
| 273 | Ron Hassey | .05 |
| 274 | Jeff Robinson | .05 |
| 275 | Steve Howe | .05 |
| 276 | Daryl Boston | .05 |
| 277 | Mark Lee | .05 |
| 278 | Jose Segura | .10 |
| 279 | Lance Blankenship | .05 |
| 280 | Don Slaught | .05 |
| 281 | Russ Swan | .05 |
| 282 | Bob Tewksbury | .05 |
| 283 | Geno Petralli | .05 |
| 284 | Shane Mack | .05 |
| 285 | Bob Scanlan | .08 |
| 286 | Tim Leary | .05 |
| 287 | John Smoltz | .10 |
| 288 | Pat Borders | .05 |
| 289 | Mark Davison | .05 |
| 290 | Sam Horn | .05 |
| 291 | Lenny Harris | .05 |
| 292 | Franklin Stubbs | .05 |
| 293 | Thomas Howard | .05 |
| 294 | Steve Lyons | .05 |
| 295 | Francisco Oliveras | .05 |
| 296 | Terry Leach | .05 |
| 297 | Barry Jones | .05 |
| 298 | Lance Parrsh | .08 |
| 299 | Wally Whitehurst | .05 |
| 300 | Bob Welch | .05 |
| 301 | Charlie Hayes | .05 |
| 302 | Charlie Hough | .05 |
| 303 | Gary Redus | .05 |
| 304 | Scott Bradley | .05 |
| 305 | Jose Quendo | .05 |
| 306 | Pete Incaviglia | .05 |
| 307 | Marvin Freeman | .05 |
| 308 | Gary Pettis | .05 |
| 309 | Joe Slusarski | .05 |
| 310 | Kevin Seitzer | .05 |
| 311 | Jeff Reed | .05 |
| 312 | Pat Tabler | .05 |
| 313 | Mike Maddux | .05 |
| 314 | Bob Milacki | .05 |
| 315 | Eric Anthony | .05 |
| 316 | Dante Bichette | .05 |
| 317 | Steve Decker | .08 |
| 318 | Jack Clark | .08 |
| 319 | Doug Dascenzo | .05 |
| 320 | Scott Leius | .05 |
| 321 | Jim Lindeman | .05 |
| 322 | Bryan Harvey | .05 |
| 323 | Spike Owen | .05 |
| 324 | Roberto Kelly | .08 |
| 325 | Stan Belinda | .05 |
| 326 | Joey Cora | .05 |
| 327 | Jeff Innis | .05 |
| 328 | Willie Wilson | .05 |
| 329 | Juan Agosto | .05 |
| 330 | Charles Nagy | .05 |
| 331 | Scott Bailes | .05 |
| 332 | Pete Schourek | .05 |
| 333 | Mike Flanagan | .05 |
| 334 | Omar Oliveres | .08 |
| 335 | Dennis Lamp | .05 |
| 336 | Tommy Greene | .08 |
| 337 | Randy Velarde | .05 |
| 338 | Tom Lampkin | .05 |
| 339 | John Russell | .05 |
| 340 | Bob Kipper | .05 |
| 341 | Todd Burns | .05 |
| 342 | Ron Jones | .05 |
| 343 | Dave Valle | .05 |
| 344 | Mike Heath | .05 |
| 345 | John Olerud | .08 |
| 346 | Gerald Young | .05 |
| 347 | Ken Patterson | .05 |
| 348 | Les Lancaster | .05 |
| 349 | Steve Crawford | .05 |
| 350 | John Candelaria | .05 |
| 351 | Mike Aldrete | .05 |
| 352 | Mariano Duncan | .05 |
| 353 | Julio Machado | .05 |
| 354 | Ken Williams | .05 |
| 355 | Walt Terrell | .05 |
| 356 | Mitch Williams | .05 |
| 357 | Al Newman | .05 |
| 358 | Bud Black | .05 |
| 359 | Joe Hesketh | .05 |
| 360 | Paul Assenmacher | .05 |
| 361 | Bo Jackson | .20 |
| 362 | Jeff Blauser | .05 |
| 363 | Mike Brumley | .05 |
| 364 | Jim Deshaies | .05 |
| 365 | Brady Anderson | .05 |
| 366 | Chuck McElroy | .05 |
| 367 | Matt Merullo | .05 |
| 368 | Tim Belcher | .05 |
| 369 | Luis Aquino | .05 |
| 370 | Joe Oliver | .05 |
| 371 | Greg Swindell | .05 |
| 372 | Lee Stevens | .05 |
| 373 | Mark Kundson | .05 |
| 374 | Bill Wegman | .05 |
| 375 | Jerry Don Gleaton | .05 |
| 376 | Pedro Guerrero | .08 |
| 377 | Randy Bush | .05 |
| 378 | Greg Harris | .05 |
| 379 | Eric Plunk | .05 |
| 380 | Jose DeJesus | .05 |
| 381 | Bobby Witt | .05 |
| 382 | Curtis Wilkerson | .05 |
| 383 | Gene Nelson | .05 |
| 384 | Wes Chamberlain | .10 |
| 385 | Tom Henke | .05 |
| 386 | Mark Lemke | .05 |
| 387 | Greg Briley | .05 |
| 388 | Rafael Ramierz | .05 |
| 389 | Tony Fossas | .05 |
| 390 | Henry Cotto | .05 |
| 391 | Tim Hulett | .05 |

| NO. | PLAYER | MINT |
|---|---|---|
| 392 | Dean Palmer | .12 |
| 393 | Glenn Braggs | .05 |
| 394 | Mark Salas | .05 |
| **No. 395 to 424—Rookie Prospects** | | |
| 395 | Rusty Meacham | .08 |
| 396 | Andy Ashby | .10 |
| 397 | Jose Melendez | .08 |
| 398 | Warren Newson | .08 |
| 399 | Frank Castillo | .08 |
| 400 | Chito Martinez | .20 |
| 401 | Bernie Williams | .15 |
| 402 | Derek Bell | .20 |
| 403 | Javier Ortiz | .08 |
| 404 | Tim Sherrill | .08 |
| 405 | Rob MacDonald | .08 |

| NO. | PLAYER | MINT |
|---|---|---|
| 406 | Phil Plantier | .35 |
| 407 | Troy Afenir | .08 |
| 408 | Gino Minutelli | .12 |
| 409 | Reggie Jefferson | .20 |
| 410 | Mike Remlinger | .08 |
| 411 | Carlos Rodriquez | .08 |
| 412 | Joe Redfield | .20 |
| 413 | Alonzo Powell | .08 |
| 414 | Scott Livingstone | .08 |
| 415 | Scott Kamieniecki | .08 |
| 416 | Tim Spehr | .12 |
| 417 | Brian Hunter | .50 |
| 418 | Ced Landrum | .15 |
| 419 | Bret Barberie | .20 |

| NO. | PLAYER | MINT |
|---|---|---|
| 420 | Kevin Morton | .10 |
| 421 | Doug Henry | .15 |
| 422 | Doug Piatt | .10 |
| 423 | Pat Rice | .15 |
| 424 | Juan Guzman | .15 |
| **No. 425 to 428—No Hit Club** | | |
| 425 | Nolan Ryan | .20 |
| 426 | Tommy Greene | .05 |
| 427 | B. Milacki, M. Williamson, M. Flanagan, G. Olson | .05 |
| 428 | Wilson Alvarez | .05 |
| **No. 429 to 430—Highlights** | | |
| 429 | Otis Nixon | .05 |
| 430 | Rickey Henderson | .15 |

| NO. | PLAYER | MINT |
|---|---|---|
| **No. 431 to 440—AL All Stars** | | |
| 431 | Cecil Fielder | .10 |
| 432 | Julio Franco | .08 |
| 433 | Cal Ripken | .15 |
| 434 | Wade Boggs | .10 |
| 435 | Joe Carter | .10 |
| 436 | Ken Griffey Jr. | .15 |
| 437 | Ruben Sierra | .10 |
| 438 | Scott Erickson | .10 |
| 439 | Tom Henke | .08 |
| 440 | Terry Steinbach | .08 |
| **No. 441 to 442—Dream Team** | | |
| 441 | Rickey Henderson | .25 |
| 442 | Ryne Sandberg | .25 |

**SERIES NO. 2 NOT
RELEASED AT PRESS TIME**

# 1989 Upper Deck . . . Complete Set of 700 Cards—Value $150.00 (Factory Set of 800 Cards—Value $200.00)

This was the premier issue of Upper Deck—the sixth major card manufacturer. Features the rookie cards of Gary Sheffield and Ken Griffey, Jr. A special feature is a small hologram on the card's back to discourage counterfeiting. The first 26 cards feature Upper Deck's selection of star rookies. Each team checklist features a drawing of a player on the team.

Ricky Jordan

Craig Biggio

Gary Sheffield

Sandy Alomar Jr.

Ken Griffey Jr.

| NO. | PLAYER | MINT |
|---|---|---|
| 1 | Ken Griffey Jr. (R) | 60.00 |
| 2 | Luis Medina (R) | .20 |
| 3 | Tony Chance (R) | .15 |
| 4 | Dave Otto | .15 |
| 5 | Sandy Alomar, Jr. (R) | 2.00 |
| 6 | Rolando Roomes (R) | .15 |
| 7 | David West (R) | .25 |
| 8 | Cris Carpenter (R) | .25 |
| 9 | Gregg Jefferies | .75 |
| 10 | Doug Dascenzo (R) | .20 |
| 11 | Ron Jones (R) | .20 |
| 12 | Luis De Los Santos (R) | .20 |
| 13 | Gary Sheffield (R) | 1.50 |
| 13 | Gary Sheffield (error) | 1.50 |
| 14 | Mike Harkey (R) | .35 |
| 15 | Lance Blankenship (R) | .15 |
| 16 | William Brennan (R) | .15 |
| 17 | John Smoltz (R) | 3.00 |
| 18 | Ramon Martinez (R) | 7.50 |
| 19 | Mark Lemke (R) | .40 |
| 20 | Juan Bell (R) | .20 |
| 21 | Rey Palacios (R) | .15 |
| 22 | Felix Jose (R) | 5.00 |
| 23 | Van Snider (R) | .15 |
| 24 | Dante Bichete (R) | .50 |
| 25 | Randy Johnson (R) | 1.00 |
| 26 | Carlos Quintana (R) | .75 |
| 27 | Star Rookie Checklist | .10 |
| 28 | Mike Schooler | .25 |
| 29 | Randy St. Claire | .12 |
| 30 | Gerald Clark (R) | .50 |
| 31 | Kevin Gross | .08 |
| 32 | Dan Firova (R) | .15 |
| 33 | Jeff Calhoun | .08 |
| 34 | Tommy Hinze | .08 |
| 35 | Ricky Jordan (R) | .35 |
| 36 | Larry Parrish | .10 |
| 37 | Bret Saberhagen | .20 |
| 38 | Mike Smithson | .08 |
| 39 | Dave Dravecky | .08 |
| 40 | Ed Romero | .08 |
| 41 | Jeff Musselman | .08 |
| 42 | Ed Hearn | .08 |
| 43 | Rance Mulliniks | .08 |
| 44 | Jim Eisenreich | .08 |
| 45 | Sil Campusano (R) | .20 |
| 46 | Mike Krukow | .10 |
| 47 | Paul Gibson (R) | .15 |
| 48 | Mike LaCoss | .08 |
| 49 | Larry Herndon | .08 |
| 50 | Scott Garreits | .08 |
| 51 | Duane Henry | .08 |
| 52 | Jim Acker | .08 |
| 53 | Steve Sax | .12 |
| 54 | Pete O'Brien | .08 |
| 55 | Paul Runge | .08 |
| 56 | Rick Rhoden | .08 |
| 57 | John Dopson (R) | .15 |
| 58 | Casey Candaele | .08 |
| 59 | Dave Righetti | .08 |
| 60 | Joe Hesketh | .08 |
| 61 | Frank DiPino | .08 |
| 62 | Tim Laudner | .08 |
| 63 | Jamie Moyer | .08 |
| 64 | Fred Toliver | .08 |
| 65 | Mitch Webster | .08 |
| 66 | John Tudor | .12 |
| 67 | John Cangelosi | .08 |

| NO. | PLAYER | MINT |
|---|---|---|
| 68 | Mike Devereaux | .15 |
| 69 | Brian Fisher | .08 |
| 70 | Mike Marshall | .10 |
| 71 | Zane Smith | .08 |
| 72 | B. Holton (error) | 1.25 |
| 72 | B. Holton (correct) | .25 |
| 73 | Jose Guzman | .08 |
| 74 | Rick Mahler | .10 |
| 75 | John Shelby | .08 |
| 76 | Jim Deshaies | .08 |
| 77 | Bobby Meacham | .08 |
| 78 | Bryn Smith | .08 |
| 79 | Joaquin Andujar | .08 |
| 80 | Richard Dotson | .08 |
| 81 | Charlie Lea | .08 |
| 82 | Calvin Schiraldi | .08 |
| 83 | Les Straker | .08 |
| 84 | Les Lancaster | .08 |
| 85 | Allan Anderson | .08 |
| 86 | Junior Oritz | .08 |
| 87 | Jesse Orosco | .08 |
| 88 | Felix Fermin | .08 |
| 89 | Dave Anderson | .08 |
| 90 | Rafael Belliard | .08 |
| 91 | Franklin Stubbs | .08 |
| 92 | Cecil Espy | .08 |
| 93 | Albert Hall | .08 |
| 94 | Tim Leary | .08 |
| 95 | Mitch Williams | .08 |
| 96 | Tracy Jones | .08 |
| 97 | Danny Darwin | .08 |
| 98 | Gary Ward | .08 |
| 99 | Neal Heaton | .08 |
| 100 | Jim Pankovits | .08 |
| 101 | Bill Doran | .08 |
| 102 | Tim Wallach | .08 |
| 103 | Joe Magrane | .08 |
| 104 | Ozzie Virgil | .08 |
| 105 | Alvin Davis | .08 |
| 106 | Tom Brookens | .08 |
| 107 | Shawon Dunston | .15 |
| 108 | Tracy Woodson | .08 |
| 109 | Nelson Liriano | .08 |
| 110 | Devon White | .12 |
| 111 | Steve Balboni | .10 |
| 112 | Buddy Bell | .08 |
| 113 | German Jimenez (R) | .15 |
| 114 | Ken Dayley | .08 |
| 115 | Andres Galarraga | .15 |
| 116 | Mike Scioscia | .08 |
| 117 | Gary Pettis | .08 |
| 118 | Ernie Whitt | .08 |
| 119 | Bob Boone | .08 |
| 120 | Ryne Sandberg | 1.25 |
| 121 | Bruce Benedict | .08 |
| 122 | Hubie Brooks | .08 |
| 123 | Mike Moore | .08 |
| 124 | Wallace Johnson | .08 |
| 125 | Bob Horner | .08 |
| 126 | Chili Davis | .08 |
| 127 | Manny Trillo | .08 |
| 128 | Chet Lemon | .10 |
| 129 | John Cerutti | .08 |
| 130 | Orel Hershiser | .20 |
| 131 | Terry Pendleton | .15 |
| 132 | Jeff Blauser | .15 |
| 133 | Mike Fitzgerald | .08 |
| 134 | Henry Cotto | .08 |

| NO. | PLAYER | MINT |
|---|---|---|
| 135 | Gerald Young | .08 |
| 136 | Luis Salazar | .08 |
| 137 | Alejandro Pena | .08 |
| 138 | Jack Howell | .08 |
| 139 | Tony Fernandez | .08 |
| 140 | Mark Grace | 1.00 |
| 141 | Ken Caminiti | .08 |
| 142 | Mike Jackson | .08 |
| 143 | Larry McWilliams | .08 |
| 144 | Andres Thomas | .08 |
| 145 | Nolan Ryan | 3.00 |
| 146 | Mike Davis | .08 |
| 147 | DeWayne Buice | .08 |
| 148 | Jody Davis | .08 |
| 149 | Jesse Barfield | .12 |
| 150 | Matte Nokes | .10 |
| 151 | Jerry Reuss | .08 |
| 152 | Rick Cerone | .08 |
| 153 | Storm Davis | .08 |
| 154 | Marvell Wynee | .08 |
| 155 | Will Clark | 1.50 |
| 156 | Luis Aguayo | .08 |
| 157 | Willie Upshaw | .08 |
| 158 | Randy Bush | .08 |
| 159 | Ron Darling | .12 |
| 160 | Kal Daniels | .15 |
| 161 | Spike Owen | .08 |
| 162 | Luis Polonia | .15 |
| 163 | Kevin Mitchell | .50 |
| 164 | Dave Gallagher (R) | .15 |
| 165 | Benito Santiago | .15 |
| 166 | Greg Gagne | .08 |
| 167 | Ken Phelps | .08 |
| 168 | Sid Fernandez | .08 |
| 169 | Bo Diaz | .08 |
| 170 | Cory Snyder | .15 |
| 171 | Eric Show | .10 |
| 172 | Ron Thompson | .08 |
| 173 | Marty Barrett | .10 |
| 174 | Dave Henderson | .15 |
| 175 | Ozzie Guillen | .08 |
| 176 | Barry Lyons | .08 |
| 177 | Kelvin Torve (R) | .15 |
| 178 | Don Slaught | .08 |
| 179 | Steve Lombardozzi | .08 |
| 180 | Chris Sabo (R) | 2.00 |
| 181 | Jose Uribe | .08 |
| 182 | Shane Mack | .08 |
| 183 | Ron Karkovice | .08 |
| 184 | Todd Benzinger | .10 |
| 185 | Dave Stewart | .15 |
| 186 | Julio Franco | .30 |
| 187 | Ron Robinson | .08 |
| 188 | Wally Backman | .08 |
| 189 | Randy Velarde | .08 |
| 190 | Joe Carter | .40 |
| 191 | Bob Welch | .08 |
| 192 | Kelly Paris | .08 |
| 193 | Chris Brown | .08 |
| 194 | Rick Reuschel | .10 |
| 195 | Roger Clemens | 1.25 |
| 196 | Dave Concepcion | .08 |
| 197 | Al Newman | .08 |
| 198 | Brook Jacoby | .08 |
| 199 | Mookie Wilson | .08 |
| 200 | Don Mattingly | .75 |
| 201 | Dick Schofield | .08 |
| 202 | Mark Gubicza | .08 |

| NO. | PLAYER | MINT |
|---|---|---|
| 203 | Gary Gaetti | .12 |
| 204 | Dan Pasqua | .08 |
| 205 | Andre Dawson | .35 |
| 206 | Chris Speier | .08 |
| 207 | Kent Tekulve | .08 |
| 208 | Rod Scurry | .08 |
| 209 | Scott Bailes | .08 |
| 210 | Rickey Henderson | 1.25 |
| 211 | Harold Baines | .08 |
| 212 | Tony Armas | .08 |
| 213 | Kent Hrbek | .15 |
| 214 | Darrin Jackson | .10 |
| 215 | George Brett | .50 |
| 216 | Rafael Santana | .08 |
| 217 | Andy Allanson | .08 |
| 218 | Brett Butler | .08 |
| 219 | Steve Jeltz | .08 |
| 220 | Jay Buhner | .35 |
| 221 | Bo Jackson | 1.50 |
| 222 | Angel Salazar | .08 |
| 223 | Kirk McCaskill | .08 |
| 224 | Steve Lyons | .08 |
| 225 | Bert Blyleven | .08 |
| 226 | Scott Bradley | .08 |
| 227 | Bob Melvin | .08 |
| 228 | Ron Kittle | .08 |
| 229 | Phil Bradley | .08 |
| 230 | Tommy John | .08 |
| 231 | Greg Walker | .08 |
| 232 | Juan Berenguer | .08 |
| 233 | Pat Tabler | .08 |
| 234 | Terry Clark (R) | .15 |
| 235 | Rafael Palmeiro | .40 |
| 236 | Paul Zuvella | .08 |
| 237 | Willie Randolph | .10 |
| 238 | Bruce Fields | .08 |
| 239 | Mike Aldrete | .08 |
| 240 | Lance Parrish | .10 |
| 241 | Gregg Maddux | .30 |
| 242 | John Moses | .08 |
| 243 | Melido Perez | .15 |
| 244 | Willie Wilson | .08 |
| 245 | Mark McLemore | .08 |
| 246 | Von Hayes | .10 |
| 247 | Matt Williams | .75 |
| 248 | John Candelaria | .12 |
| 249 | Harold Reynolds | .08 |
| 250 | Greg Swindell | .08 |
| 251 | Juan Agosto | .08 |
| 252 | Mike Felder | .08 |
| 253 | Vince Coleman | .20 |
| 254 | Larry Sheets | .08 |
| 255 | George Bell | .30 |
| 256 | Terry Steinbach | .08 |
| 257 | Jack Armstrong (R) | .25 |
| 258 | Dickie Thon | .08 |
| 259 | Ray Knight | .08 |
| 260 | Darryl Strawberry | 1.00 |
| 261 | Doug Sisk | .08 |
| 262 | Alex Trevino | .08 |
| 263 | Jeff Leonard | .08 |
| 264 | Tom Henke | .08 |
| 265 | Ozzie Smith | .40 |
| 266 | Dave Bergman | .08 |
| 267 | Tony Phillips | .08 |
| 268 | Mark Davis | .08 |
| 269 | Kevin Elster | .08 |
| 270 | Barry Larkin | .35 |

| NO. | PLAYER | MINT | NO. | PLAYER | MINT | NO. | PLAYER | MINT | NO. | PLAYER | MINT |
|---|---|---|---|---|---|---|---|---|---|---|---|
| 271 | Manny Lee | .08 | 357 | Dale Murphy (cor.) | .30 | 442 | Rob Deer | .08 | 529 | Jerry Reed | .08 |
| 272 | Tom Brunansky | .10 | 357 | Dale Murphy (err.) | 60.00 | 443 | Glenn Davis | .15 | 530 | Jack McDowell | .50 |
| 273 | Craig Biggio (R) | 1.50 | | reversed negative | | 444 | Dave Martinez | .08 | 531 | Greg Mathews | .08 |
| 274 | Jim Gantner | .08 | 358 | Mark Portugal | .08 | 445 | Bill Wegman | .08 | 532 | John Russell | .08 |
| 275 | Eddie Murray | .40 | 359 | Andy McGaffigan | .08 | 446 | Loyd McClendon | .12 | 533 | Dan Quisenberry | .08 |
| 276 | Jeff Reed | .08 | 360 | Tom Glavine | 1.00 | 447 | Dave Schmidt | .08 | 534 | Greg Gross | .08 |
| 277 | Tim Teufel | .08 | 361 | Keith Moreland | .08 | 448 | Darren Daulton | .08 | 535 | Danny Cox | .08 |
| 278 | Rick Honeycutt | .08 | 362 | Todd Stottlemyre | .35 | 449 | Frank Williams | .08 | 536 | Terry Francona | .08 |
| 279 | Guillermo Hernandez | .08 | 363 | Dave Leiper | .08 | 450 | Dan Aase | .08 | 537 | Andy Van Slyke | .20 |
| 280 | John Kruk | .08 | 364 | Cecil Fielder | 1.00 | 451 | Lou Whitaker | .08 | 538 | Mel Hall | .08 |
| 281 | Luis Alice (R) | .15 | 365 | Carmelo Martinez | .08 | 452 | Goose Gossage | .08 | 539 | Jim Gott | .08 |
| 282 | Jim Clancy | .08 | 366 | Dwight Evans | .08 | 453 | Ed Whitson | .08 | 540 | Doug Jones | .08 |
| 283 | Billy Ripken | .10 | 367 | Kevin McReynolds | .15 | 454 | Jim Walewander | .08 | 541 | Craig Lefferts | .08 |
| 284 | Craig Reynolds | .08 | 368 | Rich Gedman | .08 | 455 | Damon Berryhill | .10 | 542 | Mike Boddicker | .08 |
| 285 | Robin Yount | .50 | 369 | Len Dykstra | .08 | 456 | Tim Burke | .08 | 543 | Greg Brock | .08 |
| 286 | Jimmy Jones | .08 | 370 | Jody Reed | .15 | 457 | Barry Jones | .08 | 544 | Atlee Hammaker | .08 |
| 287 | Ron Oester | .08 | 371 | Jose Canseco | 1.50 | 458 | Joel Youngblood | .08 | 545 | Tom Bolton | .08 |
| 288 | Terry Leach | .08 | 372 | Rob Murphy | .08 | 459 | Floyd Youmans | .08 | 546 | Mike MacFarlane (R) | .15 |
| 289 | Dennis Eckersley | .20 | 373 | Mike Henneman | .08 | 460 | Mark Salas | .08 | 547 | Rich Rentiera | .15 |
| 290 | Alan Trammel | .30 | 374 | Walt Weiss | .15 | 461 | Jeff Russell | .08 | 548 | John Davis | .08 |
| 291 | Jimmy Key | .08 | 375 | Bob Dibble (R) | .75 | 462 | Darrell Miller | .08 | 549 | Floyd Bannister | .08 |
| 292 | Chris Bosio | .08 | 376 | Kirby Puckett | 1.00 | 463 | Jeff Kunkel | .08 | 550 | Mickey Tettleton | .08 |
| 293 | Jose DeLeon | .08 | 377 | Denny Martinez | .08 | 464 | Sherman Corbett | .10 | 551 | Duane Ward | .15 |
| 294 | Jim Traber | .08 | 378 | Ron Gant | 1.50 | 465 | Curtis Wilkerson | .08 | 552 | Dan Petry | .08 |
| 295 | Mike Scott | .15 | 379 | Brian Harper | .08 | 466 | Bud Black | .08 | 553 | Mickey Tettleton | .08 |
| 296 | Roger McDowell | .08 | 380 | Nelson Santovenia (R) | .20 | 467 | Cal Ripken Jr. | 1.00 | 554 | Rick Leach | .08 |
| 297 | Gary Templeton | .08 | 381 | Lloyd Moseby | .10 | 468 | John Farrell | .08 | 555 | Mike Witt | .08 |
| 298 | Doyle Alexander | .08 | 382 | Lance McCullers | .08 | 469 | Terry Kennedy | .08 | 556 | Sid Bream | .08 |
| 299 | Nick Esasky | .08 | 383 | Dave Stieb | .10 | 470 | Tom Candiotti | .08 | 557 | Bobby Witt | .08 |
| 300 | Mark McGwire | .40 | 384 | Tony Gwynn | .50 | 471 | Roberto Alomar | 1.25 | 558 | Tommy Herr | .08 |
| 301 | Darryl Hamilton (R) | .25 | 385 | Mike Flanagan | .08 | 472 | Jeff Robinson | .08 | 559 | Randy Milligan | .25 |
| 302 | Dave Smith | .08 | 386 | Bob Ojeda | .08 | 473 | Vance Law | .08 | 560 | Jose Cecena | .12 |
| 303 | Rick Sutcliffe | .08 | 387 | Bruce Hurst | .08 | 474 | Randy Ready | .08 | 561 | Mackey Sasser | .20 |
| 304 | Dave Stapleton | .10 | 388 | Dave Magadan | .15 | 475 | Walt Terrell | .08 | 562 | Carney Lansford | .08 |
| 305 | Alan Ashby | .08 | 389 | Wade Boggs | .60 | 476 | Kelly Downs | .08 | 563 | Rick Aguilera | .08 |
| 306 | Pedro Guerrero | .15 | 390 | Gary Carter | .15 | 477 | Johnny Paredes | .10 | 564 | Ron Hassey | .08 |
| 307 | Ron Guidry | .08 | 391 | Frank Tanana | .08 | 478 | Shawn Hillegas | .08 | 565 | Dwight Gooden | .40 |
| 308 | Steve Farr | .08 | 392 | Curt Young | .08 | 479 | Bob Brenly | .08 | 566 | Paul Assenmacher | .08 |
| 309 | Curt Ford | .08 | 393 | Jeff Treadway | .15 | 480 | Otis Nixon | .08 | 567 | Neil Allen | .08 |
| 310 | Claudell Washington | .08 | 394 | Darrell Evans | .08 | 481 | Johnny Ray | .08 | 568 | Jim Morrison | .08 |
| 311 | Tom Prince | .08 | 395 | Glenn Hubbard | .08 | 482 | Geno Petralli | .08 | 569 | Mike Pagliarulo | .10 |
| 312 | Chad Kreuter (R) | .15 | 396 | Chuck Cary | .08 | 483 | Stu Cliburn | .08 | 570 | Tedd Simmons | .08 |
| 313 | Ken Oberkfell | .08 | 397 | Frank Viola | .15 | 484 | Pete Incaviglia | .12 | 571 | Mark Thurmond | .08 |
| 314 | Jerry Browne | .08 | 398 | Jeff Parrett | .10 | 485 | Bria Downing | .08 | 572 | Fred McGriff | .50 |
| 315 | R.J. Reynolds | .08 | 399 | Terry Blocker (R) | .12 | 486 | Jeff Stone | .08 | 573 | Wally Joyner | .35 |
| 316 | Scott Bankhead | .08 | 400 | Dan Gladden | .08 | 487 | Carmen Castillo | .08 | 574 | Jose Bautista (R) | .15 |
| 317 | Milt Thompson | .08 | 401 | Louis Meadows (R) | .12 | 488 | Tom Niedenfuer | .08 | 575 | Kelly Gruber | .20 |
| 318 | Mario Diaz | .08 | 402 | Tim Raines | .15 | 489 | Jay Bell | .25 | 576 | Cecilo Guante | .08 |
| 319 | Bruce Ruffin | .08 | 403 | Joey Meyer | .10 | 490 | Rick Schu | .10 | 577 | Mark Davidson | .08 |
| 320 | Dave Valle | .08 | 404 | Larry Anderson | .08 | 491 | Jeff Pico (R) | .12 | 578 | Bobby Bonilla | .60 |
| 321 | Gary Varsho | .15 | 405 | Rex Hudler | .08 | 492 | Mark Parent (R) | .12 | 579 | Mike Stanley | .08 |
| 321 | Gary Varsho (error) | 2.00 | 406 | Mike Schmidt | 1.50 | 493 | Eric King | .08 | 580 | Gene Larkin | .08 |
| 322 | Paul Mirabella | .08 | 407 | John Franco | .08 | 494 | Al Nipper | .08 | 581 | Stan Javier | .08 |
| 323 | Chuck Jackson | .08 | 408 | Brady Anderson (R) | .20 | 495 | Andy Hawkins | .08 | 582 | Howard Johnson | .25 |
| 324 | Drew Hall | .08 | 409 | Don Carmen | .03 | 496 | Daryl Boston | .08 | 583 | Mike Gallego | .30 |
| 325 | Don August | .08 | 410 | Eric Davis | .35 | 497 | Ernie Riles | .08 | 583 | M. Gallego (error) | 1.25 |
| 326 | Israel Sanchez (R) | .15 | 411 | Bob Stanley | .08 | 498 | Pascual Perez | .08 | 584 | David Cone | .20 |
| 327 | Denny Walling | .08 | 412 | Pete Smith | .12 | 499 | Bill Long | .08 | 585 | Doug Jennings (R) | .20 |
| 328 | Joel Skinner | .08 | 413 | Jim Rice | .15 | 500 | Kirt Manwaring | .08 | 586 | Charlie Hudson | .25 |
| 329 | Danny Tartabull | .25 | 414 | Bruce Sutter | .10 | 501 | Chuck Crim | .08 | 587 | Dion James | .08 |
| 330 | Tony Pena | .08 | 415 | Oil Can Boyd | .08 | 502 | Candy Maldonado | .08 | 588 | Al Leiter | .10 |
| 331 | Jim Sundberg | .08 | 416 | Ruben Sierra | .75 | 503 | Dennis Lamp | .08 | 589 | Charlie Puleo | .08 |
| 332 | Jeff Robinson | .08 | 417 | Mike LaValiere | .08 | 504 | Glenn Braggs | .08 | 590 | Roberto Kelly | .40 |
| 333 | Odibbe McDowell | .08 | 418 | Steve Buechele | .08 | 505 | Joe Price | .08 | 591 | Thad Bosley | .08 |
| 334 | Jose Lind | .08 | 419 | Gary Redus | .08 | 506 | Ken Williams | .08 | 592 | Pete Stanicek | .08 |
| 335 | Paul Kilgus | .08 | 420 | Scott Fletcher | .08 | 507 | Bill Pecota | .08 | 593 | Pat Borders (R) | .35 |
| 336 | Juan Samuel | .08 | 421 | Dale Sveum | .08 | 508 | Rey Quinones | .08 | 594 | Bryan Harvey (R) | .75 |
| 337 | Mike Campbell | .10 | 422 | Bob Knepper | .08 | 509 | Jeff Bittiger (R) | .15 | 595 | Jeff Ballard | .15 |
| 338 | Mike Maddux | .08 | 423 | Luis Rivera | .08 | 510 | Kevin Seitzer | .15 | 596 | Jeff Reardon | .08 |
| 339 | Darnell Coles | .08 | 424 | Ted Higuera | .08 | 511 | Steve Bedrosian | .08 | 597 | Doug Drabek | .08 |
| 340 | Bob Dernier | .08 | 425 | Kevin Bass | .08 | 512 | Todd Worrell | .10 | 598 | Edwin Correa | .08 |
| 341 | Rafael Ramierez | .08 | 426 | Ken Gerhart | .08 | 513 | Chris James | .08 | 599 | Keith Atherton | .08 |
| 342 | Scott Sanderson | .08 | 427 | Shane Rawley | .08 | 514 | Jose Oquendo | .08 | 600 | Dave LaPoint | .08 |
| 343 | B.J. Surhoff | .08 | 428 | Paul O'Neill | .12 | 515 | David Palmer | .08 | 601 | Don Baylor | .08 |
| 344 | Billy Hatcher | .08 | 429 | Joe Orsulak | .08 | 516 | John Smiley | .08 | 602 | Tom Pagnozzi | .08 |
| 345 | Pat Perry | .08 | 430 | Jack Gutierrez | .08 | 517 | Dave Clark | .08 | 603 | Tim Flannery | .08 |
| 346 | Jack Clark | .15 | 431 | Gerald Perry | .08 | 518 | Mike Dunne | .08 | 604 | Gene Walter | .08 |
| 347 | Gary Thurman | .08 | 432 | Mike Greenwell | .40 | 519 | Ron Washington | .08 | 605 | Dave Parker | .20 |
| 348 | Timmy Jones (R) | .15 | 433 | Jerry Royster | .08 | 520 | Bob Kipper | .08 | 606 | Mike Diaz | .08 |
| 349 | Dave Winfield | .25 | 434 | Ellis Burks | .40 | 521 | Lee Smith | .08 | 607 | Chris Gwynn | .12 |
| 350 | Frank White | .08 | 435 | Ed Olwine | .08 | 522 | Juan Castillo | .08 | 608 | Odell Jones | .08 |
| 351 | Dave Collins | .08 | 436 | Dave Rucker | .08 | 523 | Don Robinson | .08 | 609 | Carlton Fisk | .35 |
| 352 | Jack Morris | .20 | 437 | Charlie Hough | .08 | 524 | Kevin Romine | .08 | 610 | Jay Howell | .08 |
| 353 | Eric Plunk | .08 | 438 | Bob Walk | .08 | 525 | Paul Molitor | .20 | 611 | Tim Crews | .08 |
| 354 | Leon Durham | .08 | 439 | Bob Brower | .08 | 526 | Mark Langston | .15 | 612 | Keith Hernandez | .15 |
| 355 | Ivan DeJesus | .15 | 440 | Bobby Bonds | .75 | 527 | Donnie Hill | .08 | 613 | Willie Fraser | .08 |
| 356 | Brian Holman (R) | .35 | 441 | Tom Foley | .08 | 528 | Larry Owen | .08 | 614 | Jim Eppard | .08 |

| NO. | PLAYER | MINT |
|---|---|---|
| 615 | Jeff Hamilton | .08 |
| 616 | Kurt Stilwell | .08 |
| 617 | Tom Browning | .08 |
| 618 | Jeff Montgomery | .15 |
| 619 | Jose Rijo | .08 |
| 620 | Jamie Quirk | .08 |
| 621 | Willie McGee | .15 |
| 622 | Mark Grant | .08 |
| 623 | Bill Swift | .08 |
| 624 | Orlando Mercado | .08 |
| 625 | John Costello | .15 |
| 626 | Jose Gonzalez | .08 |
| 627 | Bill Schroeder | .30 |
| 627 | B. Schroeder (error) | 1.50 |
| 628 | Fred Manrique | .12 |
| 628 | F. Manrique (error) | .30 |
| 629 | Ricky Horton | .08 |
| 630 | Dan Plesac | .08 |
| 631 | Alfredo Griffin | .08 |
| 632 | Chuck Finley | .30 |
| 633 | Kirk Gibson | .20 |
| 634 | Randy Myers | .08 |
| 635 | Greg Minton | .08 |

| NO. | PLAYER | MINT |
|---|---|---|
| 636 | H. Winningham (err.) | .35 |
| 636 | H. Winningham (cor.) | .12 |
| 637 | Charlie Leibrandt | .08 |
| 638 | Tim Birtsas | .08 |
| 639 | Bill Buckner | .08 |
| 640 | Danny Jackson | .10 |
| 641 | Greg Booker | .08 |
| 642 | Jim Presley | .08 |
| 643 | Gene Nelson | .08 |
| 644 | Rod Booker | .08 |
| 645 | Dennis Rasmussen | .08 |
| 646 | Juan Nieves | .08 |
| 647 | Bobby Thigpen | .08 |
| 648 | Tim Belcher | .20 |
| 649 | Mike Young | .08 |
| 650 | Ivan Calderon | .08 |
| 651 | Oswaldo Peraza (R) | .15 |
| 652 | Pat Sheridan (cor.) | .20 |
| 652 | Pat Sheridan (err.) | 25.00 |
| 653 | Mike Morgan | .08 |
| 654 | Mike Heath | .08 |
| 655 | Jay Tibbs | .08 |

| NO. | PLAYER | MINT |
|---|---|---|
| 656 | Fernando Valenzuela | .15 |
| 657 | Lee Mazzilli | .10 |
| 658 | AL Cy Young | .12 |
| 659 | AL MVP | .35 |
| 660 | AL Rookie of the Year | .10 |
| 661 | NL Cy Young | .12 |
| 662 | NL MVP | .15 |
| 663 | NL Rookie of the Year | .25 |
| 664 | ALCS MVP | .15 |
| 665 | NLCS MVP | .12 |
| 666 | World Series Moment | .15 |
| 667 | World Series MVP | .15 |
| 668 | Angels Checklist | .12 |
| 669 | Astros Checklist | .50 |
| 670 | Athletics Checklist | .35 |
| 671 | Blue Jays Checklist | .12 |
| 672 | Braves Checklist | .15 |
| 673 | Brewers Checklist | .08 |
| 674 | Cardinals Checklist | .12 |
| 675 | Cubs Checklist | .25 |
| 676 | Dodgers Checklist | .15 |
| 677 | Expos Checklist | .08 |
| 678 | Giants Checklist | .40 |

| NO. | PLAYER | MINT |
|---|---|---|
| 679 | Indians Checklist | .08 |
| 680 | Mariners Checklist | .08 |
| 681 | Mets Checklist | .30 |
| 682 | Orioles Checklist | .30 |
| 683 | Padres Checklist | .15 |
| 684 | Phillies Checklist | .30 |
| 685 | Pirates Checklist | .08 |
| 686 | Rangers Checklist | .15 |
| 687 | Red Sox Checklist | .25 |
| 688 | Reds Checklist | .15 |
| 689 | Royals Checklist | .20 |
| 690 | Tigers Checklist | .12 |
| 691 | Twins Checklist | .08 |
| 692 | White Sox Checklist | .08 |
| 693 | Yankees Checklist | .30 |
| 694 | Checklist 1-100 | .08 |
| 695 | Checklist 101-200 | .08 |
| 696 | Checklist 201-300 | .08 |
| 697 | Checklist 301-400 | .08 |
| 698 | Checklist 401-500 | .08 |
| 699 | Checklist 501-600 | .08 |
| 700 | Checklist 601-700 | .08 |

## 1989 Upper Deck Extended.... Complete Set of 100 Cards—Value $20.00

This set updates the main 1989 card set with players who had changed teams during the season, and rookies. The set was packaged in a printed box and also included with the factory sets. Features the first Upper Deck card of Gregg Olson, Tom Gordon, Todd Zeile, Jim Abbott and Jerome Walton.

Gregg Olson

Todd Zeile

Dwight Smith

Jim Abbott

Tom Gordon

| NO. | PLAYER | MINT |
|---|---|---|
| 701 | Checklist 701-800 | .10 |
| 702 | Jesse Barfield | .15 |
| 703 | Walt Terrell | .10 |
| 704 | Dickie Thon | .10 |
| 705 | Al Leiter | .10 |
| 706 | Dave LaPoint | .10 |
| 707 | Charlie Hayes (R) | .30 |
| 708 | Andy Hawkins | .10 |
| 709 | Mickey Hatcher | .10 |
| 710 | Lance McCullers | .10 |
| 711 | Ron Kittle | .10 |
| 712 | Bert Blyleven | .15 |
| 713 | Rick Dempsey | .10 |
| 714 | Ken Williams | .10 |
| 715 | Steve Rosenberg (R) | .15 |
| 716 | Joe Skalski | .10 |
| 717 | Spike Owen | .10 |
| 718 | Todd Burns (R) | .20 |
| 719 | Kevin Gross | .10 |
| 720 | Tommy Herr | .10 |
| 721 | Rob Ducey | .15 |
| 722 | Gary Green | .20 |
| 723 | Gregg Olson (R) | 1.50 |
| 724 | Greg W. Harris (R) | .40 |
| 725 | Craig Worthington | .20 |

| NO. | PLAYER | MINT |
|---|---|---|
| 726 | Tom Howard (R) | .30 |
| 727 | Dale Mohorcic | .10 |
| 728 | Rich Yett | .10 |
| 729 | Mel Hall | .10 |
| 730 | Floyd Youmans | .15 |
| 731 | Lonnie Smith | .10 |
| 732 | Wally Backman | .10 |
| 733 | Trevor Wilson (R) | .25 |
| 734 | Jose Alvarez | .20 |
| 735 | Bob Milacki (R) | .30 |
| 736 | Tom Gordon (R) | .75 |
| 737 | Wally Whitehurst | .20 |
| 738 | Mike Aldrete | .10 |
| 739 | Keith Miller | .15 |
| 740 | Randy Milligan | .15 |
| 741 | Jeff Parrett | .10 |
| 742 | Steve Finley (R) | .75 |
| 743 | Junior Felix (R) | .50 |
| 744 | Pate Harnisch (R) | .50 |
| 745 | Bill Spiers (R) | .30 |
| 746 | Hensley Meulens (R) | 1.00 |
| 747 | Juan Bell | .10 |
| 748 | Steve Sax | .10 |
| 749 | Phil Bradley | .10 |
| 750 | Rey Quinones | .10 |

| NO. | PLAYER | MINT |
|---|---|---|
| 751 | Tommy Gregg | .10 |
| 752 | Kevin Brown | .20 |
| 753 | Derek Lilliquist | .20 |
| 754 | Todd Zelle (R) | 3.00 |
| 755 | Jim Abbott (R) | 3.50 |
| 756 | Ozzie Canseco (R) | .25 |
| 757 | Nick Esasky | .20 |
| 758 | Mike Moore | .10 |
| 759 | Rob Murphy | .10 |
| 760 | Rick Mahler | .10 |
| 761 | Fred Lynn | .10 |
| 762 | Kevin Blankenship | .10 |
| 763 | Eddie Murray | .30 |
| 764 | Steve Searcy (R) | .20 |
| 765 | Jerome Walton (R) | 1.00 |
| 766 | Erik Hanson (R) | 1.25 |
| 767 | Bob Boone | .10 |
| 768 | Edgar Martinez | 1.00 |
| 769 | Jose DeJesus | .10 |
| 770 | Greg Briley (R) | .30 |
| 771 | Steve Peters | .15 |
| 772 | Rafael Palmeiro | .30 |
| 773 | Jack Clark | .15 |
| 774 | Nolan Ryan | 3.00 |
| 775 | Lance Parrish | .10 |

| NO. | PLAYER | MINT |
|---|---|---|
| 776 | Joe Girardi (R) | .25 |
| 777 | Willie Randolph | .15 |
| 778 | Mitch Williams | .10 |
| 779 | Dennis Cook (R) | .20 |
| 780 | Dwight Smith (R) | .30 |
| 781 | Lenny Harris (R) | .40 |
| 782 | Torey Lovullo (R) | .15 |
| 783 | Norm Charlton (R) | .25 |
| 784 | Chris Brown | .10 |
| 785 | Todd Benzinger | .10 |
| 786 | Shane Rawley | .10 |
| 787 | Omar Vizquel (R) | .20 |
| 788 | LaVel Freeman | .15 |
| 789 | Jeffrey Leonard | .15 |
| 790 | Eddie Williams | .10 |
| 791 | Jamie Moyer | .10 |
| 792 | Burce Hurst | .10 |
| 793 | Julio Franco | .25 |
| 794 | Claudell Washington | .10 |
| 795 | Jody Davis | .10 |
| 796 | Odibbe McDowell | .10 |
| 797 | Paul Kilgus | .10 |
| 798 | Tracy Jones | .10 |
| 799 | Steve Wilson | .15 |
| 800 | Pete O'Brien | .10 |

# 1990 Upper Deck . . . Complete Set of 700 Cards—Value $40.00

(Factory Sealed Set of 800 Cards—Value $55.00)

Features the rookie cards of Greg Vaughn, Eric Anthony, Ben McDonald, John Olerud and Todd Zeile.

Jose Offerman

Juan Gonzalez

John Olerud

Kevin Maas

Ben McDonald

| NO. | PLAYER | MINT |
|---|---|---|
| 1 | Star Rookie checklist | .10 |
| 2 | Randy Nosek (R) | .15 |
| 3 | Tom Dress (R) | .15 |
| 4 | Curt Young | .06 |
| 5 | Angels checklist | .06 |
| 6 | Luis Salazar | .06 |
| 7 | Phillies checklist | .06 |
| 8 | Jose Bautista | .06 |
| 9 | Marquis Grissom (R) | .75 |
| 10 | Dodgers checklist | .06 |
| 11 | Rick Aguilera | .06 |
| 12 | Padres checklist | .06 |
| 13 | Deion Sanders | .35 |
| 14 | Marvell Wynne | .06 |
| 15 | David West | .10 |
| 16 | Pirates checklist | .06 |
| 17 | Sammy Sosa (R) | .60 |
| 18 | Yankees checklist | .06 |
| 19 | Jack Howell | .06 |
| 20 | Special card-Schmidt | .75 |
| 21 | Robin Ventura | 1.50 |
| 22 | Brian Meyer | .15 |
| 23 | Blaine Beatty (R) | .20 |
| 24 | Mariners checklist | .75 |
| 25 | Greg Vaughn | 1.00 |
| 26 | Xavier Hernandez (R) | .15 |
| 27 | Jason Grimsley (R) | .15 |
| 28 | Eric Anthony (R) | .35 |
| 29 | Expos checklist | .06 |
| 30 | David Wells | .06 |
| 31 | Hal Morris | 1.25 |
| 32 | Royals checklist | .30 |
| 33 | Kelly Mann (R) | .15 |
| 34 | Special card-Ryan | 1.25 |
| 35 | Scott Service | .12 |
| 36 | Athletics checklist | .12 |
| 37 | Tino Martinez | 1.25 |
| 38 | Chili Davis | .06 |
| 39 | Scott Sanderson | .06 |
| 40 | Giants checklist | .12 |
| 41 | Tigers checklist | .06 |
| 42 | Scott Coolbaugh (R) | .20 |
| 43 | Jose Cano (R) | .15 |
| 44 | Jose Vizcaino (R) | .20 |
| 45 | Bob Hamelin (R) | .15 |
| 46 | Jose Offerman (R) | .50 |
| 47 | Kevin Blankenship | .12 |
| 48 | Twins checklist | .15 |
| 49 | Tommy Greene (R) | .60 |
| 50 | Special card-Clark | .35 |
| 51 | Rob Nelson | .06 |
| 52 | Chris Hammond (R) | .35 |
| 53 | Indians checklist | .06 |
| 54 | Ben McDonald (R) | 1.50 |
| 54 | B. McDonald (error) | 20.00 |
| 55 | Andy Benes | .40 |
| 56 | John Olerud (R) | 2.50 |
| 57 | Red Sox checklist | .15 |
| 58 | Tony Armas | .06 |
| 59 | George Canale (R) | .15 |
| 60 | Orioles CL (error) | 3.00 |
| 60 | Orioles CL (correct) | .15 |
| 61 | Mike Stanton (R) | .25 |
| 62 | Mets checklist | .12 |
| 63 | Kent Mercker (R) | .25 |
| 64 | Francisco Cabrera | .20 |
| 65 | Steve Avery | 3.00 |
| 66 | Jose Canseco | .75 |

| NO. | PLAYER | MINT |
|---|---|---|
| 67 | Matt Merullo | .12 |
| 68 | Cardinals checklist | .06 |
| 69 | Ron Karkovice | .06 |
| 70 | Kevin Mass (R) | 3.00 |
| 71 | Dennis Cook | .12 |
| 72 | Juan Gonzalez (R) | 6.00 |
| 73 | Cubs checklist | .06 |
| 74 | Dean Palmer (R) | 2.00 |
| 75 | Special card-Jackson | .35 |
| 76 | Rob Richie | .15 |
| 77 | Bobby Rose (R) | .15 |
| 78 | Brian DuBois (R) | .15 |
| 79 | White Sox checklist | .06 |
| 80 | Gene Nelson | .06 |
| 81 | Bob McClure | .06 |
| 82 | Rangers checklist | .06 |
| 83 | Greg Minton | .06 |
| 84 | Braves checklist | .06 |
| 85 | Willie Fraser | .06 |
| 86 | Neal Heaton | .06 |
| 87 | Kevin Tapani (R) | .75 |
| 88 | Astros checklist | .06 |
| 89 | Jim Gott (correct) | .15 |
| 89 | Jim Gott (error) | 6.00 |
| 90 | Lance Johnson | .12 |
| 91 | Brewers checklist | .15 |
| 92 | Jeff Parrett | .06 |
| 93 | Julio Machado (R) | .15 |
| 94 | Ron Jones | .06 |
| 95 | Blue Jays checklist | .06 |
| 96 | Jerry Reuss | .06 |
| 97 | Brian Fisher | .06 |
| 98 | Kevin Ritz (R) | .15 |
| 99 | Reds checklist | .06 |
| 100 | Checklist 1-100 | .06 |
| 101 | Gerald Perry | .06 |
| 102 | Kevin Appier | .40 |
| 103 | Julio Franco | .10 |
| 104 | Craig Biggio | .10 |
| 105 | Bo Jackson | .75 |
| 106 | Junior Felix | .15 |
| 107 | Mike Markey | .12 |
| 108 | Fred McGriff | .15 |
| 109 | Rick Sutcliffe | .06 |
| 110 | Pete O'Brien | .10 |
| 111 | Kelly Gruber | .15 |
| 112 | Pat Borders | .06 |
| 113 | Dwight Evans | .12 |
| 114 | Dwight Gooden | .20 |
| 115 | Kevin Batiste (R) | .20 |
| 116 | Eric Davis | .20 |
| 117 | Kevin Mitchell | .20 |
| 118 | Ron Oester | .06 |
| 119 | Brett Butler | .06 |
| 120 | Danny Jackson | .12 |
| 121 | Tommy Gregg | .06 |
| 122 | Ken Caminiti | .06 |
| 123 | Kevin Brown | .15 |
| 124 | George Brett | .20 |
| 125 | Mike Scott | .12 |
| 126 | Cory Snyder | .10 |
| 127 | George Bell | .10 |
| 128 | Mark Grace | .20 |
| 129 | Devon White | .10 |
| 130 | Tony Fernandez | .10 |
| 131 | Don Aase | .06 |
| 132 | Rance Mulliniks | .06 |

| NO. | PLAYER | MINT |
|---|---|---|
| 133 | Marty Barrett | .06 |
| 134 | Nelson Liriano | .06 |
| 135 | Mark Carreon | .06 |
| 136 | Candy Maldonado | .06 |
| 137 | Tim Birtsas | .06 |
| 138 | Tom Brookens | .06 |
| 139 | John Franco | .10 |
| 140 | Mike LaCoss | .06 |
| 141 | Jeff Treadway | .06 |
| 142 | Pat Tabler | .06 |
| 143 | Darrell Evans | .06 |
| 144 | Rafael Ramirez | .06 |
| 145 | Odibbe McDowell | .06 |
| 146 | Brian Downing | .06 |
| 147 | Curtis Wilkerson | .06 |
| 148 | Ernie Whitt | .06 |
| 149 | Bill Schroeder | .06 |
| 150 | Domingo Ramos | .06 |
| 151 | Rick Honeycutt | .06 |
| 152 | Don Slaught | .06 |
| 153 | Mitch Webster | .10 |
| 154 | Tony Phillips | .06 |
| 155 | Paul Kilgus | .06 |
| 156 | Ken Griffey, Jr. | 5.00 |
| 157 | Gary Sheffield | .15 |
| 158 | Wally Backman | .06 |
| 159 | B.J. Surhoff | .06 |
| 160 | Louie Meadows | .06 |
| 161 | Paul O'Neill | .06 |
| 162 | Jeff McKnight (R) | .15 |
| 163 | Alvaro Espinoza | .15 |
| 164 | Scott Scudder | .15 |
| 165 | Jeff Reed | .06 |
| 166 | Gregg Jefferies | .15 |
| 167 | Barry Larkin | .15 |
| 168 | Gary Carter | .15 |
| 169 | Robby Thompson | .10 |
| 170 | Rolando Roomes | .10 |
| 171 | Mark McGwire | .20 |
| 172 | Steve Sax | .15 |
| 173 | Mark Williamson | .06 |
| 174 | Mitch Williams | .06 |
| 175 | Brian Holton | .06 |
| 176 | Rob Deer | .06 |
| 177 | Tim Raines | .15 |
| 178 | Mike Felder | .06 |
| 179 | Harold Reynolds | .06 |
| 180 | Terry Francona | .06 |
| 181 | Chris Sabo | .15 |
| 182 | Darryl Strawberry | .35 |
| 183 | Willie Randolph | .15 |
| 184 | Billy Ripken | .10 |
| 185 | Mackey Sasser | .06 |
| 186 | Todd Benzinger | .06 |
| 187 | Kevin Elster | .06 |
| 188 | Jose Uribe | .06 |
| 189 | Tom Browning | .06 |
| 190 | Keith Miller | .06 |
| 191 | Don Mattingly | .25 |
| 192 | Dave Parker | .12 |
| 193 | Roberto Kelly | .12 |
| 194 | Phil Bradley | .12 |
| 195 | Ron Hassey | .06 |
| 196 | Gerald Young | .06 |
| 197 | Hubie Brooks | .06 |
| 198 | Bill Doran | .06 |
| 199 | Al Newman | .06 |

| NO. | PLAYER | MINT |
|---|---|---|
| 200 | Checklist 101-200 | .06 |
| 201 | Terry Puhl | .06 |
| 202 | Frank DiPino | .06 |
| 203 | Jim Clancy | .06 |
| 204 | Bob Ojeda | .06 |
| 205 | Alex Trevino | .06 |
| 206 | Dave Henderson | .10 |
| 207 | Henry Cotto | .06 |
| 208 | Rafael Belliard | .06 |
| 209 | Stan Javier | .06 |
| 210 | Jerry Reed | .06 |
| 211 | Doug Dascenzo | .06 |
| 212 | Andres Thomas | .06 |
| 213 | Greg Maddux | .10 |
| 214 | Mike Schooler | .10 |
| 215 | Lonnie Smith | .06 |
| 216 | Jose Rijo | .06 |
| 217 | Greg Gagne | .06 |
| 218 | Jim Gantner | .06 |
| 219 | Allan Anderson | .06 |
| 220 | Rick Mahler | .06 |
| 221 | Jim Deshaies | .06 |
| 222 | Keith Hernandez | .12 |
| 223 | Vince Coleman | .15 |
| 224 | David Cone | .10 |
| 225 | Ozzie Smith | .12 |
| 226 | Matt Nokes | .10 |
| 227 | Barry Bonds | .30 |
| 228 | Felix Jose | .35 |
| 229 | Dennis Powell | .06 |
| 230 | Mike Gallego | .06 |
| 231 | Shawon Dunston | .10 |
| 232 | Ron Gant | .30 |
| 233 | Omar Vizquel | .10 |
| 234 | Derek Lilliquist | .12 |
| 235 | Erik Hanson | .15 |
| 236 | Kirby Puckett | .30 |
| 237 | Bill Spiers | .12 |
| 238 | Dan Gladden | .06 |
| 239 | Bryan Clutterbuck | .06 |
| 240 | John Moses | .06 |
| 241 | Ron Darling | .12 |
| 242 | Joe Magrane | .10 |
| 243 | Dave Magadan | .10 |
| 244 | Pedro Guerrero | .10 |
| 245 | Glenn Davis | .12 |
| 246 | Terry Steinbach | .10 |
| 247 | Fred Lynn | .10 |
| 248 | Gary Redus | .06 |
| 249 | Kenny Williams | .06 |
| 250 | Sid Bream | .06 |
| 251 | Bob Welch | .06 |
| 252 | Bill Buckner | .06 |
| 253 | Carney Lansford | .06 |
| 254 | Paul Molitor | .12 |
| 255 | Jose DeJesus | .06 |
| 256 | Orel Hershiser | .15 |
| 257 | Tom Brunansky | .06 |
| 258 | Mike Davis | .06 |
| 259 | Jeff Ballard | .06 |
| 260 | Scott Terry | .06 |
| 261 | Sid Fernandez | .06 |
| 262 | Mike Marshall | .06 |
| 263 | Howard Johnson | .15 |
| 264 | Kirk Gibson | .12 |

| NO. | PLAYER | MINT |
|---|---|---|
| 265 | Kevin McReynolds | .10 |
| 266 | Cal Ripken, Jr. | .40 |
| 267 | Ozzie Guillen | .06 |
| 268 | Jim Traber | .06 |
| 269 | Bobby Thigpen | .06 |
| 270 | Joe Orsulak | .06 |
| 271 | Bob Boone | .06 |
| 272 | Dave Stewart | .12 |
| 273 | Tim Wallach | .06 |
| 274 | Luis Aquino | .06 |
| 275 | Mike Moore | .06 |
| 276 | Tony Pena | .06 |
| 277 | Eddie Murray | .15 |
| 278 | Milt Thompson | .06 |
| 279 | Alejandro Pena | .06 |
| 280 | Ken Dayley | .06 |
| 281 | Carmen Castillo | .06 |
| 282 | Tom Henke | .06 |
| 283 | Mickey Hatcher | .06 |
| 284 | Roy Smith | .06 |
| 285 | Manny Lee | .06 |
| 286 | Dan Pasqua | .06 |
| 287 | Larry Sheets | .06 |
| 288 | Garry Templeton | .06 |
| 289 | Eddie Williams | .10 |
| 290 | Brady Anderson | .06 |
| 291 | Spike Owen | .06 |
| 292 | Storm Davis | .06 |
| 293 | Chris Bosio | .06 |
| 294 | Jim Eisenreich | .06 |
| 295 | Don August | .10 |
| 296 | Jeff Hamilton | .06 |
| 297 | Mickey Tettleton | .06 |
| 298 | Mike Scioscia | .10 |
| 299 | Kevin Hickey | .10 |
| 300 | Checklist 201-300 | .06 |
| 301 | Shawn Abner | .06 |
| 302 | Kevin Bass | .06 |
| 303 | Bip Roberts | .06 |
| 304 | Joe Girardi | .10 |
| 305 | Danny Darwin | .06 |
| 306 | Mike Heath | .06 |
| 307 | Mike MacFarlane | .06 |
| 308 | Ed Whitson | .06 |
| 309 | Tracy Jones | .06 |
| 310 | Scott Fletcher | .06 |
| 311 | Darnell Coles | .06 |
| 312 | Mike Brumley | .06 |
| 313 | Bill Swift | .06 |
| 314 | Charlie Hough | .06 |
| 315 | Jim Presley | .06 |
| 316 | Luis Polonia | .06 |
| 317 | Mike Morgan | .06 |
| 318 | Lee Guetterman | .06 |
| 319 | Jose Oquendo | .06 |
| 320 | Wayne Tolleson | .06 |
| 321 | Jody Reed | .06 |
| 322 | Damon Berryhill | .10 |
| 323 | Roger Clemens | .35 |
| 324 | Ryne Sandberg | .35 |
| 325 | Benito Santiago | .10 |
| 326 | Bret Saberhagen | .10 |
| 327 | Lou Whitaker | .06 |
| 328 | Dave Gallagher | .06 |
| 329 | Mike Pagliarulo | .06 |
| 330 | Doyle Alexander | .06 |
| 331 | Jeffrey Leonard | .06 |
| 332 | Torey Lovullo | .10 |
| 333 | Pete Incaviglia | .10 |
| 334 | Rickey Henderson | .35 |
| 335 | Rafael Palmeiro | .15 |
| 336 | Ken Hill | .12 |
| 337 | Dave Winfield | .15 |
| 338 | Alfredo Griffin | .06 |
| 339 | Andy Hawkins | .06 |
| 340 | Ted Power | .06 |
| 341 | Steve Wilson | .10 |
| 342 | Jack Clark | .12 |
| 343 | Ellis Burks | .15 |
| 344 | Tony Gwynn | .25 |
| 345 | Jerome Walton | .15 |
| 346 | Roberto Alomar | .25 |
| 347 | Carlos Martinez | .15 |
| 348 | Chet Lemon | .06 |
| 349 | Willie Wilson | .06 |
| 350 | Greg Walker | .06 |
| 351 | Tom Bolton | .06 |
| 352 | German Gonzalez | .06 |
| 353 | Harold Baines | .06 |
| 354 | Mike Greenwell | .15 |
| 355 | Ruben Sierra | .30 |
| 356 | Andres Galarraga | .10 |
| 357 | Andre Dawson | .15 |
| 358 | Jeff Brantley | .15 |
| 359 | Mike Bielecki | .06 |
| 360 | Ken Oberkfell | .06 |
| 361 | Kurt Stillwell | .06 |
| 362 | Brian Homan | .06 |
| 363 | Kevin Seitzer | .08 |
| 364 | Alvin Davis | .10 |
| 365 | Tom Gordon | .15 |
| 366 | Bobby Bonilla | .20 |
| 367 | Carlton Fisk | .25 |
| 368 | Steve Carter | .10 |
| 369 | Joel Skinner | .06 |
| 370 | John Cangelosi | .06 |
| 371 | Cecil Espy | .06 |
| 372 | Gary Wayne | .10 |
| 373 | Jim Rice | .12 |
| 374 | Mike Dyer (R) | .15 |
| 375 | Joe Carter | .15 |
| 376 | Dwight Smith | .15 |
| 377 | John Wetteland | .15 |
| 378 | Ernie Riles | .06 |
| 379 | Otis Nixon | .08 |
| 380 | Vance Law | .10 |
| 381 | Dave Bergman | .06 |
| 382 | Frank White | .10 |
| 383 | Scott Bradley | .12 |
| 384 | Israel Sanchez | .06 |
| 385 | Gary Pettis | .06 |
| 386 | Donn Pall | .06 |
| 387 | John Smiley | .06 |
| 388 | Tom Candiotti | .10 |
| 389 | Junior Ortiz | .06 |
| 390 | Steve Lyons | .06 |
| 391 | Brian Harper | .06 |
| 392 | Fred Manrique | .10 |
| 393 | Lee Smith | .06 |
| 394 | Jeff Kunkel | .06 |
| 395 | Claudell Washington | .06 |
| 396 | John Tudor | .06 |
| 397 | Terry Kennedy | .06 |
| 398 | Lloyd McClendon | .06 |
| 399 | Craig Lefferts | .06 |
| 400 | Checklist 301-400 | .06 |
| 401 | Keith Moreland | .06 |
| 402 | Rich Gedman | .06 |
| 403 | Jeff Robinson | .12 |
| 404 | Randy Ready | .06 |
| 405 | Rick Cerone | .06 |
| 406 | Jeff Blauser | .06 |
| 407 | Larry Andersen | .06 |
| 408 | Joe Boever | .06 |
| 409 | Felix Fermin | .06 |
| 410 | Glenn Wilson | .06 |
| 411 | Rex Hudler | .06 |
| 412 | Mark Grant | .06 |
| 413 | Dennis Martinez | .06 |
| 414 | Darrin Jackson | .06 |
| 415 | Mike Aldrete | .06 |
| 416 | Roger McDowell | .06 |
| 417 | Jeff Reardon | .06 |
| 418 | Darren Daulton | .06 |
| 419 | Tim Laudner | .06 |
| 420 | Don Carman | .06 |
| 421 | Lloyd Moseby | .06 |
| 422 | Doug Drabek | .06 |
| 423 | Lenny Harris | .10 |
| 424 | Jose Lind | .06 |
| 425 | Dave Johnson | .15 |
| 426 | Jerry Browne | .12 |
| 427 | Eric Yelding | .25 |
| 428 | Brad Komminsk | .06 |
| 429 | Jody Davis | .06 |
| 430 | Mariano Duncan | .06 |
| 431 | Mark Davis | .10 |
| 432 | Nelson Santovenia | .06 |
| 433 | Bruce Hurst | .06 |
| 434 | Jeff Huson (R) | .15 |
| 435 | Chris James | .06 |
| 436 | Mark Guthrie (R) | .15 |
| 437 | Charlie Hayes | .10 |
| 438 | Shane Rawley | .06 |
| 439 | Dickie Thon | .06 |
| 440 | Juan Berenguer | .06 |
| 441 | Kevin Romine | .06 |
| 442 | Bill Landrum | .06 |
| 443 | Todd Frohwirth | .06 |
| 444 | Craig Worthington | .10 |
| 445 | Fernando Valenzuela | .15 |
| 446 | Joey Belle | 1.25 |
| 447 | Ed Whited (R) | .15 |
| 448 | Dave Smith | .06 |
| 449 | Dave Clark | .06 |
| 450 | Juan Agosta | .06 |
| 451 | Dave Valle | .06 |
| 452 | Kent Hrbek | .10 |
| 453 | Von Hayes | .06 |
| 454 | Gary Gaetti | .12 |
| 455 | Greg Briley | .15 |
| 456 | Glenn Braggs | .06 |
| 457 | Kirt Manwaring | .06 |
| 458 | Mel Hall | .06 |
| 459 | Brook Jacoby | .06 |
| 460 | Pat Sheridan | .06 |
| 461 | Rob Murphy | .06 |
| 462 | Jimmy Key | .06 |
| 463 | Nick Esasky | .06 |
| 464 | Rob Ducey | .06 |
| 465 | Carlos Quintana | .15 |
| 466 | Larry Walker (R) | .40 |
| 467 | Todd Worrell | .06 |
| 468 | Kevin Gross | .06 |
| 469 | Terry Pendleton | .06 |
| 470 | Dave Martinez | .06 |
| 471 | Gene Larkin | .06 |
| 472 | Len Dykstra | .12 |
| 473 | Barry Lyons | .06 |
| 474 | Terry Mulholland | .06 |
| 475 | Chip Hale (R) | .15 |
| 476 | Jesse Barfield | .06 |
| 477 | Dan Plesac | .06 |
| 478 | Scott Garrelts | .10 |
| 479 | Dave Righetti | .10 |
| 480 | Gus Polidor | .06 |
| 481 | Mookie Wilson | .10 |
| 482 | Luis Rivera | .06 |
| 483 | Mike Falangan | .06 |
| 484 | Dennis "Oil Can" Boyd | .06 |
| 485 | John Cerutti | .06 |
| 486 | John Costello | .06 |
| 487 | Pascual Perez | .06 |
| 488 | Tommy Herr | .10 |
| 489 | Tom Foley | .06 |
| 490 | Curt Ford | .06 |
| 491 | Steve Lake | .06 |
| 492 | Tim Teufel | .06 |
| 493 | Randy Bush | .06 |
| 494 | Mike Jackson | .06 |
| 495 | Steve Jeitz | .06 |
| 496 | Paul Gibson | .06 |
| 497 | Steve Balboni | .06 |
| 498 | Bud Black | .06 |
| 499 | Dale Sveum | .06 |
| 500 | Checklist 401-500 | .06 |
| 501 | Timmy Jones | .06 |
| 502 | Mark Portugal | .06 |
| 503 | Ivan Calderon | .06 |
| 504 | Rick Rhoden | .06 |
| 505 | Willie McGee | .10 |
| 506 | Kirk McCaskill | .10 |
| 507 | Dave LaPoint | .06 |
| 508 | Jay Howell | .06 |
| 509 | Johnny Ray | .06 |
| 510 | Dave Anderson | .06 |
| 511 | Chuck Crim | .06 |
| 512 | Joe Hesketh | .06 |
| 513 | Dennis Eckersley | .12 |
| 514 | Greg Brock | .06 |
| 515 | Tim Burke | .06 |
| 516 | Frank Tanana | .06 |
| 517 | Jay Bell | .06 |
| 518 | Guillermo Hernandez | .06 |
| 519 | Randy Kramer | .06 |
| 520 | Charles Hudson | .06 |
| 521 | Jim Corsi | .06 |
| 522 | Steve Rosenberg | .06 |
| 523 | Cris Carpenter | .06 |
| 524 | Matt Winters (R) | .15 |
| 525 | Melido Perez | .06 |
| 526 | Chris Gwynn | .12 |
| 527 | Bert Blyleven | .12 |
| 528 | Chuck Cary | .06 |
| 529 | Daryl Boston | .06 |
| 530 | Dale Mohorcic | .06 |
| 531 | Geronomi Berroa | .10 |
| 532 | Edgar Martinez | .12 |
| 533 | Dale Murphy | .20 |
| 534 | Jay Buhner | .12 |
| 535 | John Smoltz | .25 |
| 536 | Andy Van Slyke | .12 |
| 537 | Mike Henneman | .06 |
| 538 | Miguel Garcia | .06 |
| 539 | Frank Williams | .06 |
| 540 | R.J. Reynolds | .06 |
| 541 | Shawn Hillegas | .06 |
| 542 | Walt Weiss | .12 |
| 543 | Greg Hibbard (R) | .25 |
| 544 | Nolan Ryan | 1.00 |
| 545 | Todd Zeile | .75 |
| 546 | Hensley Meulens | .20 |
| 547 | Tim Belcher | .06 |
| 548 | Mike Witt | .10 |
| 549 | Greg Cadaret | .06 |
| 550 | Franklin Stubbs | .06 |
| 551 | Tony Castillo | .06 |
| 552 | Jeff Robinson | .10 |
| 553 | Steve Olin (R) | .15 |
| 554 | Alan Trammell | .10 |
| 555 | Wade Boggs | .35 |
| 556 | Will Clark | .40 |
| 557 | Jeff King | .15 |
| 558 | Mike Fitzgerald | .06 |
| 559 | Ken Howell | .06 |
| 560 | Bob Kipper | .06 |
| 561 | Scott Bankhead | .06 |
| 562 | Jeff Innis (error) | 2.50 |
| 562 | Jeff Innis (correct) | .10 |
| 563 | Randy Johnson | .10 |
| 564 | Wally Whitehurst | .10 |
| 565 | Gene Harris | .10 |
| 566 | Norm Charlton | .20 |
| 567 | Robin Yount | .20 |
| 568 | Joe Oliver | .15 |
| 569 | Mark Parent | .06 |
| 570 | John Farrell | .10 |
| 571 | Tom Glavine | .30 |
| 572 | Rod Nichols | .10 |
| 573 | Jack Morris | .15 |
| 574 | Greg Swindell | .10 |
| 575 | Steve Searcy | .15 |
| 576 | Ricky Jordan | .15 |
| 577 | Matt Williams | .25 |
| 578 | Mike LaValliere | .12 |
| 579 | Bryn Smith | .06 |
| 580 | Bruce Ruffin | .06 |
| 581 | Randy Myers | .10 |
| 582 | Rick Wrona | .10 |
| 583 | Juan Samuel | .10 |
| 584 | Les Lancaster | .06 |
| 585 | Jeff Musselman | .06 |
| 586 | Rob Dibble | .12 |
| 587 | Eric Show | .06 |
| 588 | Jesse Orosco | .06 |
| 589 | Herm Winningham | .06 |
| 590 | Andy Allanson | .06 |
| 591 | Dion James | .06 |
| 592 | Carmelo Martinez | .06 |
| 593 | Luis Quinones | .06 |
| 594 | Dennis Rasmussen | .06 |
| 595 | Rich Yett | .06 |
| 596 | Bob Walk | .06 |
| 597 | A. McGaffigan (err.) | .50 |
| 597 | A. McGaffigan (cor.) | .20 |
| 598 | Billy Hatcher | .06 |
| 599 | Bob Knepper | .06 |
| 600 | Checklist 501-600 | .06 |

| NO. | PLAYER | MINT | NO. | PLAYER | MINT | NO. | PLAYER | MINT | NO. | PLAYER | MINT |
|---|---|---|---|---|---|---|---|---|---|---|---|
| 601 | Joey Cora | .12 | 626 | Frank Viola | .12 | 651 | Eric King | .06 | 676 | Mark Gubicza | .06 |
| 602 | Steve Finley | .15 | 627 | Ted Higuera | .06 | 652 | Mike Boddicker | .06 | 677 | Greg Litton | .10 |
| 603 | Kal Daniels | .10 | 628 | Marty Pevey (R) | .15 | 653 | Duane Ward | .06 | 678 | Greg Mathews | .06 |
| 604 | Gregg Olson | .20 | 629 | Bill Wegman | .06 | 654 | Bob Stanley | .06 | 679 | Dave Dravecky | .06 |
| 605 | Dave Stieb | .06 | 630 | Eric Plunk | .06 | 655 | Sandy Alomar, Jr. | .15 | 680 | Steve Farr | .06 |
| 606 | Kenny Rogers | .10 | 631 | Drew Hall | .06 | 656 | Danny Tartabull | .12 | 681 | Miek Devereaux | .06 |
| 607 | Zane Smith | .06 | 632 | Doug Jones | .06 | 657 | Rick McCament (R) | .12 | 682 | Ken Griffey, Sr. | .06 |
| 608 | Bob Geren | .10 | 633 | Geno Petralli | .06 | 658 | Charlie Leibrandt | .06 | 683 | J. Weston (R) (correct) | .10 |
| 609 | Chad Kreuter | .06 | 634 | Jose Alvarez | .06 | 659 | Dan Quisenberry | .06 | 683 | J. Weston (error) | 4.00 |
| 610 | Mike Smithson | .06 | 635 | Bob Milacki | .12 | 660 | Paul Assenmacher | .06 | 684 | Jack Armstrong | .06 |
| 611 | Jeff Wetherby (R) | .15 | 636 | Bobby Witt | .12 | 661 | Walt Terrell | .06 | 685 | Steve Buechele | .06 |
| 612 | Gary Mielke (R) | .15 | 637 | Trevor Wilson | .10 | 662 | Tim Leary | .06 | 686 | Bryan Harvey | .06 |
| 613 | Pete Smith | .06 | 638 | Jeff Russell | .06 | 663 | Randy Milligan | .10 | 687 | Lance Blandenship | .06 |
| 614 | Jack Daugherty (R) | .15 | 639 | Mike Krukow | .06 | 664 | Bo Diaz | .06 | 688 | Dante Bichette | .06 |
| 615 | Lance McCullers | .06 | 640 | Rick Leach | .06 | 665 | Mark Lemke | .06 | 689 | Todd Burns | .10 |
| 616 | Don Robinson | .06 | 641 | Dave Schmidt | .06 | 666 | Jose Gonzalez | .06 | 690 | Dan Petry | .06 |
| 617 | Jose Guzman | .06 | 642 | Terry Leach | .06 | 667 | Chuck Finley | .15 | 691 | Kent Anderson | .10 |
| 618 | Steve Bedrosian | .06 | 643 | Calvin Schiraldi | .06 | 668 | John Kruk | .06 | 692 | Todd Stottlemyre | .10 |
| 619 | Jamie Moyer | .06 | 644 | Bob Melvin | .06 | 669 | Dick Schofield | .06 | 693 | Wally Joyner | .15 |
| 620 | Atlee Hammaker | .06 | 645 | Jim Abbott | .30 | 670 | Tim Crews | .06 | 694 | Mike Rochford | .10 |
| 621 | Rick Luecken (R) | .15 | 646 | Jaime Navarro | .15 | 671 | John Dopson | .06 | 695 | Floyd Bannister | .06 |
| 622 | Greg W. Harris | .10 | 647 | Mark Langston | .10 | 672 | John Orton (R) | .15 | 696 | Rick Reuschel | .12 |
| 623 | Pete Harnisch | .10 | 648 | Juan Nieves | .06 | 673 | Eric Hetzel | .06 | 697 | Jose DeLeon | .06 |
| 624 | Jerald Clark | .06 | 649 | Damasco Garcia | .06 | 674 | Lance Parrish | .06 | 698 | Jeff Montgomery | .10 |
| 625 | Jack McDowell | .10 | 650 | Charlie O'Brien | .06 | 675 | Ramon Martinez | .75 | 699 | Kelly Downs | .10 |
| | | | | | | | | | 700 | CL: 601-700 (error) | 2.50 |
| | | | | | | | | | 700 | CL: 601-700 (correct) | .10 |

## 1990 Upper Deck Extended. . . . Complete Set of 100 Cards—Value $15.00

This set updates the main 1990 card set with players who had changed teams during the season, and rookies.
Features the first Upper Deck card of Dave Justice.

Alex Cole · Ray Lankford · Nolan Ryan · Delino DeShields · Dave Justice

| NO. | PLAYER | MINT | NO. | PLAYER | MINT | NO. | PLAYER | MINT | NO. | PLAYER | MINT |
|---|---|---|---|---|---|---|---|---|---|---|---|
| 701 | Jim Gott | .06 | 726 | Todd Hundley (R) | .50 | 751 | Alex Cole (R) | .60 | 776 | Glenallen Hill | .10 |
| 702 | "Rookie Threats" | .50 | 727 | Scott Hemond (R) | .20 | 752 | E. Gunderson (R) | .25 | 777 | Keith Hernandez | .08 |
| 703 | Alejandro Pena | .06 | 728 | Lenny Webster (R) | .15 | 753 | Howard Farmer | .20 | 778 | Billy Hatcher | .05 |
| 704 | Willie Randolph | .06 | 729 | Jeff Reardon | .05 | 754 | Joe Carter | .15 | 779 | Marty Clary | .05 |
| 705 | Tim Leary | .06 | 730 | Mitch Webster | .05 | 755 | Ray Lankford (R) | 1.50 | 780 | Candy Maldonado | .05 |
| 706 | Chuck McElroy (R) | .15 | 731 | Brian Bohanon (R) | .15 | 756 | Sandy Alomar Jr. | .20 | 781 | Mike Marshall | .05 |
| 707 | Gerald Perry | .06 | 732 | Rick Parker | .10 | 757 | Alex Sanchez | .05 | 782 | Billy Jo Robidoux | .05 |
| 708 | Tom Brunansky | .06 | 733 | Terry Shumpert (R) | .20 | 758 | Nick Esasky | .05 | 783 | Mark Langston | .10 |
| 709 | John Franco | .06 | 734 | Ryan's No Hitter | 9.00 | 759 | Stan Belinda (R) | .20 | 784 | Paul Sorrento (R) | .12 |
| 710 | Mark Davis | .06 | 734 | Ryans 6th/300 | 1.25 | 760 | Jim Presley | .05 | 785 | Dave Hollins (R) | .50 |
| 711 | Dave Justice (R) | 8.00 | 735 | John Burkett | .25 | 761 | Gary DiSarcina (R) | .15 | 786 | Cecil Fielder | .75 |
| 712 | Storm Davis | .05 | 736 | Derrick May (R) | .25 | 762 | Wayne Edwards | .15 | 787 | Matt Young | .06 |
| 713 | Scott Ruskin (R) | .20 | 737 | Carlos Baerga (R) | .75 | 763 | Pat Combs | .10 | 788 | Jeff Huson | .06 |
| 714 | Glenn Braggs | .05 | 738 | Greg Smith (R) | .15 | 764 | Mickey Pina | .20 | 789 | Lloyd Moseby | .06 |
| 715 | Kevin Bearse (R) | .15 | 739 | Scott Sanderson | .05 | 765 | Wilson Alvarez (R) | .50 | 790 | Ron Kittle | .06 |
| 716 | Jose Nunez | .06 | 740 | Joe Kraemer | .15 | 766 | Dave Parker | .10 | 791 | Hubie Brooks | .06 |
| 717 | Tim Layana (R) | .20 | 741 | Hector Villanueva | .20 | 767 | Mike Blowers (R) | .20 | 792 | Craig Lefferts | .06 |
| 718 | Greg Myers | .05 | 742 | Mike Fetters | .10 | 768 | Tony Phillips | .05 | 793 | Kevin Bass | .06 |
| 719 | Pete O'Brien | .05 | 743 | Mark Gardner (R) | .25 | 769 | Pascual Perez | .05 | 794 | Bryn Smith | .06 |
| 720 | John Candelaria | .05 | 744 | Matt Nokes | .05 | 770 | Gary Pettis | .05 | 795 | Juan Samuel | .06 |
| 721 | Craig Grebeck (R) | .15 | 745 | Dave Winfield | .15 | 771 | Fred Lynn | .05 | 796 | Sam Horn | .06 |
| 722 | Shawn Boskie (R) | .20 | 746 | D. DeShields (R) | 1.00 | 772 | Mel Rojas (R) | .15 | 797 | Randy Myers | .06 |
| 723 | Jim Leyritz (R) | .20 | 747 | Dann Howitt (R) | .20 | 773 | David Segui (R) | .25 | 798 | Chris James | .06 |
| 724 | Bill Sampen (R) | .20 | 748 | Tony Pena | .05 | 774 | Cary Carter | .10 | 799 | Bill Gullickson | .06 |
| 725 | Scott Radinsky (R) | .20 | 749 | Oil Can Boyd | .05 | 775 | Rafael Valdez (R) | .12 | 800 | Checklist 701-800 | .06 |
| | | | 750 | Mike Benjamin (R) | .20 | | | | | | |

# 1991 Upper Deck . . . Complete Set of 700 Cards—Value $30.00 (Factory Set of 800 Cards—Value $40.00)

A new subset is Top Prospects (26 cards). 2,500 signed Baseball Heroes Ryan cards will be randomly sorted into foil packs. As in past years, a hologram to deter counterfeiting appears on the reverse side.

Henry Rodriguez

Andujar Cedeno

Travis Fryman

Todd Van Poppel

Alex Fernandez

| NO. PLAYER | MINT | NO. PLAYER | MINT | NO. PLAYER | MINT | NO. PLAYER | MINT |
|---|---|---|---|---|---|---|---|
| **No. 1 to 27—** | | 62 Tim Costo (R) | .35 | 127 Dave Stewart | .10 | 192 Walt Weiss | .05 |
| **Star Rookies** | | 63 Roger Salkeld | .50 | 128 Jay Buhner | .05 | 193 Jose Oquendo | .05 |
| 1 Star Rookie Checklist | .05 | 64 Brook Fordyce (R) | .25 | 129 Mike LaValliere | .05 | 194 Carney Lansford | .05 |
| 2 Phil Plantier (R) | 2.50 | 65 Mike Mussina (R) | .75 | 130 Scott Bradley | .05 | 195 Jeff Huson | .05 |
| 3 D.J. Dozier | .20 | 66 Dave Staton (R) | .35 | 131 Tony Phillips | .05 | 196 Keith Miller | .05 |
| 4 Dave Hansen | .25 | 67 Mike Lieberthal (R) | .30 | 132 Ryne Sandberg | .30 | 197 Eric Yelding | .05 |
| 5 Maurice Vaughn | 1.00 | 68 Kurt Miller (R) | .25 | 133 Paul O'Neill | .05 | 198 Ron Darling | .05 |
| 6 Leo Gomez | .50 | 69 Dan Peltier (R) | .20 | 134 Mark Grace | .15 | 199 John Kruk | .05 |
| 7 Scott Aldred | .15 | 70 Greg Blosser | .25 | 135 Chris Sabo | .10 | 200 Checklist 101-200 | .05 |
| 8 Scott Chiamparino | .15 | 71 Reggie Sanders (R) | .75 | 136 Ramon Martinez | .20 | 201 John Shelby | .05 |
| 9 Lance Dickson (R) | .30 | 72 Brent Mayne | .15 | 137 Brook Jacoby | .05 | 202 Bob Geren | .05 |
| 10 Sean Berry (R) | .20 | 73 Rico Brogna | .40 | 138 Candy Maldonado | .05 | 203 Lance McCullers | .05 |
| 11 Bernie Williams | .75 | 74 Willie Banks | .35 | 139 Mike Scioscia | .05 | 204 Alvaro Espinoza | .05 |
| 12 Brian Barnes (R) | .20 | 75 Len Brutcher (R) | .15 | 140 Chris James | .05 | 205 Mark Salas | .05 |
| 13 Narciso Elvira (R) | .15 | 76 Pat Kelly (R) | .50 | 141 Craig Worthington | .05 | 206 Mike Pagliarulo | .05 |
| 14 Mike Gardiner (R) | .25 | 77 Reds Checklist | .10 | 142 Manny Lee | .05 | 207 Jose Uribe | .05 |
| 15 Greg Colbrunn (R) | .20 | 78 Dodgers Checklist | .10 | 143 Tim Raines | .10 | 208 Jim DeShales | .05 |
| 16 Bernard Gilkey | .20 | 79 Giants Checklist | .07 | 144 Sandy Alomar Jr. | .10 | 209 Ron Karkovice | .05 |
| 17 Mark Lewis | .40 | 80 Padres Checklist | .07 | 145 John Olerud | .20 | 210 Rafael Ramirez | .05 |
| 18 Mickey Morandini | .15 | 81 Astros Checklist | .07 | 146 Ozzie Canseco | .10 | 211 Donnie Hill | .05 |
| 19 Charles Nagy | .15 | 82 Braves Checklist | .07 | 147 Pat Borders | .05 | 212 Brian Harper | .05 |
| 20 Geronimo Pena | .15 | 83 "Fielder's Feat" | .20 | 148 Harold Reynolds | .05 | 213 Jack Howell | .05 |
| 21 Henry Rodriguez (R) | .25 | 84 Orlando Merced (R) | .60 | 149 Tom Henker | .05 | 214 Wes Gardner | .05 |
| 22 Scott Copper | .30 | 85 Domingo Ramos | .05 | 150 R.J. Reynolds | .05 | 215 Tim Burke | .05 |
| 23 Andujar Cedeno (R) | .60 | 86 Tom Bolton | .05 | 151 Mike Gallego | .05 | 216 Doug Jones | .05 |
| 24 Eric Karros (R) | .75 | 87 Andres Santana | .30 | 152 Bobby Bonilla | .15 | 217 Hubie Brooks | .05 |
| 25 Steve Decker (R) | .35 | 88 John Dopson | .05 | 153 Terry Steinbach | .05 | 218 Tom Candiotti | .05 |
| 26 Kevin Belcher (R) | .15 | 89 Kenny Williams | .05 | 154 Barry Bonds | .20 | 219 Gerald Perry | .05 |
| 27 Jeff Conine (R) | .15 | 90 Marty Barrett | .05 | 155 Jose Canseco | .40 | 220 Jose DeLeon | .05 |
| 28 Athletics Checklist | .08 | 91 Tom Pagnozzi | .05 | 156 Gregg Jefferies | .10 | 221 Wally Whitehurst | .05 |
| 29 White Sox Checklist | .07 | 92 Carmelo Martinez | .05 | 157 Matt Williams | .15 | 222 Alan Mills | .10 |
| 30 Rangers Checklist | .07 | 93 "Save Master" | .05 | 158 Craig Biggio | .10 | 223 Alan Trammell | .10 |
| 31 Angels Checklist | .07 | 94 Pirates Checklist | .10 | 159 Daryl Boston | .05 | 224 Dwight Gooden | .20 |
| 32 Mariners Checklist | .07 | 95 Mets Checklist | .10 | 160 Ricky Jordan | .05 | 225 Travis Fryman | 1.00 |
| 33 Royals Checklist | .07 | 96 Expos Checklist | .07 | 161 Stan Belinda | .05 | 226 Joe Carter | .10 |
| 34 Twins Checklist | .07 | 97 Phillies Checklist | .08 | 162 Ozzie Smith | .12 | 227 Julio Franco | .10 |
| 35 Scott Leius | .15 | 98 Cardinals Checklist | .07 | 163 Tom Brunansky | .08 | 228 Craig Lefferts | .05 |
| 36 Neal Heaton | .05 | 99 Cubs Checklist | .10 | 164 Todd Zeile | .15 | 229 Gary Pettis | .05 |
| 37 Terry Lee (R) | .15 | 100 Checklist 1-100 | .05 | 165 Mike Greenwell | .12 | 230 Dennis Rasmussen | .05 |
| 38 Gary Redus | .05 | 101 Kevin Elster | .05 | 166 Kal Daniels | .10 | 231 Brian Downing | .25 |
| 39 Barry Jones | .05 | 102 Tom Brookens | .05 | 167 Kent Hrbek | .12 | 232 Carlos Quintana | .10 |
| 40 Chuck Knoblauch | 1.25 | 103 Mackey Sasser | .05 | 168 Franklin Stubbs | .05 | 233 Gary Gaetti | .05 |
| 41 Larry Andersen | .05 | 104 Felix Fermin | .05 | 169 Dick Schofield | .05 | 234 Mark Langston | .05 |
| 42 Darryl Hamilton | .05 | 105 Kevin McReynolds | .10 | 170 Junior Ortiz | .05 | 235 Tim Wallach | .05 |
| 43 Red Sox Checklist | .10 | 106 Dave Stieb | .08 | 171 Hector Villanueva | .10 | 236 Greg Swindell | .05 |
| 44 Blue Jays Checklist | .07 | 107 Jeffrey Leonard | .05 | 172 Dennis Eckersley | .10 | 237 Eddie Murray | .15 |
| 45 Tigers Checklist | .07 | 108 Dave Henderson | .10 | 173 Mitch Williams | .05 | 238 Jeff Manto | .05 |
| 46 Indians Checklist | .10 | 109 Sid Bream | .05 | 174 Mark McGwire | .15 | 239 Lenny Harris | .05 |
| 47 Orioles Checklist | .07 | 110 Henry Cotto | .05 | 175 Fernando Valenzuela | .10 | 240 Jesse Orosco | .05 |
| 48 Brewers Checklist | .10 | 111 Shawon Dunston | .10 | 176 Gary Carter | .10 | 241 Scott Lusader | .05 |
| 49 Yankees Checklist | .08 | 112 Mariano Duncan | .05 | 177 Dave Magadan | .08 | 242 Sid Fernandez | .05 |
| **No. 50 to 76—** | | 113 Joe Girardi | .05 | 178 Robby Thompson | .05 | 243 Jim Leyritz | .10 |
| **Top Prospects** | | 114 Billy Hatcher | .05 | 179 Bob Ojeda | .05 | 244 Cecil Fielder | .25 |
| 50 Top Prospect CL | .08 | 115 Greg Maddux | .05 | 180 Ken Caminiti | .05 | 245 Darryl Strawberry | .30 |
| 51 Kyle Abbott | .15 | 116 Jerry Browne | .05 | 181 Don Slaught | .05 | 246 Frank Thomas | 4.00 |
| 52 Juff Juden | .40 | 117 Juan Samuel | .05 | 182 Luis Rivera | .05 | 247 Kevin Mitchell | .15 |
| 53 Todd Van Poppel (R) | 2.00 | 118 Steve Olin | .05 | 183 Jay Bell | .05 | 248 Lance Johnson | .05 |
| 54 Steve Karsay (R) | .35 | 119 Alfredo Griffin | .05 | 184 Jody Reed | .05 | 249 Rick Reuschel | .05 |
| 55 Chipper Jones (R) | .50 | 120 Mitch Webster | .05 | 185 Wally Backman | .05 | 250 Mark Portugal | .05 |
| 56 Chris Johnson (R) | .15 | 121 Joel Skipper | .05 | 186 Dave Martinez | .05 | 251 Derek Lilliquist | .05 |
| 57 John Ericks | .15 | 122 Frank Viola | .10 | 187 Luis Polonia | .05 | 252 Brian Holman | .05 |
| 58 Gary Scott (R) | .35 | 123 Cory Snyder | .05 | 188 Shane Mack | .05 | 253 Rafael Valdez | .05 |
| 59 Kiki Jones | .25 | 124 Howard Johnson | .15 | 189 Spike Owen | .05 | 254 B.J. Surhoff | .05 |
| 60 Wilfredo Cordero (R) | .50 | 125 Carlos Baerga | .20 | 190 Scott Bailes | .05 | 255 Tony Gwynn | .20 |
| 61 Royce Clayton | .75 | 126 Tony Fernandez | .05 | 191 John Russell | .05 | 256 Andy Van Slyke | .10 |

| NO. | PLAYER | MINT | NO. | PLAYER | MINT | NO. | PLAYER | MINT | NO. | PLAYER | MINT |
|---|---|---|---|---|---|---|---|---|---|---|---|
| 257 | Todd Stottlemyre | .05 | 341 | Ted Higuera | .05 | 425 | Bob Welch | .05 | 509 | Greg A. Harris | .05 |
| 258 | Jose Lind | .05 | 342 | David Segui | .10 | 426 | Terry Mulholland | .05 | 510 | Mark Williamson | .05 |
| 259 | Greg Myers | .05 | 343 | Greg Cadaret | .05 | 427 | Willie Blair | .08 | 511 | Casey Candaele | .05 |
| 260 | Jeff Ballard | .05 | 344 | Robin Yount | .15 | 428 | Darrin Fletcher | .10 | 512 | Mookie Wilson | .05 |
| 261 | Bobby Thigpen | .08 | 345 | Nolan Ryan | .50 | 429 | Mike Witt | .05 | 513 | Dave Smith | .05 |
| 262 | Jimmy Kremers | .05 | 346 | Ray Lankford | .35 | 430 | Joe Boever | .05 | 514 | Chuck Carr | .10 |
| 263 | Robin Ventura | .35 | 347 | Cal Ripken Jr. | .40 | 431 | Tom Gordon | .10 | 515 | Glenn Wilson | .05 |
| 264 | John Smoltz | .12 | 348 | Lee Smith | .05 | 432 | Pedro Munoz (R) | .40 | 516 | Mike Fitzgerald | .05 |
| 265 | Sammy Sosa | .10 | 349 | Brady Anderson | .05 | 433 | Kevin Seitzer | .05 | 517 | Devon White | .05 |
| 266 | Gary Sheffield | .08 | 350 | Frank DiPino | .05 | 434 | Kevin Tapani | .05 | 518 | Dave Hollins | .10 |
| 267 | Lenny Dykstra | .10 | 351 | Hal Morris | .12 | 435 | Bret Saberhagen | .10 | 519 | Mark Eichhorn | .05 |
| 268 | Bill Spiers | .05 | 352 | Deion Sanders | .15 | 436 | Ellis Burks | .10 | 520 | Otis Nixon | .05 |
| 269 | Charlie Hayes | .05 | 353 | Barry Larkin | .10 | 437 | Chuck Finley | .10 | 521 | Terry Shumpert | .05 |
| 270 | Brett Butler | .05 | 354 | Don Mattingly | .25 | 438 | Mike Boddicker | .05 | 522 | Scott Erickson | 2.50 |
| 271 | Bip Roberts | .05 | 355 | Eric Davis | .15 | 439 | Francisco Cabrera | .05 | 523 | Danny Tartabull | .05 |
| 272 | Rob Deer | .05 | 356 | Jose Offerman | .15 | 440 | Todd Hundley | .12 | 524 | Orel Hershiser | .10 |
| 273 | Fred Lynn | .05 | 357 | Mel Rojas | .08 | 441 | Kelly Downs | .05 | 525 | George Brett | .15 |
| 274 | Dave Parker | .12 | 358 | Rudy Seanez | .10 | 442 | Dann Howitt | .10 | 526 | Greg Vaughn | .15 |
| 275 | Andy Benes | .12 | 359 | Oil Can Boyd | .05 | 443 | Scott Garrelts | .05 | 527 | Tim Naehring | .15 |
| 276 | Glenallen Hill | .05 | 360 | Nelson Liriano | .05 | 444 | Rickey Henderson | .30 | 528 | Curt Schilling | .05 |
| 277 | Steve Howard | .08 | 361 | Ron Gant | .15 | 445 | Will Clark | .30 | 529 | Chris Bosio | .05 |
| 278 | Doug Drabek | .05 | 362 | Howard Farmer | .10 | 446 | Ben McDonald | .12 | 530 | Sam Horn | .05 |
| 279 | Joe Oliver | .05 | 363 | David Justice | 1.00 | 447 | Dale Murphy | .15 | 531 | Mike Scott | .05 |
| 280 | Todd Benzinger | .08 | 364 | Delino DeShields | .10 | 448 | Dave Righetti | .05 | 532 | George Bell | .10 |
| 281 | Eric King | .05 | 365 | Steve Avery | .40 | 449 | Dickie Thon | .05 | 533 | Eric Anthony | .10 |
| 282 | Jim Presley | .05 | 366 | David Cone | .10 | 450 | Ted Power | .05 | 534 | Julio Valera | .10 |
| 283 | Ken Patterson | .05 | 367 | Lou Whitaker | .05 | 451 | Scott Coolbaugh | .05 | 535 | Glenn Davis | .10 |
| 284 | Jack Daugherty | .05 | 368 | Von Hayes | .05 | 452 | Dwight Smith | .05 | 536 | Larry Walker | .08 |
| 285 | Ivan Calderon | .05 | 369 | Frank Tanana | .05 | 453 | Pete Incaviglia | .05 | 537 | Pat Combs | .05 |
| 286 | Edgar Diaz | .08 | 370 | Tim Teufel | .05 | 454 | Andre Dawson | .15 | 538 | Chris Nabholz | .10 |
| 287 | Kevin Bass | .05 | 371 | Randy Myers | .05 | 455 | Ruben Sierra | .15 | 539 | Kirk McCaskill | .05 |
| 288 | Don Carman | .05 | 372 | Roberto Kelly | .08 | 456 | Andres Galarraga | .05 | 540 | Randy Ready | .05 |
| 289 | Greg Brock | .05 | 373 | Jack Armstrong | .05 | 457 | Alvin Davis | .05 | 541 | Mark Gubicza | .05 |
| 290 | John Franco | .05 | 374 | Kelly Gruber | .10 | 458 | Tony Castillo | .05 | 542 | Rick Aguilera | .05 |
| 291 | Joey Cora | .05 | 375 | Kevin Maas | .25 | 459 | Pete O'Brien | .05 | 543 | Brian McRae (R) | .90 |
| 292 | Bill Wegman | .05 | 376 | Randy Johnson | .05 | 460 | Charlie Leibrandt | .05 | 544 | Kirby Puckett | .20 |
| 293 | Eric Show | .05 | 377 | David West | .05 | 461 | Vince Coleman | .12 | 545 | Bo Jackson | .35 |
| 294 | Scott Bankhead | .05 | 378 | Brent Knackert | .10 | 462 | Steve Sax | .05 | 546 | Wade Boggs | .20 |
| 295 | Garry Templeton | .05 | 379 | Rick Honeycutt | .05 | 463 | Omar Olivares (R) | .12 | 547 | Tim McIntosh | .10 |
| 296 | Mickey Tettleton | .05 | 380 | Kevin Gross | .05 | 464 | Oscar Azocar | .10 | 548 | Randy Milligan | .05 |
| 297 | Luis Sojo | .05 | 381 | Tom Foley | .05 | 465 | Joe Magrane | .05 | 549 | Dwight Evans | .05 |
| 298 | Jose Rijo | .05 | 382 | Jeff Blauser | .05 | 466 | Karl Rhodes | .10 | 550 | Billy Ripken | .05 |
| 299 | Dave Johnson | .05 | 383 | Scott Ruskin | .10 | 467 | Benito Santiago | .10 | 551 | Erik Hanson | .05 |
| 300 | Checklist 201-300 | .05 | 384 | Andres Thomas | .05 | 468 | Joe Klink | .08 | 552 | Lance Parrish | .05 |
| 301 | Mark Grant | .05 | 385 | Dennis Martinez | .05 | 469 | Sil Campusano | .05 | 553 | Tino Martinez | .25 |
| 302 | Pete Harnisch | .05 | 386 | Mike Henneman | .05 | 470 | Mark Parent | .05 | 554 | Jim Abbott | .15 |
| 303 | Greg Olson | .15 | 387 | Felix Jose | .10 | 471 | Shawn Boskie | .05 | 555 | Ken Griffey, Jr. | 1.25 |
| 304 | Anthony Telford (R) | .15 | 388 | Alejandro Pena | .05 | 472 | Kevin Brown | .05 | 556 | Milt Cuyler | .35 |
| 305 | Lonnie Smith | .05 | 389 | Chet Lemon | .05 | 473 | Rick Sutcliffe | .05 | 557 | Mark Leonard (R) | .25 |
| 306 | Chris Hoiles | .15 | 390 | Craig Wilson | .12 | 474 | Rafael Palmeiro | .15 | 558 | Jay Howell | .05 |
| 307 | Bryn Smith | .05 | 391 | Chuck Crim | .05 | 475 | Mike Harkey | .05 | 559 | Lloyd Moseby | .05 |
| 308 | Mike Devereaux | .05 | 392 | Mel Hall | .05 | 476 | Jaime Navarro | .05 | 560 | Chris Gwynn | .05 |
| 309 | Milt Thompson | .05 | 393 | Mark Knudson | .05 | 477 | Marquis Grissom | .15 | 561 | Mark Whiten | .30 |
| 310 | Bob Melvin | .05 | 394 | Norm Charlton | .08 | 478 | Marty Clary | .05 | 562 | Harold Baines | .05 |
| 311 | Luis Salazar | .05 | 395 | Mike Felder | .05 | 479 | Greg Briley | .05 | 563 | Junior Felix | .10 |
| 312 | Ed Whitson | .05 | 396 | Tim Layana | .05 | 480 | Tom Glavine | .15 | 564 | Darren Lewis | .40 |
| 313 | Charlie Hough | .05 | 397 | Steve Frey | .05 | 481 | Lee Guetterman | .05 | 565 | Fred McGriff | .15 |
| 314 | Dave Clark | .05 | 398 | Bill Doran | .05 | 482 | Rex Hudler | .05 | 566 | Kevin Appier | .05 |
| 315 | Eric Gunderson | .05 | 399 | Dion James | .05 | 483 | Dave LaPoint | .05 | 567 | Luis Gonzalez (R) | .75 |
| 316 | Dan Petry | .05 | 400 | Checklist 301-400 | .05 | 484 | Terry Pendleton | .10 | 568 | Frank White | .05 |
| 317 | Dante Bichette | .05 | 401 | Ron Hassey | .05 | 485 | Jesse Barfield | .05 | 569 | Juan Agosto | .05 |
| 318 | Mike Heath | .05 | 402 | Don Robinson | .05 | 486 | Jose DeJesus | .05 | 570 | Mike Macfarlane | .05 |
| 319 | Damon Berryhill | .05 | 403 | Gene Nelson | .05 | 487 | Paul Abbott (R) | .12 | 571 | Bert Blyleven | .05 |
| 320 | Walt Terrell | .05 | 404 | Terry Kennedy | .05 | 488 | Ken Howell | .05 | 572 | Ken Griffey Sr. | .30 |
| 321 | Scott Fletcher | .05 | 405 | Todd Burns | .05 | 489 | Greg W. Harris | .05 | 573 | Lee Stevens | .20 |
| 322 | Dan Plesac | .05 | 406 | Roger McDowell | .05 | 490 | Roy Smith | .05 | 574 | Edgar Martinez | .10 |
| 323 | Jack McDowell | .10 | 407 | Bob Kipper | .05 | 491 | Paul Assenmacher | .05 | 575 | Wally Joyner | .12 |
| 324 | Paul Molitor | .12 | 408 | Darren Daulton | .05 | 492 | Geno Petralli | .05 | 576 | Tim Belcher | .05 |
| 325 | Ozzie Guillen | .05 | 409 | Chuck Cary | .05 | 493 | Steve Wilson | .05 | 577 | John Burkett | .05 |
| 326 | Gregg Olson | .08 | 410 | Bruce Ruffin | .05 | 494 | Kevin Reimer | .12 | 578 | Mike Morgan | .05 |
| 327 | Pedro Guerrero | .10 | 411 | Juan Berenguer | .05 | 495 | Bill Long | .05 | 579 | Paul Gibson | .05 |
| 328 | Bob Milacki | .05 | 412 | Gary Ward | .05 | 496 | Mike Jackson | .05 | 580 | Jose Vizcaino | .05 |
| 329 | John Tudor | .05 | 413 | Al Newman | .05 | 497 | Oddibe McDowell | .05 | 581 | Duane Ward | .05 |
| 330 | Steve Finley | .10 | 414 | Danny Jackson | .05 | 498 | Bill Swift | .05 | 582 | Scott Sanderson | .05 |
| 331 | Jack Clark | .15 | 415 | Greg Gagne | .05 | 499 | Jeff Treadway | .05 | 583 | David Wells | .05 |
| 332 | Jerome Walton | .10 | 416 | Tom Herr | .05 | 500 | Checklist 401-500 | .05 | 584 | Willie McGee | .10 |
| 333 | Andy Hawkins | .05 | 417 | Jeff Parrett | .05 | 501 | Gene Larkin | .05 | 585 | John Cerutti | .05 |
| 334 | Derrick May | .12 | 418 | Jeff Reardon | .05 | 502 | Bob Boone | .05 | 586 | Danny Darwin | .05 |
| 335 | Roberto Alomar | .12 | 419 | Mark Lemke | .05 | 503 | Allan Anderson | .05 | 587 | Kurt Stillwell | .05 |
| 336 | Jack Morris | .08 | 420 | Charlie O'Brien | .05 | 504 | Luis Aquino | .05 | 588 | Rich Gedman | .05 |
| 337 | Dave Winfield | .15 | 421 | Willie Randolph | .05 | 505 | Mark Davis | .05 | 589 | Mark Davis | .05 |
| 338 | Steve Searcy | .05 | 422 | Steve Bedrosian | .05 | 506 | Joe Orsulak | .05 | 590 | Bill Gullickson | .05 |
| 339 | Chilli Davis | .05 | 423 | Mike Moore | .05 | 507 | Dana Kiecker | .10 | 591 | Matt Young | .05 |
| 340 | Larry Sheets | .05 | 424 | Jeff Brantley | .05 | 508 | Dave Gallagher | .05 | 592 | Bryan Harvey | .05 |

| NO. | PLAYER | MINT |
|---|---|---|
| 593 | Omar Vizquel | .05 |
| 594 | Scott Lewis (R) | .15 |
| 595 | Dave Valle | .05 |
| 596 | Tim Crews | .05 |
| 597 | Mike Bielecki | .05 |
| 598 | Mike Sharperson | .05 |
| 599 | Dave Bergman | .05 |
| 600 | Checklist 501-600 | .05 |
| 601 | Steve Lyons | .05 |
| 602 | Bruce Hurst | .05 |
| 603 | Donn Pall | .05 |
| 604 | Jim Vatcher (R) | .15 |
| 605 | Dan Pasqua | .05 |
| 606 | Kenny Rogers | .05 |
| 607 | Jeff Schulz (R) | .12 |
| 608 | Brad Arnsberg | .05 |
| 609 | Willie Wilson | .05 |
| 610 | Jamie Moyer | .05 |
| 611 | Ron Oester | .05 |
| 612 | Dennis Cook | .05 |
| 613 | Rick Mahler | .05 |
| 614 | Bill Landrum | .05 |
| 615 | Scott Scudder | .05 |
| 616 | Tom Edens (R) | .12 |
| 617 | "1917 Revisited" | .05 |
| 618 | Jim Gantner | .05 |
| 619 | Darrell Akerfelds | .05 |
| 620 | Ron Robinson | .05 |
| 621 | Scott Radinsky | .05 |
| 622 | Pete Smith | .05 |
| 623 | Melido Perez | .05 |
| 624 | Jerald Clark | .05 |
| 625 | Carlos Martinez | .05 |
| 626 | Wes Chamberlain (R) | 1.00 |

| NO. | PLAYER | MINT |
|---|---|---|
| 627 | Bobby Witt | .05 |
| 628 | Ken Dayley | .05 |
| 629 | John Barfield (R) | .12 |
| 630 | Bob Tewksbury | .05 |
| 631 | Glenn Braggs | .05 |
| 632 | Jim Neidlinger (R) | .12 |
| 633 | Tom Browning | .05 |
| 634 | Kirk Gibson | .10 |
| 635 | Rob Dibble | .05 |
| 636 | "Stolen Base Leaders" | .30 |
| 637 | Jeff Montgomery | .05 |
| 638 | Mike Schooler | .05 |
| 639 | Storm Davis | .05 |
| 640 | Rich Rodriguez (R) | .12 |
| 641 | Phil Bradley | .05 |
| 642 | Kent Mercker | .15 |
| 643 | Carlton Fisk | .10 |
| 644 | Mike Bell (R) | .15 |
| 645 | Alex Fernandez | .35 |
| 646 | Juan Gonzalez | .75 |
| 647 | Ken Hill | .05 |
| 648 | Jeff Russell | .05 |
| 649 | Chuck Malone | .05 |
| 650 | Steve Buechele | .05 |
| 651 | Mike Bejamin | .15 |
| 652 | Tony Pena | .05 |
| 653 | Trevor Wilson | .05 |
| 654 | Alex Cole | .10 |
| 655 | Roger Clemens | .35 |
| 656 | "The Bashing Years" | .10 |
| 657 | Joe Grahe (R) | .12 |
| 658 | Jim Eisenreich | .05 |
| 659 | Dan Gladden | .05 |
| 660 | Steve Farr | .05 |

| NO. | PLAYER | MINT |
|---|---|---|
| 661 | Bill Sampen | .05 |
| 662 | Dave Rohde | .05 |
| 663 | Mark Gardner | .05 |
| 664 | Mike Simms (R) | .25 |
| 665 | Moises Alou | .10 |
| 666 | Mickey Hatcher | .05 |
| 667 | Jimmy Key | .05 |
| 668 | John Wetteland | .05 |
| 669 | John Smiley | .05 |
| 670 | Jim Acker | .05 |
| 671 | Pascual Perez | .05 |
| 672 | Reggie Harris | .15 |
| 673 | Matt Nokes | .05 |
| 674 | Rafael Novoa (R) | .15 |
| 675 | Hensley Muelens | .10 |
| 676 | Jeff M. Robinson | .05 |
| 677 | "Ground Breaking" | .10 |
| 678 | Johnny Ray | .05 |
| 679 | Greg Hibbard | .05 |
| 680 | Paul Sorrento | .05 |
| 681 | Mike Marshall | .05 |
| 682 | Jim Clancy | .05 |
| 683 | Rob Murphy | .05 |
| 684 | Dave Schmidt | .05 |
| 685 | Jeff Gray (R) | .12 |
| 686 | Mike Hartley | .10 |
| 687 | Jeff King | .05 |
| 688 | Stan Javier | .05 |
| 689 | Bob Walk | .05 |
| 690 | Jim Gott | .05 |
| 691 | Mike LaCoss | .05 |
| 692 | John Farrell | .05 |
| 693 | Tim Leary | .05 |
| 694 | Mike Walker | .05 |

| NO. | PLAYER | MINT |
|---|---|---|
| 695 | Eric Plunk | .05 |
| 696 | Mike Fetters | .05 |
| 697 | Wayne Edwards | .05 |
| 698 | Tim Drummond | .05 |
| 699 | Willie Fraser | .05 |
| 700 | Checklist 601-700 | .05 |

**No. SS1 to SS18—Silver Sluggers**

| No. | Player | Mint |
|---|---|---|
| SS1 | Julio Franco | 2.00 |
| SS2 | Alan Trammell | 2.00 |
| SS3 | Rickey Henderson | 6.00 |
| SS4 | Jose Canseco | 7.50 |
| SS5 | Barry Bonds | 3.00 |
| SS6 | Eddie Murray | 2.00 |
| SS7 | Kelly Gruber | 1.50 |
| SS8 | Ryne Sandberg | 7.00 |
| SS9 | Darryl Strawberry | 4.00 |
| SS10 | Ellis Burks | 1.50 |
| SS11 | Lance Parrish | 1.25 |
| SS12 | Cecil Fielder | 4.00 |
| SS13 | Matt Williams | 2.00 |
| SS14 | Dave Parker | 2.00 |
| SS15 | Bobby Bonilla | 4.00 |
| SS16 | Don Robinson | 1.25 |
| SS17 | Benito Santiago | 1.50 |
| SS18 | Barry Larkin | 2.00 |

**SPECIAL CARDS**

| No. | Card | Mint |
|---|---|---|
| — | Michael Jordan | 10.00 |
| H1 | Harmon Killebrew | 15.00 |
| H2 | Gaylord Perry | 15.00 |
| H3 | Fergie Jenkins | 15.00 |
| H4 | Title Card | 15.00 |

# 1991 Upper Deck Extended . . . Complete Set of 100 Cards—Value $12.00

This set updates the main 1991 card set with players who had changed teams during the season, and rookies. Extended cards were found in late season foil packs; the complete set was packaged in a printed box and packaged as part of the complete factory set.

Dana Allison

Reggie Jefferson

Albert Belle

Kirk Dressendorfer

Jeff Bagwell

| NO. | PLAYER | MINT |
|---|---|---|
| 701 | Mike Heath | .05 |
| 702 | "Rookie Threats" | .10 |
|  | L. Gonzalez, K. Rhodes, | |
|  | J. Bagwell | |
| 703 | Jose Mesa | .05 |
| 704 | Dave Smith | .05 |
| 705 | Danny Darwin | .05 |
| 706 | Rafael Belliard | .05 |
| 707 | Rob Murphy | .05 |
| 708 | Terry Pendleton | .12 |
| 709 | Mike Pagliarulo | .05 |
| 710 | Sid Bream | .05 |
| 711 | Junior Felix | .05 |
| 712 | Dante Bichette | .05 |
| 713 | Kevin Gross | .05 |
| 714 | Luis Sojo | .05 |
| 715 | Bob Ojeda | .05 |
| 716 | Julio Machado | .05 |
| 717 | Steve Farr | .05 |
| 718 | Franklin Stubbs | .05 |
| 719 | Mike Boddicker | .05 |
| 720 | Willie Randolph | .08 |
| 721 | Wille McGee | .08 |
| 722 | Chili Davis | .05 |
| 723 | Danny Jackson | .05 |
| 724 | Cory Snyder | .08 |

| NO. | PLAYER | MINT |
|---|---|---|
| 725 | "MVP Lineup" | .25 |
|  | A. Dawson, R. Sandberg, | |
|  | G. Bell | |
| 726 | Rob Deer | .05 |
| 727 | Rich DeLucia (R) | .20 |
| 728 | Mike Perez | .10 |
| 729 | Mickey Tettleton | .05 |
| 730 | Mike Blowers | .05 |
| 731 | Gary Gaetti | .05 |
| 732 | Brett Butler | .08 |
| 733 | Dave Parker | .12 |
| 734 | Eddie Zosky | .20 |
| 735 | Jack Clark | .12 |
| 736 | Jack Morris | .10 |
| 737 | Kirk Gibson | .08 |
| 738 | Steve Bedrosian | .05 |
| 739 | Candy Maldonado | .05 |
| 740 | Matt Young | .05 |
| 741 | Rich Garces (R) | .15 |
| 742 | George Bell | .12 |
| 743 | Deion Sanders | .25 |
| 744 | Bo Jackson | 2.00 |
| 745 | Luis Mercedes (R) | .60 |
| 746 | Reggie Jefferson | .75 |
| 747 | Pete Incaviglia | .05 |
| 748 | Chris Hammond | .10 |

| NO. | PLAYER | MINT |
|---|---|---|
| 749 | Mike Stanton | .05 |
| 750 | Scott Sanderson | .05 |
| 751 | Paul Faries (R) | .15 |
| 752 | Al Osuna (R) | .20 |
| 753 | Steve Chitren (R) | .20 |
| 754 | Tony Fernandez | .05 |
| 755 | Jeff Bagwell (R) | 4.00 |
| 756 | Kirk Dressendorfer (R) | .40 |
| 757 | Glenn Davis | .10 |
| 758 | Gary Carter | .10 |
| 759 | Zane Smith | .05 |
| 760 | Vance Law | .05 |
| 761 | Denis Boucher (R) | .25 |
| 762 | Turner Ward (R) | .25 |
| 763 | Robert Alomar | .15 |
| 764 | Albert Belle | .30 |
| 765 | Joe Carter | .15 |
| 766 | Peter Schourek (R) | .15 |
| 767 | Heathcliff Slocumb (R) | .15 |
| 768 | Vince Coleman | .12 |
| 769 | Mitch Williams | .05 |
| 770 | Brian Downing | .05 |
| 771 | Dana Allison (R) | .15 |
| 772 | Pete Harnisch | .05 |
| 773 | Tim Raines | .15 |
| 774 | Darryl Kile | .15 |

| NO. | PLAYER | MINT |
|---|---|---|
| 775 | Fred McGriff | .15 |
| 776 | Dwight Evans | .08 |
| 777 | Joe Slusarski (R) | .15 |
| 778 | Dave Righetti | .05 |
| 779 | Jeff Hamilton | .05 |
| 780 | Ernest Riles | .05 |
| 781 | Ken Dayley | .05 |
| 782 | Eric King | .05 |
| 783 | Devon White | .05 |
| 784 | Beau Allred | .12 |
| 785 | Mike Timlin (R) | .15 |
| 786 | Ivan Calderon | .05 |
| 787 | Hubie Brooks | .05 |
| 788 | Juan Agosto | .05 |
| 789 | Barry Jones | .05 |
| 790 | Wally Backman | .05 |
| 791 | Jim Presley | .08 |
| 792 | Charlie Hough | .05 |
| 793 | Larry Anderson | .05 |
| 794 | Steve Finley | .05 |
| 795 | Shawn Abner | .05 |
| 796 | Jeff M. Robinson | .05 |
| 797 | Joe Bitker | .15 |
| 798 | Eric Show | .05 |
| 799 | Bud Black | .05 |
| 800 | Checklist 701-800 | .05 |
| HH1 | Hologram—Aaron | 7.50 |

## 1991 Upper Deck Final . . . Complete Set of 100 Cards—Value $20.00

Features late season trades and rookies not included in the main set. Only sold as a complete set which was packaged in a printed box.
Includes the rookie cards of Ryan Klesko and Ryan Rodriguez.

| NO. | PLAYER | MINT |
|---|---|---|
| 1F | Diamond Skills CL | .75 |
| | R. Sanders/R. Klesko | |
| **No. 2 to 21—Diamond Skills** | | |
| 2F | Pedro Martinez (R) | 1.50 |
| 3F | Lance Dickson | .15 |
| 4F | Royce Clayton | .30 |
| 5F | Scott Bryant | .15 |
| 6F | Dan Wilson (R) | .30 |
| 7F | Dmitri Young (R) | 1.50 |
| 8F | Ryan Klesko (R) | 4.00 |
| 9F | Tom Goodwin | .20 |
| 10F | Rondell White (R) | 1.00 |
| 11F | Reggie Sanders | .35 |
| 12F | Todd Van Poppel | .60 |
| 13F | Arthur Rhodes (R) | .50 |
| 14F | Eddie Zosky | .15 |
| 15F | Gerald Williams (R) | .50 |
| 16F | Robert Eenhoorn (R) | .25 |
| 17F | Jim Thome (R) | 1.25 |
| 18F | Marc Newfield (R) | 2.50 |
| 19F | Kerwin Moore (R) | .40 |
| 20F | Jeff McNeely (R) | .75 |
| 21F | Frankie Rodriguez (R) | 2.50 |
| 22F | Andy Mota (R) | .25 |
| 23F | Chris Haney (R) | .25 |
| 24F | Kenny Lofton (R) | .60 |

| NO. | PLAYER | MINT |
|---|---|---|
| 25F | Dave Nilsson (R) | .75 |
| 26F | Derek Bell | 1.25 |
| 27F | Frank Castillo (R) | .20 |
| 28F | Candy Maldonado | .07 |
| 29F | Chuck McElroy | .07 |
| 30F | Chito Martinez (R) | 1.00 |
| 31F | Steve Howe | .07 |
| 32F | Freddie Benavides (R) | .25 |
| 33F | Scott Kamieniecki | .20 |
| 34F | Denny Neagle (R) | .60 |
| 35F | Mike Humphreys (R) | .25 |
| 36F | Mike Remlinger | .15 |
| 37F | Scott Coolbaugh | .07 |
| 38F | Darren Lewis | .20 |
| 39F | Thomas Howard | .07 |
| 40F | John Candelaria | .07 |
| 41F | Todd Benzinger | .07 |
| 42F | Wilson Alvarez | .07 |
| 43F | Patrick Lennon (R) | .60 |
| 44F | Rusty Meacham (R) | .25 |
| 45F | Ryan Bowen (R) | .30 |
| 46F | Rick Wilkins (R) | .25 |
| 47F | Ed Sprague | .15 |
| 48F | Bob Scanlan (R) | .15 |
| 49F | Tom Candiotti | .07 |
| 50F | "Perfecto" | .07 |
| | Dennis Martinez | |

| NO. | PLAYER | MINT |
|---|---|---|
| 51F | Oil Can Boyd | .07 |
| 52F | Glenallen Hill | .07 |
| 53F | Scott Livingstone (R) | .30 |
| 54F | Brian Hunter (R) | 1.25 |
| 55F | Ivan Rodriguez (R) | 3.00 |
| 56F | Keith Mitchell (R) | .75 |
| 57F | Roger McDowell | .07 |
| 58F | Otis Nixon | .07 |
| 59F | Juan Bell | .07 |
| 60F | Bill Krueger | .07 |
| 61F | Chris Donnels (R) | .30 |
| 62F | Tommy Greene | .07 |
| 63F | Doug Simons (R) | .15 |
| 64F | Andy Ashby (R) | .20 |
| 65F | Anthony Young (R) | .30 |
| 66F | Kevin Morton (R) | .25 |
| 67F | Bret Barberie | .40 |
| 68F | Scott Servais | .20 |
| 69F | Ron Darling | .07 |
| 70F | Tim Burke | .07 |
| 71F | Vicente Palacios | .07 |
| 72F | Gerald Alexander (R) | .20 |
| 73F | Reggie Jefferson | .25 |
| 74F | Dean Palmer | .50 |
| 75F | Mark Whiten | .15 |

| NO. | PLAYER | MINT |
|---|---|---|
| 76F | Randy Tomlin (R) | .40 |
| 77F | Mark Wohlers (R) | .75 |
| 78F | Brook Jacoby | .07 |
| 79F | All-Star Checklist | .60 |
| 80F | Jack Morris (AS) | .15 |
| 81F | Sandy Alomar Jr. (AS) | .07 |
| 82F | Cecil Fielder (AS) | .15 |
| 83F | Roberto Alomar (AS) | .15 |
| 84F | Wade Boggs (AS) | .15 |
| 85F | Cal Ripken (AS) | .30 |
| 86F | Rickey Henderson (AS) | .25 |
| 87F | Ken Griffey Jr. (AS) | .60 |
| 88F | Dave Henderson (AS) | .07 |
| 89F | Danny Tartabull (AS) | .07 |
| 90F | Tom Glavine (AS) | .12 |
| 91F | Benito Santiago (AS) | .07 |
| 92F | Will Clark (AS) | .25 |
| 93F | Ryne Sandberg (AS) | .30 |
| 94F | Chris Sabo (AS) | .07 |
| 95F | Ozzie Smith (AS) | .10 |
| 96F | Ivan Calderon (AS) | .07 |
| 97F | Tony Gwynn (AS) | .15 |
| 98F | Andre Dawson (AS) | .12 |
| 99F | Bobby Bonilla (AS) | .15 |
| 100F | Checklist 1F-100F (AS) | .07 |

## 1992 Upper Deck . . . Complete Set of 700 Cards—Value $35.00

New subsets included *Bloodlines* and *Diamond Skills*. Jim Abbott appeared on Upper Deck's first "public service" card. A 9-card Baseball Heroes insert and an unnumbered cover card was issued for Ted Williams. Limited edition cards were issued for special events.

| NO. | PLAYER | MINT |
|---|---|---|
| **No. 1 to 27-Star Rookies** | | |
| 1 | Star Rookie Checklist | .50 |
| 2 | Royce Clayton | .25 |
| 3 | Brian Jordan (R) | .20 |
| 4 | Dave Fleming | .25 |
| 5 | Jim Thome | .60 |
| 6 | Jeff Juden | .20 |
| 7 | Roberto Hernandez | .20 |
| 8 | Kyle Abbott | .15 |
| 9 | Chris George | .05 |
| 10 | Rob Maurer (R) | .30 |
| 11 | Donald Harris | .12 |
| 12 | Mark Wohlers (R) | .35 |
| 13 | Patrick Lennon | .20 |
| 14 | Willie Banks | .15 |

| NO. | PLAYER | MINT |
|---|---|---|
| 15 | Roger Salkeld | .30 |
| 16 | Wilfredo Cordero | .20 |
| 17 | Arthur Rhodes | .20 |
| 18 | Pedro Martinez | .60 |
| 19 | Andy Ashby | .15 |
| 20 | Tom Goodwin | .20 |
| 21 | Braulio Castillo (R) | .30 |
| 22 | Todd Van Poppel | .75 |
| 23 | Brian Williams (R) | .35 |
| 24 | Ryan Kiesko | 1.75 |
| 25 | Kenny Lofton | .35 |
| 26 | Derek Bell | .30 |
| 27 | Reggie Sanders | .25 |
| 28 | "Winfield's 400th" | .15 |
| 29 | Atlanta Checklist | .20 |

| NO. | PLAYER | MINT |
|---|---|---|
| 30 | Cincinnati Checklist | .08 |
| 31 | Houston Checklist | .06 |
| 32 | Los Angeles Checklist | .10 |
| 33 | San Diego Checklist | .10 |
| 34 | San Fran. Checklist | .08 |
| 35 | Chicago Checklist | .06 |
| 36 | Montreal Checklist | .06 |
| 37 | New York Checklist | .08 |
| 38 | Philadelphia Checklist | .06 |
| 39 | Pittsburgh Checklist | .06 |
| 40 | St. Louis Checklist | .08 |
| 41 | "Playoff Perfection" | .20 |
| 42 | J. Hernandez (R) | .15 |
| 43 | Doug Henry (R) | .25 |
| 44 | Chris Donnels | .15 |

| NO. | PLAYER | MINT |
|---|---|---|
| 45 | Mo Sanford | .15 |
| 46 | Scott Kamieniecki | .10 |
| 47 | Mark Lemke | .05 |
| 48 | Steve Farr | .05 |
| 49 | Francisco Oliveras | .05 |
| 50 | Ced Landrum | .08 |
| 51 | Top Prospect CL | .25 |
| 52 | Eduardo Perez (R) | .50 |
| 53 | Tom Nevers | .20 |
| 54 | D. Zancsaaro (R) | .25 |
| 55 | Shawn Green (R) | .35 |
| 56 | Mike Kelly | .25 |
| 57 | Dave Nilsson | .35 |
| 58 | Dmitri Young | .75 |
| 59 | Ryan Hawblitzel (R) | .30 |

| NO. | PLAYER | MINT |
|---|---|---|
| 60 | Raul Mondesi | .30 |
| 61 | Rondell White | .25 |
| 62 | Steve Hosey | .20 |
| 63 | Manny Ramirez (R) | .75 |
| 64 | Marc Newfield | .50 |
| 65 | Jeromy Burnitz | 1.00 |
| 66 | Mark Smith (R) | .50 |
| 67 | Joey Hamilton (R) | .30 |
| 68 | Tyler Green | .40 |
| 69 | John Farrell (R) | .20 |
| 70 | Kurt Miller | .15 |
| 71 | Frankie Rodriguez | .20 |
| 72 | Dan Wilson | .12 |
| 73 | Joe Vitiello (R) | .50 |
| 74 | Rico Brogna | .15 |
| 75 | David McCarty (R) | 1.00 |
| 76 | Bob Wickman | .15 |
| 77 | Brien Taylor | .15 |
| 78 | "Stay in School" | .10 |

**No. 79 to 85—Bloodlines**

| NO. | PLAYER | MINT |
|---|---|---|
| 79 | Ramon & Pedro | .40 |
| 80 | Kevin & Keith | .25 |
| 81 | Sandy Jr. & Roberto | .15 |
| 82 | Cal Jr. & Billy | .15 |
| 83 | Tony & Chris | .15 |
| 84 | Dwight & Gary | .15 |
| 85 | Ken Sr., Ken Jr. & Craig | .75 |
| 86 | California Checklist | .08 |
| 87 | Chicago Checklist | .30 |
| 88 | Kansas City Checklist | .06 |
| 89 | Minnesota Checklist | .15 |
| 90 | Oakland Checklist | .15 |
| 91 | Seattle Checklist | .06 |
| 92 | Texas Checklist | .20 |
| 93 | Baltimore Checklist | .12 |
| 94 | Boston Checklist | .10 |
| 95 | Cleveland Checklist | .06 |
| 96 | Detroit Checklist | .12 |
| 97 | Milwaukee Checklist | .08 |
| 98 | New York Checklist | .10 |
| 99 | Toronto Checklist | .08 |
| 100 | Checklist 1-100 | .05 |
| 101 | Joe Oliver | .05 |
| 102 | Hector Villanueva | .05 |
| 103 | Ed Whitson | .05 |
| 104 | Danny Jackson | .05 |
| 105 | Chris Hammond | .05 |
| 106 | Ricky Jordan | .08 |
| 107 | Kevin Bass | .05 |
| 108 | Darrin Fletcher | .05 |
| 109 | Junior Ortiz | .05 |
| 110 | Tom Bolton | .05 |
| 111 | Jeff King | .05 |
| 112 | Dave Magadan | .05 |
| 113 | Mike LaValliere | .05 |
| 114 | Hubie Brooks | .05 |
| 115 | Jay Bell | .05 |
| 116 | David Wells | .05 |
| 117 | Jim Leyritz | .05 |
| 118 | Manuel Lee | .05 |
| 119 | Alvaro Espinoza | .05 |
| 120 | B.J. Surhoff | .08 |
| 121 | Hal Morris | .10 |
| 122 | Shawon Dunston | .08 |
| 123 | Chris Sabo | .08 |
| 124 | Andre Dawson | .15 |
| 125 | Eric Davis | .12 |
| 126 | Chili Davis | .05 |
| 127 | Dale Murphy | .10 |
| 128 | Kirk McCaskill | .10 |
| 129 | Terry Mulholland | .05 |
| 130 | Rick Aguilera | .05 |
| 131 | Vince Coleman | .08 |
| 132 | Andy Van Slyke | .08 |
| 133 | Gregg Jeffries | .08 |
| 134 | Barry Bonds | .15 |
| 135 | Dwight Gooden | .15 |
| 136 | Dave Stieb | .05 |
| 137 | Albert Belle | .15 |
| 138 | Teddy Higuera | .05 |
| 139 | Jesse Barfield | .05 |
| 140 | Pat Borders | .05 |
| 141 | Bib Roberts | .05 |
| 142 | Rob Dibble | .05 |

| NO. | PLAYER | MINT |
|---|---|---|
| 143 | Mark Grace | .08 |
| 144 | Barry Larkin | .10 |
| 145 | Ryne Sandberg | .25 |
| 146 | Scott Erickson | .30 |
| 147 | Luis Polonia | .05 |
| 148 | John Burkett | .05 |
| 149 | Luis Sojo | .05 |
| 150 | Dickie Thon | .05 |
| 151 | Walt Weiss | .05 |
| 152 | Mike Scioscia | .05 |
| 153 | Mark McGwire | .15 |
| 154 | Matt Williams | .12 |
| 155 | Rickey Henderson | .30 |
| 156 | Sandy Alomar Jr. | .10 |
| 157 | Brian McRae | .15 |
| 158 | Harold Baines | .05 |
| 159 | Kevin Appier | .05 |
| 160 | Felix Fermin | .05 |
| 161 | Leo Gomez | .10 |
| 162 | Craig Biggio | .05 |
| 163 | Ben McDonald | .10 |
| 164 | Randy Johnson | .05 |
| 165 | Cal Ripken Jr. | .30 |
| 166 | Frank Thomas | 1.25 |
| 167 | Delino DeShields | .08 |
| 168 | Greg Cagne | .05 |
| 169 | Ron Karkovice | .05 |
| 170 | Charlie Leibrandt | .05 |
| 171 | Dave Righetti | .05 |
| 172 | Dave Henderson | .05 |
| 173 | Steve Decker | .10 |
| 174 | Darryl Strawberry | .20 |
| 175 | Will Clark | .25 |
| 176 | Ruben Sierra | .20 |
| 177 | Ozzie Smith | .15 |
| 178 | Charles Nagy | .05 |
| 179 | Gary Pettis | .05 |
| 180 | Kirk Gibson | .08 |
| 181 | Randy Milligan | .05 |
| 182 | Dave Valle | .05 |
| 183 | Chris Hoiles | .05 |
| 184 | Tony Phillips | .05 |
| 185 | Brady Anderson | .05 |
| 186 | Scott Fletcher | .05 |
| 187 | Gene Larkin | .05 |
| 188 | Lance Johnson | .05 |
| 189 | Greg Olson | .05 |
| 190 | Melido Perez | .05 |
| 191 | Lenny Harris | .05 |
| 192 | Terry Kennedy | .05 |
| 193 | Mike Gallego | .05 |
| 194 | Willie McGee | .08 |
| 195 | Juan Samuel | .05 |
| 196 | Jeff Huson | .05 |
| 197 | Alex Cole | .05 |
| 198 | Ron Robinson | .05 |
| 199 | Joel Skinner | .05 |
| 200 | Checklist 101-200 | .05 |
| 201 | Kevin Reimer | .05 |
| 202 | Stan Belinda | .05 |
| 203 | Pat Tabler | .05 |
| 204 | Jose Guzman | .05 |
| 205 | Jose Lind | .05 |
| 206 | Spike Owen | .05 |
| 207 | Joe Orsulak | .05 |
| 208 | Charlie Hayes | .05 |
| 209 | Mike Devereaux | .05 |
| 210 | Mike Fitzgerald | .05 |
| 211 | Willie Randolph | .05 |
| 212 | Rod Nichols | .05 |
| 213 | Mike Boddicker | .05 |
| 214 | Bill Spiers | .05 |
| 215 | Steve Olin | .05 |
| 216 | David Howard | .05 |
| 217 | Gary Varsho | .05 |
| 218 | Mike Harkey | .05 |
| 219 | Luis Aquino | .05 |
| 220 | Chuck McElroy | .05 |
| 221 | Doug Drabek | .08 |
| 222 | Dave Winfield | .12 |
| 223 | Rafael Palmeiro | .10 |
| 224 | Joe Carter | .12 |
| 225 | Bobby Bonilla | .15 |
| 226 | Ivan Calderon | .05 |

| NO. | PLAYER | MINT |
|---|---|---|
| 227 | Gregg Olson | .05 |
| 228 | Tim Wallach | .05 |
| 229 | Terry Pendleton | .05 |
| 230 | Gilberto Reyes | .05 |
| 231 | Carlos Baerga | .10 |
| 232 | Greg Vaughn | .12 |
| 233 | Bret Saberhagen | .08 |
| 234 | Gary Sheffield | .10 |
| 235 | Mark Lewis | .12 |
| 236 | George Bell | .10 |
| 237 | Danny Tartabull | .08 |
| 238 | Willie Wilson | .05 |
| 239 | Doug Dascenzo | .05 |
| 240 | Bill Pecota | .05 |
| 241 | Julio Franco | .08 |
| 242 | Ed Sprague | .05 |
| 243 | Juan Gonzalez | .30 |
| 244 | Chuck Finley | .05 |
| 245 | Ivan Rodriguez | .75 |
| 246 | Lenny Dykstra | .05 |
| 247 | Deion Sanders | .10 |
| 248 | Dwight Evans | .05 |
| 249 | Larry Walker | .05 |
| 250 | Billy Ripken | .05 |
| 251 | Mickey Tettleton | .05 |
| 252 | Tony Pena | .05 |
| 253 | Benito Santiago | .10 |
| 254 | Kriby Puckett | .20 |
| 255 | Cecil Fielder | .20 |
| 256 | Howard Johnson | .12 |
| 257 | Andujar Cedeno | .15 |
| 258 | Jose Rijo | .05 |
| 259 | Al Osuna | .05 |
| 260 | Todd Hundley | .05 |
| 261 | Orel Hershiser | .10 |
| 262 | Ray Lankford | .12 |
| 263 | Robin Ventura | .20 |
| 264 | Felix Jose | .08 |
| 265 | Eddie Murray | .10 |
| 266 | Kevin Mitchell | .10 |
| 267 | Gary Carter | .08 |
| 268 | Mike Benjamin | .05 |
| 269 | Dick Schofield | .05 |
| 270 | Jose Uribe | .05 |
| 271 | Pete Incaviglia | .05 |
| 272 | Tony Fernandez | .05 |
| 273 | Alan Trammell | .08 |
| 274 | Tony Gwynn | .20 |
| 275 | Mike Greenwell | .10 |
| 276 | Jeff Bagwell | 1.00 |
| 277 | Frank Viola | .05 |
| 278 | Randy Myers | .05 |
| 279 | Ken Caminiti | .05 |
| 280 | Bill Doran | .05 |
| 281 | Dan Pasqua | .05 |
| 282 | Alfredo Griffin | .05 |
| 283 | Jose Oquendo | .05 |
| 284 | Kal Daniels | .05 |
| 285 | Bobby Thigpen | .05 |
| 286 | Robby Thompson | .05 |
| 287 | Mark Eichhorn | .05 |
| 288 | Mike Felder | .05 |
| 289 | Dave Gallagher | .05 |
| 290 | Dave Anderson | .05 |
| 291 | Mel Hall | .08 |
| 292 | Jerald Clark | .05 |
| 293 | Al Newman | .05 |
| 294 | Rob Deer | .05 |
| 295 | Matt Nokes | .05 |
| 296 | Jack Armstrong | .05 |
| 297 | Jim Deshaies | .05 |
| 298 | Jeff Innis | .05 |
| 299 | Jeff Reed | .05 |
| 300 | Checklist 201-300 | .05 |
| 301 | Lonnie Smith | .05 |
| 302 | Jimmy Key | .05 |
| 303 | Junior Felix | .05 |
| 304 | Mike Heath | .05 |
| 305 | Mark Langston | .05 |
| 306 | Greg W. Harris | .05 |
| 307 | Brett Butler | .05 |
| 308 | Luis Rivera | .05 |
| 309 | Bruce Ruffin | .05 |
| 310 | Paul Faries | .05 |

| NO. | PLAYER | MINT |
|---|---|---|
| 311 | Terry Leach | .05 |
| 312 | Scott Brosius | .08 |
| 313 | Scott Leius | .05 |
| 314 | Harold Reynolds | .05 |
| 315 | Jack Morris | .08 |
| 316 | David Segui | .05 |
| 317 | Bill Gullickson | .05 |
| 318 | Todd Frohwirth | .05 |
| 319 | Mark Leiter | .05 |
| 320 | Jeff M. Robinson | .05 |
| 321 | Gary Gaetti | .05 |
| 322 | John Smoltz | .10 |
| 323 | Andy Benes | .10 |
| 324 | Kelly Gruber | .05 |
| 325 | Jim Abbott | .08 |
| 326 | John Kruk | .05 |
| 327 | Kevin Seitzer | .05 |
| 328 | Darrin Jackson | .05 |
| 329 | Kurt Stillwell | .05 |
| 330 | Mike Maddux | .05 |
| 331 | Dennis Eckersley | .05 |
| 332 | Dan Gladden | .05 |
| 333 | Jose Canseco | .30 |
| 334 | Kent Hrbek | .08 |
| 335 | Ken Griffey Sr. | .05 |
| 336 | Greg Swindell | .05 |
| 337 | Trevor Wilson | .05 |
| 338 | Sam Horn | .05 |
| 339 | Mike Henneman | .05 |
| 340 | Jerry Browne | .05 |
| 341 | Glenn Braggs | .05 |
| 342 | Tom Glavine | .10 |
| 343 | Wally Joyner | .10 |
| 344 | Fred McGriff | .10 |
| 345 | Ron Grant | .12 |
| 346 | Ramon Martinez | .12 |
| 347 | Wes Chamberlain | .15 |
| 348 | Terry Shumpert | .05 |
| 349 | Tim Teufel | .05 |
| 350 | Wally Backman | .05 |
| 351 | Joe Girardi | .05 |
| 352 | Devon White | .05 |
| 353 | Greg Maddux | .05 |
| 354 | Ryan Bowen | .08 |
| 355 | Roberto Alomar | .15 |
| 356 | Don Mattingly | .20 |
| 357 | Pedro Guerrero | .05 |
| 358 | Steve Sax | .05 |
| 359 | Joey Cora | .05 |
| 360 | Jim Gantner | .05 |
| 361 | Brian Barnes | .05 |
| 362 | Kevin McReynolds | .08 |
| 363 | Bret Barberie | .15 |
| 364 | David Cone | .08 |
| 365 | Dennis Martinez | .05 |
| 366 | Brian Hunter | .40 |
| 367 | Edgar Martinez | .05 |
| 368 | Steve Finely | .05 |
| 369 | Greg Briley | .05 |
| 370 | Jeff Blauser | .05 |
| 371 | Todd Stottlemyre | .05 |
| 372 | Luis Gonzalez | .15 |
| 373 | Rick Wilkins | .10 |
| 374 | Darryl Kile | .10 |
| 375 | John Olerud | .12 |
| 376 | Lee Smith | .05 |
| 377 | Kevin Maas | .15 |
| 378 | Dante Bichette | .05 |
| 379 | Tom Pagnozzi | .05 |
| 380 | Mike Flanagan | .05 |
| 381 | Charlie O'Brien | .05 |
| 382 | Dave Martinez | .05 |
| 383 | Keith Miller | .05 |
| 384 | Scott Ruskin | .05 |
| 385 | Kevin Elster | .05 |
| 386 | Alvin Davis | .05 |
| 387 | Casey Candaele | .05 |
| 388 | Pete O'Brien | .05 |
| 389 | Jeff Treadway | .05 |
| 390 | Scott Bradley | .05 |
| 391 | Mookie Wilson | .05 |
| 392 | Jimmy Jones | .05 |
| 393 | Candy Maldonado | .05 |
| 394 | Eric Yelding | .05 |

| NO. | PLAYER | MINT | NO. | PLAYER | MINT | NO. | PLAYER | MINT | NO. | PLAYER | MINT |
|---|---|---|---|---|---|---|---|---|---|---|---|
| 395 | Tom Henke | .05 | 472 | Kent Mercker | .05 | 549 | Dave Smith | .05 | 626 | Jeff Johnson | .15 |
| 396 | Franklin Stubbs | .05 | 473 | Terry Steinbach | .05 | 550 | Dan Plesac | .05 | 627 | Jeff Montgomery | .05 |
| 397 | Milt Thompson | .05 | 474 | Andres Galarraga | .08 | 551 | Alex Fernandez | .15 | 628 | Ken Hill | .05 |
| 398 | Mark Carreon | .05 | 475 | Steve Avery | .25 | 552 | Bernard Gilkey | .10 | 629 | Gary Thurman | .05 |
| 399 | Randy Velarde | .05 | 476 | Tom Gordon | .05 | 553 | Jack McDowell | .05 | 630 | Steve Howe | .05 |
| 400 | Checklist 301-400 | .05 | 477 | Cal Edlred | .05 | 554 | Tino Martinez | .12 | 631 | Jose DeJesus | .05 |
| 401 | Omar Vizquel | .05 | 478 | Omar Olivares | .10 | 555 | Bo Jackson | .30 | 632 | Bert Blyleven | .05 |
| 402 | Joe Boever | .05 | 479 | Julio Machado | .05 | 556 | Bernie Williams | .15 | 633 | Jaime Navarro | .05 |
| 403 | Bill Krueger | .05 | 480 | Bob Milacki | .05 | 557 | Mark Gardner | .05 | 634 | Lee Stevens | .05 |
| 404 | Jody Reed | .05 | 481 | Les Lancaster | .05 | 558 | Glenallen Hill | .05 | 635 | Pete Harnisch | .05 |
| 405 | Mike Schooler | .05 | 482 | John Candelaria | .05 | 559 | Oil Can Boyd | .05 | 636 | Bill Landrum | .05 |
| 406 | Jason Grimsley | .05 | 483 | Brian Downing | .05 | 560 | Chris James | .05 | 637 | Rich DeLucia | .05 |
| 407 | Grey Myers | .05 | 484 | Roger McDowell | .05 | 561 | Scott Servais | .08 | 638 | Luis Salazar | .05 |
| 408 | Randy Ready | .05 | 485 | Scott Scudder | .05 | 562 | Rey Sanchez (R) | .15 | 639 | Rob Murphy | .05 |
| 409 | Mike Timlin | .05 | 486 | Zane Smith | .05 | 563 | Paul McClellan | .08 | **No. 640 to 650—Diamond Skills** | | |
| 410 | Mitch Williams | .05 | 487 | John Cerutti | .05 | 564 | Andy Mota | .10 | 640 | Diamond Skills CL | .15 |
| 411 | Garry Templeton | .05 | 488 | Steve Buechele | .05 | 565 | Darren Lewis | .05 | 641 | Rogers Clemens | .15 |
| 412 | Greg Cadaret | .05 | 489 | Paul Gibson | .05 | 566 | Jose Melendez | .10 | 642 | Jim Abbott | .12 |
| 413 | Donnie Hill | .05 | 490 | Curtis Wilkerson | .05 | 567 | Tommy Greene | .05 | 643 | Travis Fryman | .15 |
| 414 | Wally Whitehurst | .05 | 491 | Marvin Freeman | .05 | 568 | Rich Rodriquez | .05 | 644 | Jesse Barfield | .06 |
| 415 | Scott Sanderson | .05 | 492 | Tom Foley | .05 | 569 | Heathcliff Slocomb | .05 | 645 | Cal Ripken Jr., | .25 |
| 416 | Thomas Howard | .05 | 493 | Juan Berenguer | .05 | 570 | Jose Hesketh | .05 | 646 | Wade Boggs | .15 |
| 417 | Neal Heaton | .05 | 494 | Ernest Riles | .05 | 571 | Carlton Fisk | .10 | 647 | Cecil Fielder | .15 |
| 418 | Charlie Hough | .05 | 495 | Sid Bream | .05 | 572 | Erik Hanson | .05 | 648 | Rickey Henderson | .20 |
| 419 | Jack Howell | .05 | 496 | Chuck Crim | .05 | 573 | Wilson Alvarez | .05 | 649 | Jose Canseco | .15 |
| 420 | Greg Hibbard | .05 | 497 | Mike Macfarlane | .05 | 574 | Rheal Cormier | .15 | 650 | Ken Griffey Jr. | .35 |
| 421 | Carlos Quintana | .05 | 498 | Dale Sveum | .05 | 575 | Tim Raines | .10 | 651 | Kenny Rogers | .06 |
| 422 | Kim Batiste | .12 | 499 | Storm Davis | .05 | 576 | Bobby Witt | .05 | 652 | Luis Mercedes | .20 |
| 423 | Paul Molitor | .05 | 500 | Checklist 401-500 | .05 | 577 | Roberto Kelly | .10 | 653 | Mike Stanton | .06 |
| 424 | Ken Griffey Jr. | .75 | 501 | Jeff Reardon | .05 | 578 | Kevin Brown | .05 | 654 | Glenn Davis | .06 |
| 425 | Phil Plantier | 1.00 | 502 | Shawn Abner | .05 | 579 | Chris Nabholz | .05 | 655 | Nolan Ryan | .50 |
| 426 | Denny Neagle | .15 | 503 | Tony Fossas | .05 | 580 | Jesse Orosco | .05 | 656 | Reggie Jefferson | .20 |
| 427 | Von Hayes | .05 | 504 | Cory Snyder | .05 | 581 | Jeff Brantley | .05 | 657 | Javier Ortiz | .05 |
| 428 | Shane Mack | .05 | 505 | Matt Young | .05 | 582 | Rafael Ramirez | .05 | 658 | Greg A. Harris | .05 |
| 429 | Darren Daulton | .05 | 506 | Allan Anderson | .05 | 583 | Kelly Downs | .05 | 659 | Mariano Duncan | .05 |
| 430 | Dwayne Henry | .05 | 507 | Mark Lee | .05 | 584 | Mike Simms | .08 | 660 | Jeff Shaw | .05 |
| 431 | Lance Parrish | .05 | 508 | Gene Nelson | .05 | 585 | Mike Remlinger | .05 | 661 | Mike Moore | .05 |
| 432 | Mike Humphreys | .08 | 509 | Mike Pagliarulo | .05 | 586 | Dave Hollins | .05 | 662 | Chris Haney | .08 |
| 433 | Tim Burke | .05 | 510 | Rafael Belliard | .05 | 587 | Larry Anderson | .05 | 663 | Joe Slusarski | .05 |
| 434 | Bryan Harvey | .05 | 511 | Jay Howell | .05 | 588 | Mike Gardiner | .08 | 664 | Wayne Housie (R) | .15 |
| 435 | Pat Kelly | .15 | 512 | Bob Tewksbury | .05 | 589 | Craig Lefferts | .05 | 665 | Carlos Garcia | .05 |
| 436 | Ozzie Guillen | .05 | 513 | Mike Morgan | .05 | 590 | Paul Assenmacher | .05 | 666 | Bob Ojeda | .05 |
| 437 | Bruce Hurst | .05 | 514 | John Franco | .08 | 591 | Bryn Smith | .05 | 667 | Bryan Hickerson (R) | .15 |
| 438 | Sammy Sosa | .05 | 515 | Kevin Gross | .05 | 592 | Donn Pall | .05 | 668 | Tim Belcher | .05 |
| 439 | Dennis Rasmussen | .05 | 516 | Lou Whitaker | .05 | 593 | Mike Jackson | .05 | 669 | Ron Darling | .05 |
| 440 | Ken Patterson | .05 | 517 | Orlando Merced | .15 | 594 | Scott Radinsky | .05 | 670 | Rex Hudler | .05 |
| 441 | Jay Buhner | .05 | 518 | Todd Benzinger | .05 | 595 | Brian Holman | .05 | 671 | Sid Fernandez | .05 |
| 442 | Pat Combs | .05 | 519 | Gary Redus | .05 | 596 | Geronimo Pena | .05 | 672 | Chito Martinez | .30 |
| 443 | Wade Boggs | .15 | 520 | Walt Terrell | .05 | 597 | Mike Jeffcoat | .05 | 673 | Pete Schourek | .08 |
| 444 | George Brett | .15 | 521 | Jack Clark | .08 | 598 | Carlos Martinez | .05 | 674 | A. Reynoso (R) | .15 |
| 445 | Mo Vaughan | .30 | 522 | Dave Parker | .05 | 599 | Geno Petralli | .05 | 675 | Mike Mussina | .20 |
| 446 | Chuck Knoblauch | .50 | 523 | Tim Naehring | .05 | 600 | Checklist 501-600 | .05 | 676 | Kevin Morton | .10 |
| 447 | Tom Candiotti | .05 | 524 | Mark Whiten | .12 | 601 | Jerry Don Gleaton | .05 | 677 | Norm Charlton | .05 |
| 448 | Mark Portugal | .05 | 525 | Ellis Burks | .10 | 602 | Adam Peterson | .05 | 678 | Danny Darwin | .05 |
| 449 | Mickey Morandini | .05 | 526 | Frank Castillo | .05 | 603 | Craig Grebeck | .05 | 679 | Eric King | .05 |
| 450 | Duane Ward | .05 | 527 | Brian Harper | .05 | 604 | Mark Guthrie | .05 | 680 | Ted Power | .05 |
| 451 | Otis Nixon | .05 | 528 | Brook Jacoby | .05 | 605 | Frank Tanana | .05 | 681 | Barry Jones | .05 |
| 452 | Bob Welch | .05 | 529 | Rick Sutcliffe | .05 | 606 | Hensley Meulena | .05 | 682 | Carney Lansford | .05 |
| 453 | Rusty Meacham | .12 | 530 | Joe Klink | .05 | 607 | Mark Davis | .05 | 683 | Mel Rojas | .05 |
| 454 | Keith Mitchell | .25 | 531 | Terry Bross | .05 | 608 | Eric Plunk | .05 | 684 | Rick Honeycutt | .05 |
| 455 | Marquis Grissom | .08 | 532 | Jose Offerman | .05 | 609 | Mark Williamson | .05 | 685 | Jeff Fassero | .05 |
| 456 | Robin Yount | .15 | 533 | Todd Zeile | .10 | 610 | Lee Guetterman | .05 | 686 | Cris Carpenter | .05 |
| 457 | Harvey Pulliam | .15 | 534 | Eric Karros | .25 | 611 | Bobby Rose | .05 | 687 | Tim Crews | .05 |
| 458 | Jose DeLeon | .05 | 535 | Anthony Young | .15 | 612 | Bill Wegman | .05 | 688 | Scott Terry | .05 |
| 459 | Mark Gubicza | .05 | 536 | Milt Cuyler | .10 | 613 | Mike Hartley | .05 | 689 | Chris Gwynn | .05 |
| 460 | Darryl Hamilton | .05 | 537 | Randy Tomlin | .05 | 614 | Chris Beasley (R) | .15 | 690 | Gerald Perry | .05 |
| 461 | Tom Browning | .05 | 538 | Scott Livingstone | .12 | 615 | Chris Bosio | .05 | 691 | John Barfield | .05 |
| 462 | Monty Fariss | .05 | 539 | Jim Eisenreich | .05 | 616 | Henry Cotto | .05 | 692 | Bob Melvin | .05 |
| 463 | Jerome Walton | .08 | 540 | Don Slaught | .05 | 617 | Chico Walker | .05 | 693 | Juan Agosto | .05 |
| 464 | Paul O'Neill | .05 | 541 | Scott Cooper | .15 | 618 | Russ Swan | .05 | 694 | Alejandro Pena | .05 |
| 465 | Dean Palmer | .20 | 542 | Joe Grahe | .05 | 619 | Bob Walk | .05 | 695 | Jeff Russell | .05 |
| 466 | Travis Fryman | .25 | 543 | Tom Brunansky | .08 | 620 | Billy Swift | .05 | 696 | Carmelo Martinez | .05 |
| 467 | John Smiley | .05 | 544 | Eddie Zosky | .12 | 621 | Warren Newson | .05 | 697 | Bud Black | .05 |
| 468 | Lloyd Moseby | .05 | 545 | Roger Clemens | .25 | 622 | Steve Bedrosian | .05 | 698 | Dave Otto | .05 |
| 469 | John Wehner | .15 | 546 | David Justice | .50 | 623 | Ricky Bones | .05 | 699 | Bill Hatcher | .05 |
| 470 | Skeeter Barnes | .05 | 547 | Dave Stewart | .08 | 624 | Kevin Tapani | .05 | 700 | Checklist 601-700 | .05 |
| 471 | Steve Chitren | .05 | 548 | David West | .05 | 625 | Juan Guzman | .75 | | | |

## BASEBALL CARD ALBUM (HOLDS 792 CARDS) & VINYL PAGES

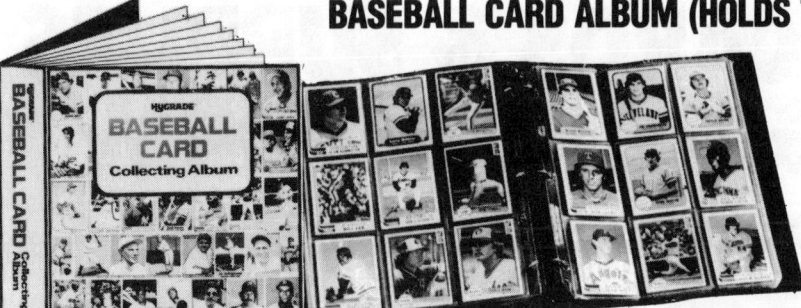

Loose-Leaf album displays and protects 792 cards. Includes 44 vinyl card holder pages. 1¾" D-ring allows vinyl pages to lie flat when album is open. Full-color cover. Entire album is covered with clear vinyl.

**PRICE $17.95...3 ALBUMS—$49.95 (save $3.90)**

**9-POCKET PLASTIC CARD PAGES**
25 ... $5.95.... 50 ... $10.95 ... 75 ...$15.95
100 ...$19.95 ...200 ... $36.95 ... 400 ...$69.95

**Baseball Card Collecting Kit**—*Everything You Need to Collect Baseball Cards!* . . . Baseball Card Album • 44 Vinyl Card Pages • 300 Baseball Cards from all 6 Manufacturers (1970 to Date) • 50 "Topps" *Original* Cards of Star Players (1982 to Date) • Card Set of 50 All-Time Greats • 5 "Reprints" of Rare Baseball Cards • Guide to Baseball Card Collecting • 184 pg. Card Catalog & Price Guide • 25 Individual Card Holders • Poster of Rare Cards • 12" x 18" Deluxe Gift Box . . . . . . . . Retail Value $59.95 / **Manufacturer's Special $39.95**

## COMPLETE CARD SETS & ASSORTMENTS

Build your card collection quickly and economically by buying *complete* card sets and assortments—at *big* savings over individual card prices. All cards are *genuine*, originals—our choice of cards, no duplicates! Complete card sets include every card issued for the year.

| Year | Complete Set | 200 Diff. | 100 Diff. | 50 Diff |
|---|---|---|---|---|
| 1991 Donruss Baseball | $34.95 (792 cards) | — | — | — |
| 1990 Donruss Baseball | 29.95 (716 cards) | — | — | — |
| 1989 Donruss Baseball | 29.95 (600 cards) | — | — | — |
| 1988 Donruss Baseball | 29.95 (660 cards) | — | — | — |
| 1987 Donruss Baseball | 90.00 (660 cards) | — | — | — |
| 1991 Fleer Baseball | 34.95 (720 cards) | — | — | — |
| 1990 Fleer Baseball | 32.95 (660 cards) | — | — | — |
| 1989 Fleer Baseball | 36.95 (660 cards) | — | — | — |
| 1988 Fleer Baseball | 49.95 (660 cards) | — | — | — |
| 1987 Fleer Baseball | 105.00 (660 cards) | — | — | — |
| 1991 Topps Baseball | 34.95 (792 cards) | — | — | — |
| 1990 Topps Baseball | 32.95 (792 cards) | — | — | — |
| 1989 Topps Baseball | 32.95 (792 cards) | $10.00 | $5.00 | — |
| 1988 Topps Baseball | 32.95 (792 cards) | 10.00 | 5.00 | — |
| 1987 Topps Baseball | 37.95 (792 cards) | 10.00 | 5.00 | — |
| 1986 Topps Baseball | 45.00 (792 cards) | 12.00 | 6.00 | — |
| 1985 Topps Baseball | 120.00 (792 cards) | 12.00 | 6.00 | — |
| 1984 Topps Baseball | 105.00 (792 cards) | 14.00 | 7.00 | — |
| 1983 Topps Baseball | 200.00 (792 cards) | 15.00 | 7.50 | — |
| 1982 Topps Baseball | 160.00 (792 cards) | 15.00 | 7.50 | — |
| 1981 Topps Baseball | 120.00 (726 cards) | — | 7.50 | — |
| 1980 Topps Baseball | — | 15.00 | — | — |

| Year | 100 Diff. | 50 Diff. | 25 Diff. | 10 Diff. |
|---|---|---|---|---|
| 1979 Topps Baseball | $14.00 | $7.00 | $3.50 | — |
| 1978 Topps Baseball | 20.00 | 10.00 | 5.00 | — |
| 1977 Topps Baseball | 20.00 | 10.00 | 5.00 | — |
| 1976 Topps Baseball | 22.00 | 11.00 | 5.50 | — |
| 1975 Topps Baseball | 35.00 | 17.50 | 8.75 | — |
| 1974 Topps Baseball | 35.00 | 17.50 | 8.75 | — |
| 1973 Topps Baseball | 40.00 | 20.00 | 10.00 | — |
| 1972 Topps Baseball | — | 20.00 | 10.00 | $4.00 |
| 1971 Topps Baseball | — | 25.00 | 12.50 | 5.00 |
| 1970 Topps Baseball | — | 25.00 | 12.50 | 5.00 |
| 1969 Topps Baseball | — | — | 18.00 | 7.50 |
| 1968 Topps Baseball | — | — | 20.00 | 8.00 |
| 1967 Topps Baseball | — | — | 20.00 | 8.00 |
| 1966 Topps Baseball | — | — | 20.00 | 8.00 |
| 1965 Topps Baseball | — | — | 20.00 | 8.00 |

## BASEBALL TEAM ASSORTMENTS

If you have a *favorite* baseball team, you'll be glad to know that you can now order *genuine*, original Topps, Donruss, Fleer, etc. cards featuring players from *just* that team! All 26 baseball teams are available.

| Team | 50 Diff. Topps 1980-Date | 150 Diff. Topps 1980-Date | 50 Diff. Donruss, Fleer Score, Upp. Deck 1981-Date | 150 Diff. Donruss, Fleer Score, Upp. Deck 1981-Date |
|---|---|---|---|---|
| A's | $7.00 | $17.00 | $7.50 | $17.50 |
| ANGELS | 5.00 | 15.00 | 5.00 | 15.00 |
| ASTROS | 5.00 | 15.00 | 5.00 | 15.00 |
| BLUE JAYS | 5.00 | 15.00 | 5.00 | 15.00 |
| BRAVES | 5.00 | 15.00 | 5.00 | 15.00 |
| BREWERS | 5.00 | 15.00 | 5.00 | 15.00 |
| CARDINALS | 6.00 | 18.00 | 6.00 | 18.00 |
| CUBS | 7.00 | 21.00 | 7.00 | 21.00 |
| DODGERS | 7.00 | 21.00 | 7.00 | 21.00 |
| EXPOS | 5.00 | 15.00 | 5.00 | 15.00 |
| GIANTS | 6.00 | 18.00 | 6.00 | 18.00 |
| INDIANS | 5.00 | 15.00 | 5.00 | 15.00 |
| MARINERS | 5.00 | 15.00 | 5.00 | 15.00 |
| METS | — | — | — | — |
| ORIOLES | 6.00 | 18.00 | 6.00 | 18.00 |
| PADRES | 5.00 | 15.00 | 5.00 | 15.00 |
| PHILS | 6.00 | 18.00 | 6.00 | 18.00 |
| PIRATES | 6.00 | 18.00 | 6.00 | 18.00 |
| RANGERS | 5.00 | 15.00 | 5.00 | 15.00 |
| REDS | 7.00 | 21.00 | 7.00 | 21.00 |
| RED SOX | 7.00 | 21.00 | 7.00 | 21.00 |
| ROYALS | 5.00 | 15.00 | 5.00 | 15.00 |
| TIGERS | 5.00 | 15.00 | 5.00 | 15.00 |
| TWINS | 5.00 | 15.00 | 5.00 | 15.00 |
| WHITE SOX | 5.00 | 15.00 | 5.00 | 15.00 |
| YANKEES | 7.00 | 21.00 | 7.00 | 21.00 |

**FOR FAST SERVICE ON CREDIT CARD ORDERS OVER $50 CALL (212) 807-7935.**

**HYGRADE SPORTS CARD CO., 5 E. 17 STREET, NEW YORK, N.Y. 10003**

Please RUSH me the items circled in this order form on your 10-day **MONEY-BACK GUARANTEE OF COMPLETE SATISFACTION.** Another order form will be sent with your merchandise. Most orders shipped within two weeks by UPS. We accept checks (must clear before shipment), money orders, Master Card and Visa. Canada, Alaska, Hawaii and P.R. please send double shipping charges. Canada customers please remit in USA funds.

**MINIMUM ORDER $20.00. MINIMUM CREDIT CARD ORDER $50.00**

☐ Master Card
☐ Visa

CREDIT CARD NUMBER

BANK NO.          EXPIRATION DATE

X _____
CREDIT CARD ORDERS REQUIRE SIGNATURE AND PHONE NUMBER OF CARD HOLDER

Name_____

Address _____
NO POST OFFICE BOXES

City/State/Zip_____

Total Amount of Merchandise Ordered ......... $_____

New York State Residents Add Sales Tax ........ $_____

Add Postage and Handling Charges ............. $_____

Minimum Order $20.00
Minimum Credit Card Order $50.00
**TOTAL AMOUNT DUE** ...... $_____

**POSTAGE AND HANDLING CHARGES**
Total Merchandise up to $24.99 (Add $3.00)
Total Merchandise $25.00-$49.99 (Add $4.00)
Total Merchandise $50.00-up (Add $5.00)

Prices effective until March, 1993 with the possible exception of card sets and assortments.

# BASEBALL CARDS & SUPPLIES CATALOG & ORDER FORM

Enjoy the convenience of shopping by mail from one of America's largest dealers—Hygrade Sports Card Co. You're backed by our guarantee that you must be satisfied with your purchase or return it within 10 days for a re-

fund. We sell *genuine,* original Topps, Donruss, Fleer, etc. cards in complete sets and assortments at *big* savings over individual card prices. Most orders shipped within one week by UPS. Select what you need and order today!

## New! 1992 Baseball Complete Card Sets...Super Special Offer!

Each card set has its own beautiful design and features all of your favorite players—Bo Jackson, Nolan Ryan, Jose Canseco, Darryl Strawberry, Rickey Henderson . . . and

more! You can buy each complete card set at a much lower price than you would pay if you bought the cards individually. And each card set is shipped in its own storage box.

### 1992 TOPPS
#### Complete Set
#### 792 Cards

**$39⁹⁵**

### 1992 DONRUSS
#### Complete Set
#### 792 Cards

**FREE BONUS!**
**Hall of Fame Puzzle**

**$59⁹⁵**

### 1992 FLEER
#### Complete Set
#### 720 Cards

**FREE BONUS!**
**Team Logo Stickers**

**$49⁹⁵**

## ORDER ALL 3 1992 BASEBALL CARD SETS ABOVE AND SAVE $9.90

*Special Price!*

- Complete 1992 Set of 792 Topps Baseball Cards
- Complete 1992 Set of 792 Donruss Baseball Cards
- Complete 1992 Set of 720 Fleer Baseball Cards

**$139⁹⁵**

## ASSORTMENTS OF "ROOKIE" CARDS

A rookie card is the player's *first* card from the main card set—and usually becomes the most popular and valuable card of his career. All cards are *genuine* originals—no duplicates!

50 Topps Rookies (1975-up) . . . . $12.95
100 Topps Rookies (1969-up) . . . . $24.95
200 Topps Rookies (1965-up) . . . . $49.95

## ASSORTMENTS OF "STAR" CARDS

Each assortment saves you money over individual card prices. Includes: Jose Canseco, Rickey Henderson, Bo Jackson, Nolan Ryan.

50 Topps (1978-up) . . . . . . . . . . $14.95
100 Topps (1976-up) . . . . . . . . . . $29.95
200 Topps (1973-up) . . . . . . . . . . $59.95
50 Donruss, Fleer, Score, U.D.   $12.95
100 Donruss, Fleer, Score, U.D.   $25.95

**HYGRADE SPORTS CARD CO.**
5 East 17th Street, New York, N.Y. 10003

Credit Card
Phone Orders
(212) 807-7935

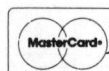